MATHEMATICS OF BUSINESS AND FINANCE

Online Lessons

- Contain highly engaging and interactive videos that use cutting-edge Cloud Learning technologies.
- Break down math concepts into logical and intuitive steps that enhance the learning process.
- Prepare students for upcoming classes, labs, and quizzes through self-study lessons.
- Contain lessons that are self-paced and are excellent for visual learners.

Online Labs

- Contain a comprehensive test-bank of real-world problems, which may be used as an assessment tool.
- Break down every answer into dynamic, step-by-step solutions that include calculator methods of solving problems.
- Provide unlimited amount of practice through algorithmically generated problems.
- Contain numerous statistical tools to analyze students' strengths and weaknesses.

Vretta™

MATHEMATICS OF BUSINESS AND FINANCE

Third Edition

Authors

Larry Daisley, *Seneca College*

Thambyrajah Kugathasan, *Seneca College*

Diane Huysmans, *OntarioLearn*

Contributing Author

Lisa MacKay, *Southern Alberta Institute of Technology*

Vretta

ISBN 978-1-927737-21-7

Mathematics of Business and Finance, Third Edition

Textbook printed in Canada

Authors: Larry Daisley, Thambyrajah Kugathasan, Diane Huysmans
Contributing Author: Lisa MacKay

Textbook Editor: Lakshmi Kugathasan
Developmental Editor: Arbana Miftari
Copy Editor: Connor Peebles
Art Director: Aleksandar Vozarevic
Solution Manual and Test Bank Editors: Paul Hansuld, Katelyn Poon, Erika De Vega

Video Tutorials: Jeff Fennell
PowerPoint Presentations: Ali Alavi, Uma Kalkar
Instructional Design: Charles Anifowose, Elisa Romeo
Technology & Data Solutions: Zach Williams, Nabil Fannoush, Ariel Sosnovsky
Marketing Director: Harsha Varlani

Expert Advice: TK Academic Consulting Inc.
Financial Designation Problems: Kaplan-Schweser course materials for Certified Financial Analyst designation
Pre-programmed Financial Calculator: Texas Instruments BAII Plus, Sharp EL-738
Turning Technologies' Student Response System (Clickers) Integrated into Powerpoint Presentations
Cases: Royal Bank of Canada
Online Resources Management System: Intromath.ca

Vretta

Brief Contents

Contents

Chapter 4

Ratios, Proportions, and Applications 120

Chapter 5

Mathematics of Merchandising 162

Chapter 13

Chapter 14

List of Cases, Tables, and Exhibits

Cases

Tables

Exhibits

Preface

A world where everyone enjoys math - the Mathematics of Business and Finance resource was created with this vision at its core. We set out to build a resource that will both help the future leaders of business achieve success in their careers, and help students develop a passion for mathematics along the way.

To optimize the learning experience, we have leveraged the cutting-edge technologies available to us to provide students with a highly immersive and engaging learning experience. Realizing that every student learns differently, students are given access to innovative online tools designed to help them master the concepts using diverse methods of learning. Students have access to interactive online lessons which give them an understanding of the concepts before class. They are also provided with access to the online lab system which tests them on all the core concepts covered throughout their course. Our aim in building the hybrid tools was to help overcome the negative perceptions associated with mathematics.

Blended learning, commonly known as hybrid learning, is a method of combining different learning environments, such as face-to-face, web-based, and mobile learning, to enhance the learning experience for all types of learners (visual, auditory, tactile, sociological, etc.). Vretta has become a world-leader in delivering blended learning solutions that are transforming the way students engage with mathematics, and has been awarded the prestigious Excellence in Learning award by the Brandon Hall Group for increasing student success using blended learning.

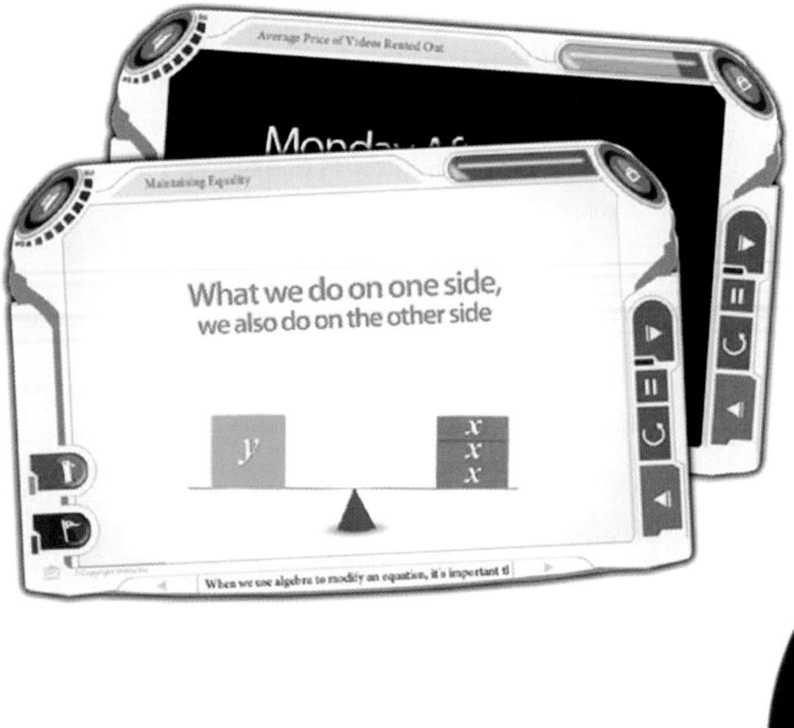

The concepts covered throughout the resource will be beneficial in supporting students to deal with repaying student loans, leasing a car, securing a mortgage, running a business, paying taxes, making investments, and much more. We have worked to build a resource that will equip our leaders of tomorrow with the core mathematical skills required to perform the day-to-day tasks demanded of them in their field of choice.

At Vretta, we believe that if you learn math, you will live smarter. We truly believe that this blended resource can help students achieve a better understanding of the concepts presented and ultimately lead to a better overall quality of life. As students embark on the journey of learning this important subject, we hope that the resources for the Mathematics of Business and Finance provide great value in helping them along the way.

Larry, Kuga, Diane, Lisa, and Team Vretta

Resources

Textbook

Language The language used in this textbook is simple and straight-forward, while maintaining the levels of sophistication required to thoroughly prepare students for the next stage in their academic and professional careers.

Pedagogies and Learning Methods Numerous pedagogies and learning methods that have been developed and proven over 30 years are incorporated into the textbook. These pedagogies have succeeded in simplifying critical mathematical concepts and significantly improving retention of concepts. The different learning methods to solve problems have also proven to cater to the varied student learning styles.

Calculator In addition to providing various methods to solve problems, the textbook contains instructions to solve problems using the Texas Instruments BAII Plus and Sharp EL-738 financial calculators, wherever applicable. The calculator instructions are designed using the images of the calculator keys, making it easy for students to follow the sequence of operations.

Spreadsheet New to the Third Edition, each of the finance chapters contains instructions on how to solve the in-text examples using spreadsheet software, wherever applicable. The spreadsheet instructions are designed to show students both the exact inputs they enter into each cell, as well as the final spreadsheet output.

Exercises The textbook has 2000+ exercises, review exercises, self-test exercises, and comprehensive cases, as well as 300+ solved examples. Problems are designed to test students on real-world, practical applications and are presented in increasing levels of difficulty, with the most difficult problems being indicated by a dot (•). The problems are categorized into pairs of similar questions to provide professors with an opportunity to solve the even-numbered problems in class and assign the odd-numbered problems as homework.

Financial Designation Problems The textbook contains problems that are used to prepare students for the first level of the Chartered Financial Analyst (CFA) professional designation exam. This will provide students with exposure to the financial career choices that will be available to them in the future. These problems are identified by a '**CFA Prep.**' icon.

Solution Manual

All problems in the end-of-section exercises, review exercises, self-test exercises, and cases have been solved using detailed step-by-step methods, including the financial calculator and spreadsheet methods, as demonstrated in the solved examples. The solution manual is available online.

PowerPoint Presentations

The animated PowerPoint presentations are available for professors to use in class. They contain both the algebraic and calculator methods of solving problems. The PowerPoint presentations are designed to work with clickers in class to gauge student understanding of concepts.

Test Bank

A comprehensive test bank, of 3000+ problems in varying levels of difficulty, that covers all concepts in the textbook is provided for professors to use as a database for exercises, quizzes, cases, group projects, or assignments.

Online Lessons

The online lessons are created as a pre-study component for students. They contain pedagogies that are highly interactive and engaging, and which teach concepts in a very logical and intuitive way. These lessons are not PowerPoint presentations but are interactive movies that have been created to enrich and enhance the learning experience. Every frame is locked to ensure that students go through the lessons sequentially as they are designed to build on learning concepts in succession. The system automatically records students' progress and performance. Once students complete a lesson, the frame unlocks itself, allowing students to navigate back and forth through the lesson. Professors, on the other hand, have administrative access which allows them to navigate through the online lessons without any restrictions.

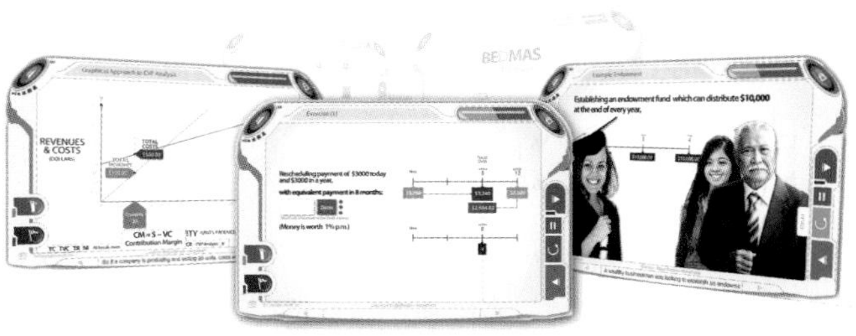

Online Labs

The online lab assessment system contains a rich comprehensive test-bank of real-world problems that are algorithmically generated and that provide students with dynamic feedback on their responses. The labs can also be customized based on course requirements. A few of the customizable features include: previewing and selecting questions, setting the number of questions, setting and modifying start and due dates, opening, closing and re-opening labs, creating new labs and quizzes, and determining the weighting and number of attempts for each question.

Administrative Tools

The following administrative tools will provide professors with the ability to monitor overall class performance and individual student performance on online lessons and labs.

Performance Dashboard for Professors

The lesson performance dashboard provides professors with the average completion percentage per chapter, including a lesson-by-lesson percentage completed visualization for the entire class. The lab performance dashboard provides them with the average percentage mark on each lab for the class. Professors can also download or export individual grades for lessons and labs to a spreadsheet or to the college's course management system.

Performance Dashboard for Students

The lesson performance dashboard provides students with their chapter completion mark, including a lesson-by-lesson percentage completed visualization. The lab performance dashboard provides them with their lab percentage marks.

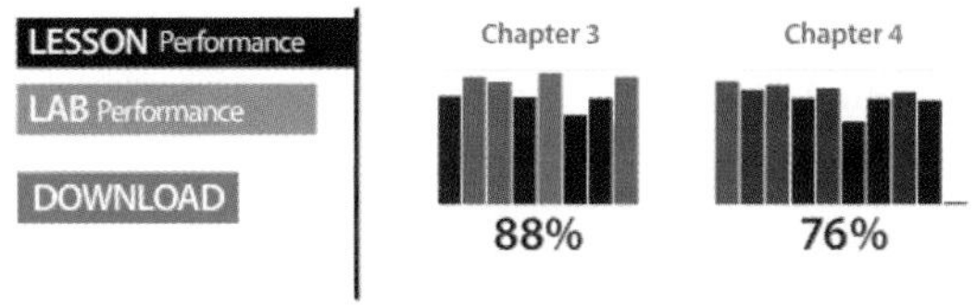

Lab Management System The lab management system is provided for administrators or subject leaders to create new labs, quizzes and case studies, preview and select questions, set the number of questions, set and modify start and due dates, open, close and re-open labs, and determine the weighting and number of attempts for each question.

Updates in the Third Edition

The content of the Third Edition textbook along with its 300+ solved problems, 2000+ exercises, and cases have been carefully reviewed by professors at various colleges in Canada. In addition to the updates to the texbook, accompanying online resources have also been updated to reflect the changes.

Spreadsheet Solutions

Full Spreadsheet Solutions provided for over **130 Examples** in Chapters 8-14

New Exercise Questions

Over **200 New Exercise Questions** added throughout the textbook

New Cases

Added **6 New Case Studies** in Chapters 9 to 13

New Examples

Examples revised, updated, and expanded throughout the textbook, with over **35 New Solved Examples** added

New Content

Modified Content

Section 1.3:	Added additional examples of reducing, comparing, and performing arithmetic with fractions
Chapter 5:	Added *Rate on C* and *Rate on S* columns to the Merchandising Calculation Table for further clarity
Section 7.4:	Modified examples and tables for further clarity
Chapters 9-10:	Added more examples and exercises involving daily compounding interest
Section 11.1:	Modified examples to show how deferred annuities can be treated as ordinary annuities or annuities due
Section 13.5:	Modified examples for further clarity

New Illustrations, Exhibits, and Tables

Up-To-Date

Acknowledgements

The authors and Vretta would like to thank the following professors for their detailed feedback on helping us update the Third Edition of the Mathematics of Business and Finance textbook and its accompanying online resources:

- Alex Tett, Northern Lakes College
- Brian Murray, Holland College
- Colleen Quinn, Seneca College
- Dianne Krasuski, Humber College
- Don Vander Klok, Lambton College
- Femi Alli, Southern Alberta Institute of Technology
- Gaspare Bonomo, Mohawk College
- Gurpreet Bhatia, Bow Valley College
- Irene Lee, Humber College
- Kaukab Kamran, Humber College
- Lori Bombier, Grande Prairie Regional College
- Margaret Dancy, Fanshawe College
- Mary Benincasa, Mohawk College
- Mohammad Hussain, Humber College
- Paul Hansuld, Lambton College
- Paul Obour, Southern Alberta Institute of Technology
- Soobia Siddiqui, Fleming College
- Valerie Webber, Mohawk College

MATHEMATICS OF BUSINESS AND FINANCE

Third Edition

Authors

Larry Daisley, *Seneca College*

Thambyrajah Kugathasan, *Seneca College*

Diane Huysmans, *OntarioLearn*

Contributing Author

Lisa MacKay, *Southern Alberta Institute of Technology*

Vretta

Chapter 1

REVIEW OF BASIC ARITHMETIC

LEARNING OBJECTIVES

- Identify place values of numbers and apply to round whole numbers, decimal numbers, and percents to the required place values.
- Determine least common multiples or denominators (LCM or LCD) and greatest common factors (GCF).
- Identify types of fractions and perform computations using fractions.
- Perform basic arithmetic operations in their proper order.
- Calculate simple arithmetic averages and weighted averages for a set of values.

CHAPTER OUTLINE

Introduction

Arithmetic is the study of numbers and includes calculations, such as addition, subtraction, multiplication, and division, that may be performed between them.

Arithmetic is the most elementary branch of mathematics. It is the study of numbers and includes calculations such as addition, subtraction, multiplication, division, etc. We use arithmetic in everyday tasks such as counting, buying, selling, estimating expenses, and checking bank balances. Arithmetic also forms the basis for all advanced technology, science, engineering, and business studies.

Throughout this textbook, we will be deriving multiple formulas related to the mathematics of business and finance. Before we can understand how these formulas work and how to properly apply them, it is essential that we gain confidence in performing arithmetic operations in the right order, using whole numbers, decimal numbers, and fractions.

In this chapter, you will review the basic arithmetic skills that are necessary for these business and finance applications.

1.1 | Place Value of Numbers and Rounding Numbers

Place Value of Whole Numbers

The position of each digit in a whole number determines the **place value** for the digit. Exhibit 1.1(a) illustrates the place value of the ten digits in the whole number 3,867,254,129. In this example, 4 is in the 'thousands' place value and represents 4,000, whereas 7 is in the 'millions' place value and represents 7,000,000.

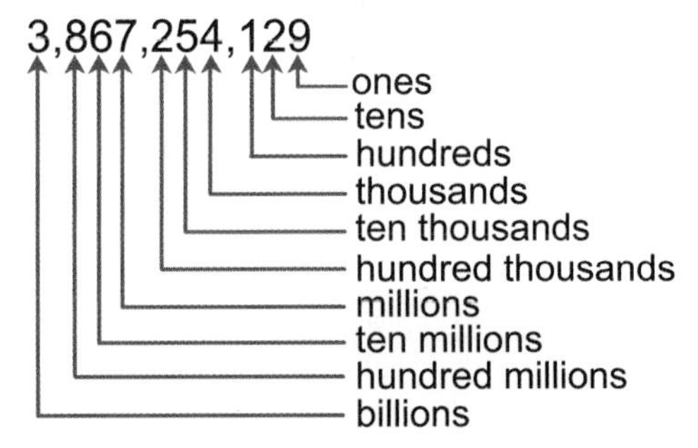

Exhibit 1.1(a): Place Value of a Ten-Digit Whole Number

We read and write numbers from left to right. A comma (or alternatively, a space) separates every three digits into groups, starting from the place value for 'ones', thereby making it easier to read a whole number.

The place value of 'ones' is 10^0 (= 1) and each place has a value 10 times the place value to its right, as shown in Table 1.1(a) below:

Table 1.1(a) Place Value Chart of Whole Numbers

10^9	10^8	10^7	10^6	10^5	10^4	10^3	10^2	10^1	10^0
1,000,000,000	100,000,000	10,000,000	1,000,000	100,000	10,000	1,000	100	10	1
Billions	**Hundred millions**	**Ten millions**	**Millions**	**Hundred thousands**	**Ten thousands**	**Thousands**	**Hundreds**	**Tens**	**Ones**

The red, vertical lines denote the positions of the commas that separate the groups of three numbers, starting from the place value for 'ones'. When written in **standard form**, the ten digit number in Exhibit 1.1(a) is written as 3,867,254,129.

3	8	6	7	2	5	4	1	2	9

This can be written in **expanded form** as follows:

- 3,000,000,000 + 800,000,000 + 60,000,000 + 7,000,000 + 200,000 + 50,000 + 4,000 + 100 + 20 + 9

Or,

- 3 billion + 800 million + 60 million + 7 million + 200 thousand + 50 thousand + 4 thousand + 1 hundred + 2 tens + 9 ones

Reading and Writing Whole Numbers

To make it easier to read and write numbers, any number larger than three digits is separated into smaller groups of three digits, starting from the last digit of the number. Each group of these three digits has a name.

Trillions			Billions			Millions			Thousands			Units		
Hundreds	Tens	Ones	Hundreds	Tens	Ones	Hundreds	Tens	Ones	Hundreds	Tens	Ones	Hundreds	Tens	Ones

Follow these steps to write large numbers in **word form**:

Step 1: Start from the group furthest to the left and write the number formed by the digits in that group, followed by the name of the group.

Step 2: Moving to the next group (to the right), write the numbers formed by this next group, followed by its name. Continue to do this for each of the groups.

Step 3: For the last group (i.e., the group furthest to the right), write the numbers formed by the group; however, for this group, do not write the name of it.

***Note:** When all three digits in a group are zero, that group is neither read nor written.*

Also, commas and hyphens are used when expressing numbers in word form.

- Commas (,) are used between the groups to separate them.
- Hyphens (-) are used to express the two digit numbers in each group; i.e., 21 to 29, 31 to 39, 41 to 49,...91 to 99.

The word 'and' does not appear in the word form of whole numbers.

For example, we write 700,629 in word form as: Seven hundred thousand, six hundred twenty-nine.

Place Value of Decimal Numbers

The position of each digit in a decimal number determines the place value of the digit. Exhibit 1.1(b) illustrates the place value of the five-digit decimal number: 0.35796.

The place value of each digit is found by decreasing powers of 10, as shown in Table 1.1(b) below:

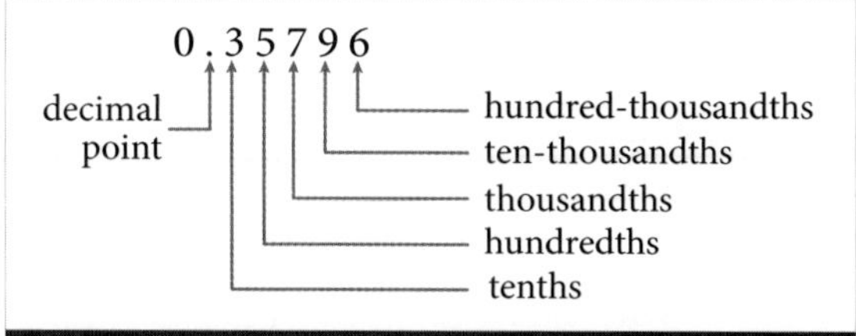

Exhibit 1.1(b): Place Value of a Five-Digit Decimal Number

Table 1.1(b) **Place Value Chart of Decimal Numbers**

$10^{-1} = \frac{1}{10}$	$10^{-2} = \frac{1}{100}$	$10^{-3} = \frac{1}{1,000}$	$10^{-4} = \frac{1}{10,000}$	$10^{-5} = \frac{1}{100,000}$
0.1	0.01	0.001	0.0001	0.00001
Tenths	**Hundredths**	**Thousandths**	**Ten-thousandths**	**Hundred-thousandths**

For example, the five-digit decimal number in Exhibit 1.1(b) is written as 0.35796 in **standard form.**

0.	3	5	7	9	6

This can be written in **expanded form** as follows:

- 0.3 + 0.05 + 0.007 + 0.0009 + 0.00006

Or,

- 3 tenths + 5 hundredths + 7 thousandths + 9 ten-thousandths + 6 hundred-thousandths

Reading and Writing Decimal Numbers

The word 'and' is used to represent the decimal point (.)

Follow these steps to read and write decimal numbers in **word form**:

Step 1: Read or write the numbers to the left of a decimal point as a whole number.

Step 2: Read or write the decimal point as 'and'.

Step 3: Read or write the number to the right of the decimal point also as a whole number, but followed by the name of the place value occupied by the digit on the far right.

- Hyphens (-) are used when expressing the place value portion of a decimal number such as ten-thousandths, hundred-thousandths, ten-millionths, hundred-millionths, etc.

For example, we write 745.023 in word form as:

Seven hundred forty-five and twenty-**three** thousandths

Whole Number Portion — Decimal Point — Decimal Portion

The last digit, three, ends in the thousandths place. Therefore, the decimal portion is $\frac{23}{1,000}$.

There are other ways of reading and writing decimal numbers as noted below.

(i) Use the word 'point' to indicate the decimal point, and, thereafter, read or write each digit individually.

For example, we read or write 745.023 as: Seven hundred forty-five point zero, two, three.

(ii) Ignore the decimal point of the decimal number and read or write the number as a whole number and include the place occupied by the digit on the far right of the decimal number.

For example,

For example, we read or write 745.023 as: Seven hundred forty-five thousand, twenty-three thousandths; i.e., $\frac{745,023}{1,000}$.

***Note:** The above two representations are not used in the examples and exercise questions within this chapter.*

Example 1.1(a) **Identifying the Place Value of a Digit and the Amount It Represents**

What is the place value of the digit 5 in each of the following numbers and what amount does it represent?

(i) 675,342 (ii) 35,721,890 (iii) 243.4759 (iv) 64.057 (v) 231.547

Solution

	(i) 675,342	(ii) 35,721,890	(iii) 243.4759	(iv) 64.057	(v) 231.547
Place Value of Digit 5	Thousands	Millions	Thousandths	Hundredths	Tenths
Amount it Represents	5,000	5,000,000	0.005	0.05	0.5

Example 1.1(b) **Identifying the Digit of a Number Given its Place Value**

In the number 320,948.751, identify the digit that occupies the following place values:

(i) Hundred thousands (ii) Ten thousands (iii) Thousands (iv) Hundredths (v) Tenths

Solution

(i) 3 (ii) 2 (iii) 0 (iv) 5 (v) 7

Example 1.1(c) **Writing Numbers in Expanded and Word Forms Given Their Standard Forms**

Write the following numbers in expanded and word forms:

(i) 43,583,621 (ii) 8,213,505,235 (iii) 478.25 (iv) 22.006 (v) 213.5078

Solution

(i) Standard form: 43,583,621
Expanded form: 40,000,000 + 3,000,000 + 500,000 + 80,000 + 3,000 + 600 + 20 + 1
Word form: Forty-three million, five hundred eighty-three thousand, six hundred twenty-one

(ii) Standard form: 8,213,505,235
Expanded form: 8,000,000,000 + 200,000,000 + 10,000,000 + 3,000,000 + 500,000 + 5,000 + 200 + 30 + 5
Word form: Eight billion, two hundred thirteen million, five hundred five thousand, two hundred thirty-five

(iii) Standard form: 478.25
Expanded form: 400 + 70 + 8 + 0.2 + 0.05
Word form: Four hundred seventy-eight and twenty-five hundredths

(iv) Standard form: 22.006
Expanded form: 20 + 2 + 0.006
Word form: Twenty-two and six thousandths

(v) Standard form: 213.5078
Expanded form: 200 + 10 + 3 + 0.5 + 0.007 + 0.0008
Word form: Two hundred thirteen and five thousand, seventy-eight ten-thousandths

Example 1.1(d) **Writing Numbers in Standard Form Given Their Word Form**

Write the following in standard form:

(i) Thirty-five thousand, eight hundred twenty-five
(ii) Three million, three hundred forty-two thousand, six hundred seventeen
(iii) Half of a million
(iv) Three-quarters of a billion

Solution

(i) 35,825
(ii) 3,342,617
(iii) Half of a million is $\frac{1}{2} \times 1{,}000{,}000 = 500{,}000$
(iv) Three-quarters of a billion is $\frac{3}{4} \times 1{,}000{,}000{,}000 = 750{,}000{,}000$

Rounding Whole Numbers and Decimal Numbers

Rounding numbers makes them easier to work with and easier to remember. Rounding changes some of the digits in a number but keeps its value close to the original. It is used in reporting large quantities or values that change often, such as in population, income, expenses, etc.

For example, the population of Canada is approximately 35 million, or Henry's car expense for this month is approximately $700.

Rounding of numbers also makes arithmetic operations faster and easier when it is not required to calculate the exact answer.

For example, if you are required to estimate the area of a rectangular plot of land that measures 114 m by 97 m, you would have to multiply 114 × 97, which will result in 11,058 m^2. However, you can get a quick estimate by rounding the measurements to the nearest ten. Rounding 114 m to the nearest ten is 110 m. Rounding 97 m to the nearest ten is 100 m. This will result in an estimated area of $110 \times 100 = 11{,}000$ m^2.

Rounding Whole Numbers to the Nearest Ten, Hundred, Thousand, etc.

Rounding whole numbers refers to changing the value of the whole number to the nearest ten, hundred, thousand, etc. It is also referred to as rounding whole numbers to multiples of 10, 100, 1000, etc.

For example,

- Rounding a whole number to the nearest ten is the same as rounding it to a multiple of 10.
- Rounding a whole number to the nearest hundred is the same as rounding it to a multiple of 100.
- Rounding an amount to the nearest $10 refers to rounding the amount to a multiple of $10.

Rounding Decimal Numbers to the Nearest Whole Number, Tenth, Hundredth, etc.

Rounding decimal numbers refers to changing the value of the decimal number to the nearest whole number, tenth, hundredth, thousandth, etc. It is also referred to as "rounding to a specific number of decimal places", indicating the number of decimal places that will be left when the rounding is complete.

For example,

- Rounding to the nearest whole number is the same as rounding without any decimals.
- Rounding to the nearest tenth is the same as rounding to one decimal place.
- Rounding to the nearest hundredth is the same as rounding to two decimal places.
- Rounding to the nearest cent refers to rounding the amount to the nearest hundredth or to two decimal places.

Rules for Rounding Whole Numbers and Decimal Numbers

Step 1: Identify the digit to be rounded (this is the place value for which the rounding is required).

Step 2: If the digit to the immediate right of the required rounding digit is less than 5 (0, 1, 2, 3, 4), do not change the value of the rounding digit.

If the digit to the immediate right of the required rounding digit is 5 or greater than 5 (5, 6, 7, 8, 9), increase the value of the rounding digit by one (round up by one number).

Step 3: For rounding whole numbers: after Step 2, change the value of all the digits that are to the right of the rounding digit to 0.

For rounding decimal numbers: after Step 2, drop all the digits that are to the right of the rounding digit.

Example 1.1(e) **Rounding Whole Numbers to the Indicated Place Values**

Round the following whole numbers to the indicated place values:

(i) 18,568 to the nearest ten

(ii) $24,643 to the nearest $100

Solution

(i) *Rounding 18,568 to the nearest ten*

- Identify the rounding digit in the tens place: 18,568 (6 is the digit in the tens place).
- The digit to the immediate right of the rounding digit is 8, which is greater than 5; therefore, increase the value of the rounding digit by one, from 6 to 7, and change the value of the digits that are to the right of the rounding digit to 0, which will result in 18,570.

Therefore, 18,568 rounded to the nearest ten (or multiple of 10) is 18,570.

(ii) *Rounding $24,643 to the nearest $100*

- Identify the rounding digit in the hundreds place: 24,643 (6 is the digit in the hundreds place).
- The digit to the immediate right of the rounding digit is 4, which is less than 5; therefore, do not change the value of the rounding digit, but change the value of the digits that are to the right of the rounding digit to 0, which will result in 24,600.

Therefore, $24,643 rounded to the nearest $100 (or multiple of $100) is $24,600.

Example 1.1(f) **Rounding Numbers (Visual Method Using a Number Line)**

Round the following numbers to the indicated place value:

(i) 627 to the nearest ten (multiples of 10)

(ii) 16.5 to a whole number

Solution

We can visualize these numbers on a number line to determine the nearest number.

(i) *Rounding 627 to the nearest ten (multiples of 10)*

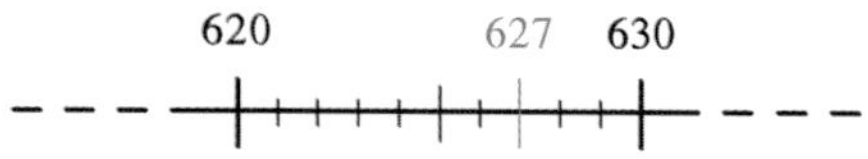

627 is closer to 630 than 620.

Therefore, 627 rounded to the nearest ten is 630.

(ii) *Rounding 16.5 to a whole number*

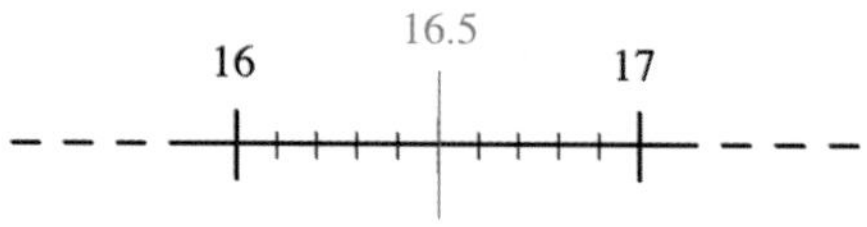

16.5 is at the mid-point of 16 and 17. By convention, if a number is exactly in the middle, we round it up.

Therefore, 16.5 rounded to a whole number is 17.

Example 1.1(g) **Rounding Decimal Numbers**

Round the following decimal numbers to the indicated place value:

(i) 268.143 to the nearest hundredth

(ii) $489.677 to the nearest cent

(iii) $39.9985 to the nearest cent

Solution

(i) *Rounding 268.143 to the nearest hundredth*

- Identify the rounding digit in the hundredths place: 268.143 (4 is the digit in the hundredths place).
- The digit to the immediate right of the rounding digit is less than 5; therefore, do not change the value of the rounding digit. Drop all the digits to the right of the rounding digit, which will result in 268.14.

Therefore, 268.143 rounded to the nearest hundredth (or to two decimal places) is 268.14.

(ii) *Rounding $489.677 to the nearest cent*

- Identify the rounding digit in the hundredths place: $489.677 (7 is the digit in the hundredths place).
- The digit to the immediate right of the rounding digit is greater than 5; therefore, increase the value of the rounding digit by one, from 7 to 8, and drop all the digits that are to the right of the rounding digit, which will result in $489.68.

Therefore, $489.677 rounded to the nearest cent (or to two decimal places) is $489.68.

(iii) *Rounding $39.9985 to the nearest cent*

- Identify the rounding digit in the hundredths place: $39.9985 (9 is the digit in the hundredths place).
- The digit to the immediate right of the rounding digit is greater than 5; therefore, increase the value of the rounding digit by one, from 9 to 10, carrying the one to the tenths place, then to the ones, then to the tens to increase 3 to 4. Finally, drop all the digits that are to the right of the hundredths place.

Therefore, $39.9985 rounded to the nearest cent (or to two decimal places) is $40.00.

Example 1.1(h)

Rounding Percents

Round the following percents to the number of decimal places indicated:

(i) 12.834% to one decimal place

(ii) 67.386% to two decimal places

(iii) 25.325% to two decimal places

Solution

(i) *Rounding 12.834% to one decimal place*

- Identify the rounding digit in the tenths place: 12.834% (8 is the digit in the tenths place).
- The digit to the immediate right of the rounding digit is less than 5; therefore, do not change the value of the rounding digit. Drop all the digits to the right of the rounding digit, which will result in 12.8%.

Therefore, 12.834% rounded to one decimal place (or nearest tenth) is 12.8%.

(ii) *Rounding 67.386% to two decimal places*

- Identify the rounding digit in the hundredths place: 67.386% (8 is the digit in the hundredths place).
- The digit to the immediate right of the rounding digit is greater than 5; therefore, increase the value of the rounding digit by one, from 8 to 9, and drop all the digits that are to the right of the rounding digit, which will result in 67.39%.

Therefore, 67.386% rounded to two decimal places (or nearest hundredth) is 67.39%.

(iii) *Rounding 25.325% to two decimal places*

- Identify the rounding digit in the hundredths place: 25.325% (2 is the digit in the hundredths place).
- The digit to the immediate right of the rounding digit is equal to 5; therefore, increase the value of the rounding digit by one, from 2 to 3, and drop all the digits that are to the right of the rounding digit, which will result in 25.33%.

Therefore, 25.325% rounded to two decimal places (or nearest hundredth) is 25.33%.

Example 1.1(i) **Rounding a Set of Percents which Add Up to 100%**

Stephanie spends 40.18% of her salary on rent, 20.61% on food, 15.62% on travel, 10.15% on entertainment, 5.5% on pet food, and saves the remaining 7.94%. Express these percents rounded to the nearest percent without decimals.

Solution

These percents rounded to the nearest percent without decimals (i.e., percent with whole number) would be:
Rent: 40%, Food: 21%, Travel: 16%, Entertainment: 10%, Pet food: 6%, and Savings: 8%.
However, the sum of these percents would result in:

$$40\% + 21\% + 16\% + 10\% + 6\% + 8\% = 101\%$$

We have to round these numbers so that they add up to 100%; therefore, 1% has to be reduced from one of these rounded numbers such that it does not have a significant effect.

Changing the largest percent will result in the smallest overall effect. If 40% is reduced to 39%, the change is $\frac{39\% - 40\%}{40\%} = -2.5\%$, but if 6% is reduced to 5%, the change is $\frac{5\% - 6\%}{6\%} = -16.67\%$.

Changing 40% has a smaller effect than changing the 6% value.
Therefore, the percents rounded to the nearest whole numbers are best represented as:
Rent: 39%, Food: 21%, Travel: 16%, Entertainment: 10%, Pet food: 6%, and Savings: 8%.

$$39\% + 21\% + 16\% + 10\% + 6\% + 8\% = 100\%$$

Do not round intermediate calculations. Round your final answer to two decimal places.

***Note:** In business and finance applications, final answers are generally rounded to the nearest hundredth (2 decimal places) for value of money (e.g., $1234.56) and percents (e.g., 4.86%).*

Estimation

Estimation is finding a number that is close to the right answer. In situations when an exact value is not required, we use an estimated value by rounding some or all of the numbers, factors, divisors, etc., so that it is easy to arrive at an answer using mental calculations.

In solving problems, particularly when using calculators, estimation helps to determine whether the calculated answer is reasonable and also helps to identify and prevent obvious mistakes. When using calculators, it is possible that numbers, operational keys, or decimal points may be incorrectly entered, leading to a wrong answer. Estimation helps to check the effective use of calculators.

We use various methods of estimation to judge whether the answer from a calculation is reasonable. The following are a few examples of estimation:

- To estimate the addition and subtraction of numbers, we may first round each number to the same place value and then add or subtract. Alternatively, we may round the numbers to their biggest place values first, and then add or subtract.

  For example, to estimate the value of 6724 + 4167 – 685,

  - by rounding to the nearest hundred, we obtain: 6700 + 4200 – 700 = 10,200
  - by rounding to the biggest place value, we obtain: 7000 + 4000 – 700 = 10,300

  Compare with the exact value: 10,206

- To estimate the product of numbers, we may round each number to its biggest place value so that it has only one non-zero digit. Then, drop all the zeroes and mentally multiply the non-zero numbers. Finally, reinstate all the zeroes that were dropped earlier. Alternatively, we may round one or two factors that can be easily multiplied mentally with the other factors.

  For example, to estimate the value of $3249 \times 504 \times 19$,

  - by rounding to the biggest place value, we obtain: $3000 \times 500 \times 20 = (3 \times 5 \times 2) \times 1{,}000{,}000 = 30 \times 1{,}000{,}000 = 30{,}000{,}000$
  - by rounding two factors, we obtain: $3249 \times 500 \times 20 = 3249 \times (5 \times 2) \times 1000 = 3249 \times 10{,}000 = 32{,}490{,}000$

  Compare with the exact value: 31,112,424

- To estimate the division of numbers, we may round each number to its biggest place value, drop the zeroes that are common to both the numerator and denominator, and divide mentally. Alternatively, we may round the numbers to multiples of a common number.

  For example, to estimate the value of $579 \div 26$,

  - by rounding to the biggest place value, we obtain: $600 \div 30 = 60 \div 3 = 20$
  - by rounding to multiples of 25, we obtain: $575 \div 25 = 23$

  Compare with the exact value rounded to the nearest two decimal places: 22.27

1.1 | Exercises

Answers to the odd-numbered problems are available at the end of the textbook.

1. Write the following numbers in (i) expanded form and (ii) word form:
   a. 7,061 b. 40,318 c. 5,249,346 d. 95,275,385
2. Write the following numbers in (i) expanded form and (ii) word form:
   a. 9,807 b. 32,045 c. 9,265,335 d. 30,673,984
3. Write the following numbers in (i) expanded form and (ii) word form:
   a. 0.35 b. 0.067 c. 41.08 d. 19.006
4. Write the following numbers in (i) expanded form and (ii) word form:
   a. 9.07 b. 0.053 c. 0.59 d. 51.002
5. Write the following in (i) standard form and (ii) expanded form:
   a. Sixty-five thousand, two hundred forty-four and thirty-four hundredths
   b. Twelve million, four hundred fifty-two thousand, eight hundred thirty-two
   c. Half of a billion d. Seven and four tenths
6. Write the following in (i) standard form and (ii) expanded form:
   a. Eight hundred thirty-three thousand, six hundred forty-one and eighty-two hundredths
   b. Thirty-two million, six hundred eighty-four thousand, two hundred fifty-six
   c. Three-quarters of a million d. Twenty-three and twenty-five thousandths
7. Write the following in standard form:
   a. Eighty-nine million, six hundred thirteen thousand, five hundred twenty-two and thirteen hundredths
   b. Sixteen million, two hundred seventeen thousand, five hundred sixty-seven
   c. Half of a million d. Eighty-seven and five tenths
8. Write the following in standard form:
   a. Nine hundred fifty thousand, six hundred fifty and five hundredths
   b. Sixty-five thousand, eight hundred fifty-six
   c. One-quarter of a billion d. Two hundred and two hundredths
9. Round the following to the indicated place values:
   a. 1645 to the nearest ten b. 9558 to the nearest thousand
   c. \$25,972 to the nearest \$1000 d. \$895 to the nearest \$10
10. Round the following to the indicated place values:
    a. 9157 to the nearest hundred b. 53,562 to the nearest ten
    c. \$7915 to the nearest \$100 d. \$1095 to the nearest \$10
11. Round the following to the indicated place values:
    a. 132.1356 to the nearest tenth b. 2.8525 to the nearest whole number
    c. \$85.4273 to the nearest cent d. \$34.9861 to the nearest cent

12. Round the following to the indicated place values:

a. 14.3575 to the nearest thousandth
b. 142.9852 to the nearest whole number
c. \$86.6246 to the nearest cent
d. \$4.0573 to the nearest cent

13. Express the following decimal numbers in their word form:

a. 6.7 b. 0.45 c. 0.034 d. 1.006

14. Express the following decimal numbers in their word form:

a. 2.4 b. 0.91 c. 0.073 d. 1.002

For Problems 15 to 18, round the percents to (i) the nearest whole percent (without decimals), (ii) the nearest percent with one decimal place, and (iii) the nearest percent with two decimal places:

15. a. 5.567% b. 29.875%
16. a. 56.596% b. 140.265%
17. a. 75.253% b. 115.796%
18. a. 8.955% b. 19.555%

For Problems 19 to 26, (i) estimate the values by first rounding the numbers to the nearest ten, and (ii) calculate the exact answer. Express answers rounded to two decimal places, wherever applicable.

19. a. 745 + 1045 b. 428 + 255 c. 326 + 1555
20. a. 357 + 245 b. 451 + 625 c. 3255 + 2105
21. a. 2449 – 2255 b. 946 – 452 c. 855 – 251
22. a. 495 – 357 b. 868 – 745 c. 1858 – 255
23. a. 58 × 75 b. 472 × 48 c. 95 × 71
24. a. 63 × 59 b. 35 × 97 c. 246 × 45
25. a. 85 ÷ 9 b. 396 ÷ 24 c. 145 ÷ 26
26. a. 78 ÷ 19 b. 245 ÷ 45 c. 38 ÷ 8
27. Estimate the values in Problems 19 and 21 by first rounding the numbers to the nearest hundred.
28. Estimate the values in Problems 20 and 22 by first rounding the numbers to the nearest hundred.
29. A prepaid phone card to make calls to Singapore for 3 hours costs \$5. Calculate the cost per minute rounded to the nearest cent.
30. A prepaid phone card to make calls to China for 1 hour costs \$2.50. Calculate the cost per minute rounded to the nearest cent.
31. 55.25% of the employees of a large software company are engineers, 35.40% are project managers and team leads, 2.40% are senior managers, and the rest are administrative staff. By rounding the given percents to the nearest percent without decimals, estimate the percent of employees that are administrative staff.
32. Amy invested 4.20% of her savings in bonds, 32.65% in stocks, 25.55% in mutual funds, and the balance in her brother's business. By rounding the given percents to the nearest percent without decimals, estimate the percent that Amy invested in her brother's business.

Express the following numbers in decimal notation.

• 33. a. $\frac{3}{10}$ b. $17\frac{9}{100}$ c. $15\frac{297}{1000}$ d. $\frac{7}{1000}$

• 34. a. $\frac{7}{10}$ b. $12\frac{7}{100}$ c. $13\frac{123}{1000}$ d. $\frac{3}{100}$

For Problems 35 to 40, estimate the values by first rounding the numbers to the nearest ten.

• 35. Girija wants to save \$6300. If she saves \$205 per month, how many months will it take her to achieve her goal?

• 36. How long will it take to travel 910 km at 63 km per hour?

• 37. An item costs \$176.92. If you give \$200 to the cashier, what will you receive as your balance?

• 38. The normal selling price of an item is \$457.50. If the item is discounted by \$70, what is the reduced price of the item?

• 39. Chandler leased a car on a 30-month term at \$475.75 per month. At the end of the lease period, he paid an additional \$12,578.90 to purchase the car. Determine the total amount Chandler paid for the car.

• 40. Mythili bought a TV and agreed to pay \$175.75 every month for ten months. A few months later, the TV went on sale for \$1699.99. How much more money than the sale price did she pay for the TV?

1.2 | Factors and Multiples

Factors of a number are whole numbers that can divide the number with no remainder. For example, factors of 12 are 1, 2, 3, 4, 6, and 12. We can express factors of a number by showing that the product of two factors will result in the number.

$12 = 1 \times 12$ or 12×1

$12 = 2 \times 6$ or 6×2

$12 = 3 \times 4$ or 4×3

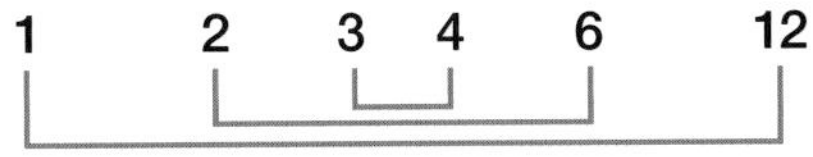

Multiples of a number are whole numbers that can be divided by the number with no remainder. For example, multiples of 10 are 10, 20, 30, 40, 50, etc. We can express multiples of a number as the product of the number and a whole number.

10×1,	10×2,	10×3,	10×4,	10×5
10,	20,	30,	40,	50

Prime Numbers and Composite Numbers

A **prime number** is a natural number (counting number) that has exactly two different factors: 1 and the number itself; i.e., prime numbers can be divided only by 1 and the number itself.

For example, 7 is a prime number because it has exactly two different factors: 1 and 7.

A **composite number** is a natural number that has at least one factor other than 1 and the number itself; i.e., all natural numbers that are not prime numbers are composite numbers.

For example, 8 is a composite number because it has more than 2 factors: 1, 2, 4, and 8.

Note: *0 and 1 are neither prime nor composite numbers because 0 is not a natural number and 1 has no other factor other than itself.*

Example 1.2(a) **Identifying Prime Numbers and Composite Numbers**

(i) Identify all the prime numbers less than 25.

(ii) Identify all the composite numbers less than 25.

Solution

(i) All the prime numbers less than 25 are: 2, 3, 5, 7, 11, 13, 17, 19, and 23.

(ii) All the composite numbers less than 25 are: 4, 6, 8, 9, 10, 12, 14, 15, 16, 18, 20, 21, 22, and 24.

Example 1.2(b) **Determining Factors of Prime Numbers**

Determine all the factors of 13.

Solution

1 and 13 are the only factors of 13.

Example 1.2(c) **Determining All Factors of Composite Numbers**

Determine all the factors of:

(i) 18 (ii) 20

Solution

(i) The factors of 18 are: 1, 2, 3, 6, 9, and 18.

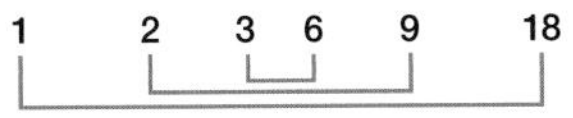

(ii) The factors of 20 are: 1, 2, 4, 5, 10, and 20.

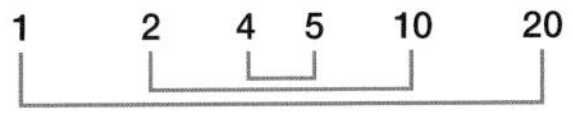

Example 1.2(d) **Determining the Prime Factors of Composite Numbers**

Determine all the prime factors of 24.

Solution

All the factors of 24 are: 1, 2, 3, 4, 6, 8, 12, and 24.

In the above factors, only 2 and 3 are prime numbers.

Therefore, the prime factors of 24 are: 2 and 3.

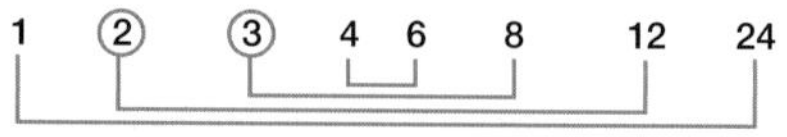

Least or Lowest Common Multiple (LCM)

The **Least Common Multiple (LCM)** of two or more natural numbers is the smallest multiple that is common to those numbers. The LCM can be determined from one of the following methods:

Method 1

- If the last digit of the number is 0, 2, 4, 6, or 8, then the number is divisible by 2.
- If the sum of the digits of the numbers is divisible by 3, then the number is divisible by 3.
- If the last digit of the number is 0 or 5, then the number is divisible by 5.

(1) First, select the largest number and check to see if it is divisible by all the other numbers. If it is, then the largest number is the LCM. If it is not, then the LCM is greater than the largest number.

(2) If the largest number is not divisible by all the other numbers, check to see if any of the numbers have any common factors between them (other than 1). If they do not, then the LCM is the product of all the numbers. If they do, then the LCM is less than the product of all the numbers.

(3) If the numbers have a common factor between them, then the LCM will be greater than the largest number, and less than the product of all the numbers. Determine the lowest multiple of the largest number that is divisible by all the other numbers. This value is the LCM.

Method 2

(1) Determine the prime factors of each of the numbers and list the different prime numbers (using a factor tree as shown in the example that follows).

(2) Count the number of times each different prime number appears in each of the factorizations.

(3) Determine the largest of these counts for each prime number.

(4) List that prime number as many times as you counted it in Step 3. The LCM is the product of all the prime numbers listed.

Example 1.2(e) **Determining the Least Common Multiple**

Determine the LCM of the following:

(i) 3, 6, and 18 (ii) 9 and 15 (iii) 3, 5, and 8

Solution

(i) *Determining the LCM of 3, 6, and 18*

Method 1

(1) The largest number, 18, is divisible by both 6 and 3.

Therefore, 18 is the LCM of 3, 6, and 18.

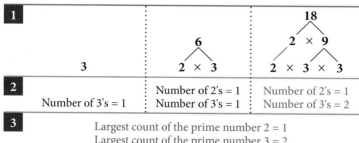

Method 2

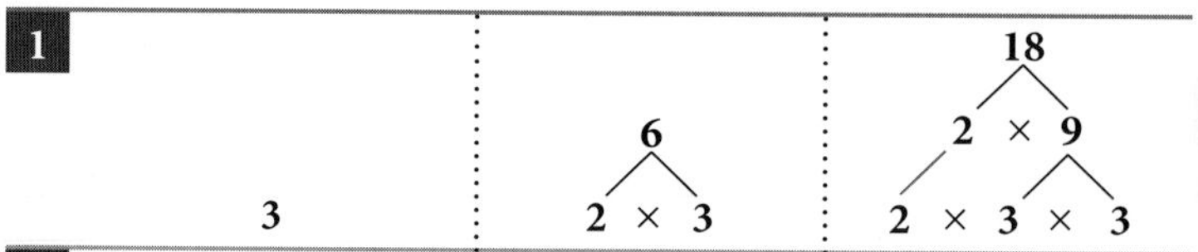

2	Number of 3's = 1	Number of 2's = 1 Number of 3's = 1	Number of 2's = 1 Number of 3's = 2
3	Largest count of the prime number 2 = 1 Largest count of the prime number 3 = 2		
4	LCM = 2 × 3 × 3 = 18		

The largest number, 18, is divisible by 6 and 3. Therefore, the LCM is the largest number, 18.

Solution *continued*

(ii) *Determining the LCM of 9 and 15*

Method 1

(1) The largest number, 15, is ***not*** divisible by 9.
Therefore, the LCM is greater than 15.

(2) Factors of 9 are: 1, 3, and 9.
Factors of 15 are: 1, 3, 5, and 15.
9 and 15 have a common factor of 3.
Therefore, the LCM is less than 9 × 15 = 135.

(3) Multiples of 15 are: 15, 30, 45...
45 is divisible by 9.
Therefore, 45 is the LCM of 9 and 15.

Method 2

Step		
1	9 = 3 × 3	15 = 3 × 5
2	Number of 3's = 2	Number of 3's = 1 Number of 5's = 1
3	Largest count of the prime number 3 = 2 Largest count of the prime number 5 = 1	
4	LCM = 3 × 3 × 5 = 45	

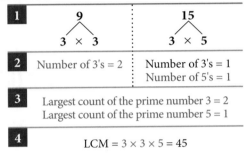

9 and 15 share a common factor of 3. Therefore, the LCM is greater than the largest number, 15, and less than the product of the numbers, 9 × 15 = 135.

(iii) *Determining the LCM of 3, 5, and 8*

Method 1

(1) The largest number, 8, is ***not*** divisible by 3 and 5.
Therefore, the LCM is greater than 8.

(2) Factors of 3 are: 1 and 3.
Factors of 5 are: 1 and 5.
Factors of 8 are: 1, 2, 4, and 8.
3, 5, and 8 do ***not*** share a common factor (other than 1).
Therefore, 3 × 5 × 8 = 120 is the LCM of 3, 5, and 8.

Method 2

Step			
1	3	5	8 = 2 × 4 = 2 × 2 × 2
2	Number of 3's = 1	Number of 5's = 1	Number of 2's = 3
3	Largest count of the prime number 2 = 3 Largest count of the prime number 3 = 1 Largest count of the prime number 5 = 1		
4	LCM = 2 × 2 × 2 × 3 × 5 = 120		

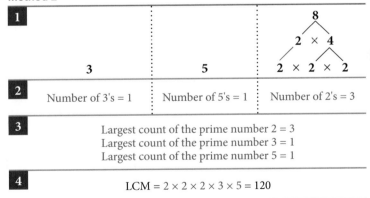

The numbers have no common factors between all of them. Therefore, the LCM is the product of all the numbers.

Example 1.2(f) **Determining the Least Common Multiple to Solve a Word Problem**

Two flashing lights are turned on at the same time. One light flashes every 12 seconds and the other flashes every 15 seconds. How often will they flash together?

Solution

In this example, we are required to determine the least common interval for both lights to flash together. Thereafter, both lights will continue to flash together at this interval (multiple).

The largest number, 15, is not divisible by 12.

12 and 15 share a common factor of 3.

Therefore, the LCM is greater than 15 and less than $12 \times 15 = 180$.

Multiples of 15 are: 15, 30, 45, 60, 75...

Multiples of 12 are: 12, 24, 36, 48, 60, 72...

The LCM of 12 and 15 is 60.

Therefore, the two flashing lights will flash together every 60 seconds (1 minute).

Least or Lowest Common Denominator (LCD)

The **Least Common Denominator (LCD)** of a set of two or more fractions is the smallest whole number that is divisible by each of the denominators. It is the least common multiple (LCM) of the denominators of the fractions.

In performing the addition and subtraction of fractions, it is necessary to determine the equivalent fraction using the least common denominator. The best choice for a common denominator is the LCD, because it makes any further simplification easier.

Example 1.2(g) **Determining the Least Common Denominator**

Determine the LCD of $\frac{4}{9}$ and $\frac{7}{15}$.

Solution

The LCD of the fractions $\frac{4}{9}$ and $\frac{7}{15}$ is the same as the LCM of the denominators 9 and 15. It is the same as in Example 1.2(e)(ii). Therefore, the LCD of $\frac{4}{9}$ and $\frac{7}{15}$ is 45.

Greatest Common Factor (GCF)

The factors that are common for two or more natural numbers are called common factors of those numbers.

The **Greatest Common Factor (GCF)** of two or more numbers is the largest common number that divides the numbers with no remainder. In other words, the GCF is the largest of all the common factors. GCF is useful when simplifying fractions. For this purpose, GCF is also known as the Greatest Common Divisor (GCD).

Example 1.2(h) **Determining the Common Factors**

Determine the common factors of 12 and 18.

Solution

The factors of 12 are: 1, 2, 3, 4, 6, 12.

The factors of 18 are: 1, 2, 3, 6, 9, 18.

Therefore, the common factors are: 2, 3, and 6.

1 is a factor that is common to all numbers but is not included in the list of common factors.

Example 1.2(i) **Determining the Greatest Common Factor**

Determine the GCF of 72, 126, and 216.

Solution

The factors of 72 are: 1, 2, 3, 4, 6, 8, 9, 12, 18, 24, 36, 72.
The factors of 126 are: 1, 2, 3, 6, 7, 9, 14, 18, 21, 42, 63, 126.

The factors of 216 are: 1, 2, 3, 4, 6, 8, 9, 12, 18, 24, 27, 36, 54, 72, 108, 216.

The common factors are: 2, 3, 6, 9, and 18.

Therefore, the GCF is 18.

Example 1.2(j) **Determining the Greatest Common Factor to Solve a Word Problem**

Three pieces of timber with lengths 24 cm, 36 cm, and 48 cm are to be cut into smaller pieces of equal length without remainders. What is the greatest possible length of each piece?

Solution

In this example we are required to determine the greatest common length of the three pieces of timber.

The factors of 24 are: 1, 2, 3, 4, 6, 8, 12, and 24.

The factors of 36 are: 1, 2, 3, 4, 6, 9, 12, 18, and 36.

The factors of 48 are: 1, 2, 3, 4, 6, 8, 12, 16, 24, and 48.

The common factors are: 2, 3, 4, 6, and 12.

The GCF is 12.

Therefore, the greatest possible length of equal piece is 12 cm.

1.2 | Exercises

Answers to the odd-numbered problems are available at the end of the textbook.

Determine all (i) the prime numbers and (ii) the composite numbers within the following ranges (excluding both the given numbers):

1. a. Between 1 and 10 b. Between 14 and 28
2. a. Between 10 and 22 b. Between 28 and 38
3. a. Between 32 and 42 b. Between 44 and 58
4. a. Between 42 and 55 b. Between 54 and 72

Determine all the prime factors of the following composite numbers:

5. a. 36 b. 28
6. a. 20 b. 34
7. a. 54 b. 65
8. a. 46 b. 21
9. a. 56 b. 60
10. a. 64 b. 49

Determine the Least Common Multiple (LCM) of the following:

11. a. 5 and 15 b. 6 and 8
12. a. 7 and 21 b. 6 and 9
13. a. 4, 6, and 18 b. 4, 10, and 12
14. a. 2, 15, and 30 b. 3, 7, and 14
15. a. 12, 40, and 48 b. 14, 28, and 42
16. a. 24, 36, and 12 b. 6, 15, and 18

Determine the Least Common Denominator (LCD) of the following:

17. a. $\frac{2}{7}$ and $\frac{3}{14}$ b. $\frac{8}{3}$ and $\frac{4}{11}$
18. a. $\frac{1}{3}$ and $\frac{32}{21}$ b. $\frac{7}{8}$ and $\frac{5}{12}$
19. a. $\frac{3}{4}, \frac{6}{15}$, and $\frac{8}{5}$ b. $\frac{1}{2}, \frac{13}{3}$, and $\frac{6}{7}$
20. a. $\frac{1}{6}, \frac{11}{4}$, and $\frac{3}{5}$ b. $\frac{2}{5}, \frac{4}{13}$, and $\frac{3}{11}$
21. a. $\frac{3}{8}$ and $\frac{5}{14}$ b. $\frac{5}{10}$ and $\frac{3}{20}$
22. a. $\frac{2}{7}$ and $\frac{3}{21}$ b. $\frac{7}{15}$ and $\frac{3}{25}$

Determine the (i) factors, (ii) common factors, and (iii) greatest common factors (GCF) of the following:

23. a. 36 and 84 b. 48 and 160
24. a. 13 and 91 b. 93 and 124
25. a. 35 and 75 b. 24 and 64
26. a. 18 and 32 b. 16 and 30
27. a. 50, 75, and 125 b. 30, 75, and 90
28. a. 40, 50, and 80 b. 12, 36, and 48
29. a. 76, 114, and 152 b. 96, 144, and 216
30. a. 33, 143, and 176 b. 85, 102, and 204
31. Two wires of lengths 96 cm and 160 cm are to be cut into pieces of equal length, without wastage. Determine the greatest possible length of each piece.
32. Two ribbons of lengths 112 cm and 154 cm are to be cut into pieces of equal length, without wastage. Determine the greatest possible length of each piece.
33. Tahrell has music lessons every 6th day and swimming lessons every 8th day. If he had his first music and swimming lessons on February 04, on which date will he have both lessons again?
34. Enea has skating lessons every 8th day and ballet lessons every 10th day. If she had her first skating and ballet lessons on March 03, on which date will she have both lessons again?

1.3 | Fractions

Definition of Fractions and Types of Fractions

A **fraction** is a rational number written as one integer divided by another non-zero integer. It is usually written as a pair of numbers, with the top number being called the numerator and the bottom number the denominator. A fraction line (horizontal bar indicating division) separates the numerator and the denominator. The use of fractions is another method of representing numbers.

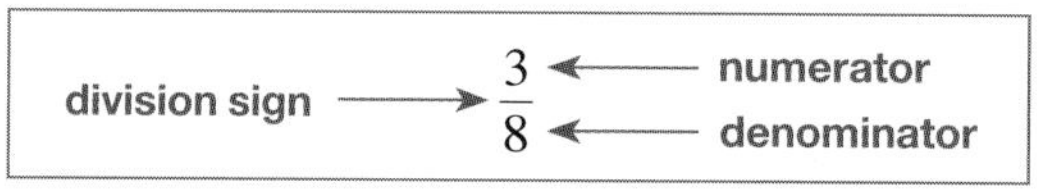

For example, $\frac{3}{8}$ (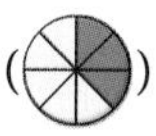) is a fraction. It is read as "three divided by eight", "three-eighths", or "three over eight", which all indicate that 3 is the numerator and 8 the denominator.

A **proper fraction** is a fraction in which the absolute value of the numerator is less than the absolute value of the denominator; i.e., the absolute value of the entire fraction is less than 1.

For example,

- $\frac{3}{8}$ (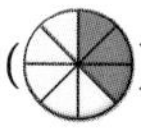) is a proper fraction.
- $\frac{-2}{5}$ in absolute value is $\frac{2}{5}$ (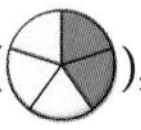), which is a proper fraction. Therefore, $\frac{-2}{5}$ is a proper fraction.

The absolute value of a number refers to the positive sign of that number.

For example, the absolute value of −2 is 2.

i.e. |−2| = 2.

An **improper fraction** is a fraction in which the absolute value of the numerator is greater than the absolute value of the denominator; i.e., the absolute value of the entire fraction is more than 1.

For example, $\frac{7}{4}$ (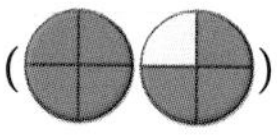) and $\frac{-3}{2}$ (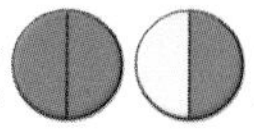) are improper fractions.

(seven quarters) (negative three halves)

A **mixed number** consists of both a whole number and a proper fraction, written side-by-side, which implies that the whole number and proper fraction are added.

For example, $3\frac{5}{8}$ implies $3 + \frac{5}{8}$

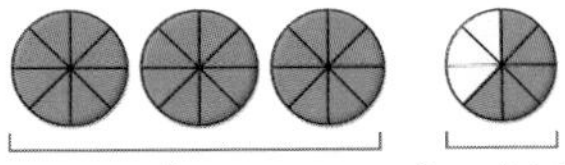

Mixed Number

$3\frac{5}{8}$ ← Fraction

↑ Whole Number

A **complex fraction** is a fraction in which one or more fractions are found in the numerator or denominator.

For example, $\dfrac{1}{\left(\frac{3}{4}\right)}$, $\dfrac{\left(\frac{2}{3}\right)}{6}$, and $\dfrac{3\frac{5}{6}}{\left(\frac{1}{8}\right)}$ are complex fractions.

Whole Number as a Fraction

Any whole number can be written as a fraction by dividing it by 1 (i.e., 1 is the denominator).

For example, $7 = \frac{7}{1}$

Reciprocal of a Fraction

Two numbers whose product is equal to 1 are called reciprocals of each other.

For example, $\frac{4}{7}$ and $\frac{7}{4}$ are reciprocals of each other because $\frac{4}{7} \times \frac{7}{4} = 1$

When the numerator and denominator of a fraction are interchanged, the resulting fraction is called the reciprocal of the original fraction.

For example, the reciprocal of 7, which is equal to $\frac{7}{1}$, is $\frac{1}{7}$

***Note:** The reciprocal of a fraction is not an equivalent fraction.*

Converting a Mixed Number into an Improper Fraction

Follow these steps to convert a mixed number into an improper fraction:

- Multiply the whole number by the denominator of the fraction and add this value to the numerator of the fraction.
- The resulting answer will be the numerator of the improper fraction.
- The denominator of the improper fraction is the same as the denominator of the original fraction in the mixed number.

For example, $3\frac{5}{8} = \dfrac{3(8) + 5}{8} = \dfrac{24 + 5}{8} = \dfrac{29}{8}$

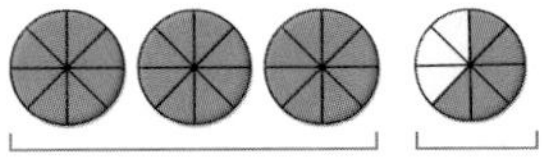

Thus, there is a total of 29 pieces, each piece being one-eighth in size.

Converting an Improper Fraction into a Mixed Number

Follow these steps to convert an improper fraction into a mixed number:

- Divide the numerator by the denominator.
- The quotient becomes the whole number and the remainder becomes the numerator of the fraction.
- The denominator of the fraction is the same as the denominator of the original improper fraction.

For example, $\frac{32}{5} = 6\frac{2}{5}$ Because,

$$\begin{array}{r} 6 \\ 5\overline{)32} \\ 30 \\ \hline 2 \end{array}$$

6 ← Quotient: whole number of the fraction

2 ← Remainder: numerator of the fraction

Converting a Fraction to its Decimal Form

A proper or improper fraction can be converted to its decimal form by dividing the numerator by the denominator.

For example, $\frac{2}{5} = 0.4$, $\frac{13}{8} = 1.625$

A mixed number can be converted to its decimal form by first converting the fractional part by dividing the numerator by the denominator, and then adding the whole number part to the decimal equivalent of the fraction.

For example,

- $3\frac{2}{5} = 3 + \frac{2}{5} = 3 + 0.4 = 3.4$
- $11\frac{3}{7} = 11 + \frac{3}{7} = 11 + 0.428571... = 11.428571...$

Converting a Fraction into an Equivalent Fraction

When both the numerator and denominator of a fraction are either multiplied by the same number or divided by the same number, the result is a new fraction called an **equivalent fraction**. Equivalent fractions imply that the old and new fractions have the same value.

For example, to determine two equivalent fractions of $\frac{2}{5}$ :

$\frac{2}{5} = \frac{2 \times 2}{5 \times 2}$ Multiplying both the numerator and denominator by 2,

$= \frac{4}{10}$ 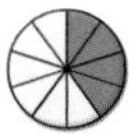

$\frac{2}{5} = \frac{2 \times 3}{5 \times 3}$ Multiplying both the numerator and denominator by 3,

$= \frac{6}{15}$ 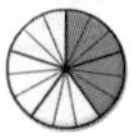

Therefore, $\frac{4}{10}$ and $\frac{6}{15}$ are equivalent fractions of $\frac{2}{5}$.

Dividing both the numerator and denominator of a fraction by the same number is called **reducing** or **simplifying** a fraction.

Consider another example to determine two equivalent fractions of $\frac{36}{60}$ 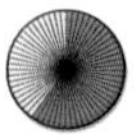:

$\frac{36}{60} = \frac{36 \div 2}{60 \div 2}$ Dividing both the numerator and denominator by 2,

$= \frac{18}{30}$ 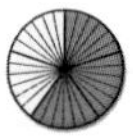

$\frac{36}{60} = \frac{36 \div 4}{60 \div 4}$ Dividing both the numerator and denominator by 4,

$= \frac{9}{15}$ 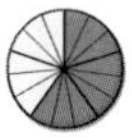

Therefore, $\frac{18}{30}$ and $\frac{9}{15}$ are equivalent fractions of $\frac{36}{60}$.

Reducing or Simplifying a Fraction

Dividing both the numerator and denominator of a fraction by the same number, which results in an equivalent fraction, is called **reducing** or **simplifying** the fraction.

For example, we can simplify $\frac{16}{20}$ as shown:

$$\frac{16}{20} = \frac{16 \div 2}{20 \div 2}$$ Dividing both the numerator and denominator by 2,

$$= \mathbf{\frac{8}{10}}$$

$$= \frac{8 \div 2}{10 \div 2}$$ Further dividing both the numerator and denominator by 2,

$$= \mathbf{\frac{4}{5}}$$

Or, $$\frac{16}{20} = \frac{16 \div 4}{20 \div 4}$$ Dividing both the numerator and denominator by 4,

$$= \mathbf{\frac{4}{5}}$$

Therefore, $\frac{8}{10}$ and $\frac{4}{5}$ are reduced fractions of $\frac{16}{20}$.

Fraction in Lowest (or Simplest) Terms

A fraction in which the numerator and denominator have no factors in common (other than 1) is said to be a **fraction in its lowest (or simplest) terms**. Any fraction can be **fully reduced** to its lowest terms by dividing both the numerator and denominator by the greatest common factor (GCF).

Example 1.3(a) **Reducing Fractions to their Lowest Terms**

Reduce the following fractions to their lowest terms.

(i) $\frac{40}{45}$ (ii) $\frac{63}{84}$

Solution

(i) The factors of 40 are: 1, 2, 4, 5, 8, 10, 20, 40.

The factors of 45 are: 1, 3, 5, 9, 15, 45.

The GCF is 5.

Therefore, dividing the numerator and denominator by the GCF, 5, results in the fraction in its lowest terms: $$\frac{40}{45} = \frac{40 \div 5}{45 \div 5} = \frac{8}{9}$$ 

(ii) The factors of 63 are: 1, 3, 7, 9, 21, 63.

The factors of 84 are: 1, 2, 3, 4, 6, 7, 12, 14, 21, 28, 42, 84.

The GCF is 21.

Therefore, dividing the numerator and denominator by the GCF, 21, results in the fraction in its lowest terms: $$\frac{63}{84} = \frac{63 \div 21}{84 \div 21} = \frac{3}{4}$$ 

Comparing Fractions

Fractions can easily be compared when they have the same denominator. If they do not have the same denominator, determine the LCD of the fractions, then convert them into equivalent fractions with the LCD as their denominators. When the denominators are the same, the larger fraction is the one with the greater numerator.

For example, $\frac{7}{12} > \frac{5}{12}$, 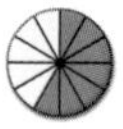 > 

Also, when the numerators are the same, the larger fraction is the one with the smaller denominator.

For example, $\frac{3}{4} > \frac{3}{8}$, 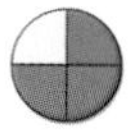 > 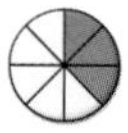

Example 1.3(b) **Comparing Fractions**

Determine which of the fractions is larger in each set of fractions given below:

(i) $\frac{9}{25}$ or $\frac{11}{25}$ (ii) $\frac{5}{12}$ or $\frac{3}{8}$ (iii) $\frac{19}{60}$ or $\frac{11}{36}$ (iv) $\frac{15}{22}$ or $\frac{15}{26}$

Solution

(i) $\frac{9}{25}$ or $\frac{11}{25}$

Since the fractions have the same denominator, 25, we can compare the numerators to identify the larger fraction.

$11 > 9$; therefore, $\frac{11}{25} > \frac{9}{25}$.

(ii) $\frac{5}{12}$ or $\frac{3}{8}$

We first determine the LCD of the fractions, which is the same as the LCM of the denominators.

The LCM of 12 and 8 is 24.

Next, convert each of the fractions to its equivalent fraction with 24 as the denominator.

Convert $\frac{5}{12}$ to an equivalent fraction with 24 as the denominator by multiplying both the numerator and denominator by 2: $\frac{5}{12} = \frac{5 \times 2}{12 \times 2} = \frac{10}{24}$.

Similarly, convert $\frac{3}{8}$ to an equivalent fraction with 24 as the denominator: $\frac{3}{8} = \frac{3 \times 3}{8 \times 3} = \frac{9}{24}$.

Since the denominators are the same, we can now compare the numerators of the two fractions to identify the larger fraction.

$10 > 9$, which implies that $\frac{10}{24} > \frac{9}{24}$; therefore, $\frac{5}{12} > \frac{3}{8}$.

(iii) $\frac{19}{60}$ or $\frac{11}{36}$

We first determine the LCD of the fractions, which is the same as the LCM of the denominators.

The LCM of 60 and 36 is 180.

Convert $\frac{19}{60}$ to an equivalent fraction with 180 as the denominator by multiplying both the numerator and denominator by 3: $\frac{19}{60} = \frac{19 \times 3}{60 \times 3} = \frac{57}{180}$.

Solution *continued*

Similarly, convert $\frac{11}{36}$ to an equivalent fraction with 180 as the denominator: $\frac{11}{36} = \frac{11 \times 5}{36 \times 5} = \frac{55}{180}$.

Since the denominators are the same, we can now compare the numerators of the two fractions to identify the larger fraction.

$57 > 55$, which implies that $\frac{57}{180} > \frac{55}{180}$; therefore, $\frac{19}{60} > \frac{11}{36}$.

(iv) $\frac{15}{22}$ or $\frac{15}{26}$

Since the fractions have the same numerator, 15, we can compare the denominators to identify the larger fraction.

$22 < 26$; therefore, $\frac{15}{22} > \frac{15}{26}$.

Basic Arithmetic Operations with Fractions

When performing additions and subtractions of fractions, it is necessary to determine their equivalent fractions using the least common denominator (LCD). When performing multiplications and divisions of fractions, it is necessary to convert any mixed number to an improper fraction.

Adding Fractions

Addition of fractions requires that the denominators of every fraction be the same. To make them the same, first determine the LCD and convert each fraction to its equivalent fraction with the LCD as the common denominator. Now, add the numerators of each of the equivalent fractions. The resulting fraction will have the common denominator, and its numerator will be the result of adding the numerators of the equivalent fractions. Express the final answer reduced to its lowest terms and as a mixed number, where applicable.

Example 1.3(c) **Adding Fractions**

(i) Add $\frac{3}{4}$ and $\frac{2}{3}$

(ii) Add $3\frac{5}{6}$ and $1\frac{5}{9}$.

Solution

(i) $\frac{3}{4} + \frac{2}{3}$

The LCM of 4 and 3 is 12 (i.e., LCD = 12). Determining the equivalent fractions using the LCD of 12,

$= \frac{9}{12} + \frac{8}{12}$

Adding the numerators and keeping the denominator,

$= \frac{17}{12}$

Converting the improper fraction to a mixed number,

$= 1\frac{5}{12}$

Therefore, the result from adding $\frac{3}{4}$ and $\frac{2}{3}$ is $1\frac{5}{12}$.

(ii) $3\frac{5}{6} + 1\frac{5}{9}$

Converting the mixed numbers to improper fractions,

$= \frac{(3 \times 6) + 5}{6} + \frac{(1 \times 9) + 5}{9}$

$= \frac{23}{6} + \frac{14}{9}$

The LCM of 6 and 9 is 18 (i.e., LCD = 18). Determining the equivalent fractions using the LCD of 18,

Solution *continued*

$= \frac{69}{18} + \frac{28}{18}$ Adding the numerators and keeping the denominator,

$= \frac{97}{18}$ Converting the improper fraction to a mixed number,

$= 5\frac{7}{18}$

Alternative Method

$3\frac{5}{6} + 1\frac{5}{9}$ Separating the whole numbers and the fractions,

$= (3 + 1) + \left(\frac{5}{6} + \frac{5}{9}\right)$ The LCM of 6 and 9 is 18 (i.e., LCD = 18). Determining the equivalent fractions using the LCD of 18,

$= (3 + 1) + \left(\frac{15}{18} + \frac{10}{18}\right)$ Adding the whole numbers and the fractions,

$= 4 + \frac{25}{18}$ Converting the improper fraction to a mixed number,

$= 4 + 1\frac{7}{18}$ Adding the whole numbers,

$= 5\frac{7}{18}$

Therefore, the result from adding $3\frac{5}{6}$ and $1\frac{5}{9}$ is $5\frac{7}{18}$.

Subtracting Fractions

The process for subtraction of fractions is the same as that of the addition of fractions. First, determine the LCD and change each fraction to its equivalent fraction having the same denominator. The resulting fraction will have the common denominator, and its numerator will be the difference of the numerators of the equivalent fractions. Express the final answer reduced to its lowest terms and as a mixed number, where applicable.

Example 1.3(d) **Subtracting Fractions**

(i) Subtract $\frac{2}{8}$ from $\frac{7}{10}$ (ii) Subtract $7\frac{2}{3}$ from $12\frac{1}{2}$.

Solution

(i) $\frac{7}{10} - \frac{2}{8}$ The LCM of 8 and 10 is 40 (i.e., LCD = 40). Determining the equivalent fractions using the LCD of 40,

$= \frac{28}{40} - \frac{10}{40}$ Subtracting the numerators and keeping the denominator,

$= \frac{18}{40} = \frac{\cancel{18}^{\,9}}{\cancel{40}_{\,20}}$ Reducing to lowest terms,

$= \frac{9}{20}$

Therefore, the result from subtracting $\frac{2}{8}$ from $\frac{7}{10}$ is $\frac{9}{20}$.

Solution *continued*

(ii) $12\frac{1}{2} - 7\frac{2}{3}$ — Converting the mixed numbers to improper fractions,

$= \frac{(12 \times 2) + 1}{2} - \frac{(7 \times 3) + 2}{3}$

$= \frac{25}{2} - \frac{23}{3}$ — The LCM of 2 and 3 is 6 (i.e., LCD = 6). Determining the equivalent fractions using the LCD of 6,

$= \frac{75}{6} - \frac{46}{6}$ — Subtracting the numerators and keeping the denominator,

$= \frac{29}{6}$ — Converting the improper fraction to a mixed number,

$= 4\frac{5}{6}$

Alternative Method

$12\frac{1}{2} - 7\frac{2}{3}$ — The LCM of 2 and 3 is 6 (i.e., LCD = 6). Determining the equivalent mixed numbers using the LCD of 6,

$= 12\frac{3}{6} - 7\frac{4}{6}$ — The fraction $\frac{4}{6}$ is greater than $\frac{3}{6}$. Therefore, we have to regroup the mixed number $12\frac{3}{6}$.

Regrouping $12\frac{3}{6} = \underbrace{11 + 1} + \frac{3}{6} = 11 + \underbrace{\frac{6}{6} + \frac{3}{6}} = 11\frac{9}{6}$

$= 11\frac{9}{6} - 7\frac{4}{6}$ — Subtracting the fractions and the whole numbers,

$= 4\frac{(9 - 4)}{6}$

$= 4\frac{5}{6}$

Therefore, the result from subtracting $7\frac{2}{3}$ from $12\frac{1}{2}$ is $4\frac{5}{6}$.

Multiplying Fractions

When multiplying two or more fractions, first convert any mixed numbers to improper fractions. Simplify the fractions, if possible, then multiply the numerators to get the new numerator and multiply the denominators to get the new denominator. Express the final answer reduced to its lowest terms and as a mixed number, where applicable.

Note: *When multiplying mixed numbers, it is incorrect to multiply the whole number part separately from the fractional parts to arrive at the answer.*

Example 1.3(e) **Multiplying Fractions**

Multiply:

(i) $\frac{3}{2} \times \frac{4}{11}$ (ii) $3\frac{1}{8} \times 2\frac{4}{5}$

Solution

(i) $\frac{3}{2} \times \frac{4}{11} = \frac{3}{\cancel{2}_1} \times \frac{\cancel{4}^2}{11}$ — Simplifying the numerators and denominators,

$= \frac{3}{1} \times \frac{2}{11}$ — Multiplying the numerators together and denominators together to get the new fraction,

$= \frac{6}{11}$

Therefore, the result of $\frac{3}{2} \times \frac{4}{11}$ is $\frac{6}{11}$.

Solution *continued*

(ii) $3\frac{1}{8} \times 2\frac{4}{5}$ — Converting the mixed numbers to improper fractions,

$= \frac{(3 \times 8) + 1}{8} \times \frac{(2 \times 5) + 4}{5}$

$= \frac{25}{8} \times \frac{14}{5} = \frac{\overset{5}{\cancel{25}}}{\underset{4}{\cancel{8}}} \times \frac{\overset{7}{\cancel{14}}}{\underset{1}{\cancel{5}}}$ — Simplifying the numerators and denominators,

$= \frac{5}{4} \times \frac{7}{1}$ — Multiplying the numerators together and denominators together to get the new fraction,

$= \frac{35}{4}$ — Converting the improper fraction to a mixed number,

$= 8\frac{3}{4}$

Therefore, the result of $3\frac{1}{8} \times 2\frac{4}{5}$ is $8\frac{3}{4}$.

Dividing Fractions

When a fraction is inverted, the resulting fraction is called the reciprocal of the original fraction.

When dividing fractions, as in multiplication, first convert any mixed numbers to improper fractions. The division of fractions is done by multiplying the first fraction by the reciprocal of the second fraction. Then, follow the procedure used in multiplication to get the final result.

Note: *Dividing by 2 is the same as multiplying by the reciprocal of 2, which is* $\frac{1}{2}$.

Example 1.3(f) **Dividing Fractions**

Divide:

(i) $\frac{15}{16}$ by $\frac{9}{20}$ (ii) $3\frac{3}{20}$ by $1\frac{4}{5}$

Solution

(i) $\frac{15}{16} \div \frac{9}{20}$ — Multiplying $\frac{15}{16}$ by the reciprocal of $\frac{9}{20}$, which is $\frac{20}{9}$,

$= \frac{15}{16} \times \frac{20}{9} = \frac{\overset{5}{\cancel{15}}}{\underset{4}{\cancel{16}}} \times \frac{\overset{5}{\cancel{20}}}{\underset{3}{\cancel{9}}}$ — Simplifying the numerators and denominators,

$= \frac{5}{4} \times \frac{5}{3}$ — Multiplying the numerators and the denominators,

$= \frac{25}{12}$ — Converting the improper fraction to a mixed number,

$= 2\frac{1}{12}$

Therefore, the result of $\frac{15}{16}$ divided by $\frac{9}{20}$ is $2\frac{1}{12}$.

Solution *continued*

(ii) $3\frac{3}{20} \div 1\frac{4}{5}$ — Converting the mixed numbers to improper fractions,

$= \frac{63}{20} \div \frac{9}{5}$ — Multiplying $\frac{63}{20}$ by the reciprocal of $\frac{9}{5}$, which is $\frac{5}{9}$,

$= \frac{63}{20} \times \frac{5}{9} = \frac{\overset{7}{\cancel{63}}}{\underset{4}{\cancel{20}}} \times \frac{\overset{1}{\cancel{5}}}{\underset{1}{\cancel{9}}}$ — Simplifying the numerators and denominators,

$= \frac{7}{4} \times \frac{1}{1}$ — Multiplying the numerators and the denominators,

$= \frac{7}{4}$ — Converting the improper fraction to a mixed number,

$= 1\frac{3}{4}$

Therefore, the result of $3\frac{3}{20}$ divided by $1\frac{4}{5}$ is $1\frac{3}{4}$.

Converting a Complex Fraction into a Proper or Improper Fraction

A complex fraction can be converted to a proper or improper fraction by dividing the numerator by the denominator and then simplifying the expression.

For example,

- $\frac{\left(\frac{7}{2}\right)}{5} = \frac{7}{2} \div 5 = \frac{7}{2} \times \frac{1}{5} = \frac{7}{10}$
- $\frac{8}{\left(\frac{9}{2}\right)} = 8 \div \frac{9}{2} = 8 \times \frac{2}{9} = \frac{16}{9}$

1.3 | Exercises

Answers to the odd-numbered problems are available at the end of the textbook.

1. Convert the following mixed numbers into improper fractions:

   a. $1\frac{3}{8}$ b. $12\frac{3}{4}$ c. $7\frac{3}{5}$ d. $9\frac{2}{3}$

2. Convert the following mixed numbers into improper fractions:

   a. $5\frac{2}{3}$ b. $5\frac{6}{7}$ c. $6\frac{4}{5}$ d. $4\frac{3}{4}$

3. Convert the following improper fractions into mixed numbers:

   a. $\frac{12}{7}$ b. $\frac{17}{8}$ c. $\frac{31}{9}$ d. $\frac{14}{5}$

4. Convert the following improper fractions into mixed numbers:

   a. $\frac{23}{12}$ b. $\frac{35}{6}$ c. $\frac{46}{5}$ d. $\frac{43}{3}$

5. Determine the missing values:

   a. $\frac{2}{3} = \frac{?}{12} = \frac{12}{?}$ b. $\frac{15}{25} = \frac{3}{?} = \frac{?}{35}$ c. $\frac{22}{12} = \frac{?}{6} = \frac{55}{?}$ d. $\frac{75}{45} = \frac{25}{?} = \frac{?}{18}$

6. Determine the missing values:

   a. $\frac{5}{5} = \frac{20}{?} = \frac{?}{24}$ b. $\frac{12}{9} = \frac{?}{18} = \frac{4}{?}$ c. $\frac{36}{42} = \frac{?}{14} = \frac{30}{?}$ d. $\frac{9}{4} = \frac{27}{?} = \frac{?}{20}$

7. Reduce the following fractions to their lowest terms:

a. $\frac{80}{12}$ b. $\frac{156}{18}$ c. $\frac{68}{10}$ d. $\frac{36}{144}$

8. Reduce the following fractions to their lowest terms:

a. $\frac{70}{15}$ b. $\frac{225}{30}$ c. $\frac{124}{48}$ d. $\frac{75}{345}$

9. Which of the following fractions is larger:

a. $\frac{9}{20}$ or $\frac{11}{20}$ b. $\frac{8}{7}$ or $\frac{13}{12}$ c. $\frac{5}{13}$ or $\frac{16}{39}$ d. $\frac{15}{23}$ or $\frac{15}{27}$

10. Which of the following fractions is smaller:

a. $\frac{7}{11}$ or $\frac{9}{11}$ b. $\frac{2}{5}$ or $\frac{3}{8}$ c. $\frac{12}{15}$ or $\frac{35}{45}$ d. $\frac{13}{15}$ or $\frac{13}{17}$

For Problems 11 to 40, perform the indicated arithmetic operations. Express the answers reduced to lowest terms and in mixed number form, wherever applicable.

11. a. $\frac{7}{9}+\frac{5}{6}$ b. $\frac{11}{20}+\frac{8}{10}$ c. $11\frac{1}{4}+5\frac{2}{3}$ d. $5\frac{2}{3}+1\frac{5}{12}$

12. a. $\frac{1}{3}+\frac{3}{8}$ b. $\frac{9}{12}+\frac{4}{5}$ c. $7\frac{1}{12}+2\frac{3}{4}$ d. $16\frac{1}{8}+1\frac{1}{2}$

13. a. $\frac{21}{13}-\frac{1}{3}$ b. $\frac{35}{18}-\frac{3}{6}$ c. $8\frac{5}{12}-4\frac{1}{2}$ d. $18\frac{5}{7}-2\frac{2}{3}$

14. a. $\frac{9}{10}-\frac{1}{2}$ b. $\frac{21}{25}-\frac{7}{8}$ c. $5\frac{5}{8}-3\frac{5}{6}$ d. $12\frac{4}{3}-5\frac{1}{3}$

15. a. $\frac{4}{5}\times\frac{23}{9}$ b. $\frac{6}{9}\times\frac{19}{12}$ c. $2\frac{7}{9}\times5\frac{2}{5}$ d. $11\frac{4}{3}\times1\frac{1}{74}$

16. a. $\frac{3}{8}\times\frac{5}{11}$ b. $3\times\frac{7}{9}$ c. $4\frac{1}{2}\times2\frac{2}{9}$ d. $9\frac{3}{5}\times1\frac{29}{96}$

17. a. $\frac{8}{12}\div\frac{2}{4}$ b. $\frac{1}{7}\div\frac{3}{5}$ c. $3\frac{1}{3}\div2\frac{2}{9}$ d. $10\frac{1}{4}\div2\frac{27}{48}$

18. a. $\frac{10}{15}\div\frac{3}{7}$ b. $\frac{3}{8}\div4$ c. $2\frac{2}{5}\div1\frac{1}{4}$ d. $23\frac{1}{2}\div8\frac{13}{16}$

19. Peter spent two-thirds of his money on rent and food and one-fourth on education. Together, what fraction of the money did he spend on rent, food, and education?

20. Tracy invested one-fifth of her savings in the stock market and two-thirds in real estate. Together, what fraction of her savings did she invest in the stock market and real estate?

21. Lily worked $5\frac{1}{2}$ hours, $6\frac{1}{4}$ hours, and $3\frac{3}{4}$ hours over the last three days. How many hours did she work in total over the three days?

22. A rain gauge collected $3\frac{2}{3}$ inches, $1\frac{1}{4}$ inches, and $2\frac{1}{2}$ inches of rain over the past three months. What was the total rainfall over the three months?

23. A wooden board measured $2\frac{1}{2}$ metres in length. It was shortened by cutting $1\frac{5}{8}$ metres from it. What is the new length of the board?

24. A tank had $4\frac{2}{3}$ litres of water. If $1\frac{2}{3}$ litres leaked from the tank, how much water was left in the tank?

25. The product of two numbers is 9. If one number is $3\frac{3}{4}$, what is the other number?

26. If a wire that is $43\frac{3}{4}$ cm long is cut into several $1\frac{1}{4}$ cm equal pieces, how many pieces were there?

27. A stack of plywood sheets measures $49\frac{1}{2}$ inches high. If each plywood sheet is three-fourths of an inch thick, how many sheets of plywood are in the stack?

28. A garment factory has $40\frac{1}{4}$ metres of cotton fabric. If $1\frac{3}{4}$ metres of the fabric is required for a dress pattern, how many dresses can be made?

29. A bottle contained 80 mg of medicine. Each dose of the medicine is $2\frac{1}{2}$ mg. How many doses were there in the bottle?

30. It took two-thirds of an hour for a machine to make one component. How many components can be made in 40 hours?

31. A company identified one-twentieth of the 320 bulbs that it received from a supplier as being defective. How many bulbs were not defective?

32. Matthew received a bonus of $6850. He spent two-thirds of this amount on a vacation. How much did he have left?

• 33. David spent one-fourth of his money on rent and one-third of the remainder on food. What fraction of his money was spent on food?

• 34. Mary spent two-fifths of her money on books and one-third of the remainder on clothes. What fraction of her money was spent on clothes?

• 35. After selling two-fifths of its textbooks, a bookstore had 810 books left. How many textbooks were in the bookstore initially?

• 36. Rose travelled two-thirds of her journey by car and the remaining 20 km by bus. How far did she travel by car?

• 37. Cheng walked $5\frac{1}{4}$ km in $1\frac{1}{2}$ hours. How many kilometres did he walk in 1 hour?

• 38. It took $15\frac{1}{4}$ hours to complete three-fourths of a project. How long did it take to complete the entire project?

• 39. Three software programmers worked $17\frac{1}{2}$ hours, $25\frac{3}{4}$ hours, and $11\frac{1}{4}$ hours, respectively, to develop an e-commerce site. If each of them was paid $18 per hour, how much did they receive in total?

• 40. It took three consultants $27\frac{3}{4}$ hours, $21\frac{1}{4}$ hours, and $18\frac{1}{2}$ hours, respectively, to design a product. If each of them was paid $55 per hour, what was the total amount paid to them?

1.4 | Order of Operations (BEDMAS)

When arithmetic expressions contain multiple operations with brackets, exponents, divisions, multiplications, additions, and subtractions, the arithmetic operation is performed in the following sequence:

1. Perform all operations within the brackets. If there is more than one bracket, start with the innermost bracket and move outwards to complete all the brackets.
2. Perform operations with exponents and roots.
3. Perform the necessary divisions and multiplications in the order in which they appear from left to right.
4. Complete the operation by performing the necessary additions and subtractions in the order in which they appear from left to right.

The order of operations - **B**rackets, **E**xponents, **D**ivisions, **M**ultiplications, **A**dditions, **S**ubtractions - can be remembered by the acronym **BEDMAS**.

Example 1.4(a) **Computing Arithmetic Expressions by Following the Order of Operations**

Compute the following arithmetic expressions:

(i) $(100 - 3 \times 24) \div 2 + 4 \times 3$ (ii) $6 + 4 \times 50 \div (8 - 3)^2 - 1$ (iii) $12 + 3^2\ [(8 \times 5) \div 5] - 7 + 2$

Solution

Order of arithmetic operations:

Brackets
Exponents
Divisions
Multiplications
Additions
Subtractions

(i)

$(100 - 3 \times 24) \div 2 + 4 \times 3$	
$= (100 - 3 \times 24) \div 2 + 4 \times 3$	Perform multiplication in the bracket.
$= (100 - 72) \div 2 + 4 \times 3$	Perform subtraction in the bracket.
$= 28 \div 2 + 4 \times 3$	Perform division and multiplication from left to right.
$= 14 + 4 \times 3$	
$= 14 + 12$	Perform addition.
$= 26$	

(ii)

$6 + 4 \times 50 \div (8 - 3)^2 - 1$	
$= 6 + 4 \times 50 \div (8 - 3)^2 - 1$	Perform the operation in the bracket.
$= 6 + 4 \times 50 \div (5)^2 - 1$	Perform the operation with the exponent.
$= 6 + 4 \times 50 \div 25 - 1$	Perform division and multiplication from left to right.
$= 6 + 200 \div 25 - 1$	
$= 6 + 8 - 1$	Perform addition and subtraction from left to right.
$= 14 - 1$	
$= 13$	

(iii)

$12 + 3^2\ [(8 \times 5) \div 5] - 7 + 2$	
$= 12 + 3^2\ [(8 \times 5) \div 5] - 7 + 2$	Perform the operation in the inner bracket.
$= 12 + 3^2\ [40 \div 5] - 7 + 2$	Perform the operation in the outer bracket.
$= 12 + 3^2(8) - 7 + 2$	Perform the operation with the exponent.
$= 12 + 9(8) - 7 + 2$	Perform multiplication.
$= 12 + 72 - 7 + 2$	Perform addition and subtraction from left to right.
$= 84 - 7 + 2$	
$= 77 + 2$	
$= 79$	

Signed Numbers

A number with no sign is considered to be positive (+). For example, $5 = +5$

Signed numbers are either positive numbers - numbers greater than zero (for example, +6, +15) - or negative numbers - numbers less than zero (for example, –4, –12).

Positive numbers may or may not have a positive (plus, "+") sign. When signed numbers are added, subtracted, multiplied, or divided, the result will be a number with a sign.

Addition and Subtraction of Signed Numbers

The following are rules to be followed while adding or subtracting signed numbers.

Adding Two Signed Numbers

a. If the signs of the two numbers are the same: disregard the sign of the numbers, add the numbers, and keep the common sign.
   For example,

   - Adding +7 and +3
     $= +7 + (+3)$
     $= +(7 + 3)$
     $= +10$
   - Adding –6 and –2
     $= -6 + (-2)$
     $= -(6 + 2)$
     $= -8$

Two signs should not be written next to each other. Brackets should be used to separate the two signs.
For example,
−7 − (+2) instead of −7 − +2
+8 + (−5) instead of +8 + −5
+10(−2) instead of +10 × −2

b. If the signs of the two numbers are different: disregard the sign of the numbers, subtract the smaller number from the larger number, and keep the sign of the larger number.
For example,

- Adding +8 and −15
$= +8 + (-15)$
$= -(15 - 8)$
$= -7$

- Adding −3 and +7
$= -3 + (+7)$
$= +(7 - 3)$
$= +4$

Subtracting Two Signed Numbers

Change the subtraction (minus) sign to addition (plus) and change the sign of the number being subtracted. Then follow the above addition rules.
For example,

- Subtracting −12 from +18
$= +18 - (-12)$
$= +18 + (+12)$
$= +(18 + 12)$
$= +30$

- Subtracting −5 from −7
$= -7 - (-5)$
$= -7 + (+5)$
$= -(7 - 5)$
$= -2$

- Subtracting −6 from −2
$= -2 - (-6)$
$= -2 + (+6)$
$= +(6 - 2)$
$= +4$

Multiplication and Division of Signed Numbers

Multiplying two signed numbers
(+) (+) = (+)
(−) (−) = (+)
(+) (−) = (−)
(−) (+) = (−)

The following are rules to be followed while multiplying or dividing two signed numbers:

a. If the sign of the two numbers are the same: their product or quotient will be positive.

For example,

- $(+5)(+4) = +20$
- $(-5)(-4) = +20$
- $\frac{+12}{+3} = +4$
- $\frac{-12}{-3} = +4$

b. If the sign of the two numbers are different: their product or quotient will be negative.
For example,

- $(+5)(-4) = -20$
- $(-5)(+4) = -20$
- $\frac{+12}{-3} = -4$
- $\frac{-12}{+3} = -4$
- $\frac{-25}{+15} = \frac{-5}{3}$ or $-\frac{5}{3}$
- $\frac{+30}{-4} = \frac{+15}{-2} = \frac{-15}{2}$ or $-\frac{15}{2}$

Dividing two signed numbers
$\frac{(+)}{(+)} = (+)$
$\frac{(-)}{(-)} = (+)$
$\frac{(-)}{(+)} = (-)$
$\frac{(+)}{(-)} = (-)$

When multiplying or dividing more than two signed numbers, group them into pairs and determine the sign using the rules for multiplication and division of signed numbers.

For example,

- $(-3)(-2)(+4)(-1)(-5)$
$= (6)(-4)(-5)$
$= (-24)(-5) = 120$

- $\frac{(-15)(+8)(-50)}{(-25)(14)}$
$= \frac{-(15 \times 8)(-50)}{-(25 \times 14)} = \frac{+(15 \times 8 \times 50)}{-(25 \times 14)}$
$= -\frac{15 \times 8 \times \cancel{50}^{2}}{{}_{1}\cancel{25} \times 14} = -\frac{15 \times 8 \times \cancel{2}^{1}}{\cancel{14}_{7}}$
$= -\frac{15 \times 8}{7} = -\frac{120}{7}$

Exponential Notation

Exponents provide a shorter way of representing the products of repeated numbers. For example, when 2 is multiplied 5 times, in standard notation, it is represented as:

$$2 \times 2 \times 2 \times 2 \times 2$$

However, when 2 is multiplied 100 times, it would be tedious to represent it using the standard notation. The shorter way to represent this repeated multiplication is by using exponents.

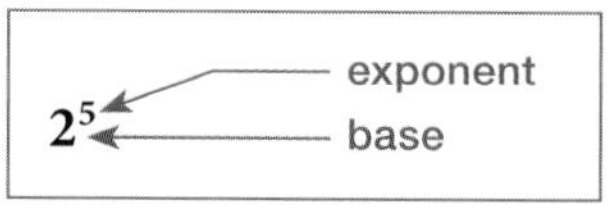

When 2 is multiplied 5 times, it is represented as 2^5 using exponents.
Similarly, if 'a' is multiplied 'n' times, it would be represented as a^n, where 'n' is a positive integer.

$$\underbrace{a \times a \times a \times a \times a \times \ldots \times a}_{n \text{ factors of } a} = a^n$$

To convert exponential notation to standard notation, expand the notation to show the repeated multiplication. The number in the exponent shows the number of times the base is multiplied.

For example, $8^4 = 8 \times 8 \times 8 \times 8$

$8^3 = 8 \times 8 \times 8$

$8^2 = 8 \times 8$

When the exponent is 1, the result is the base itself.

For example, $8^1 = 8$. This is represented by the formula $a^1 = a$.

When the exponent is 0, the result is 1.

For example, $3^0 = 1$. This is represented by the formula $a^0 = 1$.

A negative exponent indicates **dividing** by that many factors instead of multiplying.

When the exponent is negative, it is represented by $a^{-n} = \frac{1}{a^n}$, where 'n' is a positive integer.

$a^n = a \times a \times a \times a \times a \times \ldots \times a$ (multiplication of 'n' factors of 'a')

$a^{-n} = \frac{1}{a^n} = \frac{1}{a \times a \times a \times a \times a \times \ldots \times a}$ (division of 'n' factors of 'a')

Therefore, a^n and a^{-n} are reciprocals.

For example,

- $8^{-1} = \frac{1}{8^1} = \frac{1}{8}$
- $8^{-2} = \frac{1}{8^2} = \frac{1}{8 \times 8}$
- $8^{-3} = \frac{1}{8^3} = \frac{1}{8 \times 8 \times 8}$

A positive number with a negative exponent will not result in a negative answer.

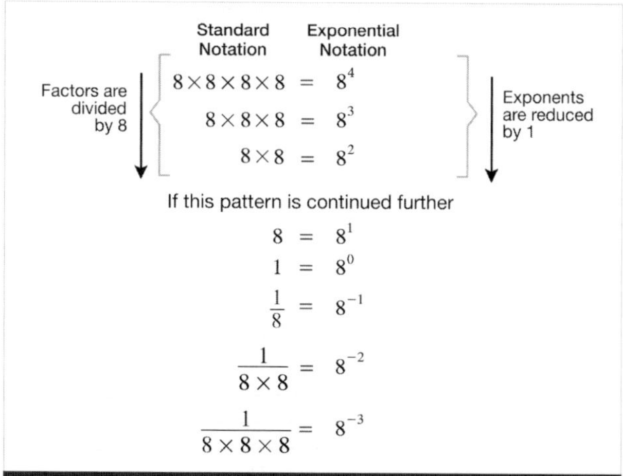

Standard Notation
Exponential Notation
Factors are divided by 8
$8 \times 8 \times 8 \times 8 = 8^4$
$8 \times 8 \times 8 = 8^3$
$8 \times 8 = 8^2$
Exponents are reduced by 1
If this pattern is continued further
$8 = 8^1$
$1 = 8^0$
$\frac{1}{8} = 8^{-1}$
$\frac{1}{8 \times 8} = 8^{-2}$
$\frac{1}{8 \times 8 \times 8} = 8^{-3}$

Exhibit 1.4: Standard and Exponential Form of Numbers

Fractions with Exponents

When a fraction has a **positive exponent**, the number in the exponent indicates the number of times the numerator is multiplied by itself and the number of times the denominator is multiplied by itself.
For example,

- $\left(\frac{2}{5}\right)^3 = \left(\frac{2}{5}\right)\left(\frac{2}{5}\right)\left(\frac{2}{5}\right) = \frac{2 \times 2 \times 2}{5 \times 5 \times 5}$
- $\frac{2^4}{3^5} = \frac{2 \times 2 \times 2 \times 2}{3 \times 3 \times 3 \times 3 \times 3}$

When a fraction has a **negative exponent**, change the fraction to its reciprocal and drop the negative sign in the exponent. After this change, the number in the exponent indicates the number of times the numerator is multiplied by itself and the denominator is multiplied by itself.
For example,

$$\left(\frac{a}{b}\right)^{-n} = \left(\frac{b}{a}\right)^{n}$$

- $\left(\frac{2}{5}\right)^{-3} = \left(\frac{5}{2}\right)^3 = \left(\frac{5}{2}\right)\left(\frac{5}{2}\right)\left(\frac{5}{2}\right) = \frac{5 \times 5 \times 5}{2 \times 2 \times 2}$

***Note:** The reciprocal of* $\frac{2}{5}$ *is* $\frac{5}{2}$.

Calculator Method to Solve Problems

The exponent key on different calculators are identified by symbols such as y^x, x^y, ^, etc. The sequence of operations to calculate the exponents also depends on the calculator. In this section, you will learn to use the Texas Instruments BA II Plus calculator to solve exponents and order of operations problems.

Example 1.4(b) **Calculating Exponents using Texas Instruments BA II Plus Calculator**

Calculate:

(i) 16^4 (ii) 5^{-4} (iii) $(1.04)^4 - 1$ (iv) $1 - (1.005)^{-4}$

Solution

(i) 16^4

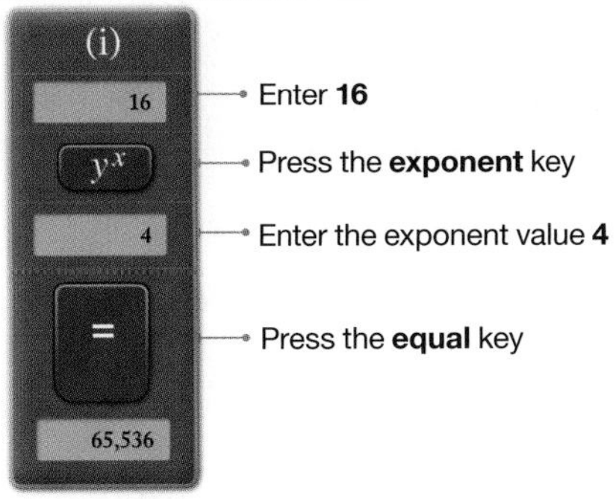

(i)
16
Enter **16**
y^x
Press the **exponent** key
4
Enter the exponent value **4**
=
Press the **equal** key
65,536

Answer: 65,536

(ii) 5^{-4}

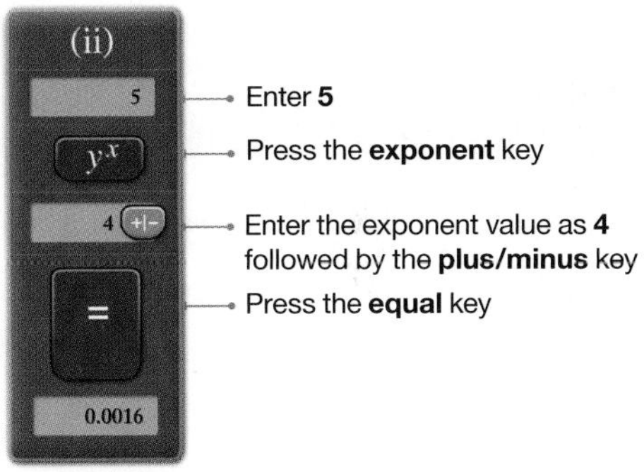

(ii)
5
Enter **5**
y^x
Press the **exponent** key
4 +|-
Enter the exponent value as **4** followed by the **plus/minus** key
=
Press the **equal** key
0.0016

Answer: 0.0016

(iii) $(1.04)^4 - 1$

(iii)
1.04
Enter **1.04**
y^x
Press the **exponent** key
4
Enter the exponent value **4**
−
Press the **subtraction** key
1
Enter **1**
=
Press the **equal** key
0.16985856

Answer: 0.1698...

(iv) $1 - (1.005)^{-4}$

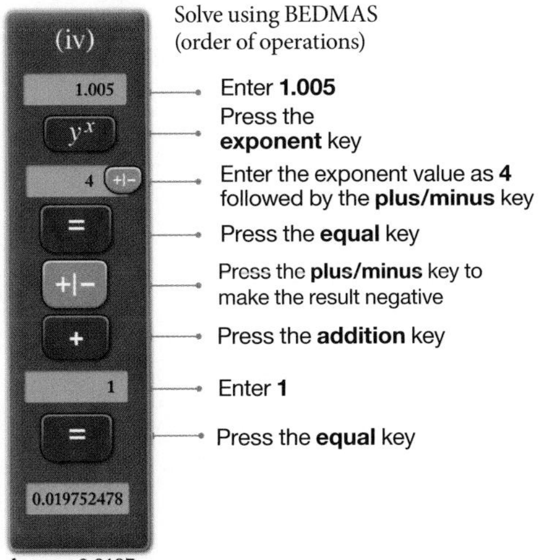

Solve using BEDMAS (order of operations)
(iv)
1.005
Enter **1.005**
y^x
Press the **exponent** key
4 +|-
Enter the exponent value as **4** followed by the **plus/minus** key
=
Press the **equal** key
+|-
Press the **plus/minus** key to make the result negative
+
Press the **addition** key
1
Enter **1**
=
Press the **equal** key
0.019752478

Answer: 0.0197...

Example 1.4(c) **Using the Store and Recall Functions to Solve Order of Operation Problems**

Solve: (i) $1380\left[\dfrac{\left(1+\frac{0.05}{12}\right)^{36}-1}{\left(\frac{0.05}{12}\right)}\right]$ (ii) $2000\left[\dfrac{1-\left(1+\frac{0.03}{4}\right)^{-12}}{\left(\frac{0.03}{4}\right)}\right]$

Solution

(i) $1380\left[\dfrac{\left(1+\frac{0.05}{12}\right)^{36}-1}{\left(\frac{0.05}{12}\right)}\right]$

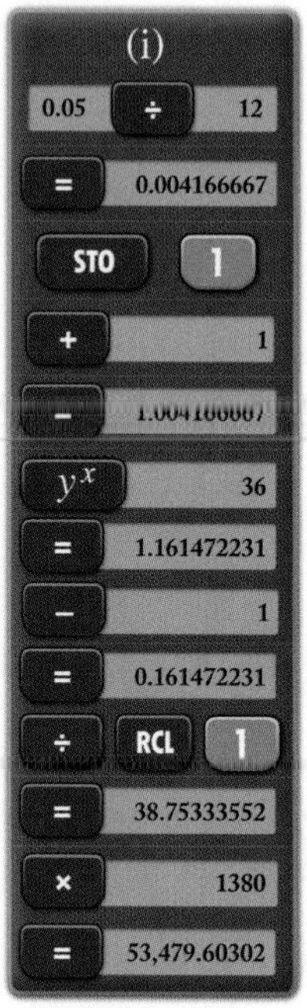

Answer: 53,479.60

(ii) $2000\left[\dfrac{1-\left(1+\frac{0.03}{4}\right)^{-12}}{\left(\frac{0.03}{4}\right)}\right]$

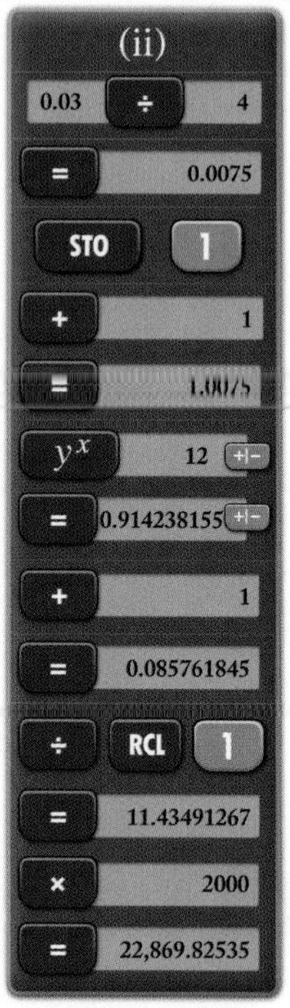

Answer: 22,869.83

1.4 | Exercises

Answers to the odd-numbered problems are available at the end of the textbook.

Evaluate Problems 1 to 18 by following the order of operations (BEDMAS).

1. a. $45 - (5 + 7)^2$ b. $18 - 8 \div 2 + 6$
2. a. $32 + (9 - 5)^3$ b. $4 \times 6 \div 2 - 5$
3. a. $128 \div (-16) \div (-2)$ b. $9(13 - 3^2) + 4$
4. a. $200 \div (-10) \div 5$ b. $20(5 - 2^2) + 5$
5. a. $(-5)(-3)(12)(-3)(-1)$ b. $31 - [(15 \div 3) \times 32 \div 2^2 \times (26 \div 13)]$
6. a. $(-1)(-3)(2)(-5)(-6)$ b. $112 - 4 \times 54 \div (5 - 2)^3 - 3$
7. a. $[(1 + 12)(1 - 5)]^2 \div (5 + 3 \times 2^2 - 4)$ b. $(-8)(2)(3)(-4)(-1)$
8. a. $3(7^2 + 2 \times 15 \div 3) - (1 + 3 \times 4)^2$ b. $(12)(1)(-7)(4)(-2)$
9. $\dfrac{8 \times 7 - 16 + 3^2 \times 2}{2^5 - (59 - 7^2) \div 2 \times 6}$
10. $\dfrac{-52 + (56 \div 8) \times 9 + 6^2}{3 \times (6 \times 4 \div 8) + 157 - 11^2}$
11. $\dfrac{6 + (8^2 - 5) - (6^2 + 13)}{60 \div 12 + [5^2 - (-2) \times (-11)]}$
12. $\dfrac{32 \div (-8) - 9 + (127 - 5^3) \times 2^3}{[(-54) \div 6 + 33] \div [(-8) \times (-3)]}$

13. $\dfrac{[(-6)\times 7+(-12)\div(-4)+3]\div 6}{[(-24)\div 8+4]\div[14-16+3]}$

14. $\dfrac{8\{9-(-2)-7[4+(-1)]\}}{-12+4[-4-(-3)]\div 7}$

15. $\dfrac{16+4(3)}{10-4+1}+\dfrac{(16+4)3}{10-(4+1)}$

16. $\dfrac{2(6)+4}{24-(7+3)}+\dfrac{2(6+4)}{24-7+3}$

17. $14-3\{[(6-9)(-4)+12](-2)\}$

18. $5(-4)-3\{(-9+6)+(-3)-4[2(-1)-7]\}$

Evaluate the following exponents:

19. a. $\left(\dfrac{2}{3}\right)^2$ b. $\left(\dfrac{1}{5}\right)^{-3}$

20. a. $\left(\dfrac{3}{4}\right)^3$ b. $\left(\dfrac{4}{7}\right)^{-2}$

21. a. $\left(\dfrac{2}{3}\right)^5$ b. $\left(\dfrac{2}{3}\right)^{-5}$

22. a. $\left(\dfrac{3}{5}\right)^3$ b. $\left(\dfrac{3}{5}\right)^{-3}$

Evaluate the following problems and round your answer to two decimal places:

23. $4500\left(1+0.005\times\dfrac{240}{365}\right)$

24. $600\left(1+0.002\times\dfrac{180}{365}\right)$

25. $1500\left(1+0.04\times\dfrac{7}{12}\right)$

26. $960\left(1+0.05\times\dfrac{3}{12}\right)$

27. $\dfrac{2500}{\left(1+0.001\times\dfrac{150}{365}\right)}$

28. $\dfrac{1250}{\left(1+0.02\times\dfrac{160}{365}\right)}$

29. $\dfrac{1800}{\left(1+0.05\times\dfrac{5}{12}\right)}$

30. $\dfrac{2700}{\left(1+0.04\times\dfrac{7}{12}\right)}$

31. $\dfrac{3000[(1.06)^5-1]}{0.06}$

32. $\dfrac{800[(1.04)^{10}-1]}{0.04}$

33. $\dfrac{1400[(1.03)^{20}-1]}{0.03}$

34. $\dfrac{750[(1.02)^{25}-1]}{0.02}$

35. $5400(1.005)^8$

36. $1275(1.03)^7$

37. $2400(1.02)^{-10}$

38. $4650(1.04)^{-6}$

- 39. $\dfrac{2400[1-(1.02)^{-8}]}{0.02}$

- 40. $\dfrac{400[1-(1.05)^{-12}]}{0.05}$

- 41. $\dfrac{950[1-(1.03)^{-15}]}{0.03}$

- 42. $\dfrac{1200[1-(1.04)^{-20}]}{0.04}$

- 43. $500\left[\dfrac{(1+0.025)^{20}-1}{0.025}\right](1+0.025)$

- 44. $1800\left[\dfrac{(1+0.075)^{24}-1}{0.075}\right](1+0.075)$

- 45. $3000\left[\dfrac{(1-0.01)^{-32}-1}{0.01}\right](1+0.01)$

- 46. $160\left[\dfrac{(1-0.0625)^{-12}-1}{0.0625}\right](1+0.0625)$

- 47. $80{,}000(1+0.02)^{\frac{43}{3}}$

- 48. $1355(1+0.055)^{\frac{55}{6}}$

- 49. $275{,}000(1+0.01)^{-\frac{43}{3}}$

- 50. $2650(1+0.035)^{-\frac{29}{6}}$

1.5 | Averages

Simple Arithmetic Average (Arithmetic Mean)

The simple arithmetic average of numbers is also often called the arithmetic mean (or mean) of numbers. It is the sum of all the values of the terms divided by the number of terms added. The answer will always be larger than the lowest value amongst the terms and smaller than the highest value amongst the terms.

Changing the order of the numbers does not change the average of the numbers and the average of a list of integers is not necessarily an integer.

Example 1.5(a) **Calculating the Arithmetic Average of Numbers**

Calculate the arithmetic average of 45, 65, 85, and 90.

Solution

$$\textit{Arithmetic average} = \frac{45 + 65 + 85 + 90}{4} = \frac{285}{4} = 71.25$$

Note: *The answer is larger than the lowest value of 45 and smaller than the highest value of 90.*

A summation method (using the summation notation, Σ) is easily generalized for any number of terms as follows:

Formula 1.5(a) **Arithmetic Average**

$$\textit{Arithmetic Average} = \frac{\textit{Sum of all values of terms}}{\textit{Number of terms}} = \frac{x_1 + x_2 + x_3 + \ldots + x_n}{n} = \frac{\sum_{i=1}^{n} x_i}{n}$$

'x_1' refers to the 1st term, 'x_2' refers to the 2nd term, etc., and 'x_n' refers to the nth term, where 'n' is the total number of terms.

Example 1.5(b) **Calculating the Average Earnings per Day**

The following are a worker's earnings for the last five days: \$150, \$225, \$350, \$270, and \$325. Determine his average earnings per day.

Solution

$$\textit{Average earnings per day} = \frac{\sum_{i=1}^{n} x_i}{n} = \frac{150 + 225 + 350 + 270 + 325}{5} = \frac{1320}{5} = \$264.00$$

Therefore, his average earning per day is \$264.00.

Example 1.5(c) **Calculating an Unknown Number Given the Other Numbers and the Average of All Numbers**

The average of six numbers is 50. If five of the numbers are 40, 25, 75, 30, and 50, what is the sixth number?

Solution

Let x represent the sixth number.

$$\frac{40 + 25 + 75 + 30 + 50 + x}{6} = 50$$

$$40 + 25 + 75 + 30 + 50 + x = 50 \times 6$$

$$220 + x = 300$$

$$x = 300 - 220 = 80$$

Or

The average of six numbers = 50

Therefore, the sum of six numbers = 50 × 6 = 300

The sum of five numbers = 40 + 25 + 75 + 30 + 50 = 220

Therefore, the sixth number is 300 – 220 = 80

Therefore, the sixth number is 80.

Example 1.5(d) **Calculating the Average of All Numbers Given the Average of Two Sets of Numbers**

If the average of a set of three numbers is 45 and the average of a different set of four numbers is 55, determine the average of all the seven numbers rounded to 2 decimal places.

Solution

If the average of a set of three numbers is 45, then the sum of the three numbers would be 45 × 3 = 135.

Similarly, the sum from the set of four numbers would be 55 × 4 = 220.

Now, the average of the seven numbers would be the sum of the seven numbers divided by 7.

$$\frac{135 + 220}{7} = 50.714285... = 50.71$$

Therefore, the average of the seven numbers is 50.71.

Weighted Average (Weighted Mean)

The weighted average is often called the weighted arithmetic mean. It is similar to an arithmetic average, but instead of each of the data points contributing equally to the final average, some data points contribute more than others.

When all the values of the terms are not of equal importance, each quantity to be averaged is assigned a different weighting factor. These weighting factors determine the relative importance of each value.

If all the weighting factors are equal, then the weighted average is the same as the arithmetic average.

For example, a student's final evaluation in a subject is often based on different components, such as quizzes, assignments, tests, exams, etc. Each component will be assigned a value by the teacher, which will help determine the student's final grade earned for the subject.

Quizzes and assignments may be worth a smaller percent of the total grade, compared to major tests and exams which may carry additional weight in the final grade earned. This means that the tests and exams carry more importance in determining a student's grade in the subject, although the successful completion of the other components will allow the student to earn the highest possible grade.

The weighted average is calculated as follows:
If $w_1, w_2, w_3, \ldots w_n$ are the weighting factors assigned for the terms and $x_1, x_2, x_3, \ldots x_n$ are the values of the terms in that order, then,

Formula 1.5(b) **Weighted Average**

$$\text{Weighted Average} = \frac{\text{Sum of the weighted values}}{\text{Sum of the weighting factors}} = \frac{w_1 x_1 + w_2 x_2 + w_3 x_3 + \ldots + w_n x_n}{w_1 + w_2 + w_3 + \ldots + w_n} = \frac{\sum_{i=1}^{n} w_i x_i}{\sum_{i=1}^{n} w_i}$$

Example 1.5(e)
Calculating the Weighted Average

The final grade of a subject is determined by three tests and a final examination. Each test is worth 20% and the final exam is worth 40%. A student received 70, 60, and 80 marks out of 100 for the tests and 95 marks out of 100 for the final exam. Calculate the student's final grade for this subject based on:

(i) The weighted average. (ii) The simple arithmetic average.

Which method is more suitable in this situation and why?

Solution

(i) *Calculating the weighted average*

Terms	Value of terms (x_i)	Weight of terms (w_i)	$w_i x_i$
Test 1	$\frac{70}{100}$	$w_1 = 20\%$	$0.20 \times \frac{70}{100} = 14\%$
Test 2	$\frac{60}{100}$	$w_2 = 20\%$	$0.20 \times \frac{60}{100} = 12\%$
Test 3	$\frac{80}{100}$	$w_3 = 20\%$	$0.20 \times \frac{80}{100} = 16\%$
Final examination	$\frac{95}{100}$	$w_4 = 40\%$	$0.40 \times \frac{95}{100} = 38\%$
		$\Sigma w_i = 100\%$	$\Sigma w_i x_i = 80\%$

Using Formula 1.5(b), *Weighted Average* $= \dfrac{\sum_{i=1}^{n} w_i x_i}{\sum_{i=1}^{n} w_i} = \dfrac{80\%}{100\%} = 80\%$

(ii) *Calculating the simple arithmetic average*

$$\textit{Arithmetic average} = \frac{\left(\frac{70}{100} + \frac{60}{100} + \frac{80}{100} + \frac{95}{100}\right)}{4} = \frac{\left(\frac{305}{100}\right)}{4} = \frac{305}{400} \times 100\% = 76.25\%$$

The simple arithmetic average does not reflect the importance given to the final examination. The weighted average of 80% reflects the greater importance given to the final exam and is the more suitable method in this situation.

Example 1.5(f)
Calculating the Grade Point Average

Jean, a first semester student at the National College of Business, received the following first semester marks along with the credit earned per subject.

Subject	Percent Mark	Credit Hours Earned
English	81%	2
Business Mathematics	97%	3
Marketing	79%	3
Computer Applications	68%	2
Accounting	72%	3
Business Management	75%	4

He planned to transfer to Hollings College of Business that required him to submit a Grade Point Average (GPA) of his performance. The college uses the students' GPA to assess their overall academic achievement. When calculating the GPA, the percent mark for each course is first converted into a grade point. The grade points for all courses are then averaged, weighted by credit hours. The school provided the following grade point conversion chart to calculate his GPA.

Percent Mark	Grade Point
80% to 100%	4.0
70% to 79%	3.3
60% to 69%	2.7
50% to 59%	1.7
40% to 49%	1.2

Based on the above information, calculate his GPA.

Solution

Subject	Percent Mark	Grade Point (x_i)	Credit Hours Earned (w_i)	Grade Point × Credit Hours Earned $w_i x_i$
English	81%	4.0	2	2 × 4.0 = 8.0
Business Mathematics	97%	4.0	3	3 × 4.0 = 12.0
Marketing	79%	3.3	3	3 × 3.3 = 9.9
Computer Applications	68%	2.7	2	2 × 2.7 = 5.4
Accounting	72%	3.3	3	3 × 3.3 = 9.9
Business Management	75%	3.3	4	4 × 3.3 = 13.2
			$\Sigma w_i = 17$	$\Sigma w_i x_i = 58.4$

Using Formula 1.5(b),

$$\textit{Weighted Average} = \frac{\sum_{i=1}^{n} w_i x_i}{\sum_{i=1}^{n} w_i} = \frac{58.4}{17} = 3.435294... = 3.44$$

Therefore, his GPA is 3.44.

Example 1.5(g) **Calculating the Weighted Average on the Return on Investments**

An investment banker assured a wealthy businesswoman, Angel, that she will receive a 14% return on her investments in a year if she invested her money with them. Angel agreed and invested her savings with the banker.

The banker created a portfolio of investments for her by investing 30% of it in high-tech stocks, 10% in oil stocks, 25% in software company startups, and the balance in a savings account. At the end of the year, the high-tech stocks grew by 18%, the oil stocks dropped by 4%, the investment in software company startups grew by 32%, and the amount in the savings account grew by 5.5%.

Did Angel's money grow by the amount that was assured to her?

Solution

Investment	Return (x_i)	Investment (w_i)	$w_i x_i$
High-tech stocks	18%	30%	0.30 × 18% = 5.4%
Oil stocks	−4%	10%	0.10 × (−4%) = −0.4%
Software companies	32%	25%	0.25 × 32% = 8.0%
Savings account	5.5%	35%	0.35 × 5.5% = 1.925%
		$\Sigma w = 100\%$	$\Sigma w_i x_i = 14.925\%$

Using Formula 1.5(b),

$$\textit{Weighted Average} = \frac{\sum_{i=1}^{n} w_i x_i}{\sum_{i=1}^{n} w_i} = \frac{14.925\%}{100\%} = 14.925\%$$

Therefore, Angel's investment grew by 14.925% which was more than the return assured to her.

Geometric Average (Geometric Mean)

When it comes to determining the average rate at which a quantity grows over a time period, the arithmetic mean is not a good measure. The geometric mean is a better measure, which allows estimating the average rate of change of growth over that period of time. It is a very useful measure in accounting and finance. It is used often in financial analysis, when analysts look at processes with compound interest.

Geometric mean is the nth root of the product of n terms.

The geometric mean is calculated by multiplying all the values of the terms together and then taking the nth root of the result (this is the same as raising the result to the power $\frac{1}{n}$), where n is the number of terms in the dataset.

If there are n terms ($x_1, x_2, x_3, x_4, x_5 ... x_n$), then the geometric mean, G, is:

Formula 1.5(c) **Geometric Mean**

$$G = \sqrt[n]{x_1 \cdot x_2 \cdot x_3 \cdot x_4 \cdot x_5 \cdot ... \cdot x_n} \quad \text{or} \quad G = \left(x_1 \cdot x_2 \cdot x_3 \cdot x_4 \cdot x_5 \cdot ... \cdot x_n\right)^{\frac{1}{n}}$$

***Note:** Geometric mean, 'G', of a set of values is the number 'G' that satisfies*

$$x_1 \cdot x_2 \cdot x_3 \cdot x_4 \cdot x_5 \cdot ... \cdot x_n = \underbrace{G \times G \times G \times G ...}_{n \text{ times}} = G^n$$

Example 1.5(h) **Determining the Geometric Mean**

Determine the geometric mean of the following five terms: 3, 4, 6, 9, 14.

Solution

Using, $G = \left(x_1 \cdot x_2 \cdot x_3 \cdot x_4 \cdot x_5 \cdot ... \cdot x_n\right)^{\frac{1}{n}}$

$$G = (3 \times 4 \times 6 \times 9 \times 14)^{\frac{1}{5}} = 6.187861... = 6.19$$

Therefore, the geometric mean is 6.19.

Example 1.5(i) **Determining the Average Annual Growth Rate**

Sam invested $100 for four years. If the growth rate for each year was 10%, 14%, 17%, and 18%, calculate the average annual growth rate using the geometric mean.

Solution

The average growth rate using the arithmetic mean $= \left[\frac{(10\% + 14\% + 17\% + 18\%)}{4}\right] = 14.75\%$

However, this is not the correct calculation in this case. The correct calculation is to determine the geometric mean, as explained below:

End of the first year, the value $= 100(1 + 0.10)$

End of the second year, the value $= 100(1 + 0.10)(1 + 0.14)$

End of the third year, the value $= 100(1 + 0.10)(1 + 0.14)(1 + 0.17)$

End of the fourth year, the value $= 100(1 + 0.10)(1 + 0.14)(1 + 0.17)(1 + 0.18)$

If 'G' is the average annual growth rate over the four-year period, then

$$100(1 + G)^4 = 100(1 + 0.10)(1 + 0.14)(1 + 0.17)(1 + 0.18)$$

$$= 100(1.10)(1.14)(1.17)(1.18)$$

$$(1 + G) = [(1.10)(1.14)(1.17)(1.18)]^{\frac{1}{4}} = 1.147073...$$

Therefore, $G = 0.147073... = 14.71\%$

1.5 | Exercises

Answers to the odd-numbered problems are available at the end of the textbook.

1. Calculate the arithmetic average of the following numbers:

   a. 12, 18, 26, and 32   b. 35.50, 86.25, 75.75, and 12.50

2. Calculate the arithmetic average of the following numbers:

   a. 50, 45, 72, and 86   b. 120.70, 118.25, 110.75, and 95.50

3. The number of hours Yara worked each of the last four weeks were: 40 hours, 35 hours, 37.5 hours, and 36 hours. Determine the average number of hours she worked per week.

4. It took Alexus the following times to commute to her office on four different days: 45 minutes, 55 minutes, 30 minutes, and 47 minutes. What is the average time it took her to commute to work?

5. The average of five numbers is 120. If four of the numbers are 118, 130, 125, and 110, what is the fifth number?

6. The average of four rates is 5.5%. If three of the rates are 6.25%, 4%, and 6.5%, what is the fourth rate?

7. The mean of 6 numbers is 50. If one of the numbers is excluded, the mean reduces by 5. Determine the excluded number.

8. The mean of 5 numbers is 27. If one of the numbers is excluded, the mean reduces by 2. Determine the excluded number.

9. The average monthly salary of 50 people is $4200. The average monthly salary of 42 of them is $3500. Calculate the average monthly salary of the remaining 8 people.

10. The average mark for a class of 40 students is 74. The 15 male students in the class have an average mark of 70. Calculate the average mark of the female students in the class.

11. The average of a set of four numbers is 60 and the average of a different set of two numbers is 50. Determine the average of all six numbers. Round your answer to two decimal places.

12. The average of a set of three grades is 85.5% and the average of a different set of four grades is 91%. Determine the average of all seven grades. Round your answer to two decimal places.

13. A footwear retailer sold 10 pairs of sneakers for $50 each, 14 pairs of leather shoes for $150 each, 3 pairs of boots for $225 each, and 6 pairs of sandals for $25 each. Calculate the average price of shoes sold based on:

    a. Weighted average.   b. Simple arithmetic average.

    Which method is more suitable in this situation and why?

14. A call center has four categories of employees, each paid a particular wage. Managers are paid $27 an hour, clerks $18 an hour, technicians $22 an hour, and administrative assistants $16 an hour. The call center has 3 managers, 22 clerks, 4 technicians, and 6 administrative assistants. Calculate the average pay per employee based on:

    a. Simple arithmetic average.   b. Weighted average (category of employees).

    Round your answer to the nearest cent.

15. The manager of a sporting goods store was given the following data regarding the sales made for the month of March.

Product	Price per unit	Items sold
Snowboards	$450.00	30
Skis	$175.00	18
Rollerblades	$230.00	22
Basketballs	$65.00	43

    What was the average price per unit sold in March? Round your answer to the nearest cent.

16. Anthony invested 40% of his money in mutual funds, 30% in real estate, and the balance in stocks. If the value of the money that he invested in mutual funds, real estate, and stocks grew by 4%, 6%, and 9%, respectively, what was the average growth on his total investment?

17. Calculate the geometric mean for the following sets of data. Express the final answer rounded to two decimal places.
    a. 4, 36 b. 2, 4, 8 c. 1.10, 1.16, 1.13, 1.18

18. Calculate the geometric mean for the following sets of data. Express the final answer rounded to two decimal places.
    a. 9, 25 b. 4, 6, 8 c. 1.08, 1.09, 1.05, 1.12

19. Henry invested $12,800 for three years. If the growth rate for each year was 5%, 6%, and 8%, calculate the average annual growth rate using the geometric mean.

20. Amanda invested $10,000 for four years. If the growth rate for each year was 3%, 5%, 6%, and 9%, calculate the average annual growth rate using the geometric mean.

1 | Review Exercises

Answers to the odd-numbered problems are available at the end of the textbook.

1. Determine the answers to the following and round to two decimal places:
   a. 75.45 ÷ 12 b. 845 ÷ 365
   c. 29.25 ÷ 4 d. 48,000 ÷ 26

2. Determine the answers to the following and round to two decimal places:
   a. 125.71 ÷ 4 b. 775 ÷ 365
   c. 56,000 ÷ 52 d. 142.75 ÷ 12

3. Determine the answers to the following and round to the nearest cent:
   a. $28.39 × 1.50 b. $37.48 × 2.00
   c. $40.75 × 2.25 d. $25.56 × 19.50

4. Determine the answers to the following and round to the nearest cent:
   a. $37.50 × 1.50 b. $37.45 × 12.25
   c. $91.38 × 6.50 d. $2.25 × 9.75

5. Determine the least common multiple (LCM) of the following:
   a. 44, 60 b. 9, 36, 64 c. 90, 165

6. Determine the least common multiple (LCM) of the following:
   a. 24, 40 b. 9, 12, 15 c. 80, 120

7. Determine the greatest common factor (GCF) of the following:
   a. 15, 25 b. 6, 8, 10 c. 25, 125, 200

8. Determine the greatest common factor (GCF) of the following:
   a. 14, 49 b. 12, 18, 20 c. 30, 75, 180

For Problems 9 to 12, express your answer as a mixed number.

9. Abigail worked $9\frac{1}{2}$, $5\frac{1}{2}$, $7\frac{1}{4}$, and $5\frac{3}{4}$ hours during the last four days. Calculate the total number of hours she worked during the four days.

10. Emily worked $3\frac{3}{4}$, $4\frac{1}{4}$, $1\frac{1}{2}$, and $2\frac{1}{2}$ hours overtime during the last four days. Calculate the number of overtime hours she worked during the four days.

11. John received a scholarship of $6000. Two-thirds of this amount was spent on tuition and one-fourth of the remaining amount was spent on books. What was the amount of the scholarship with which he was left?

12. Alyssa spent half of her bonus amount of $3500 on a vacation and invested one-third of the remaining in a mutual fund. What was the amount of the bonus with which she was left?

13. Evaluate the following:
    a. $(5 + 4)^2 - 4^3 \div 8 + 3$
    b. $(6 \times 3 - 8)^2 \div (2^3 \times 5 - 3 \times 5)$

14. Evaluate the following:
    a. $16 \div 4 \times 2 - (7 - 5)^2$
    b. $(2^3 - 3)^2 - 5 \times 20 \div (3^3 - 2)$

15. Evaluate the following and round the final answer to two decimal places:
    a. $150{,}000(1 + 0.0575)^{-9}$
    b. $\frac{800[(1.005)^{48} - 1]}{0.005}$

16. Evaluate the following and round the final answer to two decimal places:

a. $80{,}000(1 + 0.0375)^{-24}$

b. $\dfrac{250[(1.0025)^{120} - 1]}{0.0025}$

17. The average monthly salary of five employees is $4500. Four of the employees' monthly salaries are $4230, $3730, $3970, and $5420. Calculate the monthly salary of the fifth employee.

18. The average age of six employees is 35 years. The ages of five employees are 28, 32, 40, 38, and 27. Calculate the age of the sixth employee.

19. In a survey, ten people were found to have an average weight of 72 kg. When another person joined the survey, the average weight of the eleven people decreased by 2 kg. Calculate the weight of the eleventh person.

20. The average mark of fourteen students in a class was 75%. Another student took a make-up test and the class average decreased by 1%. What was the mark of the fifteenth student?

21. A store sold 20 shirts at $20 each, 35 shirts at $25 each, and 40 shirts at $30 each. Calculate the weighted average selling price per shirt.

22. In a company, 15 employees are paid $16 per hour, 11 employees are paid $22 per hour, and 14 employees are paid $25 per hour. Calculate the weighted average hourly rate of the employees rounded to the nearest cent.

1 | Self-Test Exercises

Answers to all the problems are available at the end of the textbook.

1. Peter earns $37.56 per hour. Last week he worked 32.50 hours. Calculate his weekly pay rounded to the nearest cent.

2. Estimate by rounding each number to the nearest thousand:

66,541 + 7891 + 19,725 – 13,978 – 2495

3. Determine the least common multiple (LCM) of the following:

a. 18, 24 b. 4, 10, 16 c. 18, 36, 64

4. Determine the greatest common factor (GCF) of the following:

a. 16, 20 b. 14, 35, 70 c. 24, 36, 48

5. Three software developers worked $37\frac{1}{2}$ hours, $22\frac{3}{4}$ hours, and $31\frac{1}{4}$ hours, respectively, to develop an online course. If they were each paid $20 per hour, how much did they receive in total?

6. Evaluate the following:

a. $4(8 \times 3^2 - 4^3) \div (10 + 2 \times 3)$

b. $100 \div (2 + 3)^2 - 3^2 \div 3$

7. Evaluate the following and round the final answer to two decimal places:

a. $\dfrac{1500[1 - (1.02)^{-60}]}{0.02}$

b. $2500\left(1 + \dfrac{0.09}{4}\right)^2\left(1 + \dfrac{0.06}{2}\right)^3$

8. The average sales that a business made were $42,525 for the first three months and $37,775 for the next nine months of the year. Calculate the average sales for the entire year.

9. Henry received the following marks on his first three math tests: 85%, 94%, and 89%. What mark must he receive on his fourth test to have an average of exactly 90% on the four tests?

10. Calculate the geometric mean for the following data sets:

a. 16, 81 b. $\dfrac{1}{4}, \dfrac{1}{6}, \dfrac{1}{8}$

11. Benedict invested in 250 shares of Company *A* at $15 per share, 300 shares of Company *B* at $25 per share, and 150 shares of Company *C* at $35 per share. Calculate the weighted average price per share.

1 | Summary of Formulas

Arithmetic Average | 1.5(a)

$$Arithmetic\ Average = \frac{Sum\ of\ all\ values\ of\ terms}{Number\ of\ terms} = \frac{x_1 + x_2 + x_3 + ... + x_n}{n} = \frac{\sum_{i=1}^{n} x_i}{n}$$

Weighted Average | 1.5(b)

$$Weighted\ Average = \frac{Sum\ of\ the\ weighted\ values}{Sum\ of\ the\ weighting\ factors} = \frac{w_1 x_1 + w_2 x_2 + w_3 x_3 + ... + w_n x_n}{w_1 + w_2 + w_3 + ... + w_n} = \frac{\sum_{i=1}^{n} w_i x_i}{\sum_{i=1}^{n} w_i}$$

Geometric Mean | 1.5(c)

$$G = \sqrt[n]{x_1 \cdot x_2 \cdot x_3 \cdot x_4 \cdot x_5 \cdot ... \cdot x_n} \quad \textbf{or} \quad G = \left(x_1 \cdot x_2 \cdot x_3 \cdot x_4 \cdot x_5 \cdot ... \cdot x_n\right)^{\frac{1}{n}}$$

Chapter

2

REVIEW OF BASIC ALGEBRA

LEARNING OBJECTIVES

- Perform arithmetic operations on algebraic expressions.
- Set up basic linear equations with one variable.
- Solve linear equations with one variable using various arithmetic operations.
- Use rules of exponents in simplifying expressions and solving equations involving exponents.
- Define and perform basic calculations using properties of common and natural logarithms.
- Create, rearrange, and use equations to solve for unknown variables.

CHAPTER OUTLINE

Introduction

Let us assume that you are hosting a charity event. Each ticket to this event costs \$20. How can you represent the total amount of money raised for the charity, without yet knowing the total number of attendees?

Algebra is a branch of mathematics that analyzes and solves problems using letters and symbols to represent numbers, values, etc.

If we let the letter x represent the total number of attendees, then the total amount raised for charity is equal to \$20 times x, or $20x$.

Algebra is a branch of mathematics that introduces this concept of using variables to represent numbers. These variables, together with numbers, are used to express statements and equations using mathematical operations. Algebra provides a framework to derive formulas to solve general problems, rather than finding a solution to a particular problem. Algebra will help you develop logical thinking and problem solving skills in a systematic and analytical way.

The study of algebra is required in any occupational field, including business and finance.

2.1 | Algebraic Expressions

Algebraic expressions consist of one or more terms with a combination of variables, numbers, and operational signs. In order to solve most problems in business and finance mathematics, the use of equations and formulas is necessary. These equations and formulas are formed using algebraic expressions.

In arithmetic, we use only numbers and operational signs in expressions.

For example, $25 + 15$, $75 - 22$, 8×9, $\frac{9}{4}$

In algebra, we use both numbers and variables (letters and symbols that represent varying quantities), as well as operational signs in expressions.

For example, $2x + 5$, $30 - 5y$, $6(2a + 5)$, $\frac{b+3}{2}$

Furthermore, in algebra, we use variables, numbers, and operational signs to translate word problems into equations.

For example,

- If the sum of two numbers is 100, it can be represented by the equation: $x + y = 100$.
- If $x = 40$, then $y = 60$; similarly, if $x = 10$, then $y = 90$.

In algebraic expressions involving multiplication, the number and the variable(s) are written together without the operational sign for multiplication.

For example, $5a$ means $5 \times a$, $5(a)$, or $5 \cdot a$; similarly, xy means $x \times y$, $x(y)$, or $x \cdot y$.

The following key words will help in translating word problems into algebraic expressions and equations:

Table 2.1 **Arithmetic Operations and Key Words**

Arithmetic operation	Key words
Addition (+)	add, sum, total, plus, and, more than, increased by, appreciate, rise
Subtraction (–)	subtract, difference, minus, less than, reduced by, decreased by, depreciate, fall
Multiplication (×), (•)	multiply, product, times, of
Division (÷)	divide, ratio, divided by, quotient, per
Equals (=)	is, was, gives, given by

For example,

	In words	In algebraic expression
1.	Ten more than a number	$x + 10$
2.	A number more than ten	$10 + x$
3.	A number less than twenty	$20 - x$
4.	Twenty less than a number	$x - 20$
5.	Product of five and a number	$5x$
6.	Divide 20 by a number	$\frac{20}{x}$
7.	Divide a number by 20	$\frac{x}{20}$
8.	Half of a number	$\frac{1}{2}x$ or $\frac{x}{2}$
9.	Twice a number	$2x$
10.	Ten more than the product of two numbers	$xy + 10$
11.	'x' less than 'y'	$y - x$
12.	'y' less than 'x'	$x - y$
13.	Seventy decreased by 3 times a number	$70 - 3x$
14.	'm' subtracted from 'n'	$n - m$

Terminology Used in Algebraic Expressions

Terminology	Description	Examples
Variable	Usually a single letter of the alphabet used in expressions and equations to represent a varying quantity. However, multiple letter designations are also used to represent a variable in formulas and calculator buttons.	In the expression $2m + 5n - 6$, m and n are variables. '*PV*', '*FV*', '*PMT*', etc.
Term	A number, variable, or a combination of numbers and variables which are multiplied or divided together.	$5, x, 5x^2y, 2xy, \frac{4}{a}, \frac{b}{3}$ each have 1 term. The expression $5x + y$ has 2 terms. The expression $\frac{x}{4} - y^2 + \frac{x}{y} - \frac{1}{x}$ has 4 terms.
Expression	A mathematical phrase made up of a combination of terms and operations.	Expressions with one variable: $(2x + 5), (9x - 3)$ Expressions with two variables: $(5x - 7y + 5)$, $(xy + 3x + 7)$
Coefficient	The product of all numerical factors in front of the variables of a term.	Coefficient of x^2 is 1, coefficient of $-3(2y^3)$ is -6. In the expression $5x^2 - 2y + 3$, the coefficient of the 1st term is 5, and the coefficient of the 2nd term is -2.
Constant	A term that only has a number with no variables. Sometimes a letter or symbol is used to represent a quantity that does not change.	In the expression $2x + 3y + 5$, the 3rd term, $+5$, is a constant. In the expression $5x^2 - 8$, the 2nd term, -8, is a constant. π is a constant, where $\pi = 3.14159265...$
Like terms	Terms that have the same variables and exponents. They differ only in their numerical coefficient. Constant terms are like terms.	$5x$ and $9x$ are like terms. $30a^2, -4a^2$, and $9a^2$ are like terms. $5, -9$ are like terms.
Unlike terms	Terms that have different variables or the same variables with different exponents.	$12y$ and $3y^2$ are unlike terms. x^2, x, and 1 are unlike terms.
Factors	Refer to each of the combinations of variables and/or numbers multiplied together in a term.	5 and x are factors of the term $5x$. 3, x, and y are factors of the term $3xy$.
Monomial	An algebraic expression that has only one term.	$8, 7x, 4y$, and $2xy$ are monomials.
Polynomial	Algebraic expression that has two or more terms.	$(8x^2 - 5x + 3)$ is a polynomial with 3 terms where, the 1st term is $8x^2$, the 2nd term is $-5x$, and the 3rd term is $+3$. Coefficient of the 1st term is 8, coefficient of the 2nd term is -5. The 3rd term is a constant.
Binomial	Polynomial with 2 terms.	$(4x - 3y), (x - 5), (4xy + 7x)$ are binomials.
Trinomial	Polynomial with 3 terms.	$(2x + 3y + 5), (xy + x - 2), (2x + xy + 3z)$ are trinomials.

Basic Arithmetic Operations with Algebraic Expressions

All arithmetic operations can be performed on algebraic expressions by following the applicable rules (BEDMAS, exponents, signed numbers, etc.).

Addition and Subtraction

While grouping like terms, the sign of the term moves with the term.

When adding or subtracting algebraic expressions, first collect the like terms and group them, then add or subtract the coefficients of the like terms.

Note: *If the coefficient of a term is not written, it is 1.*

Example 2.1(a) **Addition and Subtraction of Algebraic Expressions**

Add: (i) $(3x + 7)$ and $(5x + 3)$ (ii) $(4y^2 - 8y - 9)$ and $(2y^2 + 6y - 2)$

Subtract: (iii) $(x^2 + 5x - 7)$ from $(2x^2 - 2x + 3)$ (iv) $(5y^2 + 8y - 6)$ from $(-2y^2 - 7y + 5)$

Solution

When a bracket is preceded by a positive sign (+), then drop the bracket.

(i) $(3x + 7) + (5x + 3)$ Removing brackets,

$= 3x + 7 + 5x + 3$ Grouping like terms,

$= \underbrace{3x + 5x}\underbrace{+ 7 + 3}$ Adding like terms,

$= 8x + 10$

(ii) $(4y^2 - 8y - 9) + (2y^2 + 6y - 2)$ Removing brackets,

$= 4y^2 - 8y - 9 + 2y^2 + 6y - 2$ Grouping like terms,

$= \underbrace{4y^2 + 2y^2}\underbrace{- 8y + 6y}\underbrace{- 9 - 2}$ Adding and subtracting like terms,

$= 6y^2 - 2y - 11$

When a bracket is preceded by a negative sign, change the sign of every term within the bracket and drop the bracket.

(iii) $(2x^2 - 2x + 3) - (x^2 + 5x - 7)$ Expanding by distributing the negative sign to terms within the bracket,

$= 2x^2 - 2x + 3 - x^2 - 5x + 7$ Grouping like terms,

$= \underbrace{2x^2 - x^2}\underbrace{- 2x - 5x}\underbrace{+ 3 + 7}$ Adding and subtracting like terms,

$= x^2 - 7x + 10$

(iv) $(-2y^2 - 7y + 5) - (5y^2 + 8y - 6)$ Expanding by distributing the negative sign to terms within the bracket,

$= -2y^2 - 7y + 5 - 5y^2 - 8y + 6$ Grouping like terms,

$= \underbrace{-2y^2 - 5y^2}\underbrace{- 7y - 8y}\underbrace{+ 5 + 6}$ Adding and subtracting like terms,

$= -7y^2 - 15y + 11$

Multiplication

Multiplying a Monomial by a Monomial

When multiplying a monomial by a monomial, multiply the coefficients and multiply all the variables. If there are any similar variables, use the exponent notation.

Example 2.1(b) **Multiplying Monomials by Monomials**

Multiply and simplify: (i) $6x^2y$ and $5xy$ (ii) $(3a^3)$, $(-4ab)$, and $(2b^2)$

Solution

(i) $(6x^2y)(5xy)$ Grouping coefficients and variables,

$= \underbrace{(6)(5)}\underbrace{(x^2)(x)}\underbrace{(y)(y)}$ Multiplying,

$= 30x^3y^2$

Solution *continued*

(ii) $(3a^3)(-4ab)(2b^2)$ — Grouping coefficients and variables,

$= \underbrace{(3)(-4)(2)}\underbrace{(a^3)(a)}\underbrace{(b)(b^2)}$ — Multiplying,

$= -24a^4b^3$

Multiplying a Polynomial by a Monomial

When multiplying a polynomial by a monomial, multiply the monomial by **each term** of the polynomial. This is also known as the *distributive property of multiplication.*

$$a(b + c) = ab + ac$$

Then, group the like terms and simplify using addition and subtraction.

Example 2.1(c) **Multiplying Polynomials by Monomials**

(i) Multiply: $2x^3$ and $(3x^2 + 2x - 5)$

(ii) Expand and simplify: $8x(x + 3) + 4x(x - 4)$

Solution

(i) $2x^3(3x^2 + 2x - 5)$ — Expanding,

$= 6x^5 + 4x^4 - 10x^3$

(ii) $8x(x + 3) + 4x(x - 4)$ — Expanding,

$= 8x^2 + 24x + 4x^2 - 16x$ — Grouping like terms,

$= \underbrace{8x^2 + 4x^2} + \underbrace{24x - 16x}$ — Adding and subtracting like terms,

$= 12x^2 + 8x$

Multiplying a Polynomial by a Polynomial

When multiplying a polynomial by a polynomial, multiply each term of the first polynomial by each term of the second polynomial. Then, group the like terms and simplify using addition and subtraction.

Example 2.1(d) **Multiplying Polynomials by Polynomials**

Multiply and simplify:

(i) (x^2+5) and $(x - 4)$

(ii) $(x^2 + 7)$ and $(2x^2 + 5x + 2)$

(iii) $(x + 5)(2x - 6) + (3x - 4)(x - 5)$

Solution

(i) $(x^2+5)(x - 4)$ — Expanding,

$= x^3 - 4x^2 + 5x - 20$

(ii) $(x^2 + 7)(2x^2 + 5x + 2)$ — Expanding,

$= 2x^4 + 5x^3 \underbrace{+ 2x^2 + 14x^2} + 35x + 14$ — Adding like terms,

$= 2x^4 + 5x^3 + 16x^2 + 35x + 14$

Solution *continued*

(iii) $(x + 5)(2x - 6) + (3x - 4)(x - 5)$ — Expanding,

$= (2x^2 - 6x + 10x - 30) + (3x^2 - 15x - 4x + 20)$ — Removing brackets,

$= 2x^2 - 6x + 10x - 30 + 3x^2 - 15x - 4x + 20$ — Grouping like terms,

$= \underbrace{2x^2 + 3x^2}\underbrace{- 6x + 10x - 15x - 4x}\underbrace{- 30 + 20}$ — Adding and subtracting like terms,

$= 5x^2 - 15x - 10$

Division

Dividing a Monomial by a Monomial

When dividing a monomial by a monomial, group the constants and each of the variables separately and simplify them. If there are any similar variables, use the exponent notation.

Example 2.1(e) **Dividing Monomials by Monomials**

Divide and simplify: (i) $8x^2y$ by $6x$ (ii) $9x^2$ by $3x^2$

Solution

(i) $\frac{8x^2y}{6x} = \frac{8}{6} \times \frac{x^2}{x} \times y = \frac{4}{3}xy$ or $\frac{4xy}{3}$

(ii) $\frac{9x^2}{3x^2} = \frac{9}{3} = 3$

Dividing a Polynomial by a Monomial

When dividing a polynomial by a monomial, divide **each term** of the polynomial by the monomial. The process is similar to dividing a monomial by a monomial.

Example 2.1(f) **Dividing Polynomials by Monomials**

Divide: (i) $(9x^3 + 3x^2)$ by $6x$ (ii) $(2x^3 + 4x^4 + 7x)$ by $4x^4$

Solution

(i) $\frac{9x^3 + 3x^2}{6x} = \frac{9x^3}{6x} + \frac{3x^2}{6x} = \frac{3x^2}{2} + \frac{x}{2}$ or $\frac{3x^2 + x}{2}$

(ii) $\frac{2x^3 + 4x^4 + 7x}{4x^4} = \frac{2x^3}{4x^4} + \frac{4x^4}{4x^4} + \frac{7x}{4x^4} = \frac{1}{2x} + 1 + \frac{7}{4x^3}$

Evaluating Algebraic Expressions

In an algebraic expression, when we replace all the variables with numbers and simplify the expression, it is referred to as evaluating the algebraic expression. The simplified answer is the value of the expression.

Example 2.1(g) **Evaluating Algebraic Expressions**

Evaluate: (i) $2x + y$, where $x = 10$ and $y = 5$ (ii) $\frac{3xy + 3x}{2y + 5}$, where $x = 3$ and $y = 2$

Solution

(i) $2x + y$ — Substituting $x = 10$ and $y = 5$,

$= 2(10) + 5 = 20 + 5 = 25$ — [$2x$ means $2(x)$]

(ii) $\frac{3xy + 3x}{2y + 5}$ — Substituting $x = 3$ and $y = 2$,

$= \frac{3(3)(2) + 3(3)}{2(2) + 5} = \frac{18 + 9}{4 + 5} = \frac{27}{9} = 3$

Example 2.1(h) **Evaluating Algebraic Expressions Involving Exponents**

Evaluate:

(i) $\frac{(5x)^2 \times 4y}{50}$, where $x = 2$ and $y = 3$

(ii) $2(x^2 + 3x) - 5y$, where $x = 4$ and $y = -3$

Solution

(i) $\frac{(5x)^2 \times 4y}{50}$ — Substituting $x = 2$ and $y = 3$,

$= \frac{[5(2)]^2 \times 4(3)}{50} = \frac{10^2 \times 12}{50} = \frac{100 \times 12}{50} = 24$ — [Remember to follow BEDMAS rule]

(ii) $2(x^2 + 3x) - 5y$ — Substituting $x = 4$ and $y = -3$,

$= 2[(4)^2 + 3(4)] - 5(-3) = 2(16 + 12) + 15 = 56 + 15 = 71$

Factoring Algebraic Expressions with Common Factors

Factoring algebraic expressions means finding the common factors for both coefficients and the variables in all the terms. Once the factors are found, the expression will become a product of a monomial and a polynomial (or multiple polynomials).

Example 2.1(i) **Factoring Algebraic Expressions**

Factor the following:

(i) $12x + 18y$

(ii) $8y^2 + 18y$

(iii) $12xy^3 + 6xy^4 - 9x^3y^5 - 3xy^3$

(iv) $14(2x + y) - 7x(2x + y)$

Solution

(i) $12x + 18y$

$12x = 2 \times 2 \times 3 \times x$
$18y = 2 \times 3 \times 3 \times y$
} Factors 2 and 3 are common for both. Therefore, GCF = $2 \times 3 = 6$.

By dividing the original expression by the GCF 6, we obtain the other factor $(2x + 3y)$.

Therefore, $12x + 18y = 6(2x + 3y)$.

(ii) $8y^2 + 18y$

$8y^2 = 2 \times 2 \times 2 \times y \times y$
$18y = 2 \times 3 \times 3 \times y$
} Factors 2 and y are common for both. Therefore, GCF = $2(y) = 2y$.

By dividing the original expression by the GCF $2y$, we obtain the other factor $(4y + 9)$. Therefore, $8y^2 + 18y = 2y(4y + 9)$.

(iii) $12xy^3 + 6xy^4 - 9x^3y^5 - 3xy^3$ — $3xy^3$ is common for all terms. Therefore, GCF = $3xy^3$.

By dividing the original expression by the GCF $3xy^3$, we obtain the other factor $(4 + 2y - 3x^2y^2 - 1)$. Therefore, $12xy^3 + 6xy^4 - 9x^3y^5 - 3xy^3 = 3xy^3(4 + 2y - 3x^2y^2 - 1)$.

Solution *continued*

(iv) $14(2x+y) - 7x(2x+y)$

$14(2x+y) = 2 \times 7 \times (2x+y)$ } Factors 7 and $(2x + y)$ are common for both.
$7x(2x+y) = 7 \times x \times (2x+y)$ } Therefore, GCF $= 7(2x + y)$

By dividing the original expression by the GCF $7(2x + y)$, we obtain the other factor $(2 - x)$.

Therefore, $14(2x+y) - 7x(2x+y) = 7(2x+y)(2-x)$.

2.1 | Exercises

Answers to the odd-numbered problems are available at the end of the textbook.

1. Identify the following terms in the equations:
   a. 2nd term and 3rd term in $3x^2 + 7xy - 4y + 7$
   b. 3rd term and 4th term in $x^2 - 5x - y + 3$
   c. 1st term and 3rd term in $9xy + 7x - 6y + 2$

2. Identify the following terms in the equations:
   a. 1st term and 4th term in $-x^2 + 9xy + y + 7$
   b. 2nd term and 3rd term in $7xy + 4y + 7$
   c. 1st term and 3rd term in $10x^2 + 5xy - 6x + 7y$

3. State the constant term and the coefficient of all other terms in each of the following expressions:
   a. $5x^2 - 3xy + 5$
   b. $-2y^2 + 3x + 1$
   c. $-2xy^2 - 2x^2y + 7$
   d. $8y^2 - 4$

4. State the constant term and the coefficient of all other terms in each of the following expressions:
   a. $-2y^2 + 3y - 4$
   b. $y^5 - 2y^7 - 2$
   c. $2x^3 - 3x^2 + 1$
   d. $-6x^2 + 6$

For Problems 5 to 20, simplify the expressions.

5. a. $13x^2 + 8x - 2x^2 + 9x$ b. $-18y - 5y^2 + 19y - 2y^2$ c. $6x - 3x + 2y^2 + y^2$

6. a. $7x + 12x^2 - 4x + 5x^2$ b. $-14y - 2y^2 + 7y + 7y^2$ c. $9x^2 - 6x^2 + 7y - 6y$

7. a. $\dfrac{3x + 5x}{5x}$ b. $\dfrac{12y - 3y}{4y + 2y}$ c. $\dfrac{(16y)(8x)}{(4x)(8y)}$

8. a. $\dfrac{8x}{x + 5x}$ b. $\dfrac{20y - 5y}{-4y + 7y}$ c. $\dfrac{(20y)(4x)}{(2x)(5y)}$

9. a. $3[5 - 3(4 - x)] - 2 - 5[3(5x - 4) + 8] - 9x$ b. $6[4(8 - y) - 5(3 + 3y)] - 21 - 7[3(7 + 4y) - 4] + 198y$

10. a. $5 - \dfrac{1}{4}\{x - 8[3 - 5(2x - 3) + 3x] - 3\}$ b. $\dfrac{1}{5}\{y - 15[2 - 3(3y - 2) - 7y] - 4\} + 7$

11. a. $y - \{4x - [y - (2y - 9) - x] + 2\}$ b. $(x - 1) - \{[x - (x - 3)] - x\}$

12. a. $2y + \{-6y - [3x + (-4x + 3)] + 5\}$ b. $9x - \{3y + [4x - (y - 6x)] - (x + 7y)\}$

13. a. $2\{-2y + 3[4x - 2(3 + x)]\}$ b. $2y\,\{8[3(2y - 5) - (8y + 9) + 6]\}$

14. a. $2\{-7y + 8[5x - 3(4x + 6)]\}$ b. $2x - \{5[4(3x - 8) - (9x + 10)] + 14\}$

15. a. $(2y - 1)(y - 4) - (3y + 2)(3y - 1)$ b. $(2x + 3)(2x - 1) - 4(x^2 - 7)$ c. $(5x - 6)^2 - (x + 5)^2$

16. a. $(y + 4)(y - 3) + (y - 2)(y - 3)$ b. $4(2x - 1)(x + 3) - 3(x - 2)(3x - 4)$ c. $(2y - 3)^2 - (y + 3)^2$

17. a. $\dfrac{-x^2y - xy^2}{xy}$ b. $\dfrac{x^2y - 3xy^2 + 4x^2y + xy}{xy}$ c. $\dfrac{6xy^2}{7} \times \dfrac{21x^2}{y} \times \dfrac{1}{36xy^2}$

18. a. $\dfrac{-x^2y - 3xy^2}{xy}$ b. $\dfrac{3x^3y^3 + 6x^2y - 3xy^2 + 3xy}{3xy}$ c. $\dfrac{12x^2y^2}{5} \times \dfrac{15x^2}{4xy} \times \dfrac{1}{30x^3y}$

19. a. $\frac{3x+9}{14} \times \frac{7x+21}{x+3}$ b. $\frac{x^2+5x}{2x+10} \times \frac{3x+15}{4x}$ c. $\frac{5xy+15y}{4x-12} \times \frac{3x-9}{4x+12}$

20. a. $\frac{16}{3x^2y+4x} \times \frac{6x^2y+8x}{12}$ b. $\frac{3xy+4y}{8y} \times \frac{12y^2}{3x+4}$ c. $\frac{x^2+xy}{7x-14} \times \frac{14x-28}{x+y}$

21. Evaluate the following expressions, given $x = 2$ and $y = 3$:

a. $\frac{19x-5y}{9}$ b. x^2+6x+8 c. $\frac{(3x)^2+(3y)}{6y}$ d. $-2x^2+3x+8y$

22. Evaluate the following expressions, given $x = 5$ and $y = 4$:

a. $\frac{7x-5y}{3}$ b. $-x^2+10x+7$ c. $\frac{(2x)^2+(2y)}{5y}$ d. $4x^2+10x+48y$

For Problems 23 to 26, simplify and evaluate the expressions.

23. a. $6y+4y-7y$, where $y = 10$ b. $2z-z+7z$, where $z = 7$

24. a. $3x+5x-8x$, where $x = 4$ b. $3A-A+6A$, where $A = 10$

25. a. $(6x)(3x)-(5x)(4x)$, where $x = 3$ b. $(2x)(0.5x+4x)(5x+x)$, where $x = 5$

26. a. $(10x \times 4.5x)-(11x \times 4x)$, where $x = 50$ b. $(4x)(12x+0.25x)(0.5x+x)$, where $x = 3$

For Problems 27 to 30, identify like terms, group them, and simplify.

27. a. $12A+4B-7A-B$ b. $6x+8y-5x-3y+7$

28. a. $6B+8A-A-2B$ b. $14-3x+10y+4y$

29. a. $-2x+8x-12x+5y+7y$ b. $6xy^2-2x^2y-4x^2+2xy^2+3x^2y+2x^2+4$

30. a. $3x+6x-20x+8y+8y+5x$ b. $3x^2y-12xy^2-6x^2y-5xy-2xy-4xy^2$

31. Identify like terms, group them, simplify, and evaluate:

a. $3a+6b-16c-a+8b+4c+2$, where $a = 3$, $b = 2$, $c = 1$

b. x^2-x+2x^2-x, where $x = 5$

32. Identify like terms, group them, simplify, and evaluate:

a. $3x-60y-17z-2x+62y+4z+1$, where $x = 5$, $y = 8$, $z = 2$

b. $-a^2-3a+3a^2+4a$, where $a = 15$

For Problems 33 to 36, factor the expressions using GCF.

33. a. $6x^2y-3xy-9y$ b. $15y^2-12y-3$ c. $6ab^2-8ba^2$

34. a. $12a^2b-16ab-24b$ b. $33x^2-3x-11x^2$ c. $12x^2y-18y^2x$

35. a. $10ab-8bc$ b. $8a^3-4a^2$ c. $10x^2-6x-4x^2$

36. a. $6xy-9yz$ b. $10x^3-4x^2$ c. $60y^2-40y-180y^2$

For Problems 37 to 40, factor the expressions by grouping.

- 37. a. $5x(y+2)+3y+6$ b. $4y(x-5)-x^2+5x$ c. $xy-2y+5x-10$
- 38. a. $7x(m-4)+3m-12$ b. $3y(x-1)+2x^2-2x$ c. $4x-xy-20y+5y^2$
- 39. a. $x^2+x-xy-y$ b. $2x^2+3y+2x+3xy$
- 40. a. $x^2-4y+4x-xy$ b. $5x^2y-10x^2+y^2-2y$

2.2 | Simple Algebraic Equations and Word Problems

An **algebraic equation** is a mathematical sentence expressing equality between two algebraic expressions (or an algebraic expression and a number).

When two expressions are joined by an equal (=) sign, it indicates that the expression to the left of the equal sign is equal to the expression to the right of the equal sign.

For example, when two algebraic expressions, $5x + 7$ and $x + 19$, are equal, the two expressions are joined by an equal (=) sign and the equation is written as:

$$\underbrace{5x + 7}_{\text{Left side (LS)}} = \underbrace{x + 19}_{\text{Right side (RS)}}$$

The **solution** to the equation is determined by performing arithmetic operations to solve for the variable that makes the left side (LS) equal to the right side (RS).

In algebra, there are a variety of equations. In this section, you will learn one type of equation, known as a **linear equation with one variable**.

Examples of linear equations with one variable are:

$$2x = 8, \qquad 3x + 5 = 14, \qquad 5x + 7 = x + 19.$$

Equivalent Equations

Equations with the same solutions are called **equivalent equations**.

For example, $2x + 5 = 9$ and $2x = 4$ are equivalent equations because the solution $x = 2$ satisfies each equation.

Similarly, $3x - 4 = 5$, $2x = x + 3$, and $x + 1 = 4$ are equvialent equations because the solution $x = 3$ satisfies each equation.

Properties of Equality

Performing the same operation on both sides of an equation will result in an equivalent equation.

If $a = b$, then,

$b = a$	Symmetric Property	Interchanging LS and RS.
$a + c = b + c$	Addition Property	Adding the same quantity on both sides.
$a - c = b - c$	Subtraction Property	Subtracting the same quantity on both sides.
$a \times c = b \times c$	Multiplication Property	Multiplying by the same quantity on both sides.
$\frac{a}{c} = \frac{b}{c}$	Division Property, $c \neq 0$	Dividing by the same quantity on both sides.

The above properties are used to solve equations.

Equations with Decimal Coefficients

If an equation contains decimal coefficients, then the decimal coefficients can be changed to whole numbers by multiplying each term by the lowest decimal place value.

For example,

$\underline{1.25}x = \underline{0.2} + 4$	The lowest place value is hundredths. Multiplying each term by 100,
$100(1.25x) = 100(0.2) + 100(4)$	Simplifying,
$125x = 20 + 400$	Now, the equation has whole number coefficients.
$125x = 420$	

Equations with Fractional Coefficients

If an equation contains fractional coefficients, then the fractional coefficients can be changed to whole numbers by multiplying each term by the least common denominator (LCD) of all the fractions.

For example,

$\frac{2}{3}x = \frac{5}{2} + 4$	The LCD of the denominators 3 and 2 is 6. Multiplying each term by 6,
$6\left(\frac{2}{3}x\right) = 6\left(\frac{5}{2}\right) + 6(4)$	Simplifying,
$4x = 15 + 24$	Now, the equation is with whole number coefficients.
$4x = 39$	

Solving Algebraic Equations with One Variable

Use the following steps in solving algebraic equations with one variable:

Step 1: Clear the equation of fractions and/or decimals whenever possible, to make calculations and rearrangements easier.

Step 2: Expand and clear brackets in the equation, if present, by following the order of arithmetic operations (BEDMAS).

Step 3: Use the addition and subtraction properties to collect and group all **variable** terms to the **left side** of the equation and all **constants** to the **right side** of the equation.

Step 4: Use the multiplication and division properties to ensure that the coefficient of the variable is +1.

Step 5: You should now have a single variable on the left side, and one or more numbers on the right side. Compute the right side of the equation to find the solution.

Step 6: Verify the answer against the original problem.

Step 7: State your answer.

Example 2.2(a) **Solving Equations Using the Addition and Subtraction Properties**

Solve the following equations and verify the solutions:

(i) $x - 11 = 4$

(ii) $8 + x = 20$

Solution

(i) $x - 11 = 4$ — Adding 11 to both sides,

$x - 11 + 11 = 4 + 11$ — Simplifying,

$x = 15$

Verify by substituting $x = 15$:

LS $= x - 11$	RS $= 4$
$= \mathbf{15} - 11$	
$= 4$	

LS = RS

Therefore, the solution is $x = 15$.

(ii) $8 + x = 20$ — Subtracting 8 from both sides,

$8 - 8 + x = 20 - 8$ — Simplifying,

$x = 12$

Verify by substituting $x = 12$:

LS $= 8 + x$	RS $= 20$
$= 8 + \mathbf{12}$	
$= 20$	

LS = RS

Therefore, the solution is $x = 12$.

Example 2.2(b) **Solving Equations Using the Multiplication and Division Properties**

Solve the following equations and verify the solutions:

(i) $5x = 20$ (ii) $\frac{3}{8}x = 12$

Solution

(i) $5x = 20$ Dividing both sides by 5,

$\frac{5x}{5} = \frac{20}{5}$ Simplifying,

$x = 4$

Verify by substituting $x = 4$:

LS	RS
$LS = 5x$	$RS = 20$
$= 5(\mathbf{4})$	
$= 20$	

LS = RS

Therefore, the solution is $x = 4$.

(ii) $\frac{3}{8}x = 12$ Multiplying both sides by $\frac{8}{3}$ (the reciprocal of $\frac{3}{8}$),

$\frac{8}{3}\left(\frac{3}{8}x\right) = \frac{8}{3}(12)$ Simplifying,

$x = \frac{8}{\cancel{3}_1} \times \cancel{12}^4$

$x = 8 \times 4$

$x = 32$

Verify by substituting $x = 32$:

LS	RS
$LS = \frac{3}{8}x$	$RS = 12$
$= \frac{3}{8} \times \mathbf{32}$	
$= 12$	

LS = RS

Therefore, the solution is $x = 32$.

Alternative Method

$\frac{3}{8}x = 12$ Multiplying both sides by 8,

$8\left(\frac{3}{8}x\right) = 8(12)$ Simplifying,

$3x = 96$ Dividing both sides by 3,

$\frac{3x}{3} = \frac{96}{3}$ Simplifying,

$x = 32$

Example 2.2(c) **Solving Equations with Variables on Both Sides**

Solve the following equations:

(i) $3x - 8 = 12 - 2x$ (ii) $15 + 6x - 4 = 3x + 31 - x$

Solution

(i) $3x - 8 = 12 - 2x$ Adding $2x$ to both sides and simplifying,

$3x + 2x - 8 = 12 - 2x + 2x$

$5x - 8 = 12$ Adding 8 to both sides and simplifying,

$5x - 8 + 8 = 12 + 8$

$5x = 20$ Dividing both sides by 5 and simplifying,

$\frac{5x}{5} = \frac{20}{5}$

$x = 4$ Therefore, the solution is $x = 4$.

Solution *continued*

(ii) $15 + 6x - 4 = 3x + 31 - x$ — Combining like terms on both sides,

$11 + 6x = 2x + 31$ — Subtracting $2x$ from both sides and simplifying,

$11 + 6x - 2x = 2x - 2x + 31$

$11 + 4x = 31$ — Subtracting 11 from both sides and simplifying,

$11 - 11 + 4x = 31 - 11$

$4x = 20$ — Dividing both sides by 4 and simplifying,

$$\frac{4x}{4} = \frac{20}{4}$$

$x = 5$ — Therefore, the solution is $x = 5$.

Example 2.2(d) **Solving Equations with Fractions and Equations with Decimals**

Solve the following equations:

(i) $\frac{x}{3} - \frac{1}{12} = \frac{1}{6} + \frac{x}{4}$ (ii) $0.15x + 1.2 = 0.4x - 0.8$

Solution

(i) $\frac{x}{3} - \frac{1}{12} = \frac{1}{6} + \frac{x}{4}$ — LCD of 3, 4, 6, and 12 is 12. Multiplying each term by 12 and simplifying,

$$12\left(\frac{x}{3}\right) - 12\left(\frac{1}{12}\right) = 12\left(\frac{1}{6}\right) + 12\left(\frac{x}{4}\right)$$

$4x - 1 = 2 + 3x$ — Subtracting $3x$ from both sides and simplifying,

$4x - 3x - 1 = 2 + 3x - 3x$

$x - 1 = 2$ — Adding 1 to both sides and simplifying,

$x - 1 + 1 = 2 + 1$

$x = 3$ — Therefore, the solution is $x = 3$.

(ii) $0.15x + 1.2 = 0.4x - 0.8$ — Lowest decimal place value is hundredths. Multiplying each term by 100 and simplifying,

$100(0.15x) + 100(1.2) = 100(0.4x) - 100(0.8)$

$15x + 120 = 40x - 80$ — Using the symmetric property,

$40x - 80 = 15x + 120$ — Subtracting $15x$ from both sides and simplifying,

$40x - 15x - 80 = 15x - 15x + 120$

$25x - 80 = 120$ — Adding 80 to both sides and simplifying,

$25x - 80 + 80 = 120 + 80$

$25x = 200$ — Dividing both sides by 25 and simplifying,

$$\frac{25x}{25} = \frac{200}{25}$$

$x = 8$ — Therefore, the solution is $x = 8$.

Example 2.2(e) **Solving Equations Using All the Principles**

Solve the following:

(i) $8x + 7 - 3x = -6x - 15 + x$

(ii) $2(3x - 7) = 28 - 3(x + 1)$

Solution

(i)

$8x + 7 - 3x = -6x - 15 + x$	Combining like terms on both sides,
$5x + 7 = -5x - 15$	Adding $5x$ to both sides and simplifying,
$5x + 5x + 7 = -5x + 5x - 15$	
$10x + 7 = -15$	Subtracting 7 from both sides and simplifying,
$10x + 7 - 7 = -15 - 7$	
$10x = -22$	Dividing both sides by 10 and simplifying,
$\frac{10x}{10} = \frac{-22}{10}$	
$x = -2.2$	Therefore, the solution is –2.2.

(ii)

$2(3x - 7) = 28 - 3(x + 1)$	Expanding both sides,
$6x - 14 = 28 - 3x - 3$	Adding $3x$ to both sides and simplifying,
$6x + 3x - 14 = 28 - 3 - 3x + 3x$	
$9x - 14 = 25$	Adding 14 to both sides and simplifying,
$9x - 14 + 14 = 25 + 14$	
$9x = 39$	Dividing both sides by 9 and simplifying,
$\frac{9x}{9} = \frac{39}{9}$	
$x = \frac{13}{3}$	Therefore, the solution is $\frac{13}{3}$.

Examples of Writing Simple Algebraic Equations with One Variable in Word Problems

Sample word problem	Algebraic equation
Six more than a number is 15.	$x + 6 = 15$
In 20 years, Andrew will be 60 years old.	$x + 20 = 60$
Fourteen decreased by twice a number is six.	$14 - 2x = 6$
The product of five and the sum of a number and four is sixty.	$5(x + 4) = 60$
The quotient of six and a number is three.	$\frac{6}{x} = 3$

Solving Word Problems

We can follow these steps to solve word problems:

Step 1: Read the entire problem and understand the situation.

Step 2: Identify the given information and the question to be answered.

Step 3: Look for key words. Some words indicate certain mathematical operations.

Step 4: Choose a variable to represent the unknown(s).

Step 5: State what that variable represents, including the unit of measure.

Step 6: Wherever necessary, draw a simple sketch to identify the information. This helps to visualize the scenario.

Step 7: Create an equation (or set of equations) to describe the relationship between the variables and the constants in the question.

Step 8: Rearrange the equation(s) and solve for the unknowns.

Example 2.2(f) **Solving a Word Problem Using Algebraic Equations**

Harry paid a total of \$65 for a shirt and a tie. If he paid \$18 for the tie, how much did he pay for the shirt?

Solution

Let $\$x$ be the amount paid for the shirt.

The total amount paid, $x + 18 = 65$

Solving for x, $x = 65 - 18$

$x = 47$

Therefore, he paid \$47 for the shirt.

Example 2.2(g) **Solving a Word Problem Using Algebraic Equations**

Bessy's hourly rate of pay is \$5 more than that of Anna's. If both of them worked for two hours and received a total of \$70, what are their individual hourly rates of pay?

Solution

Let Anna's hourly rate be $\$x$.

Therefore, Bessy's hourly rate: $\$x + \$5$

Total amount received if both of them worked for two hours:

$$2(x) + 2(x + 5) = 70$$
$$2x + 2x + 10 = 70$$
$$4x = 70 - 10$$
$$4x = 60$$
$$x = 15$$

Therefore, Anna's hourly rate is \$15 and Bessy's hourly rate is 15 + 5 = \$20.

2.2 | Exercises

Answers to the odd-numbered problems are available at the end of the textbook.

1. Write the algebraic expression for the following:
   a. Three less than twice a number
   b. Two times a number divided by five
   c. Twenty-five increased by three times a number
   d. Six times the total of three and a number

2. Write the algebraic expression for the following:
   a. A number less than four times a number
   b. Fifteen divided by three times a number
   c. Seven times the sum of a number and five
   d. Twenty increased by twice a number

For Problems 3 to 6, write the algebraic equation and solve the equation.

3. a. The sum of a number and six is ten. b. Six times a number is seventy-two.

4. a. A number decreased by fifteen is five. b. Two-fifths a number is six.

5. a. A number divided by five is four. b. Two-thirds a number is twelve.

6. a. The product of a number and four is twenty-eight. b. A number divided by three is three.

For Problems 7 to 32, solve for the unknown using properties of equations, and round to two decimal places, wherever applicable.

7. a. $x - 20 = 10$ b. $22 = 40 - x$

8. a. $x - 25 = 17$ b. $54 = 23 - x$

9. a. $21 + x = 4$ b. $16 + x = 22$

10. a. $50 + x = 45$ b. $12 + x = 38$

11. a. $x - \frac{4}{5} = \frac{3}{5}$ b. $\frac{10}{15} = x - \frac{4}{3}$

12. a. $x - \frac{1}{6} = \frac{5}{6}$ b. $7x - 16 = 22$

13. a. $5x = 20$ b. $11x + 4 = 17$

14. a. $4x = 24$ b. $4x + 5x = 25$

15. a. $x + 0.13x = 75$ b. $x + 0.08x = 110$

16. a. $x + 0.08x = 45$ b. $4x + 5 = 25$

17. $8x + 7 - 3x = -6x - 15 + x$

18. $x - 2 - 4x = -3x - 8 + 5x$

19. $2(3x - 7) = 28 - 3(x + 1)$

20. $4(2x - 5) = 32 - 4(x - 2)$

21. $\frac{x - 5}{2} + \frac{x + 2}{3} = 41$

22. $\frac{7}{12}(2x - 1) + \frac{3}{4}(x + 1) = 3$

23. $\frac{5}{y + 4} = \frac{3}{y - 2}$

24. $\frac{3}{x + 1} = \frac{2}{x - 3}$

25. $\frac{7}{5x - 3} = \frac{5}{4x}$

26. $\frac{5}{y + 2} = \frac{3}{y}$

27. $15 + 5(x - 10) = 3(x - 1)$

28. $2(x - 3) + 3(x - 5) = 4$

29. $4(y + 7) - 2(y - 4) = 3(y - 2)$

30. $8(2y + 4) - 6(3y + 7) = 3y$

31. $4(2x - 5) = 32 - 4(x - 2)$

32. $(5 + 0.5x)(1 + 3) = -1.2(2x + 4) + 25$

33. If three times a number plus twenty is seven times that number, what is the number?

34. Fifteen less than three times a number is twice that number. What is the number?

35. A 25-metre long wire is cut into 2 pieces. One piece is 7 metres longer than the other. Calculate the length of each piece.

36. A 9-metre long pipe is cut into 2 pieces. One piece is twice the length of the other piece. Calculate the length of each piece.

37. Andy and Becky shared \$500. If Andy's share was \$150 less than Becky's, calculate the size of each of their shares.

38. A profit of \$85,750 was shared by the two partners of a business. If one partner received \$12,300 more than the other, how much did each of them receive?

39. Sam is paid \$270 a week. He worked 9 hours overtime last week and recieved \$954. Calculate his overtime pay per hour.

40. Lisa is paid \$840 a week. Her overtime rate is \$28 per hour. Last week she recieved \$1036. How many hours overtime did she work last week?

41. A 20-metre long chain is cut into two pieces. One piece is one-third $\left(\frac{1}{3}\right)$ the length of the other. Calculate the length of each piece.

42. A 18-metre long wire is cut into two pieces. One piece is four-fifths $\left(\frac{4}{5}\right)$ the length of the other. Calculate the length of each piece.

43. Fifty more than eight times a number is the same as four less than ten times the number. What is the number?

44. Eighteen less than three times a number is the same as ten more than the number. What is the number?

- 45. Movie tickets that were sold to each child were \$3 cheaper than those sold to each adult. If a family of two adults and two children paid \$34 to watch a movie at the cinema, what was the price of each adult ticket and each child ticket?
- 46. Giri had twice the number of quarters (25 cents) in his bag than dimes (10 cents). If he had a total of 54 coins, how many of them were quarters? What was the total dollar value of these coins?
- 47. Hailey's hourly rate of pay is \$3.50 more than that of Ryan's. If they worked for seven hours each and earned a total of \$248.50, calculate their individual hourly rates of pay.
- 48. A project lead and an intern worked for 30 hours each to develop a web page. The lead's hourly rate is two times that of the intern and they were paid a total of \$1620 to develop the web page. What were their individual hourly rates of pay?
- 49. Henry invested his bonus amount of \$10,000 in high-risk and low-risk stocks. His investment in high-risk stocks was \$2000 less than half his investment in low-risk stocks. What was his investment in high-risk stocks?
- 50. A retail store received a total of 1260 units of Product *A* and Product *B*. If the quantity of Product *A* was 147 less than three-fourths the quantity of Product *B*, how many units of Product *A* did they receive?

2.3 | Exponents

The concept of exponents was covered in Chapter 1, Section 1.4, where exponents were used to express repeated multiplication or division of the same numbers.

$$\underbrace{a \times a \times a \times a \ldots \times a}_{\text{'n' factors of 'a'}} = a^n \qquad \frac{1}{\underbrace{a \times a \times a \times a \ldots \times a}_{\text{'n' factors of 'a'}}} = \frac{1}{a^n} = a^{-n}$$

For example,

- $\underbrace{2 \times 2 \times 2 \times 2 \times 2}_{\text{5 factors of 2}}$ is represented by: 2^5 (5 = exponent, 2 = base)

- $\frac{1}{\underbrace{8 \times 8 \times 8}_{\text{3 factors of 8}}}$ is represented by: $\frac{1}{8^3} = 8^{-3}$ (−3 = exponent, 8 = base)

The above exponent principle is applied to express repeated multiplication of a variable or an algebraic term.

In algebra, when '*n*' is a positive integer, the general form of an exponent using variables is represented by:

- $\underbrace{x \times x \times x \times x \ldots \times x}_{\text{'n' factors of 'x'}} = x^n$

- $\frac{1}{\underbrace{x \times x \times x \times x \ldots \times x}_{\text{'n' factors of 'x'}}} = \frac{1}{x^n} = x^{-n}$

Some useful applications of exponents are provided below with corresponding examples:

The exponent button on the Texas Instruments BA II Plus calculator is the y^x button, as shown in this picture.

Table 2.3(a) Exponents As Repeated Multiplication or Division with Examples

	Exponential Form	Expanded Form	Example
(i)	$-x^n = -(x)^n$	$= -(x \times x \ldots \times x)$	$-2^5 = -(2 \times 2 \times 2 \times 2 \times 2) = -32$ $-2^4 = -(2 \times 2 \times 2 \times 2) = -16$
(ii)	$(-x)^n$	$= (-x)\,(-x)\ldots(-x)$	$(-2)^5 = (-2)(-2)(-2)(-2)(-2) = -32$ $(-2)^4 = (-2)(-2)(-2)(-2) = 16$
(iii)	$-x^{-n} = -(x)^{-n}$	$= -\dfrac{1}{x^n}$ $= -\dfrac{1}{x \times x \ldots \times x}$	$-2^{-5} = -(2)^{-5} = -\dfrac{1}{2^5}$ $= -\dfrac{1}{2 \times 2 \times 2 \times 2 \times 2} = -\dfrac{1}{32}$
(iv)	$(-x)^{-n}$	$= \dfrac{1}{(-x)^n}$ $= \dfrac{1}{(-x)(-x)\ldots(-x)}$	$(-2)^{-5} = \dfrac{1}{(-2)^5}$ $= \dfrac{1}{(-2)(-2)(-2)(-2)(-2)}$ $= \dfrac{1}{-32} = -\dfrac{1}{32}$ $(-2)^{-4} = \dfrac{1}{(-2)^4} = \dfrac{1}{(-2)(-2)(-2)(-2)} = \dfrac{1}{16}$
(v)	ax^n	$= a(x \times x \ldots \times x)$	$3x^4$, where $x = 2$, $= 3(2)^4 = 3(2 \times 2 \times 2 \times 2) = 48$
(vi)	$(ax)^n$	$= (ax)(ax)\ldots(ax)$	$(3x)^4$, where $x = 2$, $= (3 \times 2)^4 = 6 \times 6 \times 6 \times 6 = 1296$

Note: *The examples above assume that 'x' is a positive number.*

Rules of Exponents and Evaluation of Exponents

'Rules of exponents' is also referred to as 'laws of exponents' or 'properties of exponents'. When the bases of exponents are the same, there are eight basic rules, as follows:

Table 2.3(b) Rules of Exponents with Examples

	Rule	Description	Example
(i)	Product Rule	To multiply powers of the same base, write the base and add the exponents. $x^m \cdot x^n = x^{(m+n)}$	$x^4 \cdot x^3 = x^{(4+3)} = x^7$ $2^4 \cdot 2^3 = 2^{(4+3)} = 2^7 = 128$
(ii)	Quotient Rule	To divide powers of the same base, write the base and subtract the exponents. $\dfrac{x^m}{x^n} = x^{(m-n)}$	$\dfrac{x^5}{x^2} = x^{(5-2)} = x^3$ $\dfrac{3^5}{3^2} = 3^{(5-2)} = 3^3 = 27$
(iii)	Power of a Power Rule	To raise a power to another power, write the base and multiply the exponents. $(x^m)^n = x^{mn}$	$(x^4)^2 = x^{(4 \cdot 2)} = x^8$ $(2^4)^2 = 2^{(4 \cdot 2)} = 2^8 = 256$
(iv)	Power of a Product Rule	To simplify a power of a product, raise each factor to the same exponent. $(xy)^m = x^m \cdot y^m$	$(x \cdot y)^5 = x^5 \cdot y^5$ $(2 \cdot 3)^5 = 2^5 \cdot 3^5 = 32 \cdot 243$ $= 7776$

$(x^m)(x^n) = x^{m+n}$

$\dfrac{x^m}{x^n} = x^{m-n}$

$(x^m)^n = x^{mn}$

$(xy)^m = x^m y^m$

$\left(\dfrac{x}{y}\right)^m = \dfrac{x^m}{y^m}$

$\left(\dfrac{x}{y}\right)^{-m} = \left(\dfrac{y}{x}\right)^m$

$x^{-m} = \dfrac{1}{x^m}$

$x^0 = 1$

$x^1 = x$

(v)	Power of a Quotient Rule	To simplify a power of a quotient, raise each factor in the numerator and the denominator to the same exponent. $\left(\frac{x}{y}\right)^m = \frac{x^m}{y^m}$	$\left(\frac{x}{y}\right)^4 = \frac{x^4}{y^4}$ $\left(\frac{2}{3}\right)^4 = \frac{2^4}{3^4} = \frac{16}{81}$
(vi)	Negative Exponent Rule	To simplify negative exponents, write the reciprocal of the base and use a positive exponent. $\left(\frac{x}{y}\right)^{-m} = \left(\frac{y}{x}\right)^m$, $x^{-m} = \frac{1}{x^m}$, $\frac{1}{x^{-m}} = x^m$	$\left(\frac{x}{y}\right)^{-4} = \left(\frac{y}{x}\right)^4$ $\left(\frac{2}{3}\right)^{-4} = \left(\frac{3}{2}\right)^4 = \frac{81}{16}$ $x^{-5} = \frac{1}{x^5}$, $\frac{1}{x^{-5}} = x^5$ $2^{-5} = \frac{1}{2^5} = \frac{1}{32}$, $\frac{1}{2^{-5}} = 2^5 = 32$
(vii)	Zero as Exponent Rule	Any non-zero base raised to the exponent zero is equal to 1. $x^0 = 1$	$x^0 = 1$, $(xy)^0 = 1$, $\left(\frac{x}{y}\right)^0 = 1$ $5^0 = 1$, $\left(\frac{5}{3}\right)^0 = 1$
(viii)	One as Exponent Rule	Any non-zero base raised to the exponent one is equal to itself. $x^1 = x$	$x^1 = x$, $(xy)^1 = xy$, $\left(\frac{x}{y}\right)^1 = \frac{x}{y}$ $7^1 = 7$, $\left(\frac{5}{3}\right)^1 = \frac{5}{3}$

Note: *There are no rules for addition or subtraction of exponents. These operations have to be done separately.*

For example, $2^3 + 2^5 = (2 \times 2 \times 2) + (2 \times 2 \times 2 \times 2 \times 2)$
$= 8 + 32 = 40$

Example 2.3(a) **Solving Expressions Using the Product Rule and the Quotient Rule**

Solve: $(2^2)^3 \times 2^7 \div 2^9$

Solution

$$(2^2)^3 \times 2^7 \div 2^9 = 2^6 \times 2^7 \div 2^9 = 2^{(6+7-9)} = 2^4 = 16$$

Example 2.3(b) **Solving Expressions that Have Exponents with Different Bases**

Solve: $2^4 \times 3^4$

Solution

$$2^4 \times 3^4 = (2 \times 2 \times 2 \times 2) \times (3 \times 3 \times 3 \times 3) = 16 \times 81 = 1296$$

Example 2.3(c) **Solving Expressions that Have Negative Exponents**

Solve: $\left(\frac{5}{4}\right)^{-2} \times \left(\frac{2}{3}\right)^{-3}$

Solution

$$\left(\frac{5}{4}\right)^{-2} \times \left(\frac{2}{3}\right)^{-3} = \left(\frac{4}{5}\right)^2 \times \left(\frac{3}{2}\right)^3 = \frac{4^2}{5^2} \times \frac{3^3}{2^3} = \frac{\overset{2}{\cancel{16}}}{25} \times \frac{27}{\underset{1}{\cancel{8}}} = \frac{2}{25} \times \frac{27}{1} = \frac{54}{25}$$

Fractional Exponents

When the exponent, 'n', of a variable is a fraction, we call it a fractional exponent. The fractional exponent, $\frac{1}{n}$, replaces the radical sign, $\sqrt{\ }$.

For example, the square root of $x = \sqrt{x} = x^{\frac{1}{2}}$, and the cube root of $x = \sqrt[3]{x} = x^{\frac{1}{3}}$.

Similarly, the nth root of $x = \sqrt[n]{x} = x^{\frac{1}{n}}$.

Fractional exponents obey all the rules of exponents.

(i) $x^{\frac{1}{n}} = \sqrt[n]{x}$

For example, if $x = 16$ and $n = 4$, then,

$16^{\frac{1}{4}} = \sqrt[4]{16}$ (Read as the fourth root of 16)

$= 2$

(ii) $x^{\frac{m}{n}} = (x^{\frac{1}{n}})^m = \left(\sqrt[n]{x}\right)^m$

This refers to calculating the nth root of x, then raising the result to the power of m.

For example, if $x = 16$, $m = 3$, and $n = 4$, then,

$16^{\frac{3}{4}} = \left(16^{\frac{1}{4}}\right)^3 = \left(\sqrt[4]{16}\right)^3 = (2)^3 = 8$

Or

$x^{\frac{m}{n}} = (x^m)^{\frac{1}{n}} = \sqrt[n]{x^m}$

This refers to raising x to the power of m, then calculating the nth root of the result.

For example, if $x = 16$, $m = 3$, and $n = 4$, then,

$16^{\frac{3}{4}} = \left(16^{3}\right)^{\frac{1}{4}} = \sqrt[4]{16^3} = \sqrt[4]{4096} = 8$

$$x^{\frac{1}{n}} = \sqrt[n]{x}$$
$$x^{\frac{m}{n}} = (\sqrt[n]{x})^m = \sqrt[n]{x^m}$$
$$x^{-\frac{1}{n}} = \frac{1}{x^{\frac{1}{n}}} = \frac{1}{\sqrt[n]{x}}$$
$$x^{-\frac{m}{n}} = \frac{1}{x^{\frac{m}{n}}} = \frac{1}{\left(\sqrt[n]{x}\right)^m} = \frac{1}{\sqrt[n]{x^m}}$$

Note: *The first method is easier because calculating the nth root first results in a smaller number, which is easier to raise to the power of 'm'.*

(iii) $x^{-\frac{m}{n}} = \frac{1}{x^{\frac{m}{n}}} = \frac{1}{\left(\sqrt[n]{x}\right)^m}$

For example, if $x = 27$, $m = 4$, and $n = 3$, then,

$27^{-\frac{4}{3}} = \frac{1}{\left(\sqrt[3]{27}\right)^4} = \frac{1}{(3)^4} = \frac{1}{81}$

2.3 | Exercises

Answers to the odd-numbered problems are available at the end of the textbook.

For Problems 1 to 18, simplify where possible and then evaluate. Round to two decimal places, wherever applicable.

1. a. $5^4 - 4^2$ b. $4^0 - 4^4$
2. a. $10^3 - 7^2$ b. $3^0 + 3^4$
3. a. $\frac{10^6}{10^0}$ b. $\frac{3^7}{27}$
4. a. $\frac{8^5}{8^3}$ b. $\frac{5^6}{125}$
5. a. $\frac{3^9 \times 3^2}{3^5}$ b. $\frac{(2^5)^4}{4^6}$
6. a. $\frac{2^9 \times 2^1}{2^5}$ b. $\frac{(2^5)^4}{16^3}$
7. a. $-10^4 \times 10^3$ b. $(-5)^2 \times (4)^2$
8. a. $-2^4 \times 2^2$ b. $(-2)^2 \times (3)^2$
9. a. $3^{-2} \times 3^3$ b. $(2 \times 3^2)^4$
10. a. $12^{-8} \times 12^9$ b. $(5 \times 2^2)^3$
11. a. $\left(\frac{5}{2}\right)^2 \left(\frac{5}{2}\right)^3$ b. $3^4 \times 3^{(4+2)}$
12. a. $\left(\frac{5}{3}\right)^3 \left(\frac{3}{5}\right)^2$ b. $10^4 \times 10^{(3+2)}$
13. a. $(2^6)^{\frac{1}{3}}$ b. $(9)^{\frac{3}{2}}$
14. a. $(5^{15})^{\frac{1}{5}}$ b. $(16)^{\frac{3}{4}}$
15. a. $\left(\frac{2^{12}}{2^4}\right)^{\frac{1}{4}}$ b. $\left(\frac{3^9}{3^3}\right)^{\frac{1}{3}}$
16. a. $-100^2 \times (-10)^4$ b. $-5^3(-25)^3$
17. a. $\sqrt[4]{25^2 \times 25^2}$ b. $\sqrt{3^4 \times 2^4}$
18. a. $\sqrt[4]{5^2 \times 25^3}$ b. $\sqrt[5]{9^3 \times 27^4}$

For Problems 19 to 36, simplify the expressions and express your answers with positive exponents.

19. a. $x^0 \times x^4$ b. $\frac{x^6}{x^0}$ 20. a. $x^4 \times x^0$ b. $\frac{x^0}{x}$ 21. a. $\frac{x^7}{x}$ b. $(x^5)^4 \div x^3$

22. a. $\frac{x^2}{x}$ b. $(x^5)^4 \div x^{20}$ 23. a. $(5x)(4x^2)$ b. $(x^9) \times (x^2) \div x^5$ 24. a. $(3x)(6x^2)$ b. $x^{10} \times x^{20} \div x^{30}$

25. a. $-x^4 \times x^3$ b. $(-y)^4(y)^2$ 26. a. $x^6 \times (-x)^5$ b. $(-y)^5 \times (y)^1$ 27. a. $(xy^2)^4$ b. $x^{-5} \times x^7$

28. a. $x^0 \times x^{(2 \times 3)}$ b. $(x^3y^2)^5$ 29. a. $\left(\frac{x}{y}\right)^{-2}\left(\frac{x}{y}\right)^{3}\left(\frac{x}{y}\right)^{2}$ b. $\left(\frac{x}{y}\right)^{2}\left(\frac{x}{y}\right)^{-3}$ 30. a. $\left(\frac{x}{y}\right)^{4}\left(\frac{x}{y}\right)^{2}\left(\frac{x}{y}\right)^{-8}$ b. $\left(\frac{x}{y}\right)^{5}\left(\frac{x}{y}\right)^{-3}$

31. a. $(x^3)^2(x^2)^3(x^3)^{-1}$ b. $(27x^6)^{\frac{1}{3}}$ 32. a. $(x^{5-1})(x^3)^2(x^2)^{-3}$ b. $(81x^8)^{\frac{1}{4}}$ 33. a. $\left(\frac{x^9}{x^3}\right)^{\frac{1}{3}}$ b. $\frac{(-x)^3(-x)^4}{x^5}$

34. a. $\left(\frac{x^{19}}{x^4}\right)^{\frac{1}{4}}$ b. $\frac{(-x)^6(-x)^4}{x^9}$ 35. a. $\sqrt[4]{x^6x^{10}}$ b. $\sqrt[3]{x^9x^6}$ 36. a. $\sqrt[4]{x^8x^4}$ b. $\sqrt{x^{10}x^{-6}}$

2.4 | Logarithms

Logarithmic Concepts and Relation to Exponents

We know that multiplication is a quicker method for determining the answer to repeated addition.

For example, 5 + 5 + 5 + 5 + 5 + 5 + 5 is the same as 7 × 5.

Similarly, the use of logarithm is a quicker method for determining the unknown exponent.

Exponential Form

$$10^3 = 1000$$

$$5^2 = 25$$

Exponent

$$a^x = y$$

Base

Read as: base '*a*' raised to the exponent '*x*' is '*y*', or '*a*' to the power of '*x*' is '*y*'.

Logarithmic Form

$$\log_{10}1000 = 3$$

$$\log_5 25 = 2$$

$$\log_a y = x$$ ← Logarithm (exponent)

Base

Read as: logarithm of '*y*' to the base '*a*' is '*x*', log '*y*' to the base '*a*' is '*x*', or, most simply, log base '*a*' of '*y*' is '*x*'.

The base of a logarithm must be a positive number (except 1).

As seen above, a logarithm is the exponent, '*x*', to which the base, '*a*', is raised to obtain '*y*'.

Any positive number, except 1, can be used as the base for logarithms.

For example, 100 is the same as 10^2. Here, the base is 10 and the exponent is 2. Therefore, the logarithm of 100 to the base 10 is 2.

$\underbrace{10^2 = 100}_{\text{Exponential form}}$ is the same as $\underbrace{\log_{10} 100 = 2}_{\text{Logarithmic form}}$

Similarly, 125 is the same as 5^3. Here, the base is 5 and the exponent is 3; therefore, the logarithm of 125 to the base 5 is 3.

$\underbrace{5^3 = 125}_{\text{Exponential form}}$ is the same as $\underbrace{\log_5 125 = 3}_{\text{Logarithmic form}}$

$$x \underset{\log_a y}{\overset{a^x}{\rightleftarrows}} y$$

Exponents and logarithms are interchangeable.

Common Logarithms (log)

Common logarithms have base '10' and are referred to by 'log'.

Common logarithms are always to the base 10. If no base is shown in the logarithmic expression, it is assumed to have base 10 and is referred to by the symbol **'log'**.

Common Logarithmic Form	Exponential Form
$\log_{10}1000 = \log 1000 = 3$	$10^3 = 1000$
$\log_{10}100 = \log 100 = 2$	$10^2 = 100$
$\log_{10}10 = \log 10 = 1$	$10^1 = 10$
$\log_{10}1 = \log 1 = 0$	$10^0 = 1$
$\log_{10} y = \log y = x$	$10^x = y$

Example 2.4(a) **Finding Common Logarithms of Numbers**

Calculate the following common logarithms rounded to 4 decimal places:

(i) log 10,000 (ii) log 0.001 (iii) log 40 (iv) log 6.5

Solution

Using the **log** button on the calculator:

(i) $\log 10{,}000 = 4$ (ii) $\log 0.001 = -3$ (iii) $\log 40 = 1.6021$ (iv) $\log 6.5 = 0.8129$

The Texas Instruments BAII Plus calculator does not include a **log** key, as common logarithms are not used in financial math calculations.

Natural Logarithms (ln)

Natural logarithms have base 'e' and are referred to by 'ln'.

Natural logarithms, referred to by the symbol **'ln'** (pronounced "lawn"), are always to the base **'e'** where the constant $e = 2.718281...$

'e', known as Euler's number, is a special irrational number in mathematics (similar to π which is equal to 3.141592...) and is found by $\left(1+\frac{1}{n}\right)^n$ where 'n' is a very large number.

Assume $n = 100{,}000$. Then $e \approx \left(1+\frac{1}{100{,}000}\right)^{100{,}000} \approx 2.718281...$

If the base of a logarithmic expression is 'e', then it is simply expressed by **'ln'**.

To find the natural logarithm of a number with the Texas Instruments BAII Plus calculator, enter the number first then press the 'LN' key.

Natural Logarithmic Form	Exponential Form
$\log_e 1 = \ln 1 = 0$	$e^0 = 1$
$\log_e e = \ln e = 1$	$e^1 = 2.718281\ldots$
$\log_e 10 = \ln 10 = 2.302585...$	$e^{2.302585} = 10$
$\log_e 1.005 = \ln 1.005 = 0.00498754...$	$e^{0.00498754} = 1.005$

The natural logarithm key on the Texas Instruments BA II Plus calculator is the 'LN' button, as shown in this picture.

The rules of logarithms are used to evaluate the exponent 'n' in business and finance mathematics formulas, which you will study in subsequent chapters.

Note: *In the Texas Instruments BAII calculator, the common logarithm, log, of a number 'y' can be found using* $\log y = \frac{\ln y}{\ln 10}$.

For example, $\log 1000 = \frac{\ln 1000}{\ln 10} = 3$

Rules of Logarithms

Common logarithms (log) and natural logarithms (ln) follow the same rules.

Table 2.4 **Rules of Logarithms with Examples**

Rule #	Rule	Common Logarithms (log)		Natural Logarithms (ln)	
		Rule in Common Logarithmic Form	Example	Rule in Natural Logarithmic Form	Example
1	Product Rule	$\log(AB) = \log A + \log B$	$\log(50 \times 10) = \log 50 + \log 10$	$\ln(AB) = \ln A + \ln B$	$\ln(50 \times 10) = \ln 50 + \ln 10$
2	Quotient Rule	$\log\left(\frac{A}{B}\right) = \log A - \log B$	$\log\left(\frac{50}{10}\right) = \log 50 - \log 10$	$\ln\left(\frac{A}{B}\right) = \ln A - \ln B$	$\ln\left(\frac{50}{10}\right) = \ln 50 - \ln 10$
3	Power Rule	$\log(A)^n = n \log A$	$\log(50)^2 = 2 \log 50$	$\ln(A)^n = n \ln A$	$\ln(50)^2 = 2 \ln 50$
4	Zero as exponent or One as logarithm	$\log(A)^0 = \log 1 = 0$	$\log(50)^0 = \log 1 = 0$	$\ln(A)^0 = \ln 1 = 0$	$\ln(50)^0 = \ln 1 = 0$

Note: *Since* $x^0 = 1$, $10^0 = 1$ *and* $e^0 = 1$; *therefore,* $\log_{10} 1 = 0 \rightarrow \log 1 = 0$ *and* $\log_e 1 = 0 \rightarrow \ln 1 = 0$

Example 2.4(b) **Solving Equations using Common Logarithms (log)**

Solve for 'n' in the following equations:

(i) $2401 = 7^n$

(ii) $157 = 130(1.02)^n$

Solution

(i) $2401 = 7^n$ — Taking log on both sides,

$\log 2401 = \log 7^n$ — Using the Power Rule,

$\log 2401 = n \log 7$ — Isolating n,

$n = \dfrac{\log 2401}{\log 7}$ — Solving using the **log** button on the calculator,

$= \dfrac{3.380392...}{0.845098...}$

$= 4$

(ii) $157 = 130(1.02)^n$ — Dividing both sides by 130,

$\dfrac{157}{130} = (1.02)^n$ — Taking log on both sidcs,

$\log\left(\dfrac{157}{130}\right) = \log(1.02)^n$ — Using the Power Rule,

$\log\left(\dfrac{157}{130}\right) = n \log(1.02)$ — Isolating n,

$n = \dfrac{\log\left(\frac{157}{130}\right)}{\log(1.02)}$ — Solving using the **log** button on the calculator,

$= \dfrac{0.081956...}{0.008600...}$

$= 9.529612...$

Example 2.4(c) **Solving Equations using Natural Logarithms (ln)**

Solve for 'n' in the following equations:

(i) $1024 = 2^n$ (ii) $3749 = 1217(1.005)^n$

Solution

(i) $1024 = 2^n$ Taking ln on both sides,

$\ln 1024 = \ln 2^n$ Using the Power Rule,

$\ln 1024 = n \ln 2$ Isolating n,

$n = \dfrac{\ln 1024}{\ln 2}$ Solving using the LN button on the calculator,

$= \dfrac{6.931471...}{0.693147...}$

$= 10$

Alternatively, since $1024 = 2^{10}$,

$n = \dfrac{\ln 1024}{\ln 2} = \dfrac{\ln 2^{10}}{\ln 2} = \dfrac{10 \times \ln 2}{\ln 2} = 10$

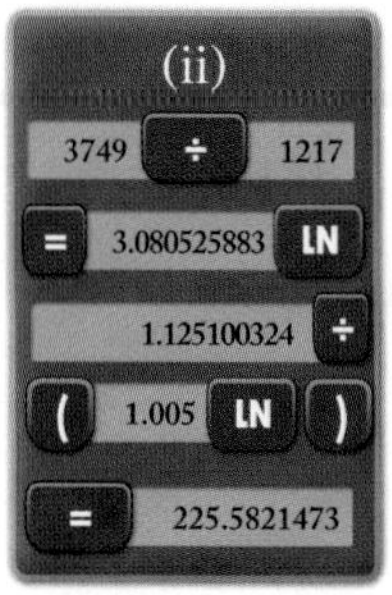

(ii) $3749 = 1217(1.005)^n$ Dividing both sides by 1217,

$\dfrac{3749}{1217} = (1.005)^n$ Taking ln on both sides,

$\ln\left(\dfrac{3749}{1217}\right) = \ln(1.005)^n$ Using the Power Rule,

$\ln\left(\dfrac{3749}{1217}\right) = n \ln 1.005$ Isolating n,

$n = \dfrac{\ln\left(\dfrac{3749}{1217}\right)}{\ln 1.005}$ Solving using the LN button on the calculator,

$= \dfrac{1.125100...}{0.004987...}$

$= 225.582147...$

2.4 | Exercises

Answers to the odd-numbered problems are available at the end of the textbook.

Express the following in logarithmic form:

1. a. $10^5 = 100{,}000$ b. $2^6 = 64$ c. $3^2 = 9$
2. a. $10^4 = 10{,}000$ b. $2^3 = 8$ c. $3^3 = 27$
3. a. $4^5 = 1024$ b. $6^5 = 7776$ c. $9^4 = 6561$
4. a. $4^4 = 256$ b. $6^4 = 1296$ c. $8^2 = 64$

Express the following in exponential form:

5. a. $\log_{10}100 = 2$ b. $\log_2 32 = 5$ c. $\log_3 729 = 6$
6. a. $\log_{10}1000 = 3$ b. $\log_2 4 = 2$ c. $\log_3 243 = 5$
7. a. $\log_4 64 = 3$ b. $\log_5 625 = 4$ c. $\log_6 216 = 3$
8. a. $\log_4 4096 = 6$ b. $\log_5 125 = 3$ c. $\log_6 1296 = 4$

Calculate the following (round to four decimal places):

9. a. ln 2250 b. ln 154 c. ln 27
10. a. ln 0.165 b. ln 1.02 c. ln 12.51
11. a. ln 10.05 b. ln 1.005 c. ln 0.675
12. a. ln 39 b. ln 276 c. ln 1550

For the following problems, solve for 'n' (round to two decimal places).

13. a. $250 = (30)^n$ b. $7500 = (45)^n + 500$
14. a. $320 = (15)^n$ b. $8000 = (35)^n + 1500$
15. a. $10{,}000 = 2000(1.2)^n$ b. $(1.05)^n = 1.31$
16. a. $15{,}000 = 5000(1.04)^n$ b. $2.5 = (1.05)^n$

Express the following as a sum or difference of two or more natural logarithms:

17. a. $\ln\left(\dfrac{3}{7}\right)$ b. $\ln(4 \times 9)$
18. a. $\ln\left(\dfrac{40}{13}\right)$ b. $\ln(7 \times 8)$
19. a. $\ln\left(\dfrac{AB}{C}\right)$ b. $\ln\left(\dfrac{X}{YZ}\right)$
20. a. $\ln\left(\dfrac{x}{ab}\right)$ b. $\ln\left(\dfrac{xy}{c}\right)$

For the following problems, express your answer as a single natural logarithm.

21. a. $\ln 8 + \ln 5$ b. $\ln 15 - \ln 3$

22. a. $\ln 25 + \ln 4$ b. $\ln 60 - \ln 15$

23. a. $2\ln 5 + 3\ln 3$ b. $5\ln 2 - 2\ln 3$

24. a. $2\ln 8 + 3\ln 3$ b. $4\ln 5 - 3\ln 2$

25. a. $2\ln 5$ b. $3\ln 6$

26. a. $5\ln 2$ b. $6\ln 3$

27. a. $5\ln \frac{a}{b}$ b. $4\ln (a \times b)$

28. a. $2\ln \frac{x}{y}$ b. $4\ln (xy)$

29. $3\ln a + 2\ln b - 5\ln c$

30. $\ln x - 2\ln y + 3\ln z$

31. $3\ln 2 + 4\ln 3 - 2\ln 4$

32. $4\ln 2 - 2\ln 3 + 3\ln 2$

For the following problems, solve for 'n' (round to two decimal places).

33. a. $n = \ln\left(\frac{4285}{4000}\right)$ b. $n = \ln\left(\frac{3645}{2175}\right)$

34. a. $n = \ln\left(\frac{6750}{3200}\right)$ b. $n = \ln\left(\frac{75{,}000}{2200}\right)$

35. a. $n = \frac{\ln\left(\frac{7200}{4725}\right)}{\ln(1.01)}$ b. $n = \frac{\ln(2.5)}{\ln(1.03)}$

36. a. $n = \frac{\ln\left(\frac{5120}{2250}\right)}{\ln(1.005)}$ b. $n = \frac{\ln(3)}{\ln(1.02)}$

• 37. $n = \frac{\ln\left[1 + \frac{0.005 \times 75{,}000}{1250}\right]}{\ln[1.005]}$

• 38. $n = \frac{\ln\left[1 + \frac{0.025 \times 60{,}000}{500}\right]}{\ln[1.025]}$

• 39. $6500 = 8000(1.02)^{-n}$

• 40. $4750 = 5250(1.015)^{-n}$

2.5 | Formulas and Applications

Formulas are similar to equations. In formulas, the relationship among many variables is written as a rule for performing calculations, so that a single variable, known as the subject of the formula, is on the left side of the equation and everything else is on the right side of the equation. To isolate one of the variables in a formula, rearrange the terms and simplify, so that only the required variable remains on the left side of the equation. Rearrangement can be performed using the rules that you have learned in the previous sections of this chapter.

To solve for a required variable using a formula, it is important to know what each symbol in the formula represents. For example, consider the formula for simple interest: $I = Prt$. In this simple interest formula, 'I' represents the amount of simple interest, 'P' represents the amount of investment or loan, also known as the principal, 'r' represents the interest rate per annum, and 't' represents the time period in years.

To solve for any one of the variables, 'I', 'P', 'r', or 't' in this simple interest formula, we can rearrange the variables, as shown below:

$$I = Prt$$ is the same as $Prt = I$

Solving for 'P' :

$$\frac{Prt}{rt} = \frac{I}{rt}$$ Dividing both sides by 'rt',

$$P = \frac{I}{rt}$$

Solving for 'r' :

$$\frac{Prt}{Pt} = \frac{I}{Pt}$$ Dividing both sides by 'Pt',

$$r = \frac{I}{Pt}$$

Solving for 't' :

$$\frac{Prt}{Pr} = \frac{I}{Pr}$$ Dividing both sides by 'Pr',

$$t = \frac{I}{Pr}$$

Example 2.5(a) **Rearranging to Isolate Variables**

Rearrange and isolate the variables indicated in the brackets:

(i) $S = C + M$ (M) (ii) $S = C + E + P$ (P)
(iii) $P = RB$ $(R \text{ and } B)$ (iv) $y = mx + b$ $(b \text{ and } m)$
(v) $S = P(1 + rt)$ (P)

Solution

If $a = b + c$,
then $b + c = a$

(i) $S = C + M$ (M)

$C + M = S$ Subtracting 'C' from both sides,

$C - C + M = S - C$

$M = S - C$

(ii) $S = C + E + P$ (P)

$C + E + P = S$ Subtracting 'C' and 'E' from both sides,

$C + E + P - C - E = S - C - E$

$P = S - C - E$

(iii) $P = RB$ (R)

$RB = P$ Dividing both sides by 'B',

$$\frac{RB}{B} = \frac{P}{B}$$

$$R = \frac{P}{B}$$

$P = RB$ (B)

$RB = P$ Dividing both sides by 'R',

$$\frac{RB}{R} = \frac{P}{R}$$

$$B = \frac{P}{R}$$

(iv) $y = mx + b$ (b)

$mx + b = y$ Subtracting 'mx' from both sides,

$mx - mx + b = y - mx$

$b = y - mx$

$y = mx + b$ (m)

$mx + b = y$ Subtracting 'b' from both sides,

$mx + b - b = y - b$

$mx = y - b$ Dividing both sides by 'x',

$$\frac{mx}{x} = \frac{y - b}{x}$$

$$m = \frac{y - b}{x}$$

(v) $S = P(1 + rt)$ (P)

$P(1 + rt) = S$ Isolating 'P' by dividing both sides by '(1 + rt)',

$$\frac{P(1 + rt)}{(1 + rt)} = \frac{S}{(1 + rt)}$$

$$P = \frac{S}{(1 + rt)}$$

Example 2.5(b) **Solving for Variables Using the Rearranged Simple Interest Formula**

In the simple interest formula $I = Prt$, determine the value for:

(i) 'I', when $P = \$1000$, $r = 5\% = 0.05$, $t = 3$ years
(ii) 'P', when $I = \$150$, $r = 3\% = 0.03$, $t = 1$ year
(iii) 'r', when $I = \$500$, $P = \$8000$, $t = 2$ years
(iv) 't', when $I = \$40$, $P = \$800$, $r = 5\% = 0.05$

Round your answers to two decimal places, wherever applicable.

Solution

(i) Substitute the values for 'P', 'r', and 't' in the formula: $I = Prt$

$$I = 1000.00 \times 0.05 \times 3 = \$150.00$$

(ii) Substitute the values for 'I', 'r', and, 't' in the rearranged formula: $P = \frac{I}{rt}$

$$P = \frac{150.00}{(0.03 \times 1)} = \$5000.00$$

(iii) Substitute the values for 'I', 'P', and 't' in the rearranged formula: $r = \frac{I}{Pt}$

$$r = \frac{500.00}{8000.00 \times 2} = 0.03125 = 3.125\% = 3.13\% \text{ (Rounded to two decimal places.)}$$

(iv) Substitute the values for 'I', 'P', and 'r' in the rearranged formula: $t = \frac{I}{Pr}$

$$t = \frac{40.00}{800.00 \times 0.05} = 1 \text{ year}$$

Example 2.5(c)

Rearranging Formulas to Isolate Variables and Solving Using the Rearranged Formulas

In the compound interest formula, $FV = PV(1 + i)^n$, rearrange and solve for the following variables, rounding to two decimal places:

(i) 'n', when $PV = \$2500$, $FV = \$8500$, $i = 4.5\% = 0.045$ (ii) 'i', when $PV = \$4800$, $FV = \$10,000$, $n = 48$

Solution

(i)

$$FV = PV(1 + i)^n$$ Dividing both sides by PV,

$$\frac{FV}{PV} = (1 + i)^n$$ Taking the natural logarithm on both sides,

$$\ln\left(\frac{FV}{PV}\right) = \ln(1 + i)^n$$ Using the Power Rule,

$$\ln\left(\frac{FV}{PV}\right) = n \times \ln(1 + i)$$ Isolating n,

$$n = \frac{\ln\left(\frac{FV}{PV}\right)}{\ln(1 + i)}$$ Substituting the given values in the rearranged formula,

$$n = \frac{\ln\left(\frac{8500.00}{2500.00}\right)}{\ln(1 + 0.045)}$$ Solving using the LN button on the calculator,

$$n = \frac{1.223775...}{0.044016...}$$

$$= 27.802408... = 27.80$$

(ii)

$$FV = PV(1 + i)^n$$ Dividing both sides by PV,

$$\frac{FV}{PV} = (1 + i)^n$$ Taking the nth root on both sides,

$$(1 + i) = \left(\frac{FV}{PV}\right)^{\frac{1}{n}}$$ Isolating i,

$$i = \left(\frac{FV}{PV}\right)^{\frac{1}{n}} - 1$$ Substituting the given values in the rearranged formula,

$$i = \left(\frac{10,000.00}{4800.00}\right)^{\frac{1}{48}} - 1$$ Solving using the exponent button on the calculator,

$$= 0.015408... = 1.54\%$$

2.5 | Exercises

Answers to the odd-numbered problems are available at the end of the textbook.

For Problems 1 to 14, rearrange and isolate the indicated variables.

1. 'C' in $S = C + M$
2. 'M' in $S = C + M$
3. 'E' in $S = C + E + P$
4. 'C' in $S = C + E + P$
5. 'B' in $P = R \times B$
6. 'R' in $P = R \times B$
7. 'r' in $S = P(1 + rt)$
8. 't' in $S = P(1 + rt)$
9. 'L' in $N = L(1 - d)$
10. 'd' in $N = L(1 - d)$
11. 'a' and 'c' in $b = \frac{ac}{1 - a}$
12. 'a' and 'c' in $b = \frac{c + ac}{a - 2}$
13. 'a' and 'b' in $c = \frac{a - c}{b}$
14. 'a' and 'b' in $c = \frac{ab - b}{4 + a}$

For Problems 15 to 34, express the answers rounded to two decimal places, wherever applicable.

In the simple interest formula $I = Prt$, determine the value for:

15. a. 'I', when $P = \$4500, r = 0.05, t = \frac{10}{12}$ b. 'P', when $I = \$20.75, r = 0.0475, t = \frac{91}{365}$
16. a. 'I', when $P = \$1200, r = 0.0325, t = \frac{8}{12}$ b. 'P', when $I = \$65.50, r = 0.0525, t = \frac{180}{365}$
17. a. 'r', when $P = \$4850, I = \$162.65, t = \frac{7}{12}$ b. 't', when $P = \$850, r = 0.035, I = \$19.50$
18. a. 'r', when $P = \$5775, I = \$296.75, t = \frac{9}{12}$ b. 't', when $P = \$9250, r = 0.075, I = \$635.94$

In the simple interest formula $S = P(1 + rt)$, determine the value for:

19. a. 'S', when $P = \$6500, r = 0.065, t = \frac{9}{12}$ b. 'P', when $S = \$8260.80, r = 0.0425, t = \frac{280}{365}$
20. a. 'S', when $P = \$1500, r = 0.075, t = \frac{4}{12}$ b. 'P', when $S = \$10{,}135.62, r = 0.0375, t = \frac{132}{365}$

In the trade discount formula $N = L(1 - d)$, determine the value for:

21. a. 'L', when $N = \$3000, d = 0.40$ b. 'd', when $L = \$900, N = \$675$
22. a. 'L', when $N = \$10{,}000, d = 0.20$ b. 'd', when $L = \$1280, N = \$1126.40$

In the compound interest formula $FV = PV(1 + i)^n$, determine the value for:

23. 'FV', when $PV = \$5000, i = 0.0375, n = 4$
24. 'FV', when $PV = \$40{,}000, i = 0.0425, n = 12$
25. 'FV', when $PV = \$2500, i = 0.0004, n = \frac{17}{12}$
26. 'FV', when $PV = \$7750, i = 0.0035, n = \frac{25}{6}$
27. 'PV', when $FV = \$7769.72, i = 0.00375, n = 24$
28. 'PV', when $FV = \$4364.12, i = 0.00475, n = 39$

In the effective interest rate formula $f = (1 + i)^m - 1$, determine the value for 'f' when:

29. $i = 0.03, m = 4$
30. $i = 0.02, m = 2$

In the periodic interest rate formula $i = \left(\frac{FV}{PV}\right)^{\frac{1}{n}} - 1$, determine the value for 'i' when:

31. $PV = \$3000, FV = \$3280.85, n = 8$
32. $PV = \$8600, FV = \$11{,}587.22, n = 24$

In the equivalent interest rate formula $i_2 = (1 + i_1)^{\frac{m_1}{m_2}} - 1$, determine the value for 'i_2' when:

33. $i_1 = \frac{0.078}{12}, m_1 = 12, m_2 = 4$
34. $i_1 = \frac{0.096}{4}, m_1 = 4, m_2 = 12$

For Problems 35 to 40, isolate the indicated variables.

- 35. In the formula $C = \frac{V_f - V_i}{V_i}$, isolate '$V_f$'
- 36. In the formula $C = \frac{V_f - V_i}{V_i}$, isolate '$V_i$'
- 37. In the formula $PV = \frac{FV}{(1 + i)^n}$, isolate '$n$'
- 38. In the formula $PV = \frac{FV}{(1 + i)^n}$, isolate '$i$'
- 39. In the formula $f = (1 + i)^m$, isolate 'm'
- 40. In the formula $f = (1 + i)^m$, isolate 'i'

2 | Review Exercises

Answers to the odd-numbered problems are available at the end of the textbook.

1. Simplify the following expressions then evaluate:
   a. $-4x^2 + 3x - 5 + 7x^2 - 2x + 3$, where $x = 2$
   b. $4x^2 - 5 + 7x - 2x^2 - x - 3$, where $x = -1$
   c. $-y^2 + 4xy + x^2 - 6y^2 - xy - 11x^2$, where $x = 1$ and $y = 2$
   d. $(x - 4)(x + 2) + 3(x + 2)$, where $x = 3$

2. Simplify the following expressions then evaluate:
   a. $3x^2 - x + 2 + x^2 - 5x - 2$, where $x = 3$
   b. $-5y^2 - 7y + 3 + y^2 - 5y + 2$, where $y = -2$
   c. $-4x^2 + 6xy - 6y^2 + 6x^2 - 2xy + 3y^2$, where $x = 2$ and $y = 1$
   d. $(y - 2)(y - 3) + 2(y - 2)$, where $y = 4$

3. Factor the following expressions, then evaluate:
   a. $6x^2 - 4x$ where $x = 1$
   b. $3y^3 - 12y^2$ where $y = -2$
   c. $7xy + 14x^2$ where $x = 1$ and $y = 2$
   d. $9x^3 - 6x^2 + 3x$ where $x = 3$

4. Factor the following expressions, then evaluate:
   a. $8y^2 - 64y$ where $y = 2$
   b. $16x^2 - 4x^3$ where $x = -1$
   c. $15y^2 + 10xy$ where $x = -1$ and $y = 2$
   d. $16x^3 + 8x^2 - 4x$ where $x = 2$

5. Write as algebraic expressions:
   a. Twelve increased by three times a number
   b. Difference between a number and five
   c. Product of three more than a number and the number
   d. Sum of ten times a number and fifteen

6. Write as algebraic expressions:
   a. Eight decreased by twice a number
   b. Six less than the total of a number and ten
   c. Sum of 15 and half of a number
   d. Product of two times a number and seven

For Problems 7 to 10, write the expression as an algebraic equation and solve.

7. a. The sum of five times a number and seventeen is forty-two.
   b. A number divided by fifteen is forty-five.

8. a. The sum of two times a number and eight is one hundred.
   b. A number divided by three is seven.

9. a. The difference between a number and ten is ten.
   b. The product of four times a number and three is thirty-six.

10. a. The product of five and a number is seventy-five.
    b. Three more than two times a number is nine.

For Problems 11 to 14, solve for the unknown variable, 'x'.

11. a. $5x - 5 = 10$ b. $\frac{x}{3} + 4 = 10$

12. a. $3x - 5 = -17$ b. $\frac{x}{4} - 2 = 1$

13. a. $12 - 3x = 3 - 4x$ b. $4(x + 4) = 24$

14. a. $4x - 2 = 13 - 6x$ b. $3(2x - 5) = 3$

15. Aran bought a shirt and a pair of pants for \$34.75. The pair of of pants cost \$9.75 more than the shirt. Calculate the cost of the shirt.

16. Mythili bought a schoolbag and a toy for \$30.45. The schoolbag cost \$5.45 more than the toy. Calculate the cost of the schoolbag.

17. Simplify and evaluate:

    a. $(-3)^2 + 2^3$ b. $(-3)^2(2^3)$ c. $\frac{2^8}{2^4}$

18. Simplify and evaluate:

    a. $(-5)^3 + 3^2$ b. $2^3(-2)^4$ c. $\frac{3^7}{3^5}$

For Problems 19 to 24, simplify the expression and express your answer with a positive exponent.

19. a. $\sqrt[3]{125}$ b. $\left(\frac{4}{9}\right)^{-\frac{1}{2}}$ c. $\frac{4^9}{4^5 \times 4^2}$

20. a. $\sqrt[5]{32}$ b. $\left(\frac{1}{8}\right)^{-\frac{2}{3}}$ c. $\frac{3^4 \times 3^2}{3^3}$

21. a. $(x^4)(3x^3)$ b. $\frac{x^6}{x^2}$ c. $\left(\frac{x^2}{y}\right)\left(\frac{x}{2y^2}\right)^2$

22. a. $(x^3)(2x^5)$ b. $\frac{x^9}{x^6}$ c. $\left(\frac{2x^2}{y}\right)\left(\frac{3x}{y^2}\right)^3$

23. a. $(8x^6)^{\frac{1}{3}}$ b. $\left(\frac{4x^3}{2y^2}\right)^3$ c. $\left(\frac{x^7}{x^0}\right)^2$

24. a. $(4x^2)^{\frac{1}{2}}$ b. $\left(\frac{3x^2}{4y^3}\right)^2$ c. $\left(\frac{x^0}{y^3}\right)^3$

• 25. Solve for 'n' and express the answer to two decimal places:

    a. $2060 = 1225(1.02)^n$ b. $5215 = (1.005)^n + 600$

• 26. Solve for 'n' and express the answer to two decimal places:

    a. $6075 = 4150(1.03)^n$ b. $4815 = (1.04)^n + 900$

• 27. Solve for 'n' and express the answer to two decimal places:

    a. $n = \left(\frac{\ln\left(\frac{2775}{1200}\right)}{\ln(1.03)}\right)$ b. $n = \frac{\ln(3)}{\ln(1.02)}$

• 28. Solve for 'n' and express the answer to two decimal places:

    a. $n = \frac{\ln\left(\frac{4950}{1250}\right)}{\ln(1.005)}$ b. $n = \frac{\ln(1200)}{\ln(5)}$

• 29. In the formula $V = \frac{1}{3}\pi r^2 h$, isolate 'r'

• 30. In the formula $V = \frac{4}{3}\pi r^3$, isolate 'r'

2 | Self-Test Exercises

Answers to all the problems are available at the end of the textbook.

1. Simplify the following expressions first, then evaluate:
    a. $2x^2 + 5x + 1 - 4 - 3x - x^2$, where $x = 2$
    b. $-3x^2 + 2x + 2x^2 - 8x + 10$, where $x = -3$
    c. $9x^2 - 4xy + y^2 - 6y^2 - 3xy + 10x^2$, where $x = 1$ and $y = 2$
    d. $5(2x - 3y) - 2(3x - 2y) + 7$, where $x = 2$ and $y = 1$

2. Factor the following expressions first, then evaluate:
    a. $18y^2 - 12y$, where $y = -2$
    b. $15y^3 + 12y^2 + 3y$, where $y = 1$
    c. $14xy - 21x^2$, where $x = 2$ and $y = 1$
    d. $8xy^2 - 6x^2y$, where $x = 1$ and $y = -1$

3. Write as algebraic expressions:
    a. Twenty-five less than three times a number
    b. A number increased by eighteen
    c. The difference between twice a number and six
    d. The quotient of a number and three

4. Write the following as an algebraic equation and solve:
    a. Nine less than twice a number is twenty-one.
    b. Twenty-two is five times a number decreased by 3.

5. Write the following as an algebraic equation and solve:
    a. Four times eight is sixteen times a number.
    b. Thirty is a product of six and a number.

6. Solve for the unknown variable 'x', using properties of equations:

a. $24 - 5x = 4$ b. $8 + 2x = 4 - 5x$

c. $\frac{x}{3} - 2 = 4$ d. $3(3x - 3) = 33$

7. A 30-metre chain is cut into two pieces. The length of one piece is $1\frac{1}{2}$ times the other. Calculate the length of each piece.

8. Twenty more than five times a number is the same as thirty less than three times the number. What is the number?

9. Simplify the expression, then evaluate:

a. $(-2)^3(-2)^4$ b. $(-5)^3 + 2^2$

c. $\frac{(-10)^5}{(-10)^2}$ d. $\sqrt[3]{27}$

e. $(216)^{\frac{1}{3}}$ f. $\frac{5^3 \times 5^4}{5^2}$

10. Simplify the expression and express your answer with a positive exponent:

a. $(3x^3)^2$ b. $(4x^2y^3)^2$

c. $(16x^0y^4)^{\frac{1}{2}}$ d. $\left(\frac{x^6}{x^2}\right)$

e. $(x^{-3}y)^2$ f. $\frac{x^{-7}x^{-3}}{x^{-10}}$

For Problems 11 to 13, solve for 'n' and express the answer rounded to two decimal places.

11. a. $n = \frac{\ln\left(\frac{2200}{1200}\right)}{\ln(1.04)}$ b. $n = \frac{\ln(1475)}{\ln(10)}$

12. a. $n = \frac{\ln(3)}{\ln(1.02)}$ b. $460 = 240(1.05)^n$

13. a. $750 = (1.05)^n + 600$ b. $1296 = 6^n$

14. In the formula $f = (1 + i)^m - 1$, solve for 'f' (rounding to four decimal places) when,

a. $i = \frac{0.05}{12}$ and $m = 2$

b. $i = 0.005$ and $m = 2$

15. In the formula $S = P(1 + rt)$,

a. Isolate 't'

b. Find the value of 't' when $S = \$1200$, $P = \$1000$, and $r = 0.10$

Chapter 3

PERCENTS, PERCENT CHANGES, AND APPLICATIONS

LEARNING OBJECTIVES

- Convert percents, fractions, and decimal numbers from one form to another.
- Solve percent problems using different methods.
- Apply percent change sign conventions to solve problems involving a change from an initial value.
- Calculate the gross pay for a pay period based on annual salary, sales commissions, hourly rate, and piecework rate.
- Calculate sales taxes and property taxes in different provinces/territories of Canada.

CHAPTER OUTLINE

3.1 Percents
3.2 Percent Changes
3.3 Payroll
3.4 Taxes

Introduction

Percent (per cent or per hundred in the literal meaning) is used to express a quantity out of 100 units and is represented by the symbol %.

For example, 'C' out of 100 = C%

A percent can be defined using:

- Fractional (ratio) notation, as in, $C\% = \frac{C}{100} = C \times \left(\frac{1}{100}\right)$ i.e., replacing % with $\times \frac{1}{100}$
- Decimal notation, as in, $C\% = 0.01C$ i.e., replacing % with × 0.01

Percent is a value expressed out of one hundred. For example, 5% is equal to five out of one hundred:

$5\% = \frac{5}{100} = 0.05$

Percents and percent changes make comparisons easy and are used often in our daily lives in making business decisions. Due to the simplicity of expression in day-to-day business statements, percents have become a widely accepted measure of expressing fractions (ratios) or decimals. Some examples of the use of percents that you would have come across include interest rates charged by banks on student loans, discounts offered at clothing stores, sales tax charged on items purchased, commission received by sales representatives on sales made, etc. The strong foundation that you will receive in this chapter will help you make intelligent business decisions in your day-to-day lives.

3.1 | Percents

Relationship Among Percents, Fractions (Ratios), and Decimals

In day-to-day business, the word *'percent'* is commonly used to represent interest rates, sales discounts, commissions, changes in quantities, etc. However, in actual calculations, fractions (ratios) or decimal equivalents are used. Therefore, it is necessary to know how to convert from one form to the other.

Converting Percents to Fractions (Ratio)

- **If the percent is a whole number,** to convert it to a fraction, remove the percent sign, divide by 100 (or multiply by $\frac{1}{100}$), and reduce to its lowest terms.

For example, to convert 60% to a fraction in its lowest terms,

$$60\% = \frac{60}{100}$$ Reduce the fraction to its lowest terms.

$$= \frac{3}{5}$$

Therefore, $60\% = \frac{3}{5}$.

- **If the percent includes a decimal number,** to convert it to a fraction, remove the percent sign, divide by 100, and change the resulting fraction to its equivalent fraction to eliminate the decimal in the numerator. Finally, reduce the fraction to its lowest terms.

For example, to convert 42.5% to a fraction:

$$42.5\% = \frac{42.5}{100}$$ Eliminate the decimal by multiplying both the numerator and denominator by 10.

$= \frac{425}{1000}$ Reduce the fraction to its lowest terms.

$= \frac{17}{40}$

Therefore, $42.5\% = \frac{17}{40}$.

- **If the percent includes a fraction or a mixed number**, either convert it to its decimal equivalent and follow the steps outlined above, or convert it to an improper fraction and follow the steps outlined below.

For example, to convert $6\frac{1}{2}\%$ to a fraction:

Method 1: Converting the fraction to its decimal equivalent

$6\frac{1}{2}\% = \frac{6\frac{1}{2}}{100}$ Rewrite the numerator in decimal form.

$= \frac{6.5}{100}$ Eliminate the decimal by multiplying both the numerator and denominator by 10.

$= \frac{65}{1000}$ Reduce the fraction to its lowest terms.

$= \frac{13}{200}$

Method 2: Converting the fraction to its improper fractional equivalent

$6\frac{1}{2}\% = \frac{6\frac{1}{2}}{100} = 6\frac{1}{2} \div 100$ Convert the mixed number to an improper fraction.

$= \frac{13}{2} \div 100$

$= \frac{13}{2} \times \frac{1}{100}$

$= \frac{13}{200}$

Therefore, $6\frac{1}{2}\% = \frac{13}{200}$.

Example 3.1(a) **Converting Percents to Fractions**

Convert each percent to its equivalent fraction or mixed number and simplify to its lowest terms.

(i) 45% (ii) $8\frac{1}{3}\%$ (iii) 6.25% (iv) 175% (v) $\frac{1}{5}\%$

Solution

(i) $45\% = \frac{45}{100} = \frac{9}{20}$

(ii) $8\frac{1}{3}\% = 8\frac{1}{3} \div 100 = \frac{25}{3} \times \frac{1}{100} = \frac{25}{300} = \frac{1}{12}$

(iii) $6.25\% = \frac{6.25}{100} = \frac{6.25}{100} \times \frac{100}{100} = \frac{625}{10{,}000} = \frac{1}{16}$

(iv) $175\% = \frac{175}{100} = \frac{7}{4} = 1\frac{3}{4}$

(v) $\frac{1}{5}\% = \frac{1}{5} \div 100 = \frac{1}{5} \times \frac{1}{100} = \frac{1}{500}$

Converting Percents to Decimal Numbers

- **If the percent is a whole number or a decimal number,** remove the '%' sign and move the decimal point two places to the left. This is the same as dividing the number by 100 and dropping the '%' sign.

Consider the following examples:

- To convert 45% to a decimal number,

  $45\% = 45.0 = 0.45$ This is the same as: $45\% = \frac{45}{100} = 0.45$

  Therefore, 45% = 0.45

- To convert 0.38% to a decimal number,

  $0.38\% = 0.38 = 0.0038$ This is the same as: $0.38\% = \frac{0.38}{100} = 0.0038$

  Therefore, 0.38% = 0.0038

- **If the percent is a fraction or a mixed number**, change it to its decimal equivalent and follow the steps as shown above.

For example, to convert $2\frac{1}{2}\%$ to a decimal number,

$2\frac{1}{2}\% = 2.5\% = 2.5 = 0.025$

Therefore, $2\frac{1}{2}\% = 0.025$.

Example 3.1(b) **Converting Percents to Decimal Numbers**

Convert each percent to its equivalent decimal number.

(i) 85% (ii) $5\frac{1}{4}\%$ (iii) 20.75% (iv) 225% (v) $\frac{2}{3}\%$

Solution

(i) $85\% = 85.0\% = 85.0 = 0.85$

(ii) $5\frac{1}{4}\% = 5.25\% = 5.25 = 0.0525$

(iii) $20.75\% = 20.75 = 0.2075$

(iv) $225\% = 225.0\% = 225.0 = 2.25$

(v) $\frac{2}{3}\% = 0.666666...\% = 0.666666... = 0.006666... = 0.00\overline{6}$

A bar over digits in a decimal number represents a repeating decimal. Here, the 6 is repeated forever.

Converting Decimal Numbers to Percents

To convert a decimal number or a whole number to a percent, move the decimal point two places to the right and insert the '%' sign. This is the same as multiplying the number by 100 and inserting the '%' sign.

Consider the following examples:

- To convert 0.35 to a percent,

  $0.35 = 0.35\% = 35\%$ This is the same as: $0.35 \times 100\% = 35\%$

  Therefore, 0.35 = 35%.

- To convert 5 to a percent,

  $5 = 5.00\% = 500\%$ This is the same as: $5 \times 100\% = 500\%$

  Therefore, 5 = 500%.

Example 3.1(c) **Converting Decimal Numbers to Percents**

Convert each of the following decimal numbers to its equivalent percent.

(i) 5.25 (ii) 0.45 (iii) 0.03 (iv) 0.002

Solution

(i) $5.25 = 5.25\% = 525\%$

(ii) $0.45 = 0.45\% = 45\%$

(iii) $0.03 = 0.03\% = 3\%$

(iv) $0.002 = 0.002\% = 0.20\%$

Example 3.1(d) **Application Problem**

If Darwin earns three times the amount that Harry earns, what percent is Darwin's earnings compared to Harry's?

Solution

Here, 'three times' has to be converted to a percent = 3 × (100%) = 300%.

Therefore, Darwin's earning is 300% of Harry's.

Note: *This also means that Darwin earns 200% more than Harry.*

Converting Fractions or Mixed Numbers to Percents

To convert a fraction or a mixed number to a percent, first convert the fraction or the mixed number to a decimal number. Then, convert the decimal number to a percent by moving the decimal point by two places to the right and inserting the % sign. This is the same as multiplying the decimals by 100 and inserting the % sign.

For example,

- To convert $\frac{3}{8}$ to a percent:

$\frac{3}{8} = 0.375$ — Convert the fraction to its decimal equivalent.

$= 0.375\%$ — Move the decimal point 2 places to the right and add the % sign.

$= 37.50\%$ — This is the same as 0.375 × 100% = 37.50%.

Therefore, $\frac{3}{8} = 37.50\%$.

- To convert $5\frac{1}{2}$ to a percent:

$5\frac{1}{2} = 5.50$ — Convert the mixed number to its decimal equivalent.

$= 5.50\%$ — Move the decimal point 2 places to the right and add the % sign.

$= 550\%$ — This is the same as 5.50 × 100% = 550%.

Therefore, $5\frac{1}{2} = 550\%$.

Example 3.1(e) **Converting Fractions and Mixed Numbers to Percents**

Convert each of the following fractions to decimals and then to its equivalent percent.

(i) $\frac{3}{25}$ (ii) $5\frac{1}{4}$ (iii) $\frac{18}{5}$ (iv) $\frac{1}{200}$

Solution

(i) $\frac{3}{25} = 0.12$

$= 0.12\% = 12\%$

(ii) $5\frac{1}{4} = 5.25$

$= 5.25\% = 525\%$

(iii) $\frac{18}{5} = 3.60$

$= 3.60\% = 360\%$

(iv) $\frac{1}{200} = 0.005$

$= 0.005\% = 0.50\%$

Example 3.1(f) **Comparing Fractions and Percents**

Out of 54 students in Class A, 43 students passed the final exam. In Class B, 78% of students passed the final exam. Which class produced the better pass rate?

Solution

Class A: Fraction of students passed $= \frac{43}{54} = 0.796296...$

Percent of students passed $= 0.796296... \times 100\%$

$= 79.629629...\%$

$= 79.63\%$

Class B: Percent of students passed $= 78.00\%$

Therefore, Class A produced a better pass rate.

Example 3.1(g) **Application Problem**

Peter and Angela are two students studying Mathematics of Finance, but at different colleges. Peter managed to secure a score of 46 out of 60 on the final exam, while Angela scored 63 out of 75. Who scored better on the exam?

Solution

By observation, it is not possible to answer the question because Peter's score is expressed on a base of 60, while Angela's score is on a base of 75. To compare their scores, we need to convert them to their percent equivalents, as shown below:

Peter's score: $\frac{46}{60} = 0.766666... \times 100\% = 76.666666...\% = 76.67\%$

Angela's score: $\frac{63}{75} = 0.84 \times 100\% = 84.00\%$

Therefore, Angela scored better than Peter on the exam.

Solving Percent Problems

There are many methods used in solving percent problems. Described below are three common methods:

Method 1: Formula Method

Every percent problem contains three variables:

Base (B): Whole quantity or value (100%). It usually follows the word 'of' or 'percent of'.

Portion (P): Portion of the whole quantity or value (portion of the base).

Rate (R): Relationship between base and portion, expressed in percent. It usually carries the sign '%' or the word 'percent'. Every percent statement can be expressed as ***P* is *R*% of *B***. The value of R is converted to its decimal or fractional equivalent in calculations.

> R% converted to a fraction (or ratio) is $\frac{R}{100}$.
>
> R% converted to a decimal is $0.01R$.

This relationship between these variables can be expressed as follows:

Portion = Rate × Base

This is represented by the formula,

Formula 3.1 **Portion**

$$P = R \times B$$

Rearranging, we obtain, $R = \frac{P}{B}$ and $B = \frac{P}{R}$.

Therefore, if any two of these quantities are known, then the third quantity can be calculated.

P, R, B triangle

Here is a triangle that can be used to help in rearranging the formula $P = R \times B$ to solve for R or B.

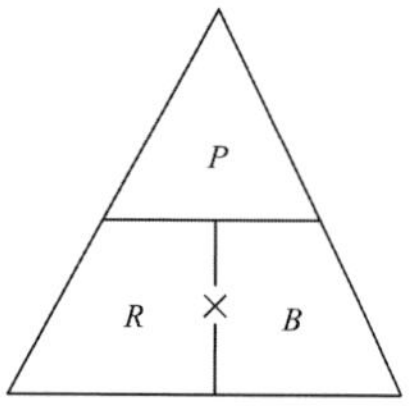

Variables beside each other at the bottom are multiplied ($R \times B$, as shown).

Variable P is divided by the variables at the bottom, R and B.

Cover the variable that you want to solve for to see the new formula.

For example, if you want to solve for 'R', the formula can be found by covering 'R' and reading the remaining variables in the above triangle, to get $R = \frac{P}{B}$.

Method 2: Portion as a Percent of Base

The whole amount or quantity is represented by 100% and is known as the **base (*B*)**. The **portion (*P*)** is a part of the base and it forms a percent, or **rate (*R*%)**, of the base. Thus, in this method, we first identify the base and portion in the problem, then we compare the portion to the base and solve for the unknown.

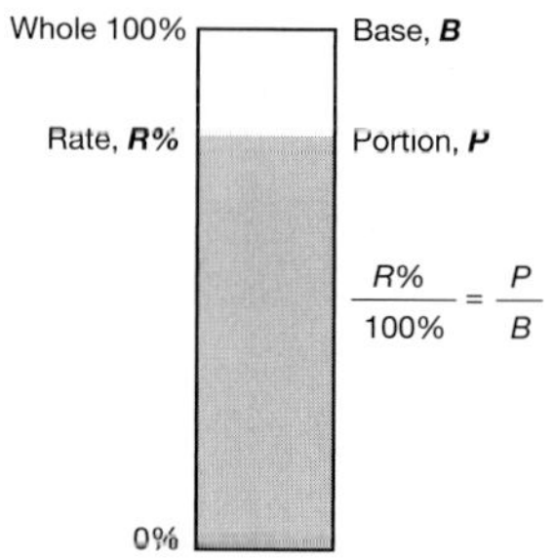

Percent	Amount
R%	Portion, P
100%	Base, B

You can use this table to separate the percents and the amounts when solving percent problems.

Method 3: Algebraic Method

Solving problems using algebraic methods involves forming an equation for an unknown value, 'x', and then solving for 'x'. In this method, we form equation(s) for the given problem (or statement) using key words to represent arithmetic operations. The following table presents some clues to remember arithmetic operations used in problems.

Table 3.1 **Operations and Key Words**

Operation symbols	Key words
Addition (+)	Add, sum, plus, and, more than, increased by, appreciate, rise
Subtraction (–)	Subtract, difference, minus, less than, decreased by, depreciate, fall
Multiplication (×) or (·)	Multiply, product, times, of
Division (÷) or (/)	Divide, ratio, per, divided by, quotient
Equal (=)	Is, was, gives, given by
Unknown value	What, how much, (usually denoted by some letter, such as 'x')

Example 3.1(h) **Calculating the Portion of a Whole Quantity**

What is 75% of $250? (Or, how much is 75% of $250?)

Solution

Method 1: Using the Formula

$R\% = 75\%$ (value with '%' sign); i.e., $R = 0.75$

$B = \$250.00$ (value after the word 'of')

$P = ?$

Using Formula 3.1, $P = R \times B$

$= 0.75 \times 250.00 = \$187.50$

Therefore, 75% of $250 is $187.50.

Solution *continued*

Method 2: Using the Portion as a Percent (%) of Base

Here, the whole amount of \$250 is the Base (B) and is represented by 100%. 75% (R%) is a Portion (P) of the whole amount, as illustrated:

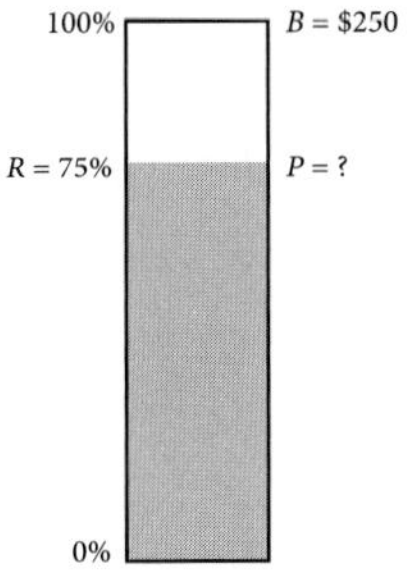

Percent	Amount
75%	\$$P$
100%	\$250

$$\frac{75\%}{100\%} = \frac{P}{250.00}$$ Cross-multiplying,

$$P = \frac{75\% \times 250.00}{100\%} = \$187.50$$

Therefore, 75% of \$250 is \$187.50.

Method 3: Using the Algebraic Method

What is 75% of \$250?

$$x = 75\% \times 250.00$$ Expressing the percent as a fraction,

$$x = \left(\frac{75}{100}\right) \times 250.00$$

$$= 0.75 \times 250.00 = \$187.50$$

Therefore, 75% of \$250 is \$187.50.

Example 3.1(i) **Calculating Rate When Portion and Base are Known**

What percent of \$775 is \$1250? (Or, \$1250 is what percent of \$775?)

Solution

Method 1: Using the Formula

B = \$775.00 (value after the word 'of'),

P = \$1250.00 (the other value),

R = ?

Using Formula 3.1, $P = R \times B$

Rearranging, $R = \frac{P}{B}$

Substituting values for 'P' and 'B', $R = \frac{1250.00}{775.00}$

$$R\% = \frac{1250.00}{775.00} \times 100\%$$

$$= 161.290322...\%$$

Method 2: Using the Portion as a Percent (%) of Base

Percent	Amount
R%	\$1250
100%	\$775

$$\frac{R\%}{100\%} = \frac{1250.00}{775.00}$$

$$R\% = \frac{1250.00 \times 100\%}{775.00}$$

$$= 161.290322...\%$$

Therefore, 161.29% of \$775 is \$1250.

Example 3.1(j) **Calculating Base When Portion and Rate are Known**

17.5% of what amount is $218.75?

Solution

Method 1: Using the Formula

$R\% = 17.5\%$ (value with '%' sign) $= 0.175$,

$B = ?$ (value after the word 'of'),

$P = \$218.75$ (the other value)

Using Formula 3.1, $P = R \times B$

Rearranging, $B = \dfrac{P}{R}$

Substituting values for 'P' and 'R', $B = \dfrac{218.75}{0.175}$

$= \$1250.00$

Method 2: Using the Portion as a Percent (%) of Base

Percent	Amount
17.5%	$218.75
100%	$B

$$\frac{17.5\%}{100\%} = \frac{218.75}{B}$$

$$B = \frac{218.75 \times 100\%}{17.5\%}$$

$$= \$1250.00$$

Therefore, 17.5% of $1250 is $218.75.

Example 3.1(k) **Calculating Portion When Rate is More Than 100%**

What is 140% of $250?

Solution

Method 1: Using the Formula

$R\% = 140\% = 1.40$,

$B = \$250$,

$P = ?$

Using Formula 3.1, $P = R \times B$

$= 1.40 \times 250.00$

$= \$350.00$

Method 2: Using the Portion as a Percent (%) of Base

Percent	Amount
140%	$P
100%	$250

$$\frac{140\%}{100\%} = \frac{P}{250.00}$$

$$P = \frac{140\% \times 250.00}{100\%}$$

$$= \$350.00$$

Therefore, 140% of $250 is $350.

Example 3.1(l) **Application Problem Based on Repeating Decimals**

Sandra owns $25\frac{1}{3}\%$ of a web development company. If the company is valued at $180,000, what is the value of Sandra's ownership in the company?

Solution

Method 1: Using the Formula

Identify the base, portion, and rate:

$B = \$180,000$

$P = ?$

$R\% = 25\frac{1}{3}\% = 25.333333...\% = 0.253333...$

(Store this value in the calculator memory)

Do not round intermediary steps in calculations. Store the value of the intermediary step in your calculator and recall it for subsequent calculations.

Using Formula 3.1, $P = R \times B$

$= 0.253333... \times 180,000.00$

$= \$45,600.00$

Alternatively, this can be solved by converting the mixed number to an improper fraction:

$B = \$180,000$

$$R\% = 25\tfrac{1}{3}\% = \frac{76}{3}\% = \frac{76}{3} \times \frac{1}{100} = \frac{76}{300}$$

Using Formula 3.1,

$$P = R \times B = \frac{76}{300} \times 180,000.00 = \$45,600.00$$

Method 2: Using the Portion as a Percent (%) of Base

Percent	Amount
$25\frac{1}{3}\%$	$\$P$
100%	$180,000

$$\frac{25\frac{1}{3}\%}{100\%} = \frac{P}{180,000.00}$$

$$P = \frac{25.333333...\% \times 180,000.00}{100\%}$$

$= \$45,600.00$

Therefore, the value of Sandra's ownership in the company is $45,600.

3.1 | *Exercises*

Answers to the odd-numbered problems are available at the end of the textbook.

For the following problems, express the answers rounded to two decimal places, wherever applicable.
Compute the missing values in Problems 1 to 4:

1.

	Percent	Decimal	Fraction in Lowest Terms
a.	80%	?	?
b.	?	0.25	?
c.	?	?	$\frac{3}{2}$
d.	$6\frac{1}{2}\%$	?	?
e.	?	0.048	?
f.	?	?	$\frac{2}{25}$

2.

	Percent	Decimal	Fraction in Lowest Terms
a.	2%	?	?
b.	?	0.245	?
c.	?	?	$\frac{5}{12}$
d.	$\frac{1}{2}\%$	?	?
e.	?	0.002	?
f.	?	?	$\frac{97}{365}$

3.

	Percent	Decimal	Fraction in Lowest Terms
a.	$10\frac{3}{5}\%$	?	?
b.	?	2.25	?
c.	?	?	$\frac{1}{400}$
d.	–26%	?	?
e.	?	–0.15	?
f.	?	?	$-\frac{7}{12}$

4.

	Percent	Decimal	Fraction in Lowest Terms
a.	$12\frac{2}{5}\%$	?	?
b.	?	1.075	?
c.	?	?	$\frac{3}{80}$
d.	–7.5%	?	?
e.	?	–0.05	?
f.	?	?	$-\frac{5}{8}$

Calculate the following:

5. a. 20% of 350 b. 12.5% of 800 c. 130% of 40
6. a. 45% of 180 b. 2.5% of 960 c. 285% of 110
7. a. 0.25% of 75 b. $\frac{1}{4}$% of 200 km c. $5\frac{1}{2}$% of \$1000
8. a. 0.755% of 120 b. $\frac{1}{8}$% of 450 km c. $12\frac{3}{4}$% of \$1260
9. a. What percent of \$100 is \$90? b. What percent of \$90 is \$100? c. 280 m is what percent of 2 km?
10. a. What percent of \$1100 is \$110.50? b. What percent of \$110.50 is \$1100? c. 180 g is what percent of 3 kg?
11. a. 15% of what amount is \$27.90? b. 120% of what amount is \$156? c. \$16.50 is 0.75% of what amount?
12. a. 30% of what amount is \$708? b. 215% of what amount is \$258? c. \$16.40 is 0.5% of what amount?
13. a. $8\frac{1}{4}$% of \$200 is how much? b. How much is $\frac{1}{4}$% of \$108? c. 0.35% of \$2700 is how much?
14. a. $25\frac{3}{4}$% of \$2680 is how much? b. How much is $\frac{3}{4}$% of 350 kg? c. 0.8% of \$275 is how much?
15. How much tax was charged on a table that costs \$250 before tax, if the tax rate is 13%?
16. The monthly gross salary of an employee is \$6250. If 26% of the salary was deducted for taxes, how much money was deducted for taxes?
17. If the 5% commission earned on sales was \$1250, what was the sales amount?
18. If the 3% interest accrued on a loan was \$210, what was the loan amount?
19. In a survey of 450 people, 117 responded 'yes'. What percent of the people surveyed responded 'no'?
20. 144 out of 600 students took Business Mathematics. What percent of students did not take the course?
21. If the population of Canada was estimated to be 36,612,500 in June 2017, and the population of Ontario was estimated to be $37\frac{1}{2}$% of Canada's population, calculate the population of Ontario, rounded up to the next whole number.
22. A company that makes video games sets sales targets of \$280,000 per year for each of its sales people. If Amanda, an excellent salesperson, achieved 250% of her target this year, calculate the value of Amanda's sales.
23. Ronald, an investment banker, sold his shares for \$18,568.50 when there was a boom in the stock market. Calculate the amount he paid for the shares if his selling price was 180.65% of the amount he paid for the shares.
24. When there was a boom in the real estate market, Lucy sold her property for \$410,440, which was 130% of the amount she paid for it. Calculate the amount she paid for the property.
25. A leading information technology company donated \$87,790 of its 2016 fiscal revenue of \$17,558,643 towards socially responsible causes. What percent of its revenue did it contribute towards these causes?

26. Evan, a business development representative of a leading pharmaceutical firm, took his client out for a dinner that cost \$180.75 before taxes. If the tax was \$23.50, calculate the tax rate.

27. Neel Corporation needed \$120,000 to purchase a machine. If it received only 25.5% of this amount from a bank, how much more money is required to purchase the machine?

28. Pamela and Martha run a business that made a profit of \$12,750. As Pamela invested a larger amount in the business, she received 57.5% of the profits, and Martha received the rest. Calculate Martha's share of the profit, in dollars.

29. Dawson purchased a pair of shoes on Boxing Day that was discounted by 10% from the original price of \$50. Calculate the amount he paid for the pair of shoes.

30. Jamie went to the mall during the holiday season to purchase a wall painting for his mother. He liked a painting that was selling for \$199.99 and which had a seasonal discount of 18% on its selling price. How much would this picture cost Jamie after the discount?

31. The actual expenditure for the construction of a local highway was 110% of the budgeted amount. If the actual expenditure was \$1,280,000, calculate the budgeted amount.

32. If Henry's actual business expenditure was \$14,480 in March and \$14,806.50 in April, which were 112% and 122% of his budgeted expenditure for March and April, respectively, calculate his total budgeted expenditure for the two months.

33. Out of 46 students in Class *A*, 33 students passed the final exam. In Class *B*, out of 37 students, 26 students passed the final exam. Which class had a better pass rate?

34. Out of 820 students who sat for the Finance Math exam in College *A*, 608 students passed. In College *B*, out of 975 students, 714 students passed the Finance Math exam. Which college had a better pass rate?

35. The attendance of a symphony in the month of December was 98,952 guests. This was 108.5% of the projected attendance. What was the projected attendance of the symphony in December?

36. The actual sales of an appliance store for a month were \$18,245. This was 82% of the budgeted sales. What were the budgeted sales for the month?

37. A moving company calculates that it pays out 9.75% of its revenue in damage claims each month. In April, the amount paid out in damage claims was \$1645.80. What was the company's revenue in April?

38. A store lost \$2350 last month due to theft. If this is equivalent to 6.25% of the total sales, what were the total sales for last month?

• 39. Assume that 350,000 people immigrated to Canada in 2016. Of these immigrants, 12.25% were from China, 9.75% were from the Philippines, and the rest were from other countries.

  a. Calculate the number of people who immigrated to Canada from China.

  b. If the combined number of immigrants from China and the Philippines constituted 0.195% of the population of Canada, calculate the population of Canada in 2016. (Round your answers up to the next whole number.)

• 40. Holly and her husband were charged \$27.80 (including taxes) for a meal at a restaurant. They tipped the waiter 15% of this amount.

  a. What was the tip amount?

  b. If the tip that they gave the waiter was 2% of all the money that the waiter earned from tips that night, calculate the total amount that the waiter earned from tips that night.

3.2 | Percent Changes

The percent by which a quantity increases or decreases from its initial value is called **percent change (%C)**. The amount of change is expressed as a percent change from its initial value.

$$\textit{Amount of Change} = \%C \times \textit{Initial Value}$$

The amount of change is the difference between the final value (V_f) and the initial value (V_i); i.e. the amount can also be calculated by subtracting the intitial value from the final value.

$$\textit{Amount of Change} = \textit{Final Value} - \textit{Initial Value}$$

Therefore,

The amount of change (increase or decrease) is expressed as a percent of the initial value.

$$\% \textit{ Change} \times \textit{Inital Value} = \textit{Final Value} - \textit{Initial Value}$$

$$\%C(V_i) = V_f - V_i$$

$$\%C = \frac{V_f - V_i}{V_i} = \frac{V_f - V_i}{V_i} \times 100\%$$

Formula 3.2 **Percent Change**

$$\%C = \frac{V_f - V_i}{V_i} \times 100\%$$

Some quantities, such as hourly rate of pay, generally increase with time, while some quantities, such as the price of an item during a sale, generally decrease.

- When there is an increase from the initial value, the final value will be more (larger) than the initial value. Therefore, the amount of change (V_f – V_i) and the %C will be positive.
- When there is decrease from the initial value, the final value will be less (smaller) than the initial value. Therefore, the amount of change (V_f – V_i) and the %C will be negative.

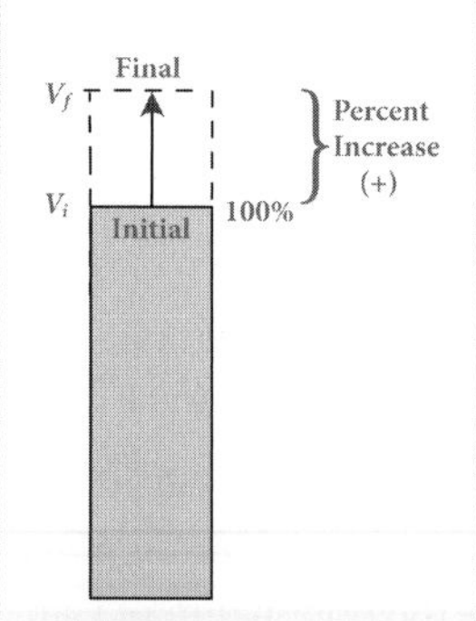

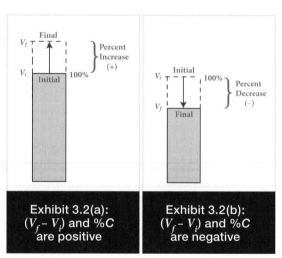

Exhibit 3.2(a): (V_f – V_i) and %C are positive

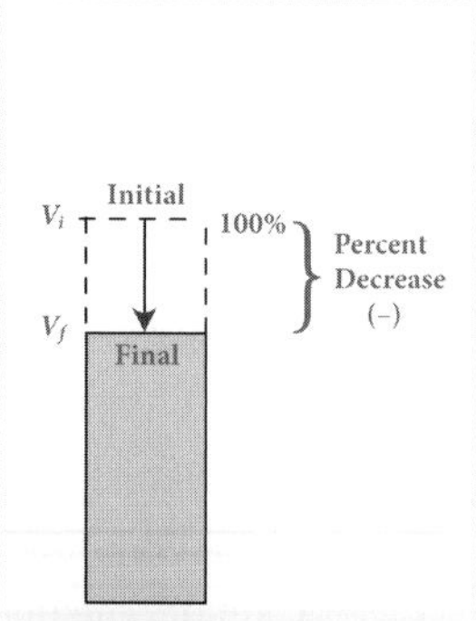

Exhibit 3.2(b): (V_f – V_i) and %C are negative

Using Formula 3.2, we can derive the equation to calculate the final value (V_f) as follows:

$$\%C = \frac{V_f - V_i}{V_i}$$ Cross-multiplying,

$$V_f - V_i = \%C \times V_i$$ Rearranging,

$$V_f = V_i + \%C(V_i)$$ Factoring out the common factor V_i,

$$V_f = V_i(1 + \%C)$$

By rearranging the above equation, we can derive the equation to calculate the inital value (V_i) as follows:

$$V_i = \frac{V_f}{1 + \%C}$$

Example 3.2(a) **Percent Change Applications**

Company *A's* profit increased from \$165,000 to \$170,000 in a year and Company *B's* profit increased from \$122,000 to \$126,000 in the same year. Which company has shown a better relative change in profit?

Solution

First, calculate the amount of change in profits:

$$Amount\ of\ Change_{Company\ A} = 170{,}000.00 - 165{,}000.00 = \$5000.00$$

$$Amount\ of\ Change_{Company\ B} = 126{,}000.00 - 122{,}000.00 = \$4000.00$$

By comparing the amounts by which the profits in Companies *A* and *B* have changed, it may be tempting to conclude that Company *A* has grown more than Company *B*. However, this comparison is incorrect, because we need to compare the *relative change* in profit for each company. This brings us to the understanding of 'percent change'.

Using Formula 3.2, $\%C = \frac{V_f - V_i}{V_i} \times 100\%$

Company A's Percent Change in Profit:

$$\%C_{Company\ A} = \frac{170{,}000.00 - 165{,}000.00}{165{,}000.00} \times 100\%$$

$$= \frac{5000.00}{165{,}000.00} \times 100\% = 0.030303... \times 100\% = 3.03\%$$

Company B's Percent Change in Profit:

$$\%C_{Company\ B} = \frac{126{,}000.00 - 122{,}000.00}{122{,}000.00} \times 100\%$$

$$= \frac{4000.00}{122{,}000.00} \times 100\% = 0.032786... \times 100\% = 3.28\%$$

Therefore, even though Company *B* had a smaller increase in profit than Company *A* during the year, Company *B* had a better relative growth compared to Company *A*.

In financial applications, it is often more important to calculate percent changes and associated values instead of relying on a mere difference between two values.

There are many methods used in solving percent change calculations. Described in the following example are four common methods used to solve a percent change problem:

Example 3.2(b) **Calculating the Final Value When the Percent Change is Positive Using Different Methods**

If a \$20 hourly rate of pay is increased by 10%, determine the new hourly rate.

Solution

Method 1: Algebraic Method

$\%C = +10\% = +0.10, \quad V_i = \$20, \quad V_f = ?$

$$Initial\ Value + Amount\ of\ Increase = Final\ Value$$

$$V_i + \%C \times V_i = V_f$$

Substituting values,

$$20.00 + 0.10(20.00) = V_f$$

$$20.00 + 2.00 = V_f$$

$$V_f = \$22.00$$

Therefore, the new hourly rate is \$22.00.

Helpful Check:
If the percent change is positive, then the final value will be greater than the initial value.

Solution *continued*

Method 2: Formula Method

$\%C = 10\%,\quad V_i = \$20,\quad V_f = ?$

Using Formula 3.2,

$$\%C = \frac{V_f - V_i}{V_i} \times 100\%$$ Substituting values,

$$10\% = \frac{V_f - 20.00}{20.00} \times 100\%$$ Eliminating the percents, (Note: 10% = 0.10 and 100% = 1)

$$0.10 = \frac{V_f - 20.00}{20.00}$$ Cross-multiplying,

$$20.00(0.10) = V_f - 20.00$$

$$2.00 = V_f - 20.00$$ Adding 20 to both sides,

$$V_f = \$22.00$$

Therefore, the new hourly rate is $22.00.

Method 3: Preprogrammed Calculator

The Texas Instruments BAII Plus has a percent change worksheet which can be used for solving percent change problems, as shown below:

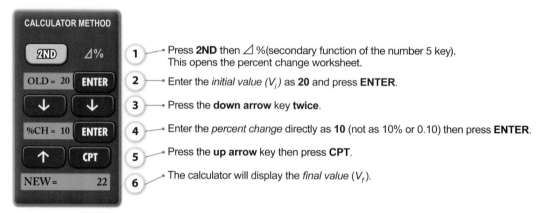

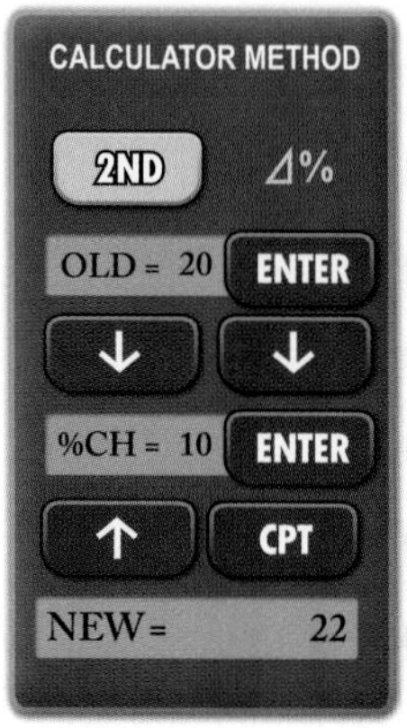

1. Press **2ND** then Δ%(secondary function of the number 5 key). This opens the percent change worksheet.
2. Enter the *initial value* (V_i) as **20** and press **ENTER**.
3. Press the **down arrow** key **twice**.
4. Enter the *percent change* directly as **10** (not as 10% or 0.10) then press **ENTER**.
5. Press the **up arrow** key then press **CPT**.
6. The calculator will display the *final value* (V_f).

Therefore, the new hourly rate is $22.00.

Note: *Refer to page 636 for instruction on how to use the calculator method.*

Method 4: Ratio-Proportion Method

In this method, the original value and final value are compared using ratios and proportions to determine the unknown.

The original value of $20 represents 100%. This is increased by 10% to a final value of 110%, as illustrated:

Percent	Amount
110%	$\$x$
100%	$20

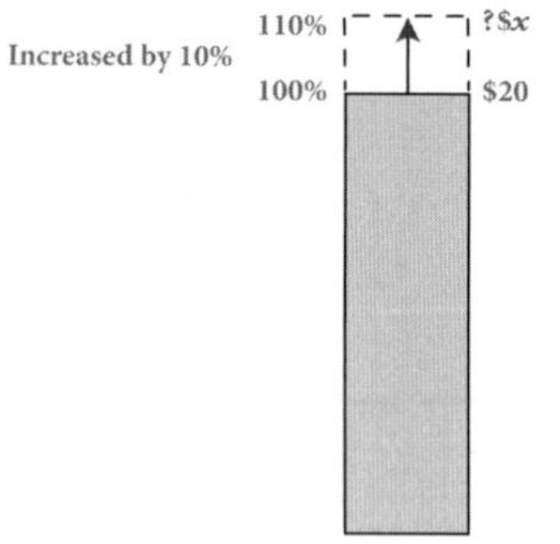

$$\frac{110\%}{100\%} = \frac{x}{20.00}$$ Cross-multiplying,

$$x = \frac{110\% \times 20.00}{100\%} = \$22.00$$

Therefore, the new hourly rate is $22.00.

Note: *There are many methods used in calculating percent change. In the following examples, the formula method and calculator method are used to solve the percent change problems. However, you can solve them using any of the four methods described in Example 3.2(b).*

Example 3.2(c) **Calculating the Initial Value when the Percent Change is Negative**

What amount decreased by 40% is $400?

Solution

$\%C = -40\%, \quad V_f = \$400, \quad V_i = ?$

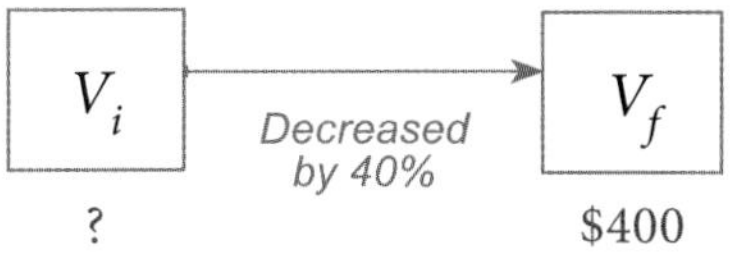

Using Formula 3.2, $\%C = \frac{V_f - V_i}{V_i} \times 100\%$

Substituting the values, $-40\% = \frac{400.00 - V_i}{V_i} \times 100\%$

Eliminating the percents, $-0.40 = \frac{400.00 - V_i}{V_i}$

Cross-multiplying, $-0.40V_i = 400.00 - V_i$

Adding V_i to both sides, $V_i - 0.40V_i = 400.00$

$0.60V_i = 400.00$

$V_i = 666.666666... = \$666.67$

Therefore, $666.67 decreased by 40% is $400.00.

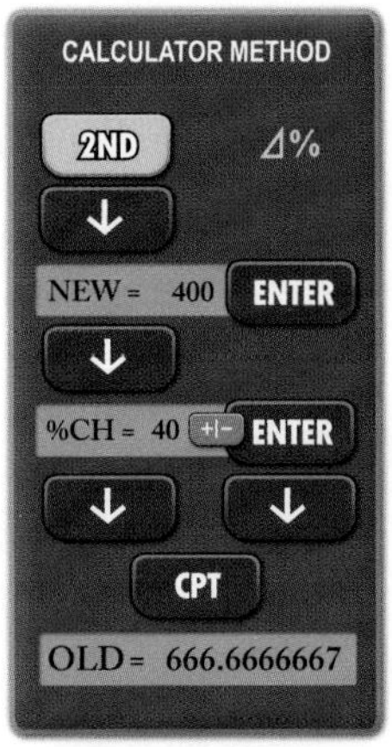

Helpful Check:
If the percent change is negative, then the final value will be smaller than the initial value.

Example 3.2(d) **Calculating the Percent Change When the Final Value is Greater than the Initial Value**

$1000 increased by what percent results in $1200?

Solution

$V_i = \$1000, \quad V_f = \$1200, \quad \%C = ?$

Using Formula 3.2, $\%C = \frac{V_f - V_i}{V_i} \times 100\%$

Substituting the values, $\%C = \frac{1200.00 - 1000.00}{1000.00} \times 100\%$

$= 20.00\%$

Therefore, $1000.00 increased by 20.00% is $1200.00.

Example 3.2(e) **Calculating the Percent Change When the Initial and Final Values are Given as a Percent**

If the Bank of Canada increases its prime lending rate from 2.25% to 3.35%, calculate the percent increase in the prime rate.

Solution

$V_i = 2.25\%, \quad V_f = 3.35\%, \quad \%C = ?$

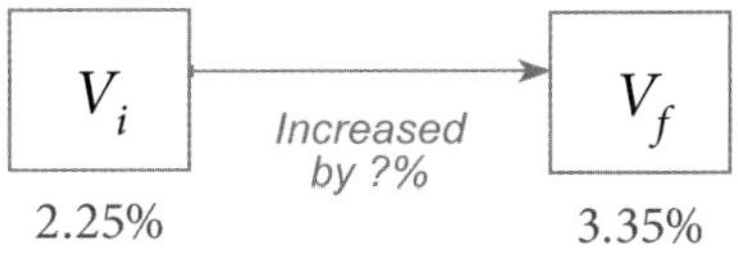

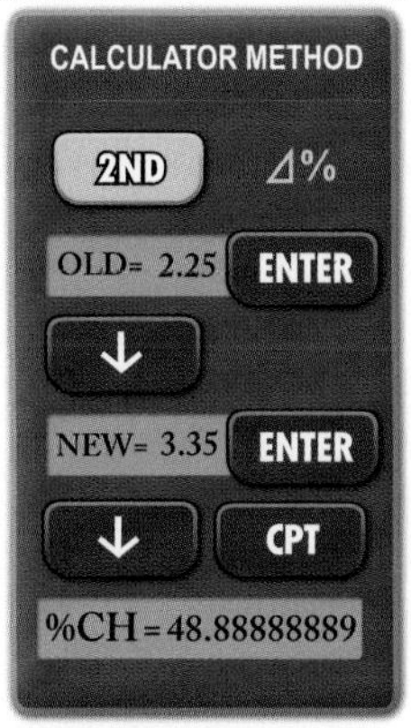

Using Formula 3.2, $\%C = \frac{V_f - V_i}{V_i} \times 100\%$

Substituting the values, $\%C = \frac{3.35\% - 2.25\%}{2.25\%} \times 100\%$

$= 0.488888... \times 100\% = 48.89\%$

Therefore, the percent increase in the prime rate is 48.89%.

Example 3.2(f) **Percent Change Comparing Unit Quantities**

A jeweler made and sold 50 g of silver chains for $90. If he reduced the weight of the silver in the chain to 45 g and reduced the price to $85.50, by what percent did the unit rate change?

Solution

Unit price of the 50 g silver chain: $\frac{90.00}{50} = \$1.80$ per gram of silver

Unit price of the 45 g silver chain: $\frac{85.50}{45} = \$1.90$ per gram of silver

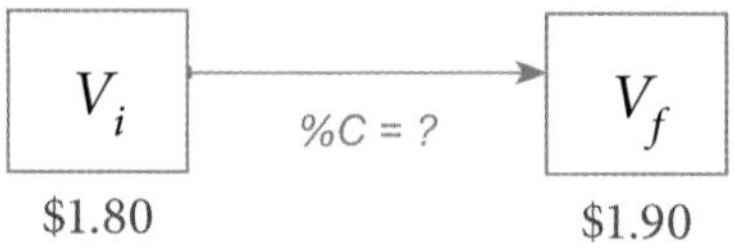

There is an increase in the unit price of the chain.

Using Formula 3.2, $\%C = \frac{V_f - V_i}{V_i} \times 100\%$

$$= \frac{1.90 - 1.80}{1.80} \times 100\%$$

$$= 0.055555\ldots \times 100\% = 5.56\% \text{ increase}$$

Therefore, the unit rate increased by 5.56%.

Example 3.2(g) **Calculating Percent Change When the Statement is Reversed**

If Ali earns 25% more than Brian, calculate the percent by which Brian's earning is less than Ali's.

Solution

Using the Algebraic Method

Let Ali's earnings be A and Brian's earnings be B.

$A = B + 25\%$ of B (or $A = 125\%$ of B)

$A = 1.25B$ Expressing B as a fraction of A,

$$B = \frac{1}{1.25}A$$

$$B = 0.80A$$

That is, B is 80% of A (which is 20% less than A).

Therefore, if Ali earns 25% more than Brian, then Brian earns 20% less than Ali.

Assuming a Value for B

Given: $A = B + 25\%$ of B

$A = 1.25B$ If $B = \$1000$, then A earns $1250.

Therefore, we need to determine the percent by which $1000 ($B$'s earning) is less than $1250 ($A$'s earning).

$1000 = 1250 - x\%$ of 1250

$x\%$ of $1250 = 1250 - 1000 = 250$

$$x\% = \frac{250}{1250} = \frac{1}{5} = \left(\frac{1}{5}\right) \times 100\% = 20\%$$

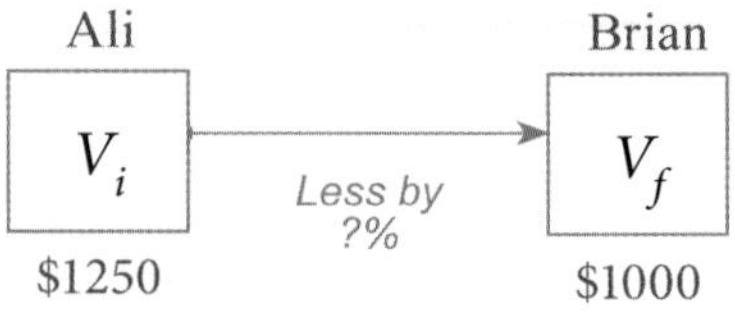

Therefore, if Ali earns 25% more than Brian, then Brian earns 20% less than Ali.

Using a Financial Calculator, Assuming a Value for Brian's Earnings

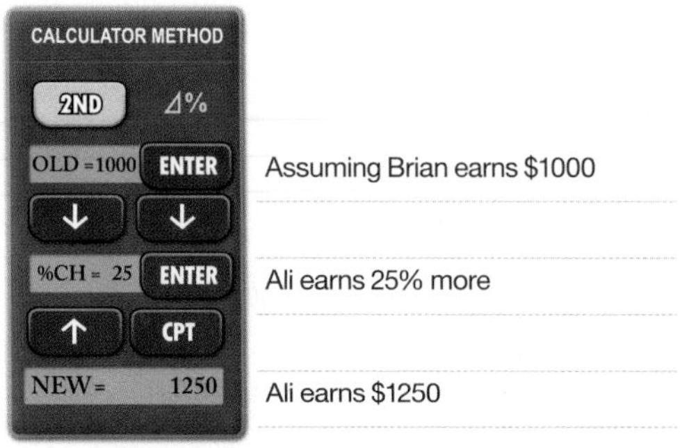

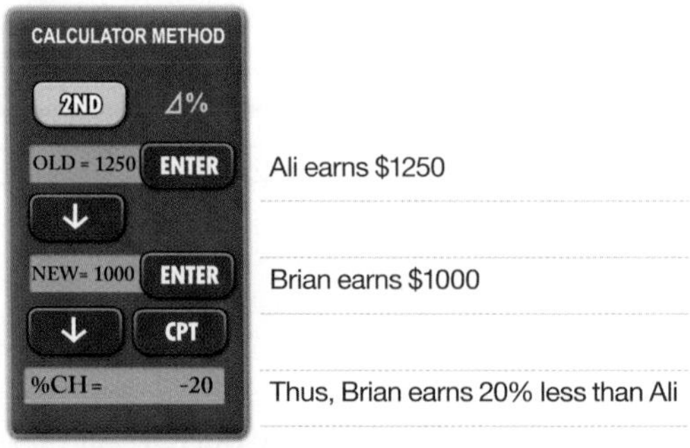

Example 3.2(h) **Calculating the Percent Change When the Value of a Currency Increases (Appreciates) or Decreases (Depreciates) Against Another Currency**

If the US dollar appreciated 10% relative to the Canadian dollar, by what percent has the Canadian dollar depreciated relative to the US dollar?

Solution

Assume the initial exchange rate as: US\$1 = C\$$x$

If the US dollar appreciated by 10%, then,

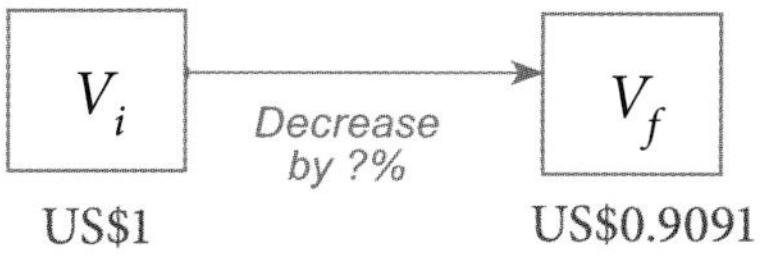

$$\text{US\$1} = \text{C\$}1.10x$$

Dividing both sides by 1.10,

$$\text{US\$}\frac{1}{1.10} = \text{C\$}x$$

$$\text{US\$}0.909090... = \text{C\$}x$$

i.e. after the US dollar appreciated by 10%, the new exchange rate is US\$0.909090... = C\$$x$

$$\text{Therefore, } V_i = \text{US\$1}, \text{ and } V_f = \text{US\$}0.909090...$$

Calculating the percent change in Canadian dollars, using Formula 3.2,

$$\%C = \frac{V_f - V_i}{V_i} \times 100\%$$

$$\%C = \frac{\text{US\$}0.909090... - \text{US\$1}}{\text{US\$1}} \times 100\% = -0.090909... \times 100\% = -9.09\%$$

Therefore, if the US dollar appreciated by 10% relative to the Canadian dollar, then the Canadian dollar depreciated by 9.09% relative to the US dollar.

3.2 | Exercises

Answers to the odd-numbered problems are available at the end of the textbook.

1. Answer the following problems, rounding your answers to two decimal places:
   a. What is \$180 increased by 70%?
   b. What is \$90 decreased by 90%?
   c. How much is \$4500 increased by 150%?
   d. What amount increased by 25.75% is 855.10 kg?
   e. What amount decreased by 10% is \$477?
   f. What amount increased by 180% is \$20.65?
   g. \$1200 decreased by what percent is \$300?
   h. 750 kg is what percent less than 1000 kg?
2. Answer the following questions, rounding your answers to two decimal places:
   a. What is \$2680 increased by 85%?
   b. What is \$880.45 decreased by 85%?
   c. How much is \$1850.50 increased by 300%?
   d. What amount increased by $90\frac{1}{2}$% is 110.49 kg?
   e. What amount increased by 28% is \$231.75?
   f. What amount increased by 600% is \$24.92?
   g. \$800 increased by what percent is \$1800?
   h. 102 km is what percent more than 85 km?
3. Last year, the revenue of Python Graphics Corporation was \$860,760. This year, the revenue grew by 280%. Calculate the revenue this year.
4. If Harley's salary of \$2000 per month is increased by 5.5%, what is his new salary?
5. A clothing retail outlet purchased clothes in bulk from a wholesaler for \$86,850. This was after a discount of $3\frac{1}{2}$% on the purchase. Calculate the original price of the clothes.
6. After a discount of $12\frac{1}{2}$%, a publishing company purchased an offset printing press for \$245,000. Calculate the original price of the machine.
7. After paying an income tax of 45%, Carla's take-home annual income was \$45,000. Calculate her income before the income tax deduction.
8. The sales tax of 13% increased the cost of a meal at a restaurant to \$34.50. What was the cost of the meal before taxes?

9. If Lilo's student loan of $12,000 will increase to $12,860 by the end of the year, calculate the percent increase of the loan.

10. If calculators that sell for $30 each are being offered online for $24 each, calculate the percent discount offered online.

11. If the current fixed mortgage rate of 5.4% rises to 6.6%, calculate the percent increase in the mortgage rate.

12. If the prime rate of 2.5% rises to 3.2%, calculate the percent increase in the prime rate.

13. The average snowfall last December in Vancouver was 14.8 cm. If the average snowfall this December decreased by 3 cm, calculate the percent decrease.

14. The average daytime temperature last July in Calgary was 20°C. If the average daytime temperature this July increased by 3°C, calculate the percent increase.

15. Kemi invested money in two types of mutual funds: $2800 in low-risk funds and $700 in high-risk funds. If the value of the low-risk funds dropped by 10% and that of the high-risk funds grew by 30%, by what percent did the total value of her investments change?

16. Gabrielle's portfolio of shares comprised of investments of $8600 and $12,400 in the telecommunications and information technology industries, respectively. If the market price of her telecommunications shares dropped by 65% and that of information technology grew by 25%, by what percent did the total value of her investments change?

17. Sandra posted an advertisement on an auction site to sell an item for 50% more than what she had paid for it. Since it did not sell within a month, she decreased the advertised price by 50% and it sold immediately. By what percent more or less than her purchase price did she sell the item?

18. If the temperature rose by 12% from the average temperature, then falls by 12%, by what percent did the final temperature increase or decrease from the average temperature?

19. After a 5% increase in value from 2014 to 2015, a house was worth $472,500. If the overall increase in the value of the house from 2014 to 2016 was 4%, calculate the value of the house in 2016.

20. The price of a share dropped by 3% from February to March down to $4.25. If the overall price fell by 5% between February and April, calculate its price in April.

21. The total cost for manufacturing a machine is $30,000. The cost of labour is 30% of the total cost. If the cost of labour increased by 5%, calculate the following:

    a. The amount by which the total cost increased.

    b. The new cost of the machine.

22. The total cost for manufacturing a TV is $2000. The cost of material is 40% of the total cost. If the cost of material decreased by 10%, calculate the following:

    a. The amount by which the total cost decreased.

    b. The new cost of the TV.

23. Tudor and Rani, two sales representatives in a company, were earning $2815 per month and $2875 per month, respectively. After a yearly appraisal, Tudor's salary increased by 14% and Rani's increased by 11%.

    a. Who had a higher salary after the appraisal?

    b. Calculate the difference in their salaries after the raise.

24. Reggie's annual salary increased from $42,000 to $46,830 this year, and his colleague Gerald's annual salary increased from $39,500 to $44,437.50.

    a. Who received a higher rate of increase this year?

    b. Calculate the difference in their salary after the increase.

• 25. The revenues of a company increased by 30% in year one and decreased by 25% in year two. What is the overall change over the two-year period?

• 26. The price of shares of a company decreased by 35% in year one and increased by 40% in year two. What is the overall change over the two-year period?

• 27. Last month, a 750 g box of cereal was sold at a grocery store for $3.00. However, this month, after the cereal manufacturer launched the same cereal in a 600 g box, the box of cereal was being sold at $2.50. By what percent did the unit rate change?

- 28. A 450 g block of butter was sold for $3.50. If the manufacturer reduced the size of the block to 250 g and sold it at a reduced price of $2.00, by what percent did the unit rate change?
- 29. The price of telecommunications shares dropped by $2.50 at the end of the first year and dropped by a further $3.45 at the end of the second year. If the price of the shares at the end of the second year was $12.55, calculate the percent change in the price of the shares each year from its price at the beginning of each year. What was the percent drop in the price over the two-year period?
- 30. Amtex Computers Inc. sells refurbished laptops online. A particular model, sold at $400 at the beginning of the year, was reduced in price by $80 at the end of the first year. At the end of the second year, the price was increased by $64. Calculate the percent change in the price of this model at the end of each year from its price at the beginning of each year. If a sale was made at the end of the second year, calculate the discount rate offered from the original price of $400.
- 31. If Roger scored 20% more than Judie, by what percent is Judie's score less than Roger's?
- 32. If Harry earns 15% more than Beary per hour, by what percent are Beary's earnings less than Harry's?
- 33. If the Canadian dollar appreciated 5% relative to the British pound, by what percent has the British pound depreciated relative to the Canadian dollar?
- 34. If the Australian dollar appreciated 15% relative to the British pound, by what percent has the British pound depreciated relative to the Australian dollar?

3.3 | Payroll

Employees of an organization receive payment from their employers for their services completed; this payment is usually given to them either as a salary or commission, or as a combination of both. Employers maintain a record called **payroll** that registers the employees' names, types of payment, and amount of payment made towards them. They also deduct part of the employees' salary to pay towards the employees' taxes, pension, savings, etc. These are called payroll deductions. The payment that the employer offers to pay an employee is called gross pay and the actual payment received after all deductions is called net pay.

In this section, we will calculate (or use) the gross pay given to employees based on:

- Annual salary
- Commissions
- Hourly rate
- Piecework rate

Annual Salary

Annual: *once a year*

Annual salary employees are usually supervisory, managerial, or professional employees who work on an annual basis and are not paid an hourly rate. Annual salary is the amount that employees are paid for services provided over a period of one year.

For example, Melinda was excited because she received her first job offer from Rubol Corp. for $50,000 per annum. In this case, Rubol Corp. has agreed to pay her a gross annual salary of $50,000.

If you are employed by an organization paying you an annual salary, your employer should provide you with the following information:

- Amount of annual salary
- Pay period (frequency of payments)
- Workweek (number of working hours per week)
- Overtime factor (used to calculate overtime rate)

Pay Period

Pay period refers to the frequency of payment (how often payments are made). In North America, there are four standard pay periods. Depending on where you work and the type of your employment, your pay period may fall into any one of the following categories:

Monthly: once a month

- **Monthly:** Once a month, 12 payments per year. (1 year = 12 months)
  For example, paydays are on the 25th of every month.

Semi-monthly: twice a month

- **Semi-monthly:** Twice a month, 24 payments per year.
  (1 year = 12 months; 2 × 12 = 24)
  For example, paydays are on the 1st and 15th of every month.

Bi-weekly: once in two weeks

- **Bi-weekly:** Once in two weeks (every other week), 26 payments per year. (1 year = 52 weeks; 52 ÷ 2 = 26)
  For example, paydays are every other Friday.

Weekly: once a week

- **Weekly:** Once a week, 52 payments per year. (1 year = 52 weeks)
  For example, paydays are every Friday.

A semi-monthly payment is not a bi-weekly payment. With semi-monthly payments, you will receive 24 payments; whereas, with bi-weekly payments, you will receive 26 payments.

One monthly payment is not equal to four weekly payments.

Note: *In the examples and exercises, we will be using 52 weekly pay periods or 26 bi-weekly pay periods per year. However, it is possible to have 53 weekly pay periods or 27 bi-weekly pay periods depending on the year and the payment days. In those circumstances, periodic payment is calculated by dividing the annual salary by the number of pay days.*

The pay for the pay period is calculated by the following formula:

Formula 3.3(a) **Pay for Pay Period**

$$\text{Pay for pay period} = \frac{\text{Annual Salary}}{\text{Number of pay periods per year}}$$

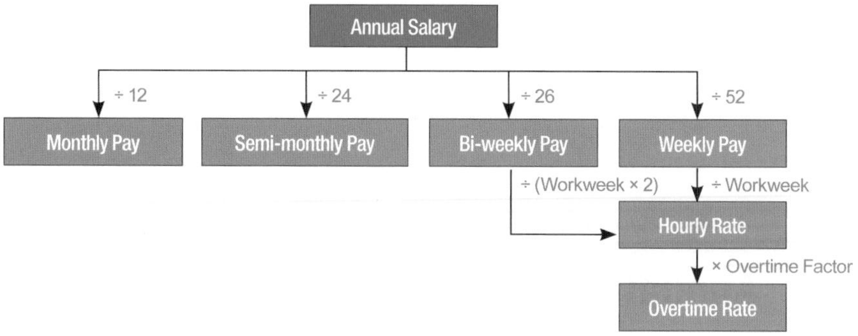

We can rearrange Formula 3.3(a) to calculate the annual salary:

$$\text{Annual Salary} = \text{Pay for pay period} \times \text{Number of pay periods per year}$$

Example 3.3(a) **Calculating Payment for Pay Period Given the Annual Salary**

Hailey works for a marketing company and receives an annual salary of $48,000. Calculate her gross pay for a pay period, if she was paid:

(i) monthly
(ii) semi-monthly
(iii) bi-weekly
(iv) weekly

Solution

(i) Monthly Pay: $\frac{\textit{Annual Salary}}{\textit{12 pay periods}} = \frac{48{,}000.00}{12}$ = \$4000.00 monthly payments

(ii) Semi-monthly Pay: $\frac{\textit{Annual Salary}}{\textit{24 pay periods}} = \frac{48{,}000.00}{24}$ = \$2000.00 semi-monthly payments

(iii) Bi-weekly Pay: $\frac{\textit{Annual Salary}}{\textit{26 pay periods}} = \frac{48{,}000.00}{26}$ = \$1846.15 bi-weekly payments

(iv) Weekly Pay: $\frac{\textit{Annual Salary}}{\textit{52 pay periods}} = \frac{48{,}000.00}{52}$ = \$923.08 weekly payments

Example 3.3(b) **Calculating Annual Salary, Equivalent Monthly and Semi-Monthly Payment, given the Weekly Pay**

Rodney is paid \$1500 weekly. Calculate the following:

(i) Annual salary (ii) Equivalent monthly pay (iii) Equivalent semi-monthly pay

Solution

Weekly Pay = \$1500.00

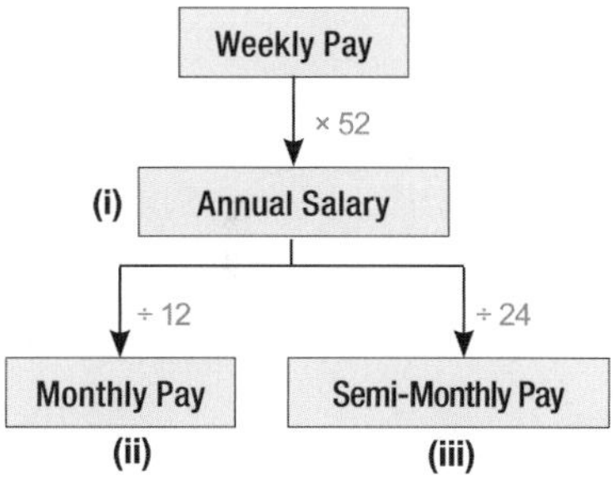

(i) *Calculating annual salary*

Number of weekly payments per year = 52

Annual Salary = Pay for pay period × Number of pay periods per year

= 1500.00 × 52

= \$78,000.00

Therefore, the annual salary is \$78,000.00.

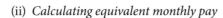

(ii) *Calculating equivalent monthly pay*

Number of monthly payments per year = 12

$$\textit{Pay for pay period} = \frac{\textit{Annual Salary}}{\textit{Number of pay periods per year}}$$

$$= \frac{78{,}000.00}{12}$$

= \$6500.00

Therefore, the equivalent monthly pay is \$6500.00.

(iii) *Calculating equivalent semi-monthly pay*

Number of semi-monthly payments per year = 24

$$\textit{Pay for pay period} = \frac{\textit{Annual Salary}}{\textit{Number of pay periods per year}}$$

$$= \frac{78{,}000.00}{24}$$

= \$3250.00

Therefore, the equivalent semi-monthly pay is \$3250.00.

Workweek (Number of Working Hours per Week)

Workweek is the total number of regular working hours. Depending on the type of profession/job, the number of regular hours you work every week may vary; 40 hours, 37.5 hours, or 35 hours are the most common number of regular working hours per week.

By knowing the number of regular hours you work per week, you can calculate your hourly rate (the amount you are paid per hour) from the following formula:

Formula 3.3(b) **Hourly Rate of Pay**

$$\textit{Hourly rate of pay} = \frac{\textit{Weekly Pay}}{\textit{Number of working hours per week}} = \frac{\textit{Weekly Pay}}{\textit{Workweek}}$$

From Formula 3.3(a), $\textit{Weekly Pay} = \frac{\textit{Annual Salary}}{\textit{52 pay periods}}$

Example 3.3(c) Calculating Hourly Rate of Pay Given Annual Salary

Trevor is being paid $41,600 per annum at Oxford Editorials. Calculate his hourly rate of pay, if he has a 40-hour workweek.

Solution

$$\textit{Weekly Pay} = \frac{\textit{Annual Salary}}{\textit{52 pay periods}}$$

$$= \frac{41{,}600.00}{52} = \$800.00 \text{ per week}$$

$$\textit{Hourly rate of pay} = \frac{\textit{Weekly Pay}}{\textit{Workweek}}$$

$$= \frac{800.00}{40} = \$20.00 \text{ per hour}$$

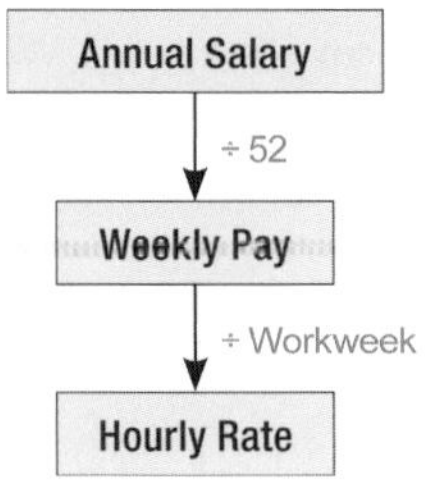

Therefore, his hourly rate of pay is $20.00 per hour.

Example 3.3(d) Calculating Hourly Rate of Pay Given the Monthly Salary

Caroline is being paid $2885 every month at Ruby Florists. Calculate her hourly rate of pay, if she has a 40-hour workweek.

Solution

Since she is paid monthly, she will receive 12 payments through the year.

$$\textit{Annual Salary} = \textit{Monthly Pay} \times 12$$

$$= 2885.00 \times 12$$

$$= \$34{,}620.00$$

$$\textit{Weekly Pay} = \frac{\textit{Annual Salary}}{\textit{52 pay periods}}$$

$$= \frac{34{,}620.00}{52} = 665.769230...$$

$$\textit{Hourly Rate of pay} = \frac{\textit{Weekly Pay}}{\textit{Workweek}}$$

$$= \frac{665.769230...}{40} = 16.644230... = \$16.64$$

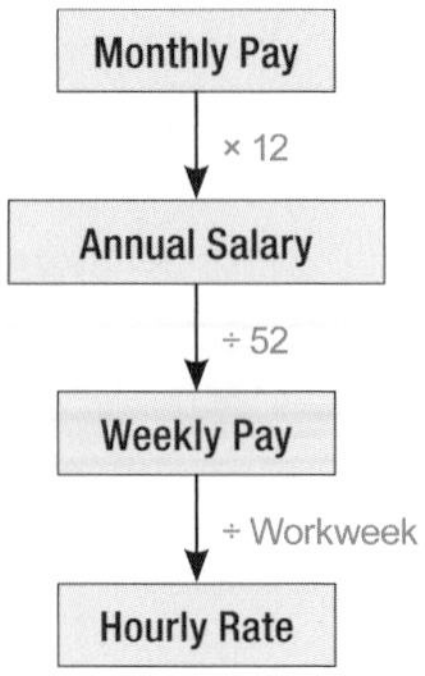

Therefore, her hourly rate of pay is $16.64 per hour.

Example 3.3(e) Calculating Semi-Monthly Payment and Bi-Weekly Payment Given the Hourly Rate of Pay

Joe is paid $25 per hour for the 40-hour workweeks at Japan Travels Inc.

(i) Calculate his semi-monthly payment.

(ii) Calculate the equivalent bi-weekly payment.

Solution

(i) $$\textit{Weekly Pay} = \textit{Hourly rate of pay} \times \textit{Workweek}$$

$$= 25.00 \times 40 = \$1000.00$$

$$\textit{Annual salary} = \textit{Weekly pay} \times 52$$

$$= 1000.00 \times 52 = \$52{,}000.00$$

$$\textit{Semi-monthly Pay} = \frac{\textit{Annual Salary}}{\textit{24 pay periods}}$$

$$= \frac{52{,}000.00}{24} = 2166.666666... = \$2166.67$$

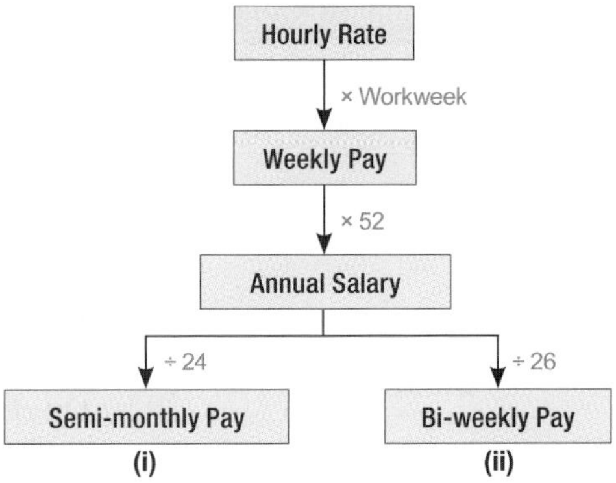

Therefore, his semi-monthly payment is $2166.67.

(ii) $$\textit{Bi-weekly Pay} = \frac{\textit{Annual Salary}}{\textit{26 pay periods}}$$

$$= \frac{52{,}000.00}{26}$$

$$= \$2000.00$$

Therefore, the equivalent bi-weekly payment is $2000.00.

Overtime Factor (Used to Calculate Overtime Rate)

If you work more than the specified number of hours per week, you will be paid extra for the additional hours worked. This extra pay is calculated using an **overtime rate**. As this is additional work performed, you would normally receive more than your regular hourly rate for the work, depending on the policy of each organization. Some organizations pay $1\frac{1}{2}$ times the regular hourly rate (time-and-a-half) for every extra hour worked and some pay 2 times the regular hourly rate (double). This factor (i.e., $1\frac{1}{2}$ times or 2 times) that employers use is called the **overtime factor**.

Example 3.3(f) **Calculating Overtime Rate of Pay**

Sally, a senior instructional designer at McMillan is paid $60,000 per annum. McMillan has a 40-hour workweek and the overtime rate is double the regular rate. Calculate Sally's overtime rate of pay.

Solution

Calculate her weekly pay and the hourly rate of pay.

$$\textit{Weekly Pay} = \frac{\textit{Annual Salary}}{\textit{52 pay periods}}$$

$$= \frac{60{,}000.00}{52} = 1153.846154...$$

$$\textit{Hourly Rate of pay} = \frac{\textit{Weekly Pay}}{\textit{Workweek}}$$

$$= \frac{1153.846154...}{40} = 28.846153...$$

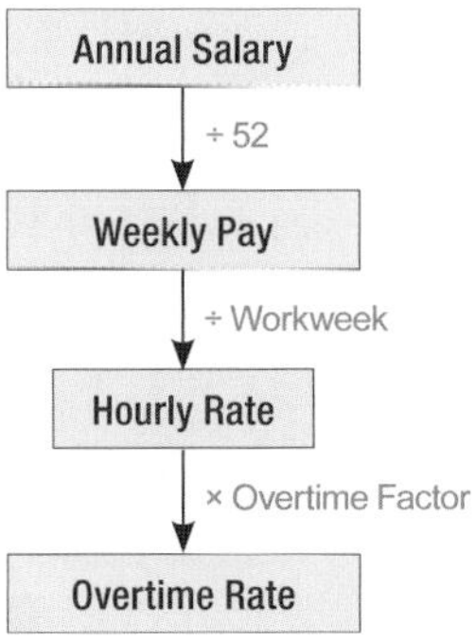

The overtime rate is double the regular rate, so the overtime factor is 2.

$$\textit{Overtime rate per hour} = \textit{Overtime factor} \times \textit{Regular hourly rate}$$

$$= 2 \times 28.846153...$$

$$= 57.692307... = \$57.69$$

Therefore, for every extra hour that Sally works (over the standard 40 hours), she will be paid $57.69 per hour.

Example 3.3(g) **Calculating Gross Pay Including Overtime Pay**

Amanda is paid an annual salary of $48,000 and is paid bi-weekly. The company has a standard 40-hour workweek and an overtime factor of $1\frac{1}{2}$. She worked 95 hours during the last pay period.

(i) Calculate Amanda's bi-weekly pay.

(ii) Calculate her gross pay (total pay without any employer deductions for taxes, Canadian pension fund, etc.) for that period.

Solution

(i) $$\textit{Bi-weekly Pay} = \frac{\textit{Annual Salary}}{\textit{26 pay periods}}$$

$$= \frac{48{,}000.00}{26} = 1846.153846...$$

Therefore, Amanda's bi-weekly pay is $1846.15.

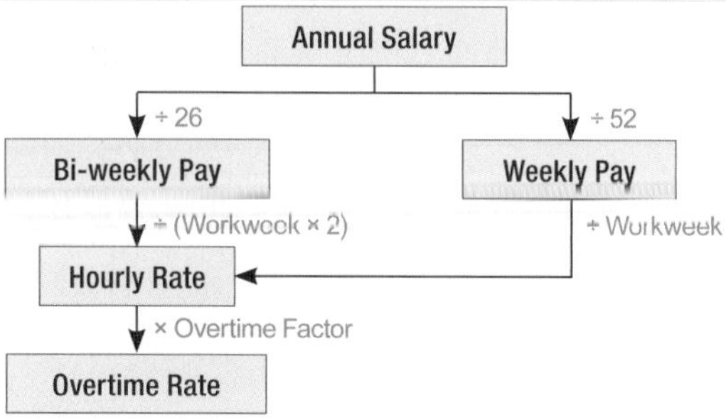

(ii)

$$\textit{Hourly Rate of Pay} = \frac{\textit{Bi-weekly Pay}}{(\textit{Workweek} \times 2)}$$

$$= \frac{1846.153846...}{(40 \times 2)}$$

$$= 23.076923...$$

Or

$$\textit{Weekly Pay} = \frac{48{,}000.00}{52} = 923.076923...$$

$$\textit{Hourly Rate of Pay} = \frac{\textit{Weekly Pay}}{\textit{Workweek}}$$

$$= \frac{923.076923...}{40} = 23.076923...$$

$$\textit{Overtime factor} = 1\tfrac{1}{2}$$

$$\textit{Overtime rate per hour} = \textit{Overtime factor} \times \textit{Regular hourly rate}$$

$$= 1\tfrac{1}{2} \times 23.076923... = \$34.615384... \text{ per hour}$$

$$\text{Number of hours worked overtime} = 95 - (40 \times 2) = 15 \text{ hours}$$

$$\text{Overtime pay for 15 hours} = 15 \times 34.615384... = 519.230769...$$

$$\textit{Gross pay for the period} = \textit{Bi-weekly pay} + \textit{Overtime pay}$$

$$= 1846.153846... + 519.230769...$$

$$= 2365.384615... = \$2365.38$$

Therefore, her gross pay for that pay period is $2365.38.

Commissions

If your employment is based on commission, your gross pay is usually based on a percent of sales for a given pay period (e.g. weekly/monthly).

Sales commissions are generally offered to encourage sales people to sell more, because the more they sell, the more money they will make.

This payment is called a sales commission and is of the following types:

- Straight commission
- Graduated commission (variable commission)
- Base salary plus commission
- Commission above quota

Straight Commission

Straight commission refers to a type of payment where the employee is paid a percent of the sales amount for the period as a salary.

Example 3.3(h) **Calculating Salary Based on Straight Commission**

Arnold's salary is 5% of the sales that he makes for the month. If the sales he makes for the month are $50,000, then what is Arnold's salary for that month?

Solution

Sales for the month: $50,000

$$\textit{Amount of commission} = 5\% \text{ of } \$50{,}000.00$$
$$= 0.05 \times 50{,}000.00$$
$$= \$2500.00$$

Therefore, Arnold's salary for the month will be $2500.00.

Graduated Commission (Variable Commission)

Graduated commission refers to a type of payment where the employee's commission rate increases gradually as his or her sales increase.

Example 3.3(i) **Calculating Salary Based on Graduated Commission**

Melissa is paid 2% sales commission for the first $10,000 of her sales. She is then paid 3% on the next $10,000 in sales, and 5% thereafter.

(i) Calculate her salary if her sales in January are $50,000.
(ii) Calculate her salary if her sales in February are $19,000.
(iii) Calculate her salary if her sales in March are $9000.
(iv) What single commission rate would represent her earnings in January?

Solution

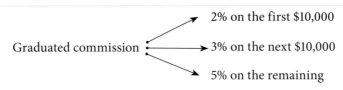

Graduated commission:
- → 2% on the first $10,000
- → 3% on the next $10,000
- → 5% on the remaining

(i) If her sales in January are $50,000:

Amount eligible for 5% commission = 50,000.00 – (10,000.00 + 10,000.00) = $30,000.00

	Sales	Rate	Commission
First	$10,000	2%	$200
Second	$10,000	3%	$300
Remaining	$30,000	5%	$1500
Total	**$50,000**		**$2000**

Therefore, her salary will be $2000.00 if her sales in January are $50,000.00.

(ii) If her sales in February are $19,000:

Amount eligible for 3% commission = 19,000.00 – 10,000.00 = $9000.00

	Sales	Rate	Commission
First	$10,000	2%	$200
Second	$9000	3%	$270
Total	**$19,000**		**$470**

Therefore, her salary will be $470.00 if her sales in February are $19,000.00.

Solution *continued*

(iii) If her sales in March are $9000:

Sales	Rate	Commission
$9000	2%	$180

Therefore, her salary will be $180.00 if her sales in March are $9000.00.

(iv) In January, she earned $2000 from sales of $50,000.

$$Single\ commission\ rate = \frac{Total\ Commissions}{Total\ Sales}$$

$$= \frac{2000.00}{50,000.00} \times 100\%$$

$$= 0.04 \times 100\% = 4.00\%$$

Therefore, a single commission rate of 4.00% would represent Melissa's earnings in January.

Base Salary Plus Commission

Base salary plus commission is the most common form of compensation (salary) paid to employees in sales environments. Organizations pay a fixed amount, called a base salary, and in addition, they pay a commission on sales made by employees.

Example 3.3(j) **Calculating Salary Based on Base Salary Plus Commission**

Elan works for Future Store and gets paid a fixed amount of $1000 per month. In addition to this, he gets paid a commission of 4% on the sales he makes. What is his total salary if he made $50,000 in sales for the month?

Solution

Base salary per month = $1000.00

Sales for the month = $50,000.00

$$Commission\ of\ 4\%\ on\ sales = 0.04 \times 50,000.00$$

$$= \$2000.00$$

$$Total\ salary = Base\ Salary + Commission$$

$$= 1000.00 + 2000.00$$

$$= \$3000.00$$

Therefore, Elan's total salary is $3000.00 if he made $50,000.00 in sales for the month.

Commission Above Quota

Commission above quota refers to a type of payment where the employee is required to sell a minimum sales amount (quota) before becoming eligible to recieve compensation based on commissions.

Example 3.3(k) **Calculating Salary Based on Base Salary Plus Commission Above Quota**

Arkady works for a tourism company that requires him to sell vacation packages. He is paid a base salary of $500 per month in addition to a 10% commission on his sales exceeding $25,000. What would be his total monthly salary if he sold $60,000 worth of vacation packages in a month?

Solution

Base salary per month = \$500.00

Sales made for the month = \$60,000.00

Sales quota for the month = \$25,000.00

$$\textit{Sales amount above quota} = 60{,}000.00 - 25{,}000.00$$
$$= \$35{,}000.00$$
$$\textit{Commission on sales above quota} = 10\% \text{ of } \$35{,}000.00$$
$$= 0.10 \times 35{,}000.00 = \$3500.00$$
$$\textit{Total salary} = \textit{Base salary} + \textit{Commission above quota}$$
$$= 500.00 + 3500.00$$
$$= \$4000.00$$

Therefore, his total monthly salary for the month would be \$4000.00.

Hourly Wages

If employees are paid hourly wages, then they are paid on an hour-by-hour basis. Pay for them is calculated as the number of hours worked multiplied by their hourly rate. The following are the minimum hourly rates set by the provinces and territories in Canada for experienced adult workers, as of October 01, 2017.

Table 3.3 **Minimum Hourly Wage Rates in Canada, as of October 01, 2017**

Province/Territory	Minimum Hourly Wage Rate	Province/Territory	Minimum Hourly Wage Rate
Alberta[1]	\$13.60	Nunavut	\$13.00
British Columbia	\$11.25	Ontario[2]	\$11.60
Manitoba	\$11.00	Prince Edward Island	\$11.25
New Brunswick	\$11.00	Quebec[3]	\$11.25
Newfoundland and Labrador	\$11.00	Saskatchewan[4]	\$10.72
Northwest Territories	\$12.50	Yukon[5]	\$11.32
Nova Scotia	\$10.85		

[1] To be increased to \$15.00 on Oct 01, 2018

[2] To be increased to \$14.00 on Jan 01, 2018, and to \$15.00 on Jan 01, 2019

[3] To be increased to \$11.75 on May 01, 2018, to \$12.10 on May 01, 2019, and to \$12.45 on May 01, 2020

[4] Rate increases annually on Oct 01 based on previous year change in the Consumer Price Index

[5] Rate increases annually on Apr 01 based on previous year change in the Consumer Price Index

Source: Human Resources and Skills Development Canada (Minimum Wage Database)

While most employees are eligible for minimum wage, some employees have jobs that are exempt from the minimum wage provisions. For example, in Ontario as of October 01, 2017, the minimum hourly wage for students is \$10.90, for liquor servers is \$10.10, and for homeworkers is \$12.80.

Hourly wage employees are also eligible for overtime pay and statutory or public holiday pay. For most employees, overtime begins after 44 hours of work in a workweek. Normal working hours, unless specified, are 8 hours per day. At least one-and-a-half times the regular rate of pay (overtime factor of 1.5) is paid for hours worked overtime.

Employees also receive their usual rate of pay on statutory or public holidays even if they do not work on those days. Employees who have worked on holidays will receive their regular pay plus additional pay at an overtime rate for the number of hours worked (based on the overtime rate for such holidays). However, the number of hours worked on holidays will not contribute towards the overtime for the workweek.

If the nature of the work requires employees to work irregular hours or to work regularly scheduled hours which vary on certain days, then the employer may average the working hours over a selected period of two or more weeks. For example, employees may be scheduled to work 10 hours per day for 4 days a week, which exceeds the standard 8-hour workday.

Also, the maximum time an employee works each week may be extended under exceptional circumstances such as during an emergency.

Unless specified in the contract of employment, an employee does not earn overtime pay on a daily basis by working more than the set number of hours for that day. Overtime is calculated only on a weekly basis or over a longer period under an averaging agreement.

Example 3.3(l) **Calculating Pay for Overtime Work in a Normal Workweek with One Statutory Holiday**

Ryan's workweek is 40 hours. His regular hourly rate of pay is $25 per hour, and the overtime rate is one-and-a-half times the regular rate of pay. For each statutory holiday, when he does not work, he receives holiday pay at his regular hourly rate for 8 hours. Anytime he is required to work on statutory holidays, he is paid at the overtime rate. Last week there was a statutory holiday, but Ryan did not work on the holiday. If he worked a total of 55 hours last week, calculate his pay for the week.

Solution

Statutory holiday hours = 8 hours (standard working day)

Regular working hours = 40 hours – 8 hours = 32 hours

Overtime hours = 55 hours – 32 hours = 23 hours

Overtime rate = (1.5 × $25.00) = $37.50

Ryan's pay for the week is calculated as follows:

Regular pay = 32 × $25.00 = $800.00

Statutory holiday pay = 8 × $25.00 = $200.00

Overtime pay = 23 × $37.50 = $862.50

Total pay = *Regular pay* + *Statutory holiday pay* + *Overtime pay*

Therefore, Ryan's total pay is ($800.00 + $200.00 + $862.50) = $1862.50.

Piecework Rate

When employment is based on the number of units produced or tasks completed (output), an employee's gross pay is calculated based on an agreed flat rate for each item or task completed, called a piecework rate.

Gross Pay = *Number of units produced (or tasks completed)* × *Rate per unit (or task)*

Therefore, a piecework rate is performance-related rather than time-related, and encourages employees to produce more units rather than spend more time. Piecework encourages employees to complete tasks more efficiently to maximize their earnings, which in turn results in greater efficiency for the company.

Piecework rate may be straight piecework rate or graduated piecework rate. In straight piecework rate, a certain amount of pay per unit of output is given regardless of the output quantity. In graduated piecework rate, the rate per unit increases above a pre-determined output level (similar to that in commissions), which provides a greater incentive to the employee to increase output.

Example 3.3(m) **Calculating Piecework Wage**

A company that manufactures tools pays its machine operators the greater of $5.50 for each item produced, or a graduated piecework rate of $5.25 per unit for the first 100 items and $6.25 per unit thereafter. Robert, a machine operator, produced 190 items last week. What was his gross pay for last week?

Solution

Gross Pay = *Number of units produced* × *Rate per unit*

Gross pay using straight piecework rate = 190 × $5.50 = $1045.00

Gross pay using graduated piecework rate = (100 × $5.25) + (90 × $6.25)

= $525.00 + $562.50

= $1087.50, which is greater than $1045.00

Therefore, Robert's gross pay for last week was $1087.50.

3.3 | Exercises

Answers to the odd-numbered problems are available at the end of the textbook.

Answer the following problems assuming that there are 52 weeks in a year. Round your final answer to two decimal places, wherever applicable.

1. Roger received a job offer for a senior graphic designer position at a reputed e-learning company and is paid a gross salary of $60,000 per annum. Calculate his periodic payments if the pay period was (a) monthly, (b) semi-monthly, (c) bi-weekly, (d) weekly.

2. A Chief Executive Officer of an investment firm receives a gross salary of $750,000 per annum. Calculate the payment for a pay period if he was paid (a) monthly, (b) semi-monthly, (c) bi-weekly, (d) weekly.

3. Nicole receives a gross pay of $1650 bi-weekly from her employer. If her employer changed her pay period to monthly from bi-weekly, calculate the monthly payment that she would receive.

4. An employee was receiving a bi-weekly pay of $800. If the employer changed the pay period to monthly from bi-weekly, what monthly payment will the employee receive?

5. Robert's compensation is to be changed from an hourly rate of $18.90 for a 40-hour workweek to a salary paid semi-monthly. For his annual earnings to remain the same, what should he be paid semi-monthly?

6. Ross' compensation is to be changed from an hourly rate of $22.50 for a 35-hour workweek to a salary paid monthly. For his annual earnings to remain the same, what should he be paid monthly?

7. Katie's hourly wage was $17 and her workweek was 35 hours. If her employer was paying her monthly, how much will she receive per month?

8. Hassan's hourly wage was $16 and his workweek was 40 hours. If his employer was paying him monthly, how much will he receive per month?

9. Al was receiving a bi-weekly salary of $2650 at a web developing company. How much would he make per hour, assuming that he is required to work 40-hour workweeks?

10. A manufacturing company, that has 40-hour workweeks, pays its machine operators $18 per hour. Calculate the annual salary and the semi-monthly payment received by each machine operator.

11. Melanie receives a semi-monthly salary of $2600 and has 37.5-hour workweeks. If she worked 10 hours overtime during her last pay period and her overtime factor is time-and-a-half, calculate her gross payment for the last pay period.

12. Ruby earns a gross annual pay of $78,000, has a 40-hour workweek, and is paid bi-weekly. If her overtime factor is time-and-a-half, calculate her gross pay for the pay period in which she worked a total of 95 hours.

13. Andrew receives an hourly wage of $30 and his regular workweek is 35 hours. He is paid bi-weekly and his overtime rate is double the regular rate. If he recieved $2640 for the last pay period, how many hours of overtime did he work during that pay period?

14. Michael receives an hourly wage of $27 and his regular workweek is 37.5 hours. He is paid bi-weekly and his overtime rate is double the regular rate. If he received $2835 for the last pay period, how many hours of overtime did he work during that pay period?

15. A real estate agent makes a commission of 2.5% on the sale of a condominium. If he sold a condominium for $450,000, calculate the commission he earned from this sale.

16. A mutual fund broker receives a commission of 1.25% on all mutual funds he sells for the month. If he sells $560,000 worth of mutual funds to his clients, what is his commission for the month?

17. James, a sales representative at a computer retail outlet, receives a commission of 3% for every computer and 5% for every monitor he sells. The selling price of each computer is $800 and the selling price of each monitor is $250. If he sold 180 computers and 120 monitors in March, calculate his sales commission for March.

18. A sales representative at an electronics outlet mall receives sales commissions of 5% on tablets, 6% on laptops, and 8% on televisions. In April, if he sold three tablets that cost $450 each, seven laptops that cost $700 each, and five televisions that cost $980 each, calculate his total sales commission earned for the month.

19. William is paid on a graduated commission scale as follows: 2% on the first $10,000 in sales, 3% on the next $15,000 in sales, and 4% on sales thereafter. His pay for the last month was $2130.
   a. What were William's sales for last month?
   b. What single commission rate would represent his earnings in the last month?

20. Peter is paid on on a graduated commission scale as follows: 3% on the first $5000 in sales; 4% on the next $20,000 in sales, and 5% on sales thereafter. His pay for the last month was $1970.
   a. What were Peter's sales for last month?
   b. What single commission rate would represent his earnings in the last month?

21. The sales commission of a pharmaceutical distribution company is structured such that its part-time sales representatives receive commissions of 5% for the first $10,000 they sell, 7% on the next $10,000, and 10% thereafter. Ivory, a new part-time sales representative of the company, has sales of $2000 in the first month, $11,000 in the second month, and $36,000 in the third month.
   a. What were her commissions for each of the first three months?
   b. What single commission rate would represent her earnings in the third month?

22. Abigail receives a graduated commission of 3% for her first $15,000 in sales, 4.5% on the next $15,000, and 5.75% thereafter.
   a. Calculate her commission if she has $60,450 in sales for the month.
   b. What single commission rate would her total earnings represent?

23. Emily is paid on a graduated commission scale of 3.5% on the first $10,000 of sales in a month, 5.0% on the next $15,000 and 7.5% on all additional sales.
   a. Calculate her pay for January in which her sales were $46,500.
   b. Calculate her sales for February in which her pay was $2375.

24. Jennifer is paid on a graduated commission scale of 4.5% on the first $15,000 of sales in a month, 6.0% on the next $20,000, and 8.5% on all additional sales.
   a. Calculate her pay for September in which her sales were $42,500.
   b. Calculate her sales for October in which her pay was $2895.

25. Sales people at a game developing company are paid a base salary of $40,000 per annum plus a commission of 7% on every sales order. If Jamie, one of the sales people, had sales orders worth $120,000 in his first year, calculate the total salary he earned during the year.

26. Jasmine is paid a base salary of $2200 bi-weekly and a commission of 8% on the sales she makes. If she had sales worth $8000 in a pay period, how much was she paid in this period?

27. Banner House Inc. gives all its sales people a base salary of $30,000 per annum and a commission of 10% on all banners that they sell over $5000. Calculate Henry's salary last month if he sold $8000 worth of banners.

28. Ryan is paid a base salary of $1500 per month. In addition to this salary, he receives a commission of 4% on sales exceeding $18,000. Calculate his total salary if he made sales of $26,000 this month.

29. Henry, a sales representative at a jewelry store, receives a 2.5% commission for the first $10,000 in sales he makes, 3% for the next $25,000, and 6% thereafter. If he was paid $1750 last month, calculate the amount of sales he made.

30. Stephen receives commissions of 3% for the first $5000 in sales he makes, 4% for the next $20,000, and 5% thereafter. If his pay last month was $2700, calculate the amount of sales he made.

31. Jessica works as a sales person in a retail store. She receives a bi-weekly salary of $975 plus 3.5% commission on sales exceeding her quota of $5000 per pay period. What were Jessica's sales if she received $1605 in pay for that pay period?

32. Samantha works in a retail store. She receives a weekly base salary of $500 plus a commission of 4.5% on sales exceeding her quota of $7500 per week. What were Samantha's sales if she received $927.50 in pay for that period?

33. Ruby had to package 1575 calculators in the production line of a factory. If she was able to package 75 calculators in two hours and her hourly rate is $30, calculate her earnings for that work.

34. Brian, an automobile production supervisor, can produce 5 doors in an 8-hour shift. If his hourly rate is $25 and he needs to produce 60 doors, calculate his earnings for that work.

• 35. Technicians on a video production team were each being paid an annual salary of $35,000, with payments being made bi-weekly. Each technician is required to work 40 hours per week and the overtime factor is time-and-a-half. Calculate each technician's earnings for the last pay period if each of them worked for 43.5 hours and 42 hours for each of the weeks during that pay period.

• 36. A software development company that had 40-hour workweeks paid each of its developers an annual salary of $60,000 (payments made bi-weekly) with an overtime factor of time-and-a-half. If each member of the team worked 46.5 hours and 48 hours for each of the weeks during the last pay period, calculate each person's payment for the last pay period.

• 37. Rayne works for a clothing boutique store as a salesperson. He receives a monthly base salary of $1000 and earns a commission on sales over $25,000. If he earned $4600 last month and he made $105,000 in sales, calculate his commission rate.

• 38. Kara's basic salary is $1250. However, she gets paid a commission on all sales she makes over $20,000. If she earned $3775 last month and she made sales of $83,125, calculate her commission rate.

• 39. Emma has a 40-hour workweek (Monday to Friday). Her regular hourly rate of pay is $20 per hour. Her rate of pay for overtime is 1.5 times her regular hourly rate. For each statutory holiday, when she does not work, she receives holiday pay at her regular hourly rate for 8 hours. Anytime she works on a statutory holiday, she receives 1.5 times her regular rate of pay. Last week there were 2 statutory holidays, and Emma worked a total of 36 hours. Assuming that she did not work on the holidays, what was her pay for last week?

• 40. Noah is a full-time barista at a coffee shop in Kelowna. He receives overtime pay for hours exceeding his regular 35-hour workweek (Monday to Friday). His regular rate of pay is $14 per hour. His overtime rate is 1.5 times the regular rate, and when he is required to work on a statutory holiday, he also receives this rate. If he does not work on a statutory holiday, he receives his regular rate for 7 hours. If Noah worked for 35 hours in a week that has 2 statutory holidays, but did not work on either holiday, calculate his pay for the week.

3.4 | Taxes

Taxes are fees that federal or provincial governments charge organizations, properties, or individuals. This is a primary source of revenue for governments.

There are numerous types of taxes in Canada, some of which are income tax, sales tax, property tax, payroll tax, etc. In this section, we will focus only on sales tax and property tax.

Sales Taxes

Sales tax is a tax paid to a governing body for the sales of certain goods and services.

In Canada, three types of sales taxes are levied. They are as follows:

- **Goods and Services Tax (GST):** levied by the federal government and applies to most supplies of goods and services made in Canada, property, and intangible goods (trademarks, internet products, etc.). The federal GST rate is 5%.

- **Provincial Sales Tax (PST):** levied by the provinces of British Columbia, Manitoba, Quebec, and Saskatchewan.
- **Harmonized Sales Tax (HST):** a combination of the GST and the PST and is levied by the provinces of New Brunswick, Newfoundland and Labrador, Nova Scotia, Ontario, and Prince Edward Island.

Goods to which the tax is applied vary by province/territory, as does the rate. The table below provides the information on applicable sales tax rates for all provinces and territories.

Table 3.4 **Summary of Sales Taxes Collected by Canadian Provinces, as of June 01, 2017**

Province/Territory	Type	PST	GST* and PST Combined / HST
Alberta	GST	-	5%
British Columbia	GST + PST	7%	12%
Manitoba	GST + PST	8%	13%
New Brunswick	HST	10%	15%
Newfoundland and Labrador	HST	10%	15%
Nova Scotia	HST	10%	15%
Ontario	HST	8%	13%
Prince Edward Island	HST	10%	15%
Quebec	GST + QST**	9.975%	14.975%
Saskatchewan	GST + PST	6%	11%
Territories of Yukon, Nunavut, and Northwest Territories	GST	-	5%

* Federal GST rate for all provinces and territories is 5%.

** Quebec Sales Tax (QST), French: Taxe de vente du Quebec (TVQ).

Source: Canada Revenue Agency: GST/HST rates

Example 3.4(a) **Calculating the Cost After Taxes in Different Provinces in Canada**

A brand new car costs $20,000 before taxes. Calculate the cost of the car after taxes in (i) Ontario, (ii) Quebec, and (iii) Alberta, using information provided in the table above.

Solution

(i) *Ontario: 13% HST*

Cost before taxes = $20,000.00

13% HST = 0.13 × 20,000.00 = $2600.00

Total cost = 20,000.00 + 2600.00

= $22,600.00

Cost before tax	100%	x	$20,000
HST	13%	$0.13x$	$2600
Total Cost	**113%**	$\mathbf{1.13x}$	$22,600

Therefore, the cost of the car after taxes in Ontario is $22,600.00.

(ii) *Quebec: 5% GST, 9.975% QST*

Cost before taxes = $20,000.00

5% GST = 0.05 × 20,000.00 = $1000.00

9.975% QST = 0.09975 × 20,000.00

= $1995.00

Total cost = 20,000.00 + 1000.00 + 1995.00

= $22,995.00

Cost before tax	100%	x	$20,000
GST	5%	$0.05x$	$1000
QST	9.975%	$0.09975x$	$1995
Total Cost	**114.975%**	$\mathbf{1.14975x}$	$22,995

Therefore, the cost of the car after taxes in Quebec is $22,995.00.

Solution *continued*

(iii) *Alberta: 5% GST, 0% PST (Nil)*

Cost before taxes = \$20,000.00

5% GST = 0.05 × 20,000.00

= \$1000.00

PST: Nil

Total cost = 20,000.00 + 1000.00

= \$21,000.00

Cost before tax	100%	x	\$20,000
GST	5%	$0.05x$	\$1000
PST	Nil	Nil	Nil
Total Cost	**105%**	$\mathbf{1.05x}$	\$21,000

Therefore, the cost of the car after taxes in Alberta is \$21,000.00.

Example 3.4(b) **Calculating the Cost Before Taxes, Given the Total Cost**

Mark spent \$70 at a restaurant in Ontario for lunch with a client. This amount included the HST (13%). Calculate the cost of the meal before taxes and the HST on the meal.

Solution

Ontario 13% HST

Cost including taxes = \$70.00

Let the cost of the meal before taxes be \$$x$.

$$x + 0.13x = 70.00$$

$$1.13x = 70.00$$

$$x = \frac{70.00}{1.13} = 61.946902... = \$61.95$$

$$13\%\ \text{HST} = 0.13x = 0.13 \times 61.95 = 8.0535 = \$8.05$$

Cost before tax	100%	x	\$61.95
HST	13%	$0.13x$	\$8.05
Total Cost	**113%**	$\mathbf{1.13x}$	**\$70.00**

Therefore, the cost before taxes was \$61.95 and HST was \$8.05.

Example 3.4(c) **Calculating the Cost Before Taxes, Given the PST**

Melody purchased a microwave in Manitoba and received a receipt for the purchase. When she reached home, she noticed that most of the numbers on the receipt were faded, except for the PST amount of \$20. Calculate the cost before taxes, GST, and total cost of the microwave.

Solution

Manitoba 5% GST, 8% PST

Let the cost before taxes be \$$x$.

$$8\%\ \text{PST} = 0.08x = \$20.00$$

$$x = \frac{20.00}{0.08} = \$250.00$$

Cost before taxes = \$250.00

5% GST = 0.05 × 250.00 = \$12.50

Total cost = \$250.00 + \$12.50 + \$20.00 = \$282.50

Cost before taxes	100%	x	\$250.00
GST	5%	$0.05x$	\$12.50
PST	8%	$0.08x$	\$20.00
Total Cost	**113%**	$\mathbf{1.13x}$	\$282.50

Therefore, the cost before taxes was \$250.00, GST was \$12.50, and total cost was \$282.50.

Property Taxes

The owner of a property (land, houses, buildings, etc.) is required to pay the municipal government (county, city council, etc.) a property tax, calculated generally as a percent of the value of the property that is being assessed. The local municipality collects this tax and this money is used to provide and mantain many of our visible services: water, snow removal, garbage collection, policing, fire protection, parks, roads, street lighting, etc.

Tax authorities assess the value of the property based on the location and purpose of use of the property. For example, the value of land used for farming will be different from that used to build apartments or houses. At the same time, the value of residences in the suburbs will be different from that of residences in commercial locations within the city.

The assessed value of a property is generally a percent of the market price (or fair market value) of that property. For example, the municipality may assess a condominium at $240,000 in the year 2016 but the market price of the condominium may be $300,000. Property taxes are charged only on the assessed value of the property and not on the purchase price or on the market value. Thus, the property tax is calculated with the following formula:

Formula 3.4(a) **Property Tax**

$$\textit{Property Tax} = \textit{Assessed value of property} \times \textit{Tax Rate}$$

Example 3.4(d) **Calculating the Property Tax Using a Property Tax Rate**

Andrew purchased an apartment for $200,000 in the city of Edmonton. The municipality assessed the value of the condominium at 70% of its purchase price. If the tax rate in this area is 1.1% per annum, how much will Andrew pay in property tax for the first year?

Solution

$$\textit{Assessed value of the condominium} = 0.70 \times 200{,}000.00 = \$140{,}000.00$$

$$\textit{Property Tax} = \textit{Assessed Value of Property} \times \textit{Tax Rate}$$

$$= 140{,}000.00 \times 0.011 = \$1540.00$$

Therefore, Andrew will have to pay $1540.00 in property tax for the first year.

Mill Rate

Property taxes are generally a percent of the assessed value of the property. It may also be expressed as a mill rate (or per mille, millage rate, millage, or mill levy), which is the amount of tax per thousand dollars of property value. For example, mill rate of 10 (10 mills) would mean your property tax rate is $10 for every $1000 worth of assessed value of property.

The property tax expressed as a mill rate is calculated by the following formula:

Formula 3.4(b) **Property Tax Expressed as a Mill Rate**

$$\textit{Property Tax} = \frac{\textit{Assessed value of property}}{1000} \times \textit{Mill Rate}$$

Example 3.4(e) **Calculating the Property Tax Using Mill Rate**

If a land is assessed for $100,000 and the property tax is 40 mills, what is the property tax amount that the land owner would have to pay?

Solution

$$\textit{Property Tax} = \frac{\textit{Assessed value of property}}{1000} \times \textit{Mill rate}$$

$$\textit{Property Tax} = \frac{100{,}000.00}{1000} \times 40 = \$4000.00$$

Therefore, the land owner would have to pay a property tax amount of $4000.00.

3.4 | Exercises

Answers to the odd-numbered problems are available at the end of the textbook.

1. The HST (13%) component of your current car purchase in Ontario is $4225. What is the amount of the total purchase price of the car, including HST?

2. The sales tax (13% HST) paid on your current property purchase in Ontario is $41,587. What is the total cost of the property including HST?

3. The HST (15%) paid for the purchase of a car in Nova Scotia is $5850. What is the total price of the car, including HST?

4. The HST (13%) paid for the purchase of a cellphone in Ontario is $176.25. What is the total price of the cellphone, including HST?

5. The total cost of a car in British Columbia including 5% GST and 7% PST is $36,400. Calculate the dollar amount of the GST.

6. The total cost of a car in Saskatchewan including 5% GST and 6% PST is $32,725. Calculate the dollar amount of the total tax (GST plus PST).

7. A business in Ontario purchased a photocopier that cost $9000 (before 13% HST) from a local dealer.
   a. Calculate the amount paid for the photocopier after taxes and the total tax paid.
   b. How much would the business pay (including taxes) for the machine in P.E.I.? (HST in P.E.I. is 15%.)

8. Luke purchased twenty laptops from Edmonton, Alberta that cost $400 each (before 5% GST).
   a. Calculate the total amount paid for the laptops after taxes and the total tax paid.
   b. How much would he pay (including taxes) for the laptops in Quebec? (GST is 5% and QST is 9.975% in Quebec.)

9. If the cost of a product (including 5% GST) in Alberta was $3230.58, calculate the cost of the same model of the product (including 15% HST) in New Brunswick. Assume that the cost before taxes in both provinces is the same.

10. A car costs $17,640 (including 5% GST) in Alberta. How much will it cost (including 5% GST and 6% PST) in Saskatchewan if the cost of the car before taxes in both provinces is the same?

11. Hansen took his family for a vacation to Halifax, Nova Scotia last summer. If his hotel room rental cost $232.50 per night (including 15% HST), calculate the amount of tax charged (HST) on the room rent per night.

12. Payal and her friend rented a hotel room in Charlottetown, P.E.I. and were charged $138 per night (including 15% HST). What was the amount of tax charged (HST) on the room rent per night?

13. Jessica purchased a table in Halifax, Nova Scotia. If the HST charged on the table was $100, calculate the cost of the table before and after HST. The HST in Nova Scotia is 15%.

14. Terrence, the purchasing manager at a furniture outlet mall in London, Ontario, purchased 5 beds and 6 dining tables for his showroom. If the total HST he paid was $410.65, calculate the total cost of the furniture purchased (including taxes). Ontario has an HST of 13%.

15. Jason Forklifts, a successful heavy equipment manufacturer in Canada, decided to expand its production line and purchased land in Mississauga, Ontario for $3,890,000. If the municipality assessed the value of the industrial land at 65% of its purchase price and the tax rate is 0.85% per annum, calculate the amount of property tax to be paid in the first year.

16. Christina purchased a townhouse for $280,000 in Toronto. If the municipality assessed the value of her house at 80% of its purchase price and the tax rate is 1.25% per annum on the assessed value, calculate the amount that she would have to pay in property tax this year.

17. A house in Manitoba is purchased at $375,000 and assessed at 80% of its purchase price. If the property tax on the house is 10 mills, calculate the amount of the property tax.

18. If an industrial plot of land in British Columbia is assessed at $845,000 and the property tax is 30 mills, what is the property tax amount that the land owner would have to pay?

19. Magazines purchased by subscriptions in Ontario prior to July 01, 2010 were taxed only 5% GST (and no PST). However, since July 1, 2010, the HST of 13% has been charged for such purchases. How much more money will you now pay for a $75 (before taxes) magazine subscription in Ontario?

20. Home renovations in Ontario prior to July 01, 2010 were taxed only 5% GST. However, since July 1, 2010, the HST of 13% has been charged for such services. How much money would you have saved on a renovation costing $85,000 before taxes, if it was done in June rather than in July 2010?

21. Textbooks are exempt from PST in Ontario. If the total cost of a book including 5% GST is $147, how much GST is paid for the textbook?

22. Home insurance is exempt from GST and only 8% PST is payable for such services in Ontario. If the insurance cost of a house in Ontario including taxes is $777.60 per year, calculate the amount of tax included in the total cost.

• 23. The property tax rate for a residential building is 1.045%.

  a. What is the property tax for a residential property that has an assessed value of $400,000?

  b. What is the property tax amount for a farmland that has an assessed value of $680,000 if the property tax for a farmland is 80% of the tax levied for residential properties?

• 24. Samantha is charged a property tax rate of 1.025% on her house.

  a. If her house is worth $180,000, how much property tax does she have to pay?

  b. If the property tax for a farmland is 75% of the tax levied for residential purposes, calculate the property tax amount that she will have to pay for a farmland with an assessed value of $750,800.

• 25. The mill rate of a residential property in a municipality is 8 mills and the property tax for an industrial property is 1.25 times that of a residential property.

  a. Calculate the property tax for a residential property assessed at $280,500.

  b. Calculate the property tax for an industrial property assessed at $460,000.

• 26. The mill rate of Derek's house in British Columbia is 6 mills and the property tax for the factory that he owns is 1.5 times that of a residential property.

  a. How much will he pay in property tax if his house is assessed at $350,000?

  b. How much property tax will he pay for his factory that is assessed at $680,000?

• 27. Jess paid property taxes of $12,352.50 over last year on her home. If the purchase price of her home was $506,250, and it is assessed at 80% of the purchase price, what is the tax rate?

• 28. If a plot of land is assessed to have a value of 125% of the purchase price of $815,000, and the property taxes due are $20,375, what is the tax rate?

• 29. Joanna, whose property is assessed at a value of $340,000, paid $5100 in property taxes last year. Calculate the mill rate.

• 30. A plot of land outside of Edmonton is assessed to be worth $1.5 million. If the property taxes for the land are $12,000, what is the mill rate?

3 | Review Exercises

Answers to the odd-numbered problems are available at the end of the textbook.

1. The marketing department's expenses rose by 30% from last year. If this year's expenses were $234,260, calculate last year's expenses.

2. A manufacturing company paid $56,400 (after a discount) for a heavy duty packing machine from Japan. If it received a discount of 21%, calculate the original price of the machine.

3. Katelyn's financial manager invested her savings in a portfolio of shares that comprised of investments of $2000, $1800, and $3100 in the infrastructure, high-tech, and garment industries, respectively. Towards the end of 2016, if the value of her shares in the infrastructure industry rose by 20% while the rest remained the same, calculate the percent change in the value of her total investments.

4. Preston's website company invests its annual savings in different mutual funds. In 2016, they invested $12,500 in high-growth funds, $5000 in medium-growth funds, and $2000 in low-growth funds. If the value of its low-growth funds dropped by 10% this year while the rest stayed the same, by what percent did the total value of its investments change?

5. A waitress is paid $18.60 per hour. If her workweek is 37.5 hours, calculate her monthly pay.

6. A teller at a bank is paid a monthly salary of $3071.25. If he works 35 hours per week, calculate his hourly rate.

7. Amy works at a pharmaceutical company as a sales representative and receives a graduated commission of 5% for the first $10,000 in sales, 6% on the next $12,000, and 7% thereafter. Calculate her commission if she makes $45,000 in sales for the month. What single commission rate would her total earnings represent?

8. A manufacturer of water purifiers offers sales people the following commission structure: 2% for the first $5000 they sell, 3% on the next $3000, and 5% thereafter. Katherine, a new sales representative, has sales of $6000 in the first month, $10,000 in the second month, and $15,000 in the third month.

   a. What were her commissions for the first three months?

   b. What single commission rate would represent her earnings in the third month?

9. Oliver is paid a base salary of $1000 per month. In addition to this salary, he receives commission on sales exceeding $20,000. His total salary for last month was $2225 and his sales were $30,000. Calculate his commission rate.

10. Heather's Leather Jacket Outlet pays all its sales representatives a base salary of $18,000 per annum and a commission on all jackets that they sell over $3000. If a sales representative's salary last month was $2500 and his sales were $11,000, calculate the commission rate.

11. Vanessa purchased a camera in New Brunswick for $1105.14 including HST(15%). What was the HST amount on the camera?

12. Nabil bought a flat screen TV in Ontario for $1175.20, including HST (13%). What was the HST amount on the TV?

13. The GST (5%) paid for a textbook in Ontario is $6.45. Calculate the price of the textbook including GST. Textbooks are exempt from PST in Ontario.

14. The total cost of a textbook in Alberta, including GST (5%), is $124.95. Calculate the amount of the GST.

15. Kristin purchased a couch, a dining set, and a bedroom set from a store in Toronto, Ontario. If she was charged $580 in HST, calculate the total amount she paid for the furniture (HST in Ontario is 13%).

16. Scarlett was shocked to learn that a restaurant charged her a tax of $50 on a meal with her family. The manager explained to her that the restaurant charges 13% HST on the amount as per the rules of the province of Ontario. Calculate the cost of her meal, including the HST.

17. Stephen and Hope purchased their first home in London, Ontario for $244,000. If the municipality assessed the value of their house at 85% of its purchase price and the tax rate is 1.15% per annum on the assessed value, calculate the amount that they would have to pay in property tax this year.

18. Marley purchased an industrial plot in Manitoba for $850,000 and it was assessed at 80% of its purchase price. If the property tax on the plot is 15 mills, calculate the amount of property tax that she would have to pay every year.

- 19. In 2012, 257,000 people immigrated to Canada. Of these, 3% were from the USA, 2% were from the UK, and the rest were from other countries.
    a. How many more people immigrated to Canada from the USA than from the UK?
    b. If the combined number of immigrants from the USA and the UK constituted 0.045% of the population of Canada, calculate the population of Canada in 2012.

    Round your answers up to the next whole number.

- 20. Madison just received the first cheque from her salary and took her family out to dinner to celebrate. The waiter who was serving her at the restaurant was very hospitable so Madison left him a tip of 20% on the bill amount of $235.60.
    a. Calculate the amount of tip that the waiter received from her.
    b. If the tip was 1% of Madison's monthly salary, calculate her monthly salary.

- 21. Holistic Energy Ltd. spends $1200, $1400, $800, and $1700 on average on replacing printer cartridges for its black & white inkjet printers, colour inkjet printers, black & white laser printers, and colour laser printers, respectively, every month.
    a. What percent of the total expenditure on printer cartridges does it spend on colour laser printers every month?
    b. If it decides to reduce the expense on both colour inkjet printers and colour laser printers by 50%, what percent of the total expenditure would it spend on black & white laser printers?

- 22. A manufacturing company has 280 production people, 21 quality inspectors, 15 sales people, 6 marketing people, and 15 people in other departments such as HR, Finance, etc.
    a. What percent of the total employees are quality inspectors?
    b. If 15% of the production people quit their jobs, what percent of the total remaining employees are quality inspectors?

- 23. Chelsea scored 15% more than Zane. By what percent is Zane's score less than Chelsea's?

- 24. If Sabrina's annual salary is 10% more than Christina's, by what percent is Christina's annual salary less than Sabrina's?

3 | Self-Test Exercises

Answers to all the problems are available at the end of the textbook.

1. Colton's store expenses for the months of July and August were $33,480 and $36,580, which were 110% and 90% of the budgeted expenditure for the months of July and August, respectively. Calculate the total budgeted expenses for the two months.

2. Sandra lives in a condominium in downtown Toronto and works for a leading telecommunications company as a multimedia specialist. She earns an annual take-home salary of $60,000, and every month she spends $1400 on rent, $600 on car expenses, $200 on a line-of-credit interest payment, $800 on miscellaneous expenses, and saves $2000.
   a. What percent of her annual take-home salary are her annual expenses?
   b. Her bank manager advised her to invest 10% of her annual take-home salary in a medium-risk mutual fund. What would this amount be every month and what percent of her current savings would this amount be?

3. Calculate the original price for a pair of shoes if Ruby paid $140 for it after receiving a discount of 7%.

4. Lindsey invested her savings in shares of her brother's engineering company. The value of the shares that she owned dropped by $1.25 at the end of the first year, and a further $2.50 at the end of the second year. If the price of the share at the end of the second year was $12.55:
   a. Calculate the percent change in the price of the share each year.
   b. What was the percent drop in the price over the two-year period?

5. The value of a currency appreciated by 20% of its value last month and then depreciated by 20% this month. By what percent did the currency appreciate or depreciate over the two-month period?

6. If the cost (including the 5% GST) of a laptop in Alberta was $850.65, calculate the cost of the same laptop in New Brunswick (including the 15% HST in New Brunswick).

7. Wesley Steel Manufacturing Ltd. was expanding its production facilities and purchased large quantities of land in Oakville, Ontario for $8,560,000. If the municipality assessed the value of the industrial land at 65% of its purchase price and the tax rate is 0.85% per annum, calculate the amount of property tax it would have to pay in its first year.

8. Gracie received a job offer as a proofreader at a national news agency and is paid a gross salary of $38,000 per annum. Calculate her periodic gross payments if she is paid (a) monthly, (b) semi-monthly, (c) bi-weekly, (d) weekly.

9. Sandra works for a film production company and receives a bi-weekly pay of $1661.54. If she has 40-hour workweeks and worked a total of 97 hours during her last pay period, calculate her gross payment for the last pay period. Assume that her overtime factor is $1\frac{1}{2}$.

10. A sales representative at a furniture store receives sales commissions of 3% on the first $10,000 of sales made, 4% on the next $15,000, and 5% thereafter. If the sales representative earned $1912.50 last month from his commissions, calculate his total sales for last month.

11. The total cost of a textbook in Alberta including 5% GST is $156.45. Calculate the amount of GST charged.

12. The total cost of a car in British Columbia including 5% GST and 7% PST is $22,000. Calculate the amount of PST charged.

CASE 3

Applying Percents in Personal and Business Scenarios

Within two months of graduating from college, Heather got a job at a pharmaceutical company, where she earns a salary of $1750 bi-weekly. Her regular workweek is 35 hours and her overtime rate is twice the regular rate of pay.

To earn additional income, Heather took up a part-time job at a call center in the evenings and weekends, where she takes orders for a pizza company. Here, she receives a base salary of $750 per month plus commission. Her commission rate is 5% on the first $5000 in sales above her monthly quota of $10,000 and 7.5% on any additional sales thereafter.

After working for six months, Heather purchased a car for $13,560 (including the 13% HST) from a dealer in Toronto. Two years later, she purchased an apartment for $180,000 in Richmond Hill. Heather continued to do really well in her earnings and this year, she invested $5000 in shares of a software company that were selling at $2.50 per share.

a. What is Heather's hourly rate of pay and the equivalent monthly pay at the pharmaceutical company?

b. If Heather worked 75 hours during a pay period at the pharmaceutical company, what would her pay have been for that period?

c. Calculate her earnings for a month at the pizza company if her sales were worth $25,000. What straight commission, to replace the salary and commissions, would have resulted in the same total earnings?

d. What were her sales last month if she received $1900 from the pizza company?

e. What was the cost of the car before the HST in Ontario and how much more would she have paid if she had purchased the car in Quebec, including the 5% GST and 9.975% QST?

f. The assessed value of her apartment is 80% of the purchase price and the property tax is 1.15% of the assessed value. Calculate her property tax amount for the year.

g. In the first six months of last year, the share price increased by 10%, but decreased by 10% over the next six months. What was the percent change in the share price over the one-year period?

h. Calculate the total value of her shares at the end of the one-year period.

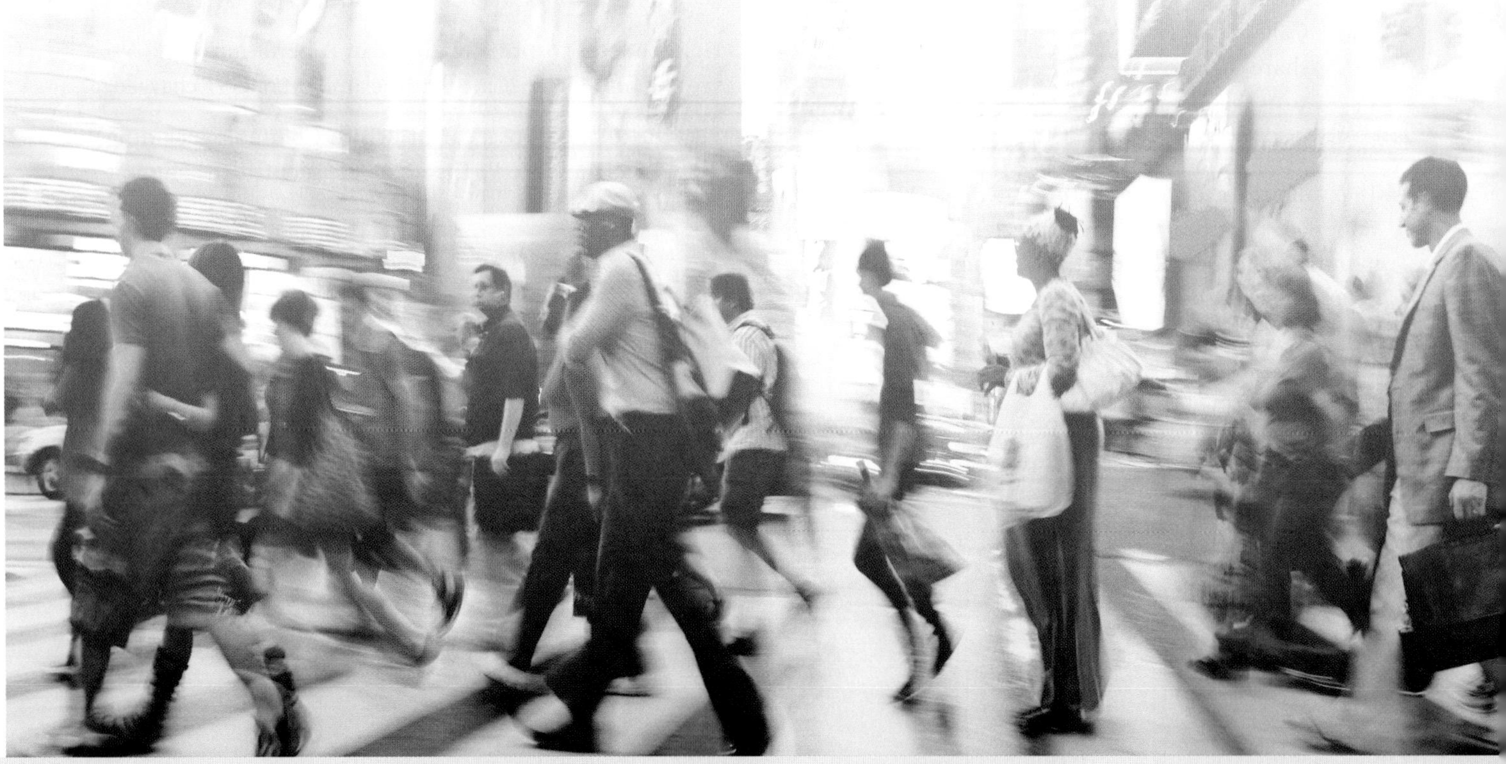

3 | Summary of Notation and Formulas

NOTATION

P = Portion

B = Base

R = Rate

$\%C$ = Percent change

V_i = Initial value

V_f = Final value

GST = Goods and Services Tax

PST = Provincial Sales Tax

HST = Harmonized Sales Tax

FORMULAS

Portion | 3.1

$$P = R \times B$$

Percent Change | 3.2

$$\%C = \frac{V_f - V_i}{V_i} \times 100\%$$

Pay for Pay Period | 3.3(a)

$$\textit{Pay for pay period} = \frac{\textit{Annual Salary}}{\textit{Number of pay periods per year}}$$

Hourly Rate of Pay | 3.3(b)

$$\textit{Hourly rate of pay} = \frac{\textit{Weekly Pay}}{\textit{Number of working hours per week}} = \frac{\textit{Weekly Pay}}{\textit{Workweek}}$$

Property Tax | 3.4(a)

$$\textit{Property Tax} = \textit{Assessed value of property} \times \textit{Tax Rate}$$

Property Tax Expressed as a Mill Rate | 3.4(b)

$$\textit{Property Tax} = \frac{\textit{Assessed value of property}}{1000} \times \textit{Mill Rate}$$

Chapter 4

RATIOS, PROPORTIONS, AND APPLICATIONS

LEARNING OBJECTIVES

- Set up and use ratios to solve allocation problems.
- Set up and use proportions to solve problems involving equivalent ratios.
- Solve problems involving pro-rating an amount using the proportion method.
- Convert currencies between countries using exchange rates and the proportion method.
- Solve problems involving buying and selling of currencies by financial institutions.
- Demonstrate the effect of currency appreciation and depreciation.
- Use exchange rates to calculate the value of goods when importing from other countries.
- Interpret and use index numbers.

CHAPTER OUTLINE

Introduction

A **ratio** is a comparison or relationship between two or more quantities with the same units. Therefore, ratios are not expressed with units.

For example, Andy (A) invested \$5000 and Barry (B) invested \$4000 in a business. The comparison of A's investment to B's investment is called the *ratio* of their investments.

Ratios are comparisons or relationships between two or more quantities.

Ratios are widely used in our day-to-day lives to compare two or more quantities. Ratios are also used by businesses to compare their performance to the previous year's performance or to industry standards.

This chapter will provide you with ample practice in using ratios and proportions. It will also provide you with a thorough understanding of the numerous applications of ratios and proportions, such as converting between currencies, buying and selling currencies, importing goods into the country, and calculating the value of currencies when they fluctuate relative to foreign currencies.

4.1 | Ratios

Expressing a Ratio of Two Quantities

When comparing two quantities, there are different ways to express the ratio. In the example given above, the ratio of A's investment of \$5000 to B's investment of \$4000 may be expressed in any of the following forms:

$A : B = 5000 : 4000$ (as a ratio, using a colon and read as '5000 is to 4000' or 'ratio of 5000 to 4000')

$\frac{A}{B} = \frac{5000}{4000}$ (as a fraction and read as '5000 over 4000')

If the decimal equivalent of the fraction is used, then it must be stated as "A's investment is 1.25 times B's investment", or $A = 1.25B$. Similarly, if the percent equivalent of the fraction is used, then it must be stated as "A's investment is 125% of B's investment".

Note: *When representing a ratio as a fraction, if the denominator is 1, the denominator (1) must still be written.*

For example, if the ratio of two quantities is $\frac{3}{1}$ then it is incorrect to state that the ratio is 3. It should be stated as $\frac{3}{1}$ or 3 : 1.

Expressing a Ratio of More than Two Quantities

When comparing more than two quantities, we use a colon (:) to represent the ratio.
For example, if A invested \$5000, B invested \$4000, and C invested \$1000 in a business, then the ratio of their investments is expressed as,

$$A : B : C = 5000 : 4000 : 1000$$

Terms of a Ratio

The quantities in a ratio are called the terms of the ratio.

For example, the terms of the ratio 5 : 7 : 19 are 5, 7, and 19.

Equivalent Ratios

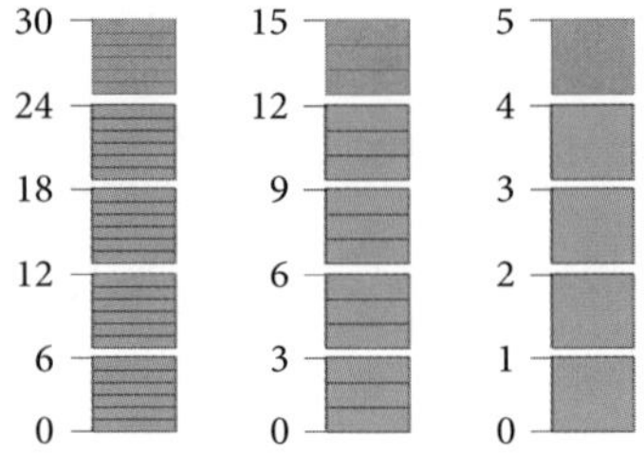

$\frac{24}{30} = \frac{12}{15} = \frac{4}{5}$

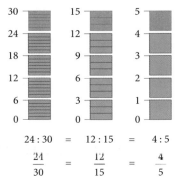

When all the terms of the ratio are multiplied by the same number or divided by the same number, the result will be an equivalent ratio. For example, when the terms of the ratio 12 : 15 are multiplied by 2, we obtain an equivalent ratio of 24 : 30.

$$12 : 15$$
$$12 \times 2 : 15 \times 2$$
$$24 : 30$$

When the terms of the ratio 12 : 15 are divided by the common factor 3, we obtain the equivalent ratio of 4 : 5.

$$12 : 15$$
$$12 \div 3 : 15 \div 3$$
$$4 : 5$$

Therefore, the ratios 12 : 15, 24 : 30, and 4 : 5 are called **equivalent ratios**.

Reducing a Ratio to its Lowest Terms

When two ratios are equivalent, they result in the same answer when reduced to their lowest terms.

A ratio is in its simplest form when the terms have no common factors other than 1.

Comparisons are easier when ratios are reduced to their lowest terms. When all the terms of a ratio are integers, the ratio can be reduced to its lowest terms by dividing all the terms by their common factors.

For example, if *A* earns \$3000, *B* earns \$4500, and *C* earns \$6000, what is the ratio of their earnings (or, compare the earnings of *A*, *B*, and *C*)? Reduce the ratio to its lowest terms.

A	:	*B*	:	*C*	
3000	:	4500	:	6000	Dividing each term by the common factor 100,
30	:	45	:	60	Dividing each term by the common factor 15,
2	:	3	:	4	The ratio is now in its lowest terms.

By reducing the ratio to its lowest terms, we can state that the earnings of $A : B : C$ are in the ratio of 2 : 3 : 4.

Example 4.1(a) **Equivalent Ratios**

Determine whether the given pairs of ratios are equivalent.

(i) 18 : 12 and 12 : 8 (ii) 20 : 24 and 15 : 20

Solution

(i) 18 : 12
$= 18 \div 6 : 12 \div 6$
$= 3 : 2$

12 : 8
$= 12 \div 4 : 8 \div 4$
$= 3 : 2$

Therefore, the given pair of ratios are equivalent.

(ii) 20 : 24
$= 20 \div 4 : 24 \div 4$
$= 5 : 6$

15 : 20
$= 15 \div 5 : 20 \div 5$
$= 3 : 4$

Therefore, the given pair of ratios are not equivalent.

Reducing Ratios When One or More of the Terms of the Ratio Are Fractions

To reduce the ratio, first convert all the terms to integers by multiplying all terms by the least common denominator, and then reduce to its lowest terms.

For example,

$\frac{2}{3} : \frac{4}{5} : 2$	Multiplying all terms by the least common denominator 15,
10 : 12 : 30	Dividing all terms by the common factor 2,
5 : 6 : 15	

Reducing Ratios When One or More of the Terms of the Ratio Are Decimals

To reduce the ratio, first convert all the terms to integers by moving the decimal place of all terms to the right by the same number of places, and then reduce to its lowest terms.

For example,

2.25 : 3.5 : 5	Moving the decimal of each term two places to the right,
225 : 350 : 500	Dividing all terms by the common factor 25,
9 : 14 : 20	

Reducing Ratios When the Terms of the Ratio Are a Combination of Fractions and Decimals

To reduce the ratio, first convert all the fractional terms to integers, then convert all the decimal terms to integers. Finally, reduce to its lowest terms.

For example,

$5.75 : \frac{9}{2} : 4$	Multiplying all terms by the common denominator 2,
11.5 : 9 : 8	Moving the decimal of each term one place to the right,
115 : 90 : 80	Dividing all terms by the common factor 5,
23 : 18 : 16	

Reducing Ratios to its Equivalent Ratio Whose Smallest Term is 1

To make the comparison of quantities easier, we can also reduce a ratio to its equivalent ratio whose smallest term is equal to 1, by dividing all the terms by the smallest value.

For example, if the investment amounts of 3 partners *A*, *B*, and *C* are \$35,000, \$78,750, and \$59,500, respectively, what is the ratio of their earnings (or, compare the earnings of *A*, *B*, and *C*)? Reduce the ratio so the smallest value is 1.

A : *B* : *C*	
35,000 : 78,750 : 59,500	Dividing each term by the smallest term, 35,000,
1 : 2.25 : 1.7	The ratio is now reduced to its equivalent ratio with the smallest term equal to 1.

By reducing it so that the smallest term is equal to 1, we can state that *B*'s investment is 2.25 times *A*'s investment, and *C*'s investment is 1.7 times *A*'s investment.

Example 4.1(b) **Reducing Ratios to Lowest Terms**

Express the following ratios as equivalent ratios in their lowest whole numbers and then reduce them to ratios where the smallest term is 1:

(i) $2\frac{7}{9} : 3\frac{1}{3} : 5$ (ii) $2.5 : 1.75 : 0.625$ (iii) $1.25 : \frac{5}{6} : 2$

Solution

(i)

$2\frac{7}{9}$	:	$3\frac{1}{3}$	:	5	Converting the terms with mixed numbers to improper fractions,
$\frac{25}{9}$	:	$\frac{10}{3}$	:	5	Multiplying each term by the least common denominator 9,
25	:	30	:	45	Dividing each term by the common factor 5,
5	:	6	:	9	Dividing each term by the smallest term 5,
1	:	1.2	:	1.8	

Therefore, $2\frac{7}{9} : 3\frac{1}{3} : 5$ reduced to its lowest terms is 5 : 6 : 9 and the equivalent ratio where the smallest term is 1 is 1 : 1.2 : 1.8.

(ii)

2.5	:	1.75	:	0.625	
2.5	:	1.75	:	0.625	Moving the decimal point of each term 3 places to the right,
2500	:	1750	:	625	Dividing each term by the common factor 125,
20	:	14	:	5	Dividing each term by the smallest term 5,
4	:	2.8	:	1	

Therefore, 2.5 : 1.75 : 0.625 reduced to its lowest terms is 20 : 14 : 5 and the equivalent ratio where the smallest term is 1 is 4 : 2.8 : 1.

(iii)

1.25	:	$\frac{5}{6}$	:	2	Multiplying each term by 6,
7.5	:	5	:	12	Moving the decimal point of each term 1 place to the right,
75	:	50	:	120	Dividing each term by the common factor 5,
15	:	10	:	24	Dividing each term by the smallest term 10,
1.5	:	1	:	2.4	

Therefore, $1.25 : \frac{5}{6} : 2$ reduced to its lowest terms is 15 : 10 : 24 and the equivalent ratio where the smallest term is 1 is 1.5 : 1 : 2.4.

Order of a Ratio

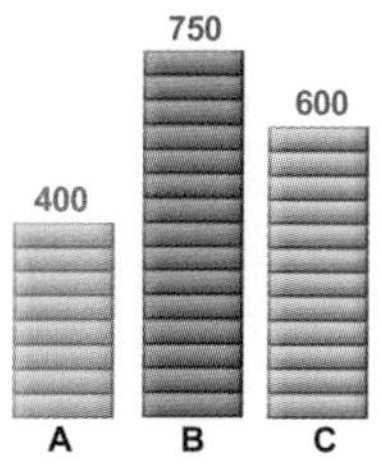

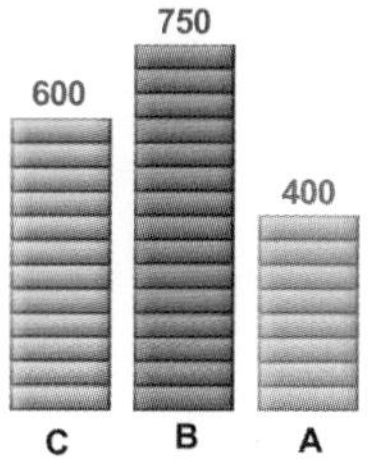

The order of presenting terms in a ratio is important.

For example, if A saves \$400, B saves \$750, and C saves \$600, then the ratio of the savings of $A : B : C$ is,

$A : B : C = 400 : 750 : 600$ Dividing each term by the common factor 50,

$= 8 : 15 : 12$

In the previous example, the ratio of the savings of $C : B : A$ is,

$C : B : A = 600 : 750 : 400$ Dividing each term by the common factor 50,

$= 12 : 15 : 8$

Notice that $C : B : A$ is not the same as $A : B : C$.

Comparing Quantities of Items That Have the Same Kind of Measure but Different Units

When writing ratios to compare quantities of items that have the same kind of measure, the units have to be the same.

For example, the ratio of 45 minutes to 2 hours is not 45 : 2. Here, in order to compare the measures of time given in different units, the measures need to be converted to the same unit.

45 minutes : 2 hours	Converting 2 hours to minutes using 1 hour = 60 minutes,
45 : 120	Dividing by the common factor 15,
3 : 8	

Converting between Common Units	
kilometre (km)	= 1000 metres (m)
metre (m)	= 100 centimetres (cm)
centimetre (cm)	= 10 millimetres (mm)
kilogram (kg)	= 1000 grams (g)
gram (g)	= 1000 milligrams (mg)
litre (L)	= 1000 millilitres (mL)
hour (h)	= 60 minutes (min)
minute (min)	= 60 seconds (sec)

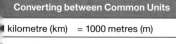

Consider another example to determine the ratio of 2.5 kilometres to 3000 metres.

2.5 km : 3000 m	Converting 2.5 km to m using 1 km = 1000 m,
2500 : 3000	Dividing by the common factor 100,
25 : 30	Dividing by the common factor 5,
5 : 6	

Example 4.1(c) **Comparing Quantities That Have the Same Kind of Measure but Different Units**

Express each of the following ratios in its simplest form:

(i) 1.2 L to 800 mL (ii) 16 weeks to 2 years

Solution

(i) 1.2 L to 800 mL

1.2 L : 800 mL	Converting 1.2 L to mL (1 L = 1000 mL),
1200 mL : 800 mL	Dividing both terms by the common factor 400,
3 : 2	

Therefore, the ratio of 1.2 L to 800 mL is 3 : 2.

Solution *continued*

(ii) 16 weeks to 2 years

16 weeks : 2 years — Converting 2 years to weeks (1 year = 52 weeks),

16 weeks : 104 weeks — Dividing both terms by the common factor 8,

2 : 13

Therefore, the ratio of 16 weeks to 2 years is 2 : 13.

Comparing Quantities of Items That Have Different Kinds of Measure

When comparing quantities of items that have different kinds of measure, the units will be different and should be included in the ratio.

For example, when baking a cake, Maggie uses 4 kilograms of flour, 2 litres of water, and 6 eggs. Therefore, the ratio of flour to water to eggs she uses while baking is,

Flour	:	Water	:	Eggs	
(kg)		(L)		(nr)	
4	:	2	:	6	Dividing by the common factor 2,
2	:	1	:	3	i.e., 2 kg Flour : 1 L of Water : 3 Eggs

Rate, Unit Rate, and Unit Price

Rate

Rate is a ratio that is used to compare two quantities with different units of measure.

For example, if a car travels 100 kilometres using 9 litres of gas, then the rate is 100 km : 9 L.

The word 'per' indicates that it is a rate and it is usually denoted by a slash '/'.

Therefore, 100 km : 9 L is usually written as 100 km per 9 L or 100 km/9 L.

Unit Rate

Unit rate represents the number of units of the first quantity (or measurements) that corresponds to one unit of the second quantity. That is, unit rate is a rate in which the rate is expressed as a quantity which has a denominator of 1.

Rate can be converted to unit rate simply by dividing the first term by the second term.

For example, a rate of 90 km in 1.5 hours, converted to unit rate:

$$\frac{90 \text{ km}}{1.5 \text{ hours}} = 60 \text{ km/hour}$$

Similarly, a rate of 75 hours in 2 weeks, converted to unit rate:

$$\frac{75 \text{ hours}}{2 \text{ weeks}} = 37.5 \text{ hours/week}$$

Unit Price

Unit price is the unit rate when it is expressed in unit currency, dollars, cents, etc. Unit price shows the cost of an item for one unit of that item. That is, the price is expressed per quantity of 1.

For example, the price of gas is \$1.36 per litre (\$1.36/L), the price of grapes is \$2 per kilogram (\$2/kg), the price of juice is \$0.75 per can, etc.

Example 4.1(d) **Calculating the Hourly Rate of Pay**

Peter worked nine hours and earned \$247.50. Calculate his hourly rate of pay.

Solution

Earnings (\$) : Working Period (h)

247.50 : 9 Dividing each term by 9 to reduce the second unit to 1,

27.50 : 1

Therefore, his hourly rate of pay is \$27.50 per hour or \$27.50/h.

Example 4.1(e) **Calculating the Cost Per Litre**

If three litres of milk cost \$4.80, what is the cost per litre of milk?

Solution

Cost (\$) : Quantity (L)

4.80 : 3 Dividing each term by 3 to reduce the second unit to 1,

1.60 : 1

Therefore, the cost of milk is \$1.60 per litre or \$1.60/L.

Sharing Quantities Using Ratios

Sharing quantities using ratios refers to the **allocation** or **distribution** of a quantity into two or more portions (or units) based on a given ratio.

For example, to share a \$1000 profit among *A*, *B*, and *C* in the ratio of 2 : 3 : 5, first add the terms in the ratio (i.e., 2, 3, and 5), which results in a total of 10 units. These 10 units represent the total profit of \$1000, where *A*'s share constitutes 2 units, *B*'s share 3 units, and *C*'s share 5 units. Each person's share can then be calculated, as shown below:

A's share is 2 units out of 10 units (\$1000),

B's share is 3 units out of 10 units (\$1000), and

C's share is 5 units out of 10 units (\$1000).

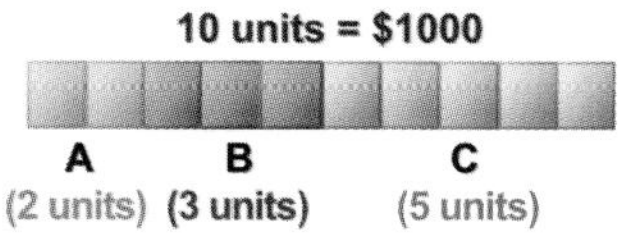

Therefore,

$$A\text{'s share} = \frac{2}{10} \text{ of } 1000 = \frac{2}{10} \times 1000 = \$200.00$$

$$B\text{'s share} = \frac{3}{10} \text{ of } 1000 = \frac{3}{10} \times 1000 = \$300.00$$

$$C\text{'s share} = \frac{5}{10} \text{ of } 1000 = \frac{5}{10} \times 1000 = \$500.00$$

Note:

- *The total shares of A, B, and C is equal to the amount of profit shared* (i.e., 200 + 300 + 500 = 1000).
- *If we reduce the ratio of the amounts shared by A, B, and C to its lowest terms, the result is the original ratio* (200 : 300 : 500 = 2 : 3 : 5).

The total of the individual portions will be equal to the original amount shared. The ratio of the individual portions, when reduced, will be equal to the original ratio.

If the order of the ratio of A's share : B's share : C's share is changed to 5 : 3 : 2 (instead of 2 : 3 : 5), their individual shares will change. Their shares are recalculated as shown below:

$$A\text{'s share} = \frac{5}{10} \times 1000 = \$500.00$$

$$B\text{'s share} = \frac{3}{10} \times 1000 = \$300.00$$

$$C\text{'s share} = \frac{2}{10} \times 1000 = \$200.00$$

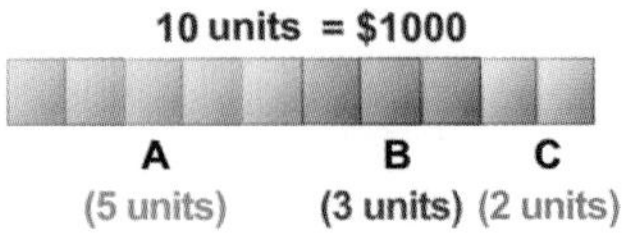

Note:

- *The total shares of A, B, and C is equal to the amount of profit shared* (i.e., 500 + 300 + 200 = 1000).
- *If we reduce the ratio of the amounts shared by A, B, and C to its lowest terms, the result is the original ratio* (500 : 300 : 200 = 5 : 3 : 2).

Example 4.1(f) **Sharing Using Ratios**

A, *B*, and *C* start a business and invest \$3500, \$2100, and \$2800, respectively. After a few months, if *C* decides to sell his shares to *A* and *B*, how much would *A* and *B* have to pay for *C*'s shares if they want to maintain their initial investment ratio?

Solution

Investments of *A*, *B*, and *C* are in the ratio of 3500 : 2100 : 2800, which can be reduced to 5 : 3 : 4.

If *A* and *B* want to maintain their investment ratio at 5 : 3, then *C*'s share (of \$2800) has to be paid for by *A* and *B* in this ratio. By adding the reduced terms of *A* and *B*, we know that *C*'s share is to be divided into a total of 8 units, as illustrated:

$$A \text{ would have to pay } C: \frac{5}{8} \times 2800.00 = \$1750.00$$

$$B \text{ would have to pay } C: \frac{3}{8} \times 2800.00 = \$1050.00$$

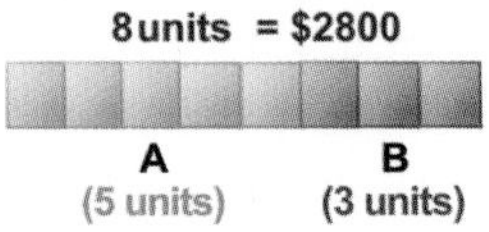

Therefore, *A* would have to pay \$1750.00 and *B* would have to pay \$1050.00 in order to maintain their initial investment ratio.

Example 4.1(g) **Application Using Equivalent Ratios**

Andrew, Barry, and Cathy invested their savings in a bank. The ratio of the investment of Andrew's to Barry's is 2 : 3 and that of Barry's to Cathy's is 4 : 5. What is the investment ratio of Andrew : Barry : Cathy?

Solution

Determine the equivalent ratio for $A : B$ and $B : C$ so that the number of units in B is the same in both cases.

This can be done by determining the equivalent ratio of $A : B$ by multiplying by 4 and that of $B : C$ by multiplying by 3.

$A : B = 2 : 3$ Multiplying both terms by 4,

$= 8 : 12$

$B : C = 4 : 5$ Multiplying both terms by 3,

$= 12 : 15$

Therefore, the investment ratio of Andrew : Barry : Cathy is 8 : 12 : 15.

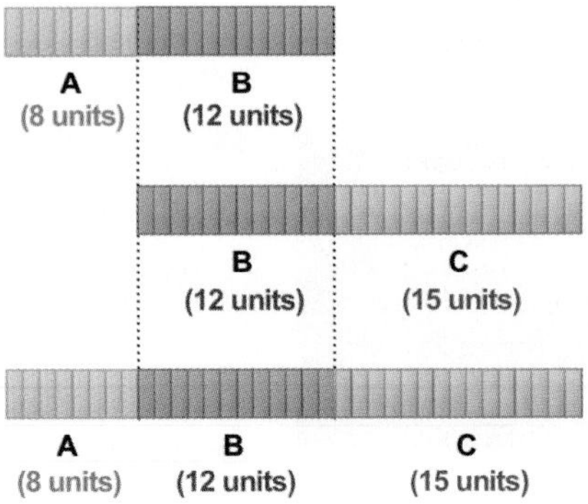

4.1 | Exercises

Answers to the odd-numbered problems are available at the end of the textbook.

1. Which of the following ratios are equivalent?

   a. 4 : 6 and 6 : 10 b. 8 : 10 and 28 : 35 c. 6 : 8 and 27 : 32 d. 16 : 22 and 64 : 88

2. Which of the following ratios are equivalent?

   a. 16 : 20 and 24 : 30 b. 10 : 12 and 35 : 42 c. 12 : 14 and 30 : 42 d. 12 : 26 and 30 : 65

3. Which of the following is not an equivalent ratio of 6 : 9 : 12?

   a. 4 : 6 : 8 b. 2 : 3 : 4 c. 1 : 2 : 3 d. 8 : 12 : 16

4. Which of the following is not an equivalent ratio of 16 : 24 : 12?

   a. 20 : 30 : 15 b. 8 : 12 : 6 c. 28 : 42 : 21 d. 24 : 36 : 18

For Problems 5 to 8, reduce the following ratios to their lowest terms and to an equivalent ratio with 1 as the smallest term.

5. a. 500 : 400 : 800 b. $12 : \frac{5}{3} : 3$ c. $1.7 : 8.5 : \frac{34}{3}$

6. a. 420 : 280 : 140 b. $65 : 91 : \frac{13}{2}$ c. $12 : 1.5 : \frac{5}{2}$

7. a. 175 : 50 : 125 b. $\frac{2}{3} : \frac{3}{5} : \frac{7}{10}$ c. $0.45 : \frac{1}{2} : 0.75$

8. a. 180 : 60 : 150 b. $\frac{3}{4} : \frac{2}{3} : \frac{11}{12}$ c. $1.2 : \frac{3}{5} : 0.8$

9. Express the following ratios reduced to their lowest terms:

   a. 30 minutes to 3 hours b. 400 m to 3.5 km c. 750 g to 12 kg d. 10 quarters to 3 dimes

10. Express the following ratios reduced to their lowest terms:

    a. 9 months to 2 years b. 990 m to 1.2 km c. 120 g to 2 kg d. 7 dimes to 4 nickels

11. What is the ratio of a Canadian dime (10¢) to a Canadian loonie ($1), reduced to its lowest terms?

12. What is the ratio of 12 minutes to 12 hours, reduced to its lowest terms?

13. An aircraft travels a distance of 3000 km in 6 hours. Calculate the ratio of the distance traveled to the time taken, reduced to a rate of kilometres per hour.

14. Speed is defined as the ratio of the distance travelled to the time taken. If Andrea, who lives in Toronto, took 6 hours to reach her parents' home in Montreal, which is 543 km away, calculate the speed at which she was travelling, reduced to a rate of kilometres per hour.

For Problems 15 to 20, identify the option that is less expensive based on unit rate.

15. 2 kg of flour for $3.30, or 5 kg of flour for $8.40
16. 3 kg of sugar for $3.90, or 5 kg of sugar for $6.25
17. 12 pencils for $4.44, or 8 pencils for $2.88
18. 6 litres of paint for $45.60, or 5 litres of paint for $37.25
19. 1.2 litres of juice for $2.16, or 0.8 litres of juice for $1.40
20. 2.2 kg of jam for $11.00, or 1.5 kg of jam for $7.20
21. An 800 g box of cereal is $5.00 and another 750 g box of cereal is $4.80. Which unit rate is better and by how much, per kg?
22. Car *A* requires 8.9 litres of gas to travel 100 km. Car *B* requires 45 litres of gas to travel 475 km. Which car has the better fuel economy?
23. If *A* earns $154 for working 8 hours and *B* earns $84 for working 5 hours, whose average hourly rate is higher, and by how much?

24. If Amanda travelled 325 km in 4 hours and 15 minutes and Ashton travelled 290 km in 3 hours and 30 minutes, whose average speed was greater and by how much?

25. Rodney, a hardware engineer, wants to install a component that is 38.2 mm in length into his laptop. The length of the installlation space provided in his laptop is 4.8 cm. Calculate the ratio of the length of the component to the installation space, in its lowest terms.

26. In a triathlon, participants are required to complete three successive events, swimming, bicycling, and running, without stopping. If they have to swim 3850 metres, bike 7 kilometres, and then run 3.5 kilometres, calculate the ratio of the distance covered by swimming to biking to running, in its lowest terms.

27. A business has 8 project leads, 12 graphic artists, 20 software developers, and 4 sales people.
    a. What is the ratio of the employees?
    b. If 2 software developers leave the business, calculate the new ratio of the employees.

28. A small stationery store has an inventory of 240 pencils, 180 pens, 120 calculators, and 300 notebooks.
    a. What is the ratio of the items?
    b. If they sell 150 notebooks, calculate the new ratio of the items.

29. Two companies share an office building and have an agreement to share the hydro bill in the ratio of 40 : 60. If the hydro bill is $360 for a month, how much should each company pay?

30. Sherrie and Alexis invested a total of $10,000 in a web design business. If the ratio of their investments is 80 : 20, how much did each of them invest?

31. Darlene, a wealthy entrepreneur, is donating $14,000 to Charities *A*, *B*, and *C* in the ratio of 6 : 1 : 3. How much money is she donating to each charity?

32. Betty divides her salary between rent, food, and entertainment in the ratio of 11 : 4 : 3. If she earns $3000 a month, how much money does she spend monthly on each category?

• 33. Lottery winnings of $50,000 are to be divided between Johnny, Greg, and Andrew in the ratio of $\frac{3}{4} : \frac{2}{5} : \frac{1}{2}$. How should the money by distributed to them?

• 34. The net profit of a company is to be divided among three partners, *A*, *B*, and *C*, in the ratio of $\frac{2}{3} : \frac{1}{6} : \frac{4}{5}$. What is each partner's share if the net profit is $44,000?

• 35. Bob, Rob, and Chuck invest $13,000, $22,000, and $18,000, respectively, to build a yacht. After the yacht was built, Bob decided to sell his share of the investment to Rob and Chuck. How much would Rob and Chuck have to pay Bob if they want to maintain the same ratio of their investments in the yacht?

• 36. Three friends, Andrew, Brooks, and Charlie, have decided to invest $8000, $12,000, and $4000, respectively, to start a software development business. If Charlie decided to leave the business, how much would Andrew and Brooks have to pay for Charlie's shares if they want to maintain their initial investment ratio?

• 37. Abbey and Baxter invested equal amounts of money in a business. A year later, Abbey withdrew $5000, making the ratio of their investments 5 : 9. How much money did each of them invest in the beginning?

• 38. Jocelyn and Haley invested equal amounts to start a business. Two months later, Jocelyn invested an additional $3000 in the business, making the ratio of their investments 11 : 5. How much money did each of them invest in the beginning?

• 39. If $A : B = 3 : 4$ and $B : C = 5 : 6$, express $A : B : C$.

• 40. If $X : Y = 2 : 5$ and $Y : Z = 6 : 7$, express $X : Y : Z$.

4.2 | Proportions and Pro-rations

Proportions

When two sets of ratios are equal, we say that they are proportionate to each other. In the proportion equation, the ratios on the left side of the equation are equal to the ratios on the right side of the equation.

Consider an example where $A : B$ is 50 : 100 and $C : D$ is 30 : 60. Reducing the ratios to their lowest terms, we obtain the ratio of $A : B$ as 1 : 2 and the ratio of $C : D$ as 1 : 2. Since these ratios are equal, they are proportionate to each other and their proportion equation is,

$$A : B = C : D$$

The proportion equation can also be formed by representing the ratios as fractions.

The fraction obtained by dividing the 1st term by the 2nd term on the left side is equal to the fraction obtained by dividing the 1st term by the 2nd term on the right side:

$$\frac{A}{B} = \frac{C}{D}$$

The above proportion equation has 4 terms. If any of the 3 terms are known, then the 4th term can be calculated using the method of cross-multiplication.

If two sets of fractions are equal, then the product obtained by cross-multiplying the fractions will be equal.

Cross-multiplication is accomplished by equating the product of the numerator of the 1st ratio and the denominator of the 2nd ratio with the product of the denominator of the 1st ratio and the numerator of the 2nd ratio.

Cross-multiplying, $\frac{A}{B} \times \frac{C}{D}$ we obtain,

$$AD = BC$$

If $A : B = C : D$

then, $\frac{A}{B} = \frac{C}{D}$

or, $\frac{A}{C} = \frac{B}{D}$

Notice that the cross-multiplication of $\frac{A}{C} = \frac{B}{D}$ also leads to the same result.

Therefore, $A : B = C : D$ is equivalent to $\frac{A}{B} = \frac{C}{D}$ and is also equivalent to $\frac{A}{C} = \frac{B}{D}$.

Similarly, this principle can be extended to proportions with sets of ratios having more than two terms.

For example, if $A : B : C = D : E : F$, then the equivalent ratio can be expressed as,

$$\frac{A}{B} = \frac{D}{E}, \quad \frac{B}{C} = \frac{E}{F}, \quad \text{and} \quad \frac{A}{C} = \frac{D}{F}$$

Cross-multiplying, $AE = BD$, $BF = CE$, and $AF = CD$

If $A : B : C = D : E : F$

then, $\frac{A}{B} = \frac{D}{E}$, $\frac{B}{C} = \frac{E}{F}$, $\frac{A}{C} = \frac{D}{F}$

or, $\frac{A}{D} = \frac{B}{E} = \frac{C}{F}$

The equivalent ratio, $A : B : C = D : E : F$

can also be illustrated in a table:

1st Term	2nd Term	3rd Term
A	B	C
D	E	F

and expressed as, $A : D = B : E = C : F$

$A : B : C = D : E : F$

In fractional form, $\frac{A}{D} = \frac{B}{E} = \frac{C}{F}$

Cross-multiplying gives the same result, $AE = BD$, $BF = CE$, and $AF = CD$

Example 4.2(a) **Solving for the Unknown Quantity in Proportions**

Determine the missing term in the following proportions:

(i) $5 : 8 = 10 : x$

(ii) $250 : x = 10 : 3$

(iii) $x : 3.8 = 5.2 : 19.76$

(iv) $2 : 2\frac{1}{2} = x : 3\frac{1}{2}$

Solution

(i) $5 : 8 = 10 : x$

1st Term	2nd Term
5	8
10	x

In fractional form, $\frac{5}{10} = \frac{8}{x}$ **Or** $\frac{5}{8} = \frac{10}{x}$

Cross-multiplying, $5x = 80$

Therefore, $x = \frac{80}{5} = 16$

(ii) $250 : x = 10 : 3$

1st Term	2nd Term
250	x
10	3

In fractional form, $\frac{250}{10} = \frac{x}{3}$ **Or** $\frac{250}{x} = \frac{10}{3}$

Cross-multiplying, $750 = 10x$

Therefore, $x = \frac{750}{10} = 75$

(iii) $x : 3.8 = 5.2 : 19.76$

1st Term	2nd Term
x	3.8
5.2	19.76

In fractional form, $\frac{x}{5.2} = \frac{3.8}{19.76}$ **Or** $\frac{x}{3.8} = \frac{5.2}{19.76}$

Cross-multiplying, $19.76x = 3.8 \times 5.2$

Therefore, $x = \frac{3.8 \times 5.2}{19.76} = 1$

(iv) $2 : 2\frac{1}{2} = x : 3\frac{1}{2}$

Converting mixed numbers to improper fractions,

$2 : \frac{5}{2} = x : \frac{7}{2}$

Multiplying each term by 2,

$4 : 5 = 2x : 7$

1st Term	2nd Term
4	5
$2x$	7

In fractional form, $\frac{4}{2x} = \frac{5}{7}$ **Or** $\frac{4}{5} = \frac{2x}{7}$

Cross-multiplying, $28 = 10x$

Therefore, $x = \frac{28}{10} = 2.8 = 2\frac{4}{5}$

Example 4.2(b) **Solving Word Problems Using Proportions**

Ben can drive a distance of 18 km using 2 litres of gas. Calculate the distance (in km) Ben can drive using 30 litres of gas.

Solution

L : km = L : km

$2 : 18 = 30 : x$

L	km
2	18
30	x

In fractional form, $\frac{2}{30} = \frac{18}{x}$ **Or** $\frac{2}{18} = \frac{30}{x}$

Cross-multiplying, $2x = 18 \times 30$

$x = \frac{18 \times 30}{2} = 270$ km

Therefore, Ben can drive a distance of 270 km using 30 litres of gas.

Example 4.2(c) **Sharing Using Proportions**

Alex (*A*), Bebeto (*B*), and Carol (*C*) decide to start a lawn mowing business together and form a partnership. *A* invests $105,000, *B* invests $140,000, and *C* invests $245,000. They agree to share the profits in the same ratio as their investments.

(i) What is the ratio of their investments in lowest terms?

(ii) In the first year of running the business, *A*'s profit was $30,000. What were *B*'s and *C*'s profits?

(iii) In the second year, their total profit was $56,000. How much would each of them receive from this total profit?

Solution

(i) *Ratio of their investments:*

$A : B : C$

105,000 : 140,000 : 245,000 — Dividing each term by the common factor 1000,

105 : 140 : 245 — Dividing each term by the common factor 5,

21 : 28 : 49 — Dividing each term by the common factor 7,

3 : 4 : 7

Therefore, the ratio of their investments in lowest terms is 3 : 4 : 7.

(ii) *A's profit was $30,000. What were B's and C's profits?*

Ratio of investment = Ratio of profit

$3 : 4 : 7 = 30{,}000 : x : y$

A	B	C
3	4	7
30,000	x	y

$\frac{3}{30{,}000} = \frac{4}{x} = \frac{7}{y}$

i.e., $\frac{3}{30{,}000} = \frac{4}{x}$

and $\frac{3}{30{,}000} = \frac{7}{y}$

Or $\frac{3}{4} = \frac{30{,}000}{x}$ and $\frac{3}{7} = \frac{30{,}000}{y}$

Cross-multiplying, $3x = 4 \times 30{,}000$ $\quad$ $3y = 7 \times 30{,}000$

$x = \frac{4 \times 30{,}000}{3}$ $\quad$ $y = \frac{7 \times 30{,}000}{3}$

$x = \$40{,}000.00$ $\quad$ $y = \$70{,}000.00$

Therefore, *B*'s profit is $40,000 and *C*'s profit is $70,000.

Solution *continued*

(iii) *In the second year, their total profit was $56,000. How much would each of them receive from this total profit?*

Since A, B, and C agreed to share profits in the same ratio as their investments, $56,000 must be shared in the ratio of 3 : 4 : 7.

By adding the terms in the ratio of their investments (3 + 4 + 7), we know that the total profit of $56,000 should be distributed over 14 units. Therefore,

$A : B : C : \text{Total} = A : B : C : \text{Total}$

$3 : 4 : 7 : 14 = A : B : C : 56{,}000$

A	B	C	Total
3	4	7	14
A	B	C	56,000

$$\frac{3}{A} = \frac{4}{B} = \frac{7}{C} = \frac{14}{56{,}000}$$

i.e.,

$$\frac{3}{A} = \frac{14}{56{,}000}, \quad \frac{4}{B} = \frac{14}{56{,}000}, \quad \frac{7}{C} = \frac{14}{56{,}000}$$

Or

$$\frac{3}{14} = \frac{A}{56{,}000}, \quad \frac{4}{14} = \frac{B}{56{,}000}, \quad \frac{7}{14} = \frac{C}{56{,}000}$$

Cross-multiplying,

$$14A = 3 \times 56{,}000 \qquad 14B = 4 \times 56{,}000 \qquad 14C = 7 \times 56{,}000$$

$$A = \frac{3 \times 56{,}000}{14} \qquad B = \frac{4 \times 56{,}000}{14} \qquad C = \frac{7 \times 56{,}000}{14}$$

$$A = \$12{,}000.00 \qquad B = \$16{,}000.00 \qquad C = \$28{,}000.00$$

Therefore, A, B, and C will receive $12,000, $16,000, and $28,000, respectively.

Pro-rations

Pro-ration is defined as sharing or allocating quantities, usually amounts of money, on a proportionate basis.

Consider an example where Kelly paid $1200 for a computer course, but decided to withdraw from the course after attending half the classes. As she attended only half the course, the college decided to refund half her tuition fee, $\frac{\$1200}{2} = \$600$. As the college calculated the refund amount proportionate to the time she attended the course, we say that the college refunded her tuition fee on a **pro-rata basis.**

A couple examples of pro-rated calculations are:

- Cancellation of insurance premiums before the end of the premium period. On cancellation, the amount refunded is calculated on a pro-rata basis.
- Employees' overtime pay, part-time pay, and vacation times are calculated on a pro-rata basis.

Example 4.2(d) **Calculating the Pro-rated Amount of a Payment**

Determine the pro-rated insurance premium for two months if the annual premium is \$4800.

Solution

Premium (\$) : time (months) = Premium (\$) : time (months)

$$4800 : 12 = x : 2$$

Premium (\$)	Time (months)
4800	12
x	2

In fractional form, $\frac{4800}{x} = \frac{12}{2}$ **Or** $\frac{4800}{12} = \frac{x}{2}$

Cross-multiplying, $4800 \times 2 = 12x$

$$\frac{9600}{12} = x$$

$$x = \$800.00$$

Therefore, the pro-rated premium for two months is \$800.

Example 4.2(e) **Calculating the Pro-rated Amount of a Refund**

Johnson paid \$200 for a 1-year, weekly subscription of a fashion journal. After receiving 15 issues of the journal, he decided to cancel his subscription. Determine Johnson's refund. Assume 1 year = 52 weeks.

Solution

Johnson paid for 52 issues, but received 15 issues; therefore, the refund is for 37 issues (52 – 15).

Issues (#) : Cost (\$) = Issues (#) : Cost (\$)

$$52 : 200 = 37 : x$$

Issues (#)	Cost (\$)
52	200
37	x

In fractional form, $\frac{52}{37} = \frac{200}{x}$ **Or** $\frac{52}{200} = \frac{37}{x}$

Cross-multiplying, $52x = 37 \times 200$

$$x = \frac{7400}{52}$$

$$x = 142.307692... = \$142.31$$

Therefore, his refund should be \$142.31.

4.2 | Exercises

Answers to the odd-numbered problems are available at the end of the textbook.

Calculate the missing terms in Problems 1 and 2.

1.
   a. $1 : 2 = 5 : x$
   b. $x : 1.2 = 3.4 : 5.8$
   c. $1 : 4\frac{1}{2} = x : 2\frac{3}{4}$
   d. $2.25 : 1\frac{1}{2} = x : 1\frac{3}{4}$
   e. $\frac{3}{4} : x = \frac{4}{11} : \frac{2}{11}$
   f. $\frac{4}{5} : \frac{3}{13} = x : \frac{5}{4}$

2.
   a. $5 : 9 = x : 3$
   b. $12.34 : 1.8 = x : 2.2$
   c. $11\frac{3}{4} : 8 = 18\frac{1}{4} : x$
   d. $4.75 : x = 6\frac{3}{4} : 3.28$
   e. $x : \frac{3}{2} = \frac{1}{3} : \frac{1}{9}$
   f. $\frac{5}{6} : \frac{1}{4} = 4 : x$

3. Michael was the lead on a research project at a large pharmaceutical company. Based on his past experience, it would take his team seven months to complete two projects. His Director of Research wants him to complete six similar projects. How long will his team take to complete all these projects?

4. A truck transporting material to a factory requires 180 litres of gas for every trip to cover 1500 km. How many litres of gas will it require to cover 1950 km?

5. Mike paid a property tax of \$400 for land that measures 110 square metres. What would his neighbour's property tax be if the size of her land is 70 square metres and she is taxed at the same rate?

6. The City of Ottawa charges $3760 in taxes per year for a 2000 square metre industrial shed. What taxes would Amazing Plastics Inc. have to pay if it has a 25,550 square metre shed in the same area?

7. On a map, 2.5 cm represents 2 km. If the distance between town *A* and town *B* on the map is 6.2 cm, how many kilometres apart are these towns?

8. On a house plan, 1.5 cm represents 1.25 metres. If the actual length of a room is 4.5 metres, how many centimetres will represent this length in the plan?

9. Jill's monthly expenses on food, transportation, and rent are in the ratio of 3 : 2 : 10. If she spends $300 on food, how much does she spend on transportation and rent?

10. Harris invested his savings in telecommunications, real estate, and technology stocks in the ratio of 4 : 5 : 3, respectively. If he invested $5450 in real estate stocks, calculate his investments in the telecommunications and technology stocks.

11. Adam, an entrepreneur, started an e-learning business with a personal investment of $110,000. He needed more funds and decided to raise money from two of his high-net-worth friends, Bill and Ted. In return for the money, he gave them ownership in his company. Based on their investments, Adam, Bill, and Ted own the company in the ratio of 11 : 5 : 2. All profits were also agreed to be shared in the ratio of their investments.
    a. Calculate Bill's and Ted's investments in the business.
    b. If the business earned a profit of $260,000 in the first year, calculate each partner's share of the profit.
    c. In the second year, if Adam earned $60,000 in profit from the business, how much did Bill and Ted make?

12. Three friends, *A*, *B*, and *C*, start a business with investments in the ratio of 2 : 3 : 1, respectively. *A* invested $9130, and all three of them agree to share profits in the ratio of their investments.
    a. Calculate *C*'s investment.
    b. If *A*'s profit was $45,000 in the first year, calculate *B*'s and *C*'s profits.
    c. In the second year, their total profit was $180,000. How much would each of them receive from this total profit?

13. If the annual salary of an employee is $45,000, calculate his weekly salary using pro-rations. Assume that there are 52 weeks in a year.

14. Addison received a job offer at a company that would pay her $2800 bi-weekly. How much is her annual salary, assuming that she will receive 26 payments in a year?

15. Angelina joined a driving school and paid $300 for twelve classes. After attending five classes, she did not like the training and wanted to cancel the remaining classes. Calculate her pro-rated refund.

16. A student paid $1400 for a course that has thirty classes. Determine the pro-rated refund she should receive if she only attended two classes before withdrawing from the course.

17. Robert paid the annual premium of $3000 for medical insurance. Three months later, he cancelled the insurance. Calculate the pro-rated refund he should receive from the insurance company.

18. The owner of a new gaming business decided to insure his servers and computers. His insurance company charged him a premium of $2000 per quarter starting January 01. If the insurance started on February 01, how much would his pro-rated insurance premiums be for the rest of the first quarter? Hint: every quarter of a year has three months.

19. Patrick and his two sisters purchased an office for $360,000. Their individual investments in the office were in the ratio of 2 : 4 : 3, respectively. After the purchase, they decided to renovate the building and purchase furniture, so each of them invested an additional $40,000. Calculate their new investment ratio after the additional investment.

20. Molly, Katie, and Timothy invested a total of $650,000 in the ratio of 2 : 4 : 7 to start a business. Two months later, each of them invested an additional $25,000 into the business. Calculate their new investment ratio after the additional investment.

21. Anthony set up a new charity fund to support needy children. For every $5 collected by the charity, the government donated an additional grant of $1.50 to the charity. At the end of three months, if his charity fund had a total of $90,000, including the government grant, calculate the amount the charity received from the government.

22. The sales tax on many products sold in Ontario is such that for every $1.00 worth of a product sold, the buyer would have to pay an additional $0.13 in taxes. If a product was being sold at an exhibition for $18,500 including taxes, calculate the amount of sales tax to be paid by the buyer.

23. Bill, Blake, and Roy invested $45,000, $75,000, and $60,000, respectively, to start an e-learning business. They realized that they required an additional $60,000 for operating the business. How much did each of them have to individually invest to maintain their original investment ratio?

24. Three wealthy business partners decided to invest $120,000, $300,000, and $180,000, respectively, to purchase an industrial plot in the outskirts of the city. They required an additional $175,000 to build an industrial shed on the land. How much did each of them have to individually invest to maintain their original investment ratio?

25. A first semester class in a college has 9 more girls than boys and the ratio of the number of girls to boys in the class is 7 : 4.
   a. How many students are there in the class?
   b. If 4 girls and 3 boys joined the class, determine the new ratio of girls to boys in the class.

26. The advisory board of a public sector company has 12 more men than women and the ratio of the number of men to women is 5 : 2.
   a. How many people are there on the board?
   b. If 4 men and 4 women joined the board, calculate the new ratio of men to women.

• 27. Paul, Oliver, and Ellie decided to start a web design company and made investments in the ratio of 2 : 3 : 4, respectively. After one year, if Paul increased his initial investment by 50% and Oliver decreased his initial investment of $4500 by 25%, determine the new ratio of their investments.

• 28. Jake, Kristen, and Destiny started a design studio and made investments in the ratio of 4 : 7 : 8, respectively, out of which Destiny's investment was $12,000. Calculate the new ratio of their investments if Jake and Destiny increased their investments by 25% and 50%, respectively.

• 29. To estimate the number of tigers in a forest, a team of researchers tagged 91 tigers and released them into the forest. Six months later, 25 tigers were spotted, out of which 7 had tags. How many tigers are estimated to be in the forest?

• 30. Researchers were conducting a study to estimate the number of frogs in a pond. They put a bright yellow band on the legs of 45 frogs and released them into the pond. A few days later, 12 frogs were spotted, out of which 5 had bands. How many frogs are estimated to be in the pond?

4.3 | Exchange Rates and Applications

Exchange Rates

Exchange rates are used to convert currencies between countries.

The exchange rate, also called the foreign exchange rate or forex rate, is used to convert currencies between countries. Therefore, knowing the exchange rate would allow you to calculate the amount of a currency required to purchase one unit of another currency.

For example, to convert Canadian currency to US currency, it is important to know how many Canadian dollars are equivalent to one US dollar, or vice versa.

The value of a currency may fluctuate constantly during the day and the exchange rate may vary accordingly. For example, at 1:00 pm EST on March 01, 2017, US$1 was equal to C$1.3342 and C$1 was equal to US$0.7495. Therefore, the exchange rate on that date and time was US$1 = C$1.3342 and C$1 = US$0.7495.

Currency Cross-Rate Table

Currency exchange rates are generally displayed in a table called the 'Currency Cross-Rate Table' for quick reference.

Exchange rates presented in the currency cross-rate table below are as of March 01, 2017 at 1:00 pm EST.

Common currencies and their symbols

Canadian dollar:	C$
US dollar:	US$
Euro:	€
British pound:	£
Japanese yen:	¥
Swiss franc:	CHF
Australian dollar:	A$

Table 4.3(a) **Currency Cross-Rate Table, as of March 01, 2017**

(One unit of)

(Equivalent to)

Symbol	C$	US$	€	£	¥	CHF	A$
C$	1.0000	1.3342	1.4095	1.6435	0.011738	1.3247	1.0226
US$	0.7495	1.0000	1.0565	1.2318	0.008798	0.9929	0.7665
€	0.7095	0.9466	1.0000	1.1660	0.008328	0.9398	0.7255
£	0.6085	0.8118	0.8576	1.0000	0.007142	0.8060	0.6222
¥	85.191	113.661	120.079	140.013	1.0000	112.849	87.118
CHF	0.7549	1.0072	1.0641	1.2407	0.008861	1.0000	0.7720
A$	0.9779	1.3047	1.3784	1.6072	0.011479	1.2954	1.0000

The vertical columns of the table represent one unit of the currency to be converted and the horizontal rows represent the equivalent value of it in another currency.

For example, US$1 = C$1.3342 and £1 = CHF1.2407.

Based on the exchange rates in Table 4.3(a), the exchange rates of foreign currencies in Canadian dollars and vice versa are presented in Table 4.3(b) for easy reference.

Table 4.3(b) **Exchange Rates of Foreign Currencies per Canadian Dollar and Vice Versa**

Foreign Currency	Symbol	C$ per Unit of Foreign Currency	Units of Foreign Currency per C$
US dollar	**US$**	1.3342	0.7495
Euro	**€**	1.4095	0.7095
British pound	**£**	1.6435	0.6085
Japanese yen	**¥**	0.011738	85.191
Swiss franc	**CHF**	1.3247	0.7549
Australian dollar	**A$**	1.0226	0.9779

For calculations involving conversion from one currency to another, we will either use the cross-reference table or exchange rates provided in the question. We will be using the method of proportions to solve examples that follow.

Example 4.3(a) Currency Conversion from Canadian Dollar to US Dollar

Based on the exchange rates provided in Table 4.3(a) (Currency Cross-Rate Table), how many US dollars will you receive when you convert C$400?

Solution

From the cross-rate table, US$1 = C$1.3342

US$: C$ = US$: C$

$1 : 1.3342 = x : 400$

US$	C$
1	1.3342
x	400

In fractional form, $\frac{1}{x} = \frac{1.3342}{400}$ **Or** $\frac{1}{1.3342} = \frac{x}{400}$

Cross-multiplying, $x = \frac{400}{1.3342} = 299.805126... = \text{US\$}299.81$

Therefore, you will receive US$299.81 when you convert C$400.00.

Example 4.3(b) Currency Conversion from C$ to US$ and from US$ to C$

If US$1 = C$1.3342, then (i) how much will you receive if you convert US$1000 to Canadian dollars, and (ii) how much will you receive if you convert C$1000 to US dollars?

Solution

(i) US$: C$ = US$: C$

$1 : 1.3342 = 1000 : x$

US$	C$
1	1.3342
1000	x

In fractional form, $\frac{1}{1000} = \frac{1.3342}{x}$ **Or** $\frac{1}{1.3342} = \frac{1000}{x}$

Cross-multiplying and solving, $x = \text{C\$}1334.20$

Therefore, you will receive C$1334.20 when you convert US$1000.00.

(ii) US$: C$ = US$: C$

$1 : 1.3342 = x : 1000$

US$	C$
1	1.3342
x	1000

In fractional form, $\frac{1}{x} = \frac{1.3342}{1000}$ **Or** $\frac{1}{1.3342} = \frac{x}{1000}$

Cross-multiplying and solving, $x = 749.512816... = \text{US\$}749.51$

Therefore, you will receive US$749.51 when you convert C$1000.00.

Example 4.3(c) Converting from One Currency to Another Currency, Given Exchange Rates

Samantha is travelling from Canada to London on vacation. If £1 = C$1.6435, then how much will she receive if she converts C$1000 to British pounds?

Solution

£ : C$ = £ : C$

$1 : 1.6435 = x : 1000$

£	C$
1	1.6435
x	1000

In fractional form, $\frac{1}{x} = \frac{1.6435}{1000}$ **Or** $\frac{1}{1.6435} = \frac{x}{1000}$

Cross-multiplying and solving, $x = 608.457560... = £608.46$

Therefore, she will receive £608.46 when she converts C$1000.00.

Example 4.3(d) **Series of Currency Conversions**

If US$1 = C$1.3342 and C$1 = A$0.9779, calculate the amount of US dollars you will receive with 100 Australian dollars.

Solution

First, determine how many Canadian dollars you will receive with A$100.

C$: A$ = C$: A$

$1 : 0.9779 = x : 100$

C$	A$
1	0.9779
x	100

In fractional form, $\frac{1}{x} = \frac{0.9779}{100}$ **Or** $\frac{1}{0.9779} = \frac{x}{100}$

Cross-multiplying and solving, x = C$102.259944...

Now, determine how many US dollars you will receive with C$102.259944...

US$: C$ = US$: C$

$1 : 1.3342 = x : 102.259944...$

US$	C$
1	1.3342
x	102.259944...

In fractional form, $\frac{1}{x} = \frac{1.3342}{102.259944...}$ **Or** $\frac{1}{1.3342} = \frac{x}{102.259944...}$

Cross-multiplying and solving, x = 76.645139... = US$76.65

Therefore, you will receive US$76.65 when you convert A$100.00.

Example 4.3(e) **Series of Currency Conversions and Converting Back to the Original Currency**

Martha, a globetrotter, travelled from Canada to the US with C$3000 as backup cash. In the US, she converted this amount to US dollars. From there, she traveled to Japan. While in Japan, she converted her US dollars to Japanese yen. She finally returned to Canada and converted the Japanese yen to Canadian dollars.

(i) How many US dollars did she have as backup cash during her stay in the US?

(ii) How many Japanese yen did she have while she was in Japan?

(iii) Determine if she received her original amount of C$3000 when she converted her Japanese yen back to Canadian dollars.

Use these exchange rates: C$1 = US$0.7495, US$1 = ¥113.661, and C$1 = ¥85.191.

Solution

(i) *How many US dollars did she have as backup cash during her stay in the US?*

C$: US$ = C$: US$

$1 : 0.7495 = 3000 : x$

C$	US$
1	0.7495
3000	x

In fractional form, $\frac{1}{3000} = \frac{0.7495}{x}$ **Or** $\frac{1}{0.7495} = \frac{3000}{x}$

Cross-multiplying and solving, x = US$2248.50

Therefore, she had US$2248.50 in the US.

Solution *continued*

(ii) *How many Japanese yen did she have while she was in Japan?*

US$: ¥ = US$: ¥

1 : 113.661 = 2248.50 : x

US$	¥
1	113.661
2248.50	x

In fractional form, $\frac{1}{2248.50} = \frac{113.661}{x}$ **Or** $\frac{1}{113.661} = \frac{2248.50}{x}$

Cross-multiplying and solving, x = ¥255,566.7585

Therefore, she had ¥255,566.7585 in Japan.

(iii) *Determine if she received her original amount of C$3000 when she converted her Japanese yen back to Canadian dollars.*

C$: ¥ = C$: ¥

1 : 85.191 = x : 255,566.7585

C$	¥
1	85.191
x	255,566.7585

In fractional form, $\frac{1}{x} = \frac{85.191}{255{,}566.7585}$ **Or** $\frac{1}{85.191} = \frac{x}{255{,}566.7585}$

Cross-multiplying and solving, x = 2999.926735... = C$2999.93

Therefore, she would receive C$2999.93 in Canada.

Note: *The slight difference of C$0.07 is because of rounding every time she converts a currency.*

Buying and Selling Currencies

If you would like to convert currencies, you should go to a bank or other financial institution that is authorized to purchase and sell currencies. These financial institutions usually have different exchange rates for buying and selling currencies, which they refer to as their 'buy rate' and 'sell rate'. They use the actual currency exchange rates and their rate of commission to create their own buying and selling rates for each currency. The commission is charged for their services on these transactions.

Example 4.3(f) **Currency Conversion Including Commission in Buying or Selling Currencies**

Sarah plans to travel to the US from Canada and approaches a local bank to purchase US$1000. Assume US$1 = C$1.3342 and the bank charges a commission of 0.75% to sell or buy US dollars.

(i) How much in Canadian dollars would Sarah have to pay for US$1000?

(ii) If Sarah changes her plan and wishes to convert US$1000 back to Canadian dollars, how much will she receive from the same bank, assuming the same exchange rate and the same commission rate?

Solution

When buying or selling currencies, it does not matter if you calculate the commission first and then convert the value, or vice versa. You will always get the same answer.

(i) *How much in Canadian dollars would she have to pay for US$1000?*

US$: C$ = US$: C$

1 : 1.3342 = 1000 : x

US$	C$
1	1.3342
1000	x

In fractional form, $\frac{1}{1000} = \frac{1.3342}{x}$ **Or** $\frac{1}{1.3342} = \frac{1000}{x}$

Cross-multiplying and solving, x = C$1334.20

When you buy currencies, you will pay the converted amount and the financial institution's commission.

US$1000 =	C$1334.20	Amount in C$ before the bank's commission.
0.0075 × 1334.20 =	+C$10.0065	Adding bank's 0.75% commission,
Total =	C$1344.21	Amount that Sarah will pay the bank.

Or,

$$C\$1334.20(1 + 0.0075) = 1344.2065 = C\$1344.21$$

Therefore, Sarah would have to pay C$1344.21 for US$1000.00.

(ii) *If Sarah changes her plan and wishes to convert US$1000 back to Canadian dollars, how much will she receive from the same bank, assuming the same exchange rate and the same commission rate?*

When you sell currencies, you will receive the converted amount less the financial institution's commission.

US$1000 =	C$1334.20	As calculated in (i)
0.0075 × 1334.20 =	–C$10.0065	Subtracting bank's 0.75% commission,
Total =	C$1324.19	Amount the bank will pay Sarah.

Or,

$$C\$1334.20(1 - 0.0075) = 1324.1935 = C\$1324.19$$

Therefore, Sarah will receive C$1324.19 from the bank.

Example 4.3(g) **Calculating a Bank's Rate of Commission to Sell Currencies**

A bank in Calgary has the following buy and sell rates against Canadian dollars:

Country	Currency name	Buy Rate	Sell Rate
Brazil	reals	0.3615	0.4290

(i) Calculate the cost of 500 Brazilian reals based on the exchange rate of R$1 = C$0.3927.

(ii) Calculate the bank's commission amount in Canadian dollars and the rate of commission (%) to sell 500 Brazilian reals.

Solution

(i) R$500 based on the exchange rate:

R$: C$ = R$: C$

1 : 0.3927 = 500 : x

R$	C$
1	0.3927
500	x

In fractional form, $\frac{1}{500} = \frac{0.3927}{x}$ **Or** $\frac{1}{0.3927} = \frac{500}{x}$

Cross-multiplying and solving, $x = C\$196.35$

It would cost C$196.35 based on the exchange rate.

(ii) R$500 based on the bank's selling rate: 500.00 × 0.4290 = C$214.50

It would cost C$214.50 based on the bank's selling rate.

Therefore, the bank's commission amount is C$214.50 – C$196.35 = C$18.15

Although exchange rates may be the same, the buying and selling rates may be different at different financial institutions because of varying commissions.

Using $R = \frac{P}{B}$,

$$\text{Rate of commission} = \frac{\text{Amount in Commission in C\$}}{\text{Amount based on exchange rate in C\$}} \times 100\%$$

$$= \frac{18.15}{196.35} \times 100\% = 0.092436... \times 100\% = 9.24\%$$

Therefore, the bank's selling commission rate is 9.24%.

Example 4.3(h) **Calculating a Bank's Rate of Commission to Buy Currencies**

The same bank in Calgary has the following buy and sell rates against Canadian dollars:

Country	Currency name	Buy Rate	Sell Rate
South Africa	rand	0.0868	0.1036

(i) Calculate the cost of 2000 South African rands using the exchange rate of 1 rand = C$0.0949.

(ii) Calculate the bank's commission amount in Canadian dollars and the rate of commission (%) to buy 2000 South African rands.

Solution

(i) 2000 rands based on the exchange rate:

rand : C$ = rand : C$

1 : 0.0949 = 2000 : x

rand	C$
1	0.0949
2000	x

In fractional form, $\frac{1}{2000} = \frac{0.0949}{x}$ **Or** $\frac{1}{0.0949} = \frac{2000}{x}$

Cross-multiplying and solving, $x = \text{C\$}189.80$

It would cost C$189.80 based on the exchange rate.

(ii) 2000 rands based on the bank's buying rate: 2000.00 × 0.0868 = C$173.60

You would receive C$173.60 according to the bank's buying rate.

Therefore, the bank's commission amount is C$189.80 – C$173.60 = C$16.20

Using $R = \frac{P}{B}$, Rate of commission $= \frac{\text{Amount in Commission in C\$}}{\text{Amount based on exchange rate in C\$}} \times 100\%$

$$= \frac{16.20}{189.80} \times 100\% = 0.085353... \times 100\% = 8.54\%$$

Therefore, the bank's buying commission rate is 8.54%.

Currency Appreciation and Depreciation

The value of a currency can increase or decrease relative to the value of another currency.

For example, the exchange rate on December 01, 2014 was C$1 = US$0.881504. This means that on December 01, 2014 you were able to buy US$0.88 with C$1.

However, on December 01, 2016, the exchange rate changed to C$1 = US$0.751058. This means that on December 01, 2016 you were able to buy US$0.75 with C$1.

As you were able to purchase fewer US dollars with C$1 on December 01, 2016 than on December 01, 2014, the value of the Canadian currency weakened or depreciated relative to the US currency; i.e., the value of the US currency strengthened or appreciated relative to the Canadian currency.

Understanding the Effect of Currency Appreciation and Depreciation

When a currency appreciates, consumers will pay less for foreign goods and services. When a currency depreciates, consumers will pay more for foreign goods and services.

When the Canadian dollar appreciates in value compared to other currencies:

- It is cheaper for Canadian businesses to import from foreign countries and the consumer will benefit as the price on imported goods will drop.
- Export of goods to foreign countries and the demand for Canadian goods and services will decrease as foreign countries receive less money when exchanging their currencies.

When the Canadian dollar depreciates in value compared to other countries:

- It is cheaper for foreign businesses to import more goods from Canadian businesses. It will cost more money for Canadian businesses to import goods from foreign countries and therefore, consumers will pay more for imported goods.
- When more Canadian goods are exported, the country must produce more goods and the employment rate will increase.

Example 4.3(i) **Application of Exchange Rate Fluctuation**

A large chocolate distributor in Canada purchased chocolates from a supplier in Switzerland two years ago for CHF100,000 when the exchange rate between the Canadian dollar and the Swiss franc was C$1.177797 = CHF1. This year, it wanted to make a similar purchase as the purchase price of the chocolates did not change in Swiss francs; however, the exchange rate changed to C$1.317385 = CHF1.

(i) Calculate the amount of increase or decrease this year in the cost of the chocolates in Canadian dollars, compared to two years ago.

(ii) Which currency appreciated relative to the other?

Solution

(i) *Cost of chocolates in Canadian dollars two years ago:*

C$: CHF = C$: CHF

1.177797 : 1 = x : 100,000

C$	CHF
1.177797	1
x	100,000

In fractional form, $\frac{1.177797}{x} = \frac{1}{100{,}000}$ **Or** $\frac{1.177797}{1} = \frac{x}{100{,}000}$

Cross-multiplying and solving, x = C$117,779.70

i.e. the cost of chocolates in Canadian dollars two years ago = C$117,779.70.

Cost of chocolates in Canadian dollars this year:

C$: CHF = C$: CHF

1.317385 : 1 = x : 100,000

C$	CHF
1.317385	1
x	100,000

In fractional form, $\frac{1.317385}{x} = \frac{1}{100{,}000}$ **Or** $\frac{1.317385}{1} = \frac{x}{100{,}000}$

Cross-multiplying and solving, x = C$131,738.50

i.e. the cost of chocolates in Canadian dollars this year = C$131,738.50.

Therefore, the cost of the chocolates has increased by 131,738.50 – 117,779.70 = C$13,958.80

(ii) From the two exchange rates, we see that this year you can purchase more Canadian dollars with 1 Swiss franc; therefore, the value of the Swiss franc has appreciated relative to the value of the Canadian dollar.

Importing Goods from Another Country

When you import an item, the authorities at the border will convert the value of the goods to the local currency based on current exchange rates and may impose an import duty or customs duty, which is the tax a government charges on imported goods. In addition to providing revenue for the government, import duties help to protect domestic trade from overseas products. Import duties vary depending on the product and/or the country of origin.

Importing goods to Canada is almost always subject to import duty and is normally charged on the converted rate in Canadian dollars. GST (Goods and Services Tax), PST (Provincial Sales Tax), or HST (Harmonized Sales Tax) will then be charged on the total value of the goods including duty.

Higher duties are applied on certain types of products as well as items of luxury or high dollar value.

Example 4.3(j) **Calculating the Cost of Importing Goods from Another Country**

Robert, who resides in Toronto, drove down to Buffalo, USA on Black Friday to purchase a leather jacket at a discounted price. He paid US$650 (including taxes) for the jacket that costs C$1000 (including taxes) in Canada. While driving back into Canada, the customs authorities at the border charged a duty of 18% for the jacket. He also paid 13% HST on the amount after the duty was applied. Calculate the total amount he spent on the jacket and determine if it worked out to be cheaper for him to drive down to Buffalo to purchase this jacket. Assume US$1 = C$1.3342.

Solution

US$: C$ = US$: C$

$1 : 1.3342 = 650 : x$

US$	C$
1	1.3342
650	x

$$\frac{1}{650} = \frac{1.3342}{x} \quad \textbf{Or} \quad \frac{1}{1.3342} = \frac{650}{x}$$

x = C$867.23 — Value of the jacket in C$ based on the given exchange rate

Total cost including duty and HST:
650(1.3342)(1.18)(1.13) = 1156.36

$867.23
$1023.3314
$1156.364482

Value of the jacket	= C$867.23	
Add 18% duty	= C$156.1014	(18% × 867.23) Amount of duty
Value including duty	= C$1023.3314	
Add 13% HST	= C$133.033082	(13% × 1023.3314) Amount of HST
Total cost	= C$1156.364482	

Therefore, the total amount he paid for the jacket was C$1156.36.

It was more expensive for him to purchase the leather jacket from Buffalo. He would have saved C$156.36, plus the time and other costs related to driving down to Buffalo if he had bought the jacket in Canada.

4.3 | Exercises

Answers to the odd-numbered problems are available at the end of the textbook.

1. Using £1 = CHF1.2407, US$1 = C$1.3342, and £1 = C$1.6435, convert the following:
   a. CHF200 to British pounds (£)
   b. C$3000 to US dollars (US$)
   c. US$5000 to Canadian dollars (C$)
   d. £10 to Canadian dollars (C$)

2. Using ¥1 = C$0.011738, CHF1 = US$0.9929, £1 = CHF1.2407, and CHF1 = C$1.3247, convert the following:
   a. C$18,000 to Japanese yen (¥)
   b. US$2850 to Swiss francs (CHF)
   c. £18 to Swiss francs (CHF)
   d. CHF850,935 to Canadian dollars (C$)

3. A bank in London, Ontario charges 2.25% commission to buy and sell currencies. Assume that the current exchange rate is US$1 = C$1.3342.
   a. How many Canadian dollars will you receive from the bank if you sell US$1375?
   b. How much commission will you pay the bank for this transaction?

4. A bank in Toronto charges 2.5% commission to buy and sell currencies. Assume that the current exchange rate is US$1 = C$1.3342.
   a. How many Canadian dollars will you have to pay to purchase US$1500?
   b. How much commission in Canadian dollars (C$) will you pay the bank for the above transaction?

5. Jo-Ann's mother sent her ¥50,000 as a graduation gift and she wanted to convert the Japanese yen into Canadian dollars. If the bank was charging 0.90% commission, calculate how many Canadian dollars she received. Assume that the exchange rate was C$1 = ¥85.191.

6. Hailey found US$100 in her attic and sold it to a bank that charged her a commission of 0.25%. How much did she receive from the bank? Assume that the exchange rate was C$1 = US$0.7495.

7. Emma-Lee purchased US$10,000 from a bank in the US, which charged her a commission of 0.80%, and sold the US dollars to a bank in Canada, which charged her a 0.25% commission. How much money did she lose or gain? Assume that the exchange rate was C$1 = US$0.7495.

8. Ronald planned to travel to Australia from Canada and purchased 5000 Australian dollars. A week later, he decided to cancel his trip and wanted to convert his Australian dollars back to Canadian dollars at the same bank. Did he lose any money by converting the money twice? If so, how much did he lose? Assume that the bank charged a commission of 0.5% to sell and 0.75% to buy currencies. Assume that the exchange rate was C$1 = A$0.9779.

9. If C$1 = £0.6085 and £1 = US$1.2318, how many Canadian dollars will you receive with US$1000?

10. If C$1 = ¥85.191 and ¥1 = US$0.008798, how many Canadian dollars will you receive with US$1000?

11. If £1 = US$1.2318 and A$1 = US$0.7665, determine the exchange rate for one Australian dollar to British pounds.

12. If €1 = ¥120.079 and C$1 = ¥85.191, determine the exchange rate one for Canadian dollar to euro.

13. Suppose the exchange rate changes from C$1 = A$0.9779 to C$1 = A$1.1385; what will be the change in the value of a machine in Australian dollars if it costs C$3000?

14. Suppose the exchange rate changes from C$1 = £0.6085 to C$1 = £0.6754; what will be the change in the value of a printer in British pounds if it costs C$280?

15. Bernie, a senior sales representative at a multinational company, travelled from Canada to Japan via the UK. He left Canada with C$8000. When he reached the UK, he converted all his cash to British pounds. The conversion rate was £1 = C$1.6435. After spending £1000, he left for Japan where he converted the remaining British pounds to Japanese yen at an exchange rate of ¥1 = £0.007142. He spent ¥125,400 in Japan and finally returned to Canada. Based on the information in this question, calculate the number of Canadian dollars he received when he converted the remaining Japanese yen to Canadian dollars.

16. Kristin saved up C$3000 to use for her travels during her summer holidays. She first travelled from Toronto to Switzerland, where she converted all her Canadian dollars to Swiss francs at an exchange rate of C$1 = CHF0.7549. She spent CHF1452 and then travelled to London, where she converted the remaining Swiss francs to British pounds at an exchange rate of CHF1 = £0.8060. She spent £570.34 in London before returning to Toronto. Based on the information in this question, how many Canadian dollars did she receive when she converted the remaining British pounds to Canadian dollars?

17. A Canadian businesswoman purchased an all-in-one printer for ¥80,000 while in Japan on business. On returning to Canada, she had to pay 15% customs duty, 5% GST, and 8% PST. What was the total cost of the printer in Canadian dollars if the exchange rate was ¥1 = C$0.011738?

18. What would it cost, in Canadian dollars, to import a set of Swiss skis priced at CHF850 and subject to an import duty of 10% and 13% HST if the exchange rate is CHF1 = C$1.3247?

19. Noah, who lives in Vancouver, purchased a piece of equipment from Australia for A$535,280. He was charged 18% duty, 5% GST, and 7% PST to import it. Calculate the total cost of the equipment. Assume that the exchange rate was C$1 = A$0.9779.

20. A wholesaler in Ontario purchased a shipment of fruits from Australia for A$15,000. If his shipment was subject to a customs duty of 5% and 13% HST, calculate the total cost of the shipment to the wholesaler in Ontario. Assume that the exchange rate was C$1 = A$0.9779.

• 21. A bank in London, Ontario has a buying rate of CHF1 = C$1.2717. If the exchange rate is CHF1 = C$1.3247, calculate the rate of commission that the bank charges.

• 22. A bank in London, Ontario has a selling rate of £1 = C$1.6912. If the exchange rate is £1 = C$1.6435, calculate the rate of commission that the bank charges.

• 23. The following table provides you with exchange rates of different currencies on December 01, 2014 and December 01, 2016.

December 01, 2014	December 01, 2016
C$1 = US$0.881504	US$1 = C$1.331455
C$1 = €0.705813	€1 = C$1.419632
C$1 = £0.559974	£1 = C$1.677576

Did the Canadian dollar appreciate or depreciate relative to the (a) US dollar (US$), (b) euro (€), or (c) British pound (£) over the two year period? Explain your answer.

• 24. The following table provides you with exchange rates of different currencies on December 01, 2014 and December 01, 2016.

December 01, 2014	December 01, 2016
C$1 = A$1.034610	A$1 = C$0.987338
C$1 = ¥104.136457	¥1 = C$0.011663
C$1 = CHF0.849042	CHF1 = C$1.317386

Did the Canadian dollar appreciate or depreciate relative to the (a) Australian dollar (A$), (b) Japanese yen (¥), or (c) Swiss franc (CHF) over the two year period? Explain your answer.

• 25. Helix, a motorbike manufacturer in Canada, has two paint suppliers - one is in the US and the other is in Mexico. This month, the value of the Canadian currency appreciated relative to the US dollar but remained the same relative to the Mexican peso. If the paint suppliers did not change the price of the paint, in which country can it purchase more paint for the same amount of Canadian dollars and why?

• 26. Bob, a resident of Canada, was contemplating purchasing a motorbike from either the US or Mexico. The cost of the bike, including shipment and taxes, after converting to Canadian dollars was the same whether purchased in the US or Mexico. A month later, the Canadian currency depreciated against the Mexican peso but remained the same relative to the US dollar. Where will Bob purchase the bike for the lowest cost and why?

• 27. If the Canadian dollar appreciated by US$0.1115 relative to the US dollar, what would be the new value of the Canadian dollar per US dollar? Assume that the current exchange rate is US$1 = C$1.3342.

• 28. If the US dollar depreciated by C$0.0899 relative to the Canadian dollar, what would be the new value of the US dollar per Canadian dollar? Assume that the current exchange rate is C$1 = US$0.7495.

• 29. Harris purchased a set of golf clubs from the US for US$900. He had to pay 18% customs duty and 13% HST to import it. Calculate the total cost of the clubs. If a similar set of clubs cost C$1300 plus 13% HST, was it cheaper for him to buy it from the US? Assume that the exchange rate was US$1 = C$1.3342.

• 30. Joanne purchased a laptop from Los Angeles, California for US$900 and brought it back with her to Toronto. At the US-Canada border, she was asked to pay customs duty of 14% on the laptop. In addition, she had to pay 13% HST. If the same model of laptop was available in Toronto for C$1500 including HST, was it cheaper for her to purchase the laptop from the US? Assume that the current exchange rate was US$1 = C$1.3342.

4.4 | Index Numbers and Applications

Index Numbers

***Index Numbers** are used to express the relative value of items compared to a base value.*

The price of various items constantly fluctuates at different points in time. You may have noticed that the cost of transportation, entertainment, education, housing, etc., have constantly been on the rise. Index numbers are used to quantify such economic changes over time.

An **index number** is a comparison of the value of an item on a selected date to the value of the same item on a designated date, known as the base date.

This can be expressed using a proportion equation, as follows:

$$\text{Index Number on selected date} : \text{Value of Item on selected date} = \text{Index Number on base date} : \text{Value of Item on base date}$$

Representing this in fractional form, we get,

$$\frac{\text{Index Number on selected date}}{\text{Index Number on base date}} = \frac{\text{Value of Item on selected date}}{\text{Value of Item on base date}} \quad \textbf{Or} \quad \frac{\text{Index Number on selected date}}{\text{Value of Item on selected date}} = \frac{\text{Index Number on base date}}{\text{Value of Item on base date}}$$

The index number on the base date is usually set as 100 to align the index numbers with percents.

$$\frac{\text{Index Number on selected date}}{100} = \frac{\text{Value of Item on selected date}}{\text{Value of Item on base date}} \quad \textbf{Or} \quad \frac{\text{Index Number on selected date}}{\text{Value of Item on selected date}} = \frac{100}{\text{Value of Item on base date}}$$

Cross-multiplying either of these equations, we obtain,

Formula 4.4(a) **Index Number on a Selected Date**

$$\text{Index Number on selected date} = \frac{\text{Value of Item on selected date}}{\text{Value of Item on base date}} \times 100$$

The index number on the base date is 100 and is the comparative centre of the index numbers. That is, if the index number on a selected date is lower than 100, the value of the item has decreased since the base date; if the index number on a selected date is higher than 100, the value of the item has increased since the base date.

Base period is the year from which the percent change is calculated. Any year can be the base period.

The difference between the index number of an item on a selected date and 100 represents the percent change in value of that item between the selected date and the base period.

For example, if the index number for an item on a selected date is 120.5, then the value of the item is 20.5% above the base period price of 100 for the same item.

Example 4.4(a) **Calculating the Index Number and Percent Change in Price of Gasoline in 2016 Using 2010 as the Base Year**

The price of gasoline (gas) in 2010 was \$0.91 per litre and in 2016 it increased to \$1.05 per litre.

(i) Calculate the index number for the price of gas in 2016 using 2010 as the base year.

(ii) Calculate the percent change in the price of gas from 2010 to 2016.

Solution

(i)

	Year	Index	Price ($)
Base Year	2010	100	0.91
	2016	x	1.05

In fractional form, $\frac{100}{x} = \frac{0.91}{1.05}$

Cross-multiplying, $x = \frac{1.05}{0.91} \times 100$

$= 115.384615...$

$= 115.38$

Or

Using Formula 4.4(a),

$$\text{Index Number on selected date} = \frac{\text{Value of Item on selected date}}{\text{Value of Item on base date}} \times 100$$

$$\text{Index Number}_{2016} = \frac{1.05}{0.91} \times 100$$

$= 115.384615... = 115.38$

Therefore, the index number for the price of gas in 2016 is 115.38 using 2010 as the base year.

CALCULATOR METHOD

2ND Δ%
OLD = 0.91 ENTER
↓
NEW = 1.05 ENTER
↓ CPT
%CH = 15.38461538

(ii) Since 2010 is referred to as the base date,

Index number for 2010 is 100.

Index number for 2016 is 115.38.

Percent change = (115.38 – 100)% = 15.38%.

Or

Using the percent change formula, Formula 3.2,

$$\%C = \frac{V_f - V_i}{V_i} \times 100\%$$

$$= \frac{1.05 - 0.91}{0.91} \times 100\%$$

$= 0.153846... \times 100\% = 15.38\%$

Therefore, the price of gas in 2016 has increased by 15.38% from its price in 2010.

Example 4.4(b) Calculating the Index Number and Percent Change in the Price of Basic Cable TV in 2016 Using 2005 as the Base Year

The price of basic cable TV in 2005 was $39 per month and it decreased to $25 per month in 2016.

(i) Calculate the index number for the price of basic cable TV in 2016 using 2005 as the base year.

(ii) Calculate the percent change in the price of basic cable TV from 2005 to 2016.

Solution

(i)

	Year	Index	Price ($)
Base Year	2005	100	39
	2016	x	25

In fractional form, $\frac{100}{x} = \frac{39.00}{25.00}$

Cross multiplying, $x = \frac{25.00}{39.00} \times 100$

$= 64.102564...$

$= 64.10$

Or

Using Formula 4.4(a),

$$\text{Index Number on selected date} = \frac{\text{Value of Item on selected date}}{\text{Value of Item on base date}} \times 100$$

$$\text{Index Number}_{2016} = \frac{25.00}{39.00} \times 100$$

$= 64.102564... = 64.10$

Therefore, the index number for basic cable TV in 2016 is 64.10 using 2005 as the base year.

CALCULATOR METHOD

2ND Δ%
OLD = 39 ENTER
↓
NEW = 25 ENTER
↓ CPT
%CH = –35.8974359

(ii) Since 2005 is referred to as the base date,

Index number for 2005 is 100.

Index number for 2016 is 64.10.

Percent change = (64.10 – 100)% = –35.90%

Or

Using the percent change formula, Formula 3.2,

$$\%C = \frac{V_f - V_i}{V_i} \times 100\%$$

$$= \frac{25.00 - 39.00}{39.00} \times 100\%$$

$= -0.358974... \times 100\% = -35.90\%$

Therefore, the price of basic cable TV in 2016 decreased by 35.90% from its price in 2005.

Consumer Price Index (CPI)

***The Consumer Price Index (CPI)** is an indicator of changes in consumer prices experienced by Canadians.*

The Consumer Price Index (CPI) is a good example of how useful index numbers can be in day-to-day life. CPI is an indicator of changes in consumer prices. In Canada, Statistics Canada obtains this number by calculating the cost of a fixed basket of goods and services purchased by consumers and comparing this cost over time. This basket is composed of around 600 different goods and services classified under eight major categories. Every product has a unique place in this classification. The composition of the Canadian CPI Basket in 2016 is provided in Table 4.4(a).

Table 4.4(a) **CPI Basket Composition**

	Components of CPI Basket	Percent
1.	Food	16.45%
2.	Shelter	26.79%
3.	Recreation, education, and reading	11.02%
4.	Health and personal care	4.98%
5.	Transportation	19.48%
6.	Clothing and footwear	5.68%
7.	Household operations, furnishings, and equipment	13.01%
8.	Alcoholic beverages and tobacco products	2.58%
		99.99%

Source: Statistics Canada: Consumer Price Index Basket Basket Share (%) by Consumer Price Index Component

Note: *Figures do not add to 100% due to rounding.*

CPI is calculated by comparing the cost of a fixed basket of items at a particular period to the cost at the base period. The CPI value is usually rounded to one decimal place.

CPI for Canada is calculated and issued by Statistics Canada on a monthly basis and is released during the third week of the following month (around the 20th).

For example, CPI for October 2016 was released on November 18, 2016. (CPI for for October 2016 = 129.1).

When there are considerable changes in consumer spending pattern, the base period for CPI is adjusted periodically by Statistics Canada. In 2004, the base period was changed from 1992 to 2002, which is the current base period used in CPI calculations (CPI for 2002 = 100).

The annual CPI from 2002 to 2016 is provided in Table 4.4(b).

Table 4.4(b) **CPI from the Year 2002 to 2016**

Year	2002 (BASE YEAR)	2003	2004	2005	2006	2007	2008	2009	2010	2011	2012	2013	2014	2015	2016
CPI	100.0	102.8	104.7	107.0	109.1	111.5	114.1	114.4	116.5	119.9	121.7	122.8	125.2	126.6	128.4

Source: Statistics Canada: Consumer Price Index, historical summary

Example 4.4(c) **Calculating the Cost of the Basket of Goods and Services in 2016 and the Percent Change from the Base Year**

The basket of goods and services cost $16,500 in 2002. Using the CPI for 2016 from Table 4.4(b):

(i) Calculate the cost of the basket of goods and services in 2016.

(ii) What is the percent change in the cost of the basket of goods and services from 2002 to 2016?

Solution

(i)

Year	Index	Price ($)
2002	100	16,500
2016	128.4	x

In fractional form, $\frac{100}{128.4} = \frac{16{,}500.00}{x}$

Cross multiplying, $x = \frac{128.4 \times 16{,}500.00}{100}$

$= \$21{,}186.00$

Or

Using Formula 4.4(a),

$$\textit{Index Number on selected date} = \frac{\textit{Value of Item on selected date}}{\textit{Value of Item on base date}} \times 100$$

$$128.4 = \frac{x}{16{,}500.00} \times 100$$

$$x = \frac{128.4 \times 16{,}500.00}{100}$$

$$= \$21{,}186.00$$

Therefore, the cost of the basket of goods and services in 2016 is $21,186.00.

CALCULATOR METHOD

2ND Δ%
OLD = 16,500 ENTER
↓
NEW = 21,186 ENTER
↓ CPT
%CH = 28.4

(ii) CPI for 2002 is 100.

CPI for 2016 is 128.4.

Percent change = (128.4 – 100)% = 28.4%

Or

Using the percent change formula, Formula 3.2,

$$\%C = \frac{V_f - V_i}{V_i} \times 100\%$$

$$= \frac{21{,}186.00 - 16{,}500.00}{16{,}500.00} \times 100\%$$

$$= 0.284 \times 100\% = 28.4\%$$

Therefore, the percent change in the cost from 2002 to 2016 is 28.4%.

Example 4.4(d) **Changing the Base Year to 2012, Calculate the New CPI for Years 2013 to 2015 and the Percent Changes**

Refer to the CPI numbers provided in Table 4.4(b) and answer the following questions:

(i) If 2012 was used as a base year for CPI calculations instead of 2002, what would be the new CPI in 2013, 2014, and 2015?

(ii) Determine the percent change of the CPI between 2012 and 2015 using the old CPI numbers (when 2002 was the base year).

(iii) Determine the percent change of the CPI between 2012 and 2015 using the new CPI numbers (when 2012 is the base year).

Provide your answers rounded to one decimal place.

Solution

(i) Using Formula 4.4(a),

$$\textit{Index Number on selected date} = \frac{\textit{Value of Item on selected date}}{\textit{Value of Item on base date}} \times 100$$

$$\textit{New Index Number}_{2013} = \frac{122.8}{121.7} \times 100 = 100.903862... = 100.9$$

$$\textit{New Index Number}_{2014} = \frac{125.2}{121.7} \times 100 = 102.875924... = 102.9$$

$$\textit{New Index Number}_{2015} = \frac{126.6}{121.7} \times 100 = 104.026294... = 104.0$$

	Index Number	
Year	Original	New
2012	121.7	100.0
2013	122.8	100.9
2014	125.2	102.9
2015	126.6	104.0

Therefore, if 2012 was used as the base year, the CPI for 2013, 2014, and 2015 would be 100.9, 102.9, and 104.0, respectively.

CALCULATOR METHOD

2ND Δ%
OLD = 121.7 ENTER
↓
NEW = 126.6 ENTER
↓ CPT
%CH = 4.026294166

(ii) *Calculating the percent change of the CPI between 2012 and 2015, using the old CPI numbers (when 2002 was the base year):*

Using the percent change formula, Formula 3.2,

$$\%C = \frac{V_f - V_i}{V_i} \times 100\% = \frac{126.6 - 121.7}{121.7} \times 100\%$$

$$= 0.040262... \times 100\% = 4.0\%$$

Therefore, the percent change of the CPI, using the old CPI numbers, is 4.0%.

Solution *continued*

(iii) *Calculating the percent change of the CPI between 2012 and 2015, using the new CPI numbers (when the 2012 is the base year):*

CPI for 2012 is 100.0.

CPI for 2015 is 104.0

Percent change = (104.0 – 100.0)% = 4.0%

Therefore, the percent change of the CPI, using the new CPI numbers, is 4.0% .

Note: *The percent change between 2012 and 2015 is the same, regardless of which year is used as a base year.*

Inflation Rate and Real Income

When prices increase, CPI also increases; inflation rate is the rate of change in CPI over a period of time.

Normally, the inflation rate is calculated on an annual basis using the CPI for two consecutive years.

Formula 4.4(b) **Inflation Rate**

$$\text{Inflation Rate (from Year A to Year B)} = \frac{CPI_{\text{Year B}} - CPI_{\text{Year A}}}{CPI_{\text{Year A}}} \times 100\%$$

Inflation is a rise on the general level of prices of goods and services in an economy over time.

Inflation is crucial in financial planning because $100 to be received in the future is worth less than $100 received today. Unless our income rises to match the price increase (inflation), we will not be able to maintain the same standard of living as before. For this reason, wages of workers, private and public pension programs, personal income tax deductions, social and welfare payments, spousal and child support payments, etc., are adjusted periodically based on the changes in CPI.

Real income is the income after adjusting for inflation and is calculated as follows:

Formula 4.4(c) **Real Income**

$$\text{Real Income} = \frac{\text{Money Income}}{CPI} \times 100$$

Real income refers to the amount of goods and services you can buy now compared to that which you purchased in another time period with the same amount of dollars. If you received a salary increase of 2% and the inflation was 3%, then your real income is decreased by 1%. Money income refers to the dollar amount of income without taking into account the purchasing power, inflation, or other factors that may affect income's value.

Example 4.4(e) **Calculating the Inflation Rate, Given CPI**

If the CPI was 126.6 in 2015 and 128.4 at the end of 2016, what would be the inflation rate in 2016?

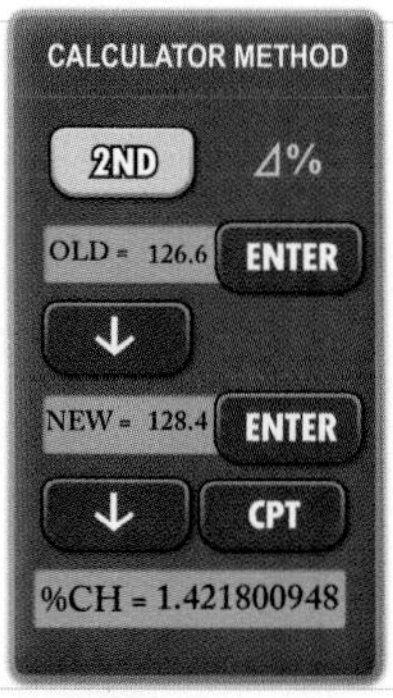

$$\text{Inflation Rate} = \frac{CPI_{2016} - CPI_{2015}}{CPI_{2015}} \times 100\%$$

$$\text{Inflation Rate} = \frac{128.4 - 126.6}{126.6} \times 100\%$$

$$= 0.014218... \times 100\%$$

$$= 1.4\%$$

Therefore, the inflation rate in 2016 would be 1.4%.

Example 4.4(f) **Calculating the Real Income**

Peter's income was $30,000 in 2002 (base year), $40,000 in 2008, and $43,500 in 2014. The CPI was 114.1 in 2008 and 125.2 in 2014. Determine Peter's real income in 2008 and 2014.

Solution

$$\textit{Real Income} = \frac{\textit{Money Income}}{\textit{CPI}} \times 100$$

$$\textit{Real Income in 2008} = \frac{40{,}000.00}{114.1} \times 100 = 35{,}056.96757...$$

$$= \$35{,}056.97$$

$$\textit{Real Income in 2014} = \frac{43{,}500.00}{125.2} \times 100 = 34{,}744.40895...$$

$$= \$34{,}744.41$$

	Year	CPI	Money Income	Real Income
Base Year	2002	100	$30,000.00	$30,000.00
	2008	114.1	$40,000.00	$35,056.97
	2014	125.2	$43,500.00	$34,744.41

Peter's real income in 2008 is $35,056.97 and his real income in 2014 is $34,744.41.

Purchasing Power of a Dollar

Purchasing Power is the value of a currency expressed in terms of the amount of goods or services that one unit of money can buy. The value of a dollar does not remain the same when there is inflation; inflation decreases the amount of goods and services you are able to purchase. We use CPI to measure the purchasing power of a dollar:

Formula 4.4(d) **Purchasing Power of a Dollar**

$$\textit{Purchasing Power of a Dollar} = \frac{\$1}{\textit{CPI}} \times 100$$

Table 4.4(c) **Purchasing Power of a Dollar Table**

Year	2002 (BASE YEAR)	2003	2004	2005	2006	2007	2008	2009	2010	2011	2012	2013	2014	2015	2016
CPI	100.0	102.8	104.7	107.0	109.1	111.5	114.1	114.4	116.5	119.9	121.7	122.8	125.2	126.6	128.4
Purchasing power of a dollar	$1	0.9728	0.9551	0.9346	0.9166	0.8969	0.8764	0.8741	0.8584	0.8340	0.8217	0.8143	0.7987	0.7899	0.7788

Note: *The Purchasing Power of a dollar was calculated using Formula 4.4 (d).*

Example 4.4(g) **Calculating the Purchasing Power of a Dollar, Given CPI**

If the CPI was 125.2 for 2014 and 126.6 for 2015, determine the purchasing power of the dollar for the two years. Compare with the base year 2002 (CPI = 100).

Solution

$$\textit{Purchasing Power in 2014} = \frac{\$1}{125.2} \times 100 = 0.798722...$$

$$\textit{Purchasing Power in 2015} = \frac{\$1}{126.6} \times 100 = 0.789889...$$

Therefore, the dollar in 2014 could purchase 79.87% of what could be purchased in 2002, and the dollar in 2015 could purchase 78.99% of what could be purchased in 2002.

Stock Index

Standard and Poor's Financial Services LLC (S&P) is an American company that publishes financial research and analyses on stocks, bonds, and commodities.

A stock index or stock market index is an application of index numbers being used to measure the performance of a section of the market. For example, the Standard and Poor's Toronto Stock Exchange Composite (S&P/TSX) index reflects the share prices of all the companies trading on the Toronto Stock Exchange. Here, the 'basket' composed of ordinary goods and services that all consumers use on average is replaced by a portfolio composed of the shares of the big companies that are listed on the Toronto Stock Exchange. This index is an indicator of the health of the Toronto Stock Exchange. If the S&P/TSX increases, it means that the overall value of the shares in the Exchange is increasing; it is important to note that individually, some companies may be performing better than others, but collectively, the companies are performing well. The base value used for the S&P/TSX is 1000, set in 1975. S&P/TSX can be calculated as follows:

Formula 4.4(e) **S&P/TSX Composite Index**

$$\textit{S\&P/TSX Composite Index} = \frac{\textit{Value of portfolio on selected date}}{\textit{Value of portfolio on base date}} \times 1000$$

In December 2016, the S&P/TSX index reached 15,300, which means that the value of the portfolio in 2016 was 15.3 times its value in 1975.

Example 4.4(h) **Calculating the S&P/TSX Composite Index**

If the S&P/TSX portfolio cost \$200,000 in 1975, and the same portfolio cost \$2,729,000 in 2015, calculate the S&P/TSX Composite Index.

Solution

$$\textit{S\&P/TSX Composite Index} = \frac{\textit{Value of portfolio on selected date}}{\textit{Value of portfolio on base date}} \times 1000$$

Substituting values,

$$= \frac{2{,}729{,}000.00}{200{,}000.00} \times 1000$$

$$= 13{,}645$$

Therefore, in 2015, the S&P/TSX Composite Index was 13,645.

4.4 | Exercises

Answers to the odd-numbered problems are available at the end of the textbook.

For Problems 1 to 4, round your answer to two decimal places.

1. Determine the index number for 2011 and 2016 for the value of a car using 2005 as the base year.

Year	2005	2011	2016
Value of Car	\$32,000	\$37,000	\$43,000

2. Determine the index number for 2010 and 2015 for the price of a tire using 2002 as the base year.

Year	2002	2010	2015
Price of a Tire	\$35	\$60	\$86

3. Determine the index number for 2016 for the price of a monthly metro pass for adults and students using 2002 as the base year.

Year	Metro Pass Adult	Metro Pass Student
2002	\$98.75	\$83.25
2016	\$141.50	\$112.00

4. Determine the index number for 2016 for the cost of an adult and child movie ticket using 2006 as the base year.

Year	Movie Ticket Adult	Movie Ticket Child
2006	\$9.00	\$6.00
2016	\$13.50	\$9.00

For the following problems, round monetary values to two decimal places and all other values to one decimal place, unless otherwise indicated.

Use the CPI from year 2002 to 2016 provided in Table 4.4(b) for Problems 5 to 16.

5. a. Compute the new index for years 2014 and 2015, using 2013 as the base year.
   b. Compute the percent change in index between 2014 and 2015.
6. a. Compute the new index for years 2014 and 2015, using 2010 as the base year.
   b. Compute the percent change in index between 2014 and 2015.
7. a. Compute the new index for years 2013 and 2014, using 2015 as the base year.
   b. Compute the percent change in index between 2013 and 2014.
8. a. Compute the new index for years 2012 and 2013, using 2014 as the base year.
   b. Compute the percent change in index between 2012 and 2013.
9. If an item was worth $2500 in 2009, how much was it worth in 2013 and 2015?
10. If an item was worth $4000 in 2008, how much was it worth in 2012 and 2014?
11. If an item was worth $2000 in 2005, how much was it worth in 2012 and 2015?
12. If an item was worth $5000 in 2006, how much was it worth in 2011 and 2014?
13. What real income in 2016 would be equivalent to an income of $60,000 in 2010?
14. What real income in 2016 would be equivalent to an income of $50,000 in 2008?
15. Calculate the inflation rate for the period 2012 to 2016.
16. Calculate the inflation rate for the period 2005 to 2015.
17. The college tuition fee for the year 2008 was $3200. What would the tuition fee be for the year 2016 if the tuition fee increased with the inflation rate during this period?
18. Tony earned $58,000 in 2002. How much would he have earned in 2016 if his earnings grew with the inflation rate during this period?
19. Undergraduate students paid an average of $5760 in tuition fees in 2014. The tuition fees increased to an average of $5960 in 2015. Does the tuition increase match the inflation? If not, how much should the tuition fees have been in 2015, to align with inflation?
20. Yara was paid a salary of $46,000 in 2012. Her salary increased to $48,000 in 2014. Should Jara be happy with this increase? Justify your answer.
21. Calculate the purchasing power of a dollar for 2012 and 2015 relative to the base year 2002. Round your answer to four decimal places.
22. Calculate the purchasing power of a dollar for 2011 and 2014 relative to the base year 2002. Round your answer to four decimal places.

Use the following data for Problems 23 to 26.

End of the Year	2009	2010	2011	2012	2013	2014	2015	2016
S&P/TSX Index	11,746	13,443	11,955	12,541	13,622	14,754	13,010	15,288

23. If you had invested $25,000 at the end of 2010, what would have been the value at the end of 2016?
24. If you had invested $75,000 at the end of 2009, what would have been the value at the end of 2016?
25. What amount invested at the end of 2012 would have resulted in a value of $50,000 at the end of 2016?
26. What amount invested at the end of 2011 would have resulted in a value of $150,000 at the end of 2016?

4 | Review Exercises

Answers to the odd-numbered problems are available at the end of the textbook.

1. Christopher, an investment banker, invests all his yearly earnings in stocks of high-tech, mining, and garment industries in the ratio of 2 : 5 : 7, respectively. Calculate his investment in mining stocks if his investment in high-tech stocks was $18,540.

2. The ratio of the driving distance from London to Hamilton, London to Mississauga, and London to Toronto is 3 : 4 : 5, respectively. If the distance from London to Hamilton is 125 km, calculate the distance from London to Mississauga and from London to Toronto.

3. Three college classmates, Sandra, Meghan, and Bob, decided to start a small business and invest $1000, $2500, and $3500, respectively. If Bob decided to leave the business, how much did Sandra and Meghan have to pay for Bob's shares if they wanted to maintain their initial investment ratio?

4. Anthony decided to build a shopping complex with his two brothers, Adrian and Andrew. They invested $200,000, $860,400, and $750,000, respectively. After the complex was built, Adrian decided to sell his share of the investment to Anthony and Andrew. How much did each of them have to pay if they wanted to maintain the same ratio of their investments in the complex?

5. If Lillian, a graphic designer, receives an annual salary of $55,000, calculate her weekly salary using pro-rations. Assume that there are 52 weeks in a year.

6. As the CFO of a technology company, Tyler receives 26 bi-weekly payments of $6000 each throughout the year. The company decided to change the pay period from bi-weekly to monthly. What will be Tyler's monthly payment?

7. Owen, Jamie, and Wayne invested a total of $800 in the ratio of 3 : 4 : 5 , respectively, to purchase a billiards table for their clubhouse. After the table was delivered, each invested an additional $200 to purchase balls and cue sticks. Calculate their new investment ratio after their additional investment.

8. Gregory, his wife, and his mother jointly purchased an estate for $1,350,000. Their individual investments in the estate were in the ratio of 5 : 3 : 1, respectively. Each of them decided to invest an additional $250,000 to develop the estate into a small family resort. Calculate their new investment ratio after the additional investment.

9. Dustin and Gina were classmates who graduated together from college. Dustin found a job as a banker that pays him $189 for 9 hours of work and Gina found a job as a freelance artist that pays her $174 for 8 hours of work. Who is being paid a higher hourly rate and by how much is it higher than the other person's hourly rate?

10. Jeffrey purchased a racing motorbike and Chris purchased a cruising motorbike. Jeffrey travelled 765 km from Toronto to New York City and covered this journey in 8 hours and 20 minutes. Chris travelled 165 km from Toronto to Buffalo in 2 hours and 10 minutes. Based on this information, whose average speed was greater and by how much was it greater (in km/h) than the other person's average speed?

11. Lena, Maxwell, and Calvin invested $3750, $8000, and $6250, respectively, to start a video production studio. The company did very well in the first year and they wanted to invest an additional $5250 to expand their business. How much did each of them have to individually invest to maintain their original investment ratio?

12. David, an investment banker, invested $5000, $4300, and $3600 in stocks of three different companies. The market showed potential to grow so he decided to invest an additional $2000 in stocks of the same companies. How did he invest this amount into stocks of the three companies to maintain the original investment ratio?

13. A bank in Vancouver, British Columbia has a selling rate of €1 = C$1.4687. If the exchange rate is €1 = C$1.4095, calculate the rate of commission that the bank charges.

14. A bank in Calgary, Alberta has a buying rate of ¥1 = C$0.011362. If the exchange rate is ¥1 = C$0.011738, calculate the rate of commission that the bank charges to buy currencies.

15. What amount in 2015 had the same purchasing power as $500 in 2005? Use the CPI provided in Table 4.4(b).

16. What amount in 2014 had the same purchasing power as $10,000 in 2008? Use the CPI provided in Table 4.4(b).

• 17. A software company in Canada outsourced 20 software development projects to Malaysia for 30,500 Malaysian ringgits (RM) last year. How many projects can it outsource this year for the same amount of Canadian dollars as spent last year if the cost to do the job remains the same but the exchange rate changed from C$1 = RM3.162524 last year to C$1 = RM3.351163 this year. Assume that each of the projects has the same value.

• 18. A telecommunications company in Vancouver hired an outsourced support team of 50 people from Italy. It paid them €20,000 per person this year. If the exchange rate changes from C$1 = €0.704408 to C$1 = €0.659402 next year, calculate the number of people the telecommunications company can afford to hire for the support job. Assume that the cost to hire the people remains the same and the telecommunications company's yearly budget to hire people next year is the same as this year.

• 19. Ellen bought clothes in Los Angeles, California for US$1500 by converting her Canadian currency when the exchange rate was C$1 = US$0.9481. She then returned to Toronto and had to pay customs duty of 14% and HST of 13% on the clothes at the Canada-US border based on that day's exchange rate of C$1 = US$0.9589. Calculate the total amount she spent on the clothes in Canadian dollars.

• 20. Alexandria went to Florida and purchased a laptop for US$650 by converting her Canadian currency when the exchange rate was C$1 = US$0.9485. After a month, she returned to Vancouver but the exchange rate fluctuated and was C$1 = US$0.9589 on the day of her return. At the border she paid customs duty of 14% and HST of 13% on the laptop based on that day's exchange rate. Calculate the total amount she spent on the laptop in Canadian dollars.

• 21. If the ratio of sugar to flour in a pie is 2 : 3 and that of flour to salt is 2 : 1, calculate the ratio of sugar : flour : salt in the pie.

• 22. If the ratio of sales people to marketing people in an organization is 5 : 4 and the ratio of marketing people to finance people is 5 : 2, what is the ratio of sales people : marketing people : finance people in the organization?

4 | Self-Test Exercises

Answers to all the problems are available at the end of the textbook.

1. If the Canadian dollar appreciated by US$0.0050 relative to the US dollar, what would be the new value of the Canadian dollar per US dollar? Assume the current exchange rate is US$1 = C$1.3342.

2. If C$1 = ¥85.191 and ¥1 = US$0.008798, how many Canadian dollars will you receive with US$1000?

3. For every $30 that a not-for-profit foundation transferred to a relief fund, the government donated $10 towards the same cause. After two months of fundraising, the foundation had a total of $8500 including the government's contribution. Calculate the amount donated by the government.

4. Henry had a plan for a house he was building. If the scale ratio was 1 : 75 (i.e., the ratio of the measurements in the plan to the actual size was 1 : 75), calculate the width of the garage door, in metres, if it measured 5.75 cm on the plan.

5. Antonio paid a yearly subscription amount of $250 to receive a business magazine monthly. After receiving two issues, he cancelled his subscription. Calculate the pro-rated refund he should receive from the magazine company.

6. Georgia received her grandfather's American currency collection as part of her inheritance. She decided to sell the collection to a bank when the exchange rate was C$1 = US$0.9324. The bank charged her a commission of 0.35%. How much did she receive from the bank, assuming that she was only able to sell US$40 of the collection?

7. Cheryl, a student at a college in Toronto, decided to travel to Switzerland and purchased CHF750 from her bank. However, two weeks later she cancelled her trip and converted the Swiss francs back to Canadian dollars at the same bank. Did she lose any money by converting the money twice? If so, how much did she lose? Assume C$1 = CHF0.7549 and that the bank charged a commission of 0.25% to sell and buy currencies.

8. What amount of earnings in 2005 had the same purchasing power as $1000 in 2015? Use the CPI provided in Table 4.4(b).

• 9. Zain and Cassie invested equal amounts of money in a business. A year later, Zain withdrew $10,000 making the ratio of their investments 3 : 5. How much money did each of them invest in the beginning?

• 10. Andrew's earnings to Bill's was in the ratio of 5 : 6 and Bill's to Cathy's was in the ratio of 5 : 7. What was the ratio of the earnings of Andrew : Bill : Cathy?

• 11. Russel, who lives in Halifax, Nova Scotia, purchased a dining table set from Brazil for 800 Brazilian reals (R$). At the Canadian border, he was charged 18% duty and 15% HST to bring the table back home. Calculate the total amount he spent on the dining table. The exchange rate was C$1 = R$2.223483.

CASE 4

Applying Ratios in Business

Lana, Ann, and Cecilia, three budding entrepreneurs, formed a partnership to start a Belgian waffle restaurant in Toronto. They required funds to lease a place, hire staff, and purchase equipment and furniture. Their initial investments were in the ratio of 5 : 7 : 11, respectively, and Ann's contribution was $14,700. Once the restaurant was ready for business, at the suggestion of Cecilia, the marketing specialist in the team, each of them contributed an additional $6300 for marketing and advertising expenses.

During the initial stage of operation of the restaurant, additional funds for miscellaneous expenses (repairs, maintenance, etc.) were required and the three partners decided to raise their total investment in their partnership to $87,400 while maintaining their original proportionate partnership. Also, the partners agreed that half of the annual profit would be shared equally and the other half be shared in the ratio of their original investments. At the end of the first year, the total profit was $36,225.

Lana converted one-third of her profits to British pounds (£) and saved the balance in her bank in Toronto. Ann converted two-fifths of her profits to Swiss francs (CHF) and saved the balance in her bank in Toronto. Cecilia drove down to New York City and spent an amount equivalent to US$3000, including service charges, on clothes and designer accessories. On her return to Toronto, she converted the rest to Euros (€) at her bank and went on a vacation to France.

Assume the following exchange rates in answering the following:
C$1 = US$0.7495, C$1 = £0.6085, C$1 = CHF0.7549, C$1 = €0.7095

a. Calculate the amount initially invested by Lana and Cecilia.

b. Determine the investment ratio of the three partners after their contributions for marketing and advertising expenses.

c. Calculate the amount contributed by each partner for miscellaneous expenses that was necessary to raise their total investment to $87,400 and to maintain the original proportionate partnership of 5 : 7 : 11.

d. What was the share of the profits of each partner?

e. How much did Lana save in British pounds and Ann save in Swiss francs, if the bank charged a commission of 0.75% for each transaction?

f. After two months, if the British pound appreciated by 10% relative to the Canadian dollar and Swiss francs depreciated by 10% relative to the Canadian dollar, what was the equivalent value of money in Canadian dollars that Lana and Ann invested in British pounds and Swiss francs, respectively?

g. On her return from New York, at the Canada-US border, Cecilia paid 18% customs duty and 13% HST on the goods that she purchased. What was the total cost of her clothes and accessories in Canadian dollars? Note: HST is calculated on the amount that includes import duty.

h. How many Euros did Cecilia receive when she converted the balance of her profits if the bank's commission was 2%?

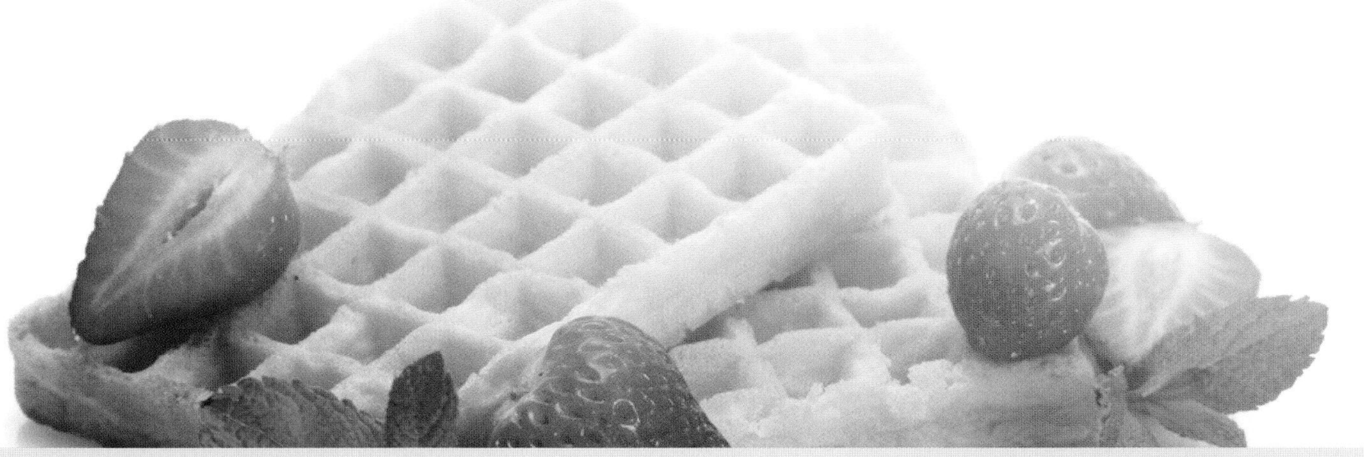

4 | Summary of Notation and Formulas

NOTATION

CPI = Consumer Price Index

FORMULAS

Index Number on a Selected Date | 4.4(a)

$$\textit{Index Number on selected date} = \frac{\textit{Value of Item on selected date}}{\textit{Value of Item on base date}} \times 100$$

Inflation Rate | 4.4(b)

$$\textit{Inflation Rate (from Year A to Year B)} = \frac{CPI_{\textit{Year B}} - CPI_{\textit{Year A}}}{CPI_{\textit{Year A}}} \times 100\%$$

Real Income | 4.4(c)

$$\textit{Real Income} = \frac{\textit{Money Income}}{CPI} \times 100$$

Purchasing Power of a Dollar | 4.4(d)

$$\textit{Purchasing Power of a Dollar} = \frac{\$1}{CPI} \times 100$$

S&P/TSX Composite Index | 4.4(e)

$$\textit{S\&P/TSX Composite Index} = \frac{\textit{Value of portfolio on selected date}}{\textit{Value of portfolio on base date}} \times 1000$$

Chapter

5

MATHEMATICS OF MERCHANDISING

LEARNING OBJECTIVES

- Solve problems involving a single trade discount rate or a series of trade discount rates, and calculate the equivalent trade discount rate for a series of trade discount rates.
- Solve problems involving cash discounts for full and partial payments.
- Calculate the amount of markup and rate of markup on cost and selling price of items.
- Calculate the amount of markdown and rate of markdown on selling price of items.
- Perform calculations involving markup and markdown in calculating profit or loss.
- Calculate the net rates of markup and markdown.

CHAPTER OUTLINE

5.1 Trade Discounts

5.2 Payment Terms and Cash Discounts

5.3 Markup

5.4 Markdown

5.5 Applications of Markup and Markdown

5.6 Net Rate of Markup and Markdown

Introduction

Merchandising is an essential part of commerce and involves the buying and selling of goods.

Have you ever wondered why prices of items sold at wholesalers like 'Costco' and 'Wal-Mart' are cheaper than prices of the same items sold at a convenience store; why prices of items are cheaper online than at retail outlets; or how a 'Dollar Store' manages to sell items for a very cheap price? Large distributors buy directly from manufacturers to reduce the cost of the product offered to consumers. Online stores have less overhead expenses, employee time, storage costs, etc., which enable them to pass on the savings to customers. Although stores like the 'Dollar Store' make small profits on each item sold, they make high overall profits by selling large quantities of items. Pricing responsibilities such as these, and many more, lie in the hands of a seasoned merchandiser. This chapter will provide you with the basic analytical skills and terminology used in retail management that a merchandiser should possess to make intelligent business decisions.

Merchandising

Merchandising is a process that involves the buying and selling of goods (merchandise) from the manufacturer, to the final sale of those goods to the consumers. The process can include discounting, promoting, advertising, etc. Typically, manufactured goods are sold to consumers through a chain of distributors, wholesalers, and retailers. This is known as a merchandising chain or distribution chain.

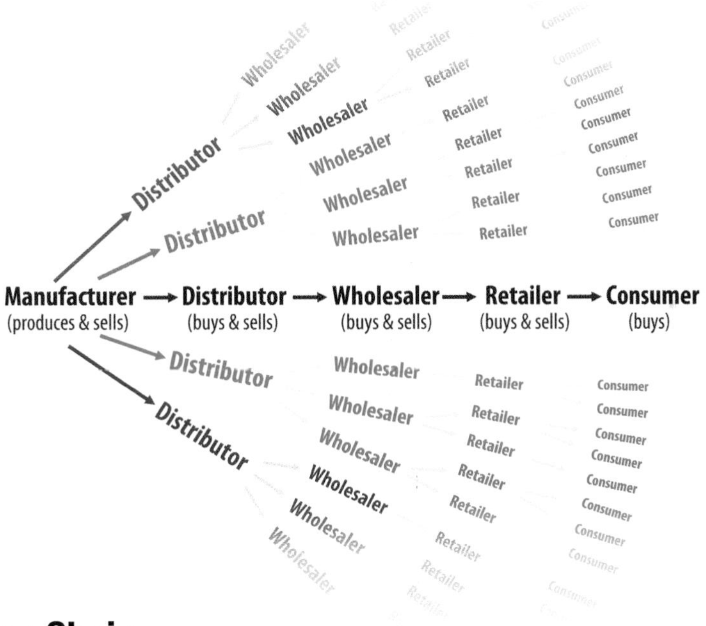

Distribution Chain

Having fewer members in the distribution chain will usually result in a lower selling price of the product to the consumers.

- The illustration above is a typical distribution chain for most organizations. Some organizations may skip one or two members in this chain. For example, in some organizations, retailers may obtain goods directly from the manufacturer while in others, distributors may act as wholesalers and supply directly to retailers.
- Each manufacturer could have numerous distributors, wholesalers, retailers, or consumers located locally or in different countries depending on the type and nature of the organization, product, and consumer.
- Each member in this chain makes profits, except the consumer, as the consumer is only a buyer and not a seller.
- The selling price of a product at each stage of the distribution chain depends on many factors such as demand, competition, the cost of the product, operating costs, or the profit necessary to stay in business.

5.1 | Trade Discounts

*The **list price** is the price quoted by a supplier for a product.*

*A **trade discount** is a reduction on the list price of a product.*

*The **net price** is the price of a product after deducting trade discounts from the list price.*

Manufacturers usually determine the price at which a product can be sold to the consumer. This is known as the manufacturer's suggested retail price (MSRP), catalogue price, or **list price**.

When a manufacturer sells the product to the distributor, the manufacturer deducts a certain amount from their list price, usually a percent of the list price. This is known as a **trade discount**.

The distributor in turn offers a trade discount on their list price to the wholesaler and the wholesaler offers a trade discount to the retailer. The price each of them pays for the product after the trade discount is known as their **net price (N)**.

As the product goes through the distribution chain, the trade discount becomes smaller and smaller. Trade discounts are generally offered to increase sales, to reward valuable customers, to encourage large quantity purchases, to promote a new or seasonal product, etc.

Single Trade Discount

When one discount is offered by the seller to the buyer, it is known as a single trade discount. The amount of trade discount is calculated by multiplying the single trade discount rate (d) and the list price (L).

$$\textit{Amount of trade discount} = \textit{Trade discount rate } (d) \times \textit{List price } (L)$$

This can be written as the following formula:

Formula 5.1(a) **Amount of Trade Discount**

$$\textit{Amount of trade discount} = d \times L$$

By rearranging Formula 5.1(a), we can derive the formula to calculate the trade discount rate, d, as follows:

$$d = \frac{\textit{Amount of trade discount } (d \times L)}{\textit{List price } (L)}$$

The net price (N) is calculated by subtracting the amount of trade discount ($d \times L$) from the list price (L).

$$\textit{Net price } (N) = \textit{List Price } (L) - \textit{Amount of trade discount } (d \times L)$$

$$N = L - d \times L$$

Factoring out the common factor, 'L', results in the following formula for Net Price:

Formula 5.1(b) **Net Price**

$$N = L(1 - d)$$

$(1 - d)$ is the complement of the discount rate (d). It is known as the Net Cost Factor (NCF). The NCF is the percent of the list price that has to be paid by the buyer.

$$NCF = 100\% - \textit{discount}\% = (1 - d)$$

Therefore, the Net Price can also be calculated by multiplying the list price by the complement of the discount rate (or NCF).

$$N = L(1 - d)$$

$$N = L(NCF)$$

Example 5.1(a) **Calculating the Amount of Trade Discount and the Net Price, Given List Price and Rate of Trade Discount**

The list price of an item is \$640. The trade discount is 20%. Calculate the amount of trade discount and the net price of the item.

Solution

$L = \$640.00, \quad d = 20\% = 0.20, \quad N = ?$

$$\textit{Amount of trade discount} = d \times L$$
$$= 640.00 \times 0.20 = \$128.00$$
$$\textit{Net Price, } N = \textit{List price } (L) - \textit{Amount of trade discount } (d \times L)$$
$$= 640.00 - 128.00 = \$512.00$$

Or,

$$\textit{Net Price, } N = L(1 - d) = 640.00(1 - 0.20)$$
$$= 640.00 \times 0.80 = \$512.00$$
$$\textit{Amount of trade discount} = \textit{List price } (L) - \textit{Net price } (N)$$
$$= 640.00 - 512.00 = \$128.00$$

Therefore, the amount of trade discount is \$128.00 and the net price of the item is \$512.00.

Example 5.1(b) **Calculating the List Price and the Amount of Trade Discount, Given Net Price and Rate of Trade Discount**

After a 40% trade discount, the net price of an item is \$420. Calculate the list price of the item and the amount of trade discount.

Solution

$d = 40\% = 0.40, \quad N = \$420.00, \quad L = ?$

Using Formula 5.1(b), $N = L(1 - d)$

Rearranging, $L = \dfrac{N}{(1 - d)} = \dfrac{420.00}{(1 - 0.40)} = \dfrac{420.00}{(0.60)} = \$700.00$

Using Formula 5.1(a), $\textit{Amount of trade discount} = d \times L$

$$= 0.40 \times 700.00 = \$280.00$$

Or,

$$\textit{Amount of trade discount} = L - N$$
$$= 700.00 - 420.00 = \$280.00$$

Therefore, the list price is \$700.00 and the amount of trade discount is \$280.00.

Example 5.1(c) **Calculating the List Price and the Net Price, Given the Rate and Amount of Trade Discount**

An item is purchased after a trade discount of 25% and the amount of trade discount received is \$150. Calculate the list price and net price of the item.

Solution

$d = 25\% = 0.25, \quad d \times L = \$150.00, \quad L = ?, \quad N = ?$

Using Formula 5.1(a), $\textit{Amount of trade discount} = d \times L$

Rearranging, $L = \dfrac{\textit{Amount of trade discount } (d \times L)}{d}$

Substituting the values, $L = \dfrac{150.00}{0.25} = \$600.00$

Using Formula 5.1(b), $N = L(1 - d) = 600.00(1 - 0.25)$

$$= 600.00 \times 0.75 = \$450.00$$

Or,

$$N = \textit{List price} - \textit{Amount of trade discount}$$
$$= 600.00 - 150.00 = \$450.00$$

Therefore, the list price is \$600.00 and the net price is \$450.00.

Example 5.1(d) **Calculating the Trade Discount Rate, Given List Price and Net Price**

The list price is \$500 and the net price is \$400 for an item. What is the trade discount rate?

Solution

$L = \$500.00, \quad N = \$400.00, \quad d = ?$

$$\textit{Amount of trade discount} = L - N$$

$$\textit{Amount of trade discount} = 500.00 - 400.00 = \$100.00$$

$$d \times L = 100.00$$

Rearranging, $d = \frac{100.00}{L} = \frac{100.00}{500.00} = 0.20 = 20\%$

Or,

Using Formula 5.1(b), $N = L(1 - d)$

Substituting the values, $400.00 = 500.00(1 - d)$

Expanding, $400.00 = 500.00 - 500.00d$

Rearranging, $500.00d = 500.00 - 400.00$

$$d = \frac{100.00}{500.00} = 0.20 = 20\%$$

Therefore, the trade discount rate is 20%.

Series of Trade Discounts

As explained earlier, trade discounts are provided for various reasons. At times, a buyer may qualify to receive more than one trade discount rate on the list price of a product. In this case, the buyer may be offered a series of trade discount rates (also known as multiple discount rates or chain discount rates). These series of trade discounts are always applied in sequence, one after the other; i.e., the second discount is applied on the amount after the first discount and the third discount is applied on the amount after the first and second discounts, etc.

Series of trade discount rates are never added to determine a single trade discount rate.

Trade discounts of 10% followed by 5%, and followed by 2%, are not equal to 17%.

For example, three trade discounts - a 10% seasonal discount, a 5% large purchase discount, and a 2% new product discount - were offered on a product listed at \$1000. If a buyer is eligible for all three trade discounts, then the net price and amount of discount are calculated as follows:

The series of trade discount rates are usually written as 10%, 5%, and 2%.

$$\textit{Net price after the } 1^{st} \textit{ discount} = 1000.00(1 - 0.10) = 1000.00 \times 0.90 = \$900.00$$

Similarly, $\textit{Net price after the } 2^{nd} \textit{ discount} = 900.00(1 - 0.05) = 900.00 \times 0.95 = \$855.00$

and, $\textit{Net price after the } 3^{rd} \textit{ discount} = 855.00(1 - 0.02) = 855.00 \times 0.98 = \$837.90$

Therefore, $\textit{Net price after the series of three trade discounts} = \$837.90$

and, $\textit{Amount of trade discount} = 1000.00 - 837.90 = \$162.10$

Example 5.1(e) **Calculating the Net Price of an Item After Two Trade Discounts**

A manufacturer offers a trade discount of 10% for volume purchases and an additional discount of 5% for end-of-season purchases. How much would you pay for an item with a list price of \$800 if you qualify for both discounts? What is the amount of the trade discount?

Solution

$$\textit{Net price after the } 1^{st} \textit{ trade discount} = 800.00(1 - 0.10) = 800.00 \times 0.90 = \$720.00$$

Similarly, $\textit{Net price after the } 2^{nd} \textit{ trade discount} = 720.00(1 - 0.05) = 720.00 \times 0.95 = \$684.00$

Therefore, $\textit{Amount of the trade discount} = \textit{List price} - \textit{Net price after } 2^{nd} \textit{ discount}$

$$= 800.00 - 684.00 = \$116.00$$

Therefore, you would pay \$684.00 for the item and the amount of trade discount is \$116.00.

Calculating the Net Price of an Item Using the Formula for Series of Trade Discounts

Let the list price of an item be 'L' and the series of trade discounts be $d_1, d_2, d_3, ... d_n$.

Net price after the 1st *trade discount* $= L(1 - d_1)$

Similarly, *Net price after the* 2nd *trade discount* $= L(1 - d_1)(1 - d_2)$

and, *Net price after the* 3rd *trade discount* $= L(1 - d_1)(1 - d_2)(1 - d_3)$

and, *Net price after the* n^{th} *trade discount* $= L(1 - d_1)(1 - d_2)(1 - d_3) ... (1 - d_n)$

Therefore, the formula for the net price after a series of trade discounts is,

Formula 5.1(c) **Net Price After a Series of Trade Discounts**

$$N = L(1 - d_1)(1 - d_2)(1 - d_3) ... (1 - d_n)$$

Example 5.1(f) **Calculating the Net Price of an Item After a Series of Trade Discounts**

A wholesaler offers a retailer the following three discounts on the $1250 list price of an item: 15% for an end-of-season sale, 10% for a large quantity purchase, and 5% for paying cash on delivery. Calculate the net price of the item if a retailer qualifies for all three discounts.

Solution

Using Formula 5.1(c), $N = L(1 - d_1)(1 - d_2)(1 - d_3)$

Substituting values, $N = 1250.00(1 - 0.15)(1 - 0.10)(1 - 0.05)$

$$N = 1250.00(0.85)(0.90)(0.95) = \$908.44$$

$$1250.00(0.85) = \$1062.50$$

$$\$1062.50(0.90) = \$956.25$$

$$\$956.25(0.95) = \$908.4375$$

Therefore, the net price of the item is $908.44.

Example 5.1(g) **Comparing the Net Price of Similar Items that Have Different List Prices and Trade Discounts**

An electronics manufacturer, Rudolph Electronics, offers HDTVs for a list price of $3500 each, offering trade discounts of 30% and 5%. Another manufacturer, Best Tech Electronics, offers a similar model of HDTVs for $3430 each, offering trade discounts of 20% and 15%. Which offer is cheaper and by how much?

Solution

Using Formula 5.1(c), $N = L(1 - d_1)(1 - d_2)$

Substituting values for Rudolph Electronics, $N_{Rudolph} = 3500.00(1 - 0.30)(1 - 0.05)$

$= 3500.00(0.70)(0.95)$

$= \$2327.50$

Substituting values for Best Tech Electronics, $N_{Best\ Tech} = 3430.00(1 - 0.20)(1 - 0.15)$

$= 3430.00(0.80)(0.85)$

$= \$2332.40$

The difference in price = 2332.40 – 2327.50 = $4.90

Therefore, Rudolph Electronic's offer is $4.90 cheaper than that of Best Tech Electronics.

Example 5.1(h) **Calculating the Additional Discount Rate to Match the Net Price of Similar Items**

Company *A* sells a product at a list price of $300 with trade discounts of 20% and 5%. Company *B* sells a similar product at a list price of $375 with a trade discount of 10%. What further trade discount rate must Company *B* offer to match the price of the product offered by Company *A*?

Solution

Using Formula 5.1(c), $N = L(1 - d_1)(1 - d_2)$

Substituting values for Company *A*, $N_A = 300.00(1 - 0.20)(1 - 0.05)$

$= 300.00(0.80)(0.95) = \$228.00$

Substituting values for Company *B*, $N_B = 375.00(1 - 0.10)$

$= 375.00(0.90) = \$337.50$

Company *B* has to provide an additional trade discount of 337.50 – 228.00 = $109.50

Using rearranged Formula 5.1(a),

$$\text{Trade discount rate} = \frac{\text{Amount of trade discount } (d \times L)}{\text{List price } (L)}$$

$$\text{Additional discount rate} = \frac{109.50}{337.50} \times 100\% = 0.324444... \times 100\% = 32.44\%$$

Therefore, Company *B* should provide an additional trade discount rate of 32.44% to match the price of the product available at Company *A*.

Alternative Method

Let the additional discount offered by Company *B* be *d*%.

N_A after trade discounts of 20% and 5% = N_B after trade discounts of 10% and *d*%

$$300.00(1 - 0.20)(1 - 0.05) = 375.00(1 - 0.10)(1 - d)$$

Rearranging and solving for *d*, $228.00 = 337.50(1 - d)$

$228.00 = 337.50 - 337.50d$

$$d = \frac{337.50 - 228.00}{337.50}$$

$= 0.324444... = 32.44\%$

Therefore, Company *B* should provide an additional trade discount rate of 32.44% to match the price of the product offered by Company *A*.

Single Equivalent Trade Discount Rate for a Series of Trade Discount Rates

As explained in the previous section on series of trade discount rates, we cannot simply add trade discount rates to get the single equivalent trade discount rate. We can, however, derive a formula to calculate the single equivalent trade discount rate for a series of trade discount rates.

Let d_e be the single equivalent trade discount rate for a series of trade discount rates $d_1, d_2, d_3, ..., d_n$.

From Formula 5.1(b), $N = L(1 - d_e)$

From Formula 5.1(c), $N = L(1 - d_1)(1 - d_2)(1 - d_3) ... (1 - d_n)$

Equating the above 2 formulas, $L(1 - d_e) = L(1 - d_1)(1 - d_2)(1 - d_3) ... (1 - d_n)$

Dividing by *L* on both sides, $(1 - d_e) = (1 - d_1)(1 - d_2)(1 - d_3) ... (1 - d_n)$

Rearranging the above will result in the formula for a single equivalent trade discount rate for a series of trade discount rates:

Formula 5.1(d) **Single Equivalent Trade Discount Rate**

$$d_e = 1 - [(1 - d_1)(1 - d_2)(1 - d_3) \ldots (1 - d_n)]$$

Example 5.1(i) **Calculating a Single Equivalent Trade Discount Rate for a Series of Trade Discount Rates**

If an item with a list price of $1000 is discounted under a series of trade discounts of 10%, 5%, and 2%, what is the single equivalent trade discount rate that represents all these three trade discount rates?

Solution

Method 1: Using the Single Equivalent Trade Discount Rate Formula

Using Formula 5.1(d), $d_e = 1 - [(1 - d_1)(1 - d_2)(1 - d_3)]$

Substituting values, $= 1 - [(1 - 0.10)(1 - 0.05)(1 - 0.02)]$

$= 0.1621 = 16.21\%$

Therefore, the single equivalent trade discount rate that represents the series of three trade discount rates is 16.21%.

Method 2: Using the Amount of Trade Discount And List Price

$L = \$1000.00$

Using Formula 5.1(c), $N = L(1 - d_1)(1 - d_2)(1 - d_3)$

Substituting values, $= 1000.00(1 - 0.10)(1 - 0.05)(1 - 0.02)$

$= \$837.90$

So, *Amount of trade discount* $= L - N$

$= 1000.00 - 837.90 = \$162.10$

Trade discount rate, $d = \dfrac{\textit{Amount of trade discount } (d \times L)}{\textit{List price } (L)}$

$$d_e = \frac{162.10}{1000.00} = 0.1621 = 16.21\%$$

Therefore, the single equivalent trade discount rate that represents the series of three trade discount rates is 16.21%.

Method 3: Using the Net Price Formula for a Series of Trade Discounts and the Equivalent Single Trade Discount Rate

$L = \$1000.00$

For a series of trade discounts:

Using Formula 5.1(c), $N = L(1 - d_1)(1 - d_2)(1 - d_3)$

Substituting values, $= 1000.00(1 - 0.10)(1 - 0.05)(1 - 0.02)$

$= \$837.90$

For the equivalent trade discount d_e:

Using Formula 5.1(b) $N = L(1 - d_e)$

$= 1000.00(1 - d_e)$

Equating both equations, $837.90 = 1000.00(1 - d_e)$

Solving for d_e, $837.90 = 1000.00 - 1000.00d_e$

$1000.00d_e = 1000.00 - 837.90$

$$d_e = \frac{1000.00 - 837.90}{1000.00} = 0.1621 = 16.21\%$$

Therefore, the single equivalent trade discount rate that represents the series of three trade discount rates is 16.21%.

Example 5.1(j) **Calculating the List Price, Given the Net Price and a Series of Trade Discount Rates**

Jason, a retailer, paid $1349.46 for a flat screen TV at a Boxing Day sale after receiving three successive discounts of 15%, 10%, and 2% on the TV. What was the list price of the TV?

Solution

Using Formula 5.1(c), $N = L(1 - d_1)(1 - d_2)(1 - d_3)$

Rearranging, $L = \dfrac{N}{(1 - d_1)(1 - d_2)(1 - d_3)}$

$= \dfrac{1349.46}{(1 - 0.15)(1 - 0.10)(1 - 0.02)}$

$= \dfrac{1349.46}{0.7497}$

$= \$1800.00$

Therefore, the list price of the TV was $1800.00.

Example 5.1(k) **Calculating the Additional Trade Discount Rate Required**

An item is listed for $3000, less discounts of 15%, 10%, and 5%. What further rate of discount should be offered to reduce the net price to $2000?

Solution

Using Formula 5.1(c), $N = L(1 - d_1)(1 - d_2)(1 - d_3)$

$= 3000.00(1 - 0.15)(1 - 0.10)(1 - 0.05)$

$= \$2180.25$

Further discount of $2180.25 – $2000.00 = $180.25 should be offered to reduce the net price to $2000.

Trade discount rate, $d = \dfrac{\textit{Amount of trade discount } (d \times L)}{\textit{List price } (L)}$

$= \dfrac{180.25}{2180.25}$

$= 0.082674... = 8.27\%$

Therefore, a further discount of 8.27% should be offered to reduce the net price to $2000.00.

5.1 | Exercises

Answers to the odd-numbered problems are available at the end of the textbook.

For the following problems, express the answers rounded to two decimal places, wherever applicable.
Calculate the missing values for Problems 1 to 4.

1.

	List Price (L)	Single Trade Discount Rate (d)	Amount of Trade Discount (d × L)	Net Price (N)
a.	?	20%	$375.00	?
b.	?	?	$27.60	$202.40
c.	$800.00	?	?	$368.00
d.	$500.00	?	$10.00	?

2.

	List Price (*L*)	Single Trade Discount Rate (*d*)	Amount of Trade Discount ($d \times L$)	Net Price (*N*)
a.	?	5%	$50.50	?
b.	?	?	$217.50	$652.50
c.	$12,600.00	?	?	$630.00
d.	$30,750.00	?	$3843.75	?

3.

	List Price (*L*)	Series of Trade Discount Rates	Equivalent Trade Discount Rate (d_e)	Net Price (*N*)	Amount of Trade Discount ($d \times L$)
a.	$540.00	20%, 10%	?	?	?
b.	?	22%, 12.5%, 10%	?	?	$760.00
c.	?	$5\frac{1}{2}$%, 3%, 1%	?	$2512.00	?
d.	$1200.00	10%, 6%, *d*%	?	$984.74	?

4.

	List Price (*L*)	Series of Trade Discount Rates	Equivalent Trade Discount Rate (d_e)	Net Price (*N*)	Amount of Trade Discount ($d \times L$)
a.	$850.00	10%, 5%	?	?	?
b.	?	5%, 4%, 3%	?	?	$80.50
c.	?	$5\frac{1}{2}$%, 2%, 1%	?	$1854.50	?
d.	$625.00	5%, 4%, *d*%	?	$558.60	?

5. The net price of a snow blower is $503.40 after a trade discount of 25%. What is the list price?

6. The net price of a lawn mower is $197.60 after a trade discount of 35%. What is the list price?

7. The list price of a fan is $165. During a sale, a trade discount rate of 8% was offered.
   a. What is the amount of the trade discount?
   b. What is the net price of each fan?

8. A new model of golf shoes are listed at $110 per pair. During a sale, a trade discount rate of 15% was offered.
   a. What is the amount of trade discount offered per pair of shoes?
   b. What is the net price per pair of shoes?

9. An accounting software was sold at $780 per package after a trade discount rate of 10.5%.
   a. What was the list price of the software?
   b. What was the amount of discount?

10. A distributor of batteries received complete payment of $8560.50 for ten automobile batteries that it sold to a wholesaler after a trade discount of 12%.
    a. What was the list price of each battery?
    b. What was the amount of discount offered for each battery?

11. A trade discount rate of 5% on a shipment of designer clothes resulted in a trade discount amount of $20,400.
    a. What was the list price of the shipment of designer clothes?
    b. What was the net price of the shipment of designer clothes?

12. A trade discount rate of 15% on a product resulted in a trade discount amount of $18,200.
    a. What was the list price of the product?
    b. What was the net price of the product?

13. A retail store purchased a shipment of coffee at a net price of $787.20. If this shipment was listed at $960.00, calculate the trade discount rate.

14. The list price of canned foods at a wholesaler's outlet is $50 and the net price is $46. What is the trade discount rate?

15. Annabel's store is selling a newly released camera for $465.50 each. Vashti's store is selling the same model for $490. What rate of discount should Vashti's store offer to match the price of the camera at Annabel's store?

16. Muskoka Tools Depot is selling snow blowers for $725 each. The same model blowers are being offered by Dixie Appliances for $667 each. What rate of discount should Muskoka Tools Depot offer to match the lower price?

17. A clothing wholesaler listed a dress for $280 and offered a standard trade discount rate of 10%. The dress did not sell for two months, so she offered an additional trade discount rate of 12% on the dress during a clearance sale. Calculate the amount of discount offered if both discounts are offered during a final sale.

18. A distributor of kitchen appliances could not sell a blender that was listed at $80.50 even after a trade discount of 25%. He decided to discount it further and offered an additional trade discount of 25%. If the distributor sold the blender at this new price, calculate the amount of trade discount offered on the list price.

19. Is a series of trade discount rates of 20%, 10%, and 5% equivalent to a single trade discount rate of 31.60%?

20. Is a series of trade discount rates of 50%, 40%, and 10% equivalent to a single trade discount rate of 85%?

21. The owner of a manufacturing plant offers his distributors trade discounts of 5%, 5%, and 1%. He wanted to standardize these discounts and offer just one discount that was equivalent to these three discounts. What equivalent trade discount rate should he offer?

22. A list price is discounted under a series of three trade discount rates of 12% each. What is the single equivalent trade discount rate that represents these three discount rates?

23. Three trade discount rates of 5% each are offered on an airplane ticket that is listed at $1200.
    a. What is the net price of the ticket?
    b. What is the amount of discount offered?

24. Towards the end of winter, a distributor is selling leather jackets that were listed for $600 with the following three discounts: 15%, 10%, and 5%.
    a. What is the net price of the leather jacket?
    b. What is the amount of trade discount?

25. Marissa paid $190.57 for a printer that she purchased after receiving trade discounts of 20%, 15%, and 5%.
    a. What was the list price of the printer?
    b. What single equivalent trade discount rate represents the series of discounts received?

26. A shoe retailer received three trade discounts of 15% each on a pair of shoes that he purchased for $42.99.
    a. What was the list price of the pair of shoes?
    b. What single equivalent trade discount rate represents the series of discounts received?

27. A retail store sells a pair of shoes for $82.00, less 15%. A department store sells the same item for $99.90, less 20%.
    a. Which store is offering the item for a cheaper price and by how much?
    b. What additional trade discount rate must the store with the higher price provide to match the lower price?

28. A retail store lists a jacket for $290.00, less 18%. A department store list the same pair of gloves for $265.00, less 12%.
    a. Which store is offering the item for a cheaper price and by how much?
    b. What additional trade discount rate must the store with the higher price provide to match the lower price?

29. A computer store lists a laptop at $600.00, less two trade discounts of 15% and 10%. An electronic store lists the same model laptop at $590.00, less one trade discount of 25%.
    a. Which store is offering the laptops for a cheaper price and by how much?
    b. What further trade discount rate must the store with the higher price provide to match the lower price?

30. A popular model of a tablet is being sold by Digital Inc. at a list price of $825.00, less two trade discounts of 8% and 7%. The same model of tablet is also being sold by an online store for $900.00, less a trade discount of 15%.
    a. Which store is offering the tablet for a cheaper price and by how much?
    b. What further trade discount rate must the supplier with the higher price provide to match the lower price?

31. An item is listed for $280, less discounts of 25%, 15%, and 10%. What further rate of discount must be offered to reduce the net price to $150?

32. Skis are listed by a manufacturer for $850, less trade discounts of 30% and 15%. What further rate of discount must be offered to reduce the net price to $450?

• 33. A distributor in Northern Canada lists a product for $8700 with trade discount rates of 10%, 8%, and 4%. Another distributor in Western Canada lists the same model of the product for $8800 with trade discount rates of 11% and 8%. The product is also listed online for $8900 with a single trade discount rate of 22%.
    a. What is the net price in each case?
    b. Where is the product available the cheapest?

• 34. Martin, the purchasing manager at a distribution company, was asked to source steel tubes. He received the following quotes from vendors: Vendor *A*: $20,600, offering trade discount rates of 10%, 8%, and 7.5%; Vendor *B*: $20,600, offering trade discount rates of 11% and 10%; Vendor *C*: $20,600, offering a trade discount rate of 20%.
    a. What is the net price in each case?
    b. Whose offer is the least expensive?

• 35. A pet food company in Toronto, Ontario lists a bag of food for $22 with trade discount rates of 8% and 4%. At the same time, a company in Orillia, Ontario lists the same food for $21.50 with trade discount rates of 7% and 5%.
    a. Which company is offering the food for a cheaper price?
    b. What further trade discount rate must the company with the higher price provide to match the lower price?

• 36. A specific model of computer servers are being sold by Company *A* for $26,500 each, offering trade discounts of 7% and 6%, and by Company *B* for $35,500 each, offering trade discount rates of 12% and 2%.
    a. Which company is offering the servers for a cheaper price?
    b. What further trade discount rate must the company with the higher price provide to match the lower price?

5.2 | Payment Terms and Cash Discounts

A cash discount is the amount of discount on the net price (invoice amount) that is offered by a seller to a buyer to encourage early payment of the invoice. Cash discounts are expressed as a percent of the net price and have a time limit, after which, the full net price amount is due. A sample invoice with a description of its payment terms is illustrated in Exhibit 5.2.

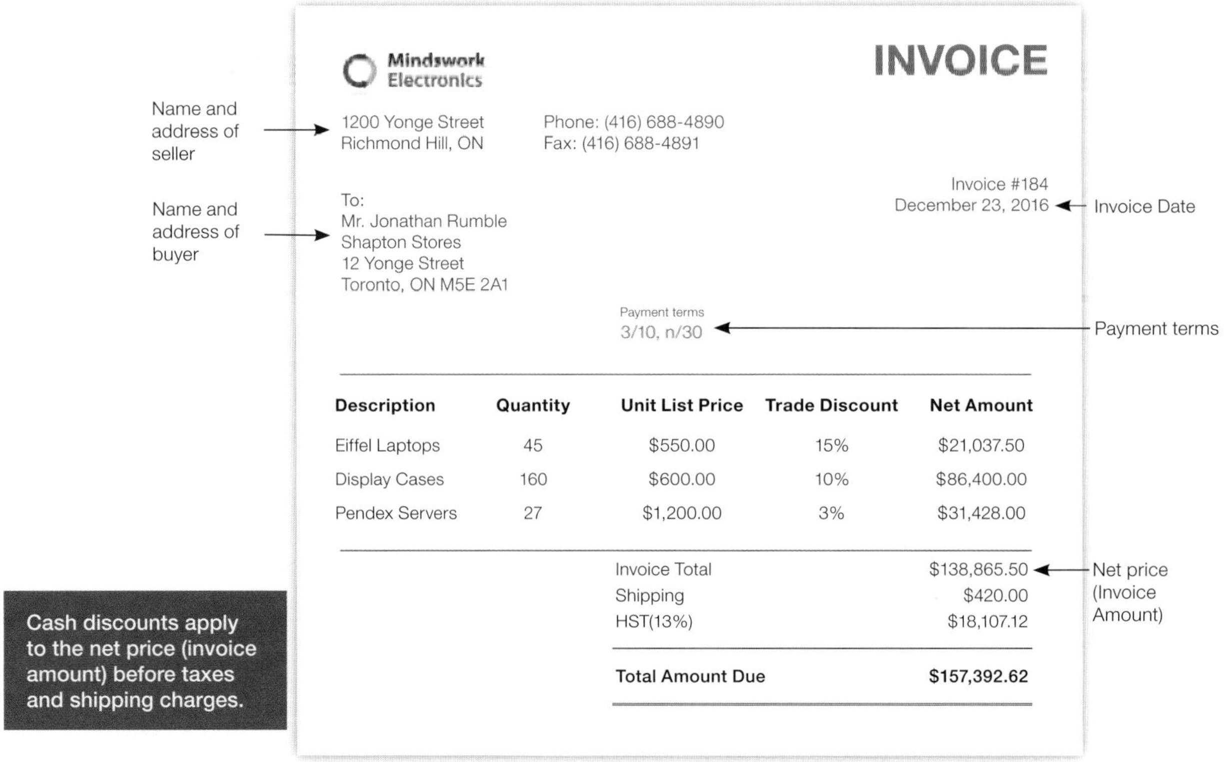

Mindswork Electronics

INVOICE

1200 Yonge Street
Richmond Hill, ON

Phone: (416) 688-4890
Fax: (416) 688-4891

Invoice #184
December 23, 2016

To:
Mr. Jonathan Rumble
Shapton Stores
12 Yonge Street
Toronto, ON M5E 2A1

Payment terms
3/10, n/30

Description	Quantity	Unit List Price	Trade Discount	Net Amount
Eiffel Laptops	45	$550.00	15%	$21,037.50
Display Cases	160	$600.00	10%	$86,400.00
Pendex Servers	27	$1,200.00	3%	$31,428.00

Invoice Total	$138,865.50
Shipping	$420.00
HST(13%)	$18,107.12
Total Amount Due	**$157,392.62**

Exhibit 5.2: Sample Invoice with Description of Payment Terms

In the invoice from 'Mindswork Electronics' in Exhibit 5.2, the 'payment terms' are 3/10, n/30. This provides information on cash discount terms, the discount period, and the credit period for the payment. Payment terms that end without any reference or code indicate that the payment follows 'ordinary dating', which will be explained later in this section.

The first term, 3/10 (read as three-ten), is the discount period, which implies that the buyer will receive a cash discount of 3% if the payment is made within 10 days of the invoice date. The buyer will not receive a discount after the discount period of 10 days.

The second term, n/30 (read as net thirty), is the credit period, which implies that the buyer is expected to settle the full payment within 30 days of invoice date (in other words, the full payment is expected within 20 days from the end of the discount period). If the buyer does not settle the full payment within the credit period, a late-penalty may be applied in addition to the invoice amount.

To count the days in the payment terms, the invoice date (December 23, 2016) is considered as day '0', December 24 is day '1', December 25 is day '2', and so on (or simply add 10 days to December 23, that is, 33 days. December has 31 days so the remaining two days are in January). Therefore, 10 days from the invoice date is January 02, 2017, and 30 days from the invoice date is January 22, 2017, as shown in the following time-line diagram:

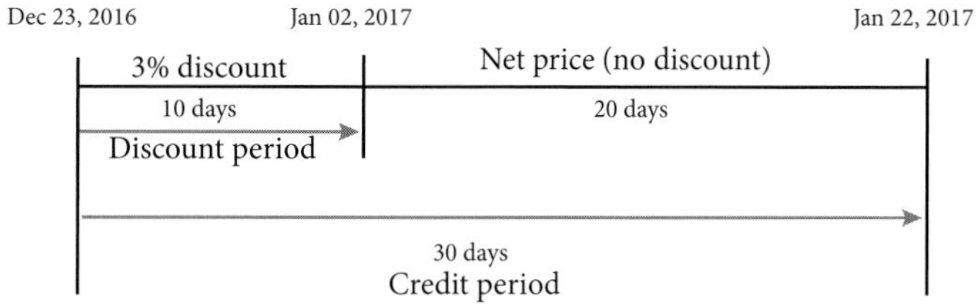

Description of payment terms 3/10, n/30 for the above invoice dated December 23, 2016 are:

- 3% discount for payment made on or before January 02, 2017 (discount period).
- Net price is due for payment made after January 02, 2017, but on or before January 22, 2017 (credit period).

Note:

- *If the credit period is not stated, it is understood that the full payment is expected within twenty days from the end of the discount period: i.e., if only 3/10 is provided in the payment terms, it is understood that the payment terms are 3/10, n/30.*
- *Determining the time period in days between dates can also be calculated using the days table or a financial calculator as explained in Chapter 8, Section 8.1, Pages 295 and 296.*

Example 5.2(a) **Calculating the Payment Amounts, Given Ordinary Dating Payment Terms**

Shawn purchased inventory for his factory and received an invoice for \$180,750 dated January 25, 2017 with payment terms 3/10, 2/30, n/45. What amount will settle the invoice if paid on: (i) February 03, (ii) February 04, (iii) February 24, (iv) February 25, or (v) March 11?

Solution

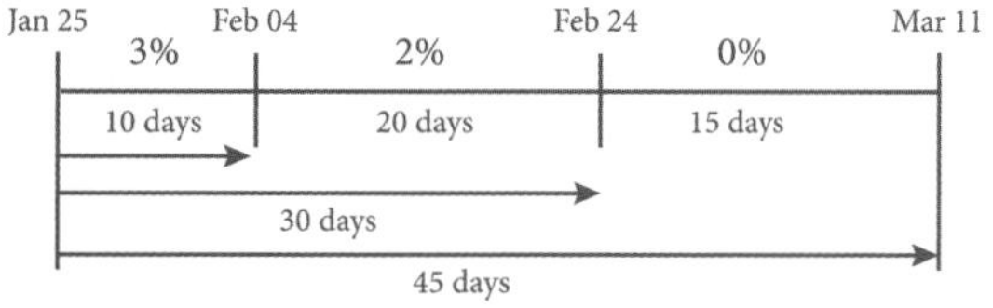

From the time-line diagram above,

- 3% discount for payment made on or before February 04 (1st discount period).
- 2% discount for payment made after February 04, but on or before February 24 (2nd discount period).
- Net price is due for payments made after February 24, but on or before March 11 (credit period).

(i) *If paid on February 03:*

He receives a 3% discount on his invoice as it falls within the first 10 days of the invoice date.

Therefore, he has to pay: $180,750.00(1 - 0.03) = 180,750.00 \times 0.97 = \$175,327.50$

(ii) *If paid on February 04:*

He receives a 3% discount on his invoice as it falls on the 10th day of the invoice date.

Therefore, he has to pay: $180,750.00(1 - 0.03) = 180,750.00 \times 0.97 = \$175,327.50$

(iii) *If paid on February 24:*

He receives a 2% discount on his invoice as it falls on the 30th day of the invoice date (which is after 10 days but less than or equal to 30 days).

Therefore, he has to pay: $180,750.00(1 - 0.02) = 180,750.00 \times 0.98 = \$177,135.00$

(iv) *If paid on February 25:*

The net price has to be paid as it falls after the 30th day of the invoice date.

Therefore, he has to pay: \$180,750.00

(v) *If paid on March 11:*

The net price has to be paid as it falls on the 45th day (last day of credit period) of the invoice date.

Therefore, he has to pay: \$180,750.00

Payment Terms

There are three ways by which payment terms are generally stated in an invoice.

Ordinary Dating

In the previous examples for cash discounts, the payment terms are without any reference or code at the end of the terms and are known as ordinary dating terms. For example, the payment terms 3/20, n/45, refer to ordinary dating where a 3% discount is offered if the payment is made within 20 days of the invoice date and where payment has to be settled within 25 days from the end of the discount period.

End-Of-Month Dating (E.O.M.)

When E.O.M. is included at the end of the payment terms, it refers to 'end-of-month dating' where the discount period and credit period start from the end of the month of the invoice date.

For example, if an invoice dated February 12, 2017 has payment terms 3/10, n/30, E.O.M., then the discount period and credit period start from the last day of the invoice month, which is February 28, 2017. Therefore, a 3% cash discount is offered if a payment is made on or before 10 days following the end-of-month date (with the end-of-month date being day '0'), which is March 10, 2017, and the invoice is expected to be settled on or before March 30, 2017.

When E.O.M. or R.O.G. is not specified in the payment terms of an invoice, it is ordinary dating.

E.O.M. terms are generally stated without the credit period. If the credit period is not stated, it is understood that the full payment is expected within twenty days from the end of the discount period: i.e., if 3/10, E.O.M. is provided in the payment terms, it is understood that the payment terms are 3/10, n/30, E.O.M.

Receipt-Of-Goods Dating (R.O.G.)

When R.O.G. is included at the end of the payment terms, it refers to 'receipt-of-goods dating' where the discount period and credit period start from the date of receipt of goods.

For example, if an invoice dated March 12, 2017 has payment terms: 4/10, n/30, R.O.G. and goods are received on March 21, 2017, then the discount period and credit period start from March 21, 2017. Therefore, a 4% cash discount is offered if the payment is made on or before 10 days from the date the goods were received (with date of the receipt of goods being day '0,' so simply add 10 to March 21), which is March 31, 2017, and the invoice is expected to be settled on or before April 20, 2017.

Note: *When E.O.M or R.O.G is specified, any payments made before the start of the first discount period, will qualify for the first discount rate.*

Example 5.2(b) **Calculating the Payment Amounts, Given E.O.M. Dating Payment Terms**

An invoice dated March 25, 2017 for $65,000 has payment terms: 2/10, E.O.M. What payment will settle the invoice if it is paid on: (i) March 28, (ii) April 06, or (iii) April 11?

Solution

E.O.M. is specified at the end of the payment terms. Therefore, the discount period starts from the last day of the invoice month, which is March 31. As the credit period is not stated, it is understood that the full payment is expected within 20 days from the end of the discount period, i.e., n/30.

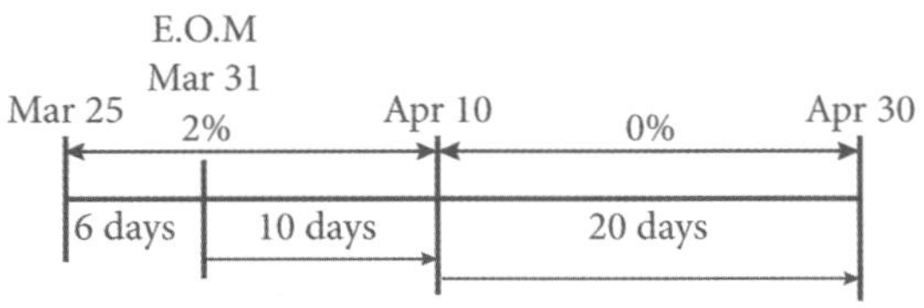

- 2% discount for payment made on or before April 10 (discount period).
- Net price is due for payments made after April 10, but on or before April 30 (credit period).

(i) *If paid on March 28:*
The date falls before the start of the first discount period and will qualify for the 2% discount rate.
Therefore, payment amount = 65,000.00(1 – 0.02) = $63,700.00

(ii) *If paid on April 06:*
The date falls within the 2% discount period.
Therefore, payment amount = 65,000.00(1 – 0.02) = $63,700.00

Solution *continued*

(iii) *If paid on April 11:*
The date falls after the discount period, but within the credit period.
Therefore, the net payment is due and the payment amount is $65,000.00.

Example 5.2(c) **Calculating the Payment Amounts, Given R.O.G. Dating Payment Terms**

A $50,000 invoice dated March 20 has payment terms 5/10, n/30, R.O.G. The goods were received on March 25.

(i) When does the discount period end?
(ii) When does the credit period end?
(iii) What is the amount of cash discount if the invoice is settled on April 02?

Solution

R.O.G. is specified at the end of the payment terms. Therefore, the discount period starts from the date of receipt of the goods, which is March 25.

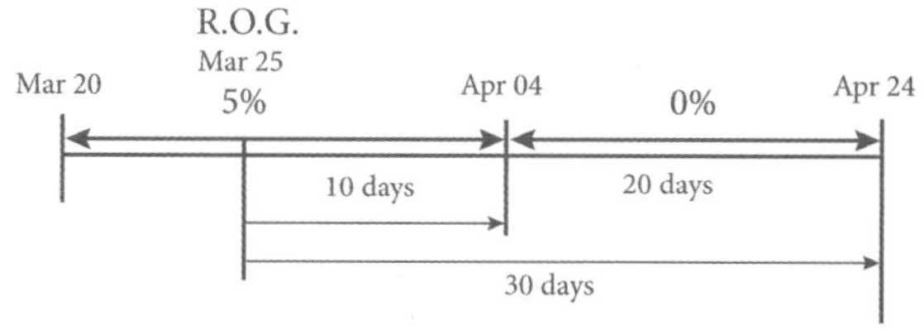

(i) The discount period ends on April 04, i.e., 10 days after R.O.G.

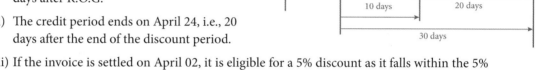

(ii) The credit period ends on April 24, i.e., 20 days after the end of the discount period.

(iii) If the invoice is settled on April 02, it is eligible for a 5% discount as it falls within the 5% discount period.
Therefore, the amount of cash discount = 50,000.00(0.05) = $2500.00

Partial Payments

For any payment made within the discount period, the amount *credited* will be greater than the amount *paid*.

A partial payment is a portion of the invoice amount that a buyer pays within the discount period to take advantage of a cash discount. The cash discount is applied to the amount paid. Therefore,

Not all sellers allow buyers to make partial payments and receive cash discounts on the portion of invoice paid.

$$\text{Amount Paid} = \text{Amount Credited} - \text{Amount of Discount}$$

$$= \text{Amount Credited} - (d \times \text{Amount Credited})$$

$$= \text{Amount Credited}(1 - d) \qquad [\text{Compare with } N = L(1 - d)]$$

If the *full* payment is made within the discount period, the amount credited is the invoice amount.

$$\text{Amount Credited} = \frac{\text{Amount Paid}}{(1 - d)}$$

The amount credited to the account is the partial payment plus the partial cash discount, as calculated using the following formula:

Formula 5.2 **Amount Credited**

$$\text{Amount Credited} = \frac{\text{Amount Paid}}{(1 - d)}$$

The cash discount is only applied on the amount paid within the discount period and not on the invoice amount. If a payment of $1000 is made within the 10% discount period, the amount credited would be $\frac{1000.00}{(1 - 0.10)}$ = $1111.11 (i.e., $1000 payment in the 10% cash discount period has the equivalent value of $1111.11).

Example 5.2(d) **Calculating the Payment Amount When a Partial Payment is Made Within the Discount Period**

Rolaxes Industries purchased a large 4-colour printing machine and received an invoice of $150,000 dated March 17, 2017 with payment terms 2/10, n/30. If it made a partial payment of $50,000 on March 20 and settled the balance on April 08, calculate the total amount paid for the machine.

Solution

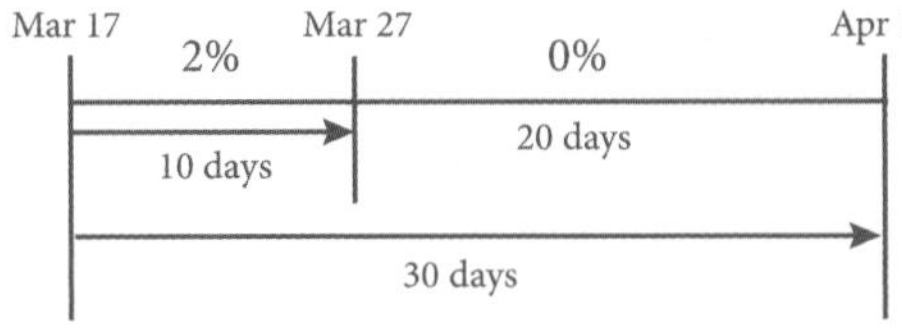

- 2% discount for the payment made on or before March 27 (discount period).
- Net price due for payments made after March 27, but on or before April 16 (credit period).

When amounts represent physical transactions, they are generally rounded to two decimal places before being used in further calculations.

The payment of $50,000 on March 20 was within the 2% discount period. Therefore, the printing company would have received a credit equivalent to: $\frac{50{,}000.00}{(1 - 0.02)} = 51{,}020.40816... = \$51{,}020.41$

Therefore, the balance that they would then have had to pay is,

$$150{,}000.00 - 51{,}020.41 = \$98{,}979.59$$

The balance payment on April 08 fell outside the discount period, but within the credit period. Since the company would not have received any discount on this amount, it would have had to pay $98,979.59.

Therefore, the total amount paid for the machine = 50,000.00 + 98,979.59 = $148,979.59

Example 5.2(e)

Calculating the Payment Amount When Two Partial Payments are Made Within the Discount Periods

Rianna furnished three floors of her office with new furniture and received an invoice dated January 15, 2017 for $250,000 with the following terms: 3/10, 2/30, n/45.

(i) If she paid $100,000 on January 25, 2017, what was the balance to be paid?

(ii) What was the amount of the second payment made on February 14, 2017 that reduced the balance to $70,000?

(iii) If she settled the balance on March 01, 2017, what was her total payment for the furniture?

Solution

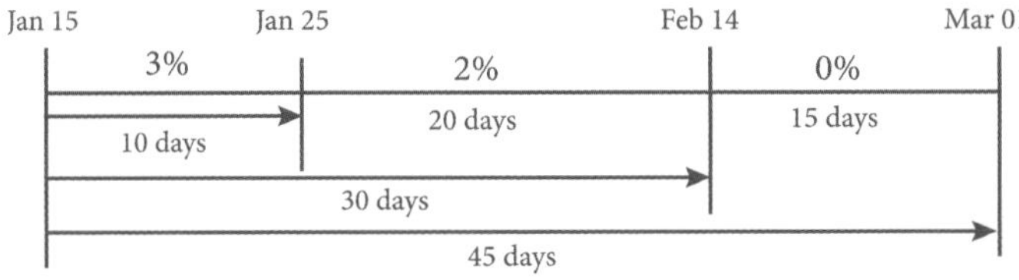

- 3% discount for payment made on or before January 25 (1st discount period).
- 2% discount for payment made after January 25, but on or before February 14 (2nd discount period).
- Net price due for payment made after February 14, but on or before March 01 (credit period).

(i) $100,000 paid on January 25 was within the 3% discount period

$$\textit{Amount Credited} = \frac{\textit{Amount Paid}}{(1 - d)} = \frac{100{,}000.00}{(1 - 0.03)} = 103{,}092.7835... = \$103{,}092.78$$

Balance on that invoice after this payment on January 25:

$$250{,}000.00 - 103{,}092.78 = \$146{,}907.22$$

(ii) Since the balance after the second payment was $70,000, the amount credited at the time the second payment was made should have been:

$$146{,}907.22 - 70{,}000.00 = \$76{,}907.22$$

$$\textit{Amount Credited} = \frac{\textit{Amount Paid}}{(1 - d)}$$

$$76{,}907.22 = \frac{\textit{Amount Paid}}{(1 - 0.02)}$$

$$76{,}907.22 = \frac{\textit{Amount Paid}}{0.98}$$

$$\textit{Amount paid} = 76{,}907.22 \times 0.98 = 75{,}369.0756 = \$75{,}369.08$$

Therefore, $75,369.08 was the amount of the second payment she made on February 14.

Solution *continued*

(iii) Her balance payment of $70,000 on March 01 was not eligible for any discounts and she should have paid the net price of $70,000.

Therefore, her total payment = 100,000.00 + 75,369.08 + 70,000.00 = $245,369.08

5.2 | Exercises

Answers to the odd-numbered problems are available at the end of the textbook.

Identify the last date of the discount period and the credit period for the payment terms with ordinary dating in Problems 1 and 2.

1.

	Invoice Date	Payment Terms	Last Date of Discount Period	Last Date of Credit Period
a.	January 01, 2017	3/10, n/30	?	?
b.	March 15, 2017	2.5/7, n/45	?	?
c.	April 25, 2017	3/10, 1/30, n/45	?	?
d.	July 22, 2017	2.5/10, 1.5/30, n/60	?	?

2.

	Invoice Date	Payment Terms	Last Date of Discount Period	Last Date of Credit Period
a.	February 18, 2017	2/10, n/30	?	?
b.	October 06, 2016	3/10, n/45	?	?
c.	February 25, 2017	2/7, 1/30, n/45	?	?
d.	August 23, 2016	3/10, 2.5/30, n/60	?	?

3. Foresteel Inc., a manufacturer of steel tubes, purchased raw materials from Premier Controls Ltd. and received an invoice for $20,500 dated February 28, 2017 with the following terms: 2/10, n/45. What amount does Foresteel Inc. have to pay to settle the invoice if paid on the following dates of 2017:

   a. March 10? b. March 11? c. April 14?

4. The purchasing department of a leading information technology company received an invoice of $260,800 for the purchase of new computers for its software development team. The invoice was dated February 14, 2017 and had the following payment terms: 2/7, n/45. What amount does the company have to pay to settle the invoice on the following dates of 2017:

   a. February 21? b. February 22? c. March 31?

5. A payment of $2500 was paid during the discount period on an invoice for $4775 with payment terms 2/15, n/30. What further payment, after the discount period, will settle this invoice?

6. A payment of $1250 was paid during the discount period on an invoice for $3150 with payment terms 3/10, n/30. What further payment, after the discount period, will settle this invoice?

7. Ella purchased some furniture for her office and received an invoice for $18,800 dated September 16, 2017 with payment terms 3/7, 1/30, n/60. What amount does she have to pay on October 16, 2017 to settle this invoice?

8. What payment on November 21, 2016 will settle an invoice for $3150 dated October 22, 2016 with payment terms 3/10, 1.5/30, n/60?

9. DCM Clocks received the following two invoices from its supplier: $27,500 on December 19, 2016 and $22,500 on January 08, 2017. If the payment terms on both the invoices were 2/10, 1/30, n/60, calculate the amount that must be paid by DCM Clocks to settle both of these invoices on January 18, 2017.

10. A publisher received an invoice for $180,750 on October 20, 2016 and another invoice of $145,000 on November 09, 2016 from its printer. The payment terms on both the invoices were 3/10, 1.5/30, n/45. What amount must be paid by the publisher to settle both of these invoices on November 19, 2016.

11. Three invoices for the amounts of $35,800, $25,000, and $40,650 were received on March 22, 2017, April 21, 2017, and May 14, 2017, respectively. If the payment terms are 3/7, 1/30, n/60, calculate the amount that must be paid on May 21, 2017 to settle all three invoices.

12. How much must be paid on December 20, 2016 to settle three invoices of values $125,750, $85,000, and $12,200 that were received on November 19, 2016, November 20, 2016, and December 10, 2016, respectively. The payment terms are 3/10, 1/30, n/45.

13. Nina received an invoice for $10,263 dated March 18, 2017 with payment terms 2.5/10, n/30 for the purchase of fertilizer for her vineyard. If she made a partial payment of $5000 on March 28 and settled the balance amount on April 17, what was the total amount paid for the fertilizer?

14. A retailer purchased winter clothes from a wholesaler and received an invoice for $40,618 dated November 25, 2016 with payment terms 3/15, n/30. If the retailer made a partial payment of $20,000 on December 10 and settled the balance on December 23, calculate the total amount paid for the clothes.

15. Suzanne received goods shipped to her from Halifax along with an invoice of $3000 that had payment terms 2.5/10, n/30. If she made a partial payment of $1000 during the discount period, calculate the balance on the invoice.

16. Whitney, the owner of a recording studio, received an invoice for $2500 that had payment terms 1/15, n/30. If she made a partial payment of $2000 during the discount period, calculate the balance on the invoice.

17. Nancy and Nikki run a very successful bakery in Oshawa, Ontario. On July 29, 2016 they received an invoice of $1750 with payment terms 3/7, 1.5/30, n/45 from their flour supplier. If they made a partial payment of $1250 on August 28, 2016, calculate the outstanding balance.

18. If a payment of $5000 was made on October 05, 2016 against an invoice for $30,000 dated September 05, 2016 with payment terms 3/10, 2/30, n/60, calculate the outstanding balance.

19. A purchasing manager of a beverage bottling factory received a shipment of raw materials with an invoice for $132,500 with payment terms 3/10, n/30. What payment should he make within the discount period to reduce the balance to $50,000?

20. An invoice for $56,000 has payment terms 1.25/15, n/45. What payment should be made within the discount period to reduce the balance to $25,000?

21. The purchasing department of a manufacturing company received an invoice for $280,550 with payment terms 2/10, n/30. What payment should be made within the discount period to reduce the balance by $30,000?

22. A purchasing manager received a shipment of raw materials with an invoice for $120,000 with terms 2.5/10, n/30. What payment should he make within the discount period to reduce the balance by $100,000?

23. Pamela, the purchasing manager, received an invoice for $290,000 dated March 17, 2016 with payment terms 2/7, 1.5/30, n/45. She made a first payment of $140,500 on March 24, a second payment of $100,000 on April 16, and the balance on May 01.
    a. What was the balance amount after the first payment?
    b. What was the amount paid on May 01?

24. A company received an invoice dated October 20, 2016 with terms 1.5/10, 0.5/30, n/60 for an amount of $150,860. It made a first payment of $65,500 on October 30, 2016, a second payment of $40,250 on November 19, 2016, and the balance on December 19, 2016.
    a. What was the balance amount after the first payment?
    b. What was the amount paid on December 19, 2016?

Identify the last date of the discount period and the credit period for the payment terms with E.O.M. and R.O.G. dating in Problems 25 and 26.

25.

	Invoice Date	Payment Terms	Date Goods Were Received (R.O.G.)	Last Date of Discount Period	Last Date of Credit Period
a.	August 12, 2016	3/10, E.O.M.	August 15, 2016	?	?
b.	July 01, 2016	1.5/10, E.O.M.	July 05, 2016	?	?
c.	February 21, 2017	3/7, n/30, R.O.G.	February 27, 2017	?	?
d.	June 12, 2017	2.5/10, n/45, R.O.G.	July 16, 2017	?	?

26.

	Invoice Date	Payment Terms	Date Goods Were Received (R.O.G.)	Last Date of Discount Period	Last Date of Credit Period
a.	June 30, 2017	2/10, E.O.M.	July 05, 2017	?	?
b.	October 18, 2016	1.5/10, E.O.M.	October 25, 2016	?	?
c.	April 20, 2017	2/7, n/30, R.O.G.	May 10, 2017	?	?
d.	August 02, 2017	1.5/10, n/45, R.O.G.	August 23, 2017	?	?

27. An invoice for $120,800 dated January 27, 2017 for a shipment of furniture has payment terms 3/15, E.O.M. What payment will settle the invoice if it is paid on:

a. January 31? b. February 15? c. March 01?

28. Built-in Installers received an invoice dated February 24, 2017 for $83,500 for electrical appliances that it purchased. If the payment terms on the invoice were 2/10, E.O.M., what payment would settle the invoice if it is paid on:

a. February 27? b. March 10? c. March 30?

29. Meghan, the owner of a brewery in Toronto, receives a shipment of barley on May 05, 2018 with an invoice dated May 01, 2018 valued at $30,600 and cash discount payment terms 3/10, n/30, R.O.G. What cash discount would she receive if the invoice is settled on the following dates:

a. May 10? b. May 15? c. June 04?

30. Starlight, a Kingston based production company, shipped a truck-load of lighting equipment to a client in Halifax. The invoice of $175,000 for the equipment was dated August 02, 2016. The equipment was received by the client on September 10, 2016. If the payment terms were 2.5/10, n/45, R.O.G., what cash discount would the client receive if the invoice is settled on the following dates:

a. September 10? b. September 25? c. October 10?

• 31. A department store received an invoice for $5625, dated February 25, 2017 with payment terms 3.0/10, 1.5/20, n/30. What payment on March 17 will reduce the balance by $2500?

• 32. A publisher received an invoice for $12,675 dated February 28, 2017 with payment terms 3/7, 1.5/15, n/30. What payment on March 15 will reduce the balance by $7500?

• 33. A hardware store received an invoice for $6375 dated March 26, 2017 with payment terms 3/7, 1.5/15, n/30.

a. What payment on April 02 will reduce the balance owed to $2000?

b. What further payment needs to be made on April 10 to settle the balance?

• 34. An electronic store received an invoice for $8200 dated January 23, 2017 with payment terms 2.5/10, 1.5/20, n/30.

a. What payment on February 02 will reduce the balance owed to $4000?

b. What further payment needs to be made on February 12 to settle the balance?

• 35. Markus received an invoice dated April 25, 2016 for $22,760 with the following terms: 3/10, 2/30, n/45.

a. If he paid $10,000 on May 05, what is the outstanding balance?

b. After making the first payment on May 05, calculate the amount of the second payment made on May 25 that reduced the balance to $5000.

c. What was the total payment (assuming that the balance was paid during the non-discount period)?

• 36. Lucy was in charge of sourcing chemicals for her pharmaceutical company. She received 300 shipments of chemicals for $280,400 with an invoice dated October 12, 2016 and payment terms 2/10, 1/30, n/45.

a. If she pays $100,000 on October 22, what is the outstanding balance?

b. What was the amount of the second payment that she made on November 11 if it reduced the balance to $69,288.89?

c. What was her total payment for the chemicals (assuming that the balance was paid during the non-discount period)?

5.3 | Markup

Markup (*M*) is the amount that a business adds to the **cost (*C*)** of the product to arrive at the **selling price (*S*)** of the product.

$$Selling\ Price\ (S) = Cost\ (C) + Markup\ (M)$$

This can be written as the following formula:

Formula 5.3(a)

Selling Price

$$S = C + M$$

The cost (*C*) of the product is the amount paid for the item after both trade and cash discounts have been applied.

The amount of markup (*M*), also known as margin or gross profit, is the difference between the selling price and the cost of the product (as from Formula 5.3(a)). Markup includes the business' **overhead expenses (*E*)** and the desired **operating profit (*P*)** of the business.

Overhead expenses (*E*), also known as operating expenses, include expenses such as salary, rent, utilities, insurance, advertising, etc., that are necessary to operate the business. Operating profit (*P*), also known as profit, is the amount of desired profit that is necessary to stay in the business.

$$Markup\ (M) = Overhead\ Expenses\ (E) + Operating\ Profit\ (P)$$

This can be written as the following formula:

Formula 5.3(b)

Amount of Markup

$$M = E + P$$

Combining the earlier two formulas, the formula for selling price (*S*) can be expressed as follows:

Formula 5.3(c)

Selling Price

$$S = C + E + P$$

Rate of Markup

The markup, expressed as a dollar amount (the amount of markup), can also be expressed as a percent (the rate of markup) calculated as a ratio on cost or on selling price, as shown below:

Formula 5.3(d)

Rate of Markup on Cost

$$Rate\ of\ markup\ on\ cost = \frac{M}{C} \times 100\%$$

Formula 5.3(e)

Rate of Markup on Selling Price (Gross Profit Margin)

$$Rate\ of\ markup\ on\ selling\ price = \frac{M}{S} \times 100\%$$

The relationship among C, E, P, M, and S as expressed by the above algebraic equations (or formulas) can be represented by the illustration in Exhibit 5.3(a) below:

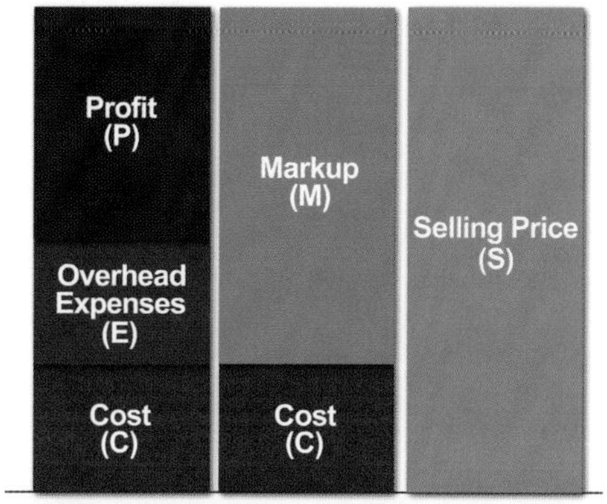

Exhibit 5.3(a): Relationship Among C, E, P, M, and S

Many retailers markup their product on selling price rather than on cost as information on selling price is easily available to them.

The relationship established by the algebraic equations (or formulas), which is illustrated in Exhibit 5.3(a), can also be represented by a table, as shown in Table 5.3, which allows the entry of values against those variables.

Table 5.3: Merchandising Calculation Table

	Amount	Rate	
		on C	on S
P			
$+E$			
M			
$+C$			
S			

The first column represents the variables and their relationship in a vertical form, as expressed in the equations.

For example, markup (M) is the sum of the operating profit (P) and the overhead expenses (E), as in the formula, $M = E + P$.

Similarly, selling price (S) is the sum of markup (M) and cost (C), as in the formula, $S = C + M$.

The second column, 'Amount', represents the dollar amount of the variables.

For example, if the cost of an item is $2500, then $2500 will be entered in the second column beside 'C'.

The third column, 'Rate', represents any of the variables as a percent on C or S, which is written under the 'on C' or 'on S' column.

For example, if the rate of markup on cost is 25%, (i.e., $M = 25\%$ of C), then 25% will be entered in the 'on C' column beside the variable 'M'. Similarly, if the overhead expense on selling price is 10%, (i.e., $E = 10\%$ of S), then 10% will be entered in the 'on S' column beside the variable 'E'.

This table is a useful tool for solving problems as it will allow you to organize the information provided and easily identify the values that need to be calculated, without repeatedly writing the same formulas.

	Amount	Rate	
		on C	on S
P			
$+E$			10%
M		25%	
$+C$	$2500.00		
S			

Example 5.3(a) **Markup Calculations, Given the Profit, Expenses, and Cost**

A store purchases printers for \$800 each. The overhead expenses on each printer are \$200 and the store has an operating profit of \$400 per printer.

(i) What is the amount of markup per printer?

(ii) What is the selling price per printer?

(iii) What is the rate of markup on cost?

(iv) What is the rate of markup on selling price?

Solution

Method 1: Using Formulas

Based on the information provided, $C = \$800.00$, $E = \$200.00$, $P = \$400.00$.

(i) Markup, $M = E + P = 200.00 + 400.00 = \$600.00$

Therefore, the amount of markup is \$600.00.

(ii) Selling Price, $S = C + M = 800.00 + 600.00 = \$1400.00$

Or, $S = C + E + P = 800.00 + 200.00 + 400.00 = \$1400.00$

Therefore, the selling price of each printer is \$1400.00.

(iii) *Rate of markup on cost* $= \dfrac{M}{C} \times 100\% = \dfrac{600.00}{800.00} \times 100\% = 0.75 \times 100\% = 75.00\%$

Therefore, the rate of markup on cost is 75.00%.

(iv) *Rate of markup on selling price* $= \dfrac{M}{S} \times 100\% = \dfrac{600.00}{1400.00} \times 100\% = 0.428571... \times 100\% = 42.86\%$

Therefore, the rate of markup on selling price is 42.86%.

Method 2: Using Table 5.3

Enter the known quantities for the variables and identify the quantities that are to be calculated.

(i) $M = E + P = \$600.00$

(ii) $S = C + M = \$1400.00$

(iii) $\dfrac{M}{C} = \dfrac{600.00}{800.00} = 0.75 = 75.00\%$

(iv) $\dfrac{M}{S} = \dfrac{600.00}{1400.00} = 0.428571... = 42.86\%$

	Amount	Rate	
		on C	on S
P	\$400.00		
$+ E$	\$200.00		
M	\$600.00	75.00%	42.86%
$+ C$	\$800.00		
S	\$1400.00		

Example 5.3(b) **Markup Calculations, Given the Cost, and Rate of Markup and Expenses on Cost**

A wholesaler purchases a product for \$2000 and has a rate of markup of 40% on cost. The overhead expenses are 20% on cost. Calculate the selling price, operating profit, amount of markup, and rate of markup on selling price.

Solution

Method 1: Using Formulas

Cost, $C = \$2000.00$

Markup, $M = 0.40C = 0.40(2000.00) = \$800.00$

Selling Price, $S = C + M = 2000.00 + 800.00 = \$2800.00$

Overhead expenses, $E = 0.20C = 0.20(2000.00) = \$400.00$

Solution *continued*

Using Formula 5.3(b), $M = E + P$

Substituting the values, $800.00 = 400.00 + P$

Solving for P, $P = 800.00 - 400.00 = \$400.00$

$$\textit{Rate of markup on selling price} = \frac{M}{S} \times 100\%$$

$$= \frac{800.00}{2800.00} \times 100\% = 0.285714... \times 100\% = 28.57\%$$

Therefore, the selling price is \$2800.00, the operating profit is \$400.00, the amount of markup is \$800.00, and the rate of markup on selling price is 28.57%.

Method 2: Using Table 5.3

Enter the known quantities for the variables and identify the quantities that are to be calculated.

$M = 0.40C = 0.40(2000.00) = \$800.00$

$E = 0.20C = 0.20(2000.00) = \$400.00$

$P = M - E = 800.00 - 400.00 = \$400.00$

$S = C + M = 2000.00 + 800.00 = \$2800.00$

$$\frac{M}{S} = \frac{800.00}{2800.00} = 0.285714... = 28.57\%$$

	Amount	Rate	
		on C	on S
P	\$400.00		
$+ E$	\$400.00	20.00%	
M	\$800.00	40.00%	28.57%
$+ C$	\$2000.00		
S	\$2800.00		

Example 5.3(c)

Markup Calculations, Given the Markup and Profit and Expenses on Selling Price

A retailer purchases a camera from a wholesaler, and marks up the product by \$200. If the operating profit is 18% on selling price and the overhead expenses are 14% on selling price, determine the selling price, cost, overhead expenses, and operating profit.

Solution

Method 1: Using Formulas

$M = \$200.00, P = 0.18S, E = 0.14S$

Using Formula 5.3(b), $M = E + P$

Substituting values, $200.00 = 0.14S + 0.18S$

Solving for S, $200.00 = 0.32S$

$S = \$625.00$

Using Formula 5.3(a), $S = C + M$

Substituting values, $625.00 = C + 200.00$

Solving for C, $C = \$425.00$

Overhead expenses, $E = 0.14S = 0.14(625.00) = \$87.50$

Operating profit, $P = 0.18S = 0.18(625.00) = \$112.50$

Therefore, the selling price is \$625.00, the cost is \$425.00, the overhead expenses are \$87.50, and the operating profit is \$112.50.

Method 2: Using Table 5.3

	Amount	Rate	
		on C	on S
P	\$112.50		18%
$+ E$	\$87.50		14%
M	\$200.00		32%
$+ C$	\$425.00		
S	\$625.00		

Example 5.3(d)

Markup Calculations, Given the Selling Price and Rate of Markup on Selling Price

Madison, a retailer, sells a handbag for \$800. The rate of markup on selling price for this bag is 40%. Calculate her cost for the bag and the markup amount.

Solution

Method 1: Using Formulas

$S = \$800.00$

$M = 0.40S = 0.40(800.00) = \$320.00$

Using Formula 5.3(a), $S = C + M$

Substituting the values, $800.00 = C + 320.00$

Solving for C, $C = \$480.00$

Therefore, the bag cost her $480.00 and her markup amount is $320.00.

Method 2: Using Table 5.3

	Amount	Rate on C	Rate on S
P			
+ E			
M	$320.00		40%
+ C	$480.00		
S	$800.00		

Example 5.3(e)

Markup Calculations, Given the Selling Price and Rate of Markup on Cost

Alba, a wholesaler of an electronic item, sells each item for $600. If she has a rate of markup of 25% on the cost of the item, calculate the cost of each item.

Solution

Method 1: Using Formulas

$S = \$600.00,\ M = 0.25C$

Using Formula 5.3(a), $S = C + M$

Substituting the values, $600.00 = C + 0.25C$

Solving for C, $600.00 = 1.25C$

$C = \$480.00$

Therefore, the cost of each item is $480.00.

Method 2: Using Table 5.3

	Amount	Rate on C	Rate on S
P			
+ E			
M		25%	
+ C	$480.00	100%	
S	$600.00	125%	

Break-Even Price (BE)

The break-even (*BE*) price of a product refers to the selling price of an item, which only includes the cost (*C*) and the overhead expenses (*E*) of the product. Therefore, when a product is sold at a break-even price, there is no profit gained or loss incurred ($P = 0$).

Break-even price (BE) = Cost (C) + Overhead Expenses (E)

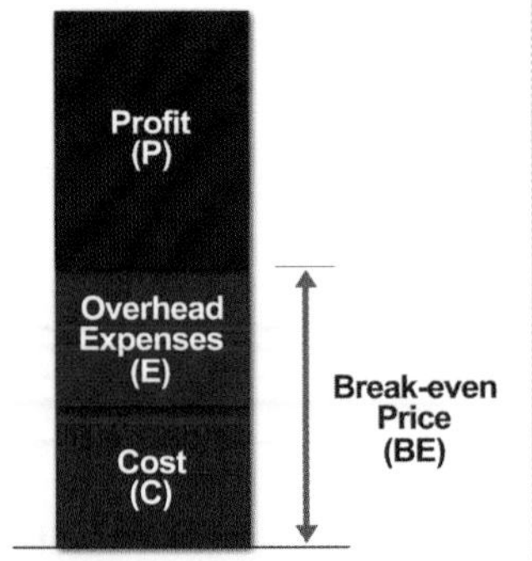

Exhibit 5.3(b): Break-Even Price (*BE*)

Formula 5.3(f)

Break-Even Price

$$BE = C + E$$

At break-even, profit or loss is 0.

From Formula 5.3(c), $S = C + E + P$

At break-even, $S = BE + 0$

$S = BE$

Therefore, at break-even, the break-even price (*BE*) is the selling price (*S*).

Example 5.3(f)

Calculating the Break-Even Price

A furniture store received trade discounts of 10% and 8% on the list price of $1250 on a dining table and planned to sell it for $1700 so that the operating profit would be 20% on cost. If the store was unable to sell the table for this amount, what minimum selling price would allow it to break-even?

Solution

Using Formula 5.1(c), $N = L(1 - d_1)(1 - d_2)$

$N = 1250.00(1 - 0.10)(1 - 0.08) = \$1035.00$

Therefore, $C = \$1035.00$.

Method 1: Using Formulas

$S = \$1700.00$, $C = \$1035.00$

$P = 0.20C = 0.20(1035.00) = \$207.00$

Using Formula 5.3(a), $S = C + M$

Substituting values, $1700.00 = 1035.00 + M$

Solving for M, $M = \$665.00$

Using Formula 5.3(b), $M = E + P$

Substituting values, $665.00 = E + 207.00$

Solving for E, $E = \$458.00$

Method 2: Using Table 5.3

	Amount	Rate	
		on C	on S
P	\$207.00	20%	
$+ E$	\$458.00		
M	\$665.00		
$+ C$	\$1035.00		
S	\$1700.00		

In order to break even, the minimum selling price would be the break-even price, which is equal to $C + E$.

Using Formula 5.3(f), $BE = C + E = 1035.00 + 458.00 = \$1493.00$

Therefore, the break-even price or selling price to break even would be \$1493.00.

Example 5.3(g)

Calculating the Selling Price, Given the Profit and Expenses as a Percent of Cost

The cost of an item to a store is \$360. The store's overhead expense is 12% on cost and the store wants to have an operating profit of 15% on cost.

(i) Calculate the regular selling price of the item.

(ii) Calculate the rate of markup on cost.

(iii) Calculate the break-even price.

Solution

$C = \$360.00$

$E = 0.12C = 0.12(360.00) = \$43.20$

$P = 0.15C = 0.15(360.00) = \$54.00$

Method 1: Using Formulas

(i) Using Formula 5.3(c), $S = C + E + P$

$= 360.00 + 43.20 + 54.00$

$= \$457.20$

Therefore, the regular selling price of the item was \$457.20.

(ii) Using Formula 5.3(a), $S = C + M$

Substituting values, $457.20 = 360.00 + M$

Solving for M, $M = \$97.20$

$$\textit{Rate of markup on cost} = \frac{M}{C} \times 100\% = \frac{97.20}{360.00} \times 100\%$$

$$= 0.27 \times 100\% = 27\%$$

Therefore, the rate of markup on cost is 27%.

(iii) Using Formula 5.3(f), $BE = C + E$

$= 360.00 + 43.20 = \$403.20$

Therefore, the break-even price is \$403.20.

Method 2: Using Table 5.3

	Amount	Rate	
		on C	on S
P	\$54.00	15%	
$+ E$	\$43.20	12%	
M	\$97.20	27%	
$+ C$	\$360.00		
S	\$457.20		

5.3 | Exercises

Answers to the odd-numbered problems are available at the end of the textbook.

For the following problems, express the answers rounded to two decimal places, wherever applicable. Calculate the missing values in Problems 1 to 4.

1.

	Cost	Amount of Markup	Selling Price	Rate of Markup on Cost	Rate of Markup on Selling Price
a.	$48.00	$12.00	?	?	?
b.	?	?	$192.00	60%	?
c.	$88.00	?	?	25%	?
d.	$42.00	?	?	?	$33\frac{1}{3}\%$
e.	?	?	$70.00	?	$66\frac{2}{3}\%$

2.

	Cost	Amount of Markup	Selling Price	Rate of Markup on Cost	Rate of Markup on Selling Price
a.	$120.00	$30.00	?	?	?
b.	?	?	$280.00	40%	?
c.	$160.00	?	?	20%	?
d.	$64.00	?	?	?	28%
e.	?	?	$150.00	?	40%

3.

	Cost	Amount of Markup	Selling Price	Profit	Overhead Expenses	Rate of Markup on Cost	Rate of Markup on Selling Price
a.	$1200.00	?	?	$350.00	$280.00	?	?
b.	$7450.50	?	$10,500.00	?	$1375.40	?	?
c.	?	?	?	$400.00	$200.00	20.5%	?
d.	$6.60	?	?	$3.50	?	?	40%
e.	?	$20.50	?	?	$8.20	5%	?

4.

	Cost	Amount of Markup	Selling Price	Profit	Overhead Expenses	Rate of Markup on Cost	Rate of Markup on Selling Price
a.	$400.00	?	?	$250.00	$150.00	?	?
b.	$1010.75	?	$1200.00	?	$110.35	?	?
c.	?	?	?	$125.50	$46.80	30%	?
d.	$40.80	?	?	$8.50	?	?	20%
e.	?	$284.50	?	?	$70.75	25%	?

5. Marlin buys a box of printer cartridges for $1000 and is selling them for $1200.
   a. What is the rate of markup on cost?
   b. What is the rate of markup on selling price?

6. Ivy purchases phones for $280.50 each and is selling them for $300 each.
   a. What is the rate of markup on cost?
   b. What is the rate of markup on selling price?

7. A laptop trader purchases laptops for $450 each. The overhead expense is $50 and operating profit is $200 per laptop.
   a. What is the rate of markup on cost?
   b. What is the rate of markup on selling price?

8. A car dealership purchases a particular car model for $16,500 each. The dealership's overhead expenses are $1250 and its operating profits are $3000 per car.
   a. What is the rate of markup on cost?
   b. What is the rate of markup on selling price?

9. A computer assembly firm purchases computer parts at $225 per computer. The operating expenses are 25% on cost and rate of markup is 60% on cost.
   a. What is the selling price of each computer?
   b. What is the operating profit per computer?

10. Rugged Hardware, a local store in London, purchases industrial toolkits from its distributor for $180 each. Its operating expenses are 15% on cost and rate of markup is 35% on cost.
    a. What is Rugged Hardware's selling price of each toolkit?
    b. What is Rugged Hardware's operating profit per toolkit?

11. Rafael, a successful clothing designer, creates designer leather jackets, marks them up by 90% on selling price, and sells them for $1200 each. What is his cost to create each jacket?

12. As Amber Cupcakes is the only cupcake shop in the area, the owner sells her cupcakes for a premium. The rate of markup on each cupcake is 95% on selling price. If she sells each cupcake for $4.25, what is her cost to make each cupcake?

13. If the cost of a product is $480.75 and it has a 20% rate of markup on selling price, calculate the selling price of the product.

14. A calendar reseller purchases calendars for $5 each and applies a 14.50% markup on selling price. What is the selling price of each calendar?

15. Rudolf, a cloth merchant, sells special fabric for $10 per metre. What is the amount of markup if the rate of markup on cost is 30%?

16. A distributor has a rate of markup of 30% on cost of its textbooks. If it sells each textbook for $100, what is the amount of markup?

17. The cost of a desk lamp to a store is $125. The store's overhead expenses are 25% on cost and the operating profit is 20% on selling price.
    a. Calculate the regular selling price of the desk lamp.
    b. Calculate the rate of markup on selling price.

18. A furniture retailer paid $649 for a desk. The retailer's operating profit is 22% on selling price and the overhead expenses are 18% on cost.
    a. Calculate the regular selling price of the desk.
    b. Calculate the rate of markup on selling price.

19. A store sells humidifiers for $67.50 each. The store's operating expenses are 40% on cost and the operating profit is 20% on selling price.
    a. Calculate the cost of a humidifier.
    b. Calculate the rate of markup on cost.

20. A store sells crystal chandeliers for $2500 each. The store's operating expenses are 20% on cost and their operating profit is 15% on selling price.
    a. Calculate the cost of a chandelier.
    b. Calculate the rate of markup on cost.

21. Kathy has a 20% rate of markup on cost of the magazines that she sells at her store. What is the rate of markup on selling price of the magazines?

22. A car dealership sold a used car at a 35.25% rate of markup on cost. What was the rate of markup on selling price?

23. Amanda and Rakesh had an 18% rate of markup on selling price of the shoes that they sold at their store. Calculate the rate of markup on cost.

24. If a car dealership sold its brand new cars at a rate of markup of 40% on selling price, calculate the rate of markup on cost.

25. A manufacturer of vertical blinds purchases raw materials for $18 per set of blinds and has a markup of $124 per set of blinds. Its operating profit is 60% on selling price. What are its overhead expenses per set of blinds?

26. Zack's operating profit is 35% on selling price for the cameras that he sells at his store. He purchases them for $145 per camera and has a markup of $82 per camera. What are his overhead expenses per camera?

27. Danilo and his wife operate a restaurant where they sell all their meals for $14 each. The markup on each meal is $4.50 and overhead expenses are 20% of the selling price.
    a. How much does it cost them to make each meal?
    b. What is their operating profit per meal?

28. Domenica's store sells an item for $5.50 each. The overhead expenses are 15% on selling price and markup on each item is $1.25.
    a. What is the cost of each item?
    b. What is the operating profit per item?

29. A distributor purchases a machine for $185,000, less discounts of 5% and 3%. It then sells the machine to a client at a price, which includes 35% profit on selling price and overhead expenses of 20% on selling price.
    a. How much did it cost to purchase the machine?
    b. What was the selling price of the machine?

30. A clothing merchant purchases a container shipment of clothes for $35,000, less discounts of 10% and 5%. He sells it to a customer at a price which includes 20% profit on selling price and overhead expenses of 25% on selling price.
    a. How much did it cost him to purchase the container of clothes?
    b. What was the selling price of the container of clothes?

31. Zarita sells clay pots at her pottery studio for $30 each. The overhead expenses are $12 per pot and operating profit is 30% on selling price.
    a. What is her amount of markup per pot?
    b. How much does it cost her to purchase each pot?

32. Anna sells earrings at her store for $45.20 per pair. Her overhead expenses are $6 per pair and she makes 40% operating profit on selling price.
    a. What is her amount of markup per pair of earrings?
    b. How much does it cost her to purchase each pair of earrings?

• 33. Henry purchased two computers for $1000 each. If he applies a rate of markup of 35% on cost for the first computer and a rate of markup of 25% on selling price for the second computer, which computer is he selling for a cheaper price and by how much?

• 34. Lynn and Kim own two competing convenience stores. Both of them purchase a similar shipment of chocolate bars for $2500 every month to sell at their stores. If Lynn has a rate of markup of 45% on cost of her chocolate bars and Kim has a rate of markup of 30% on selling price of her chocolate bars, which store sells the shipment of chocolate bars for a cheaper price and by how much?

• 35. Kayla, a retailer, received successive trade discounts of 20% and 5% on a listed price of $2340 for each computer system that she purchased from a wholesaler. If her overhead expenses were 40% on cost, calculate the minimum price at which she would have had to sell the computers to break-even.

• 36. A battery trader received successive trade discounts of 8% and 6% on the list price of $22,450 for a container shipment of batteries from an overseas country. If the trader's overhead expenses are 18% on cost, calculate the minimum price at which he must sell the batteries to break-even.

5.4 | Markdown

Markdown (*D*) is the amount by which the selling price (*S*) of a product is reduced to determine the sale price or **reduced selling price (S_{Red})**. In business, the selling price of an item is often reduced for various reasons, such as competition, clearance of seasonal items, out-of-fashion items, etc.

The relationship is expressed by the following formula:

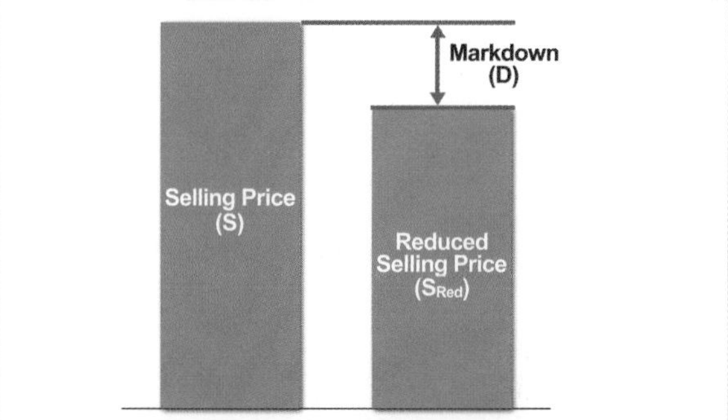

Exhibit 5.4(a): Relationship Among S, D, and S_{Red}

Formula 5.4(a) **Reduced Selling Price**

$$S_{Red} = S - D$$

Amount of Markdown and Rate of Markdown

Markdown can be expressed as a dollar amount or as a percent (the rate of markdown) of the selling price, as shown below:

Formula 5.4(b) **Amount of Markdown**

$$D = S - S_{Red}$$

Formula 5.4(c) **Rate of Markdown**

$$Rate\ of\ markdown = \frac{D}{S} \times 100\%$$

If the rate of markdown is 20%, then, $D = 0.20S$.

Unless otherwise stated, rate of markdown is calculated as a percent of the selling price.

The relationship among S, D, and S_{Red} as outlined in Formula 5.4(a) and Formula 5.4(b) and the relationship among S, C, E, P, and M, learned in Section 5.3 (Exhibit 5.3(a)), is incorporated into Exhibit 5.4(b).

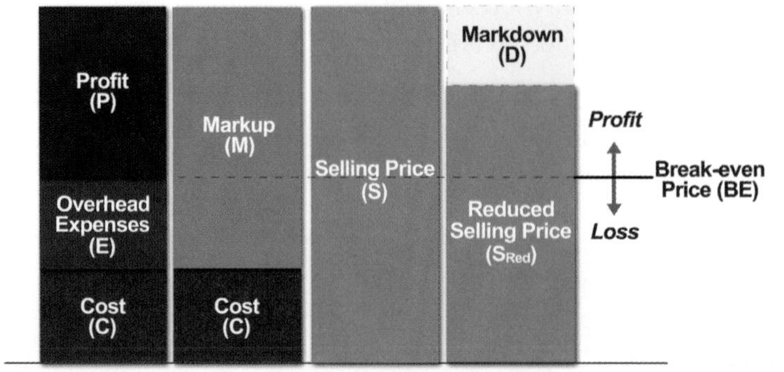

Exhibit 5.4(b): Relationship Among C, E, P, M, S, D, and S_{Red}

Table 5.4: Merchandising Calculation Table

	Amount	Rate	
		on C	on S
P			
$+E$			
M			
$+C$			
S			
$-D$			
S_{Red}			

The relationship established by the algebraic equations (formulas), which is illustrated in Exhibit 5.4(b), can also be represented using Table 5.4, an extension to Table 5.3.

Example 5.4(a) **Markdown Calculations, Given the Selling Price and Sale Price**

A pair of sunglasses regularly sells for \$185 each. Calculate the rate of markdown if each pair of sunglasses was sold for \$129.50 during a sale.

Solution

Method 1: Using Formulas

$S = \$185.00,\ S_{Red} = \$129.50$

Using Formula 5.4(b), $D = S - S_{Red}$

$= 185.00 - 129.50 = \$55.50$

Using Formula 5.4(c), $\textit{Rate of markdown} = \frac{D}{S} \times 100\%$

$= \frac{55.50}{185.00} \times 100\%$

$= 0.30 \times 100\% = 30\%$

Therefore, the rate of markdown was 30%.

Method 2: Using Table 5.4

	Amount	Rate	
		on C	on S
P			
$+E$			
M			
$+C$			
S	\$185.00		
$-D$	-\$55.50		30%
S_{Red}	\$129.50		

Example 5.4(b) **Calculating the Amount of Markdown and Reduced Selling Price**

A used car dealer purchases cars for \$9450 each and marks them up by 20% on selling price. At the beginning of the year, the dealer marks down its cars by 10%.

(i) Calculate the amount of markdown.

(ii) What is the reduced selling price of the car?

Solution

Method 1: Using Formulas

$C = \$9450.00$, $M = 0.20S$

Using Formula 5.3(a), $S = C + M$

$$S = 9450.00 + 0.20S$$

$$0.80S = 9450.00$$

$$S = \$11{,}812.50$$

(i) $D = 0.10S = 0.10(11{,}812.50) = \$1181.25$

Therefore, the amount of markdown is \$1181.25.

(ii) Using Formula 5.4(a), $S_{Red} = S - D$

$$= 11{,}812.50 - 1181.25$$

$$= \$10{,}631.25$$

Therefore, the reduced selling price is \$10,631.25.

Method 2: Using Table 5.4

	Amount	Rate	
		on C	on S
P			
$+E$			
M			20%
$+C$	\$9450.00		80%
S	\$11,812.50		100%
$-D$	−\$1181.25		10%
S_{Red}	\$10,631.25		

Example 5.4(c) **Calculating the Rate of Discount to Match the Competitor's Sale Price**

The same model calculator is sold for \$40 at Store *A* and \$38 at Store *B*. In the summer, Store *A* offers a discount of 15% on the calculator. What rate of discount should Store *B* offer to match the sale price of the calculator available in Store *A*?

Solution

Method 1: Using Formulas

For Store A,

$S = \$40.00$, $D = 0.15S = 0.15(40.00) = \$6.00$

$S_{Red} = S - D = 40.00 - 6.00 = \$34.00$

For Store B,

$S = \$38.00$

To match the sale price of the calculators sold in Store A,

$D = 38.00 - 34.00 = \$4.00$

$$\textit{Rate of markdown} = \frac{D}{S} \times 100\% = \frac{4.00}{38.00} \times 100\% = 0.105263... \times 100\% = 10.53\%$$

Therefore, Store *B* should offer a discount of 10.53% to match the sale price of calculators sold in Store *A*.

Method 2: Using Table 5.4

For Store *A*:

	Amount	Rate	
		on C	on S
P			
$+E$			
M			
$+C$			
S	\$40.00		
$-D$	−\$6.00		15.00%
S_{Red}	\$34.00		

For Store *B*:

	Amount	Rate	
		on C	on S
P			
$+E$			
M			
$+C$			
S	\$38.00		
$-D$	−\$4.00		10.53%
S_{Red}	\$34.00		

Example 5.4(d) **Calculating the Rate of Markdown to Sell at the Cost Price**

A distributor purchased hard drives for $250 each and sells them with a markup of 25% on cost. At the end of the financial year, the distributor wanted to clear the inventory so it sold the hard drives at the cost price. Calculate the rate of markdown.

Solution

Method 1: Using Formulas

$C = \$250.00,\ M = 0.25C = 0.25(250.00) = \$62.50$

Using Formula 5.3(a), $S = C + M$

$= 250.00 + 62.50 = \$312.50$

$S_{Red} = C = \$250.00$

Using Formula 5.4(b), $D = S - S_{Red}$

$= 312.50 - 250.00 = \$62.50$

Using Formula 5.4(c), $\text{Rate of markdown} = \dfrac{D}{S} \times 100\%$

$= \dfrac{62.50}{312.50} \times 100\%$

$= 0.20 \times 100\% = 20\%$

Therefore, the rate of markdown is 20%.

Method 2: Using Table 5.4

	Amount	Rate	
		on C	on S
P			
+ E			
M	$62.50	25%	
+ C	$250.00		
S	$312.50		
– D	–$62.50		20%
S_{Red}	$250.00		

Example 5.4(e) **Calculating the Rate of Markdown, Reduced Selling Price, and Rate of Markup on Sale Price**

A store purchases SLR cameras for $540 each. The store's overhead expenses are 20% on cost and it wants an operating profit of $200 on the sale of each camera. Since the store is unable to sell its cameras at the regular selling price, it marks down the price by $127.20.

(i) What is the rate of markdown?

(ii) What is the reduced selling price (or sale price)?

(iii) What is the rate of markup on sale price?

Solution

Method 1: Using Formulas

$C = \$540.00,\ P = \$200.00,\ D = \$127.20$

$E = 0.20C = 0.20(540.00) = \$108.00$

Using Formula 5.3(c), $S = C + E + P$

$= 540.00 + 108.00 + 200.00 = \$848.00$

(i) Using Formula 5.4(c),

$\text{Rate of markdown} = \dfrac{D}{S} \times 100\% = \dfrac{127.20}{848.00} \times 100\%$

$= 0.15 \times 100\% = 15\%$

Therefore, the rate of markdown is 15%.

(ii) Reduced selling price (or sale price),

Using Formula 5.4(a), $S_{Red} = S - D$

$= 848.00 - 127.20 = \$720.80$

Therefore, the reduced selling price is $720.80.

(iii) $\text{Markup on sale price} = S_{Red} - C = 720.80 - 540.00 = \$180.80$

$\text{Rate of markup on sale price} = \dfrac{180.80}{720.80} \times 100\% = 0.250832... \times 100\% = 25.08\%$

Therefore, the markup on sale price is 25.08%.

Method 2: Using Table 5.4

	Amount	Rate	
		on C	on S
P	$200.00		
+ E	$108.00	20%	
M	$308.00		
+ C	$540.00		
S	$848.00		
– D	–$127.20		15%
S_{Red}	$720.80		

5.4 | Exercises

Answers to the odd-numbered problems are available at the end of the textbook.

For the following problems, express the answers rounded to two decimal places, wherever applicable. Calculate the missing values in Problems 1 and 2 below.

1.

	Cost	Amount of Markup	Selling Price	Rate of Markup on Cost	Rate of Markup on Selling Price	Amount of Markdown	Rate of Markdown	Reduced Selling Price
a.	$50.75	$14.25	?	?	?	$5.50	?	?
b.	$211.25	?	?	?	?	$12.50	5.00%	?
c.	?	$101.12	?	?	?	?	2.50%	$2174.25
d.	$315.00	?	?	?	30.00%	$210.00	?	?
e.	$950.00	?	?	26.00%	?	?	12.00%	?
f.	?	?	$15,000.00	25.00%	?	?	?	$12,750.00

2.

	Cost	Amount of Markup	Selling Price	Rate of Markup on Cost	Rate of Markup on Selling Price	Amount of Markdown	Rate of Markdown	Reduced Selling Price
a.	$250.50	$89.50	?	?	?	$42.75	?	?
b.	$851.57	?	?	?	?	$230.50	18.00%	?
c.	?	$47.00	?	?	?	?	5.00%	$570.00
d.	$5.25	?	?	?	25.00%	$1.25	?	?
e.	$176.25	?	?	25.00%	?	?	20.00%	?
f.	?	?	$8640.00	40.00%	?	?	?	$7344.00

3. A stereo that regularly sells for $200 at a store is marked down by 20%.
   a. What is the amount of discount offered?
   b. What is the reduced selling price of the stereo?

4. Harris Steels was unable to sell steel rods when there was a slump in the construction industry, so it offered a 60% markdown on the regular selling price of $80.
   a. Calculate the amount of discount offered.
   b. What is the reduced selling price of the steel rods?

5. Grand Prairie Sportmart, a sporting goods store, regularly sells its snowboards at $800 each. However, as winter was coming to an end, it reduced the price to $680. Calculate the amount of markdown on the snowboards and the corresponding rate of markdown.

6. Charlottetown Winter Wear sells its sports jackets for $1450 each. However, when the store received a large corporate order to supply sports jackets, it sold them for $900 each. Calculate the amount of markdown and the corresponding rate of markdown.

7. Alessandria, a resident of Toronto, drives to Buffalo every year on Black Friday to purchase clothes from the retail outlets there. The markdown at the outlet this year was 70% on Black Friday and she spent $1000 on clothes. Calculate the regular selling price of the clothes she purchased and the amount of discount she received this year.

8. Tao was excited that he purchased a brand new car for $22,400 from a car dealership after it was marked down by 8%. Calculate the regular selling price of the car and the amount of markdown he received.

9. Company A and Company B sell the same model camera for \$115 and \$130, respectively. During a sale, Company A offers a discount of 10% on the camera. What should Company B's rate of markdown be on the camera to match Company A's sale price?

10. Ken's electronic store sells tablets for \$395 each and Henry's electronic store sells the same model tablet for \$373. During a Boxing Day sale, Ken offers a discount of 15% on the tablet. What rate of markdown should be offered by Henry to match the sale price of the tablet offered by Ken?

11. An item is sold for \$35 at a store in Brandon, Manitoba and for \$47.50 at a store in Selkirk, Manitoba. If the store in Brandon offers a discount of \$5.50 on this item, what rate of markdown should be offered by the store in Selkirk to match the sale price of the item in Brandon?

12. A car dealership in Kensington sells a new model for \$28,900. The same model is sold in Cornwall for \$27,600. If the dealership in Kensington offers a discount of \$4,850 on the car, what rate of markdown should the dealership in Cornwall offer to match the sale price of the car in Kensington?

13. A store purchases a product for \$2.50 each and sells it with a markup of 14% on cost. To clear inventory, the store sells the product at cost. Calculate the rate of markdown.

14. Galleria Sports World purchases skates for \$25.50 each and sells them at a markup of 30% on cost. During a clearance sale, the store sells the skates at the cost price. Calculate the rate of markdown.

15. It costs a manufacturing firm \$12,500 to build a machine and the markup is 45% on selling price. During a sale, the price of the machine is marked down to the cost price. Calculate the rate of markdown.

16. Slave Lake Shoe Source purchases ladies shoes for \$35 each pair and has a markup of 60% on selling price. What is the rate of markdown on these shoes if it sells them at the cost price during a New Year's sale?

17. During a sale, HomeMart marks down its utensils by 40%. If the amount of markdown on an expensive dinner set is \$435, calculate the regular selling price and sale price of the dinner set.

18. Collingwood Ski & Board marked down its skis by 25% towards the end of the season. If the amount of markdown is \$180.50, calculate the regular selling price and sale price of a pair of skis.

19. Thomas owns a successful furniture distribution store. He purchases dining table sets at \$200 each from a wholesaler and sells them after a markup of 120% on cost. Every summer he runs a seasonal sale and offers a markdown of 30%. Calculate the regular selling price and the discounted selling price of the set.

20. It costs a manufacturer \$18,450 to build a machine. The company sells the machines at a markup of 75% on cost. During a low demand season, it discounts the machine by 25% and sells it. Calculate the regular selling price and the discounted selling price of the machine.

21. CompuWare Outlet buys portable hard-disks for \$500 each and has a rate of markup of 60% on selling price. During a sale, it offers a markdown of 75%. Calculate the following for each hard-disk:
    a. Regular selling price.
    b. Reduced selling price.

22. It costs a manufacturer \$3150 to make a product. The rate of markup is 25% on selling price and it offers a markdown of 15% during a discount period.
    a. What is the regular selling price?
    b. What is the reduced selling price during the discount period?

23. The markup on an item is \$28 and the rate of markup on selling price is 20%. If the discount offered is 15%, calculate the regular selling price and reduced selling price of the item.

24. A furniture dealer has a markup of \$36 per table. If this represented an 18% rate of markup on the selling price, calculate the regular selling price. If the dealer offered a discount of 15% during a sale, calculate the reduced selling price per table.

25. Shirts were purchased for $12.50 each and were marked up by $16.75. During Christmas, they were discounted by $5.85 per shirt.
    a. What is the rate of markdown?
    b. What is the reduced selling price per shirt?

26. It costs a tailor $2.50 to make a fabric laptop case. The markup is $10 per case. During a sale, he offers a discount of $1.25 per case.
    a. What is the rate of markdown?
    b. What is the reduced selling price?

27. Madelyn, a shoe store owner, purchases snow boots for $60 each and has a rate of markup of 25% on cost. Every January, she marks them down to a reduced selling price of $52.50.
    a. What is the regular selling price of the boots?
    b. What is the rate of markdown in January?

28. Casey buys chocolates for $7 and marks them up by 30% on cost. During a sale, he marks them down to $7.25.
    a. What is the regular selling price of the chocolates?
    b. What is the rate of markdown during a sale?

• 29. A computer store's markup on selling price of a computer is 15% and the amount of markup is $217.35. During a sale, the item was marked down to sell at break-even price. If the stores overhead expense is 10% on cost, calculate the rate of markdown during the sale.

• 30. An electronic store's markup on selling price of a camera is 25% and the amount of markup is $36.95. During a sale, the item was marked down to sell at break-even price. If the stores overhead expense is 15% on cost, calculate the rate of markdown during the sale.

• 31. A retailer's rate of markup on cost of an item is 20% and the markup amount is $80. During a sale, the item was marked down by 30%.
    a. Calculate the regular selling price.
    b. Calculate the reduced selling price.

• 32. Pete's Wheels n' Spokes has a rate of markup on cost of 25% on a model of bikes. This represents a markup amount of $40. At the end of summer, the store offers a discount of 30%.
    a. Calculate the regular selling price.
    b. Calculate the discounted selling price.

5.5 | Applications of Markup and Markdown

Calculating the Reduced Profit or Loss at Sale Price

When a product is sold at its break-even price, there is neither profit gained nor loss incurred. As described earlier, the break-even price of a product is the selling price of an item, which includes the cost (C) and overhead expenses (E) of the product.

At the reduced selling price (S_{Red}), the desired or operating profit (P) will be reduced by the amount equal to the amount of markdown (D), as shown in the diagram below:

$P_{Red} = P - D$
$P_{Red} = S_{Red} - BE$

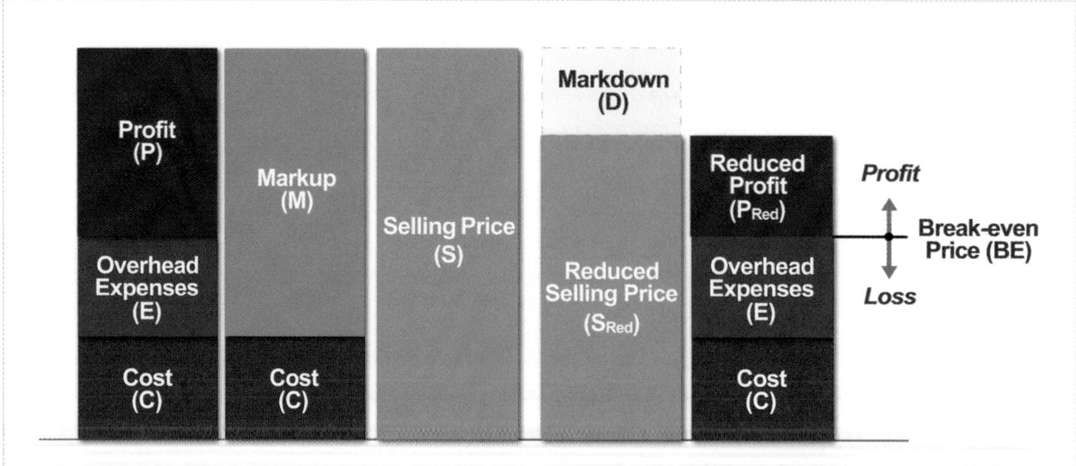

Exhibit 5.5: Reduced Profit or Loss After Markdown

From the above diagram, you will also note the following:

- If Markdown (**D**) < Profit (**P**), then the **reduced profit (P_{Red})** will be positive. Also, S_{Red} will be greater than BE. Therefore, there will be reduced profit at the sale price.
- If Markdown (**D**) = Profit (**P**), then P_{Red} will be 0. Also, S_{Red} will be equal to BE. Therefore, there will be neither profit nor loss at the sale price.
- If Markdown (**D**) > Profit (**P**), then P_{Red} will be negative. Also, S_{Red} will be less than BE. Therefore, there will be loss at the sale price.

There may also be situations when an item is sold below cost (for example, out of season sales, discontinued product, etc.). In such situations, Markdown (D) > Markup (M) and P_{Red} will be negative.

Therefore, we can conclude that

$$P_{Red} = S_{Red} - BE$$
$$= S_{Red} - (C + E)$$

If P_{Red} is negative, then there is a loss at sale price.

Removing the brackets results in the following formula:

Formula 5.5(a) **Reduced Profit**

$$P_{Red} = S_{Red} - C - E$$

We can also express P_{Red} in terms of profit (P) and markdown (D).

From Formula 5.5(a), $P_{Red} = S_{Red} - C - E$

Substituting $S_{Red} = S - D$ from Formula 5.4(a),

$$P_{Red} = S - D - C - E$$

Regrouping, $P_{Red} = (S - C - E) - D$

Substituting $P = (S - C - E)$ from Formula 5.3(c) results in the following formula:

Formula 5.5(b) **Reduced Profit**

$$P_{Red} = P - D$$

The relationship established by the algebraic equations (or formulas) illustrated in Exhibit 5.5 can also be represented using Table 5.5, an extension of Table 5.4.

Table 5.5: Merchandising Calculation Table

	Amount	Rate on C	Rate on S
P			
$+ E$			
M			
$+ C$			
S			
$- D$			
S_{Red}			
$- C$ (−BE)			
$- E$ (−BE)			
P_{Red}			

Example 5.5(a)

Calculating the Profit or Loss at Sale Price

A store that purchases printers for $800 each has overhead expenses of $200 on each printer. The store wants to sell each printer for an operating profit of $400. During a sale, it offers a markdown rate of 25%. At the sale price, calculate the store's profit or loss.

Solution

Method 1: Using Formulas

$C = \$800.00, E = \$200.00, P = \$400.00, D = 0.25S$

Using Formula 5.3(c), $S = C + E + P$

$= 800.00 + 200.00 + 400.00$

$= \$1400.00$

Therefore, $D = 0.25(1400.00) = \$350.00$

Using Formula 5.4(a), $S_{Red} = S - D$

$= 1400.00 - 350.00 = \$1050.00$

Thus, using Formula 5.5(a),

$P_{Red} = S_{Red} - C - E$

$= 1050.00 - 800.00 - 200.00$

$= \$50.00$ profit

Or, using Formula 5.5(b),

$P_{Red} = P - D$

$= 400.00 - 350.00$

$= \$50.00$ profit

Therefore, at the sale price, the store's profit is $50.00.

Method 2: Using Table 5.5

		Amount	Rate on C	Rate on S
	P	$400.00		
	+ E	$200.00		
	M	$600.00		
	+ C	$800.00		
	S	$1400.00		
	– D	–$350.00		25%
	S_{Red}	$1050.00		
–BE	– C	–$800.00		
–BE	– E	–$200.00		
	P_{Red}	$50.00		

Example 5.5(b)

Calculating the Profit or Loss and the Amount of Markup at Sale Price

An item costs $500, the overhead expenses are 20% on cost, and the operating profit is 30% on cost. The item is marked down by 25% during a sale.

(i) What is the profit or loss on the sale of this item?

(ii) What is the amount of markup at sale price?

Solution

Method 1: Using Formulas

$C = \$500.00, D = 0.25S$

$E = 0.20C = 0.20(500.00) = \$100.00$

$P = 0.30C = 0.30(500.00) = \$150.00$

(i) Using Formula 5.3(c), $S = C + E + P$

$= 500.00 + 100.00 + 150.00$

$= \$750.00$

Therefore, $D = 0.25(750.00) = \$187.50$

Using Formula 5.4(a), $S_{Red} = S - D$

$= 750.00 - 187.50$

$= \$562.50$

Using Formula 5.5(a), $P_{Red} = S_{Red} - C - E$

$= 562.50 - 500.00 - 100.00$

$= -\$37.50 = \$37.50$ loss

Therefore, at the sale price, the store's loss is $37.50.

Method 2: Using Table 5.5

		Amount	Rate on C	Rate on S
	P	$150.00	30%	
	+ E	$100.00	20%	
	M	$250.00		
	+ C	$500.00		
	S	$750.00		
	– D	–$187.50		25%
	S_{Red}	$562.50		
–BE	– C	–$500.00		
–BE	– E	–$100.00		
	P_{Red}	–$37.50		

Solution *continued*

(ii) *Markup on sale price* $= S_{Red} - C$

$= 562.50 - 500.00 = \$62.50$

Therefore, the amount of markup at sale price is $62.50.

Example 5.5(c) **Calculating the Selling Price, Profit or Loss, and Rate of Markdown at Break-Even Price**

It costs a manufacturer $1794 to build a machine. The company's operating profit is 20% on selling price and the markup is 35% on selling price.

(i) What is the selling price of the machine?

(ii) During a trade show, if the company offered a discount of 17.5%, what was its profit or loss on the sale of each machine?

(iii) What should be the rate of markdown to sell the machines at the break-even price?

Solution

Method 1: Using Formulas

$C = \$1794.00,\ P = 0.20S,\ M = 0.35S$

(i) Using Formula 5.3(a), $S = C + M$

$$S = 1794.00 + 0.35S$$
$$0.65S = 1794.00$$
$$S = \$2760.00$$

Therefore, the selling price of the machine is $2760.00.

(ii) $D = 0.175S = 0.175(2760.00) = \$483.00$

Rearranging Formula 5.3(b), $E = M - P$

$$= 0.35S - 0.20S = 0.15S$$
$$= 0.15(2760.00) = \$414.00$$

Using Formula 5.4(a), $S_{Red} = S - D$

$$= 2760.00 - 483.00 = \$2277.00$$

Using Formula 5.5(a), $P_{Red} = S_{Red} - C - E$

$$= 2277.00 - 1794.00 - 414.00$$
$$= \$69.00 \text{ profit}$$

Therefore, it made a profit of $69.00 on the sale of each machine.

(iii) The machines are being sold at break-even.

Using Formula 5.3(f), $BE = C + E = 1794.00 + 414.00 = \$2208.00$

Using Formula 5.4(b), $D = S - S_{Red} = 2760.00 - 2208.00 = \$552.00$

Using Formula 5.4(c), $\text{Rate of markdown} = \frac{D}{S} \times 100\% = \frac{552.00}{2760.00} \times 100\% = 0.20 \times 100\% = 20\%$

Therefore, the rate of markdown to sell the machine at the break-even price would be 20%.

Method 2: Using Table 5.5

	Amount	Rate on C	Rate on S
P			20.00%
$+E$	$414.00		15.00%
M			35.00%
$+C$	$1794.00		65.00%
S	$2760.00		100.00%
$-D$	–$483.00		17.50%
S_{Red}	$2277.00		
$-C$ (–BE)	–$1794.00		
$-E$ (–BE)	–$414.00		
P_{Red}	$69.00		

Example 5.5(d) **Calculating the Cost and Rate of Markdown at Sale Price and Cost Price**

A manufacturer sells printers for $108.50 each. The operating profit is 30% on cost and markup is 75% on cost.

(i) How much does it cost the company to manufacture each printer?

(ii) Calculate the rate of markdown offered during a sale if it made a profit of $5.58 per printer.

(iii) What should be the rate of markdown offered to sell the printers at its cost price?

Solution

Method 1: Using Formulas

$S = \$108.50,\ P = 0.30C,\ M = 0.75C$

(i) Using Formula 5.3(a), $S = C + M$

$$108.50 = C + 0.75C$$
$$1.75C = 108.50$$
$$C = \$62.00$$

Therefore, it costs $62.00 to manufacture each printer.

(ii) $P_{Red} = \$5.58$

Using Formula 5.3(b), $M = E + P$

$$0.75C = E + 0.30C$$
$$E = 0.45C = 0.45(62.00)$$
$$E = \$27.90$$

Using Formula 5.5(a), $P_{Red} = S_{Red} - C - E$

$$5.58 = S_{Red} - 62.00 - 27.90$$
$$S_{Red} = \$95.48$$

Using Formula 5.4(b), $D = S - S_{Red}$

$$= 108.50 - 95.48 = \$13.02$$

Using Formula 5.4(c), $Rate\ of\ markdown = \frac{D}{S} \times 100\% = \frac{13.02}{108.50} \times 100\%$

$$= 0.12 \times 100\% = 12\%$$

Therefore, the rate of markdown is 12%.

(iii) $S_{Red} = C = \$62.00$

Using Formula 5.4(b), $D = S - S_{Red} = 108.50 - 62.00 = \$46.50$

Using Formula 5.4(c), $Rate\ of\ markdown = \frac{D}{S} \times 100\% = \frac{46.50}{108.50} \times 100\%$

$$= 0.428571... \times 100\% = 42.86\%$$

Therefore, the rate of markdown to sell the printers at the cost price should be 42.86%

Method 2: Using Table 5.5

	Amount	Rate on C	Rate on S
P		30%	
$+E$	$27.90	45%	
M		75%	
$+C$	$62.00	100%	
S	$108.50	175%	
$-D$	–$13.02		12%
S_{Red}	$95.48		
$-C$ (–BE)	–$62.00		
$-E$ (–BE)	–$27.90		
P_{Red}	$5.58		

Example 5.5(e) **Calculating the Profit or Loss at Selling Price, Sale Price, and Break-Even Price**

Amelia, a retailer of electronic goods, purchases 1000 HDTVs from a distributor after trade discounts of 10% and 8% on the list price of $600 per unit. She marks up the HDTVs by 55% on selling price and sells 660 units at the regular selling price. During a sale, she offers a markdown of 10% and sells another 300 units at the sale price. She finally sells the remaining units at the break-even price. Her overhead expenses are 20% on selling price.

(i) What is the price at which 660 units were sold?

(ii) What is the price at which 300 units were sold?

(iii) What is the break-even price at which the remaining units were sold?

(iv) What is the total profit or loss from the sale of 1000 units?

Solution

Using Formula 5.1(c), $N = L(1 - d_1)(1 - d_2)$

$N = 600.00(1 - 0.10)(1 - 0.08) = \$496.80$

Therefore, $C = \$496.80$.

(i) Using Formula 5.3(a), $S = C + M$

$S = 496.80 + 0.55S$

$0.45S = 496.80$

$S = \$1104.00$

Therefore, 660 units were sold at \$1104.00 per unit.

(ii) $D = 0.10S = 0.10(1104.00) = \$110.40$

Using Formula 5.4(a), $S_{Red} = S - D$

$= 1104.00 - 110.40 = \$993.60$

Therefore, 300 units were sold at \$993.60 per unit.

(iii) $E = 0.20S = 0.20(1104.00) = \$220.80$

Using Formula 5.3(f), $BE = C + E$

$= 496.80 + 220.80 = \$717.60$

	Amount	Rate on C	Rate on S
P	\$386.40		
$+E$	\$220.80		20%
M	\$607.20		55%
$+C$	\$496.80		45%
S	\$1104.00		100%
$-D$	–\$110.40		10%
S_{Red}	\$993.60		
$-C$ (–BE)	–\$496.80		
$-E$ (–BE)	–\$220.80		
P_{Red}	\$276.00		

This is the profit for each unit sold at the regular selling price (P).

This is the profit for each unit sold at the sale price (P_{Red}).

Therefore, the break-even price at which the remaining units were sold is \$717.60.

(iv) Total cost of 1000 units = $1000 \times 496.80 = \$496{,}800.00$

Total operating expenses = $1000 \times 220.80 = \$220{,}800.00$

Total selling price = $(660 \times 1104.00) + (300 \times 993.60) + (40 \times 717.60)$

$= \$1{,}055{,}424.00$

Total Profit = $S - C - E$

$= 1{,}055{,}424.00 - 496{,}800.00 - 220{,}800.00$

$= \$337{,}824.00$

Or, using the table, Total Profit = $(660 \times 386.40) + (300 \times 276.00) + (40 \times 0.00)$

$= \$337{,}824.00$

Therefore, the total profit from the sale of 1000 units was \$337,824.00.

5.5 | Exercises

Answers to the odd-numbered problems are available at the end of the textbook.

For the following problems, express the answers rounded to two decimal places, wherever applicable.

Calculate the missing values for Problems 1 and 2.

1.

	Cost	Amount of Markup	Selling Price	Operating Profit	Overhead Expenses	Rate of Markup on Cost	Rate of Markup on Selling Price	Rate of Markdown	Reduced Selling Price	Reduced Profit
a.	?	?	\$2150.00	\$850.00	\$300.00	?	?	25.00%	?	?
b.	\$900.25	?	?	\$600.00	\$200.50	?	?	35.00%	?	?
c.	\$15.75	?	?	\$2.18	?	15.50%	?	5.50%	?	?
d.	?	?	\$678.75	?	\$76.50	?	25.00%	12.50%	?	?
e.	?	\$656.50	\$4555.50	?	\$140.75	?	?	?	\$4180.00	?
f.	\$38.00	?	\$59.50	\$10.00	?	?	?	?	?	–\$2.50

2.

	Cost	Amount of Markup	Selling Price	Operating Profit	Overhead Expenses	Rate of Markup on Cost	Rate of Markup on Selling Price	Rate of Markdown	Reduced Selling Price	Reduced Profit
a.	?	?	$12.00	$2.50	$3.00	?	?	17.00%	?	?
b.	$450.75	?	?	$40.50	$80.50	?	?	5.00%	?	?
c.	$1.50	?	?	$0.25	?	30.00%	?	5.50%	?	?
d.	?	?	$12,400.00	?	$1280.50	?	23.00%	9.00%	?	?
e.	?	$180.50	$750.50	?	$45.75	?	?	?	$710.50	?
f.	$12.50	?	$18.50	$4.00	?	?	?	?	?	–$1.30

3. Hermois Fine Diamonds purchased Canadian solitaire diamonds for $2800. The markup on these diamonds is 15% on cost and the operating expenses are 10% on cost.
   a. Calculate the regular selling price of each diamond and the profit made.
   b. During a sale, if the company offers a markdown of 15%, calculate the reduced selling price and profit or loss it makes at the sale price.

4. Harold, the owner of Sweet Tunes Music, purchased acoustic guitars for $80 each and has marked them up by 20% on cost. The overhead expenses were 10% on cost.
   a. Calculate the regular selling price of each guitar and the profit made.
   b. If he decides to offer a markdown of 5%, what would be the reduced selling price and profit or loss he would make on the sale of each guitar?

5. Amanda purchases flowers for $2 each and her regular selling price is $4.25.
   a. If she makes a profit of $1.85 on each flower, calculate her overhead expenses per flower.
   b. During Valentine's Day, if she offers a rate of markdown of 20%, calculate the reduced selling price and the profit or loss that she makes on the sale of each flower.

6. FootWorks purchases shoes for $30 each pair and sells them at a regular price of $42 each pair.
   a. If the profit made is $5.25 per pair, calculate the overhead expense per pair.
   b. If the discount offered during a Boxing Week sale is 20%, calculate the reduced selling price and the profit or loss made on the sale of each pair.

7. Jacy, a reseller of printers, purchases printers for $300 each and marks them up by 40% on cost to make a profit of $70 on each printer. If he marks them down by 10% during a sale, calculate his profit or loss on each printer at the sale price.

8. Andreya is in the business of buying and selling expensive yachts. She recently bought a yacht for $420,500 and marked it up by 20% on cost, hoping to make a profit of $70,000. Since she was unable to sell it for many months, she marked down the price by 30% and managed to find a buyer. Calculate her profit or loss on the yacht at the sale price.

9. An electronic toy costs $300, the overhead expenses are 30% on cost, and the operating profit is 20% on cost. The item is marked down by 10% during a sale.
   a. What is the profit or loss on the sale of this item?
   b. What is the amount of markup at sale price?

10. Jesse makes a 10% profit on cost of belts which he purchases at $15 each. The overhead expenses are 25% on cost. During a sale, he marked the belts down by 10%.
    a. What is the profit or loss on the sale of this item?
    b. What is the amount of markup at sale price?

11. A professional SLR camera that regularly sells for $750 is sold after a markdown of 20%. If the break-even price is $590, calculate the profit or loss made on the sale of this camera.

12. The regular selling price of cell phones at a store is $125 each. During a sale, it was sold at a markdown of 45%. Calculate the profit or loss made on the sale of the cell phone if the break-even price is $75.

13. Miranda purchases office furniture from a wholesaler listed at $800, less discounts of 20% and 10%. She has overhead expenses of 20% on cost and wants to have an operating profit of 30% on cost.
    a. Calculate the regular selling price of the office furniture.
    b. After listing the item for one month, she marked it down by 10%. Calculate the profit or loss that she made at the reduced selling price.
    c. What is the maximum amount of markdown that she can offer so that she breaks even on the sale?

14. Gabriella was in the business of purchasing sculptures from Brazil and selling them in Toronto at her boutique. On one consignment listed at $2400, she received trade discounts of 10%, 8%, and 6%. The overhead expenses were 15% of her costs and she wanted to make a profit of 20% on cost.
    a. Calculate the regular selling price of the sculptures.
    b. Calculate the loss or profit she will make if she decides to markdown the selling price by 15%.
    c. Calculate the maximum amount of markdown that she can offer so that she breaks even on the sale.

15. The cost of an item is $450 and it is marked up by 35% on selling price. During a sale, it is marked down to sell at the break-even price. If the overhead expenses are 15% on regular selling price, calculate the rate of markdown.

16. Karina owns a boutique where she sells designer dresses. She purchases the dresses for $280 each and has a rate of markup of 30% on selling price. At the end of every season, she has a sale and marks down the dresses to sell them at the break-even price. If the overhead expenses are 10% on the regular selling price, calculate the rate of markdown on these dresses.

17. The profit of an item from the regular selling price of $500 is $150. If a 20% markdown is offered during a sale, calculate the profit or loss at the sale price.

18. Hollis Sound Equipment Ltd. makes a profit of $100 on an acoustic guitar that it sells at the regular selling price of $600. During a Boxing Week sale, if it marked down the guitar by 20%, calculate the profit or loss at the sale price.

• 19. A distributor purchases industrial fans for $147 each. Its profit is 10% on selling price and markup is 30% on selling price.
    a. What is the regular selling price of the fans?
    b. During a trade show, if the distributor offers a markdown of 7.5% on its fans, calculate the reduced profit or loss made per fan.
    c. What is the rate of markdown to sell the fans at the break-even price?

• 20. The cost of manufacturing a product is $42. The factory has a profit of 42% on selling price and markup of 65% on selling price.
    a. What is the regular selling price of the product?
    b. During a trade show event, if the factory offers a markdown of 40%, calculate the reduced profit or loss made per product.
    c. What is the rate of markdown offered to sell the products at the break-even price?

• 21. A distributor sells water cooling units for $880 each. The operating profit is 25% on cost and markup is 60% on cost.
    a. Calculate the cost per cooling unit.
    b. Calculate the rate of markdown offered during a sale if it made a profit of $49.50 per machine.
    c. What should be the rate of markdown offered to sell the machines at the cost price?

• 22. Martha's Steel Warehouse has an operating profit of 15.50% on cost and a markup of 35% on cost. It sells construction steel bars for $1255.50 per ton.
    a. Calculate the cost of the bars per ton.
    b. Calculate the rate of markdown offered during a sale if it made a profit of $100 per ton.
    c. What should be the rate of markdown offered to sell the bars at the cost price?

• 23. A distributor purchased golf sets for $625 each, less 20% and 10%. Its profit is 10% on cost and markup is 30% on selling price. During a sale, the golf sets were marked down to $629.00.
    a. What was the regular selling price?
    b. What was the rate of markdown?
    c. At the sale price, what was the profit or loss?

• 24. Maggie purchased designer bags for $242.88 each, less 12% and 8%. The markup is 35% on selling price and the operating profit is 15% on cost. During a sale, the designer bags were marked down to $260.00.

a. What was the regular selling price?

b. What was the rate of markdown?

c. At the sale price, what was the profit or loss?

• 25. High Tech Heaven purchased laptops for $263.50 each, less 10%. The store's rate of markup is 25% on selling price and the store's profit is 15% on cost. During a sale, the laptops were marked down and sold at break-even price.

a. What was the regular selling price of each laptop?

b. What was the sale price?

c. What was the rate of markdown offered during the sale?

• 26. A retailer purchased shirts for $50 each, less 10%. The retailer has a markup of 20% on selling price and a profit of 10% on cost. During a sale, the shirts were marked down and sold at break-even price.

a. What was the regular selling price of each shirt?

b. What was the sale price?

c. What was the rate of markdown offered during the sale?

• 27. A retail store purchased 180 shirts for $35 each. It sold 120 shirts at a markup of 60% on cost. During an off-season, it sold another 40 shirts at a markup of 20% on cost. A few months later, it sold the remaining shirts at 25% below cost to clear the inventory.

a. What was the selling price of each of the 120 shirts, 40 shirts, and 20 shirts?

b. If the overhead expenses are 20% on cost, what was the total operating profit?

• 28. A designer purchased 70 dresses from an overseas tailor for $140 each. When the shipment arrived, she identified 40 of the dresses to be of very high quality, 20 of medium quality, and the remaining of low quality. She sold the high quality dresses at an 80% markup on cost, the medium quality dresses at 40% markup on cost, and the low quality dresses at 10% below cost.

a. What was the selling price of each of the high, medium, and low quality dresses?

b. If the overhead expenses are 30% on cost, what was the total operating profit?

• 29. A supplier purchased 1000 mousepads for $5 each. She sold 500 pads at their regular selling price of $12 each, 300 at a markdown of 20%, and the remaining at a price to break-even. The overhead expenses are 20% on cost.

a. Calculate her total profit or loss made from the sale of all mousepads.

b. What was the rate of markdown and amount of markdown offered on the remaining mousepads that were sold at break-even?

• 30. Rodney runs Handheld Hardware Inc. in Mississauga, Ontario. He purchases 400 phones from a distributor with trade discounts of 12% and 5% on the list price of $50 per phone. He sold 300 phones at the regular selling price of $75 each and offered a markdown of 25% on the next 75 phones. To ensure that he completes the stock, he sold the rest at break-even. The store's overhead expenses are 10% on cost.

a. Calculate his total profit or loss made from the sale of the phones.

b. What is the rate of markdown and amount of markdown offered on the remaining phones that are being sold at break-even?

5.6 | Net Rate of Markup and Markdown

In Sections 5.3 to 5.5, you learned that in business, goods are usually sold at a higher price than their cost (C) and the amount added to the cost in determining the selling price (S) of an item is the amount of markup (M), which is necessary to cover the overhead expenses (E) and the desired operating profit (P) of the business.

You also learned both the formula method (horizontal analysis) and table method (vertical analysis) for solving problems involving cost, expense, profit, markup, selling price, rate of markup on cost, rate of markup on selling price, markdown (D), rate of markdown, and calculating the reduced profit or loss (P_{Red}) when goods are sold at a reduced selling price or sale price (S_{Red}).

Businesses sell goods on discounts by a percent reduction of the selling price and often sell goods at different prices at different points of time, for various reasons. If all goods are sold at the same price, then the average amount of markup per unit would be the difference between the unit selling price and the unit cost. However, this is not the case in business most of the time because the selling price differs after each markdown.

When goods are sold at different selling prices, the original markup (M) on the item will be reduced, because the cost of the item remains the same. The Net Amount of Markup is the difference between the total sale price and the total cost.

This relationship is expressed by the following formula:

Formula 5.6(a) **Net Amount of Markup**

$$Net\ Amount\ of\ Markup = Total\ Sales - Total\ Cost$$

In this section, you will learn to perform calculations involving the net rate of markup and the net rate of markdown.

Net Rate of Markup

The term net rate of markup refers to the net amount of markup based on the total cost or on the total sales. This is calculated as follows:

Step 1: Calculate the total cost (i.e., cost of all the items purchased).

Step 2: Calculate the total sales (i.e., revenue from the sales of items at different selling prices).

Step 3: Calculate the net amount of markup by subtracting the total cost from the total sales.

Step 4: The net rate of markup on total cost is calculated by determining the ratio of the net amount of markup to the total cost and converting it to a percent.

Step 5: The net rate of markup on total sales is calculated by determining the ratio of the net amount of markup to the total sales and converting it to a percent.

Formula 5.6(b) **Net Rate of Markup Based on Total Cost**

$$Net\ Rate\ of\ Markup\ based\ on\ Total\ Cost = \frac{Net\ Amount\ of\ Markup}{Total\ Cost} \times 100\%$$

Formula 5.6(c) **Net Rate of Markup Based on Total Sales**

$$\textit{Net Rate of Markup based on Total Sales} = \frac{\textit{Net Amount of Markup}}{\textit{Total Sales}} \times 100\%$$

Example 5.6(a) **Understanding the Relationship Among Total Cost, Total Sales, and Net Rate of Markup**

A retailer purchased 100 printers at $150 each, marked them up at 40% on cost, and sold 70 printers at the regular selling price. During a sale, it offered a markdown of 20% and sold the remaining printers. Calculate the following:

(i) Total cost of the printers.

(ii) Total sales.

(iii) Net amount of markup.

(iv) Net rate of markup based on total cost.

Solution

Enter the known values for the variables and identify those that are to be calculated.

$C = \$150.00$

$M = 0.40C = 0.40(150.00) = \$60.00$

$S = C + M = 150.00 + 60.00 = \$210.00$

$D = 0.20S = 0.20(210.00) = \$42.00$

$S_{Red} = S - D = 210.00 - 42.00 = \$168.00$

	Amount	Rate on C	Rate on S	Qty	Total Amount
M	$60.00	40%			
$+ C$	$150.00			100	$15,000.00
S	$210.00			70	$14,700.00
$- D$	$42.00		20%		
S_{Red}	$168.00			30	$5040.00

(i) Total Cost = 100×150.00

= $15,000.00

(ii) Total Sales = $(70 \times 210.00) + (30 \times 168.00)$

= $14,700.00 + 5040.00$

= $19,740.00

(iii) Using Formula 5.6(a),

Net Amount of Markup = *Total Sales* – *Total Cost*

= $19,740.00 - 15,000.00$

= $4740.00

	Amount	Rate on C	Rate on S
Net Markup	$4740.00	31.60%	
+ Total Cost	$15,000.00		
Total Sales	$19,740.00		

(iv) Using Formula 5.6(b),

$$\textit{Net Rate of Markup based on Total Cost} = \frac{\textit{Net Amount of Markup}}{\textit{Total Cost}} \times 100\%$$

$$= \frac{4740.00}{15,000.00} \times 100\%$$

$$= 0.316 \times 100\% = 31.60\%$$

Example 5.6(b) **Understanding the Relationship Among Total Cost, Total Sales, and Net Rate of Markup**

A furniture store sells chairs at $400 each. The rate of markup on selling price of the chairs is 70%. At the beginning of the month, the store purchased 250 chairs. Halfway through the month, it had sold 160 of these chairs at the regular selling price and they decided to offer a markdown of 35% on the remaining chairs. All remaining chairs were sold at the reduced selling price. Calculate the following:

(i) Total cost of the chairs.

(ii) Total sales.

(iii) Net amount of markup.

(iv) Net rate of markup based on total sales.

Solution

Enter the known values for the variables and identify those that are to be calculated.

	Amount	Rate on C	Rate on S	Qty	Total Amount
M	\$280.00		70%		
$+C$	\$120.00			250	\$30,000.00
S	\$400.00			160	\$64,000.00
$-D$	\$140.00		35%		
S_{Red}	\$260.00			90	\$23,400.00

$S = \$400.00$

$M = 0.70S = 0.70(400.00) = \$280.00$

$C = S - M = 400.00 - 280.00 = \$120.00$

$D = 0.35S = 0.35(400.00) = \$140.00$

$S_{Red} = S - D = 400.00 - 140.00 = \$260.00$

(i) Total Cost $= 250 \times 120.00$

$= \$30{,}000.00$

(ii) Total Sales $= (160 \times 400.00) + (90 \times 260.00)$

$= 64{,}000.00 + 23{,}400.00$

$= \$87{,}400.00$

(iii) Using Formula 5.6(a),

Net Amount of Markup = *Total Sales* – *Total Cost*

$= 87{,}400.00 - 30{,}000.00$

$= \$57{,}400.00$

	Amount	Rate on C	Rate on S
Net Markup	\$57,400.00		65.68%
+ Total Cost	\$30,000.00		
Total Sales	\$87,400.00		

(iv) Using Formula 5.6(c),

$$\textit{Net Rate of Markup based on Total Sales} = \frac{\textit{Net Amount of Markup}}{\textit{Total Sales}} \times 100\%$$

$$= \frac{57{,}400.00}{87{,}400.00} \times 100\%$$

$$= 0.656750... \times 100\% = 65.68\%$$

Net Rate of Markdown and Discount

Markdown is the devaluation of the selling price of the product and is usually offered to sell items faster, to match a competitor's price, for the clearance of seasonal items, etc. Whereas, **discount** is a reduction in the selling price of the product and is based on the customer making the purchase. For example, discounts are usually offered to frequent buyers, employees, senior citizens, etc.

Net Rate of Markdown

Markdown is always calculated on the original selling price.

The amount of markdown is calculated by applying the rate of markdown to the original selling price. In situations where a store offers two (or more) markdowns, these percents must be calculated on the original selling price to determine the amount of markdown. The **net rate of markdown** is the sum of all the rates of markdowns. For example, the net rate of markdown for two successive rates of markdowns of 20% and 10% is 30%.

Example 5.6(c) **Calculations, Given Two Successive Rates of Markdowns**

The regular selling price of an item is \$120. During a sale, the store offered a markdown of 30% and during a clearance sale, the store offered an additional markdown of 10%.

(i) What is the sale price of the item during the clearance sale?

(ii) What is the net amount of markdown during the clearance sale?

(iii) What is the net rate of markdown?

Solution

(i) Reduced selling price after the first markdown of 30%:

$S_{Red\ 1} = S - D_1$
$= 120.00 - 0.30S$
$= 120.00 - 0.30(120.00)$
$= \$84.00$

Reduced selling price after the additional markdown of 10%:

$S_{Red\ 2} = S_{Red\ 1} - D_2$
$= 84.00 - 0.10S$
$= 84.00 - 0.10(120.00)$
$= \$72.00$

(ii) *Net Amount of Markdown* $= S - S_{Red\ 2}$
$= 120.00 - 72.00$
$= \$48.00$

(iii) *Net Rate of Markdown* $= \frac{48.00}{120.00} \times 100\%$
$= 0.40 \times 100\%$
$= 40\%$

Alternative Method

(i) We can combine the markdowns to calculate the reduced selling price:
Net Rate of Markdown = 30% + 10% = 40%

$S_{Red} = S - D$
$= 120.00 - 0.40S$
$= 120.00 - 0.40(120.00)$
$= \$72.00$

(ii) *Net Amount of Markdown* $= 0.40 \times 120.00$
$= \$48.00$

(iii) *Net Rate of Markdown* = 30% + 10% = 40%

Net Rate of Discount

Discount is always calculated on the previous selling price or sale price.

The amount of discount is calculated by applying the rate of discount to the previous selling price or to the sale price, if the item had already been reduced. In situations where a store offers two (or more) discounts, the second discount is calculated on the reduced price after the first discount. The third discount is calculated on the reduced price after the second discount, and so on. The **net rate of discount** is calculated as a percent of the total discounts to the original selling price. For example, the net rate of discount for two successive rates of discounts of 20% and 10% is **not equal** to 30%.

Example 5.6(d) **Calculations, Given Two Successive Rates of Discounts**

The regular selling price of an item is $120. During a sale, the store offered a discount of 30% with an additional discount of 10% for loyalty card holders.

(i) What is the sale price of the item for a loyalty card holder?

(ii) What is the net amount of discount for a loyalty card holder?

(iii) What is the net rate of discount?

Solution

(i) Reduced selling price after the first discount of 30%:

$S_{Red\ 1} = S - 0.30S$
$= 120.00 - 0.30(120.00) = \$84.00$

Solution *continued*

Reduced selling price after the additional discount of 10% for loyalty card holders:

$$S_{Red\,2} = S_{Red1} - 0.10S_{Red1}$$
$$= 84.00 - 0.10(84.00) = \$75.60$$

(ii) $Net\ Amount\ of\ Discount = S - S_{Red\,2}$
$$= 120.00 - 75.60$$
$$= \$44.40$$

(iii) $Net\ Rate\ of\ Discount = \frac{44.40}{120.00} \times 100\%$
$$= 0.37 \times 100\%$$
$$= 37\%$$

Alternative Method

(i) Since the reductions are similar to series of discounts, the reduced selling price can be calculated as follows:

$$S_{Red} = 120.00(1 - 0.30)(1 - 0.10)$$
$$= \$75.60$$

(ii) $Net\ Amount\ of\ Discount = 120.00 - 75.60$
$$= \$44.40$$

(iii) $Net\ Rate\ of\ Discount = \frac{44.40}{120.00} \times 100\%$
$$= 0.37 \times 100\%$$
$$= 37\%$$

Example 5.6(e)

Calculating the Net Rate of Markup based on Total Cost When Items are Sold at Different Prices, Given Two Successive Rates of Markdowns

On Time Clock Shop purchased 250 units of a particular model of watches. The cost was $75 per watch and the regular selling price was $120 per watch. The company sold 175 units at the regular selling price. During a sale, it offered a markdown of 25% and sold another 50 units. The remaining units were sold after an additional markdown of 10%. Determine the net rate of markup based on total cost.

Solution

Series of markdown rates are always calculated on the original selling price (S).

$$Total\ Cost = 250 \times 75.00 = \$18{,}750.00$$
$$S = \$120.00$$
$$S_{Red\,1} = S - D_1 = 120.00 - 0.25(120.00) = \$90.00$$
$$S_{Red\,2} = S_{Red\,1} - D_2 = 90.00 - 0.10(120.00) = \$78.00$$
$$Total\ Sales = (175 \times 120.00) + (50 \times 90.00) + (25 \times 78.00)$$
$$= 21{,}000.00 + 4500.00 + 1950.00$$
$$= \$27{,}450.00$$

$$Net\ Amount\ of\ Markup = Total\ Sales - Total\ Cost$$
$$= 27{,}450.00 - 18{,}750.00$$
$$= \$8700.00$$

$Net\ Rate\ of\ Markup\ based\ on\ Total\ Cost$
$$= \frac{Net\ Amount\ of\ Markup}{Total\ Cost} \times 100\%$$
$$= \frac{8700.00}{18{,}750.00} \times 100\%$$
$$= 0.464 \times 100\%$$
$$= 46.40\%$$

Therefore, the net rate of markup based on total cost is 46.40%.

	Amount	Rate on C	Rate on S	Qty	Total Amount
M					
$+ C$	$75.00			250	$18,750.00
S	$120.00			175	$21,000.00
$- D_1$	$30.00		25%		
$S_{Red\,1}$	$90.00			50	$4500.00
$- D_2$	$12.00		10%		
$S_{Red\,2}$	$78.00			25	$1950.00

	Amount	Rate on C	Rate on S
Net Markup	$8700.00	46.40%	
Total Cost	$18,750.00		
Total Sales	$27,450.00		

Solution *continued*

Alternative Method

Markup at which 175 watches were sold = 120.00 – 75.00
= $45.00

Markup at which 50 watches were sold = 90.00 – 75.00
= $15.00

Markup at which 25 watches were sold = 78.00 – 75.00
= $3.00

Net Amount of Markup = (175 × 45.00) + (50 × 15.00) + (25 × 3.00) = $8700.00

Total Cost = 250 × 75.00 = $18,750.00

$$\textit{Net Rate of Markup based on Total Cost} = \frac{8700.00}{18{,}750.00} \times 100\% = 0.464 \times 100\% = 46.40\%$$

Example 5.6(f) **Calculating the Net Rate of Markup based on Total Sales when Items are Sold at Different Prices, Given Two Successive Rates of Markdowns**

A store that sells cameras purchased 120 units at $180 each. It expects to sell 50% of the units at the regular selling price of $275 each, 30% after a markdown of 20%, and the remaining at cost. Calculate the net rate of markup based on total sales.

Solution

Total Cost = 120 × 180.00 = $21,600.00

S = $275.00

$S_{Red\ 1} = S - D_1 = 275.00 - 0.20(275.00) = \$220.00$

$S_{Red\ 2} = C = \$180.00$

Total Sales = (60 × 275.00) + (36 × 220.00) + (24 × 180.00)
= 16,500.00 + 7920.00 + 4320.00
= $28,740.00

Net Amount of Markup = *Total Sales* – *Total Cost*
= 28,740.00 – 21,600.00
= $7140.00

Net Rate of Markup based on Total Sales

$$= \frac{\textit{Net Amount of Markup}}{\textit{Total Sales}} \times 100\%$$

$$= \frac{7140.00}{28{,}740.00} \times 100\%$$

= 0.248434... × 100%
= 24.84%

	Amount	Rate on C	Rate on S	Qty	Total Amount
M					
$+C$	$180.00			120	$21,600.00
S	$275.00			60	$16,500.00
$-D_1$	$55.00		20%		
$S_{Red\ 1}$	$220.00			36	$7920.00
$-D_2$					
$S_{Red\ 2}$	$180.00			24	$4320.00

	Amount	Rate on C	Rate on S
Net Markup	$7140.00		24.84%
Total Cost	$21,600.00		
Total Sales	$28,740.00		

Therefore, the net rate of markup based on total sales is 24.84%.

Applications of Net Rate of Markup

The following examples illustrate various applications of net rate of markup.

Example 5.6(g) **Calculating the Selling Price and Rate of Markup on Selling Price, Given the Net Rate of Markup based on Total Sales**

A company purchases items for $12 each. The company maintains a net rate of markup of 40% based on total sales. It estimates that out of 600 items, 400 will be sold at the regular selling price, 80 will be sold at a reduced price of $15 each, and the remaining items will be sold at cost.

(i) What should be the regular selling price of the items to maintain the net rate of markup of 40% based on total sales?

(ii) What is the rate of markup on the regular selling price?

Solution

(i) $C = \$12.00$ $S_{Red\ 1} = \$15.00$ $S_{Red\ 2} = C = \$12.00$ $S = ?$

Total Cost = 600 × 12.00 = \$7200.00

We know that the net amount of markup is 40% of the total sales.

$$Total\ Sales = Net\ Amount\ of\ Markup + Total\ Cost$$

$$Total\ Sales = (0.40 \times Total\ Sales) + 7200.00$$

$$(0.60 \times Total\ Sales) = 7200.00$$

$$Total\ Sales = \frac{7200.00}{0.60} = \$12{,}000.00$$

	Amount	Rate on C	Rate on S
Net Markup			40%
Total Cost	\$7200.00		60%
Total Sales	\$12,000.00		100%

Therefore, the total amount of sales was \$12,000.00.

Now we can calculate the price at which 400 items were sold (regular selling price).

80 items were sold at \$15.00 each.

The number of items sold at cost = 600 – 400 – 80 = 120 i.e., 120 items were sold at \$12.00 each.

Therefore,

$$\text{Total Sales} = (400 \times S) + (80 \times S_{Red\ 1}) + (120 \times S_{Red\ 2})$$

$$12{,}000.00 = (400 \times S) + (80 \times 15.00) + (120 \times 12.00)$$

$$12{,}000.00 = 400S + 2640.00$$

$$400S = 9360.00$$

$$S = \frac{9360.00}{400} = \$23.40$$

	Amount	Rate on C	Rate on S	Qty	Total Amount
M	\$11.40		48.72%		
$+ C$	\$12.00			600	\$7200.00
S	\$23.40			400	\$9360.00
$- D_1$					
$S_{Red\ 1}$	\$15.00			80	\$1200.00
$- D_2$					
$S_{Red\ 2}$	\$12.00			120	\$1440.00

Therefore, the regular selling price should be set at \$23.40 for the company to maintain a net rate of markup of 40% based on total sales.

(ii) Calculating the rate of markup on the regular selling price,

$$S = C + M$$

$$23.40 = 12.00 + M$$

$$M = \$11.40$$

$$Rate\ of\ markup\ on\ the\ regular\ selling\ price = \frac{M}{S} \times 100\% = \frac{11.40}{23.40} \times 100\% = 0.487179... \times 100\% = 48.72\%$$

Therefore, the rate of markup on the regular selling price is 48.72%.

Example 5.6(h)

Calculating the Reduced Selling Price and Rate of Markdown, Given the Net Rate of Markup based on Total Cost

A store purchases appliances for \$450 and sells them at \$720 each. Last month, the store purchased 200 appliances. It sold 50% of the appliances at the regular selling price, 30% at a reduced price, and the balance at cost.

(i) What should be the reduced selling price to maintain a net rate of markup of 40% based on total cost?

(ii) What is the rate of markdown offered during the sale?

Solution

(i) $C = \$450.00$ $S = \$720.00$ $S_{Red\,2} = C = \$450.00$ $S_{Red\,1} = ?$

Total Cost = 200 × 450.00 = \$90,000.00

Net rate of markup based on total cost is 40%.

$$\textit{Total Sales} = \textit{Net Amount of Markup} + \textit{Total Cost}$$
$$= (0.40 \times \textit{Total Cost}) + \textit{Total Cost}$$
$$= (0.40 \times 90{,}000.00) + 90{,}000.00$$
$$= 36{,}000.00 + 90{,}000.00 = \$126{,}000.00$$

	Amount	Rate on C	Rate on S
Net Markup	\$36,000.00	40%	
Total Cost	\$90,000.00	100%	
Total Sales	\$126,000.00	140%	

Now we can calculate the reduced selling price at which 30% of the items were sold.

50% of items = 0.50 × 200 = 100 were sold at the regular selling price of \$720.00

30% of items = 0.30 × 200 = 60 were sold at a reduced selling price.

Remaining items, 200 – 100 – 60 = 40, were sold at cost, \$450.00

Therefore,

$$\text{Total Sales} = (100 \times S) + (60 \times S_{Red\,1}) + (40 \times S_{Red\,2})$$
$$126{,}000.00 = (100 \times 720.00) + (60 \times S_{Red\,1}) + (40 \times 450.00)$$
$$126{,}000.00 = 72{,}000.00 + (60 \times S_{Red\,1}) + 18{,}000.00$$
$$(60 \times S_{Red\,1}) = \$36{,}000.00$$
$$S_{Red\,1} = \frac{36{,}000.00}{60} = \$600.00$$

	Amount	Rate on C	Rate on S	Qty	Total Amount
M					
$+C$	\$450.00			200	\$90,000.00
S	\$720.00			100	\$72,000.00
$-D_1$	\$120.00		16.67%		
$S_{Red\,1}$	\$600.00			60	\$36,000.00
$-D_2$					
$S_{Red\,2}$	\$450.00			40	\$18,000.00

Therefore, the reduced selling price should be set at \$600.00 for the company to maintain a net rate of markup of 40% based on total cost.

(ii) Calculating the rate of markdown:

$$D = S - S_{Red} = 720.00 - 600.00 = \$120.00$$

$$\textit{Rate of markdown} = \frac{D}{S} \times 100\% = \frac{120.00}{720.00} \times 100\% = 0.166666... \times 100\% = 16.67\%$$

Therefore, the rate of markdown offered during the sale is 16.67%.

5.6 | Exercises

Answers to the odd-numbered problems are available at the end of the textbook.

For the following problems, express the answers rounded to two decimal places, wherever applicable.

1. Steve's Cash n' Carry purchased 80 pencil cases at \$6.50 each and marked them up by 25% on cost and sold 75% of the pencil cases at the regular selling price. During a sale, it sold the remaining pencil cases after a markdown of 10%. Calculate the following:
   a. Total cost of the pencil cases.
   b. Total sales of the pencil cases at the two different prices.
   c. Net amount of markup.
   d. Net rate of markup based on total cost.

2. Circuit World purchased 175 monitors at \$125 each and marked them up by 35% on cost and sold 90 of the monitors at the regular selling price. During a sale, the store sold the remaining monitors after a markdown of 25%. Calculate the following:
   a. Total cost of the monitors.
   b. Total sales of the monitors at the two different prices.
   c. Net amount of markup.
   d. Net rate of markup based on total cost.

3. Proctor Electronics has a markup of 60% on the selling price of its portable chargers. Last month, the store purchased 140 items and sold 80 at the regular selling price of $85. During a weekend sale, a 25% markdown was offered, following which 45 items were sold at the reduced price and the remaining sold at cost. Calculate the following:
   a. Total cost of the portable chargers.
   b. Total sales of the portable chargers.
   c. Net amount of markup.
   d. Net rate of markup based on total sales.

4. Jay owns a local store where he sells garden equipment. He sells each unit of equipment at a price of $420, which includes a markup of 25% on the selling price. During a sale, he reduced the selling price by 35% and sold nine items. When a new model of the equipment was introduced to the market, Jay sold five of the remaining items at cost. If there were 30 items in stock initially, calculate the following:
   a. Total cost of the equipment.
   b. Total sales of the equipment.
   c. Net amount of markup.
   d. Net rate of markup based on total sales.

5. Mountains Outwear offers a markdown of 30% on parka jackets during their semi-annual sale. During a clearance sale, the store offers an additional markdown of 15%. If the original price of the jackets is $350, calculate the following:
   a. The sale price during the clearance sale.
   b. The amount of total markdown offered.
   c. The net rate of markdown.

6. An online store sells tablets at a price of $250 each. The store had a week-long sale and offered a markdown of 35% on the tablets during the week, and an additional 10% markdown during the weekend.
   a. What was the sale price of the tablets during the weekend?
   b. What was the total amount of markdown?
   c. What net rate of markdown was offered during the week-long sale?

7. Lily's boutique sells handmade scarves for $120. During a sale, a discount of 25% was offered with an additional discount of 5% offered to customers with Lily's loyalty cards.
   a. At what price will the cardholders purchase the scarves?
   b. What is the total amount of discount offered on the scarves?
   c. What is the net rate of discount?

8. A wholesale store sells membership cards for a price of $60. Once a year, the store offers a discount of 15% on the cards for customers and an additional 10% discount for its employees.
   a. Calculate the price that employees will pay during the sale.
   b. Calculate the total amount of discount offered to employees.
   c. Calculate the net rate of discount offered to employees.

9. A bookstore was selling a boxset of a popular series of books for $90. In December, the store offered a markdown of 25% for the holidays.
   a. What is the net rate of markdown if the store offered an additional 10% markdown for customer loyalty?
   b. What is the net rate of discount if the store offered an additional 10% discount for customer loyalty?

10. The regular selling price of a coffee table is $320. The furniture store that carries the coffee table was having a store-wide sale and offered a markdown of 30% on all items.
    a. What is the net rate of markdown if the store offered an additional 5% markdown for students?
    b. What is the net rate of discount if the store offered an additional 5% discount for students?

11. Nail & Hammer Shack purchased 225 table fans of a particular make. The unit cost was $25.50 and the regular selling price was $49 each. The store sold 120 table fans at the regular selling price. During a sale, it sold another 60 at a markdown of 20%. The remaining units were sold at an additional markdown of 10%. Determine the net rate of markup based on total cost.

12. Ace of Diamonds purchased 70 diamond bracelets at $225 each and the regular selling price was $300. The store sold 50% of the diamond bracelets at the regular selling price. During a sale, it sold another 25 at a markdown of 15%. The remaining units were sold at an additional markdown of 10%. Determine the net rate of markup based on total cost.

13. A store purchased 500 DVDs at $3.60 each. The store expects to sell 300 DVDs at the regular selling price of $6, another 150 DVDs after a markdown of 20%, and the remaining DVDs at cost. Calculate the net rate of markup based on total sales.

14. Book World purchased 150 financial calculators at $22.50. The store expects to sell 72 units at the regular price of $40, another 45 units after a markdown of 15%, and the remaining units at cost. Calculate the net rate of markup based on total sales.

15. It costs $150 for a furniture store in Toronto to make its famous bookshelves. At the beginning of the year, the store had 210 items in stock. It sold 90 items at the regular selling price, 60% of the remaining items at a reduced price of $210 and the balance at cost.

    a. What was the regular selling price of the bookshelves if the store maintained a net rate of markup of 30% based on total sales?

    b. What will be the rate of markup on the regular selling price?

16. A store purchased 75 notebooks at a price of $2.30 each. It sold 25 notebooks at the regular selling price, 30 at a markdown price of $5.50, and the remaining at cost.

    a. What was the regular selling price of the notebooks if the store maintained a net markup rate of 60% based on total sales?

    b. What will be the rate of markup on the regular selling price?

5 | Review Exercises

Answers to the odd-numbered problems are available at the end of the textbook.

For the following problems, express the answers rounded to two decimal places, wherever applicable.

1. A ream of paper was sold by a distributor for $15.75 after a trade discount of 7%. What is the amount of discount offered by the distributor?

2. A wholesaler paid a net price of $180,446.50 for the shipment of a container load of raw materials. If the trade discount offered was 18%, calculate the amount of discount received on the container load of raw materials.

3. A distributor listed machines for $12,400 each in his warehouse and offered a standard trade discount of 10%. Since the machines did not sell for four months, he offered an additional trade discount of 15%. What is the amount of trade discount offered on each machine?

4. A wholesaler listed firewood at $2 per kg. Last winter, he offered trade discounts of 10% and 5% to a retailer. What was the amount of trade discount per kg offered to the retailer?

5. A wholesaler in Calgary sells a bag of basmati rice at a listed price of $11, less 5% and 3%. Another wholesaler in Edmonton sells the same brand of rice at a listed price of $11.25, less 8%. What additional trade discount rate must the wholesaler in Edmonton offer to match the price of the bag sold in Calgary?

6. Company *A*'s quotation was $850,000, less 15% and 8% for a supply of steel rods. Company *B*'s quotation was $1,140,000, less 20% and 20% for the rods. What additional trade discount rate should the bidder with the higher quote provide to match the quote of the other bidder?

7. A wine rack listed for $900 was sold after trade discounts of 50%, 25%, and 15%.

    a. What is the net price?

    b. What is the single equivalent trade discount rate that represents these trade discounts?

8. A grocery chain purchased its meat from a supplier for $750, less trade discounts of 10%, 5%, and 3%.

    a. What is the net price?

    b. What is the single equivalent trade discount rate that represents these discounts?

9. A publishing company delivered textbooks worth $45,000 to a college bookstore. The invoice is dated August 18, 2016 and has the following payment terms: 2.5/7, 2/30, n/45. What amount paid by the bookstore to the publisher will settle the invoice on: (a) August 25, (b) September 17, and (c) October 02?

10. A video production studio sent Harry an invoice of $18,500 for the creation of an advertising video for his designer clothes. The invoice was dated April 05, 2017 and had the following payment terms 3/10, 2/30, n/60. Calculate the amount paid by Harry and the cash discount if the invoice was settled on (a) April 15, 2017, (b) May 05, 2017, and (c) June 04, 2017.

11. A calendar retailer purchases calendars for $5 each and has a 14.5% markup on selling price. What is the selling price of each calendar?

12. If the cost of a product is $480.75 and it has a 20% rate of markup on selling price, calculate the selling price of the product.

13. A shoe store purchases a new model of walking shoes at $60 per pair. The store's operating expenses are 10% on cost and the rate of markup on cost is 40%.
    a. What is the selling price per pair of shoes?
    b. What is the rate of markup on selling price?
    c. What is the amount of operating profit on each pair of shoes?

14. Vanessa, a florist, purchases roses for $1.50 each. Her operating expenses are 22% on cost and operating profit is 60% on cost.
    a. What is the selling price of each rose?
    b. What is the rate of markup on selling price?
    c. What is the amount of operating profit on each rose?

15. Emma runs a speciality food store in Toronto where she sells organic carrots for $4 per kg. The rate of markup is 80% on cost.
    a. Calculate the cost of the carrots per kg.
    b. What is the amount of markup?

16. A watch store in a mall has a markup rate of 35% on cost of its watches. They sell each watch for $440.
    a. Calculate the cost of each watch.
    b. What is the amount of markup?

17. Rodney, the owner of Rodney's Gear, purchases jeans at $25 per pair from a distributor and sells them after a markup of 80% on cost. During the summer, he offers a markdown of 20% for college students.
    a. What is the regular selling price of each pair of jeans?
    b. What is the discounted selling price of each pair of jeans?

18. Home World purchased a new model of cutlery for $125 and has a markup rate of 60% on selling price. During a sale, the store offered a markdown of 50%.
    a. What is the regular selling price of the cutlery?
    b. What is the reduced selling price of the cutlery?

19. The cost of an oven is $65.00. The rate of markup based on cost is 45%. During a sale, the oven was marked down by 30%. Calculate the following:
    a. Amount of markup.
    b. Selling price.
    c. Amount of markdown.
    d. Sale price.
    e. Amount of markup at sale price.

20. The cost of a frying pan set is $15.50. The rate of markup based on cost is 25%. During a sale, the set was marked down by 10%. Calculate the following:
    a. Amount of markup.
    b. Selling price.
    c. Amount of markdown.
    d. Sale price.
    e. Amount of markup at sale price.

● 21. A computer assembly company received a shipment of monitors from its supplier with an invoice of $185,650 dated October 20, 2017 with payment terms 3/10, 2/30, n/45.
    a. If the company paid $75,000 on October 30, 2017, what was the balance to be paid?
    b. What further payment on November 19, 2017 will reduce the balance to $50,000?
    c. If the invoice is settled with a balance payment on December 04, 2017, what was the total payment for the shipment?

● 22. Maya, the general manager at Fitness World, received a shipment of new equipment for her gym. The invoice dated March 04, 2016 was for $30,000 with payment terms 3/10, 2.5/30, n/60.
    a. If she made a payment of $10,000 on March 14, 2016, calculate the balance amount on the invoice.
    b. What further payment on April 03, 2016, will reduce the balance to $2000?
    c. If the invoice was settled with a balance payment on May 03, 2016, what was the total payment for the shipment?

● 23. A wholesaler listed a printer for $150 with trade discounts of 15% and 10%. Tyler purchased this printer and showcased it for sale in his computer store. The overhead expenses are 30% on cost and the desired profit is 25% on cost. To clear the item, he offered a markdown of 20%.
    a. Calculate the regular selling price of the printer.
    b. Calculate Tyler's profit or loss at the clearance price.
    c. What is the maximum markdown rate he can offer to sell at the break-even price?

• 24. Ella buys a machine for $8500, less discounts of 20% and 15%. The overhead expenses are 8% on cost and she plans to make a profit of 60% on cost.

a. What is the regular selling price?

b. What is the profit or loss if she offers a markdown of 22%?

c. What is the maximum markdown rate she can offer to sell at the break-even price?

• 25. Fit Life store purchases its workout equipment at $900 each and sells them at a price of $1200. Out of 80 items, the store sold 60% of the items at the regular selling price, 25% at the sale price, and the remaining at cost.

a. What was the store's sale price if they maintain a net rate of markup of 25% based on total cost?

b. What was the rate of markdown offered during the sale?

• 26. Enda's Fashion store purchases its dresses at a cost of $120. The store estimates that they will sell 60% of 130 items currently in stock at a price of $220, 30% at a sale price, and the balance at cost.

a. What was the store's sale price if they maintain a net rate of markup of 60% based on total cost?

b. What was the rate of markdown offered during the sale?

5 | Self-Test Exercises

Answers to all the problems are available at the end of the textbook.

For the following problems, express the answers rounded to two decimal places, wherever applicable.

1. The net price of an item after trade discounts of 40%, 10%, and 5% is $1077.30.

a. What is the list price of the item?

b. Calculate the equivalent trade discount rate of the series of discount rates.

c. What is the amount of discount offered?

2. A clothing distributor in Ajax, Ontario sells a designer suit for $1500, less 30%. Another distributor in Oshawa, Ontario sells a similar designer suit for $1440, less 25%.

a. Which distributor offers the cheaper price for the suit?

b. What further trade discount rate should the distributor with the more expensive suit offer to match the price of the suit offered by the other distributor?

3. A newspaper company received an invoice for $180,540 dated August 28, 2018 with payment terms 2/10, 1.5/30, n/45 for the supply of a truckload of paper. Calculate the cash discount the newspaper company would receive if the invoice was paid on:

a. September 07, 2018.

b. September 27, 2018.

c. October 12, 2018.

4. Amanda received an invoice dated June 10, 2016 with payment terms 3/10, E.O.M. She made a payment of $42,360 on July 10, 2016, which settled the entire invoice amount. Calculate the invoice amount.

5. A tractor dealership purchases tractors for $55,000 each. The operating expenses are 20% on cost and the profit is 15% on cost. During a sale, the dealership offers a markdown of 25%. Calculate the profit or loss made at the sale price.

6. Molly imported a dresser and marked it up by 35% on cost. The amount of markup was $157.50.

a. How much did she pay for the dresser?

b. What is the markup as a percent of the selling price?

7. If the markup on a phone is 40% of its selling price, calculate the markup as a percent on cost.

8. The cost of stereo equipment is $72.50 each. The rate of markup based on selling price is 60%. During a sale, the equipment was marked down by 25%. Calculate the following:

a. Selling price.

b. Amount of markup.

c. Amount of markdown.

d. Sale price.

e. Amount of markup at sale price.

- 9. Timothy, an entrepreneur, received a shipment of clothes on March 25, 2017 and an invoice for $50,000 dated March 15, 2017 with terms 3/10, n/30, R.O.G. What payment on April 04, 2017 would reduce the balance:
    a. by $20,000?
    b. to $20,000?

- 10. Lily had to settle an invoice of $170,000 dated July 09, 2017 with terms of 3/7, 2/30, n/45. She made a payment of $140,000 on July 16, 2017 and another payment of $20,000 on August 08, 2017.
    a. What was the balance after the first payment?
    b. What was the balance after the second payment?
    c. What payment amount will settle the invoice on August 23?

- 11. A stationery store in Mississauga has operating expenses of 20% on selling price and the operating profit is 25% on selling price. During a sale, the laser printers were marked down by 30%. What is the profit or loss at sale price if they purchased the laser printers at $600 each?

- 12. William purchased dress shirts and sold them at his store for $75 each. The overhead expenses are 18% on cost and operating profit is 12% on cost.
    a. What rate of markdown is required to sell the shirts at break-even?
    b. What rate of markdown is required to sell the shirts at cost?

CASE 5

Merchandising Cycle of a Product: Manufacturer to Consumer

Isabelle, a college student, enjoyed this chapter on the Mathematics of Merchandising and wanted to see for herself how a product moves through the merchandising cycle from a manufacturer to the consumer. During her 2017 summer holidays, she decided to study the merchandising cycle at her father's clothing store that was located in Halifax.

While she was at the store, it purchased 1000 dress shirts that were listed for $45 each, less 10%, 8%, and 6% from a garment manufacturer in Vancouver. The store's operating expenses are 35% on selling price and rate of markup is 60% on selling price.

The store sold 400 shirts at the regular selling price. During a sale, it offered a markdown of 20% and sold another 250 shirts. It sold another 200 shirts at the break-even price and the remaining shirts at cost.

Answer the following questions by rounding to two decimal places, wherever applicable.

a. What was the cost per shirt to the store?

b. What was the total amount of discount received on the purchase of the shirts from the garment manufacturer?

c. What was the equivalent discount rate that represents the three trade discount rates?

d. What was the regular selling price per shirt at which 400 shirts were sold?

e. What was the sale price per shirt at which 250 shirts were sold?

f. What was the break-even price per shirt at which 200 shirts were sold?

g. What was the rate of markdown from the regular selling price that would price the shirt to sell at break-even?

h. What was the rate of markdown from the regular selling price that would price the shirt to sell at cost?

i. What was the total profit or loss from the sale of the 1000 shirts?

5 | Summary of Notation and Formulas

NOTATION

L = List price

d = Single discount rate

$d \times L$ = Amount of trade discount

d_e = Single equivalent discount rate to a series of discount rates

N = Net price

C = Cost

M = Markup

S = Selling price (or regular selling price)

E = Overhead expenses (or operating expenses)

P = Operating profit (or profit)

D = Markdown

BE = Break-even price

S_{Red} = Reduced selling price (or sale price)

P_{Red} = Reduced profit

FORMULAS

Amount of Trade Discount | 5.1(a)

$$\text{Amount of trade discount} = d \times L$$

Net Price | 5.1(b)

$$N = L\,(1 - d)$$

Net Price After a Series of Trade Discounts | 5.1(c)

$$N = L\,(1 - d_1)\,(1 - d_2)\,(1 - d_3) \ldots (1 - d_n)$$

Single Equivalent Trade Discount Rate | 5.1(d)

$$d_e = 1 - [(1 - d_1)\,(1 - d_2)\,(1 - d_3) \ldots (1 - d_n)]$$

Amount Credited | 5.2

$$\text{Amount Credited} = \frac{\text{Amount Paid}}{(1 - d)}$$

Selling Price | 5.3(a)

$$S = C + M$$

Amount of Markup | 5.3(b)

$$M = E + P$$

Selling Price | 5.3(c)

$$S = C + E + P$$

Rate of Markup on Cost | 5.3(d)

$$\text{Rate of markup on cost} = \frac{M}{C} \times 100\%$$

Rate of Markup on Selling Price | 5.3(e)

$$\text{Rate of markup on selling price} = \frac{M}{S} \times 100\%$$

Break-Even Price | 5.3(f)

$$BE = C + E$$

Reduced Selling Price | 5.4(a)

$$S_{Red} = S - D$$

Amount of Markdown | 5.4(b)

$$D = S - S_{Red}$$

Rate of Markdown | 5.4(c)

$$\text{Rate of markdown} = \frac{D}{S} \times 100\%$$

Reduced Profit | 5.5(a)

$$P_{Red} = S_{Red} - C - E$$

Reduced Profit | 5.5(b)

$$P_{Red} = P - D$$

If P_{Red} is negative, then there is a loss at sale price.

Table 5.5: Merchandising Calculation Table

		Amount	Rate on C	Rate on S
	P			
	$+E$			
	M			
	$+C$			
	S			
	$-D$			
	S_{Red}			
$-BE$	$-C$			
	$-E$			
	P_{Red}			

Net Amount of Markup | 5.6(a)

$$\text{Net Amount of Markup} = \text{Total Sales} - \text{Total Cost}$$

Net Rate of Markup Based on Total Cost | 5.6(b)

$$\text{Net Rate of Markup based on Total Cost} = \frac{\text{Net Amount of Markup}}{\text{Total Cost}} \times 100\%$$

Net Rate of Markup Based on Total Sales | 5.6(c)

$$\text{Net Rate of Markup based on Total Sales} = \frac{\text{Net Amount of Markup}}{\text{Total Sales}} \times 100\%$$

Chapter

6 LINEAR SYSTEMS

LEARNING OBJECTIVES

- Apply the rectangular coordinate system in drawing graphs.
- Graph linear equations.
- Analyze the systems of linear equations.
- Solve systems of linear equations with two variables.

CHAPTER OUTLINE

Introduction

A **linear equation** is an algebraic equation with one or two variables (each to the power of one), which produces a straight line when plotted on a graph.

Linear equations are algebraic equations with one or two variables, where the variables are all raised to the power of one. Linear equations produce a straight line when plotted on a graph.

- Examples of linear equations with one variable are:

  $3x - 5 = 0$ $\quad$ $5y + 7 = 0$

- Examples of linear equations with two variables are:

  $2x + 3y - 6 = 0$ $\quad$ $y = 4x + 9$

Linear equations commonly have two variables, generally represented by the variables x and y.

A *system* of linear equations is a set of linear equations considered together. The simplest linear system is a system with two equations and two variables.

Many word problems may be solved easily by translating the word problems to systems of equations with two (or more) variables. The process of determining the values of the variables for which the equations are true is known as 'solving the system of equations'. In this chapter, we will learn to solve systems of linear equations with two variables using both graphical and algebraic methods.

6.1 | The Cartesian Coordinate System

Graphs are used to provide information in a visual form to illustrate the relationship between variables easily and clearly. Graphs of equations refer to a drawing that represents the solutions to that set of equations.

Graphs are drawn on a **rectangular coordinate system** known as the **Cartesian coordinate system** (invented by René Descartes). This system uses two perpendicular number lines: one horizontal and the other vertical, each referred to as an **axis**, which cross each other at zero (0), known as the **origin**.

The horizontal number line (moving to the left or the right) is known as the **X-axis** and the vertical number line (moving up or down) is known as the **Y-axis**, as illustrated in Exhibit 6.1(a).

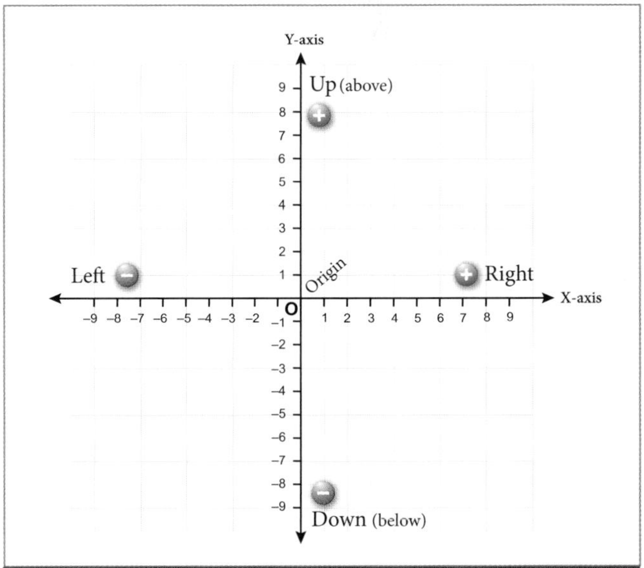

Exhibit 6.1(a): Rectangular Coordinate System

Sign Convention

The numbers to the **right** of the origin along the X-axis are **positive** and those to the left are negative. The numbers **above** the origin along the Y-axis are **positive** and those below are negative.

The purpose of the rectangular coordinate system and the sign convention is to locate a point relative to the X- and Y-axes and in reference to the origin 'O'.

Ordered pairs are used to locate a point in the coordinate system. The ordered pair (x, y) describes a point in the plane by its x- and y- coordinates.

For example, the coordinate of a point P written as an ordered pair (2, 3) refers to the point P which is 2 units to the right and 3 units above, in reference to the origin, as illustrated in Exhibit 6.1(b).

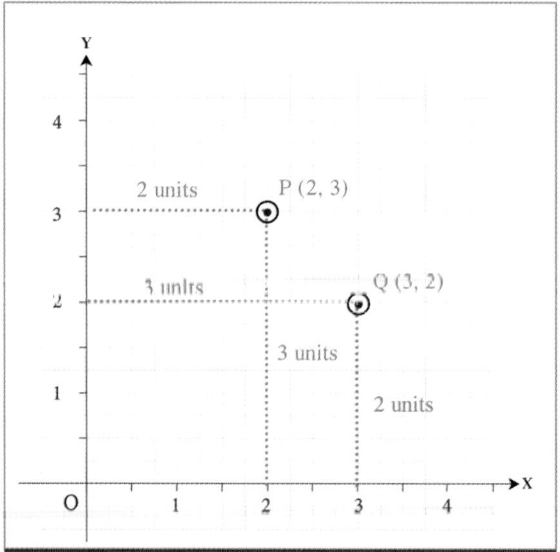

Exhibit 6.1(b): Ordered Pairs

Note:

- The first value in the bracket is the x-coordinate (horizontal distance from the Y-axis) and the second value in the bracket is the y-coordinate (vertical distance from the X-axis) of the point; i.e., x-coordinate of point P is 2 units and y-coordinate of point P is 3 units, as illustrated in Exhibit 6.1(b).
- It is referred to as a rectangular coordinate system because the x- and y-coordinates form a rectangle with the X- and Y- axes.
- It is important to identify the coordinate numbers in their order. They are known as ordered pairs because the order in which they appear determines the position of the points on the graph. Changing their order will result in a different point.

Pay close attention to the order in which coordinate pairs are written. The first coordinate refers to the horizontal distance from the origin and the second coordinate refers to the vertical distance from the origin.

- (2, 3) and (3, 2) are different points.
- (2, 3) refers to a point 'P', which is 2 units to the right of the origin and 3 units above the origin.
- (3, 2) refers to a point 'Q', which is 3 units to the right of the origin and 2 units above the origin.

Quadrants

The X- and Y- axes divide the coordinate plane into 4 parts, known as **quadrants**. Quadrants are numbered counter-clockwise from one (I) to four (IV), as illustrated in Exhibit 6.1(c).

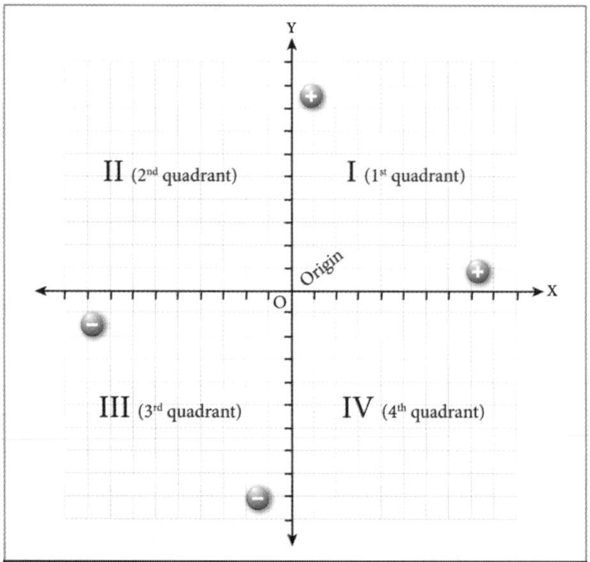

Exhibit 6.1(c): Quadrants

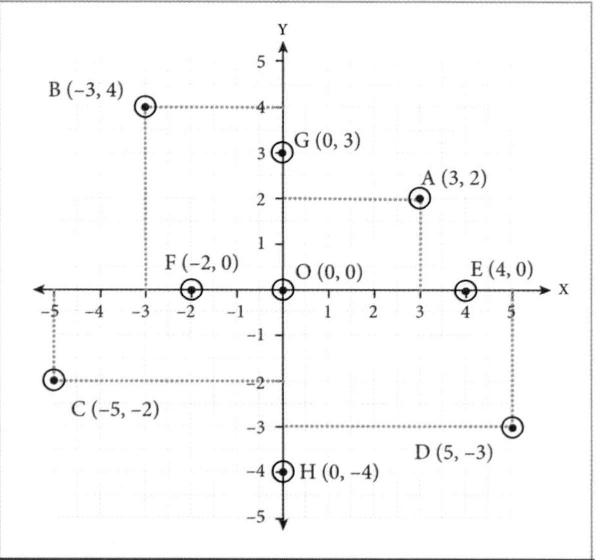

Exhibit 6.1(d): Coordinates in Different Quadrants

The table below shows the sign convention of coordinates in each of the quadrants with examples that are plotted on the graph in Exhibit 6.1(d).

Table 6.1 **Sign Convention of Coordinates in Different Quadrants, Axes, and Origin**

Quadrant/ Axis/Origin	Sign of x-coordinate	Sign of y-coordinate	Example as plotted in Exhibit 6.1(d)
I	Positive (+)	Positive (+)	A (3, 2)
II	Negative (−)	Positive (+)	B (−3, 4)
III	Negative (−)	Negative (−)	C (−5, −2)
IV	Positive (+)	Negative (−)	D (5, −3)
X-Axis	Positive (+) or Negative (−)	Zero (0)	E (4, 0) F (−2, 0)
Y-Axis	Zero (0)	Positive (+) or Negative (−)	G (0, 3) H (0, −4)
Origin	Zero (0)	Zero (0)	O (0, 0)

6.1 | Exercises

Answers to the odd-numbered problems are available at the end of the textbook.

1. Plot the following points on a graph:
   a. A (−3, 5) b. B (5, −3) c. C (0, −4)
   d. D (6, 0) e. E (−2, −4) f. F (5, 2)

2. Plot the following points on a graph:
   a. A (−6, 0) b. B (4, −2) c. C (0, −7)
   d. D (8, 0) e. E (−3, −5) f. F (5, 5)

3. In which quadrant or axis do the following points lie?
   a. A (−1, 2) b. B (5, −1) c. C (3, 5)
   d. D (−4, 0) e. E (−2, −7) f. F (0, 5)

4. In which quadrant or axis do the following points lie?
   a. A (1, 6) b. B (4, −3) c. C (−7, 3)
   d. D (6, 0) e. E (−1, −13) f. F (0, −7)

5. Plot the following pairs of points on a graph and calculate the length of each horizontal line joining the pairs of points:
   a. (3, 4) and (5, 4) b. (−7, 1) and (2, 1) c. (−5, 3) and (0, 3) d. (−2, −2) and (6, −2)

6. Plot the following pairs of points on a graph and calculate the length of each vertical line joining the pairs of points:
   a. (5, 6) and (5, 2) b. (7, 2) and (7, −4) c. (−3, 5) and (−3, 0) d. (−3, 5) and (−3, −4)

• 7. Three vertices of a square, ABCD, have points A (−3, 3), B (1, 3), and C (1, −1). Determine the coordinates of the 4th vertex, D.

• 8. Three vertices of a rectangle, PQRS, have points P (−3, 4), Q (6, 4), and R (6, −1). Determine the coordinates of the 4th vertex, S.

• 9. A vertical line has a length of 7 units and the coordinates of one end of the line is (1, 5). Determine the possible coordinates of the other end of the line.

• 10. A horizontal line has a length of 6 units and the coordinates of one end of the line is (−1, 3). Determine the possible coordinates of the other end of the line.

6.2 | Graphing Linear Equations

A linear equation is an algebraic equation with one or two variables (each with an exponent of one), which produces a straight line when plotted on a graph.

Examples of linear equations with one variable are:

$3x - 5 = 0$, $x - 3 = 0$, $5y + 7 = 0$, $y + 2 = 0$

Examples of linear equations with two variables are:

$2x - 3y + 3 = 0$, $y = 2x + 3$, $4y = 3x$, $x + y = 0$

Linear equations with two variables are generally represented by the variables x and y and expressed either in the standard form of $Ax + By = C$ (A, B, and C are integers) or in the slope-intercept form of $y = mx + b$ (m and b are integers or fractions).

The process of determining the values of the variables for which the equation(s) are true is known as solving the equations. Linear equations with two variables have infinite pairs of values as solutions; therefore, it is convenient to represent these solutions by drawing a graph.

Linear Equations in Standard Form

For an equation in standard form, the value of A is usually positive.

The 'standard' form for a linear equation with two variables, x and y, is written as $\boldsymbol{Ax + By = C}$, where A, B, and C are integers, A is positive, and A, B, and C, have no common factors other than 1.

For example, consider the following simple linear equation with two variables: $2x - y = -3$.

This equation is in the standard form of $Ax + By = C$, where $A = 2$, $B = -1$, and $C = -3$.

Example 6.2(a) **Writing Linear Equations in Standard Form**

Write the following linear equations in standard form:

(i) $\frac{2}{3}x + \frac{1}{2}y - 3 = 0$ (ii) $5 - 2x - 3y = 0$

Solution

(i) $\frac{2}{3}x + \frac{1}{2}y - 3 = 0$ Multiplying each term by the LCD of 6 and simplifying,

$4x + 3y - 18 = 0$ Rearranging,

$4x + 3y = 18$

Therefore, the equation $\frac{2}{3}x + \frac{1}{2}y - 3 = 0$, in standard form, is $4x + 3y = 18$.

(ii) $5 - 2x - 3y = 0$ Rearranging,

$-2x - 3y = -5$ Multiplying each term by -1,

$2x + 3y = 5$

Therefore, the equation $5 - 2x - 3y = 0$, in standard form, is $2x + 3y = 5$.

Linear Equations in Slope-Intercept Form

The 'slope-intercept' form for a linear equation with two variables, x and y, is written in the form of $\boldsymbol{y = mx + b}$, where $\boldsymbol{m}$ and $\boldsymbol{b}$ are either integers or fractions. '$\boldsymbol{m}$' represents the slope and '$\boldsymbol{b}$' represents the y-intercept.

For example, consider a simple linear equation such as $y = 2x + 3$. This equation is in the slope-intercept form of $y = mx + b$, where the slope, $m = 2$, and the y-intercept, $b = 3$.

Example 6.2(b) **Writing Linear Equations in Slope-Intercept Form**

Write the following linear equations in slope-intercept form and identify the slope and the y-intercept.

(i) $4x + 3y = 18$ (ii) $6x = 25y + 40$

Solution

(i) $4x + 3y = 18$ Rearranging to have the y term on the left,

$3y = -4x + 18$ Dividing each term by 3 and simplifying,

$y = -\frac{4}{3}x + 6$ This is in the form $y = mx + b$.

Therefore, the slope, $m = -\frac{4}{3}$ and the y-intercept, $b = 6$.

(ii) $6x = 25y + 40$ Rearranging to have the y term on the left,

$-25y = -6x + 40$ Multiplying each term by -1,

$25y = 6x - 40$ Dividing each term by 25 and simplifying,

$y = \frac{6}{25}x - \frac{8}{5}$ This is in the form $y = mx + b$.

Therefore, the slope, $m = \frac{6}{25}$ and the y-intercept, $b = -\frac{8}{5}$.

Graphing Linear Equations Using a Table of Values

Steps in drawing the graph of a linear equation using a table of values:

Drawing a linear graph requires only two points. However, at least three points will ensure that the formed line truly represents the given linear equation.

Step 1: Create a table of values and choose a value for the variable x.

Step 2: Compute the corresponding value for the variable y using the given equation.

Step 3: The value of x and the computed value of y will produce the ordered pair (x, y).

Step 4: Repeat Steps 1 to 3 two more times to create three unique ordered pairs.

Step 5: Plot the ordered pairs (points) on the coordinate system, choosing a suitable scale.

Step 6: Join the points with a straight line.

Step 7: Label the graph with the equation of the line.

For example, consider the equation $y = 2x + 3$.

Create a table representing x, y, and the ordered pair (x, y), as shown below. Choose a value for x, determine the coresponding value for y, and form the ordered pair (x, y).

$y = 2x + 3$			
x	y	(x, y)	
1	5	(1, 5)	Choose $x = 1$, $y = 2(1) + 3 = 5$
2	7	(2, 7)	Choose $x = 2$, $y = 2(2) + 3 = 7$
3	9	(3, 9)	Choose $x = 3$, $y = 2(3) + 3 = 9$

Plot the ordered pairs (1, 5), (2, 7), and (3, 9) on the grid of the coordinate system and draw a line through these points as shown in Exhibit 6.2(a).

Label the graph with the equation of the line $y = 2x + 3$.

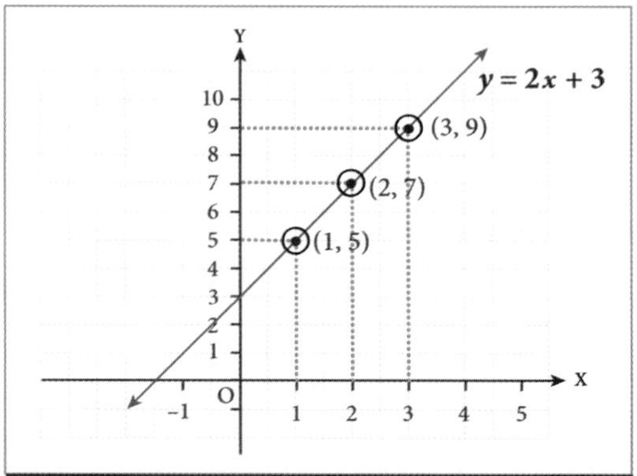

Exhibit 6.2(a): Graphing a Linear Equation Using a Table of Values

Graphing Linear Equations Using the x-intercept and the y-intercept

We may use the x-intercept and y-intercept as two points to draw a linear graph and use a third point to test the drawn line.

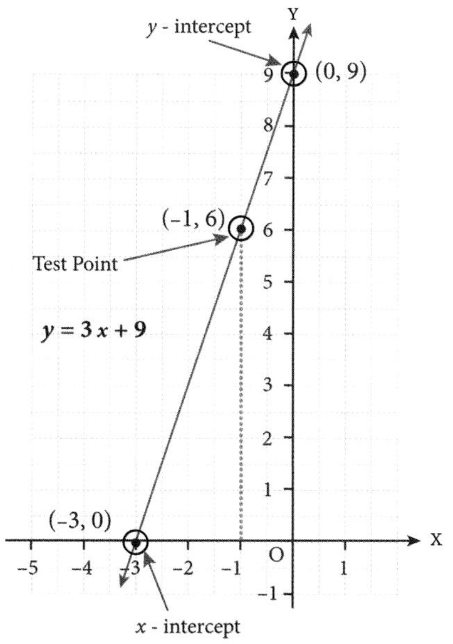

Exhibit 6.2(b): Graphing a Linear Equation Using the x-intercept and the y-intercept.

Let us consider another equation, $y = 3x + 9$.

The **x-intercept** is the point at which the line crosses the X-axis and where the y-coordinate is zero.

Substituting $y = 0$ in the above equation and solving for x,

$$0 = 3x + 9, \text{ thus, } x = -3.$$

Therefore, the x-intercept has the point (–3, 0).

The **y-intercept** is the point at which the line crosses the Y-axis and where the x-coordinate is zero.

Substituting $x = 0$ in the above equation and solving for y,

$$y = 3(0) + 9, \text{ thus, } y = 9.$$

Therefore, the y-intercept has the point (0, 9).

We can now graph the linear equation $y = 3x + 9$ by joining the x- and y-intercepts with a straight line.

To test the line, let us use another point as a test point on this line.

Let $x = -1$. Substituting this in the equation,

$$y = 3(-1) + 9 = 6$$

Therefore, the test point is (–1, 6).

Since the point (–1, 6), when plotted on the graph, falls on the line, it verifies that the plotted line represents the equation.

Graphing Linear Equations Using the Slope and the y-intercept

As noted earlier, a linear equation in the form of $y = mx + b$ is known as the equation in slope-intercept form, where 'm' is the slope and 'b' is the y-intercept. If the equation is in the standard form $Ax + By + C = 0$, it can be rearranged to be expressed in the slope-intercept form, $y = mx + b$.

The Slope and y-intercept of a Line

The slope (m) is the steepness of the line relative to the X-axis. It is the ratio of the change in value of y (known as the 'rise') to the corresponding change in value of x (known as the 'run').

If P (x_1, y_1) and Q (x_2, y_2) are two different points on a line, then the slope of the line between the points PQ is,

$$m = \frac{\text{Change in } y \text{ value}}{\text{Change in } x \text{ value}} = \frac{\Delta y}{\Delta x} = \frac{\text{Rise}}{\text{Run}} = \frac{y_2 - y_1}{x_2 - x_1}$$

as illustrated in the following exhibits (Exhibit 6.2(c) and Exhibit 6.2(d)):

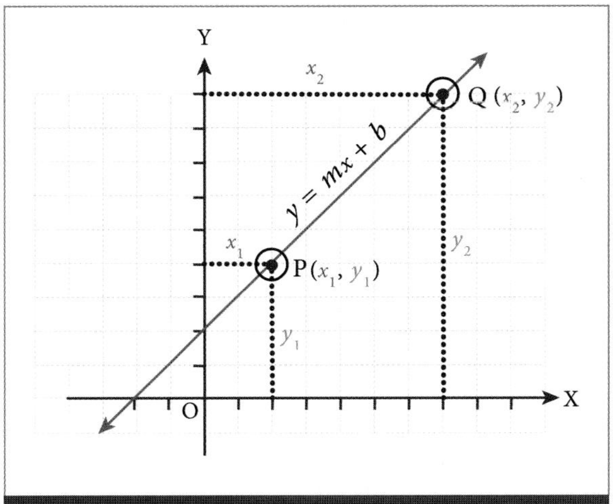

Exhibit 6.2(c): Coordinates of Points P and Q

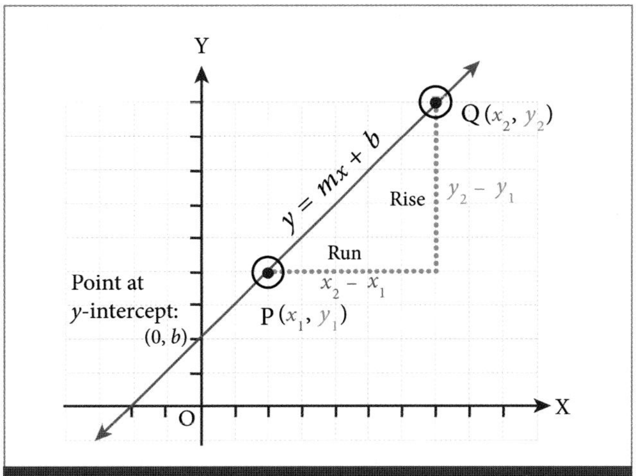

Exhibit 6.2(d): Rise and Run Between Points P and Q

As defined earlier, the y-intercept (b) is the point where the line crosses the Y-axis and is calculated by substituting zero for the x-coordinate of the equation.

Example 6.2(c)

Determining the Slope and y-intercept of an Equation and Graphing the Equation

Determine the slope and y-intercept of the linear equation $-2x + 3y - 12 = 0$ and graph the equation.

Solution

Rearranging, $-2x + 3y - 12 = 0$

$$3y = 2x + 12$$

Therefore, $$y = \frac{2}{3}x + 4$$

This is in the form $$y = mx + b,$$

where the y-intercept, $b = 4$, and the slope, $m = \frac{2}{3}$.

Therefore, (0, 4) is a point on the line, and slope,

$$m = \frac{\text{Change in } y \text{ value}}{\text{Change in } x \text{ value}} = \frac{\text{Rise}}{\text{Run}} = \frac{2}{3}$$

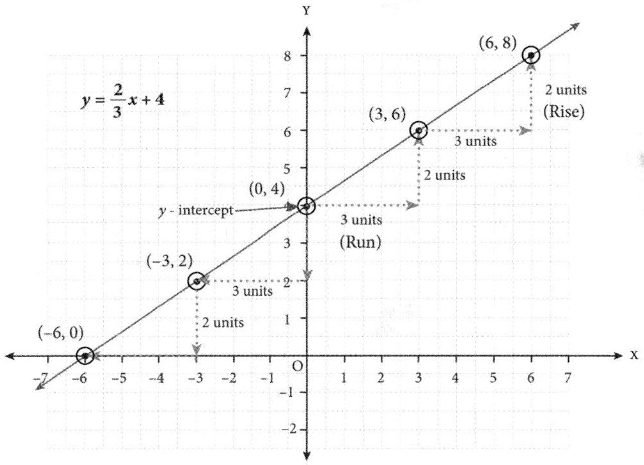

Representing this on a graph:

(i) First, plot the y-intercept point (0, 4).

(ii) From this point, move 3 units to the right and then move 2 units up to locate the new point (3, 6). This is the same as moving 2 units up, then 3 units to the right to locate the new point (3, 6).

(iii) Similarly, from the point (3, 6), move 3 units to the right and 2 units up to locate another point (6, 8).

(iv) Draw the line through these points to graph the equation.

Or,

(i) Plot the y-intercept point (0, 4).

(ii) From this point, move 2 units down and then move 3 units to the left to locate the new point (–3, 2).

(iii) Similarly, from the point (–3, 2), move 2 units down and then 3 units left to locate another point (–6, 0).

(iv) Draw the line through these points to graph the equation.

Note: *All the points located by moving in opposite directions will lie on the same line.*

Example 6.2(d) **Graphing a Linear Equation, Given in the Slope-Intercept Form**

Graph the equation $y = -\frac{3}{4}x - 2$.

Solution

The equation is in the form $y = mx + b$.

Therefore, the slope, $m = \frac{\text{Change in } y \text{ value}}{\text{Change in } x \text{ value}} = \frac{\text{Rise}}{\text{Run}} = -\frac{3}{4}$

$$m = \frac{-3}{4} \text{ or } \frac{3}{-4}$$

The y-intercept, $b = -2$, is indicated by the point $(0, -2)$.

First, plot the point $(0, -2)$. Then, using the slope, $m = \frac{-3}{4}$, from the point $(0, -2)$, move 4 units to the right and 3 units down to locate the new point, $(4, -5)$.

Alternatively, first plot the point $(0, -2)$. Then, using the slope, $m = \frac{3}{-4}$, from the point $(0, -2)$, move 4 units to the left and 3 units up to locate another point on the line, $(-4, 1)$.

Draw a line through these points to graph the equation.

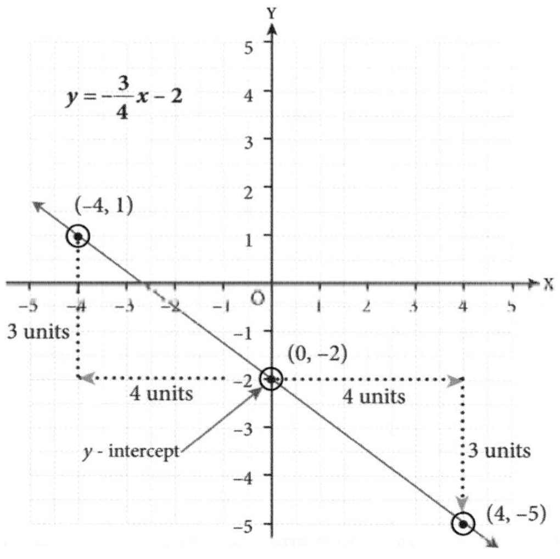

The sign of the coefficient 'm' of the equation $y = mx + b$ indicates the direction of the line.

If the sign of the coefficient 'm' is positive, then the line slopes upwards to the right, as illustrated in Exhibit 6.2(e).

If the sign of the coefficient of 'm' is negative, then the line slopes downwards to the right, as illustrated in Exhibit 6.2(f).

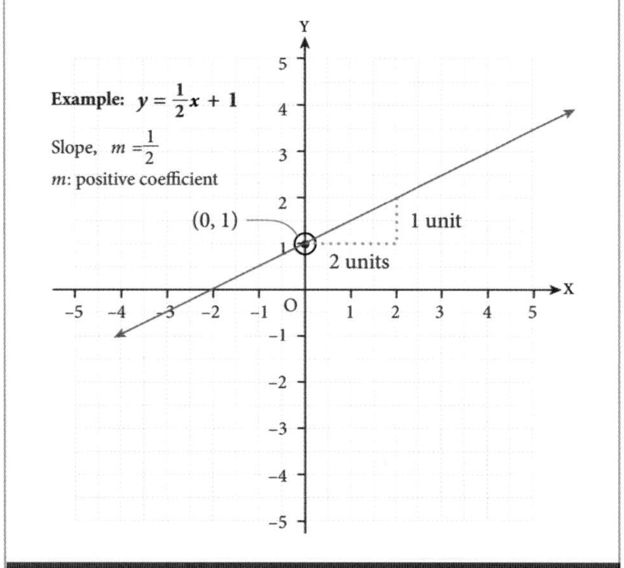

Exhibit 6.2(e): Slope of a Line When 'm' is Positive

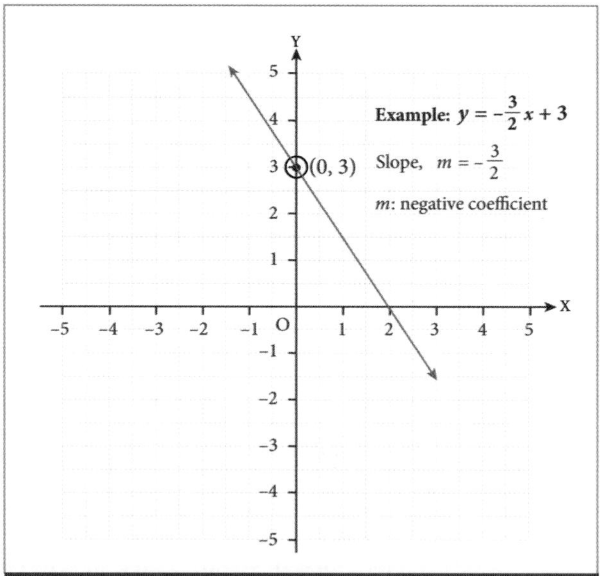

Exhibit 6.2(f): Slope of a Line When 'm' is Negative

- The absolute value of the coefficient 'm' of the equation $y = mx + b$ indicates the steepness of the line.

For example, a higher value for a slope indicates a steeper incline, as illustrated in Exhibit 6.2(h). A lower value for a slope indicates a gentler incline, as illustrated in Exhibit 6.2(i)

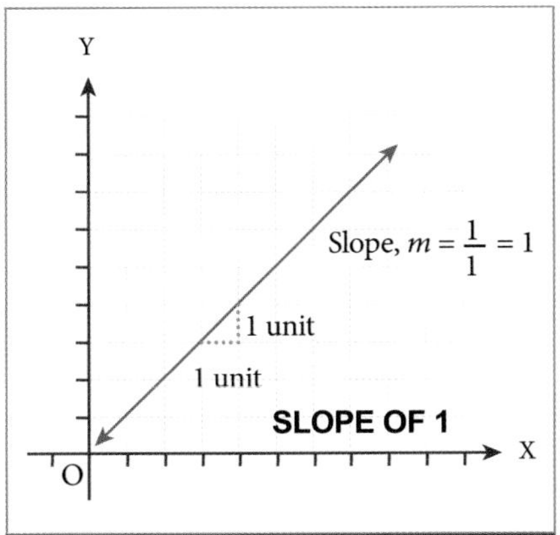

Exhibit 6.2(g): Slope Equal to 1

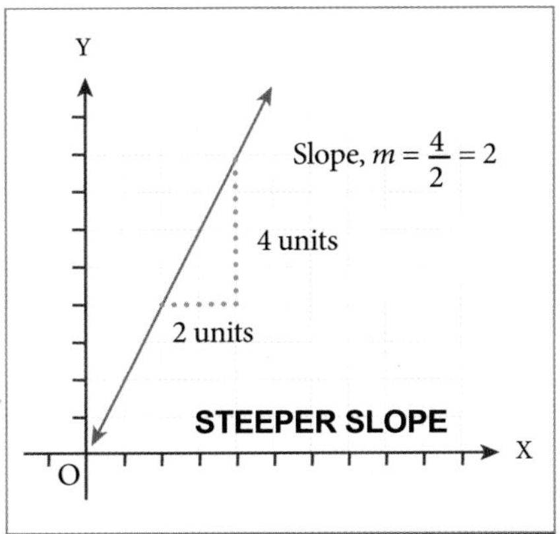

Exhibit 6.2(h): Slope Greater than 1

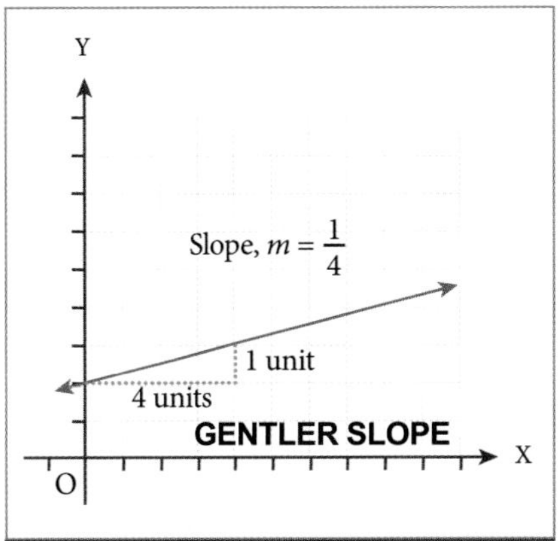

Exhibit 6.2(i): Slope Less than 1

- The slope of a line parallel to the X-axis is zero; i.e., if the slope of a line is zero, then the line is horizontal, as shown in Exhibit 6.2(j).

For example, in the equation, $y = 3$ ($y = 0x + 3$), the slope is zero and the value of the y-coordinate is 3 for all values of x. Therefore, the line is horizontal and passes through (0, 3), as illustrated in Exhibit 6.2(j).

- The slope of a line parallel to the Y-axis is undefined; i.e., if the slope of a line is undefined, then the line is vertical, as shown in Exhibit 6.2(k).

For example, in the equation, $x = 2$, the value of the x-coordinate is 2 for all values of y. Therefore, the line is vertical and passes through (2, 0), as illustrated in Exhibit 6.2(k).

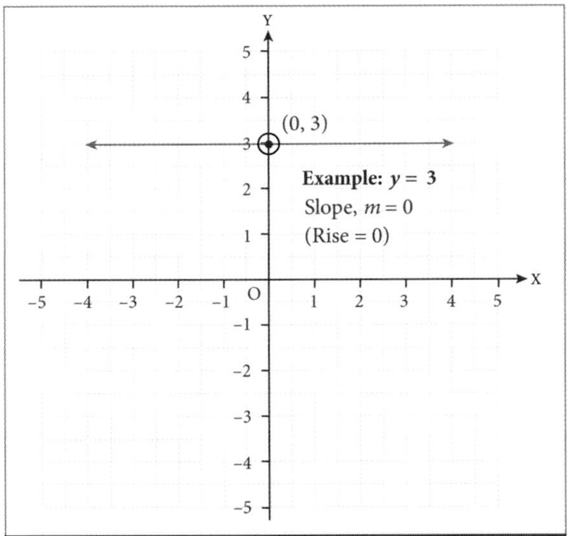

Exhibit 6.2(j): Slope of a Line Parallel to the X-axis

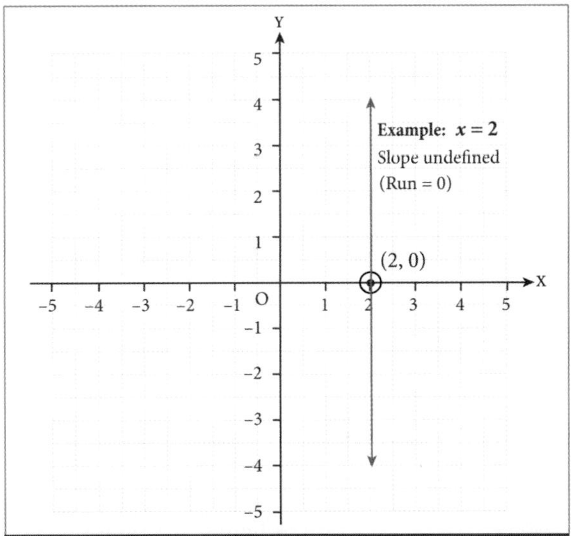

Exhibit 6.2(k): Slope of a Line Parallel to the Y-axis

If the line slopes upwards to the right, then the slope is positive.
If the line slopes downwards to the right, then the slope is negative.
If the line is parallel to the X-axis, then the slope is zero.
If the line is parallel to the Y-axis, then the slope is undefined.

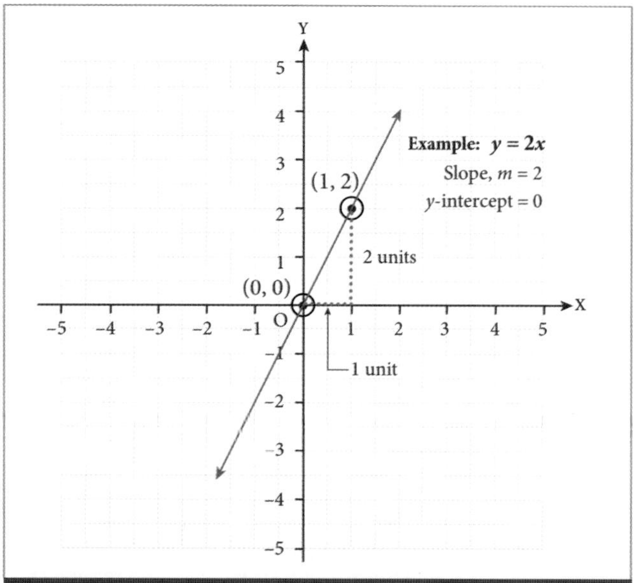

Exhibit 6.2(l): Slope of a Line When the y-intercept is 0

- An equation with a y-intercept equal to 0 will have the graph passing through the origin.

For example, in the equation, $y = 2x$, the slope, $m = 2 = \frac{2}{1}$, and the y-intercept = 0. Therefore, the line passes through (0, 0), as illustrated in Exhibit 6.2(l).

Example 6.2(e) **Determining the Equation of a Line, Given the Slope and One Point**

Determine the equation of a line having a slope of –2 and passing through (3, 5).

Solution

$m = -2$, point = (3, 5)

Step 1: Replace m with the given slope

Substituting for m in the slope-intercept equation $y = mx + b$,

$y = -2x + b$

Step 2: Substitute the ordered pair into the equation to solve for b

Substituting the coordinates of the given point (3, 5) in the above equation to solve for b,

$5 = -2(3) + b$, thus, $b = 5 + 6 = 11$

Step 3: Write the equation of $y = mx + b$ with m and the calculated value of b

Therefore, the equation of the line is $y = -2x + 11$.

Example 6.2(f) **Determining the Slope and the Equation of a Line, Given Two Points**

Determine the equation of a line that passes through points (3, 2) and (4, 5).

Solution

Step 1: Calculate the slope

$$m = \frac{\text{Change in } y \text{ value}}{\text{Change in } x \text{ value}} = \frac{y_2 - y_1}{x_2 - x_1} = \frac{5 - 2}{4 - 3} = \frac{3}{1}$$

Step 2: Replace m with the calculated slope

Substituting for m in the slope-intercept equation $y = mx + b$,

$y = 3x + b$

Step 3: Substitute one ordered pair into the equation to solve for b

Substituting the coordinate (3, 2) into the above equation to solve for b,

$2 = 3(3) + b$, thus, $b = 2 - 9 = -7$

Step 4: Write the equation $y = mx + b$ with the calculated values of m and b

Therefore, the equation of the line is $y = 3x - 7$.

Example 6.2(g) **Determining the Equation of a Line in the Standard Form, Given a Graph**

Determine the equation of the line in standard form that is plotted in the coordinate axis below:

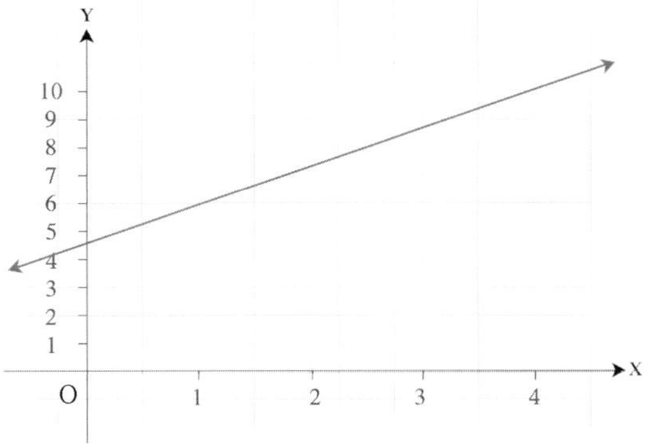

Solution

Start by choosing any 2 points (with integer coordinates) on the line: e.g., (1, 6) and (4, 10).

The slope of the line is, $m = \dfrac{y_2 - y_1}{x_2 - x_1} = \dfrac{10 - 6}{4 - 1} = \dfrac{4}{3}$

Let the equation be, $y = mx + b$

Therefore, $y = \dfrac{4}{3}x + b$

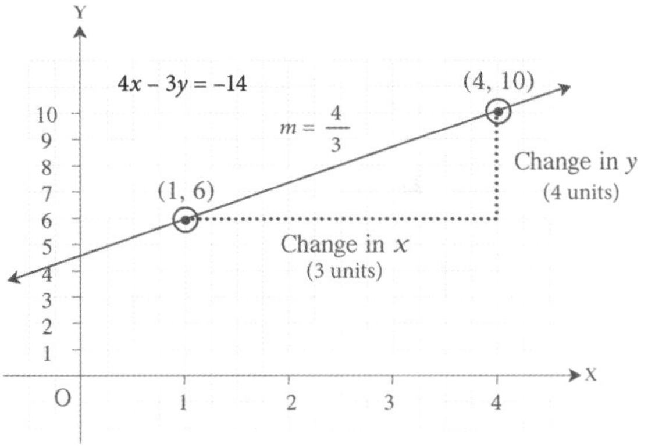

Substituting the coordinates of one of the points (1, 6) into the above equation,

$$6 = \frac{4}{3}(1) + b$$

Solving for b, $b = 6 - \dfrac{4}{3}(1) = \dfrac{14}{3}$

Therefore, the equation of the line is,

$$y = \frac{4}{3}x + \frac{14}{3}$$

This is in the slope-intercept form.

Multiplying both sides by 3,

$$3y = 4x + 14$$

Rearranging, $4x - 3y = -14$

Therefore, the equation of the line in standard form is $4x - 3y = -14$.

6.2 | Exercises

Answers to the odd-numbered problems are available at the end of the textbook.

1. For the equation $2x + 3y = 18$, determine the missing value of the following ordered pairs:
   a. (3, ?) b. (–6, ?) c. (0, ?) d. (?, 0) e. (?, –4) f. (?, 2)

2. For the equation $x + 5y = 20$, determine the missing value of the following ordered pairs:
   a. (0, ?) b. (–15, ?) c. (5, ?) d. (?, 6) e. (?, –3) f. (?, 0)

Write the following equations in slope-intercept form:

3. a. $6x + 4y + 3 = 0$ b. $2x - 3y + 15 = 0$

4. a. $2x + 9y - 18 = 0$ b. $2x - 5y - 20 = 0$

Write the following equations in standard form:

5. a. $y = \frac{5}{2}x + 1$ b. $y = -\frac{3}{4}x - 3$

6. a. $y = \frac{2}{5}x - 1$ b. $y = -\frac{4}{3}x + 4$

Graph the following equations using a table of values:

7. a. $y = x + 3$ b. $y = -5x + 1$

8. a. $y = 3x + 2$ b. $y = -2x + 3$

9. a. $2x + y + 1 = 0$ b. $2x - y - 3 = 0$

10. a. $4x + y + 2 = 0$ b. $x - y - 1 = 0$

11. Determine the points of the x-intercepts and y-intercepts for the following equations:
   a. $3x + y = -2$ b. $x + y - 3 = 4$ c. $y = 2x + 4$

12. Determine the points of the x-intercepts and y-intercepts for the following equations:
   a. $5x + y = -3$ b. $x + y - 4 = 7$ c. $y = 4x + 1$

13. Point 'A' is in the 3rd quadrant and Point 'B' is in the 1st quadrant. Determine the sign of the slope of the line AB.

14. Point 'C' is in the 4th quadrant and Point 'D' is in the 2nd quadrant. Determine the sign of the slope of the line CD.

Determine the slope and point of the y-intercept of the following equations and graph the equations:

15. $2x - 3y - 18 = 0$

16. $5x - 2y + 10 = 0$

17. $-4x + 7y - 21 = 0$

18. $-7x + 8y - 32 = 0$

Determine the equation of the line that passes through the following points:

19. (1, 2) and (5, 2)

20. (5, 0) and (4, 5)

21. (–3, –5) and (3, 1)

22. (–4, –7) and (5, 2)

Determine the equation of the following lines that have:

23. Slope = 1 and passing through (2, 6).

24. Slope = –5 and passing through (3, –2).

25. Slope = 2 and passing through the origin.

26. Slope = 4 and passing through the origin.

27. x-intercept = 4 and y-intercept = –5.

28. x-intercept = –3 and y-intercept = 3.

Determine the slope of the line passing through:

29. (2, 1) and (6, 1)

30. (–5, 4) and (3, –1)

31. (–6, 4) and (2, 4)

32. (5, 6) and (5, –4)

33. The slope of a line is 3. The line passes through A (4, y) and B (6, 8). Determine y.

34. The slope of a line is 2. The line passes through A (x, 8) and B (2, 4). Determine x.

35. Points A (2, 3), B (6, 5), and C (10, y) are on a line. Determine y.

36. Points D (3, 2), E (6, 5), and F (x, 1) are on a line. Determine x.

Determine the equation of the lines (in standard form) for the graphs shown in Problems 37 and 38.

• 37.

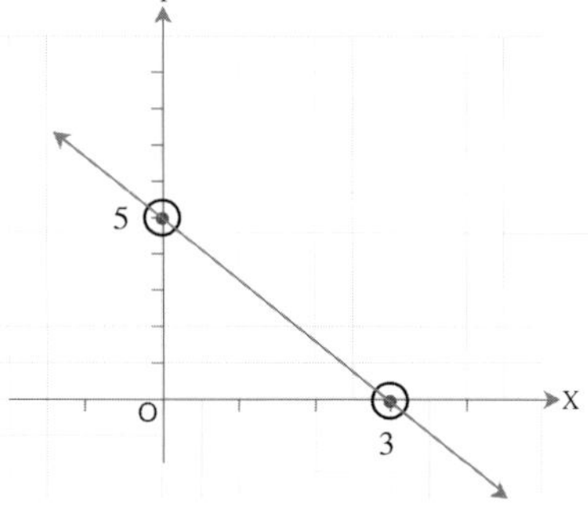

• 38.

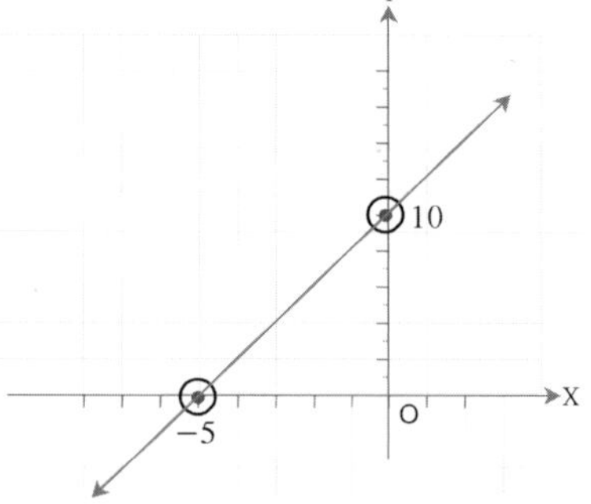

• 39. Hanna charges \$20 for the first shirt that you purchase at her store. However, for every additional shirt, she charges \$15. Write an equation that shows the relationship between her total revenue (y) and number of shirts sold (x). If you plot a graph of y vs. x, what is the point of the y-intercept and slope of the line that represents the equation?

• 40. An online music store charges \$2 for the first song that you download. For every additional song you download, you will be charged only \$1.50. Write an equation that shows the relationship between the total revenue (y) and the number of songs sold (x). If you plot a graph of y vs. x, what is the y-intercept and slope of the line that represents the equation?

6.3 | Solving Systems of Linear Equations with Two Variables Graphically

Two or more equations analyzed together are referred to as systems of equations. In this section, we will be analyzing two linear equations with two variables.

The solution to a system of two equations with two variables is an ordered pair of numbers (coordinates) that satisfy both equations.

If the graph of an equation is linear, then every point on the line is a solution to that equation. If we graph a system of two linear equations, then the point at which the two lines intersect will be a solution to both lines.

The following steps will help to solve systems of two linear equations with two variables graphically:

Step 1: Rewrite both equations in the form of $y = mx + b$ (or $Ax + By = C$).

Step 2: Graph one of the equations using any of the previously defined methods. The graph will be a straight line.

Step 3: Graph the second equation on the same axes as in Step 2. It will be another straight line.

Step 4: If the two lines intersect at a point, then the point of intersection is the solution to the given system of equations, also known as an ordered pair (x, y).

Step 5: Check the solution obtained by substituting the values for the variables in each of the original equations. If the answer satisfies the equations, then it is the solution to the given system of equations.

Note: *In Step 2, the order in which the equations are graphed or the method used to graph the equations does not matter.*

Graphs of linear equations may intersect at one point, may not intersect, or may coincide.

- If they intersect at one point (lines are non-parallel and intersecting), it indicates that there is one solution, as in Exhibit 6.3(a).
- If they do not intersect (lines are parallel and distinct), it indicates that there is no solution, as in Exhibit 6.3(b).
- If they coincide (lines are parallel and coincident), it indicates that there are infinite solutions, as in Exhibit 6.3(c).

Consistent and Inconsistent Systems

A system of linear equations that has **one or many solutions** is a **consistent linear system.**

A system of linear equations that has **no solution** is an **inconsistent linear system.**

Dependent and Independent Equations

If the system of linear equations has **many solutions,** then the **equations are dependent**.

If the system of linear equations has **one or no solution,** then the **equations are independent.**

Non-Parallel and Intersecting Lines

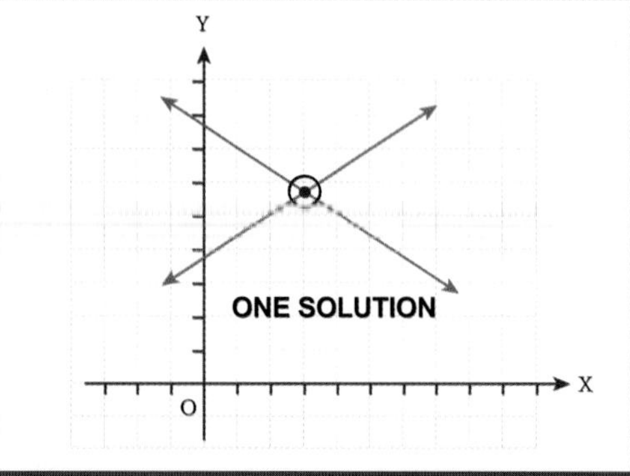

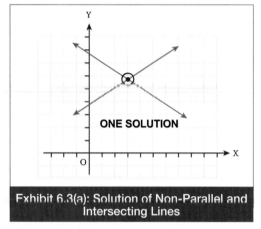

Exhibit 6.3(a): Solution of Non-Parallel and Intersecting Lines

Slope of lines:	Different
***y*-intercept:**	May or may not be same (will be different, unless the lines intersect on the Y-axis or at the origin)
Number of solutions:	One
System:	Consistent
Equations:	Independent

Parallel and Distinct Lines

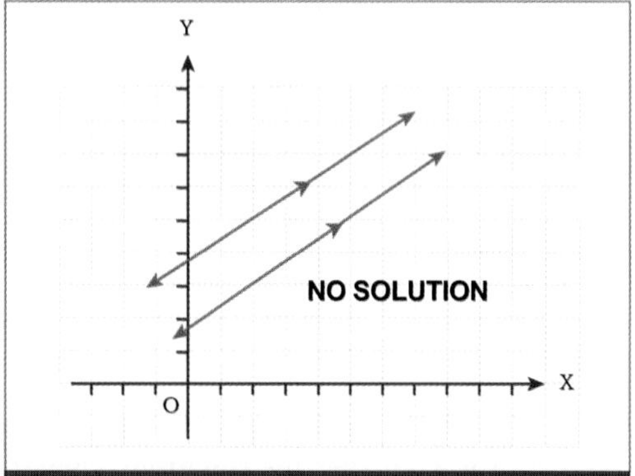

Exhibit 6.3(b): Solution of Parallel and Distinct Lines

Slope of lines:	Same
***y*-intercept:**	Different
Number of solutions:	None
System:	Inconsistent
Equations:	Independent

Parallel and Coincident Lines

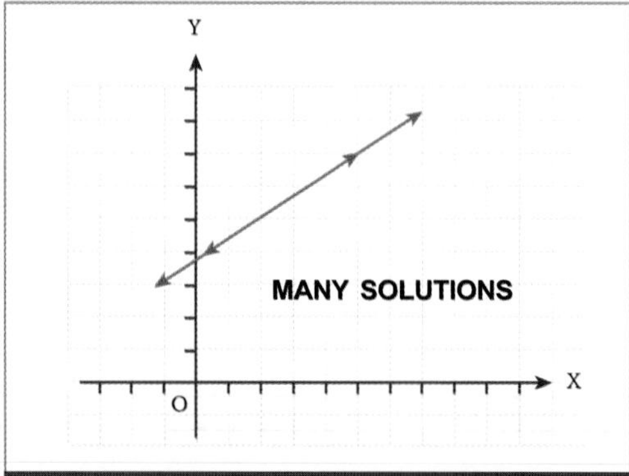

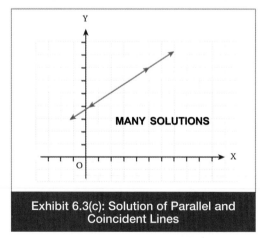

Exhibit 6.3(c): Solution of Parallel and Coincident Lines

Slope of lines:	Same
***y*-intercept:**	Same
Number of solutions:	Infinite
System:	Consistent
Equations:	Dependent

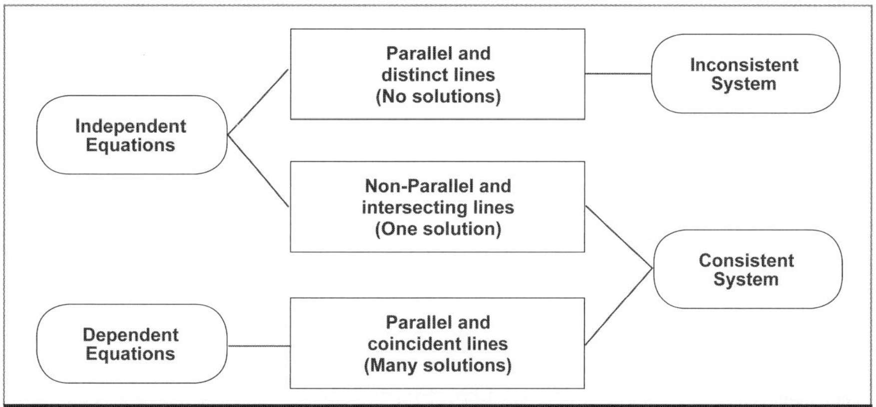

Exhibit 6.3(d): Classification of System of Equations

Example 6.3(a) **Solving and Classifying a System of Linear Equations**

Solve the following system of linear equations by graphing and classifying the system as consistent or inconsistent and the equations as dependent or independent.

$y = x + 1$ Equation (1)

$y = -x + 3$ Equation (2)

Solution

Equation (1): $y = x + 1$

Slope, $m = 1 = \frac{1}{1}$

$b = 1$, therefore, y-intercept has the point (0, 1).

Equation (2): $y = -x + 3$

Slope, $m = -1 = \frac{-1}{1}$

$b = 3$, therefore, y-intercept has the point (0, 3).

Plot the graph using the slope-intercept method. The two lines intersect at a common point (1, 2), i.e., the solution (1, 2) satisfies both equations.

Therefore, the system is consistent and the equations are independent.

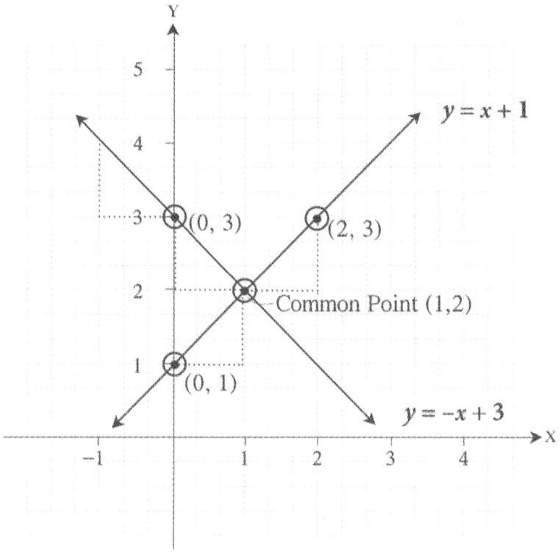

Example 6.3(b) **Classifying a System of Linear Equations**

Solve the following system of linear equations by graphing and classifying the system as consistent or inconsistent and the equations as dependent or independent.

$y = -3x + 3$ Equation (1)

$y = -3x - 2$ Equation (2)

Solution

Equation (1): $y = -3x + 3$

Slope, $m = -3 = \dfrac{-3}{1}$

$b = 3$, therefore, y-intercept has the point (0, 3).

Equation (2): $y = -3x - 2$

Slope, $m = -3 = \dfrac{-3}{1}$

$b = -2$, therefore, y-intercept has the point (0, −2).

The lines have the same slope but different y-intercepts. Therefore, the lines are parallel and distinct; i.e., they have no solutions.

The system is inconsistent and the equations are independent.

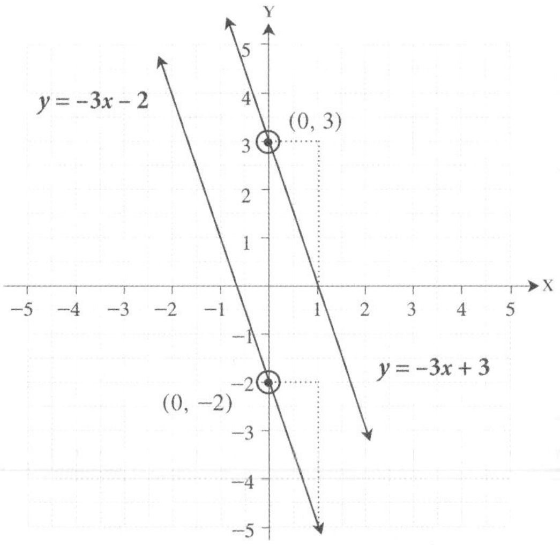

6.3 | Exercises

Answers to the odd-numbered problems are available at the end of the textbook.

Solve the following systems of linear equations by graphing:

1. $y = 3x - 2$ and $y = -7x + 8$
2. $y = -x + 2$ and $2y = -2x + 6$
3. $y = -4x + 7$ and $2y + 8x = 14$
4. $y = 3x + 9$ and $y = x - 4$
5. $y = 2x + 6$ and $2y = -3x + 6$
6. $y = -2x + 3$ and $2y + 4x = 6$
7. By determining the slope and y-intercept of each pair of equations in Problems 3 and 5, classify the system of linear equations as dependent or independent.
8. By determining the slope and y-intercept of each pair of equations in Problems 4 and 6, classify the system of linear equations as dependent or independent.
9. By determining the slope and y-intercept of each pair of equations in Problems 3 and 5, classify the system of linear equations as consistent or inconsistent.
10. By determining the slope and y-intercept of each pair of equations in Problems 4 and 6, classify the system of linear equations as consistent or inconsistent.
11. Determine the value of 'A' for which the lines $Ax - 2y - 5 = 0$ and $8x - 4y + 3 = 0$ are parallel.
12. Determine the value of 'A' for which the lines $Ax + 3y = 6$ and $3x + 2y = 10$ are parallel.
13. Determine the value of 'B' for which the lines $3x - 2y + 8 = 0$ and $6x - By - 3 = 0$ are parallel.
14. Determine the value of 'B' for which the lines $3x + By = 5$ and $2x - 3y = 1$ are parallel.

Solve the following systems of linear equations by graphing:

15. $5x + y + 9 = 0$ and $x - 3y + 5 = 0$
16. $3x - 2y + 1 = 0$ and $y + 4x - 6 = 0$
17. $3x + 2y = -4$ and $y + \dfrac{3}{2}x + 2 = 0$
18. $2x - y = 6$ and $6x - 3y = 15$
19. $4x - 2y = 6$ and $-2y + 4x - 8 = 0$
20. $2y - x - 6 = 0$ and $y = \dfrac{1}{2}x + 3$

6.4 | Solving Systems of Linear Equations with Two Variables Algebraically

Solving systems of linear equations using algebraic methods is the most accurate for the following reasons:

- It eliminates graphing errors.
- It gives the exact answer with systems of equations that contain fractions or that have fractional answers.

There are two methods involved in solving systems of linear equations. They are the **substitution method** and the **elimination method**.

The Substitution Method

The substitution method is preferable when the coefficient of any one of the variables is either 1 or –1 in either one of the equations in the system.

In this method, the following steps are used to solve systems of two linear equations with two variables:

Step 1: Solve one of the equations for either x or y.

Step 2: Substitute that result into the second equation to obtain an equation with one variable.

Step 3: Solve the equation obtained from the step above for that variable.

Step 4: Substitute that value into any one of the equations to determine the value of the other variable.

Example 6.4(a) **Solving a System of Linear Equations by Substituting for the Variable 'y'**

Solve this system:

$y - 3x + 2 = 0$ Equation (1)

$2y + x - 10 = 0$ Equation (2)

Solution

From Equation (1),

$$y - 3x + 2 = 0$$
$$y = 3x - 2$$

Substituting this in Equation (2),

$$2y + x - 10 = 0$$
$$2(3x - 2) + x - 10 = 0$$

Solving for 'x',

$$6x - 4 + x - 10 = 0$$
$$7x = 14$$
$$x = 2$$

Substituting $x = 2$ in Equation (1),

$$y = 3x - 2 = 3(2) - 2 = 4$$

Therefore, the solution is (2, 4).

Example 6.4(b) **Solving a System of Linear Equations by Substituting for the Variable 'x'**

Solve this system:

$x + 2y = 6$ Equation (1)

$4x + 3y = 4$ Equation (2)

Solution

From Equation (1), $x = 6 - 2y$

Substituting in Equation (2), $4(6 - 2y) + 3y = 4$

Solving for 'y', $24 - 8y + 3y = 4$

$$20 = 5y$$

$$y = 4$$

Substituting $y = 4$ in Equation (1),

$$x = 6 - 2y = 6 - 2(4) = -2$$

Therefore, the solution is (−2, 4).

The Elimination Method

The elimination method is preferable when none of the the variables' coefficients are either 1 or −1, in either one of the equations in the system.

In this method, the following steps are used to solve systems of two linear equations with two variables:

Step 1: Write both equations in the form $Ax + By = C$.

Step 2: Simplify the equations to eliminate fractions.

Step 3: Choose a variable to eliminate.

Step 4: Multiply one or both equations by a constant to obtain the least common multiple for the coefficient of the variable to be eliminated.

Step 5: Add or subtract the two equations so that the variable is eliminated.

Step 6: Solve the equation for the remaining variable.

Step 7: Substitute that value into any one of the equations to determine the value of the other variable.

Example 6.4(c) **Solving a System of Linear Equations by Eliminating the Variable 'x'**

Solve this system:

$2x + 3y = 13$ Equation (1)

$-3x + 6y = 12$ Equation (2)

Solution

Choose the variable 'x' to eliminate. It has coefficients of 2 and −3.

Multiplying Equation (1) by 3, and multiplying Equation (2) by 2,

$3(2x + 3y) = 3(13)$

$6x + 9y = 39$ Equation (3)

$2(-3x + 6y) = 2(12)$

$-6x + 12y = 24$ Equation (4)

Adding Equations (3) and (4),

$$(6x + 9y) + (-6x + 12y) = 39 + 24$$

$$6x - 6x + 9y + 12y = 63$$

$$21y = 63$$

$$y = \frac{63}{21} = 3$$

Substituting $y = 3$ in Equation (1),

$$2x + 3y = 13$$

$$2x + 3(3) = 13$$

Solving for 'x', $2x = 13 - 9$

$$2x = 4$$

$$x = 2$$

Therefore, the solution is (2, 3).

Example 6.4(d) **Solving a System of Linear Equations by Eliminating the Variable 'y'**

Solve this system:

$3x + 2y = 8$ Equation (1)

$8x + 5y = 18$ Equation (2)

Solution

Choose the variable 'y' to eliminate. It has coefficients of 2 and 5.

Multiplying Equation (1) by 5,

$15x + 10y = 40$ Equation (3)

Multiplying Equation (2) by 2,

$16x + 10y = 36$ Equation (4)

Subtracting Equation (3) from (4),

$x = -4$

Substituting $x = -4$ into Equation (1),

$3(-4) + 2y = 8$

Rearranging, $2y = 20$

$y = 10$

Therefore, the solution is (–4, 10).

Example 6.4(e) **Solving a System of Linear Equations Containing Fractions by Elimination**

Solve this system:

$\frac{x}{5} + 7y = \frac{29}{10}$ Equation (1)

$\frac{x}{3} + \frac{5y}{2} = \frac{1}{4}$ Equation (2)

Solution

First, simplify the equations to eliminate the fractions.

Multiplying Equation (1) by the LCD, 10,

$2x + 70y = 29$ Equation (3)

Multiplying Equation (2) by the LCD, 12,

$4x + 30y = 3$ Equation (4)

Choose the variable 'x' to eliminate. It has coefficients of 2 and 4.

Multiplying Equation (3) by 2,

$4x + 140y = 58$ Equation (5)

Subtracting Equation (4) from (5),

$110y = 55$

$y = 0.5$

Substituting $y = 0.5$ in Equation (3),

$2x + 70(0.5) = 29$

Rearranging, $2x = -6$

$x = -3$

Therefore, the solution is (–3, 0.5).

Example 6.4(f) **Solving Systems of Equations by Elimination**

Anna invested a total of $10,000 in Funds *A* and *B*. The amount in Fund *A* earned an interest of 4% per annum and the amount in Fund *B* earned an interest of 5% per annum. If the total interest earned from both these funds at the end of one year was $470, how much did she invest in each fund?

Solution

Let the amount invested in Fund *A* be $*A*, and the amount invested in Fund *B* be $*B*.

$$A + B = 10{,}000 \qquad \text{Equation (1)}$$

Also, $$4\%(A) + 5\%(B) = 470$$

$$0.04A + 0.05B = 470 \qquad \text{Equation (2)}$$

Choose the variable '*B*' to eliminate.

It has coefficients of 1 and 0.05.

Multiplying Equation (1) by 0.05,

$$0.05A + 0.05B = 500 \qquad \text{Equation (3)}$$

Subtracting Equation (2) from Equation (3),

$$(0.05A + 0.05B) - (0.04A + 0.05B) = 500 - 470$$

$$0.01A = 30$$

$$A = 3000$$

Substituting $A = 3000$ in Equation (1),

$$3000 + B = 10{,}000$$

$$B = 7000$$

Therefore, she invested $3000 in Fund *A* and $7000 in Fund *B*.

6.4 | Exercises

Answers to the odd-numbered problems are available at the end of the textbook.

Solve the following systems of equations by using the substitution method:

1. a. $y - 3x + 8 = 0$ and $y - x + 4 = 0$ b. $3x - 2y = 8$ and $x + 3y = 15$
2. a. $4x - 7y + 6 = 0$ and $x - 3y + 2 = 0$ b. $6x - 9y + 2 = 0$ and $x - 2y - 5 = 0$
3. a. $5x + 4y = 14$ and $x - 3y = -1$ b. $3x - 2y = 20$ and $y + 4x = 23$
4. a. $x - 9y = 6$ and $3x - 7y = 16$ b. $9x - 2y = 12$ and $5y + 3x = 21$
5. a. $x - 3y = 12$ and $5x + 2y = 9$ b. $7x - 5y + 3 = 0$ and $-3x + y + 1 = 0$
6. a. $3x + y = -8$ and $3x - 4y = -23$ b. $6x - 5y + 13 = 0$ and $-3x + y - 8 = 0$

Solve the following systems of equations by using the elimination method:

7. a. $3y + 2x = 24$ and $2x - 2y = 14$ b. $5x + 3y = 19$ and $3x - 5y = -9$
8. a. $7x - 3y = -5$ and $5x - 9y = 7$ b. $5x - 3y = 2$ and $3x - 5y = 7$
9. a. $5x - 7y = 19$ and $2x + 3y = -4$ b. $2y + 3x = 14$ and $9x - 4y = 2$
10. a. $9x + 8y = 10$ and $3x + 2y = 4$ b. $3x - 5y = 4$ and $5x + 3y = -16$
11. a. $5x - 2y + 1 = 0$ and $2x - 3y - 4 = 0$ b. $3y + 7x = 15$ and $3x + 5y + 1 = 0$
12. a. $4x + 5y = 11$ and $2x + 3y = 5$ b. $9y + 4x - 1 = 0$ and $4x + 5y + 3 = 0$

Solve the following systems of equations:

13. $0.5x - 0.3y = -1.2$ and $0.2x - 0.7y = 0.1$
14. $1.2x + 0.6y = 0$ and $3.5x + 1.7y = 0.01$
15. $0.4x - 0.5y = -0.8$ and $0.3x - 0.2y = 0.1$
16. $0.2x - 0.3y = -0.6$ and $0.5x + 0.2y = 2.3$
17. $0.7x - 0.4y = 2.9$ and $0.6x - 0.3y = 2.4$
18. $1.5x + y = 1$ and $0.8x + 0.7y = 1.2$

Solve the following systems of equations:

19. $\frac{x}{5}+\frac{y}{6}=3$ and $\frac{x}{2}-\frac{y}{3}=3$

20. $\frac{x}{6}-\frac{y}{3}=\frac{2}{3}$ and $\frac{x}{4}-\frac{y}{12}=-\frac{3}{2}$

21. $\frac{5x}{3}-\frac{5y}{2}=-5$ and $\frac{x}{3}-\frac{y}{4}=2$

22. $\frac{x}{4}-\frac{y}{2}=2$ and $\frac{x}{6}+\frac{2y}{3}=\frac{4}{3}$

23. $\frac{x}{4}+\frac{y}{2}=2\frac{1}{4}$ and $\frac{2x}{3}+\frac{y}{6}=\frac{3}{2}$

24. $\frac{3x}{10}+\frac{y}{5}=\frac{1}{2}$ and $\frac{x}{3}+\frac{y}{3}=\frac{1}{2}$

25. $4(x-3)+5(y+1)=12$ and $(y+7)-3(x+2)=1$

26. $4(x+3)-3(y+4)=21$ and $2(x+4)+5(y-3)=10$

27. $2(x-2)-3(y-1)=11$ and $5(x+1)+2(y-4)=8$

28. $3(x+1)-6(y+2)=6$ and $5(2x-4)+7(y+1)=-17$

29. $3(2x+1)-2(y+7)=-1$ and $4(x+5)+3(y-1)=28$

30. $2(3x+2)+5(2y+7)=13$ and $3(x+1)-4(y-1)=-15$

31. Meals for two adults and three children cost $48, whereas meals for three adults and two children cost $52. Determine the cost of the meal for one adult.

32. Three DVDs and four movie tickets cost $94, whereas four DVDs and three movie tickets cost $81. How much did one DVD cost?

33. The sum of the ages of a son and his father in years was 92. The difference in their ages was 28. How old were the son and father?

34. The sum of two numbers is 56 and their difference is 22. What are the numbers?

35. Benjamin invested a portion of $25,000 at 3% per annum and the remainder at 4% per annum. The total interest on the investment for the first year was $900. How much did he invest at each rate?

36. Naomi invested a portion of $10,000 at 4% per annum and the remainder at 2.5% per annum. The total interest on the investment for the first year was $370. How much did she invest at each rate?

37. Company *A* charged a one-time setup fee of $40 and $1.25 per page to print a book. Company *B* charged a one-time setup fee of $25 and $1.30 per page to print a book.
    a. Where would it have been cheaper to print a book that has 160 pages?
    b. How many pages should a book have for both companies to charge the same amount in printing cost?

38. Arthur's Electric Company charged $75 for a service call and an additional $45 per hour to repair a furnace. Vladimir's Furnaces Inc. charged $40 for a service call and an additional $50 per hour to repair the same furnace.
    a. Where would it have been cheaper to repair a furnace if it took 8 hours for the repair job?
    b. How many hours of work would have resulted in both companies charging the same amount for the repair?

39. 450 tickets were sold at an opera in Calgary. Tickets for adults were sold for $9.50 each and tickets for children were sold for $5.50 each. If a total of $3675 was collected from ticket sales, how many tickets of each kind were sold?

40. Maggie had 50 bills consisting of $20 bills and $5 bills. The total dollar value of the bills was $310. How many of each type of bill did she have?

6 | Review Exercises

Answers to the odd-numbered problems are available at the end of the textbook.

1. In which quadrant or axis do the following points lie?
   a. A (5, −1) b. B (−2, 3) c. C (3, 0)
   d. D (4, −2) e. E (2, 0) f. F (0, 4)

2. In which quadrant or axis do the following points lie?
   a. A (−4, 5) b. B (−5, 0) c. C (−2, −7)
   d. D (0, −3) e. E (6, 6) f. F (5, 4)

3. Plot the following points and join them in the order A, B, C, D. Identify the type of quadrilateral and determine its area and perimeter.
   a. A (6, −3) b. B (6, −6)
   c. C (−2, −6) d. D (−2, −3)

4. Plot the following points and join them in the order P, Q, R, S. Identify the type of quadrilateral and determine its area and perimeter.
   a. P (−2, 4) b. Q (−8, 4)
   c. R (−8, −2) d. S (−2, −2)

5. Graph the following equations using a table of values with four points:
   a. $4x - y = 2$ b. $x + y - 4 = 0$
   c. $y = \frac{1}{2}x + 2$

6. Graph the following equations using a table of values with four points:
   a. $2x + 3y = 12$ b. $x + 2y - 4 = 0$
   c. $y = -\frac{1}{3}x - 2$

7. Graph the following equations using the x-intercept, y-intercept, and another point.
   a. $3x - 4y = 12$ b. $x - 2y - 6 = 0$
   c. $y = 4x$

8. Graph the following equations using the x-intercept, y-intercept, and another point.
   a. $x - 2y = -1$ b. $3x + y - 4 = 0$
   c. $x = 2y$

9. Graph the following equations using the slope and y-intercept method.
   a. $y = 4x + 6$ b. $y = -\frac{3}{4}x - 1$
   c. $3x + 2y - 12 = 0$

10. Graph the following equations using the slope and y-intercept method.
    a. $y = 5x + 4$ b. $y = -\frac{1}{3}x - 1$
    c. $2x + 3y + 6 = 0$

11. Determine the equation of the line that passes through the following points:
    a. (3, 2) and (7, 5) b. (5, −4) and (−1, 4)
    c. (1, −2) and (4, 7)

12. Determine the equation of the line that passes through the following points:
    a. (4, 6) and (2, 4) b. (0, −7) and (−6, −1)
    c. (3, −4) and (−1, 4)

13. The slope of a line is 2 and it passes through A (2, 3) and B (−1, y). Determine 'y' and the equation of the line.

14. The slope of a line is −3 and it passes through P (2, −2) and Q (x, 7). Determine 'x' and the equation of the line.

15. Henry worked in a computer store and earned $500 a month plus a commission of 10% on the sales he made. The relationship between his earnings (y) in a month and the number of computers he sold (x) is expressed by the equation $y = 500 + 0.10x$.
    a. What would his commission be if his earnings were $14,000 in a month?
    b. What would his earnings be if his sales were $250,000 in a month?

16. The fixed costs (FC) of a factory for the month were \$5000 and the variable costs (VC) to manufacture each product were \$5 per unit. The total costs (TC) for the month were the sum of the FC and VC per unit multiplied by the number of products produced and sold (x). The relationship between TC, FC, VC, and x is expressed by the equation $TC = FC + (VC)x$.

    a. What would be the total cost if 90 products were sold this month?

    b. How many products were sold this month if the total cost was \$11,375?

17. Solve the following pairs of equations by using the graphing method:

    a. $y = -2x - 1$ and $y = 3x - 11$

    b. $2x - 3y - 6 = 0$ and $x + 2y - 10 = 0$

    c. $2y = x$ and $y = -x + 3$

18. Solve the following pairs of equations by using the graphing method:

    a. $y = 2x + 3$ and $y = -2x - 1$

    b. $3x + 4y - 5 = 0$ and $2x - y + 4 = 0$

    c. $3y = 2x$ and $y = -3x + 11$

19. Solve the following pairs of equations by using the substitution method:

    a. $x + 4y = 8$ and $2x + 5y = 13$

    b. $x + 4y + 12 = 0$ and $9x - 2y - 32 = 0$

    c. $3x + 2y = 5$ and $y = 2x - 1$

20. Solve the following pairs of equations by using the substitution method:

    a. $x + y = 3$ and $2x - y = 12$

    b. $x - y - 1 = 0$ and $2x + 3y - 12 = 0$

    c. $4x + 3y = 12$ and $9 - 3x = y$

21. Solve the following pairs of equations by using the elimination method:

    a. $8x + 7y = 23$ and $7x + 8y = 22$

    b. $9x - 2y = -32$ and $x + 4y = -12$

    c. $4x + 3y = 12$ and $18 - 6x = 2y$

22. Solve the following pairs of equations by using the elimination method:

    a. $2x + y = 8$ and $3x + 2y = 7$

    b. $5x - 2y + 3 = 0$ and $3x - 2y - 1 = 0$

    c. $2x + y + 2 = 0$ and $6x = 2y + 9$

23. The difference of two numbers was 5. The sum of three times the larger number and two times the smaller number was 25. What were the numbers?

24. Henry loaned a total of \$5000 to his friends, Ben and Chris. He charged Ben an interest of 2% per annum and Chris an interest of 2.5% per annum. If he earned a total interest of \$110 from both of them at the end of the year, what were the loan amounts given to each of them?

6 | Self-Test Exercises

Answers to all the problems are available at the end of the textbook.

1. Three vertices of a rectangle ABCD have points A (–3, 4), B (5, 4), and C (5, –1). Determine the coordinate of the 4th vertex and the area of the rectangle.

2. Determine the slope and y-intercept of the line $2x - 3y + 6 = 0$.

3. Determine the equation of the line in standard form that passes through the points P(–4, 5) and Q(1, 1).

4. Given the following slopes (m) and y-intercepts (b), write the equations in standard form:

   a. $m = -\frac{1}{2}$, $b = -4$

   b. $m = \frac{2}{3}$, $b = -2$

5. Determine the x-intercept, y-intercept, and another point on the line and graph the following lines:

   a. $y = 2x - 3$

   b. $2x - 3y + 9 = 0$

6. Write the equation of a line in standard form that is parallel to $3x - 2y + 9 = 0$ and passes through the point (–6, –3).

   (Hint: Parallel lines will have the same slope.)

7. Solve the system of equations by using the graphical method:

   a. $y = 3x + 6$ and $6x - 2y + 12 = 0$

   b. $2x + 3y + 4 = 0$ and $3x - y + 7 = 0$

8. Solve the system of equations by using the substitution method:

   a. $2x + 4y + 6 = 0$ and $y - 3x + 9 = 0$

   b. $3x + y = -8$ and $2x + 3y = 4$

9. Solve the system of equations by using the elimination method:

   a. $6x - 4y + 3 = 0$ and $4x - 6y - 3 = 0$

   b. $3x + 5y - 19 = 0$ and $5x - 2y + 11 = 0$

10. The equation of a line is $8x - By - 6 = 0$. If the line passes through (1, –2), find the value of 'B' and write the equation in slope-intercept form.

11. A restaurant charged \$15 for an adult meal and \$8 for a child meal. On a weekend, the restaurant sold 200 meals in total, for \$2475. What was the quantity of each type of meal sold during this weekend?

12. Chan invested a portion of \$10,000 at 5.5% per annum and the remainder at 3.5% per annum. The total interest on his investment for the first year was \$470. How much did he invest at each rate?

Chapter 7

BREAK-EVEN AND COST-VOLUME-PROFIT ANALYSIS

LEARNING OBJECTIVES

- Examine the terms used in break-even analysis and their relation to each other.
- Indicate the assumptions and limitations used in break-even analysis.
- Calculate the break-even point in terms of number of units produced and total revenue.
- Use cost and revenue functions in cost-volume-profit (CVP) analysis.
- Use a preprogrammed financial calculator in CVP analysis.
- Use the contribution margin (CM) per unit approach in CVP analysis.
- Use the contribution margin (CM) percent approach in CVP analysis.
- Use break-even charts in CVP analysis.

CHAPTER OUTLINE

7.1 Break-Even Analysis

7.2 Cost-Volume-Profit (CVP) Analysis

7.3 Contribution Margin Per Unit Approach to CVP Analysis

7.4 Contribution Margin Percent Approach to CVP Analysis

7.5 Graphical Approach to CVP Analysis (Break-Even Chart)

Introduction

In any business, the goal is to make a profit. To achieve this goal, the total revenue from the business should exceed the total costs associated with it. Revenue is earned from the sales of the product manufactured or produced, but there are numerous costs incurred in manufacturing or producing a product before selling it. Therefore, it is important to determine the number of units of the product that need to be produced and sold in order to cover all of the costs related to producing it.

Break-even is when the number of units of the product produced and sold cover all the costs related to producing it.

When the number of units of the product produced and sold cover all the costs related to producing it, the business is said to break even. The point at which the total revenue or total sales is equal to the total costs is known as the **break-even point**. At the break-even point, the profit (net income) or loss is zero; i.e., there is no profit made or loss incurred.

The break-even point is generally expressed in terms of volume (or quantity produced and sold). It may also be expressed in terms of total revenue. Any quantity that is produced and sold over this break-even point will result in a profit, while any quantity that is produced and sold below this break-even point will result in a loss.

Therefore, a good understanding of how revenue and costs change with the quantity produced and sold is important. It is also necessary to understand the relationships among fixed costs, variable costs, selling price, etc. To be competitive in the market, businesses should look into ways of lowering their costs by reducing fixed costs and unit variable costs, while optimizing the quantity of items produced and sold, as well as by analyzing the resulting effects on their revenue. In this chapter, you will learn to answer some of the important questions in making such business decisions using the following techiques: (i) break-even analysis, (ii) cost-volume-profit (CVP) analysis, (iii) contribution margin (CM) per unit approach, (iv) contribution margin (CM) percent approach, and (v) graphical approach (break-even charts).

7.1 | Break-Even Analysis

Break-even analysis is one of the techniques used to determine the sales level (both in quantity and revenue) at which a business neither earns a profit nor incurs a loss.

To understand break-even analysis, and to determine the break-even point, it is necessary to define the following terms and understand how they relate to each other.

Terms Used in Break-Even Analysis

There are several types of costs to consider in a business and these are classified into the two most relevant categories: fixed costs (FC) and total variable costs (TVC).

Fixed Costs (FC)

Fixed costs (FC) are always for a period of time.

Fixed costs (FC) are costs that remain the same regardless of the number of items produced to sell. Fixed costs are calculated for a specific time period (per annum, per month, etc.) and are based on the production of a predetermined quantity of products - known as the maximum quantity or capacity of the facility - for that period.

Examples of fixed costs are administrative salaries, rent or lease of a facility, utility costs, insurance costs, property taxes, equipment rental or depreciation, and marketing and advertising costs.

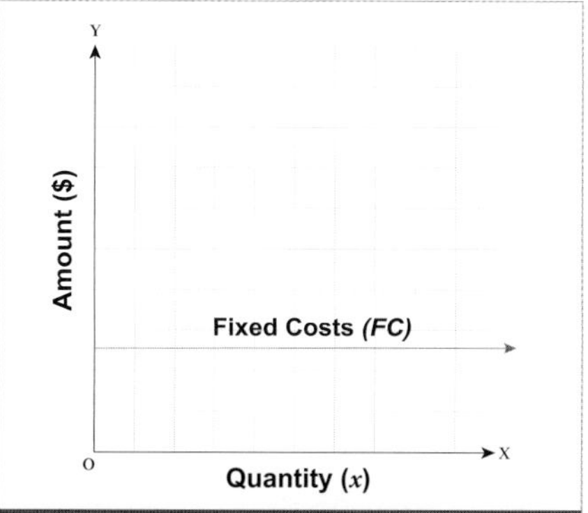

Exhibit 7.1(a): Graph of Fixed Costs vs. Quantity

Total Variable Costs (TVC)

Total variable costs (TVC) are costs that vary directly with the number of units of items produced. Examples of total variable costs are cost of all materials, cost of labour, and revenue-related costs, such as sales commission, royalties, etc., that are necessary to produce the number of items for the specific period. If no quantity is produced, then the total variable costs are zero.

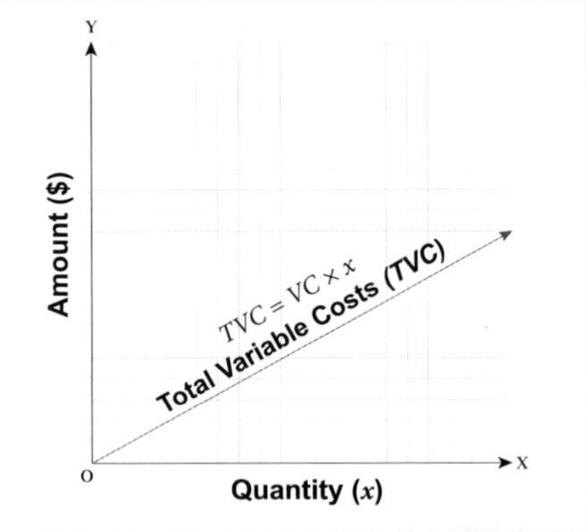

Exhibit 7.1(b): Graph of Total Variable Costs vs. Quantity

Variable Costs per Unit (VC)

The variable costs per unit (VC) is the ratio of the total variable costs to the total number of units produced. These are costs from producing one unit of the item:

Variable costs (VC) and selling price (S) are always expressed per unit.

$$VC = \frac{TVC}{x}$$

where x is the number of units produced and sold.

Rearranging results in the following formula for TVC:

Formula 7.1(a) **Total Variable Costs**

$$TVC = VC \times x$$

Total Costs (TC)

The sum of the fixed costs (FC) and total variable costs (TVC) is the total cost (TC) of the business and is expressed by the following formula:

Formula 7.1(b) **Total Costs**

$$TC = FC + TVC$$

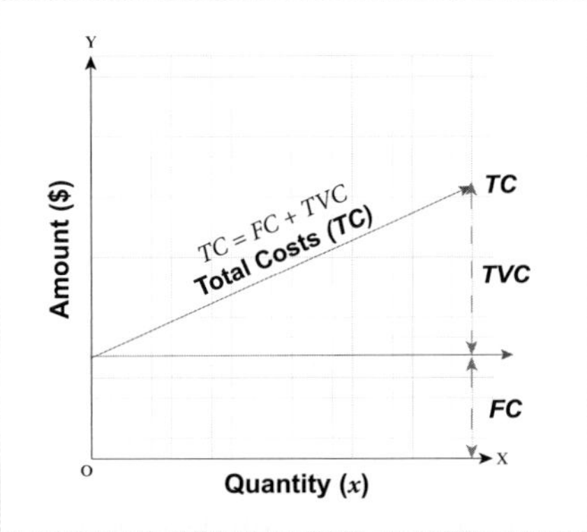

Exhibit 7.1(c): Graph of Total Costs vs. Quantity

Selling Price per Unit (S)

The selling price per unit (S) is the amount a business charges its customers to buy a single unit of item produced. Selling price per unit is critical in calculating the revenue for the business.

Total Revenue (TR)

The total revenue (TR) is the amount of money received or brought into the business from the sales of the items produced and is expressed by the following formula, where x is the number of units produced and sold:

Formula 7.1(c) **Total Revenue**

$$TR = S \times x$$

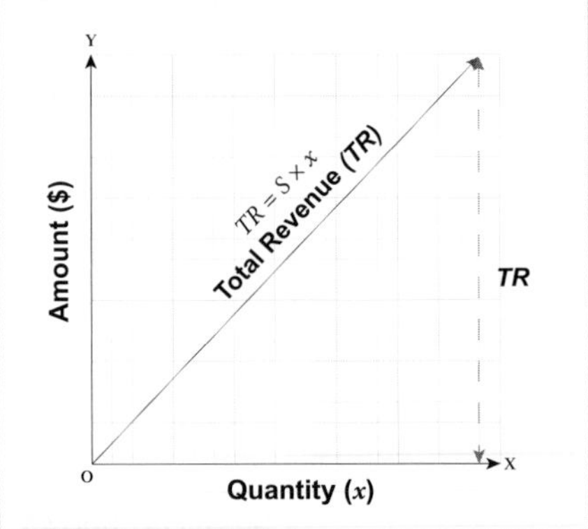

Exhibit 7.1(d): Graph of Total Revenue vs. Quantity

Profit or Net Income (*NI*)

Net income (*NI*) defines the success of the business by determining the difference between the total revenue (*TR*) earned and the total costs (*TC*) incurred in the business.

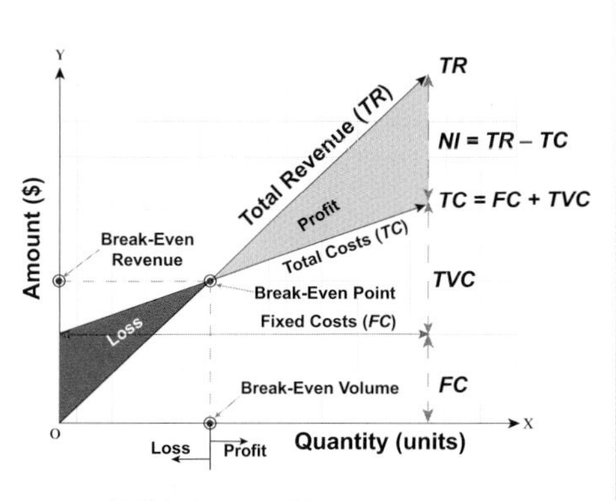

Exhibit 7.1(e): Graph of Total Costs vs. Quantity Produced and Total Revenue vs. Quantity Sold

Formula 7.1(d)

Net Income

$$NI = TR - TC$$

If the total revenue exceeds the total costs, then there is a net profit. If the total revenue is less than the total costs, then there is a net loss. If the total revenue is equal to the total costs, then the business breaks even.

If $TR > TC$, then $NI > 0$	(Profit)
If $TR = TC$, then $NI = 0$	(Break-Even)
If $TR < TC$, then $NI < 0$	(Loss)

Formula 7.1(e)

At the break-even point

$$\text{At the break-even point, } TR = TC$$

Contribution Margin (*CM*) per Unit

Contribution margin (*CM*) per unit is the difference between the selling price per unit (*S*) and the variable costs per unit (*VC*). It is shown in the following formula:

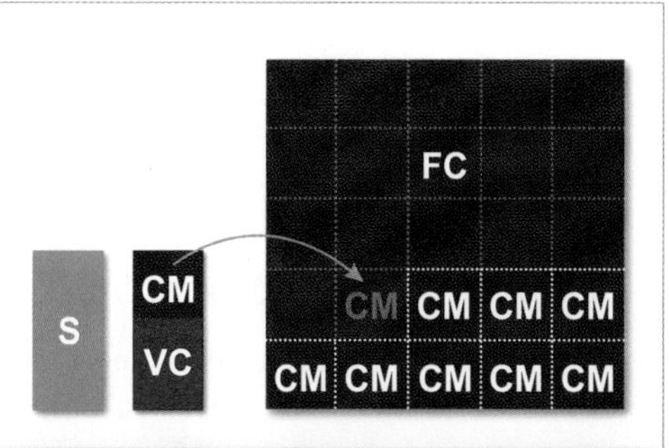

Exhibit 7.1(f): *CM* from the sale of each unit is first used to cover *FC*

Formula 7.1(f)

Contribution Margin per Unit

$$CM = S - VC$$

The contribution amount from the sale of all units during a period is first used to cover the fixed costs (*FC*).

If the contribution amount from the sale of all units exceeds the fixed costs for a period, then there is a profit; similarly, if the contribution amount from the sale of all units is less than the fixed costs, then there is a loss.

Contribution Ratio (*CR*)

This is the ratio of the contribution margin (*CM*) to the selling price (*S*) and is expressed as a percent, as shown in the following formula:

Formula 7.1(g)

Contribution Ratio

$$CR = \frac{CM}{S} \times 100\%$$

Assumptions and Limitations

There are a number of assumptions made and limitations present in break-even analysis and cost-volume-profit analysis in this chapter. These assumptions are made to focus on the main concepts in this topic and to simplify theoretical calculations. However, in practical situations, variations to these assumptions must be taken into account before making business decisions. This is accomplished using more advanced mathematical models.

The following are the assumptions and limitations in this chapter:

(i) Selling price per unit (S) is constant and is not affected by a change in the number of units sold; i.e., Total Revenue ($TR = S \times x$) is a linear function.

(ii) Quantity of items (x) produced is equal to the quantity of items sold.

(iii) Fixed Costs (FC) remain the same throughout the specified period.

(iv) Variable Costs per unit (VC) is constant and is not affected by a change in the number of units sold; i.e., Total Cost ($TC = FC + VC \times x$) is a linear function where $VC \times x = TVC$.

(v) When multiple products are produced in a company, the ratio of various products produced remains constant.

Break-Even Point

Break-even point: *The point at which the total revenue (TR) equals the total costs (TC).*

As explained earlier, the break-even point in a business is when the total revenue from sales is equal to the total costs. The break-even point may be expressed in terms of the number of units produced or in terms of the total revenue.

The break-even point can be lowered by any or all of the following measures:

- Reducing the variable costs per unit (VC) by using more cost-effective scheduling or technology.
- Reducing the fixed costs (FC) by using cost-control measures in marketing, rentals, etc.
- Increasing the selling price (S). However, businesses may be reluctant to increase the price of the product due to competitors' selling price of similar items.
- Rounding up to the next unit when calculating the number of units (x) to earn a little more profit than a loss.

Break-Even Analysis Using a Financial Calculator

If you are routinely solving break-even problems, a pre-programmed calculator, like the Texas Instruments BA II Plus calculator, will help you solve them quickly, without the need for you to remember any formulas.

The exhibit below shows the methods to access your worksheet and the five break-even variables (fixed costs, variable costs per unit, selling price per unit, profit, and quantity) as seen in your calculator. It also refers to the corresponding algebraic variables. You will get a better idea on how to use your calculator by working through Examples 7.1(a) and 7.1(b).

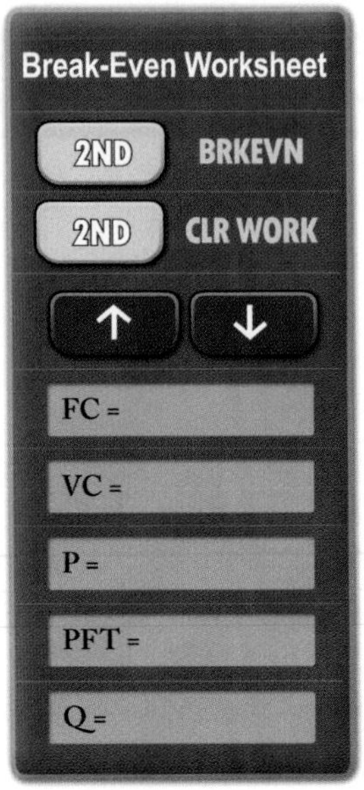

Press the **2ND** key then the **BRKEVN** key (secondary function of the number **6** key) to open the break-even worksheet.

Press the **2ND** key then the **CLR WORK** key (secondary function to the **CE|C** key) to clear all values from memory.

Press the **up** and **down arrow** keys to access the different break-even variables.

Fixed Costs — Represented by 'FC' in algebraic calculations.

Variable Costs per unit — Represented by 'VC' in algebraic calculations.

Selling Price per unit — Represented by 'S' in algebraic calculations.

Profit — Represented by 'NI' in algebraic calculations.

Quantity — Represented by 'x' in algebraic calculations.

Note: *At the break-even point, $PFT = 0$*

Example 7.1(a) **Calculating the Break-Even Point in Terms of the Number of Units Produced**

A company manufactures calculators and sells them at \$50 each. The fixed costs are \$4000 per month and the variable costs per unit are \$32. Calculate the number of units needed to be manufactured and sold per month to break even.

Solution

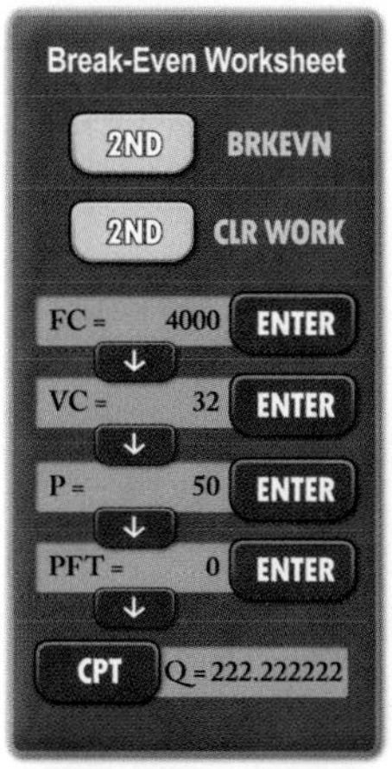

$S = \$50.00, \quad FC = \$4000.00, \quad VC = \$32.00$

Let x be the number of units needed per month to break even.

Using Formula 7.1(c), $TR = S \times x = 50.00x$

Using Formula 7.1(b), $TC = FC + TVC$

Substituting TVC with Formula 7.1(a), $= FC + (VC \times x)$

Substituting values, $= 4000.00 + 32.00x$

At the break-even point, $TR = TC$

Therefore, $50.00x = 4000.00 + 32.00x$

Solving for x, $18.00x = 4000.00$

$x = 222.222222...$

$= 223$ units

The number of units produced must be rounded up to the next whole number.

Therefore, 223 units need to be manufactured and sold per month to break even.

Example 7.1(b) **Calculating the Break-Even Point in Terms of the Total Revenue**

Rubber King must produce 3200 tires per month to break even. The fixed costs per month are \$12,850 for administrative salaries, \$18,600 for rent and utilities, \$2400 for insurance costs, and \$4550 for equipment rental. The variable costs are \$10 per tire for material and \$30 per tire for labour.

(i) What is the total revenue per month required to break even?

(ii) What is the selling price per tire at the break-even point?

Solution

Fixed Costs, FC = Administrative Salaries + Rent and Utilities + Insurance Costs + Equipment Rental

= 12,850.00 + 18,600.00 + 2400.00 + 4550.00 = \$38,400.00 per month

Variable Costs, VC = Material + Labour = 10.00 + 30.00 = \$40.00 per tire

$x = 3200$ units

(i) *Calculating the total revenue per month required to break even*

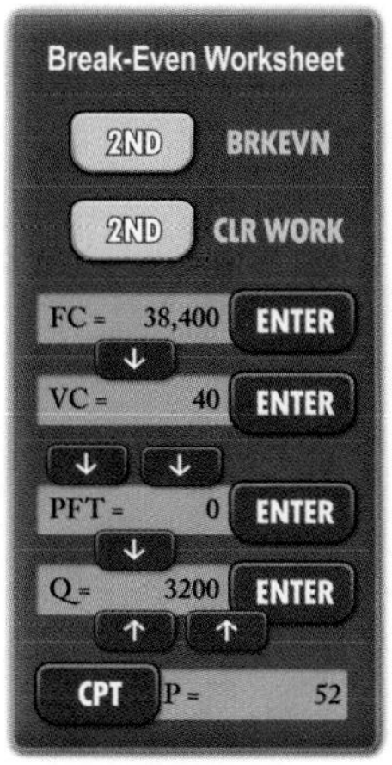

Using Formula 7.1(b), $TC = FC + TVC$

Substituting TVC with Formula 7.1(a), $= FC + (VC \times x)$

Substituting values, $= 38{,}400.00 + (40.00 \times 3200)$

Total Cost at the break-even point, $= \$166{,}400.00$

At the break-even point, $TR = TC$

Therefore, the total revenue required to break even is \$166,400 per month.

(ii) *Calculating the selling price per tire at the break even point*

Let 'S' be the selling price per unit.

Using Formula 7.1(c), $TR = S \times x$

Substituting values, $166{,}400.00 = S(3200)$

$S = \$52.00$

Therefore, the selling price per tire at the break-even point is \$52.

7.1 | Exercises

Answers to the odd-numbered problems are available at the end of the textbook.

Calculate the missing values and express the answers rounded to two decimal places:

1.

	Fixed Costs (FC) per month	Variable Costs (VC) per unit	Selling Price (S) per unit	Break-Even Volume (x) per month	Total Variable Cost at Break-Even (TVC) per month	Total Revenue (TR) per month at Break-Even
a.	$1000	$3	$13	?	?	?
b.	$8000	$70	?	200	?	?
c.	$5890	?	$156	62	?	?
d.	?	$45	$91	50	?	?

2.

	Fixed Costs (FC) per month	Variable Costs (VC) per unit	Selling Price (S) per unit	Break-Even Volume (x) per month	Total Variable Cost at Break-Even (TVC) per month	Total Revenue (TR) per month at Break-Even
a.	$8400	$25	$36	?	?	?
b.	$125,000	$450	?	1000	?	?
c.	$720	?	$74	20	?	?
d.	?	$30	$50	400	?	?

3. A company sells items for $75 each. The variable costs are $58 per item and the fixed costs are $4250 per month. How many items does the company have to sell per month to break even?

4. ClockWork sells clocks for $150. The fixed costs are $7800 per month and variable costs are $111 per clock. How many clocks does it have to sell per month to break even?

5. The selling price per unit of a product is $30, the fixed costs per month are $12,560, and the total variable costs per month are $11,440 at the break-even point. Calculate the number of units required to break even.

6. Harris owns a DVD manufacturing factory that produces DVDs and sells them for $0.30 each. The fixed costs are $8640 per month and the total variable costs at the break-even point are $1800 per month. Calculate the number of DVDs he needs to produce and sell per month to break even.

7. A small manufacturing company that produces and sells snow boots has variable costs of $65 per pair of boots. The fixed costs are $2100 per month and it has to sell 84 pairs of boots to break even.
   a. What is the total revenue at the break-even point?
   b. What is the selling price per pair of boots?

8. A manufacturing company has to produce and sell 225 items every month to break even. The company's fixed costs are $2227.50 per month and variable costs are $10 per item.
   a. What is the total revenue at the break-even point?
   b. What is the selling price per item?

9. Digital Displays Inc. makes computer monitors and sells them for $317 each. To break even, it needs to sell 500 monitors per month. If the fixed costs are $8500 per month, calculate the variable costs per monitor.

10. A company that manufactures electronic items sells them for $155 each. It needs to sell 700 items per month to break even. If the fixed costs are $24,500 per month, what are the variable costs per item?

11. In order to break even, a manufacturer is required to sell 250 chairs every week. The total revenue per week at the break-even point is $27,000 and the fixed costs are $10,220 per week. Calculate the variable costs per chair.

12. Alora and Jacey run a company that manufactures and sells injection moulding machines. It needs to sell 520 machines per month to break even and the total revenue at the break-even point is $45,000. Calculate the variable costs per machine if the fixed costs are $26,000 per month.

13. A company manufactures skis and sells them for $400 per pair. The variable costs to manufacture each pair are $290 and the break-even volume is 740 pairs per month.
   a. What is the total revenue at the break-even point?
   b. What are the fixed costs per month?

14. Chu-Hua Inc. manufactures automobile components and sells them for $15.40 each. The variable costs to manufacture each component are $12 and the company needs to sell 625 components per month to break even.
    a. What is the total revenue at the break-even point?
    b. What are the fixed costs per month?

• 15. A manufacturing company pays $16,700 per month for rent and utilities, $41,850 for administrative salaries, $4800 for insurance costs, and $62,789 for equipment rental. The variable costs are $45 per unit for material and $62 per unit for labour. It needs to manufacture and sell 3100 units to break even.
    a. What is the selling price per unit?
    b. What is the total revenue per month to break even?

• 16. A factory that manufactures and sells computer hard-drives pays $20,000 per month for rent and utilities, $120,850 per month for management salaries, and $37,500 per month for equipment rental and lease. The variable costs are $55 per unit for material and $120 per unit for labour. The factory needs to sell 2445 units to break even.
    a. What is the selling price per hard-drive?
    b. What is the total revenue per month to break even?

7.2 | Cost-Volume-Profit (CVP) Analysis

The Cost-Volume-Profit (*CVP*) analysis examines the relationship among Fixed Costs (*FC*), Variable Costs per Unit (*VC*), Selling Price per Unit (*S*), Total Costs (*TC*), Total Revenue (*TR*), Net Income (*NI*), Sales Volume (x), etc.

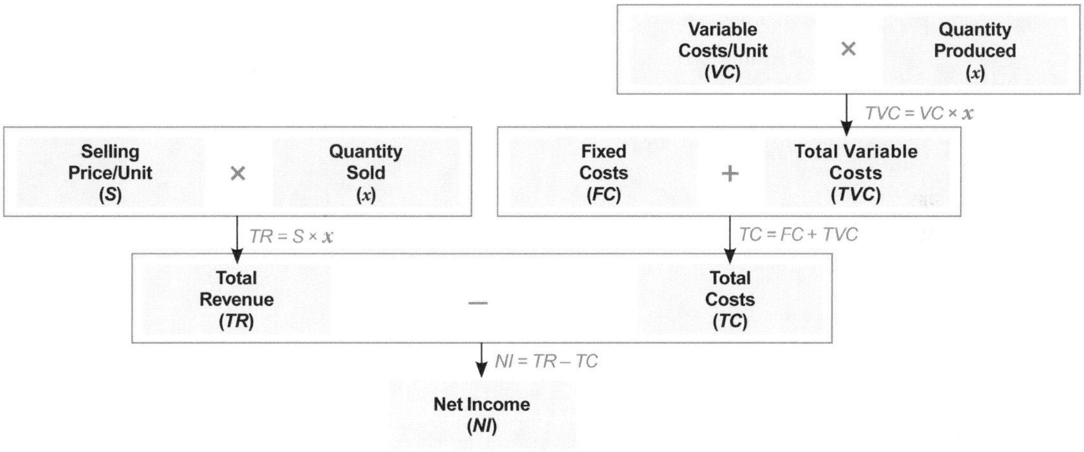

Cost-Volume-Profit (*CVP*) analysis can be used to determine the volume and revenue required to break even, to achieve target profit, and to analyse the effects of change in Fixed Costs, Variable Costs, Selling Price, etc.

Cost-Volume-Profit (*CVP*) analysis commences with the following profit equation:

Profit or Net Income (NI) = Total Revenue (TR) – Total Costs (TC)

$NI = TR - TC$ Rearranging,

$TR = TC + NI$ Substituting $TR = S \times x$ from Formula 7.1(c) and $TC = FC + TVC$ from Formula 7.1(b),

$S \times x = FC + TVC + NI$ Substituting $TVC = VC \times x$ from Formula 7.1(a),

Formula 7.2(a) **Cost-Volume-Profit Analysis**

$$S \times x = FC + (VC \times x) + NI$$

When *TR* > *TC*, *NI* is positive (i.e., profit), as illustrated in Exhibit 7.2(a).

Using Formula 7.2(a) to solve for the number of units, x,

$$S \times x = FC + (VC \times x) + NI$$

Rearranging,

$$(S \times x) - (VC \times x) = FC + NI$$

Factoring,

$$x\,(S - VC) = FC + NI$$

Rearranging and isolating x results in the following formula:

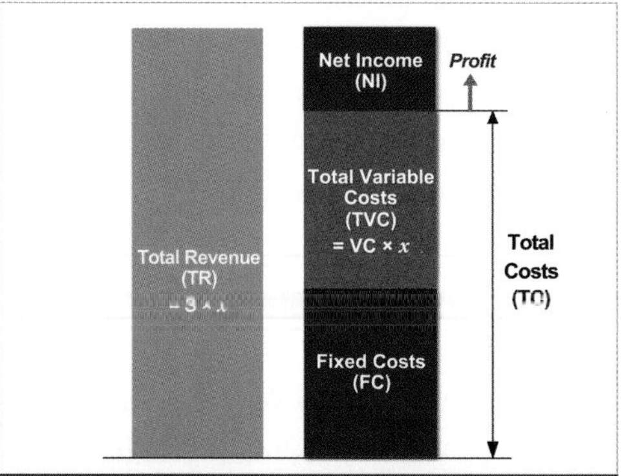

Exhibit 7.2(a): When *TR* > *TC*, *NI* is Positive (Profit)

Formula 7.2(b) **Number of Units**

$$x = \frac{FC + NI}{(S - VC)}$$

When *TR* = *TC*, *NI* = 0 (i.e., break-even), as illustrated in Exhibit 7.2(b).

Therefore, from Formula 7.2(b), the number of units produced and sold is,

$$x = \frac{FC}{(S - VC)}$$

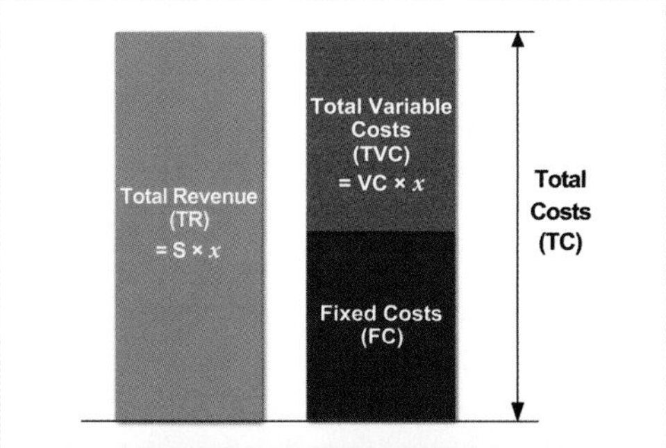

Exhibit 7.2(b): When *TR* = *TC*, *NI* is Zero (Break-Even)

When *TR* < *TC*, *NI* is negative (i.e., loss), as illustrated in Exhibit 7.2(c).
Therefore, when calculating the number of units produced and sold using Formula 7.2(b), *NI* is entered as a negative number as it is a loss.

$$x = \frac{FC - NI}{(S - VC)}$$

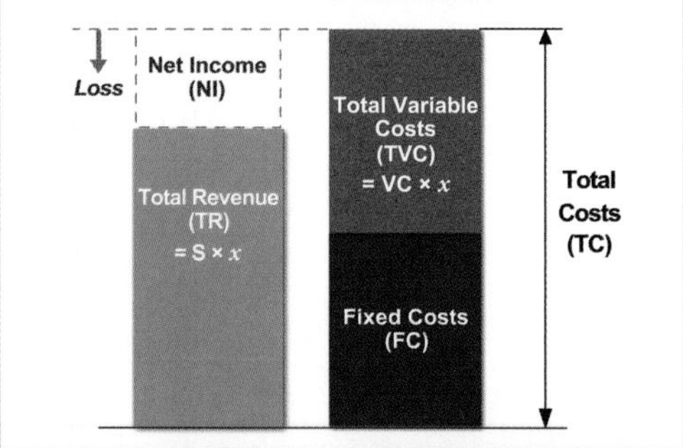

Exhibit 7.2(c): When *TR* < *TC*, *NI* is Negative (Loss)

CVP analysis can be performed using either the formulas from 7.1, or the rearranged formulas from 7.2, as shown in the following examples:

Example 7.2(a)

Using Formulas in Cost-Volume-Profit (CVP) Analysis

Sam has a printing company that prints textbooks, which are then sold to customers. His printing facility can produce a maximum of 3000 textbooks per annum (capacity of the facility). The fixed costs per annum are $100,000, the variable costs per unit are $75, and the selling price per unit is $125.

(i) Calculate the number of books he should produce and sell per year to break even.

(ii) In 2015, he produced and sold 1200 textbooks. Did he make a profit or incur a loss and by what amount?

(iii) In 2016, he produced and sold 2250 textbooks. Did he make a profit or incur a loss and by what amount?

(iv) In 2017, 80% of the facility was utilized to produce textbooks. Calculate the profit made or loss incurred if all textbooks that were produced were sold.

(v) In 2018, he wanted a profit of $40,000. How many books did he have to produce and sell and what percent of the facility would he have utlitized?

(vi) What is the maximum profit per annum that he can expect from the facility?

Solution

Capacity = 3000 textbooks, S = $125.00, FC = $100,000.00, VC = $75.00

(i) *Calculating the number of textbooks to be produced and sold per year to break even*

Assume that he has to produce and sell x textbooks to break even.

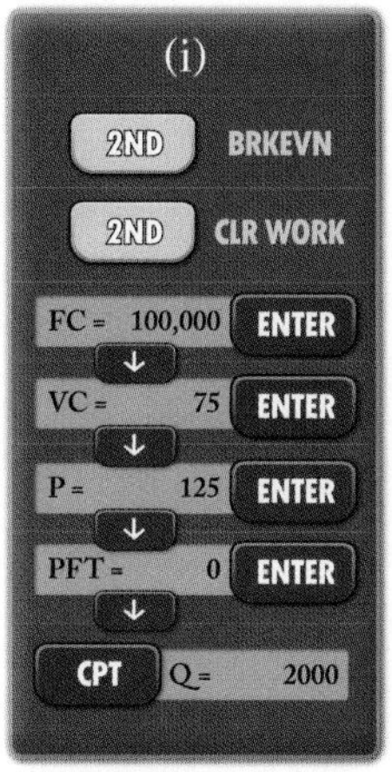

Using Formula 7.1(c), Total revenue, $TR = S \times x = 125.00x$

Using Formula 7.1(b), Total costs, $TC = FC + (VC \times x) = 100{,}000.00 + 75.00x$

At the break-even point, $TR = TC$

So, $125.00x = 100{,}000.00 + 75.00x$

Solving for x, $125.00x - 75.00x = 100{,}000.00$

$$50.00x = 100{,}000.00$$

$$x = \frac{100{,}000.00}{50.00} = 2000 \text{ units per year}$$

Therefore, Sam should produce and sell 2000 textbooks per year to break even.

(ii) *Calculating the amount of profit made or loss incurred when 1200 textbooks were produced and sold in 2015*

It is not necessary to re-enter FC, VC, and P as they have not changed.

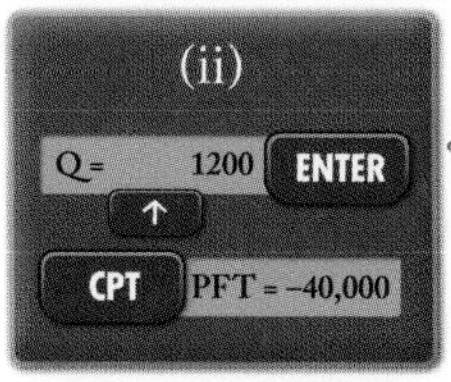

He would have incurred a loss since the 1200 textbooks produced in 2015 is less than the break-even volume of 2000 textbooks per year.

Using Formula 7.1(c), $TR = S \times x = 125.00 \times 1200 = \$150{,}000.00$

Using Formula 7.1(b), $TC = FC + (VC \times x) = 100{,}000.00 + (75.00 \times 1200) = \$190{,}000.00$

Using Formula 7.1(d), $NI = TR - TC = 150{,}000.00 - 190{,}000.00 = -\$40{,}000.00$ (loss)

Therefore, he incurred a loss of $40,000 in 2015.

(iii) *Calculating the amount of profit made or loss incurred when 2250 textbooks were produced and sold in 2016*

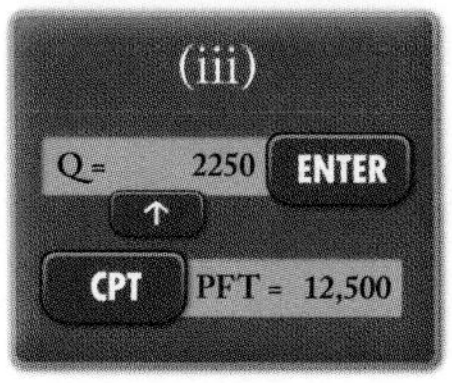

He would have made a profit since the 2250 textbooks produced in 2016 is greater than the break-even volume of 2000 textbooks per year.

Using Formula 7.1(c), $TR = S \times x = 125.00 \times 2250 = \$281{,}250.00$

Using Formula 7.1(b), $TC = FC + (VC \times x) = 100{,}000.00 + (75.00 \times 2250) = \$268{,}750.00$

Using Formula 7.1(d), $NI = TR - TC = 281{,}250.00 - 268{,}750.00 = \$12{,}500.00$ profit

Therefore, he made a profit of $12,500 in 2016.

Solution *continued*

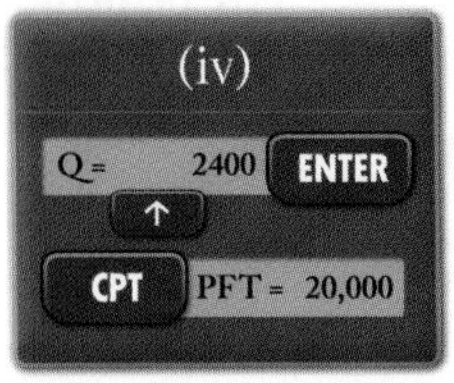

(iv) *Calculating the amount of profit made or loss incurred when 80% of the facility was utilized to produce and sell books in 2017*

$$\text{Capacity} = 3000 \text{ textbooks}$$

$$80\% \text{ of } 3000 = 2400 \text{ textbooks}$$

This is greater than the break-even volume of 2000 textbooks and therefore, he would have made a profit.

Using Formula 7.1(c), $TR = S \times x = 125.00 \times 2400 = \$300{,}000.00$

Using Formula 7.1(b), $TC = FC + (VC \times x) = 100{,}000.00 + (75.00 \times 2400) = \$280{,}000.00$

Using Formula 7.1(d), $NI = TR - TC = 300{,}000.00 - 280{,}000.00 = \$20{,}000.00$ profit

Therefore, he made a profit of \$20,000 in 2017.

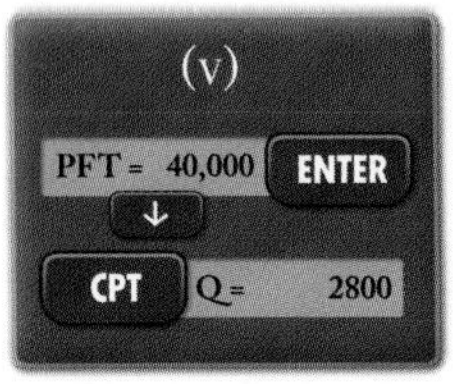

(v) *Calculating the number of books to be produced and sold and the percent of the facility utilized if a profit of \$40,000 was required in 2018*

Using Formula 7.1(d), $NI = TR - TC$

$$NI = S \times x - (FC + VC \times x)$$

Substituting values, $40{,}000.00 = 125.00x - (100{,}000.00 + 75.00x)$

Solving for x, $40{,}000.00 = 125.00x - 100{,}000.00 - 75.00x$

$$140{,}000.00 = 50.00x$$

Therefore, $x = \dfrac{140{,}000.00}{50.00} = 2800$ units in 2018

To make a profit of \$40,000, Sam would have to produce and sell 2800 textbooks in 2018, out of a maximum of 3000 textbooks.

$$\text{Percent of the facility utilized} = \frac{\text{Quantity produced}}{\text{Capacity of the facility}} \times 100\%$$

$$= \frac{2800}{3000} \times 100\% = 0.933333... \times 100\% = 93.33\%$$

Therefore, he would have to produce and sell 2800 textbooks in 2018 and he would have utilized 93.33% of his facility.

(vi) *Calculating the maximum amount of profit expected from the facility*

He should utilize 100% of the facility to maximize profit. Therefore, he should produce and sell 3000 textbooks (capacity of the facility).

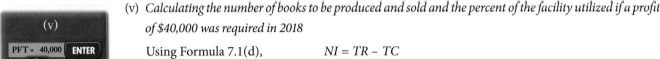

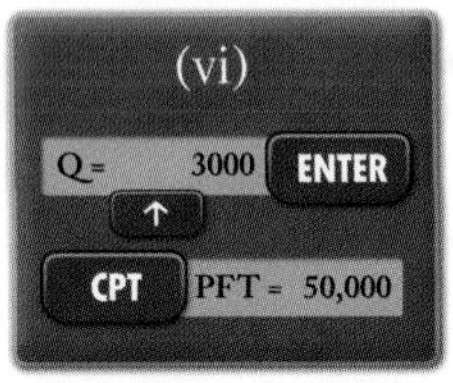

Using Formula 7.1(c), $TR = S \times x = 125.00 \times 3000 = \$375{,}000.00$

Using Formula 7.1(b), $TC = FC + (VC \times x) = 100{,}000.00 + (75.00 \times 3000) = \$325{,}000.00$

Using Formula 7.1(d), $NI = TR - TC = 375{,}000.00 - 325{,}000.00 = \$50{,}000.00$ profit

Therefore, he can expect a maximum profit of \$50,000 per annum from his facility.

Example 7.2(b) **CVP Analysis Where there are Several Fixed Costs and Variable Costs**

A furniture manufacturer who sells chairs for \$210 each has the following monthly fixed costs: \$2500 in rent, \$350 in utilities, and \$150 in insurance. The variable costs to produce each chair are \$60 for the material and 3 hours of labour at \$30 per hour. The manufacturer has a capacity to produce 125 chairs in a month.

(i) Calculate the break-even volume, break-even revenue, and break-even as a percent of capacity per month.

(ii) What was the cost of labour at the break-even point?

(iii) If the profit last month was \$1800, how many chairs were produced and sold?

Solution

Capacity = 125 chairs, $S = \$210.00$

$$FC = \text{Rent} + \text{Utilities} + \text{Insurance}$$
$$= 2500.00 + 350.00 + 150.00 = \$3000.00 \text{ per month}$$
$$VC = \text{Material cost} + \text{Labour costs}$$
$$= 60.00 + (30.00 \times 3) = \$150.00 \text{ per chair}$$

(i) *Calculating the break-even volume, break-even revenue, and break-even as a percent of capacity per month*

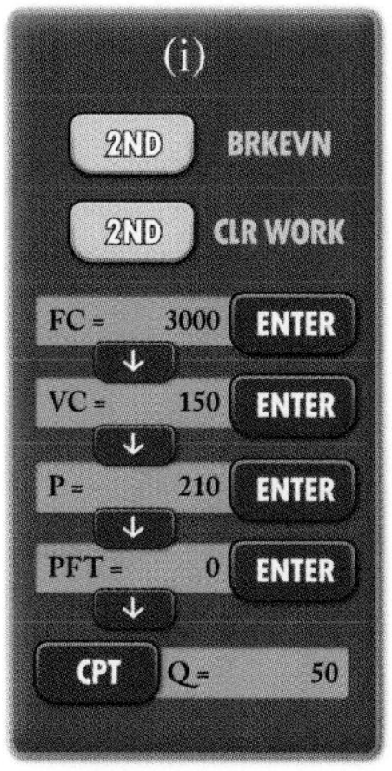

Assume that it needs to produce and sell 'x' chairs per month to break even.
At the break-even point, $NI = 0$.

Using Formula 7.2(a), $S \times x = FC + (VC \times x) + NI$

Substituting values, $210.00x = 3000.00 + 150.00x + 0$

Solving for x, $60.00x = 3000.00$

$x = 50$ units per month

Or

Using Formula 7.2(b),

$$x = \frac{FC + NI}{(S - VC)}$$
$$= \frac{3000.00 + 0}{(210.00 - 150.00)}$$
$$= 50 \text{ units per month}$$

Therefore, the break-even volume is 50 chairs per month.

$$TR = S \times x = 210.00 \times 50 = \$10{,}500.00$$

Therefore, the break-even revenue is \$10,500 per month.

$$\text{Break-even as a percent of capacity} = \frac{\text{Break-even volume}}{\text{Capacity}} = \frac{50}{125} = 0.40 = 40\%$$

Therefore, the break-even as a percent of capacity is 40%.

(ii) *Calculating the cost of labour to break even*

From (i), Break-even volume per month = 50 chairs

Given, Time (labour) to produce 1 chair = 3 hours

Time (labour) to produce 50 chairs = 3 × 50 = 150 hours

Given, Cost per hour of labour = \$30.00

Cost for 150 hours of labour = 30.00 × 150 = \$4500.00

Therefore, the cost of labour to break even is \$4500.

(iii) *Calculating the number of chairs produced and sold if the profit last month was \$1800*

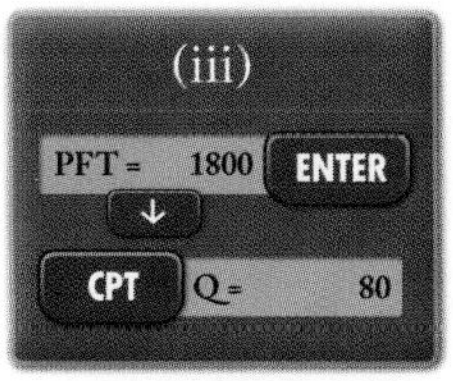

Using Formula 7.2(a), $S \times x = FC + (VC \times x) + NI$

Substituting values, $210.00x = 3000.00 + 150.00x + 1800.00$

Solving for x, $60.00x = 4800.00$

$x = 80$ units per month

Or

Using Formula 7.2(b),

$$x = \frac{FC + NI}{(S - VC)}$$
$$= \frac{3000.00 + 1800.00}{(210.00 - 150.00)}$$
$$= 80 \text{ units per month}$$

Therefore, if the profit last month was \$1800, 80 chairs were produced and sold.

Example 7.2(c)

CVP Analysis When the Selling Price and/or Fixed Costs Change

Pierre runs a small garment manufacturing company. He has fixed costs of \$2500 per month and variable costs of \$25 per unit. He sells each garment for \$35 per unit and has a capacity of producing 450 garments per month.

(i) Calculate the break-even volume, break-even revenue, and break-even as a percent of capacity per month.

(ii) If the selling price increases by 10%, calculate the new break-even volume per month.

(iii) If the fixed costs decrease by \$250 per month with no changes to the variable costs and selling price, calculate the new break-even volume per month.

(iv) If the fixed costs increase by 5% and he decreases his selling price by 10%, calculate the new break-even volume per month if there were no changes to the variable costs.

Solution

Capacity = 450 garments, S = \$35.00, FC = \$2500.00, VC = \$25.00

(i) *Calculating the break-even volume, break-even revenue, and break-even as a percent of capacity per month*

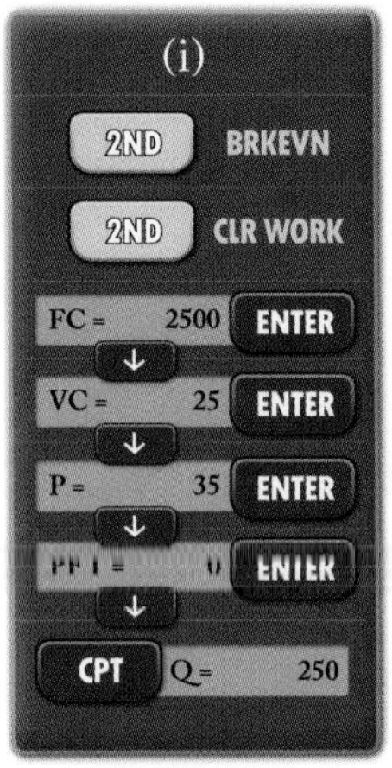

Assume that he sells x garments per month.

Using Formula 7.1(a), $TVC = VC \times x = 25.00x$

Using Formula 7.1(c), $TR = S \times x = 35.00x$

Using Formula 7.1(b), $TC = FC + TVC = 2500.00 + 25.00x$

At the break-even point, $TR = TC$

$$35.00x = 2500.00 + 25.00x$$

Solving for x, $10.00x = 2500.00$

$$x = 250 \text{ units per month}$$

Therefore, the break-even volume is 250 garments per month.

$$TR = S \times x = 35.00 \times 250 = \$8750.00$$

Therefore, the break-even revenue is \$8750 per month.

$$\text{Break-even as a percent of capacity} = \frac{\text{Break-even volume}}{\text{Capacity}} = \frac{250}{450} = 0.555555... = 55.56\%$$

Therefore, the break-even as a percent of capacity is 55.56%.

(ii) *Calculating the new break-even volume per month if the selling price increases by 10%*

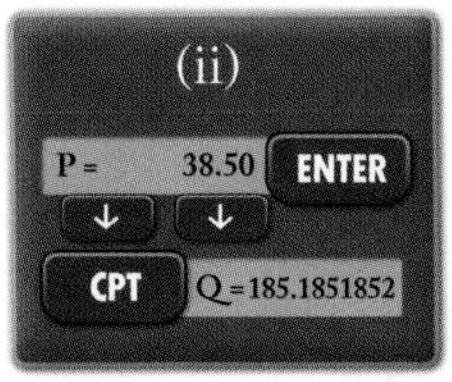

New selling price, $S = 35.00 \times 1.10 = \$38.50$

Using Formula 7.1(c), $TR = S \times x = 38.50x$

From (i), $TC = FC + TVC = 2500.00 + 25.00x$

At the break-even point, $TR = TC$

$$38.50x = 2500.00 + 25.00x$$

Solving for x, $13.50x = 2500.00$

$$x = 185.185185... = 186 \text{ units per month}$$

The number of units produced must be rounded up to the next whole number.

Therefore, the new break-even volume is 186 garments per month.

(iii) *Calculating the new break-even volume per month if the fixed costs are reduced by \$250 per month with no changes to the variable costs and selling price*

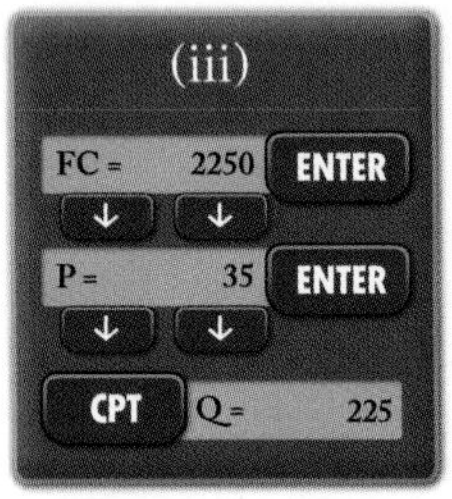

New fixed costs, $FC = 2500.00 - 250.00 = \$2250.00$

From (i), $TVC = VC \times x = 25.00x$

$TR = S \times x = 35.00x$

Using Formula 7.1(b), $TC = FC + TVC = 2250.00 + 25.00x$

At the break-even point, $TR = TC$

$$35.00x = 2250.00 + 25.00x$$

Solving for x, $10.00x = 2250.00$

$$x = 225 \text{ units per month}$$

Therefore, the new break-even volume is 225 garments per month.

(iv) *Calculating the new break-even volume per month if the fixed costs increase by 5%, selling price decreases by 10%, and there are no changes to the variable costs*

New fixed costs, $FC = 2500.00 \times 1.05 = \$2625.00$

New selling price, $S = 35.00 \times (1 - 0.10) = \$31.50$

From (i), $TVC = VC \times x = 25.00x$

Solution
continued

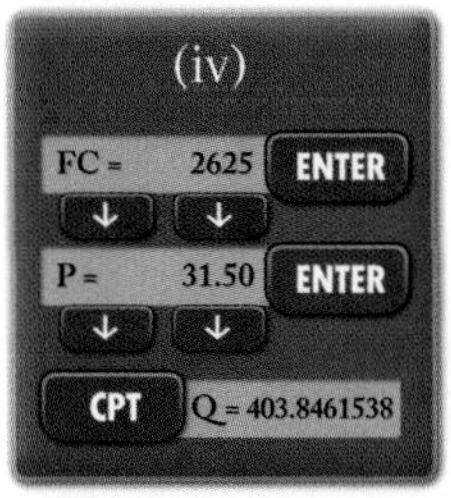

Using Formula 7.1(c), $TR = S \times x = 31.50x$

Using Formula 7.1(b), $TC = FC + TVC = 2625.00 + 25.00x$

At the break-even point, $TR = TC$

$$31.50x = 2625.00 + 25.00x$$

Solving for x,

$$6.50x = 2625.00$$

$$x = 403.846153... = 404 \text{ units per month}$$

Therefore, the new break-even volume is 404 garments per month.

7.2 | Exercises

Answers to the odd-numbered problems are available at the end of the textbook.

1. Oyster Ink sells pens for $3 each. The fixed costs are $1900 per month, variable costs are $0.50 per pen, and the production capacity is 1000 pens per month.
   a. Calculate the break-even volume, break-even revenue, and break-even as a percent of capacity per month.
   b. What is the profit or loss made if 880 pens are produced and sold in a month?

2. A machine manufacturer sells each machine for $8000. The fixed costs are $280,455 per annum, variable costs are $1800 per machine, and the production capacity is 60 machines in a year.
   a. Calculate the break-even volume, break-even revenue, and break-even as a percent of capacity per annum.
   b. What is the profit or loss made if 40 machines are produced and sold in a year?

3. Fu's firm has the capacity to produce a maximum of 6000 items per annum. The fixed costs are $385,500 per annum, variable costs are $5 per item, and he sells each item for $80.
   a. Calculate the break-even volume, break-even revenue, and break-even as a percent of capacity per annum.
   b. If he produced and sold 5100 items in a year, what was the profit made or loss incurred?
   c. What is the maximum profit per year that he can expect from his firm?

4. Sandra's company has a machine that can produce a maximum of 50,000 components per annum. She sells each component for $3.50. The fixed costs are $36,000 per annum and variable costs are $0.35 per component.
   a. Calculate the break-even volume, break-even revenue, and break-even as a percent of capacity per annum.
   b. If she produced and sold 13,500 components in a year, what was the profit made or loss incurred?
   c. What is the maximum profit per year that she can expect from her company?

5. The manager of an e-learning company identified a new course that it could create and sell for $90 per student. The costs for adding this new course to its product offering would be $1800 per month to lease additional space, $300 per month for insurance, $5000 per month for support staff, $4000 per month for sales staff, and variable costs of $2 per student. The maximum number of students is 500 per month.
   a. For the company to break even, how many students would have to purchase the course each month?
   b. If the company made a profit of $32,460 last month, how many students purchased the course?

6. Olga was planning to set up a business where she would purchase paintings for $1000 per unit and sell them for $1600 per unit. She wanted to conduct a break-even analysis and identified the following costs for running her business: $4450 per month for store leasing, $50 per month for website hosting fee, $5000 per month for staff salary, $2000 per month for advertising costs, and $25 per unit for labour charges to pack the paintings.
   a. How many paintings would she have to sell per month to break even?
   b. If she wants to make a profit of $23,000 in a month, how many paintings would she have to sell?

7. A manufacturer sells a product for $200 per unit. The variable costs are $120 per unit and the fixed costs are $50,000 per month.
   a. How many units would the manufacturer have to sell per month to break even?
   b. If the fixed costs are increased by 10% and the variable costs are increased by 15%, what should be the new selling price to have the same break-even volume per month?

8. A manufacturer sells a product for $115 per unit. The variable costs are $75 per unit and the firm's fixed costs are $39,000 per month.
    a. How many units would the manufacturer have to sell per month to break even?
    b. If the fixed costs are increased by 15% and the variable costs are increased by 10%, what should be the new selling price to have the same break-even volume per month?

9. Last year, a manufacturer selling a product at $97 per unit had a net income of $78,000. The unit variable costs to produce the item were $45 per unit and the annual fixed costs were $260,000. This year, the fixed costs decreased by 5% and the variable costs decreased by 10%. If the same number of units as last year is produced and sold, what should have been the new selling price to have resulted in the same profit as last year?

10. Last year, a manufacturer selling a product at $145 per unit had a net income of $82,500. The unit variable costs to produce the item are $90 per unit and their annual fixed costs are $165,000. This year, the fixed costs decreased by 10% and the variable costs decreased by 5%. If the same number of units as last year is produced and sold, what should have been the new selling price to have resulted in the same profit as last year?

11. The annual fixed costs of operating a company that manufactures doors are $95,000. The variable costs are $170 per unit and the selling price of each door is $360. The company's net income for last year was $47,500. This year, the fixed costs decreased by 20% and the variable costs increased to $225. If the selling price remained the same, how many doors does the company need to sell this year to earn the same profit as last year?

12. The annual fixed costs of operating a company that manufactures office tables are $36,000. The variable costs are $95 per unit and the selling price of each table is $360. The company's net income for last year was $22,500. This year, the fixed costs decreased by 10% and the variable costs increased to $105. If the selling price remained the same, how many office tables does the company need to sell this year to earn the same profit as last year?

• 13. Sylvester, the CEO of a manufacturing company, decided to expand the product offering of his business to include the manufacture of a specialized automotive unit. To include this product, his business would incur fixed costs of $120,000 per year and variable costs of $750 per unit. He plans to sell each unit for $1250.
    a. Calculate the number of units he would have to manufacture to break even.
    b. While manufacturing the unit, he realized that he required an additional fixed cost of $3000 per year, and also realized that to be more competitive in the market he had to reduce the selling price by 20%. Calculate the new break-even quantity.

• 14. Samantha and Baxter start a business that manufactures cutting tools. They sell the tools for $80 each. Their monthly fixed costs are $3800 for the building lease and utilities and $2800 for salaries. The cost of supplies for each tool is $12.
    a. To break even, how many tools do they have to sell every month?
    b. If the cost of supplies for each tool is reduced to $10 and they hire one more person for $2000 per month, calculate the minimum number of tools that they would have to sell to ensure that they do not incur a loss.

• 15. Gandolf Financial Training pays $4000 per month for rent and utilities and $600 per month for auto insurance. The company pays its training consultants $100 per hour. The training sessions are conducted by one training consultant and typically last for 4 hours. The company charges its clients $1000 for a session.
    a. How many sessions should the company sell per month to break even?
    b. If the company wants to make a profit of $22,400 in a month, how many sessions should be sold?
    c. How many trainers will the company need to employ per month if it wants to make a profit of $22,400 per month? Assume that a training consultant works for 30 hours per month.

• 16. Innovative Detailing Services pays $8500 per month for rent and utilities and $850 per month for workers' insurance. The company pays its engineers $50 per hour. The client consulting sessions are conducted by one engineer and typically lasts for 3 hours. The company charges its clients $500 for a session.
    a. How many sessions should the company sell per month to break even?
    b. If the company wants to make a profit of $102,650 in a month, how many sessions should be sold?
    c. How many engineers will the company need to employ per month if it wants to make a profit of $102,650 per month? Assume that an engineer works for 160 hours per month.

7.3 | Contribution Margin Per Unit Approach to CVP Analysis

As defined in Section 7.1, the contribution margin (CM) per unit is the amount remaining from the sales per unit after deducting the variable costs per unit.

$$CM = S - VC \qquad \text{From Formula 7.1(f)}$$

We know that the number of units produced (x) is

$$x = \frac{FC + NI}{(S - VC)} \qquad \text{From Formula 7.2(b)}$$

At the break-even point, $NI = 0$

Therefore, $$x_{BE} = \frac{FC}{(S - VC)}$$

Substituting $CM = (S - VC)$ in the above formula, we obtain,

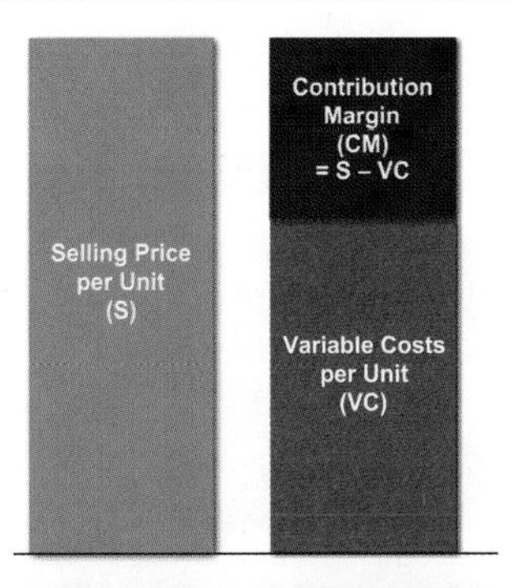

Exhibit 7.3: $CM = S - VC$

Formula 7.3

Number of Units at the Break-Even Point

$$x_{BE} = \frac{FC}{CM}$$

Every unit produced above the break-even volume results in a profit equal to the amount of contribution margin per unit. Similarly, every unit produced below the break-even volume results in a loss equal to the amount of contribution margin per unit.

The contribution margin from each unit produced and sold is used to cover fixed costs (FC) until the break-even point is reached.

Once the break-even volume is reached, every unit produced above the break-even volume will result in a profit equal to the contribution margin amount.

If the contribution margin from the number of units produced and sold is not sufficient to cover the fixed costs, then a loss occurs; i.e., every unit produced below the break-even volume will result in a loss equal to the contribution margin amount.

For example, if $FC = \$100{,}000$, $S = \$125$ per unit, and $VC = \$75$ per unit,

$$CM = S - VC$$
$$= 125 - 75$$
$$= \$50.00 \text{ per unit}$$

$$\text{Break-even volume, } x_{BE} = \frac{FC}{CM}$$
$$= \frac{100{,}000}{50}$$
$$= 2000 \text{ units}$$

Therefore, every unit produced above the break-even volume of 2000 units results in a profit of \$50.00 and every unit produced below the break-even volume of 2000 units results in a loss of \$50.00.

Example 7.3(a)

Using the Contribution Margin (CM) Per Unit Approach in Cost-Volume-Profit (CVP) Analysis to Solve Example 7.2(a)

Sam has a printing company that prints textbooks, which are then sold to customers. His printing facility can produce a maximum of 3000 textbooks per annum (capacity of the facility). The fixed costs per annum are \$100,000, the variable costs per unit are \$75, and the selling price per unit is \$125.

(i) Calculate the number of books he should produce and sell per year to break even.

(ii) In 2015, he produced and sold 1200 textbooks. Did he make a profit or incur a loss and by what amount?

(iii) In 2016, he produced and sold 2250 textbooks. Did he make a profit or incur a loss and by what amount?

(iv) In 2017, 80% of the facility was utilized to produce and sell textbooks. Calculate the profit made or loss incurred.

(v) In 2018, he wanted a profit of \$40,000. How many books did he have to produce and sell and what percent of the facility would he have utlizized?

(vi) What is the maximum profit per annum that he can expect from the facility?

Solution

Capacity = 3000 textbooks, S = \$125.00, FC = \$100,000.00, VC = \$75.00

Let us first calculate his contribution margin per textbook.

$CM = S - VC = 125.00 - 75.00 = \$50.00$ per unit

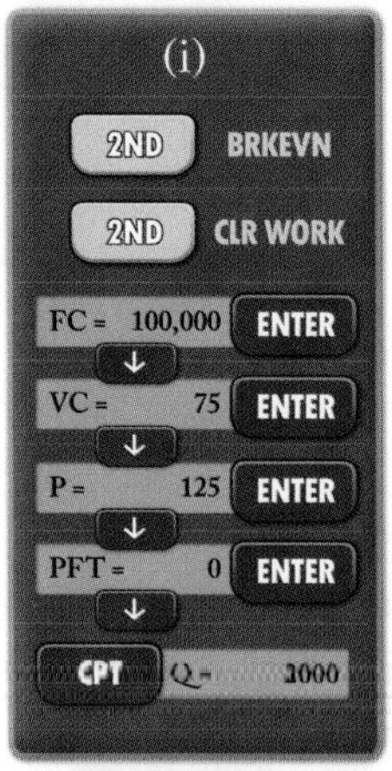

(i) *Calculating the number of textbooks to be produced and sold per year to break even*

Using Formula 7.3,

$$x_{BE} = \frac{FC}{CM}$$

$$= \frac{100{,}000.00}{50.00} = 2000 \text{ units}$$

Therefore, Sam should produce and sell 2000 textbooks per year to break even.

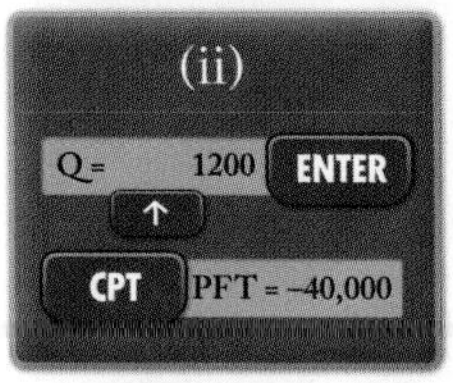

(ii) *Calculating the amount of profit made or loss incurred when 1200 textbooks were produced and sold in 2015*

If Sam sold 1200 textbooks in 2015, then this was 800 textbooks below the break-even volume of 2000 textbooks per year; therefore, he incurred a loss.

Since CM = \$50 per textbook, the amount of loss = 800 × 50.00 = \$40,000.00.

Therefore, he incurred a loss of \$40,000 in 2015.

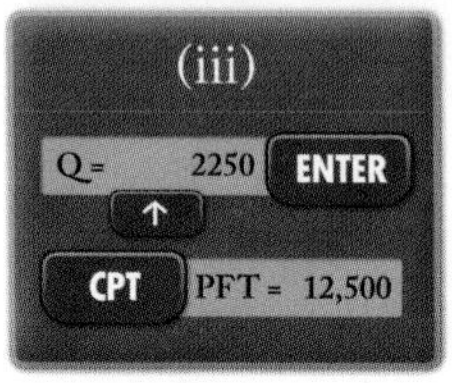

(iii) *Calculating the amount of profit made or loss incurred when 2250 textbooks were produced and sold in 2016*

If Sam sold 2250 textbooks in 2016, then this was 250 textbooks above the break-even volume of 2000 textbooks per year; therefore, he made a profit.

Since CM = \$50 per textbook, the amount of profit is 250 × 50.00 = \$12,500.00.

Therefore, he made a profit of \$12,500 in 2016.

(iv) *Calculating the amount of profit made or loss incurred when 80% of the facility was utilized to produce and sell textbooks in 2017*

Capacity = 3000 textbooks

80% of 3000 = 2400 textbooks

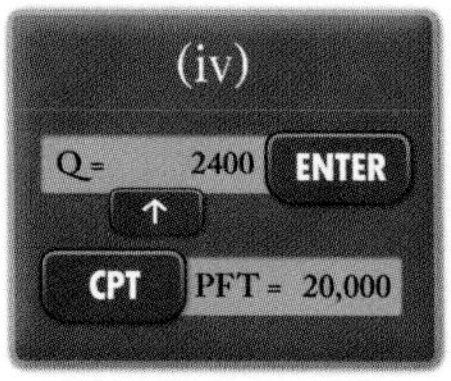

This was 400 textbooks above the break-even volume of 2000 textbooks per year; therefore, he made a profit.

Since CM = \$50 per textbook, the amount of profit is 400 × 50.00 = \$20,000.00.

Therefore, he made a profit of \$20,000 in 2017.

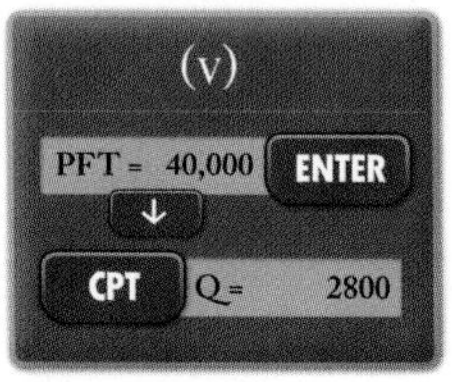

(v) *Calculating the number of textbooks to be produced and sold and the percent of the facility utilized if a profit of \$40,000 was required in 2018*

Since he wanted a profit of \$40,000, he should have produced textbooks above the break-even volume of 2000 textbooks per year.

The number of units above the break-even volume that he had to produce and sell to earn a profit of \$40,000:

$$\textit{Textbooks to Produce} = \frac{40{,}000.00}{50.00} = 800 \text{ units}$$

Therefore, he had to produce and sell (2000 + 800) = 2800 textbooks per year.

$$\textit{Percent of the facility utilized} = \frac{2800}{3000} \times 100\% = 0.933333... \times 100\% = 93.33\%$$

In order to produce and sell 2800 textbooks in 2018, 93.33% of the facility would have been utilized.

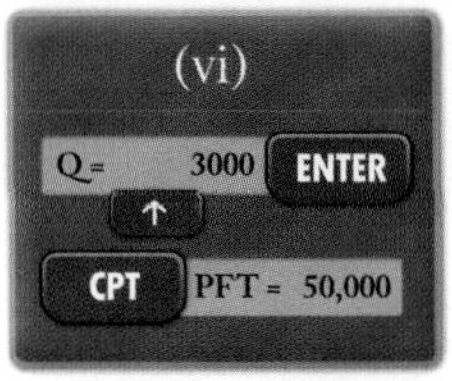

(vi) *Calculating the maximum amount of profit expected from the facility*

This would be 1000 textbooks above the break-even volume of 2000 textbooks per year. Therefore, the profit would be $1000 \times 50.00 = \$50,000$ per year.

Example 7.3(b) **Using the Contribution Margin (CM) Per unit Approach in Cost-Volume-Profit (CVP) Analysis**

An audio equipment manufacturer produced and sold 725 sound systems and made a net income of \$50,000 last year, with total revenues of \$1,015,000. The manufacturer's break-even volume is 600 units.

(i) Calculate the selling price of each sound system.

(ii) Calculate the variable costs for each sound system.

(iii) Calculate the fixed costs per year.

Solution

$NI = \$50,000.00, \quad TR = \$1,015,000.00, \quad x = 725, \quad x_{BE} = 600$

(i) *Calculating the selling price of each sound system*

Using Formula 7.1(c), $TR = S \times x$

$$1,015,000.00 = S \times 725$$

$$S = \frac{1,015,000.00}{725} = \$1400.00$$

Therefore, the selling price of each sound system was \$1400.

(ii) *Calculating the variable costs for each sound system*

The manufacturer produced 725 sound systems last year.

This is 125 units above the break-even volume of 600 units, contributing to a profit of \$50,000.

$$125 \times CM = 50,000.00$$

Therefore, $CM = \frac{50,000.00}{125} = \$400.00$

Using Formula 7.1(f), $CM = S - VC$

$$400.00 = 1400.00 - VC$$

$$VC = \$1000.00 \text{ per unit}$$

Therefore, the variable costs for each sound system were \$1000 per unit.

(iii) *Calculating the fixed costs per year*

Using Formula 7.3, $x_{BE} = \frac{FC}{CM}$

$$600 = \frac{FC}{400.00}$$

Rearranging, $FC = 600 \times 400.00 = \$240,000.00$ per year

Therefore, the fixed costs per year are \$240,000.

7.3 | Exercises

Answers to the odd-numbered problems are available at the end of the textbook.

Calculate the missing values for Problems 1 and 2.

1.

	Fixed Costs (*FC*) per period	Variable Costs (*VC*) per unit	Selling Price (*S*) per unit	Total Variable Costs (*TVC*) per period	Total Revenue (*TR*) per period	Total Costs (*TC*) per period	Net Income (*NI*) per period	Number of units produced and sold (*x*)
a.	$9000	?	$65	?	?	$31,500	$33,500	?
b.	?	$75	$145	?	?	$168,500	?	1200
c.	$1440	?	?	$22,500	$33,750	?	?	750
d.	?	?	$135	$62,500	?	?	$62,200	1500

2.

	Fixed Costs (*FC*) per period	Variable Costs (*VC*) per unit	Selling Price (*S*) per unit	Total Variable Costs (*TVC*) per period	Total Revenue (*TR*) per period	Total Costs (*TC*) per period	Net Income (*NI*) per period	Number of units produced and sold (*x*)
a.	$22,500	?	$910	?	?	$364,500	$418,100	?
b.	?	$280	$420	?	?	$55,480	?	170
c.	$120,800	?	?	$342,000	$570,000	?	?	1900
d.	?	?	$1480	$37,800	?	?	$4,300	30

3. The variable costs to manufacture a digital appliance are $280 per appliance and the selling price is $800 per appliance. The fixed costs are $44,720 per month.
   a. Calculate the contribution margin per appliance.
   b. Calculate the number of appliances that need to be sold per month to break even.

4. Jonathan repairs tubs and jacuzzis for $350 per job. His fixed costs are $1400 per month and variable costs are $30 per job.
   a. Calculate the contribution margin per job.
   b. Calculate the number of repairs he needs to make per month to break even.

5. Bobble Roofing charges a flat rate of $1400 for insulating roofs of townhouses. Monthly administrative costs of the company are $3880, cost of supplies is $130 per job, and wages are $300 per job. Calculate the company's profit or loss in a month if it insulated 15 roofs in a particular month.

6. A solar water heater distributor buys water heaters for $5850 and sells them for $7600 each. If he pays $2000 per month as lease and utilities for his store, $5950 per month for staff salary, and $800 per month for marketing, calculate the amount of profit made or loss incurred in a month if he sold 4 heaters.

7. Ching Lan Inc. makes hats and sells them for $28 each. The fixed costs are $2613 per month and the company needs to sell 300 hats to break even.
   a. What is the contribution margin per hat?
   b. What are the variable costs per hat?
   c. What is the net income per month at 50% above break-even volume?

8. Dmytro runs a small company that makes skates and sells them for $450 each pair. He needs to sell 190 pairs of skates to break even and has fixed costs of $28,500 per annum.
   a. What is the contribution margin per pair of skates?
   b. What are the variable costs per pair of skates?
   c. What is the net income per annum if he sells 100 units above the break-even point?

9. Belle Inc. makes bags and sells them for $36 each. The total revenue at the break-even point is $81,000 per month and the contribution margin per bag is $27.
   a. Calculate the break-even volume.
   b. Calculate the fixed costs per month.
   c. Calculate the total revenue if the company sells 2500 bags in a month.

10. Elise and her friend Eloi developed an online car repair training course and sell it for $62.50 per course. The contribution margin per course is $20 and to break even they need to have a total revenue of $175,000 per annum.
    a. Calculate the break-even volume.
    b. Calculate the fixed costs per annum.
    c. Calculate the total revenue if they sell 3000 courses this year.

11. A company is producing electric heaters. The fixed manufacturing costs are $12,500 per month and the administration costs are $11,500 per month. Materials and labor costs are $72 per unit, marketing costs are $48 per unit, and the selling commission is 10% of the selling price. If the selling price is $200 per unit, how many units must be produced for a profit of $18,000 per month?

12. A company is producing humidifiers. The fixed manufacturing costs are $18,000 per month and the administration costs are $9000 per month. Materials and labor costs are $35 per unit, marketing costs are $4 per unit, and the selling commission is 8% of the selling price. If the selling price is $75 per unit, how many units must be produced for a profit of $13,500 per month?

13. A manufacturer sells a new product for $150 per unit. Fixed manufacturing costs are $12,500 per month, and the administrative costs are $5000 per month. Variable costs are $85 per unit plus a royalty of 10% on the selling price.
    a. If the manufacturer wants a profit of $15,000 per month, how many units must be sold?
    b. If the selling price is reduced by 10%, how many more units must be sold to earn the same profit as before?

14. A manufacturer sells a new product for $280 each. Fixed manufacturing costs are $22,500 per month, and the administrative costs are $12,500 per month. Variable costs are $126 per unit plus a royalty of 5% on the selling price.
    a. If the manufacturer wants a profit of $21,000 per month, how many units must be sold?
    b. If the selling price is reduced by 15%, how many more units must be sold to earn the same profit as before?

• 15. Zenith Lighting Inc. makes chandeliers and sells them for $650 each. The costs for administrative salaries, rent, and utilities are $28,000 per month. The company also recruits a full-time sales person for a base salary of $3402.50 per month to sell the chandeliers. The sales person's commission on the sale of each chandelier is 5% on the selling price. The variable costs (excluding the sales commission) are $220 per chandelier and the company can only produce a maximum of 100 chandeliers every month. Calculate the maximum profit that can be made in a month.

• 16. Rehan, a first semester student at a college, decided to start a trading business buying formal dress shirts for $10 from an overseas country and selling them to his college peers for $35 each. As he is not good at selling, he hired his friend Ruby to sell these shirts and paid her 10% on the selling price as commission on every shirt she sold. If he spent a flat rate of $20 on storage charges every month and could only purchase a maximum of 500 shirts every month from his overseas vendor, calculate the maximum monthly profit that he can make in his business.

7.4 | Contribution Margin Percent Approach to CVP Analysis

In the previous sections, you learned Cost-Volume-Profit (*CVP*) analysis and the Contribution Margin (*CM*) Per Unit approach to *CVP* analysis.

The *CM* per unit approach provides information on the dollar amount from each unit of sales that is available to cover the fixed costs and contribute towards the operating profits (Net Income).

In this section, you will learn about the Contribution Margin (*CM*) Percent approach to *CVP* analysis, which provides information on the percent of each sales dollar that is available to cover fixed costs and contribute to the net income.

Contribution Margin (*CM*) Percent

The Total Contribution Margin (*TCM*) as a percent of the Total Revenue (*TR*) is called the Contribution Margin (*CM*) Percent.

$$\text{Total Contribution Margin} = \text{Total Revenue} - \text{Total Variable Costs}$$

Therefore,
$$\text{CM Percent} = \frac{\text{Total Revenue} - \text{Total Variable Costs}}{\text{Total Revenue}} \times 100\%$$

Formula 7.4(a)

Contribution Margin Percent

$$\text{CM Percent} = \frac{TR - TVC}{TR} \times 100\%$$

For example, if the total sales are \$200,000 and the total variable costs are \$140,000, then,

Using Formula 7.4(a),
$$\text{CM Percent} = \frac{200{,}000 - 140{,}000}{200{,}000} \times 100\% = \frac{60{,}000}{200{,}000} \times 100\% = 30\%$$

The contribution margin percent is most useful when the increase or decrease in sales is measured in sales amount.

The ***CM percent*** measures the effect on net income when the sales revenue increases or decreases; i.e., for each dollar increase in sales, the total contribution will increase by the amount equal to the *CM* percent, and the net income will also increase by the amount equal to the *CM* percent, provided that the fixed costs remain the same. In the above example, if \$20,000 in sales are added (with no change in fixed costs), then the net income will increase by 30% of \$20,000, which is equal to \$6000.

The net income, using the *CM* Percent (or *TCM*), can be calculated as follows:

Cross-multiplying Formula 7.4(a), $TR - TVC = \text{CM Percent} \times TR$

Substituting $TVC = TC - FC$, $TR - (TC - FC) = \text{CM Percent} \times TR$

$TR - TC + FC = \text{CM Percent} \times TR$

Substituting $TR - TC = NI$, $NI + FC = \text{CM Percent} \times TR$

Solving for NI, $NI = \text{CM Percent} \times TR - FC$

$NI = TCM - FC$

Formula 7.4(b)

Net Income

$$NI = (\text{CM Percent} \times TR) - FC \quad \textbf{or} \quad NI = TCM - FC$$

The relationship among Total Revenue (Sales Amount), Total Variable Costs, Total Contribution Margin, Contribution Margin Percent, Fixed Costs, and Net Income is shown in the following diagram in a table form (vertical analysis):

	Percent of Sales	Total Amount
Total Revenue		*TR*
– Total Variable Costs		*TVC*
Total Contribution Margin		*TCM*
– Fixed Costs		*FC*
Net Income		*NI*

Example 7.4(a) **Calculating the Total Revenue Required to Break Even and to Make a Profit, and Calculating the Net Income, Given the Total Revenue**

The variable costs of a company are 80% of sales and their fixed costs are $180,000.

(i) What is the total revenue at break-even?

(ii) What is the total revenue to earn a net income of $50,000?

(iii) What is the net income if the total revenue is $600,000?

Solution

(i) Given, $TVC = 0.80TR$

At BE, $NI = 0$

Therefore, $TCM = FC = \$180{,}000.00$

Also, $TCM = TR - TVC$

$= TR - 0.80TR = 0.20TR$

Therefore, $180{,}000.00 = 0.20TR$

$$TR = \frac{180{,}000.00}{0.20}$$

$TR = \$900{,}000.00$

	% of Sales	Total Amount
TR	100%	$900,000.00
– *TVC*	80%	
TCM	20%	$180,000.00
– *FC*		$180,000.00
NI		0

Therefore, at break-even, the total revenue is $900,000.

(ii) Using Formula 7.4(b), $NI = TCM - FC$

$TCM = FC + NI$

Substituting values, $= 180{,}000.00 + 50{,}000.00$

$= \$230{,}000.00$

Also, from (i), $TCM = 0.20TR$

Therefore, $230{,}000.00 = 0.20TR$

$$TR = \frac{230{,}000.00}{0.20}$$

$TR = \$1{,}150{,}000.00$

	% of Sales	Total Amount
TR	100%	$1,150,000.00
– *TVC*	80%	
TCM	20%	$230,000.00
– *FC*		$180,000.00
NI		$50,000.00

Therefore, to earn a net income of $50,000, the total revenue should be $1,150,000.

(iii) From (i), $TCM = 0.20TR$

$= 0.20 \times 600{,}000.00$

$TCM = \$120{,}000.00$

Using Formula 7.4(b), $NI = TCM - FC$

$= 120{,}000.00 - 180{,}000.00$

$NI = -\$60{,}000.00$ (loss)

	% of Sales	Total Amount
TR	100%	$600,000.00
– *TVC*	80%	
TCM	20%	$120,000.00
– *FC*		$180,000.00
NI		–$60,000.00

Therefore, if the total revenue is $600,000, the company will incur a loss of $60,000.

Example 7.4(b) **Calculating the Change in Net Income when the Selling Price Increases and the Sales Volume Decreases**

A manufacturer of air-conditioning units has fixed costs of $150,000 and sales revenue of $800,000. The variable costs are of 75% of sales.

(i) What is the net income?

(ii) What is the amount of change in the net income if the company increases the selling price by 5%?

(iii) What is the amount of change in the net income, if the company increases the selling price by 5% and as a result the sales volume decreases by 10%?

Solution

(i) Given, $TVC = 0.75TR$

Using, $TCM = TR - TVC$

$= TR - 0.75TR = 0.25TR$

$= 0.25 \times 800{,}000.00$

$TCM = \$200{,}000.00$

Using Formula 7.4(b), $NI = TCM - FC$

$= 200{,}000.00 - 150{,}000.00$

$NI = \$50{,}000.00$

	% of Sales	Total Amount
TR	100%	$800,000.00
– *TVC*	75%	$600,000.00
TCM	25%	$200,000.00
– *FC*		$150,000.00
NI		$50,000.00

Therefore, the net income is $50,000.

(ii) New $TR = 800{,}000.00(1 + 0.05) = \$840{,}000.00$

New $TCM = 840{,}000.00 - 600{,}000.00 = \$240{,}000.00$

New $NI = 240{,}000.00 - 150{,}000.00 = \$90{,}000.00$

Therefore, the new net income is $90,000.

Amount of change = New NI – Original NI

$= 90{,}000.00 - 50{,}000.00 = \$40{,}000.00$

	Original		New
	% of Sales	Total Amount	Total Amount
TR	100%	$800,000.00	$840,000.00
– *TVC*	75%	$600,000.00	$600,000.00
TCM	25%	$200,000.00	$240,000.00
– *FC*		$150,000.00	$150,000.00
NI		$50,000.00	$90,000.00

Therefore, if the company increases the selling price by 5%, the net income will increase by $40,000.

(iii) The new total revenue must account for both the increase in price and decrease in sales.

New $TR = 800{,}000.00(1 + 0.05)(1 - 0.10) = \$756{,}000.00$

As the sales volume decreased by 10%, the total variable costs will also decrease by 10% (TVC decreases with the decrease in the number of units sold).

New $TVC = 600{,}000.00(1 - 0.10) = \$540{,}000.00$

New TCM = New TR – New TVC

$= 756{,}000.00 - 540{,}000.00 = \$216{,}000.00$

New NI = New $TCM - FC$

$= 216{,}000.00 - 150{,}000.00 = \$66{,}000.00$

Therefore, the new net income is $66,000.00.

Solution *continued*

Amount of change = New NI – Original NI

= 66,000.00 – 50,000.00 = $16,000.00

	Original		New
	% of Sales	Total Amount	Total Amount
TR	100%	$800,000.00	$756,000.00
– TVC	75%	$600,000.00	$540,000.00
TCM	25%	$200,000.00	$216,000.00
– FC		$150,000.00	$150,000.00
NI		$50,000.00	$66,000.00

Therefore, if the company increases the selling price by 5% and as a result the sales volume decreases by 10%, the net income will increase by $16,000.

Example 7.4(c) **Calculating the Change in Selling Price when the Variable Costs and Fixed Costs Increase**

The variable costs of a manufacturing company are 60% of the sales and the fixed costs are $60,000. The company makes a profit of $25,000. If its variable costs increase by 15% and fixed costs increase to $70,000, by what percent should the company increase the selling price to earn the same profit of $25,000? Assume that there is no increase in the volume of units sold.

Solution

Using Formula 7.4(b), $NI = TCM - FC$

Substituting values, $25{,}000.00 = TCM - 60{,}000.00$

$TCM = \$85{,}000.00$

Also, $TCM = TR - TVC$

$= TR - 0.60TR = 0.40TR$

Therefore, $0.40TR = 85{,}000.00$

$$= \frac{85{,}000.00}{0.40} = \$212{,}500.00$$

Therefore, the original sales revenue is $212,500.

New TVC = Old $TVC \times (1 + 0.15)$

$= 0.60(212{,}500.00) \times 1.15 = \$146{,}625.00$

Using Formula 7.4(b), New NI = New TCM – New FC

Substituting values, 25,000.00 = New TCM – 70,000.00

New TCM = $95,000.00

Also, New TCM = New TR – New TVC

Therefore, 95,000.00 = New TR – 146,625.00

New TR = $241,625.00

Therefore, the new sales revenue is $241,625.

Solution
continued

	Original		New
	% of Sales	Total Amount	Total Amount
TR	100%	$212,500.00	$241,625.00
– *TVC*	60%	$127,500.00	$146,625.00
TCM	40%	$85,000.00	$95,000.00
– *FC*		$60,000.00	$70,000.00
NI		$25,000.00	$25,000.00

Calculating the percent increase in sales revenue:

Using Formula 3.2, $\%C = \frac{V_f - V_i}{V_i} \times 100\%$

$$= \frac{241{,}625.00 - 212{,}500.00}{212{,}500.00} \times 100\%$$

$$= 0.137058... \times 100\% = 13.71\%$$

Therefore, to earn the same profit, the company should increase its selling price by 13.71%.

7.4 | Exercises

Answers to the odd-numbered problems are available at the end of the textbook.

1. The manufacturer of a product has fixed costs of $150,000 per year. The variable costs are 60% of selling price. What is the sales revenue at break-even?

2. The variable costs of a computer manufacturing company are 80% of selling price. If its fixed costs are $550,000 per annum, calculate their sales revenues to break-even.

3. A bike manufacturing company has fixed costs of $220,000. The variable costs are 75% of sales.
   a. What is the sales revenue at break-even?
   b. What is the sales revenue to earn a net income of $80,000?
   c. What is the net income if the sales revenue is $950,000?

4. Ruby Bags Inc. has fixed costs of $45,000. The variable costs are 60% of sales.
   a. What is the sales revenue for the company to break-even?
   b. What is the sales revenue to make a profit of $20,000?
   c. What is the profit or loss if the sales revenue is $90,000?

5. A company that produces cameras has fixed costs of $75,000 per annum and sales revenue of $650,000. The variable costs are of 70% of sales.
   a. What is the net income?
   b. What is the amount of change in the net income if the company increases the selling price by 10%?
   c. What is the amount of change in the net income, if the company increases the selling price by 10% and as a result the sales volume decreases by 5%?

6. Laser Tech has fixed costs of $250,000 per annum and sales revenue of $1,300,000. The variable costs are of 65% of sales.
   a. What is the profit or loss?
   b. What is the amount of change in the net income if the company decreases the selling price by 5%?
   c. What is the amount of change in the net income, if the company decreases the selling price by 5% and as a result the sales volume increases by 10%?

7. The variable costs of a manufacturing company are 75% of the sales and the fixed costs are $85,000. The company makes a profit of $15,000. If its variable costs increase by 5% and fixed costs increase to $100,000, by what percent should the company increase the selling price to earn the same profit of $15,000? Assume that there is no increase in the volume of units sold.

8. Structures Inc., a steel manufacturing company, has fixed costs of $150,000. Their net income is $25,000 and variable costs are 40% of sales. If its fixed costs increase to $175,000 and variable costs increase by 5%, by what percent should the company change the selling price to earn the same profit of $25,000? Assume that there is no change in the number of units sold.

9. A manufacturing company has fixed costs of $120,000 per annum and the variable costs are 40% of sales. If the variable costs increased to 60% of sales, what additional sales must be made to break-even?

10. Square Technology Solutions has fixed costs of $66,000 per annum and its variable costs are 85% of sales. If the variable costs increased to 90% of sales, what additional sales must be made to break-even?

7.5 | Graphical Approach to CVP Analysis (Break-Even Chart)

A break-even chart is a graphical representation of the following on the same axes:

1. Fixed costs
2. Total costs at various levels of quantity produced
3. Total revenue at various levels of quantity sold

The vertical axis (Y-axis) of the graph represents the total cost or total revenue (in dollars) and the horizontal axis (X-axis) of the graph represents the quantity of items produced or sold (in number of units).

These graphs are useful tools in break-even analysis and make it easy to observe the way total costs and total revenue change with the quantity produced and sold. It also makes it easy to see the point at which neither profit is made nor loss is incurred in the business (i.e., break-even point) and the amount of profit or loss if the quantity produced and sold is known.

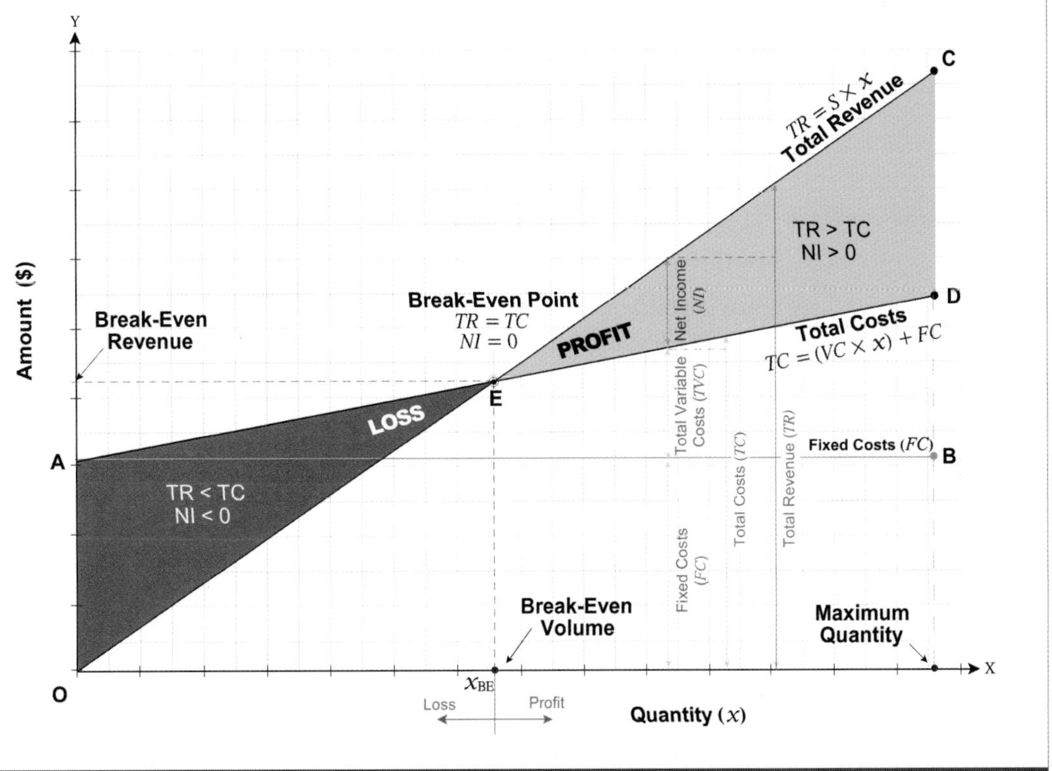

Exhibit 7.5: Graph of Total Costs vs. Quantity Produced and Total Revenue vs. Quantity Sold

The quantity produced and sold above the break-even volume will result in a profit for a business while that below the break-even volume will result in a loss.

As sales increase, net income becomes less negative until it equals zero ($NI = 0$). At this point, it reaches the break-even point. The intersection point of the two graphs represents the break-even point, where the total revenue and the total costs from the business are equal.

Therefore, sales before the break-even point would result in a negative net income ($NI < 0$) indicating a **loss**, while sales after the break-even point will result in a positive net income ($NI > 0$), indicating a **profit**.

Creating and Understanding a Break-Even Chart

Step 1: Drawing and labelling the X-axis and Y-axis

- Draw a horizontal axis (X-axis) to represent the quantity (x) produced and sold. Use a suitable scale with equal incremental markings from 0 to the maximum quantity. Label the X-axis as "Quantity (x)".
- Draw a vertical axis (Y-axis) to represent the Total Revenue (TR) or Total Costs (TC). Use a suitable scale and equal incremental markings from 0 to the maximum total revenue. Label the Y-axis as "Amount ($)".
- Mark the point "O" where the X-axis and Y-axis intersect each other. The point "O" is the origin with coordinates (0, 0).

Step 2: Drawing the Fixed Costs Line

Determine the Fixed Costs (FC) and mark a point "A" to represent this amount on the Y-axis. Through this point, draw a line "AB" parallel to X-axis. This is the "Fixed Costs line".

Step 3: Drawing the Total Revenue Line and Total Costs Line

- The Total Revenue function, $TR = S \times x$, is a linear function represented by line "OC".
- The Total Costs function, $TC = (VC \times x) + FC$, is a linear function represented by line "AD".

Create a table of values by choosing the two end points ($x = 0$ and $x =$ maximum quantity) and their corresponding TR and TC values to draw the two lines. To confirm the linearity of each line, include another value for x between the two points (as a test point) in the table of values.

Step 4: Determining the break-even point, break-even volume, break-even revenue, and the profit and loss areas

- Mark the point "E" where the Total Revenue line (OC) and the Total Cost line (AD) intersect. The point "E" is the break-even point, where there is neither profit nor loss.
- The break-even volume is the x-coordinate of the break-even point E.
- The break-even revenue is the y-coordinate of the break-even point E.
- Any quantity produced and sold greater than the break-even volume will generate a profit. The area indicating a profit is the section ECD, where the Total Revenue line (OC) is above the Total Costs line (AD). The amount of profit for any quantity above the break-even volume is represented by the vertical distance between the two lines EC and ED.
- Any quantity produced and sold less than the break-even volume will generate a loss. The area indicating a loss is the section OAE, where the Total Revenue line (OC) is below the Total Cost line (AD). The amount of loss for any quantity below the break-even volume is represented by the vertical distance between the two lines AE and OE.

Example 7.5(a) **Creating a Break-Even Chart, Determining Break-Even Revenue and Break-Even Volume, and Computing Break-Even as Percent of Capacity (Maximum Quantity)**

Johnathan's company has a capacity to produce and sell 300 chairs per month. The fixed costs are $5000 per month, variable costs are $30 per chair, and selling price is $70 per chair.

(i) Draw a detailed break-even chart showing the fixed costs line, total costs line, total revenue line, break-even point, and profit and loss areas.

(ii) Determine the break-even volume and break-even revenue, and compute the break-even as a percent of the capacity.

Solution

(i)

Step 1: *Drawing and Labelling the X-axis and Y-axis*

The maximum quantity is 300 chairs; therefore, the X-axis must extend to at least 300.

The maximum revenue is 300 × $70.00 = $21,000.00; therefore, the Y-axis must extend to at least 21,000.

Step 2: *Drawing the Fixed Costs Line*

The fixed costs are $5000.00; therefore, draw the horizontal line (AB) from A (0, 5000) to represent the *Fixed Costs line.*

Step 3: *Drawing the Total Revenue Line* and *Total Costs Line*

- Total Revenue function, $TR = S \times x = 70.00 \times x$
- Total Costs function, $TC = (VC \times x) + FC = (30.00 \times x) + 5000.00$

Create a table of values when $x = 0$ and 300 (maximum quantity) and choose $x = 100$ (any number in between) as the third point.

x	0	100	300
TR	0	7000	21,000
TC	5000	8000	14,000

Using these coordinates, construct OC to represent the *Total Revenue line* and AD to represent the *Total Costs line.*

Step 4: *Determining the Break-Even Point*

Mark the point E where the *Total Revenue line* (OC) and the *Total Cost line* (AD) intersect.

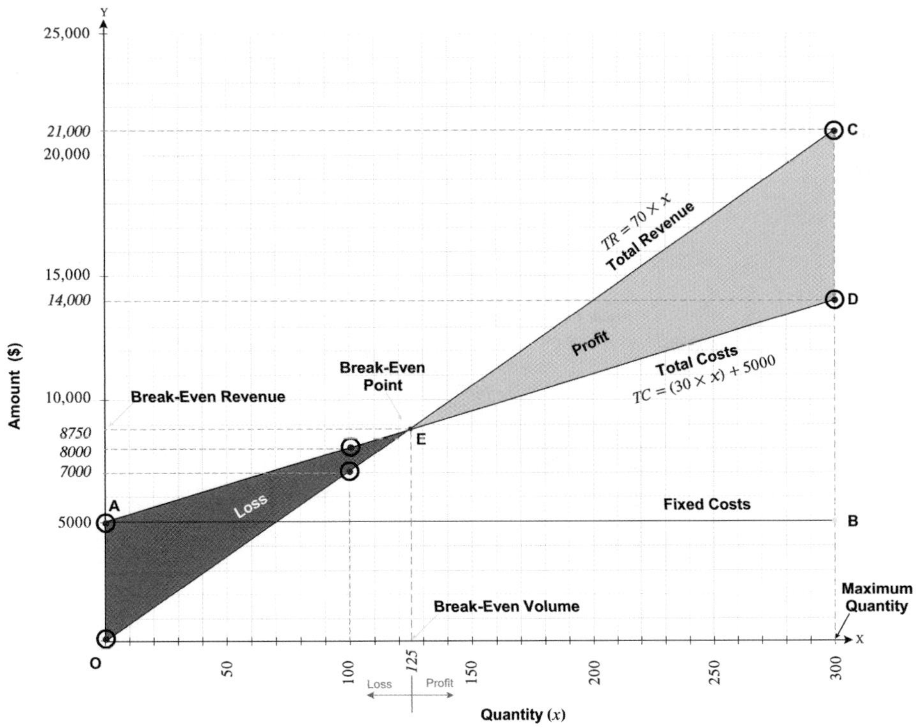

Solution *continued*

(ii) *Determining the break-even volume*

The x-coordinate of the break-even point (E) is 125.

Therefore, the break-even volume is 125 chairs.

Determining the break-even revenue

The y-coordinate of the break-even point (E) is 8750.

Therefore, the break-even revenue is $8750.

Computing the break-even as a percent of the capacity

$$\textit{Break-even as a percent of the capacity} = \frac{\textit{Break-even volume}}{\textit{Capacity}}$$

$$= \frac{125}{300} = 0.416666... = 41.67\%$$

Therefore, the break-even as a percent of capacity is 41.67%.

Example 7.5(b) Using Break-Even Charts for CVP Analysis

Answer the following referring to Example 7.5(a).

(i) What was the amount of profit or loss if 210 chairs were produced and sold in a month?

(ii) What was the amount of profit or loss if 60 chairs were produced and sold in a month?

(iii) What is the maximum profit that can be expected in a month?

Solution

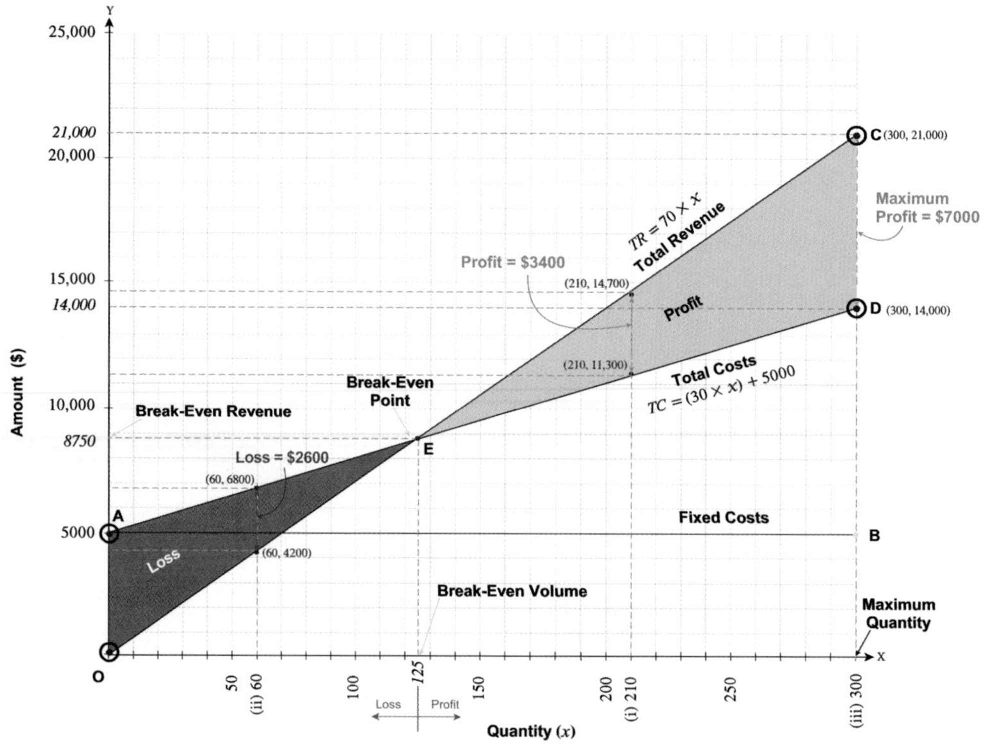

Solution *continued*

(i) *Determining the amount of profit or loss if 210 chairs were produced and sold in a month*

If 210 chairs were produced and sold, then this was 85 chairs above the break-even volume of 125 chairs per month; therefore, a profit was made.

The amount of profit is calculated by subtracting the value for the y-coordinate in line AD (i.e., TC), from the y-coordinate in line OC (i.e., TR), when $x = 210$.

When $x = 210$, $TR = \$14{,}700.00$, and $TC = \$11{,}300.00$

$$TR - TC = 14{,}700.00 - 11{,}300.00 = \$3400.00$$

Therefore, a profit of $3400 was made by producing and selling 210 chairs in a month.

(ii) *Determining the profit or loss if 60 chairs were produced and sold in a month*

If 60 chairs were produced and sold, then this was 65 chairs below the break-even volume of 125 chairs per month; therefore, a loss was incurred.

The amount of loss is calculated by subtracting the value for the y-coordinate in line AD (i.e., TC), from the y-coordinate in line OC (i.e., TR), when $x = 60$.

When $x = 60$, $TR = \$4200.00$, and $TC = \$6800.00$

$$TR - TC = 4200.00 - 6800.00 = -\$2600.00$$

Therefore, a loss of $2600 was incurred by producing and selling 60 chairs in a month.

(iii) *Determining the maximum profit that can be expected in a month*

Maximum profit can be expected at capacity, i.e., when $x = 300$.

This is 175 chairs above the break-even volume of 125 chairs per month.

The amount of profit is calculated by subtracting the value for the y-coordinate in line AD (i.e., TC), from the y-coordinate in line OC (i.e., TR), when $x = 300$.

When $x = 300$, $TR = \$21{,}000.00$ and $TC = \$14{,}000.00$

$$TR - TC = 21{,}000.00 - 14{,}000.00 = \$7000.00$$

Therefore, $7000 would be the maximum profit per month that can be expected.

Example 7.5(c) **Using Break-Even Charts for CVP Analysis when *FC*, *VC*, and *S* Change**

Answer the following referring to Example 7.5(a).

If the fixed costs increased by 20% per month, variable costs increased by $10 per chair, and Jonathan increased the selling price per chair to $80, determine the new break-even volume and new break-even revenue.

Solution

New $FC = 5000.00(1 + 0.20) = \$6000.00$ per month

New $VC = 30.00 + 10.00 = \$40.00$ per unit

New $S = \$80.00$ per unit

Creating the new break-even chart

- Drawing the new *Fixed Costs line*

Draw the new horizontal line (AB) from A (0, 6000) to represent the new *Fixed Costs line.*

- Drawing the new *Total Revenue line* and new *Total Costs line*

Graph the following linear functions:

Total Revenue function, $TR = S \times x = 80.00 \times x$

Total Costs function, $TC = (VC \times x) + FC = (40.00 \times x) + 6000.00$

Solution *continued*

Create a table of values when $x = 0$ and 300 (maximum quantity) and choose $x = 100$ (any number in between) as the third point.

x	0	100	300
TR	0	8000	24,000
TC	6000	10,000	18,000

Using these coordinates, construct OC to represent the new *Total Revenue line* and AD to represent the new *Total Costs line.*

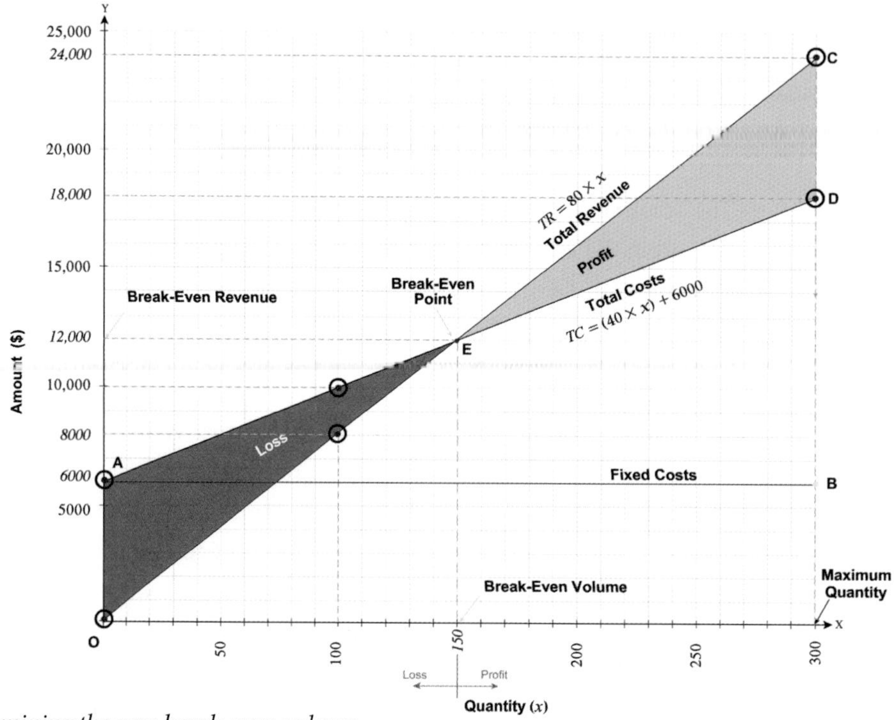

Determining the new break-even volume

The x-coordinate of the break-even point (E) is 150.

Therefore, the new break-even volume is 150 chairs.

Determining the new break-even revenue

The y-coordinate of the break-even point (E) is 12,000.

Therefore, the new break-even revenue is $12,000.

7.5 | Exercises

Answers to the odd-numbered problems are available at the end of the textbook.

1. The market research for the production and sale of a new pair of boots indicates that it can be sold for $185 per pair. The variable costs are $95 per pair and the fixed costs are $8100 per period. The production capacity is 180 pairs per period.
   a. Draw a detailed break-even chart showing the fixed costs line, total costs line, total revenue line, break-even point, and profit and loss areas.
   b. Determine the break-even volume and break-even revenue, and compute the break-even as a percent of the production capacity.

2. The market research for the production and sale of a new dress indicates that it can be sold for $175 per dress. The variable costs are $85 per dress and the fixed costs are $7200 per period. The production capacity is 300 units per period.
   a. Draw a detailed break-even chart showing the fixed costs line, total costs line, total revenue line, break-even point, and profit and loss areas.
   b. Determine the break-even volume and break-even revenue, and compute the break-even as a percent of the production capacity.

3. Chenkowski Motors was selling an automotive component for $170 per unit. The variable costs are $80 per unit and the fixed costs are $6300 per period. The production capacity is 190 units per period.
   a. Draw a detailed break-even chart showing the fixed costs line, total costs line, total revenue line, break-even point, and profit and loss areas.
   b. Determine the break-even volume and break-even revenue, and compute the break-even as a percent of the production capacity.
   c. What was the amount of profit or loss if 50 components were sold in a period?
   d. What is the maximum profit that can be expected in a period?

4. An electronics manufacturer was selling an electronic gadget for $155 per unit. The variable costs are $65 per unit and the fixed costs are $7200 per period. The production capacity is 250 units per period.
   a. Draw a detailed break-even chart showing the fixed costs line, total costs line, total revenue line, break-even point, and profit and loss areas.
   b. Determine the break-even volume and break-even revenue, and compute the break-even as a percent of the production capacity.
   c. What was the amount of profit or loss if 150 gadgets were sold in a period?
   d. What is the maximum profit that can be expected in a period?

5. A firm manufactures a product which sells for $12 per unit. The variable costs consist of two parts: the variable manufacturing costs are $6 per unit and the variable selling costs are $1.50 per unit. The fixed costs are $2475 for the period. The capacity is 1500 units per period.
   a. Draw a detailed break-even chart showing the fixed costs line, total costs line, total revenue line, break-even point, and profit and loss areas.
   b. Determine the break-even volume and break-even revenue, and compute the break-even as a percent of the capacity.
   c. What is the new break-even point in units if the fixed costs are increased by $1095 in a period and the variable manufacturing costs per unit are decreased by 10%?

6. A machine manufacturing firm sells a small component for $25 per unit. The variable costs consist of two parts: the variable manufacturing costs are $12.50 per unit and the selling costs are $2.50 per unit. The fixed costs for the period are $3600. The capacity is 600 units per period.
   a. Draw a detailed break-even chart showing the fixed costs line, total costs line, total revenue line, break-even point, and profit and loss areas.
   b. Determine the break-even volume and break-even revenue, and compute the break-even as a percent of the capacity.
   c. What is the new break-even point in units if the fixed costs are decreased by $625 in a period and the variable manufacturing costs per unit are increased by 10%?

7. A new product can be sold for $165 according to market research. The variable costs are $90 per unit, fixed costs are $8625 per period, and the production capacity is 475 units.
   a. Draw a detailed break-even chart showing the fixed costs line, total costs line, total revenue line, break-even point, and profit and loss areas.
   b. Determine the break-even volume and break-even revenue, and compute the break-even as a percent of the capacity.
   c. What is the new break-even point in units when the selling price is decreased by $5 and the fixed costs per period are increased to $10,150?

8. A new product can be sold for $175 according to market research. The variable costs are $95 per unit, the fixed costs are $9600 per period, and the capacity is 520 units.
   a. Draw a detailed break-even chart showing the fixed costs line, total costs line, total revenue line, break-even point, and profit and loss areas.
   b. Determine the break-even volume and break-even revenue, and compute the break-even as a percent of the capacity.
   c. What is the new break-even point in units when the selling price is decreased by $5 and the fixed costs per period are increased to $10,875?

9. A publisher sells a new travel book for $65 per book. The fixed costs are $37,000 per year, publishing costs per book are $40, and the royalty paid to the author is 10% of the selling price per book. The publisher has a capacity to sell 10,000 books in a year.
   a. Draw a detailed break-even chart showing the fixed costs line, total costs line, total revenue line, break-even point, and profit and loss areas.
   b. Determine the break-even volume and break-even revenue, and compute the break-even as a percent of the capacity.
   c. If the fixed costs increased by 20% per year, publishing costs increased by $5 per book, and the publisher increased the selling price per book to $80, determine the new break-even volume and the new break-even revenue.

10. A new cookbook is being sold for $25 each. The publisher's fixed costs are $25,500 per year, publishing costs are $14 per book, and the royalty paid to the author is 10% of the selling price. The publisher has a capacity to sell 12,000 books in a year.
   a. Draw a detailed break-even chart showing the fixed costs line, total costs line, total revenue line, break-even point, and profit and loss areas.
   b. Determine the break-even volume and break-even revenue, and compute the break-even as a percent of the capacity.
   c. If the fixed costs increased by 15% per year, publishing costs increased by $6 per book, and the publisher increased the selling price per book to $30, determine the new break-even volume and the new break-even revenue.

7 | Review Exercises

Answers to the odd-numbered problems are available at the end of the textbook.

1. A nursery sells a bouquet of roses for $14 each. The variable costs are $8.50 per bouqet and the fixed costs per week are $2700.
   a. Calculate the break-even number of bouquets to be sold per week.
   b. What is the net income in a week in which 900 bouquets are sold?
   c. Calculate the number of bouquets to be sold to earn a profit of $1000 per week.

2. Don makes portable hard-drives that he sells for $81 each. The variable costs per drive are $33 and the fixed costs per week are $1200.
   a. Calculate the number of drives he needs to sell per week to break even.
   b. What net income will he make in a week in which he sells 35 drives?
   c. If he wants to make a profit of $960 in a week, how many drives must he sell?

3. Token's Toys sells them at $12.50 each. The variable costs per toy are $7.50 and fixed costs are $20,000 per year.
   a. What are the contribution margin and contribution ratios?
   b. How many toys must be sold per year for a net income of $48,000 per year?
   c. What will be the net income in a year in which 10,000 toys were sold?

4. Andy K. Fiddles makes violins and sells them for $286 each. The variable costs per violin are $111 and fixed costs are $31,500 per year.
   a. What are the contribution margin and contribution ratios?
   b. How many violins must be sold per year for a net income of $63,000 per year?
   c. What will be the net income in a year in which 450 violins were sold?

5. A publishing company sells its biology textbooks for $125 each. The office overhead costs are $48,000 per year, equipment maintenance costs are $18,000 per year, printing costs are $40 per textbook, and advertisement and promotional costs are $2875 per year. In addition, the author receives a royalty that is 10% on the selling price.
   a. How many books must be sold per year to break even?
   b. Calculate the net income with the sale of 3500 books per year.
   c. How many books must be sold in a year to earn a net income of $435,000?

6. AWM Inc., a plastic chair manufacturing company, produces chairs and sells them for $28 each. The office overhead costs are $33,500 per year, machine maintenance and rental costs are $20,500 per year, production costs are $8.60 per chair, and the sales team receives a commission of 5% on the selling price.
   a. How many chairs must be sold in a year to break even?
   b. Calculate the net income with the sale of 8000 chairs per year.
   c. How many chairs must be sold in a year to earn a net income of $40,000 for the year?

7. To achieve a total revenue target of $86,400 per month, Henry has to make and sell 320 components. If his company can sell a maximum of 600 components, the variable costs per component are $150, and the fixed costs are $54,000 per month, calculate the following:
   a. The selling price of each component.
   b. The new break-even volume per month if the fixed costs decrease by $6000 per month.
   c. The new break-even volume as a percent of the capacity.

8. Kawai purchased a new printing machine and started a small printing shop. As per his calculations, to earn a revenue of $5000 per month, he needs to sell printouts of 25,000 pages per month. If the printing machine has a capacity of printing 40,000 sheets per month, the variable costs are $0.02 per sheet, and the fixed costs are $1800 per month, calculate:
   a. The selling price of each printout.
   b. The new break-even point per month if the fixed costs decrease by $360 per month.
   c. The new break-even point as a percent of the capacity.

9. Xing-fu and his business partner manufacture car tires and sells them for $105 per tire. The fixed costs are $85,800 per year and variable costs are $45 per tire.
   a. How many units would they be required to sell to make a net income of $75,000 per year?
   b. Find the break-even point per year if the variable costs increase by $5 per tire.

10. Ivan Daniels Consulting charges $275 per hour for its consulting services. The fixed costs are $780,000 per annum and variable costs are $25 per hour.
    a. Calculate the net income assuming that the annual sales are $2,579,500.
    b. How many hours of consultation service would the company be required to provide to make a net income of $3,000,000 per year?
    c. Find the break-even point if the variable costs increase by $10 per hour.

11. The market research for a new product indicates that the product can be sold for $300 per unit. The manufacturing costs are $120 per unit, the selling costs are $20 per unit, and the fixed costs are $14,400 per period. The production capacity is 400 units per period.
    a. Draw a detailed break-even chart showing the fixed costs line, total costs line, total revenue line, break-even point, and profit and loss areas.
    b. Determine the break-even volume and break-even revenue, and compute the break-even as a percent of the capacity.
    c. What is the break-even point in units if the fixed costs are increased by $2456 in a period and the manufacturing cost per unit is decreased by 10%?

12. Urban Riders Ltd. has introduced a new mountain bike that can be sold for $290 per unit. The variable costs are $115 per unit and the fixed costs are $5250 per period. The production capacity is 100 units per period.
    a. Draw a detailed break-even chart showing the fixed costs line, total costs line, total revenue line, break-even point, and profit and loss areas.
    b. Determine the break-even volume and break-even revenue, and compute the break-even as a percent of the capacity.
    c. What is the break-even in dollars if fixed costs are reduced to $3800 in a period and variable cost per unit is increased by 20%?

13. Tom has a garment manufacturing factory that has the capacity to make and sell 700 dress shirts per week. He sells each shirt for $16 to wholesalers, have fixed costs of $2880 per week, and variable costs of $9.60 per shirt.
    a. Calculate the contribution margin and contribution ratio.
    b. What sales amount per week will result in a net income of $960 for the week?
    c. What will be the net income at capacity?

14. A magazine company has the capacity to print and sell 200,000 magazines per month. It sells each magazine for $4.50, has fixed costs of $520,000 per month, and variable costs of $0.50 per magazine.
    a. Calculate the contribution margin and contribution ratio.
    b. What sales amount will result in a net income of $21,000 for the month?
    c. What will be the net income at capacity?

15. A company that produces hard-drives has fixed costs of $85,000. The variable costs are 75% of the sales. The company makes a profit of $30,000. If its variable costs increase by 5% and fixed costs increase by $15,000, by what percent should the company increase the selling price to earn the same profit of $30,000? Assume that there is no increase in the volume of units sold.

16. Four-legged Industries, a furniture manufacturing company, has fixed costs of $55,000. Their net income is $25,000 and variable costs are 45% of sales. If its fixed costs increase by $12,000 and variable costs increase by 5%, by what percent should the company change the selling price to earn the same profit of $25,000? Assume that there is no change in the number of units sold.

• 17. A company that makes keyboards sells them for $65 each. The fixed costs are $8400 per month and variable costs are $23 per keyboard. It can make and sell a maximum of 350 keyboards per month.
    a. What is the break-even revenue and volume per month?
    b. What is the number of keyboards that it would have to sell to earn a net income of $5600 per month?
    c. What is the net income at capacity if the variable costs decreased by $3 per keyboard?

• 18. A company sells an item for $25 each. It has fixed costs of $2025 per month and variable costs of $2.50 per item. It has the capacity to produce 3000 items per month.
    a. What is the break-even revenue and volume per month?
    b. What is the number of items that it would have to provide to earn a net income of $6750 per month?
    c. What is the net income at capacity if the variable costs decreased by $0.50 per item?

• 19. A business has the capacity to manufacture 600 electronic components per annum that it sells for $500 each. The variable costs are $250 per component and the fixed costs are $100,000 per year.
    a. What quantity should it sell in a year to earn a net income of $60,000 per year?
    b. What is the net income per year at capacity?
    c. Calculate the quantity that it needs to sell to earn a net income of $60,000 per year if the selling price of the component is reduced by 10% and variable costs are increased by 10%.

• 20. An industrial water cooler manufacturer, has the capacity to produce 4500 water coolers every year. It sells each cooler for $350. The variable costs are $180 per cooler and fixed costs are $250,000 per year.
    a. How many coolers should it sell to earn a net income of $500,000 per year?
    b. What is the net income per year at capacity?
    c. Calculate the number of coolers that it needs to sell to earn a net income of $300,000 per year if the selling price of the cooler is reduced by 5% and variable costs are increased by 10%.

• 21. An automobile plant produced 9000 cars and lost $6,000,000 last year. The total revenue for the year was $135,000,000. The break-even volume of the plant is 10,000 cars.
    a. Calculate the selling price of each car.
    b. Calculate the variable costs for each car.
    c. Calculate the fixed costs per year.

• 22. A garment manufacturing company produced and sold 2800 dress shirts and made a net income of $1750 last year. The total revenue for the year was $35,000. The break-even volume of the company is 2200 shirts.
    a. Calculate the selling price of each shirt.
    b. Calculate the variable costs for each shirt.
    c. Calculate the fixed costs per year.

7 | Self-Test Exercises

Answers to all the problems are available at the end of the textbook.

1. Audrey Manufacturing is evaluating the introduction of a new product that would have a unit selling price of $100. The total annual fixed costs are estimated to be $200,000 and the unit variable costs are projected at $60.
   a. What sales volume (in units) per year is required to break even?
   b. What volume is required to generate an income of $100,000 per year?

2. A manufacturer of major appliances provided the following information: the capacity of the facility is 900 units per month, the fixed costs are $175,000 per month, and the variable costs are $360 per unit. The product currently sells for $640.
   a. What is the break-even volume as a percent of capacity?
   b. If the variable costs decreased by $20 per unit, what would be the net income per month at capacity?

3. A publishing company decided to create a new textbook in chemistry to be sold to bookstores for $120 each. The costs for adding this new textbook to its products are: $2000 per month rent for additional space for its editorial and research team, $330 per month insurance costs for the building, $4250 per month for support staff, $2500 per month for sales and marketing. The variable cost per textbook is $18.
   a. Calculate the break-even volume.
   b. If the profit last month was $55,460, how many textbooks did it sell?

4. A manufacturer sells an item for $45 each. It has fixed costs of $3000 per month and it needs to sell 480 items to break even.
   a. What are the variable costs per item?
   b. What is the contribution margin (CM) per item?
   c. What is the net income per month at 60% above break-even volume?

• 5. A company manufactures a product that currently sells for $30. The fixed costs are $100,000 per year and the variable costs are $20. The capacity of the production facility is 50,000 units per year.
   a. How many units must be produced to attain a net income of $80,000 per year?
   b. If sales dropped to 50% of the capacity and the selling price reduced by $3 per unit, what would be the net income?

• 6. A manufacturer of ovens sells them for $2050 each. The variable costs are $1400 per unit. The manufacturer's factory has annual fixed costs of $2,100,000.
   a. Given the expected sales volume of 3000 units for this year, what will be this year's net income?
   b. How many units must the manufacturer produce to break even if the fixed costs increased by 10%?

• 7. Abban manufactures a product that sells very well. The capacity of his facility is 50,000 units per month. The fixed costs are $150,000 per month and the variable costs are $12 per unit. The product currently sells for $20.
   a. What total revenue is required for a net income of $100,000 per month?
   b. If he produced and sold 75% of the capacity and the variable costs decreased by 25%, what was the net income for the month?

• 8. Last year, a battery manufacturing company in Winnipeg incurred a loss of $835,000 by producing and selling 45,000 batteries. The total revenue for the year was $12,600,000 and the break-even volume of the company is 49,900 batteries.
   a. What is the selling price of each battery?
   b. What are the fixed costs per year and variable costs per battery?

- 9. A retail store has fixed costs of $180,000 per year and a capacity to store and sell 850 dishwashers every year. It sells each unit for $500 and the variable costs are $140 per unit.

   a. How many units should it sell to earn a net income of $45,000 per year?

   b. What is the net income per year at capacity?

   c. Calculate the number of units it needs to sell to earn a net income of $45,000 per year if it decides to reduce the selling price of each unit by 15% and variable costs increase by 15%.

- 10. Rudolf manufactures a particular brand of pens and sells them for $40 each. The total revenue from these pens at the break-even point is $70,520 per month and the contribution margin per pen is $12.

   a. What are the fixed costs?

   b. What is the break-even volume?

   c. What is the total revenue if he sells 1500 pens per month?

CASE 7

Cost-Volume-Profit Analysis at a Manufacturing Company

Madison is the newly appointed manager of Spark Communications, a small computer monitor manufacturing company based out of Halifax, Nova Scotia. During her first few days on the job, she collected the following data about the company:

The company has the capacity to produce 750 monitors per month and is currently producing 525 monitors every month and selling it to a wholesaler. The company's expenses are: rent of $4000 per month, salaries of $12,500 per month, insurance of $1500 per month, materials at $6 per monitor, labour of $35 per monitor, and sales commissions of $19 per monitor. Each monitor is sold for $105.

a. What is the contribution margin and the contribution ratio?

b. What is the break-even volume and break-even revenue per month?

c. How much net income per month would be earned at the current level of production?

d. At the current level of production, what percent of the facility is utilized?

e. Madison decided to increase the quantity produced to the facility's capacity and reduce the selling price from $105 to $95. What would be the impact of this decision on the company's net income?

f. At the new selling price of $95, another store wanted to purchase an additional 750 units per month on a regular basis. Madison expanded the facility by renting additional space, which increased the fixed costs by 25% and doubled the capacity of the facility. What would be the company's net income per month if it were operating at 100% of the new facility's capacity?

7 | Summary of Notation and Formulas

NOTATION

TR = Total Revenue

TC = Total Costs

VC = Variable Costs per unit

TVC = Total Variable Costs

FC = Fixed Costs for a specific period

x = Number of units produced and sold

S = Selling Price per unit

NI = Net Income

CM = Contribution Margin (per unit)

CR = Contribution Ratio

TCM = Total Contribution Margin

FORMULAS

Total Variable Costs | 7.1(a)

$$TVC = VC \times x$$

Total Costs | 7.1(b)

$$TC = FC + TVC$$

Total Revenue | 7.1(c)

$$TR = S \times x$$

Net Income | 7.1(d)

$$NI = TR - TC$$

At the break-even point | 7.1(e)

At the break-even point, TR = TC

Contribution Margin per Unit | 7.1(f)

$$CM = S - VC$$

Contribution Ratio | 7.1(g)

$$CR = \frac{CM}{S} \times 100\%$$

Cost-Volume-Profit Analysis | 7.2(a)

$$S \times x = FC + (VC \times x) + NI$$

Number of Units | 7.2(b)

$$x = \frac{FC + NI}{(S - VC)}$$

Number of Units at the Break-Even Point | 7.3

$$x_{BE} = \frac{FC}{CM}$$

Contribution Margin Percent | 7.4(a)

$$CM\ Percent = \frac{TR - TVC}{TR} \times 100\%$$

Net Income | 7.4(b)

$NI = (CM\ Percent \times TR) - FC$ **or** $NI = TCM - FC$

Chapter

8 SIMPLE INTEREST AND APPLICATIONS

LEARNING OBJECTIVES

- Demonstrate the concept of simple interest.
- Determine the number of days between two calendar dates using different methods, including the pre-programmed financial calculator method.
- Calculate the amount of interest, principal, time, interest rate, and maturity value of investments and loans.
- Calculate equivalent payments that replace another payment or a series of payments.
- Use simple interest in solving problems involving business applications such as demand loans, promissory notes, discounting, treasury bills, and commercial papers.

CHAPTER OUTLINE

8.1 Calculating the Amount of Simple Interest

8.2 Calculating Principal, Interest Rate, Time, and Maturity Value

8.3 Calculating Equivalent Payments

8.4 Applications of Simple Interest

Introduction

Interest is a fee paid by borrowers to lenders for using money temporarily.

Given a choice, would you prefer to receive $1000 today or $1000 in 1 year? Even though the amounts are the same, it is preferable to receive $1000 today, so that you can invest the sum in a bank and earn interest on the investment over time.

Interest is a fee paid by borrowers to lenders for using money temporarily. Interest is an expense when we borrow money and an income when we invest money. Many business transactions involve either lending money to or borrowing money from a financial institution, such as a bank or a credit union.

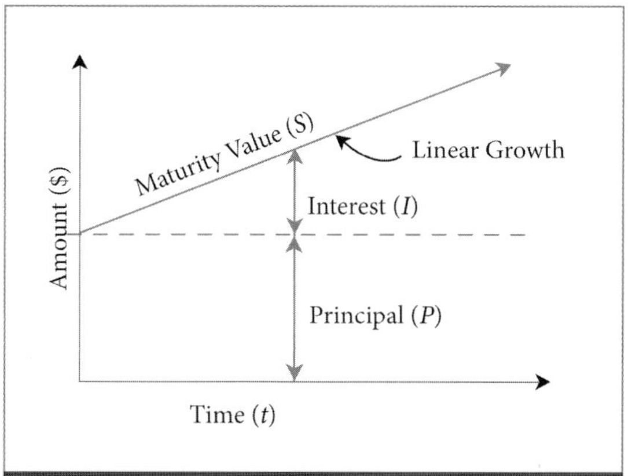

Exhibit 8(a): Under Simple Interest, Money Grows Linearly

For example, when we invest money, a financial institution uses our money, and therefore pays us interest for the use of the money for the time period it has been invested. Similarly, when we borrow money from a financial institution, we pay interest to them for the use of the money for the time period borrowed, unless otherwise specified. In both cases, when money is returned after a period of time, interest is added to the original amount borrowed. Therefore, as time goes by, the value of money increases by the amount of interest earned for that period. This is called the **time value of money**: money grows with time when it is invested or borrowed at a particular interest rate.

In **simple interest** calculations, interest is calculated only on the initial amount invested or borrowed at the specified simple interest rate for the whole term. For this reason, simple interest is usually used for short term investments or loans. In this chapter, you will learn the fundamental relationship between the time value of money and the amount of simple interest charged or earned.

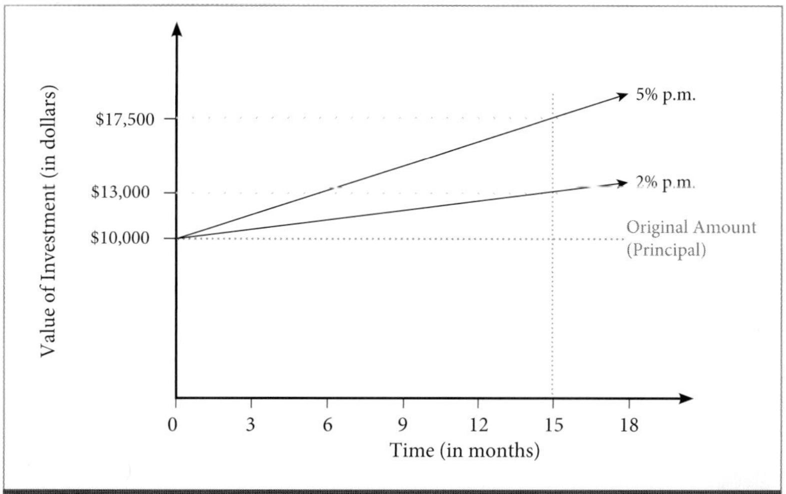

Exhibit 8(b): Graph showing the Maturity Value at Different Simple Interest Rates

For long term investments or loans, compound interest is used, where interest is calculated on the amount borrowed or invested in addition to the interest earned periodically. You will learn about compound interest in Chapter 9.

8.1 | Calculating the Amount of Simple Interest

In simple interest calculations, the amount of interest, for a period of time, is calculated as a percent of the amount invested or borrowed. This percent is referred to as the rate of interest (or interest rate), which is always stated for a unit period of time; i.e., r% per annum (r% p.a. or r% per year).

In simple interest calculations, interest is calculated only on the principal for the whole term.

For example,

- Interest for \$1000 at 10% p.a. for 1 year $= 1000 \times 0.10 \times 1 = \$100.00$
- Interest for \$1000 at 10% p.a. for 3 years $= 1000 \times 0.10 \times 3 = \$300.00$

In calculations, interest rate, 'r', is used as a decimal or fractional equivalent of the percent rate.

Similarly, interest for \$$P$ at r% p.a. for t years $= P \times r \times t$

Therefore, *Amount of Interest = Principal × Rate × Time Period*

This can be written as the following formula:

Formula 8.1 **Amount of Interest**

$$I = Prt$$

Notation

I = **Amount of interest** is the amount (in dollars) charged or earned for borrowing or investing the principal amount for a period of time.

P = **Principal (or Present Value)** is the amount borrowed or invested (or the discounted value or the proceeds) at the beginning of a period.

r = **Simple interest rate** is the rate at which the principal is borrowed or invested. It is expressed as a percent for a given period of time, usually per year, unless otherwise specified; if the interest rate is r%, it is understood that r% is an annual interest rate (r% p.a.).

t = **Time period** is the period of time for which the principal amount is borrowed or invested during which interest is charged or earned.

Interest can be calculated either using a 365-day year (called the exact interest method) or a 360-day year (called the ordinary interest method). We follow the exact interest method in this textbook.

Note: *Since $r \times t$ refers to the interest percent of the principal $\left(r \times t = \frac{I}{P}\right)$ the units for 'r' and 't' should match. For example,*

- *If 'r' is per annum (r% p.a.), then 't' should be in years.*
- *If 'r' is per month (r% p.m.), then 't' should be in months.*

Usually, the unit of 't' is converted to match the unit of 'r' using 1 year = 12 months or 1 year = 365 days.

Example 8.1(a) **Calculating 'I' When 't' is Expressed in Years**

Sabrina borrowed \$4250 from her friend for 2 years. If she was charged a simple interest rate of 6% p.a., how much interest would she have to pay on the loan?

Solution

P = \$4250.00, r = 6% p.a. = 0.06 p.a., t = 2 years (unit of 't' and unit of 'r' are the same)

Using Formula 8.1, $I = Prt$

Substituting values, $I = (4250.00)(0.06)(2)$

$= \$510.00$

Therefore, Sabrina would have to pay an interest amount of \$510.00 on the loan.

Using Spreadsheets to Solve Problems

Once you understand the formulas involved in calculations, spreadsheets, such as Microsoft Excel or Google Sheets, can be useful tools for solving problems related to simple interest calculations.

In spreadsheets, each box or cell is labelled with letters (A, B, C,...) for columns and numbers (1, 2, 3,...) for rows. For example, B2 refers to the cell along column B and row 2. To enter a value in a cell, click on the cell, type the value and press enter.

To calculate the amount of simple interest using the formula $I = Prt$, we will set up the spreadsheet as follows:

	A	B
1		Calculating *I*
2	***P***	B2
3	***r***	B3
4	***t***	B4
5		
6	***I***	B6
7		

- In cell B2, enter the amount of **principal, '*P*'**.
- In cell B3, enter the **simple interest rate, '*r*'**.
- In cell B4, enter the **time period, '*t*'**; the unit of ***t*** must match the unit of ***r***.
- In cell B6, enter the **amount of interest, '*I*'**.

Solving Example 8.1(a) using a spreadsheet is shown below:

Example 8.1(b) **Using a Spreadsheet to Solve Example 8.1(a)**

Sabrina borrowed \$4250 from her friend for 2 years. If she was charged a simple interest rate of 6% p.a., how much interest would she have to pay on the loan?

Solution

Set up the spreadsheet to include variables P, r, t, and I as shown.

	A	B
1		Calculating *I*
2	***P***	\$4,250.00
3	***r***	6.00%
4	***t***	2
5		
6	***I***	\$510.00
7		

- To enter the **principal, '*P*'**, select cell B2. Type **\$4250.00** and press **Enter**.
- To enter the **simple interest rate, '*r*'**, select cell B3. Type **6.00%** and press **Enter**.
- To enter the **time period, '*t*'**, select cell B4. Type **2** and press **Enter**.
- To calculate the amount of **simple interest**, **'*I*'**, using the formula *I* = *Prt*, select cell B6. Type **'=B2*B3*B4'** and press **Enter**. Alternatively, select B6 and type '=', select B2 and type '*', select B3 and type '*', select B4 and press **Enter**. The amount of simple interest, '*I*', will be displayed in cell B6.

Therefore, Sabrina would have to pay an interest amount of \$510.00 on the loan.

Note: *Spreadsheet solutions to the examples are identified with an icon containing the page number and are available at the end of the chapter.*

Example 8.1(c)

Calculating 'I' When 't' is Expressed in Months

Calculate the amount of interest earned from an investment of \$1750 for 9 months at 4.5% p.a.

Solution

Page 325

$P = \$1750.00$, $r = 4.5\%$ p.a. $= 0.045$ p.a., $t = 9$ months

Method 1: Match the unit of 't' to that of 'r'

$$t = 9 \text{ months} = \frac{9}{12} \text{ years} = 0.75 \text{ years}$$

Using Formula 8.1, $I = Prt$

Substituting values, $I = (1750.00)(0.045)(0.75)$

$= 59.0625 = \$59.06$

Method 2: Match the unit of 'r' to that of 't'

$$r = 0.045 \text{ p.a.} = \frac{0.045}{12} \text{ p.m.}$$

Using Formula 8.1, $I = Prt$

Substituting values, $I = (1750.00)\left(\frac{0.045}{12}\right)(9)$

$= 59.0625 = \$59.06$

Therefore, an interest amount of \$59.06 will be earned.

Example 8.1(d)

Calculating 'I' When 't' is Expressed in Days

Calculate the amount of interest charged on a loan of \$3200 at 6% p.a. for 125 days.

Solution

Page 325

Matching the unit of 't' to that of 'r'

$P = \$3200.00$, $r = 6\%$ p.a. $= 0.06$ p.a., $t = 125 \text{ days} = \frac{125}{365} \text{ years}$

Using Formula 8.1, $I = Prt$

Substituting values, $I = (3200.00)(0.06)\left(\frac{125}{365}\right)$

$= 65.753424... = \$65.75$

Therefore, an interest amount of \$65.75 will be charged.

Example 8.1(e)

Calculating 'I' When 't' is Expressed in Days and 'r' is Expressed Per Month

Calculate the amount of interest earned on an investment of \$2275 earning interest at 0.75% p.m. for 90 days.

Solution

Page 325

Method 1: Match the unit of 't' to that of 'r'

$P = \$2275.00$, $r = 0.75\%$ p.m. $= 0.0075$ p.m.

$$t = 90 \text{ days} = \left(\frac{90}{365} \times 12\right) \text{ months}$$

Using Formula 8.1, $I = Prt$

$$I = (2275.00)(0.0075)\left(\frac{90}{365} \times 12\right)$$

$= 50.486301... = \$50.49$

Method 2: Convert the units of 'r' and 't' to years

$P = \$2275.00$, $r = 0.75\%$ p.m. $= 0.0075 \times 12$ p.a. $= 0.09$ p.a.

$$t = 90 \text{ days} = \frac{90}{365} \text{ years}$$

Using Formula 8.1, $I = Prt$

$$I = (2275.00)(0.09)\left(\frac{90}{365}\right)$$

$= 50.486301... = \$50.49$

Therefore, an interest amount of \$50.49 is earned.

Example 8.1(f) **Calculating 'I' When 't' is Expressed in Years and 'r' is Expressed Per Month**

Calculate the amount of interest earned on an investment of \$5680 at 0.25% p.m. for $1\frac{1}{2}$ years.

Page 325

Solution

Method 1: Match the unit of 't' to that of 'r'

$P = \$5680.00, \quad r = 0.25\% \text{ p.m.} = 0.0025 \text{ p.m.}$

$t = 1\frac{1}{2} \text{ years} = 1\frac{1}{2} \times 12 \text{ months} = 18 \text{ months}$

Using Formula 8.1, $I = Prt$

$$I = (5680.00)(0.0025)(18)$$

$$= \$255.60$$

Method 2: Match the unit of 'r' to that of 't'

$P = \$5680.00, \quad r = 0.25\% \text{ p.m.} = 0.0025 \times 12 \text{ p.a.} = 0.03 \text{ p.a.}$

$t = 1\frac{1}{2} \text{ years} = \frac{3}{2} \text{ years}$

Using Formula 8.1, $I = Prt$

$$I = (5680.00)(0.03)\left(\frac{3}{2}\right)$$

$$= \$255.60$$

Therefore, an interest amount of \$255.60 is earned.

Determining the Time Period in Days Between Dates

Since simple interest is mostly used for loans or investments with short time periods, it is necessary to calculate the time period in days, unless it is stated in months or years. The time period in days is then converted to its equivalent in years to use as 't' in the simple interest formula.

- The following months have 31 days: *January, March, May, July, August, October,* and *December.*
- The following months have 30 days: *April, June, September,* and *November.*
- There are 28 days in *February*, except in leap years, when there are 29 days.
- Leap years occur every 4 years. For example, 2004, 2008, 2012, 2016, 2020, etc. are leap years.
- Century years can be leap years only if they are divisible by 400. For example, 1800, 1900, 2100, 2200, and 2300 are not leap years; however, 2000 and 2400 are leap years.

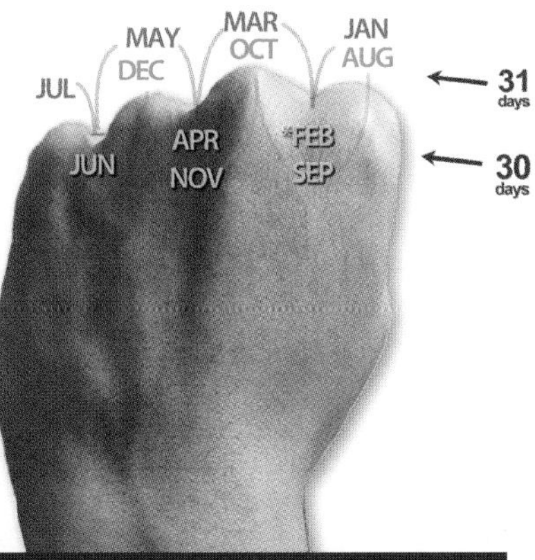

Exhibit 8.1: Days in Each Month

An Easy Way to Remember the Number of Days in Each Month

Make a fist with one hand, hiding your thumb.

Using your other hand, start counting January, February, March, April, May, June, July, on the knuckle and the space in between the knuckles, as shown in blue on the left.

When you reach the end, go back to the first knuckle and continue counting August, September, October, November, and December, as shown in green.

All months that fall on a knuckle have 31 days and the others have 30 days, except for February, which has 28 days (or 29 in a leap year).

Described below are three methods to determine the number of days for a time period between two dates:

Method 1: Determining the Number of Days Using Calendar Days in Each Month

When calculating the number of days in a time period, you must either exclude the first day or the last day in the day count.

While counting the number of days in a time period, we include either the first day or the last day of the investment or loan, but not both days.

Financial institutions generally include the first day of the period and exclude the last day. This is done because they base their financial calculations on the end of the day's closing balance. On the first day, as you would either borrow or invest money, the closing balance would not be zero. However, on the last day of the period, since you would either pay-back the loan or withdraw the investment making the closing balance zero, financial institutions would not include the last day in calculations.

For example, the number of days between January 25 and February 05 is:

January 25 to January 31:	7 days (First day included)
February 01 to February 05:	4 days (Last day excluded)

Therefore, there are 11 days between January 25 and February 05.

In the following two examples, we have illustrated calculations that:

- include the first day and exclude the last day, as done by financial institutions, and
- exclude the first day and include the last day.

Example 8.1(g) Calculating the Number of Days in a Time Period During a Non-Leap Year and Expressing it in Years

Calculate the number of days in the time period from October 18, 2016 to April 05, 2017.

Solution

Including the first day and excluding the last day

October: 14 days
(First day included, counting from October 18 to October 31 = 14 days)

November: 30 days

December: 31 days

January: 31 days

February: 28 days
(Year 2017 is not a leap year)

March: 31 days

April: 4 days
(Last day excluded, counting from April 01 to April 04 = 4 days)

Total number of days = 169 days

$(t = \frac{169}{365}$ years$)$

Excluding the first day and including the last day

October: 13 days
(First day excluded, counting from October 19 to October 31 = 13 days, or 31 – 18 = 13 days)

November: 30 days

December: 31 days

January: 31 days

February: 28 days
(Year 2017 is not a leap year)

March: 31 days

April: 5 days
(Last day included, counting from April 01 to April 05 = 5 days)

Total number of days = 169 days

$(t = \frac{169}{365}$ years$)$

Example 8.1(h) Calculating the Number of Days in a Time Period During a Leap Year and Expressing it in Years

Calculate the number of days in the time period from January 15, 2016 to March 20, 2016.

Solution

Including the first day and excluding the last day

January: 17 days
(First day included, counting from January 15 to January 31 = 17 days)

February: 29 days
(Year 2016 is a leap year)

March: 19 days
(Last day excluded, counting from March 01 to March 19 = 19 days)

Total number of days = 65 days

$(t = \frac{65}{365}$ years$)$

Excluding the first day and including the last day

January: 16 days
(First day excluded, counting from January16 to January 31 = 16 days, or 31 – 15 = 16)

February: 29 days
(Year 2016 is a leap year)

March: 20 days
(Last day included, counting from March 01 to March 20 = 20 days)

Total number of days = 65 days

$(t = \frac{65}{365}$ years$)$

In this textbook, we will always calculate the time period in years (t) using 365 days, even during a leap year.

Method 2: Determining the Number of Days Using a Days Table

In this method, we use a table that has the days of the year serially numbered from 1 to 365 as shown in Table 8.1. The number of days between two dates that are in the same calendar year is determined by calculating the difference between the serial numbers of those dates in the table.

Table 8.1 **Days Table**

DAY OF MONTH	JAN	FEB	MAR	APR	MAY	JUN	JUL	AUG	SEP	OCT	NOV	DEC	DAY OF MONTH
	DAY OF THE YEAR												
1	1	32	60	91	121	152	182	213	244	274	305	335	**1**
2	2	33	61	92	122	153	183	214	245	275	306	336	**2**
3	3	34	62	93	123	154	184	215	246	276	307	337	**3**
4	4	35	63	94	124	155	185	216	247	277	308	338	**4**
5	5	36	64	95	125	156	186	217	248	278	309	339	**5**
6	6	37	65	96	126	157	187	218	249	279	310	340	**6**
7	7	38	66	97	127	158	188	219	250	280	311	341	**7**
8	8	39	67	98	128	159	189	220	251	281	312	342	**8**
9	9	40	68	99	129	160	190	221	252	282	313	343	**9**
10	10	41	69	100	130	161	191	222	253	283	314	344	**10**
11	11	42	70	101	131	162	192	223	254	284	315	345	**11**
12	12	43	71	102	132	163	193	224	255	285	316	346	**12**
13	13	44	72	103	133	164	194	225	256	286	317	347	**13**
14	14	45	73	104	134	165	195	226	257	287	318	348	**14**
15	15	46	74	105	135	166	196	227	258	288	319	349	**15**
16	16	47	75	106	136	167	197	228	259	289	320	350	**16**
17	17	48	76	107	137	168	198	229	260	290	321	351	**17**
18	18	49	77	108	138	169	199	230	261	291	322	352	**18**
19	19	50	78	109	139	170	200	231	262	292	323	353	**19**
20	20	51	79	110	140	171	201	232	263	293	324	354	**20**
21	21	52	80	111	141	172	202	233	264	294	325	355	**21**
22	22	53	81	112	142	173	203	234	265	295	326	356	**22**
23	23	54	82	113	143	174	204	235	266	296	327	357	**23**
24	24	55	83	114	144	175	205	236	267	297	328	358	**24**
25	25	56	84	115	145	176	206	237	268	298	329	359	**25**
26	26	57	85	116	146	177	207	238	269	299	330	360	**26**
27	27	58	86	117	147	178	208	239	270	300	331	361	**27**
28	28	59	87	118	148	179	209	240	271	301	332	362	**28**
29	29		88	119	149	180	210	241	272	302	333	363	**29**
30	30		89	120	150	181	211	242	273	303	334	364	**30**
31	31		90		151		212	243		304		365	**31**

Note: *For leap years, February 29 becomes day number 60. Therefore, you will need to add one day to any date that includes February 29 in a leap year.*

Example 8.1(i) **Calculating the Number of Days Within a Single Calendar Year**

Calculate the number of days in the time period from February 18, 2017 to May 17, 2017.

Solution

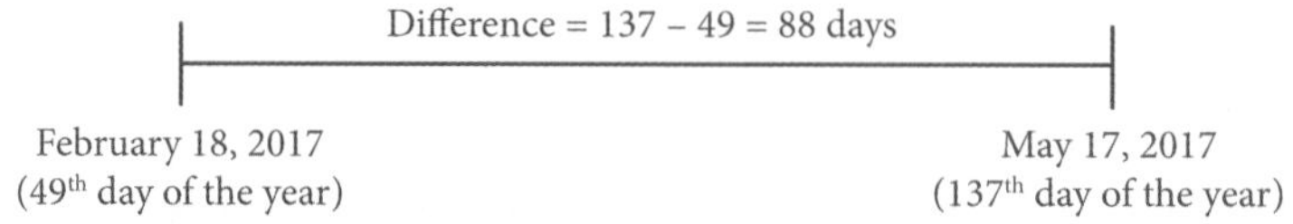

Therefore, the number of days in the time period = 88 days ($t = \frac{88}{365}$ years).

Example 8.1(j) **Calculating the Number of Days in a Time Period During a Non-Leap Year When the Time Period is Over Two Calendar Years**

Calculate the number of days in the time period from October 18, 2017 to April 05, 2018.

Solution

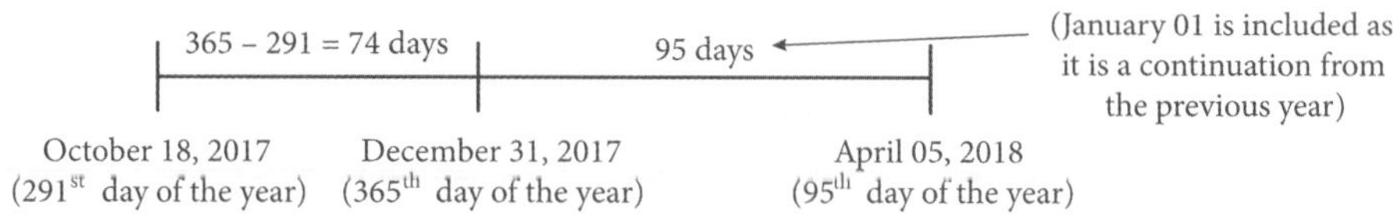

Therefore, the number of days in the time period = 74 + 95 = 169 days ($t = \frac{169}{365}$ years).

Example 8.1(k) **Calculating the Number of Days in a Time Period During a Leap Year**

Calculate the number of days in the time period from January 15, 2016 to March 20, 2017.

Solution

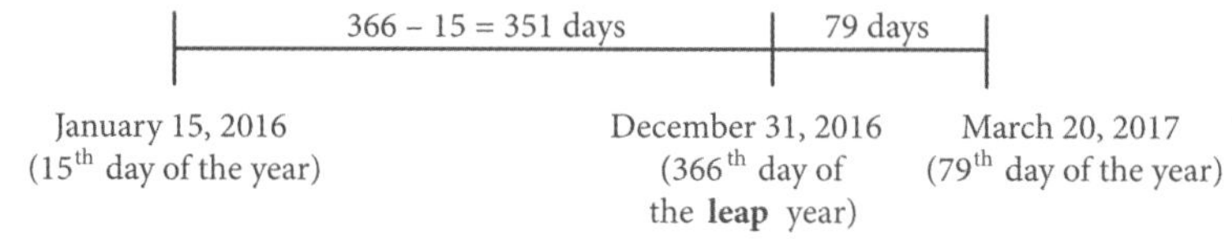

Therefore, the number of days in the time period = 351 + 79 = 430 days ($t = \frac{430}{365}$ years).

Method 3: Determining the Number of Days Using a Financial Calculator

You can use a financial calculator, such as the Texas Instruments BA II Plus, to determine the number of days in a time period as illustrated below:

The following example will illustrate the use of the calculator to determine the number of days.

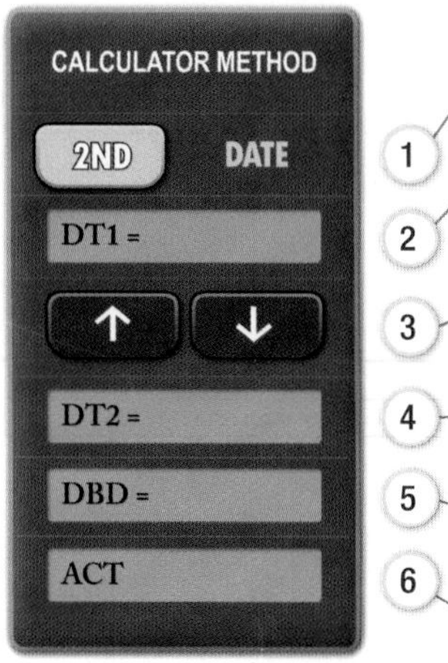

1. Pressing the **2ND** button then **DATE** (*secondary function of* **1**) will take you to the date worksheet to determine the number of days between two dates.
2. *Date 1* is the earlier date or the first date you will enter. Dates are shown in mm-dd-yyyy format and entered as mm.ddyy (you will understand this better while working through an example).
3. The **up arrow** and **down arrow** buttons are used to toggle between different items in the date worksheet.
4. *Date 2* is the later date or the second date you will enter. If you enter the dates in a reverse order you will get a negative value for the number of days.
5. *Days between dates* will give you the number of days between the first date entered and the second date entered. It includes the first day and excludes the last day in the calculation.
6. The *ACT* setting shows you that the setting for your date worksheet takes the *actual* number of days into consideration: i.e., it includes adjustments for leap years. If it is set to *360*, change it by pressing **2ND** then **SET** (*secondary function of* **ENTER**) to get *ACT*.

Example 8.1(I) **Calculating the Number of Days in a Time Period Using a Financial Calculator**

Calculate the number of days in the time period from October 18, 2017 to April 05, 2018.

Solution

age 325

Spreadsheets can also be used to calculate the number of days between 2 dates. The spreadsheet solution for this example is shown on page 325.

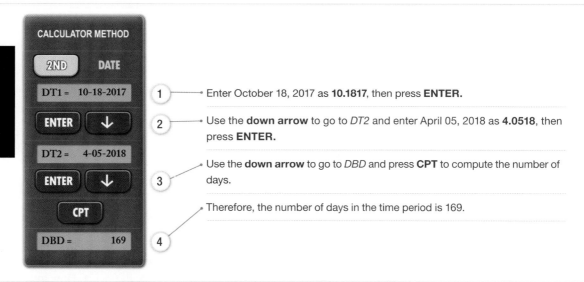

1. Enter October 18, 2017 as **10.1817**, then press **ENTER.**
2. Use the **down arrow** to go to *DT2* and enter April 05, 2018 as **4.0518**, then press **ENTER.**
3. Use the **down arrow** to go to *DBD* and press **CPT** to compute the number of days.
4. Therefore, the number of days in the time period is 169.

8.1 | Exercises

Answers to the odd-numbered problems are available at the end of the textbook.

For the following problems, express the answers rounded to two decimal places, wherever applicable.

1. Calculate the number of days in the following time periods and express it in terms of years:
   a. January 01, 2017 to February 19, 2017
   b. February 26, 2018 to December 02, 2018
   c. November 23, 2016 to April 04, 2017
   d. August 25, 2015 to September 06, 2016

2. Calculate the number of days in the following time periods and express it in terms of years:
   a. August 18, 2017 to September 19, 2017
   b. January 23, 2018 to October 06, 2018
   c. July 18, 2016 to July 18, 2017
   d. October 19, 2015 to November 06, 2016

3. Calculate the amount of interest earned on the following investments:

	Principal	Rate	Time period
a.	$200	10% p.a.	200 days
b.	$2200	4% p.a.	April 15, 2017 to November 01, 2017
c.	$5605	1.2% p.m.	January 24, 2017 to February 15, 2018
d.	$150	0.8% p.m.	1 year and 9 months

4. Calculate the amount of interest earned on the following investments:

	Principal	Rate	Time period
a.	$20,000	5% p.a.	250 days
b.	$200	12% p.a.	November 06, 2016 to February 28, 2017
c.	$800	1.10% p.m.	March 15, 2017 to August 25, 2018
d.	$500	0.75% p.m.	2 years and 3 months

5. What was the amount of interest charged on a loan of $12,500 received on January 18, 2017 and settled on April 24, 2017 if the interest rate on the loan was 3.25% p.a.?

6. Saira invested $3450 into a savings account that was earning 2.5% p.a. If she invested this amount on May 25, 2017, how much interest did she make by November 23, 2017?

7. Salma earned 2.2% p.a. on a short-term investment of $5000. Calculate the interest amount earned on this investment if she deposited the money on November 18, 2016 and withdrew it on February 23, 2017.

8. On December 25, 2016, Amy borrowed $4750 from Cynthia at 5.5% p.a. If she repaid the amount on April 27, 2017, calculate the amount of interest charged on the loan.

9. Owen lent Hua $5000 at 5% p.a. simple interest for 1 year and 3 months. Calculate the amount of interest charged at the end of the term.

10. Madison won a prize amount of $1500 and she deposited the entire amount into a savings account at a local bank. How much interest would she have earned after 18 months if interest on the savings account was 3% p.a.?

11. Nathan obtained a loan of $750 to purchase a bike. How much interest would Nathan have to pay at the end of 11 months if the loan was at an interest rate of 5.5% p.a.?

12. Ernie wanted to purchase a motorbike but was short $4350. He approached his friend who agreed to lend him the amount, as long as he paid back the money in 4 months at an interest rate of 6% p.a. How much interest would Ernie have to pay his friend at the end of 4 months?

13. Brenda withdrew $8000 from her business and deposited this amount into a savings account on January 02, 2015. If the account provided her with an interest rate of 4% p.a., calculate the amount of interest she would earn by March 15, 2016.

14. Kumar's website development business was doing well and he wanted to lend the surplus earnings he made to his friend who was in need of money. He lent $5000 at 6% p.a. to his friend on February 7, 2015. Calculate the amount of interest his friend had to pay on July 11, 2016.

15. Benjamin borrowed $2500 from a money lender. If the money lender charges interest at 12.5% p.a., calculate the amount of interest Benjamin had to pay the lender at the end of 20 days.

16. Zack wanted to propose to his girlfriend and decided to purchase a diamond ring. The ring he liked was selling for $3200 but he only had $1500 with him. His friend, Ethan, agreed to lend him the remaining amount at an interest rate of 12% p.a. If Zack returned the money in 40 days, calculate the amount of interest he had to pay Ethan for the loan.

17. Aidan borrowed $5000 from a lender at 1.5% p.m. If he repaid the amount in 45 days, calculate the amount of interest he had to pay.

18. Maya had a savings account with a bank in Canada that was providing her with a very low interest rate of 0.05% p.m. If she deposited $10,000 in her savings account, calculate the amount of interest she earned after 60 days.

19. Which rate is more attractive for a lender of a loan: 9.8% p.a. or 0.85% p.m.? Explain your answer.

20. Lian's friend offered to lend her $1000 at an interest rate of 6.5% p.a. However, her sister offered her the same amount at 0.52% p.m. Who was charging her a smaller amount of interest for the loan? Explain your answer.

21. Angelo took a loan of $2500 from a bank at 4.6% p.a. for 18 months and gave it to his friend Alisa as a loan at a rate of 6.0% p.a. At the end of 18 months, how much interest should Alisa have paid Angelo? Of this amount, how much interest should Angelo have paid the bank?

22. Mike borrowed $3250 from a bank at 3.8% p.a. for 15 months and gave it to Trish as a loan at a rate of 4.5% p.a. At the end of 15 months, how much interest should Trish have paid Mike? Of this amount, how much interest should Mike have paid the bank?

23. Aba invested $5200 for 210 days at 0.4% p.m. Tabitha invested the same amount for the same period but at 4.3% p.a. Who earned more and by how much?

24. Caroline invested $4500 for 180 days at 0.35% p.m. Cole invested the same amount for the same period but at 4.4% p.a. Who earned more and by how much?

- 25. Jada invested a total of $7500. Out of this, $3500 was invested at 4.6% p.a. and the remainder at 0.4% p.m. Calculate the total interest earned from both investments after 8 months.
- 26. Babiya borrowed a total of $3250 to pay for college fees. $2000 of this was from a bank at 6.25% p.a. and the remainder from a credit union at 0.9% p.m. Calculate the total interest she should have paid after 9 months for both the loans.
- 27. Yara took a loan of $2600 for 180 days at 11% p.a. How much more or less money would be required to pay off the loan if the interest rate is 1.2% p.m. instead of 11% p.a.?
- 28. Afsoon invested $9500 for 320 days at 8% p.a. How much more or less interest would he have earned on the investment if his money was growing at an interest rate of 0.75% p.m. instead of 8% p.a.?
- 29. John deposited $5000 in a bank at a simple interest rate for 6 months. If the interest rate was 2% higher than that offered by the bank, how much more interest would he have earned?
- 30. Lisa invested $6000 in a savings account at a simple interest rate for 2 years. If the interest rate was 1.5% higher than that offered by the savings account, how much more interest would she have earned?

8.2 | Calculating Principal, Interest Rate, Time, and Maturity Value

In simple interest calculations, depending on the information provided, the simple interest Formula 8.1 can be rearranged to solve for the unknown variable, as shown below:

Using Formula 8.1, $I = Prt$

Therefore, $Prt = I$

Dividing both sides by,

(i) *rt*, we obtain the principal, $P = \frac{I}{rt}$

(ii) *Pt*, we obtain the simple interest rate, $r = \frac{I}{Pt}$

(iii) *Pr*, we obtain the time period, $t = \frac{I}{Pr}$

P, r, t Triangle

Here is a triangle that can be used to help in rearranging the formula $I = Prt$ to solve for the variable *P*, *r*, or *t*.

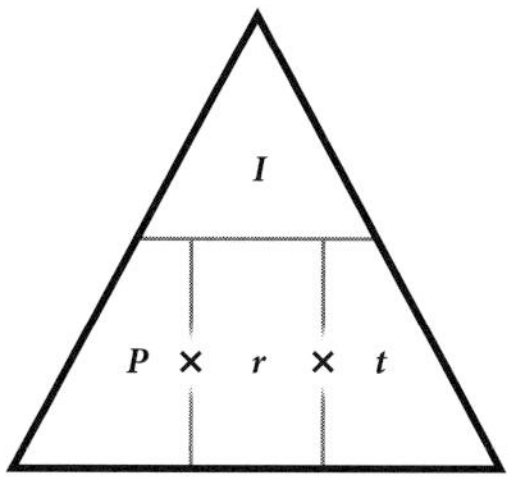

Variables beside each other at the bottom are multiplied ($P \times r \times t$, as shown).

Variable I is divided by the variables at the bottom.

To obtain a formula to find *P*, *r*, or *t*, cover that variable and read the remaining variables in the triangle.

For example, if you want to solve for '*P*', the formula can be found by covering '*P*' and reading the remaining variables in the triangle, to obtain $P = \frac{I}{rt}$.

Example 8.2(a) **Calculating the Principal**

A 5-month term deposit at Andrew's bank offers a simple interest rate of 3.5% p.a. If Andrew earned an interest amount of \$75 over the 5-month period, how much did he deposit in this term deposit?

Page 325

Solution

$I = \$75.00,\quad r = 3.5\%\text{ p.a.} = 0.035\text{ p.a.},\quad t = 5\text{ months} = \frac{5}{12}\text{ years}$

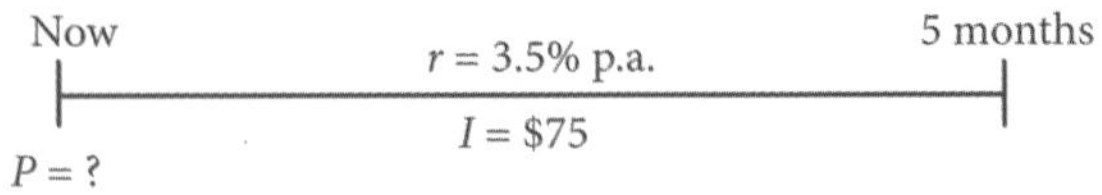

Rearranging Formula 8.1, $P = \frac{I}{rt}$

$$= \frac{75.00}{0.035 \times \frac{5}{12}}$$

$$= 5142.857143... = \$5142.86$$

Therefore, Andrew deposited \$5142.86 in his term deposit to earn an interest amount of \$75.00.

Example 8.2(b) **Calculating the Time Period**

The simple interest charged on a short-term loan of \$30,000 at 9.5% p.a. was \$1900.

(i) What was the term expressed in months?

(ii) What was the term expressed in days (rounded up to the next day)?

Page 325

Solution

$I = \$1900.00,\quad P = \$30{,}000.00,\quad r = 9.5\%\text{ p.a.} = 0.095\text{ p.a.}$

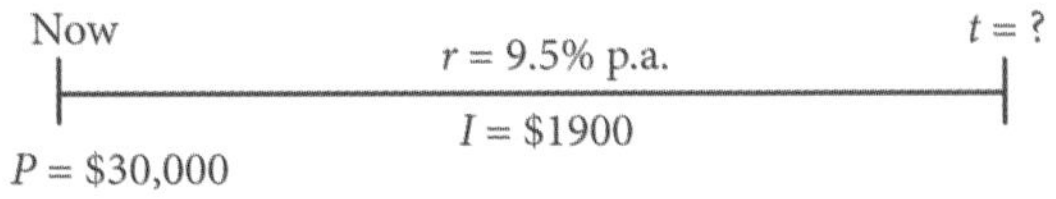

Do not round intermediate steps. When using a calculator, use the store and recall functions, as illustrated on Page 636.

Rearranging Formula 8.1,

$$t = \frac{I}{Pr}$$

$$t = \frac{1900.00}{30{,}000.00 \times 0.095}\text{ years}$$

$$= 0.666666...\text{ years}$$

(i) Expressing 't' in months

$t = 0.666666... \times 12$ months

$= 7.999999...$ months

$= 8$ months

Therefore, the term was 8 months.

(ii) Expressing 't' in days (rounded up to the next day)

$t = 0.666666... \times 365$ days

$= 243.333333...$ days

$= 244$ days

Therefore, the term was 244 days.

Example 8.2(c) **Calculating the Rate of Interest**

Calculate the rate of simple interest per annum offered on savings of \$2900 if the interest earned is \$170 over a period of 8 months.

Page 326

Solution

Method 1: Using unit of 't' in years

$I = \$170.00,\ P = \$2900.00,\ t = 8\text{ months} = \frac{8}{12}\text{ years}$

Rearranging Formula 8.1,

$$r = \frac{I}{Pt} = \frac{170.00}{\left(2900.00 \times \frac{8}{12}\right)}$$

$$= 0.087931\ldots = 8.79\%\text{ p.a.}$$

Method 2: Using unit of 't' in months

$I = \$170.00,\quad P = \$2900.00,\quad t = 8\text{ months}$

Rearranging Formula 8.1,

$$r = \frac{I}{Pt} = \frac{170.00}{2900.00 \times 8}$$

$$= 0.007327\ldots = 0.73\%\text{ p.m}$$

$$= 0.007327... \times 12\text{ p.a.}$$

$$= 0.087931... = 8.79\%\text{ p.a.}$$

Therefore, the rate of interest is 8.79% p.a.

Calculating the Maturity Value

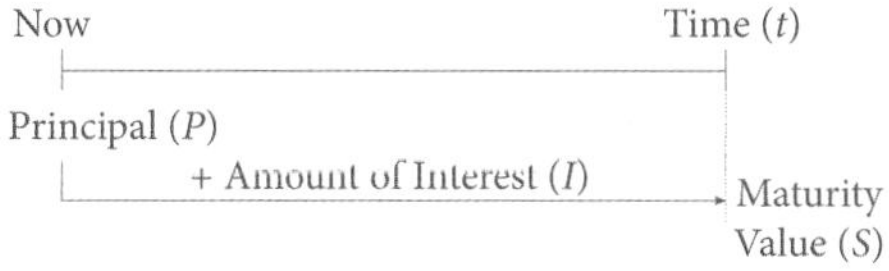

Maturity value (S) is the accumulated value (or future value) of the principal over a period of time. It is the sum of the principal amount and the amount of interest.

Therefore, *Maturity Value = Principal + Amount of Interest,* as shown in the following formula:

Formula 8.2(a)

Maturity Value

$$S = P + I$$

This can be rearranged to obtain, $I = S - P$

And, $P = S - I$

Formulas 8.1 and 8.2(a) can be combined by substituting for 'I' as follows:

$I = Prt$ From Formula 8.1

$S = P + I$ From Formula 8.2(a)

Substituting 'I' from Formula 8.1 into Formula 8.2(a),

$S = P + Prt$

Factoring out the common factor 'P', results in the following formula:

Formula 8.2(b)

Maturity Value

$$S = P(1 + rt)$$

Dividing both sides by $(1 + rt)$ and rearranging the equation to isolate P,

Formula 8.2(c)

Principal

$$P = \frac{S}{(1 + rt)} \quad \textbf{or} \quad P = S(1 + rt)^{-1}$$

Example 8.2(d)

Calculating the Maturity Value and Amount of Interest

Selena received an amount of \$700 from a pawnbroker at an interest rate of 1.5% p.m. Calculate the maturity value of her loan and amount of interest she would have to pay at the end of four months.

Solution

age 326

$P = \$700.00,$ $r = 1.5\%$ p.m. $= 0.015$ p.m., $t = 4$ months

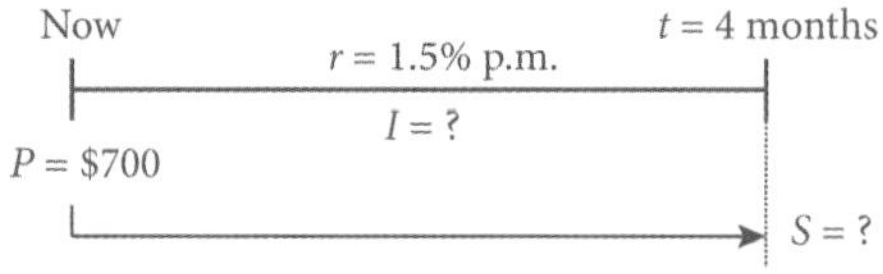

Using Formula 8.2(b), $S = P(1 + rt)$

$S = 700.00(1 + 0.015 \times 4)$

$= \$742.00$

Therefore, the maturity value of her loan is \$742.00.

Using Formula 8.2(a), $S = P + I$

Rearranging, $I = S - P$

$= 742.00 - 700.00$

$= \$42.00$

Therefore, the interest she would have to pay is \$42.00.

Example 8.2(e) Calculating the Principal and Amount of Interest

At the end of ten months, Gwyneth had \$2264.50 in a fund that was growing at a simple interest rate of 8% p.a.

(i) What was the principal amount invested?

(ii) What was the interest earned?

Solution

Page 326

$S = \$2264.50$, $r = 8\%$ p.a. $= 0.08$ p.a., $t = 10$ months $= \frac{10}{12}$ years

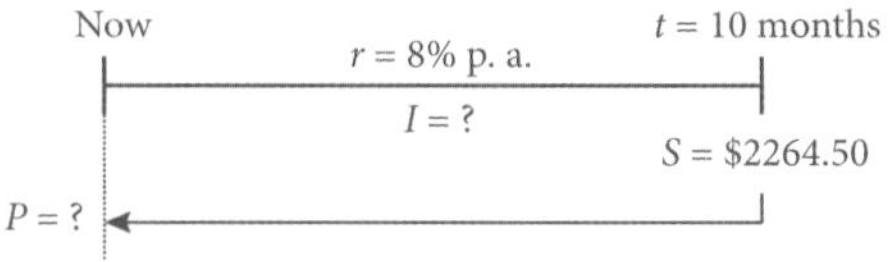

(i) Using Formula 8.2(c),

$$P = \frac{S}{(1 + rt)} = \frac{2264.50}{\left(1 + 0.08 \times \frac{10}{12}\right)}$$

$$= 2122.968750... = \$2122.97$$

Or,

$$P = S(1 + rt)^{-1} = 2264.50\left(1 + 0.08 \times \frac{10}{12}\right)$$

$$= 2122.968750... = \$2122.97$$

Therefore, she invested \$2122.97.

(ii) Using Formula 8.2(a),

$$S = P + I$$

$$I = S - P$$

$$= 2264.50 - 2122.97$$

$$= \$141.53$$

Therefore, she earned \$141.53 in interest.

Example 8.2(f) Calculating the Interest Paid and Maturity Value of a Loan with Varying Interest Rates

Peter obtained a loan on April 13, 2017 for \$4200 at 4.1% p.a. simple interest. On June 01, 2017, the prime rate increased and the rate on the loan changed to 4.35% p.a. If the loan was repaid on July 15, 2017, what was the interest paid on the loan? What was the maturity value of the loan on this date?

Solution

Page 326

$P = \$4200$ is the principal amount of the loan.

April 13 to June 01 = 49 days, $t_1 = \frac{49}{365}$ years, $r_1 = 4.1\%$ p.a.

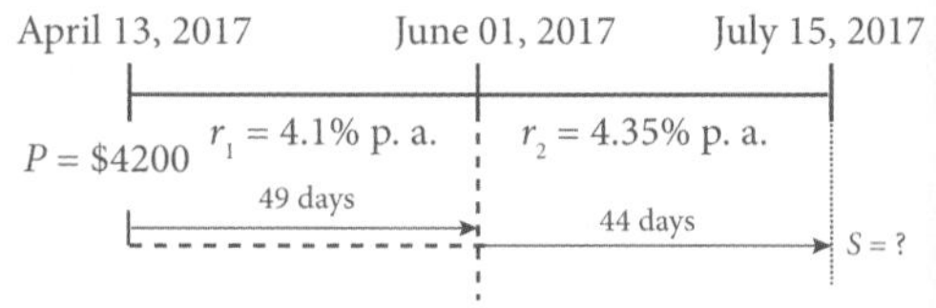

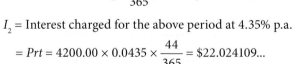

I_1 = Interest charged for the above period at 4.1% p.a.

$$= Prt = 4200.00 \times 0.041 \times \frac{49}{365} = \$23.117260...$$

June 01 to July 15 = 44 days, $t_2 = \frac{44}{365}$ years, $r_2 = 4.35\%$ p.a.

I_2 = Interest charged for the above period at 4.35% p.a.

$$= Prt = 4200.00 \times 0.0435 \times \frac{44}{365} = \$22.024109...$$

Therefore, the interest paid on the loan was 23.117260... + 22.024109... = 45.141369... = \$45.14

Using Formula 8.2(a), $S = P + I$

$$= 4200.00 + 45.14 = \$4245.14$$

Therefore, the maturity value of the loan was \$4245.14.

8.2 | Exercises

Answers to the odd-numbered problems are available at the end of the textbook.

For the following problems, express the answers rounded to two decimal places, wherever applicable.

Calculate the missing values for Problems 1 and 2.

1.

	Principal Amount	Date of Receiving Loan	Date of Repayment	Interest Rate	Amount of Interest Earned
a.	$12,400.00	July 16, 2017	August 05, 2018	?% p.a.	$1862.50
b.	?	April 19, 2017	September 09, 2017	18% p.a.	$280.40
c.	$19,865.00	August 08, 2017	?	5% p.a.	$375.50
d.	$1675.00	?	January 18, 2018	7.2% p.a.	$163.00

2.

	Principal Amount	Date of Investment	Date of Maturity	Interest Rate	Amount of Interest Earned
a.	$26,850.00	December 12, 2016	April 19, 2017	?% p.a.	$724.75
b.	?	May 01, 2017	October 06, 2017	12% p.a.	$180.75
c.	$180.00	September 17, 2017	?	5% p.a.	$12.00
d.	$7890.00	?	February 12, 2018	10.8% p.a.	$295.00

3. Calculate the maturity value of $5000 invested at 4.75% p.a. from August 21, 2017 to February 14, 2018.

4. Calculate the maturity value of $2750 invested at 5.15% p.a. from June 15, 2017 to January 05, 2018.

5. How much should be invested at 4.8% p.a. on September 11, 2017 to have it accumulate to $3000 on March 07, 2018?

6. How much should be invested at 5.2% p.a. on November 15, 2017 to have it accumulate to $7500 on April 28, 2018?

7. Vincent received a loan at 4.5% p.a. simple interest for 6 months. If he was charged an interest of $135 at the end of the period, what was the principal amount of the loan?

8. Chelsea invested her savings in an account at 2.5% p.a. simple interest for 9 months. If she earned an interest of $37.50 at the end of the term, what was the principal amount of the investment?

9. On March 3, 2017, Heather received a loan at 8% p.a. simple interest. She settled the loan on December 16, 2017. If she was charged an interest of $420, calculate the principal amount of the loan.

10. On November 23, 2017, Maya paid her uncle $868.75 in interest for a loan that he had given her on June 12, 2017. Calculate the amount she borrowed from him if he charged her interest of 12% p.a. simple interest.

11. Morgan received a loan of $10,000 from his friend. If he was charged an interest of $218.75 at the end of seven months, calculate the annual rate of simple interest on the loan.

12. Caitlin invested $5000 in an account for six months. If she earned an interest of $62.50 at the end of the term, calculate the annual rate of simple interest on the investment.

13. What annual rate of simple interest was charged on a loan of $4600 that was issued to Mary on August 15, 2015, if she settled the loan on September 03, 2016 with $380.50 in interest?

14. Layla received an academic achievement prize of $4000 from her college. She deposited this money on August 08, 2015 into a savings account. If the interest she earned when she withdrew the money on October 09, 2016 was $75.75, determine the annual rate of simple interest.

15. Lenny was charged an interest of $850 for a loan amount of $21,000 that he borrowed for 120 days. What monthly rate of simple interest was charged?

16. Zoey borrowed $2250 from her friend Tamer for her vacation to Halifax. If he charged her $120 in interest for 180 days, calculate the monthly simple interest rate charged.

17. Lydia borrowed $7400 at 7.35% p.a. simple interest. How many months did she take to repay the loan if she was charged an interest of $317.25?

18. Roshan invested $9180 in an account that was earning simple interest at a rate of 3.75% p.a. How many months did it take for his investment to earn an interest of $172.10?

19. Fred borrowed $8600 at 6.45% p.a. simple interest and repaid the loan on October 15, 2017. If he was charged a simple interest amount of $151.97, when did he receive the loan?

20. George repaid a $14,500 loan with $655.48 in simple interest on April 28, 2017. If the simple interest rate was 8.25% p.a., when did he receive the loan?

21. On March 03, 2017, Heather received a loan of $4000 at 8% p.a. simple interest. She settled the loan with an interest of $276.16. Calculate the date of repayment.

22. What is the date of repayment of a $6200 loan at 9.6% p.a. simple interest, if the loan was received on July 07, 2016 and the simple interest was $366.90?

23. How long in years and months will it take for an investment of $2000 earning 5.75% p.a. simple interest to grow to $2134.16?

24. A loan of $6500 at 4.5% p.a. simple interest was settled by paying $6865.60. What was the term of the loan in years and months?

25. Carolina invested $400 in her savings account for a period of six months. If the savings account was offering her a simple interest rate of 2.5% p.m., calculate the maturity amount of her investment and the interest she earned at the end of the time period.

26. Gladys received a loan of $700 from her aunt to purchase a new bike. She had to repay the loan in 45 days at a simple interest rate of 7% p.a. Calculate the total amount she would have had to repay her aunt and the interest charged at the end of the time period.

27. On March 20, 2017, Rachel deposited $50,000 into a short-term investment fund at 3.25% p.a. simple interest. Calculate the interest earned and the maturity amount on June 30, 2017.

28. On February 15, 2017, Sophia deposited the profits of her business into a savings account at 5% p.a. simple interest. On September 25, 2017, the amount matured to $18,546.75. Calculate the amount invested and the interest earned.

29. Karl invested his savings in a short term fund that was offering a simple interest rate of 4% p.a. Calculate the principal amount invested and the interest earned during the period if the maturity value of the investment at the end of 320 days was $20,720.

30. Isabella heard that if she invested her savings in a 91-day short-term investment at her local bank, she would earn interest at a simple interest rate of 3.5% p.a. Calculate the amount she invested and the interest earned from this investment if she received $11,950 at the end of the period.

31. Calculate the amount that Nicholas lent his friend and the interest he earned if his friend repaid him $3684.50 (including interest) at the end of 80 days. Assume that Nicholas charged his friend a simple interest rate of 5% p.a.

32. Sophia invested money into a savings account at 3% p.a. simple interest. At the end of six months, the amount matured to $31,312.75. What was the amount invested and the interest earned?

33. If the interest earned on an investment that is growing at 0.42% p.m. simple interest for 180 days is $250, calculate the principal and maturity amount of this investment.

34. If Rachel earned $20 as interest by lending a certain amount at 2% p.m. to her friend for 3 months, calculate the amount she lent to her friend and the amount she received from her friend at the end of the loan period.

35. Alejandro obtained a loan for $8500 on October 26, 2016 at 4.25% p.a. On January 01, 2017, the interest rate on the loan changed to 5.25% p.a. What was the total interest paid on the loan if he paid off the loan on June 30, 2017? What was the maturity value of the loan on this date?

36. Gwen invested $10,000 on April 24, 2016 at 5.15% p.a. On September 18, 2016, the interest rate changed to 4.95% p.a. What was the total interest earned by March 15, 2017? What was the maturity value of the investment on this date?

37. An investment of $18,750 grew to $19,193.75 in ten months. If the interest rate on the fund was 0.5% more than the original rate, what would have been the maturity value of the investment?

38. A loan of $3700 charging simple interest for 1 year and 3 months requires a repayment of $3954.38. If 1% was deducted from the interest rate, what would have been the repayment amount?

• 39. The maturity value of an investment is twice the amount invested. If the investment earns 7.5% p.a. simple interest, what is the term of the investment? Express your answer in years and months.

• 40. The maturity value of an investment is three times the amount invested. The interest is 7.95% p.a. simple interest. What is the term of the investment in years and days, rounded up to the next day?

• 41. Ben invested a certain amount at 6% p.a. and another $6000 at 7% p.a. After 15 months, the total interest from both investments was $716.50. Calculate the amount that was invested at 6% p.a.

• 42. Sandra invested a certain amount at 4% p.a. and another $6000 at 4.2% p.a. After 18 months, the total interest from both investments was $1098. Calculate the amount that was invested at 4% p.a.

• 43. An investment at a simple interest rate accumulates to $2970 in 2 years and to $3080 in 3 years. Calculate the amount invested and the interest rate per annum.

• 44. An investment at a simple interest rate accumulates to $7950 in 1 year and to $8400 in 2 years. Calculate the amount invested and the interest rate per annum.

8.3 | Calculating Equivalent Payments

Time value of money: A dollar is worth more today than a dollar in the future since it can be invested today to earn interest over time.

We have learned that the value of money changes over a period of time when invested or borrowed at an interest rate (time value of money).

For example, $1000 invested or borrowed today is neither equivalent to $1000 a year ago nor equivalent to $1000 a year from now. Assuming that money earns 10% p.a. simple interest, $1000 is equivalent to:

- $909.09 a year ago, or
- $1100 a year from now.

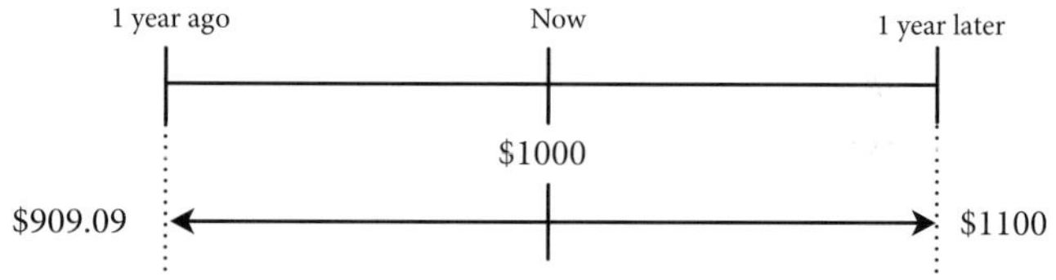

There may be times when it is necessary to change or reschedule the due date of a payment for various reasons. When the due date is changed, the value of money on the new date is called the equivalent value; i.e., a new value equivalent to the value of money on the old date.

Equivalent Payment of a Single Payment

If the rescheduled date of a payment is after the due date, it is similar to moving money in the forward direction (left to right). Therefore, the equivalent value of the payment on the rescheduled date is calculated using Formula 8.2(b):

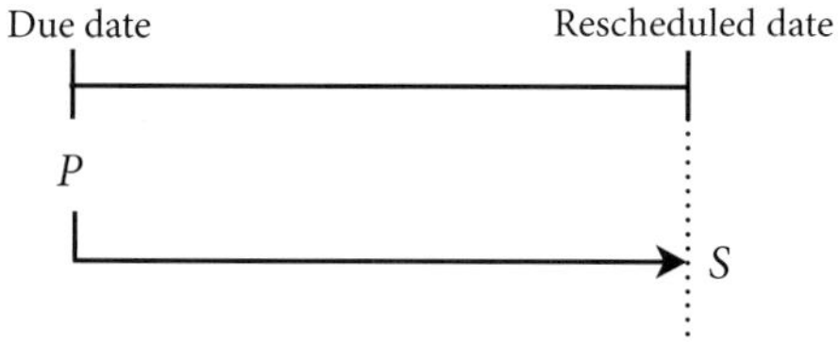

$$S = P(1 + rt)$$

If the rescheduled date of a payment is before the due date, it is similar to moving money in the reverse direction (right to left). Therefore, the equivalent value of the payment on the rescheduled date is calculated using Formula 8.2(c):

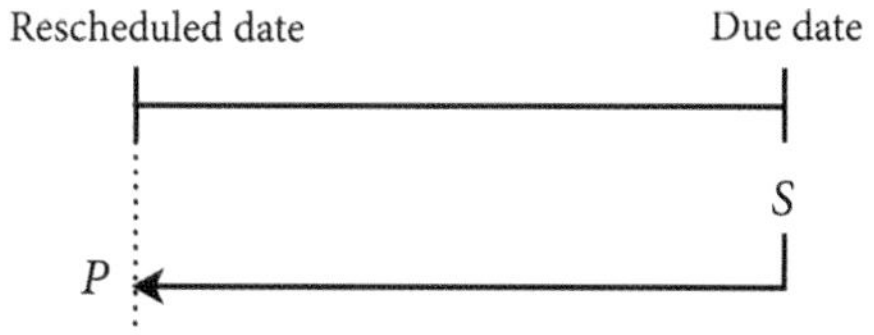

$$P = \frac{S}{(1 + rt)} \text{ or } P = S(1 + rt)^{-1}$$

Example 8.3(a) **Equivalent Payment of a Single Payment being Received in the Future**

Phil realizes that he is unable to repay a matured loan amount of \$2500 that is due today. If he is charged 5% p.a. (simple interest) for this loan, what equivalent payment is required to repay this amount in 6 months?

Solution

Page 326

$P = \$2500.00, \quad r = 5\% \text{ p.a.} = 0.05 \text{ p.a.}, \quad t = 6 \text{ months} = \frac{6}{12} \text{ years}$

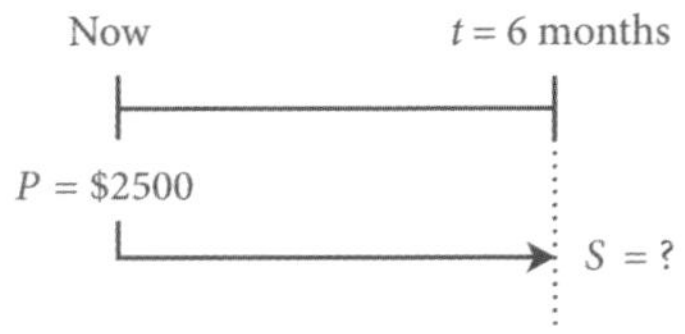

Using Formula 8.2(b), $S = P(1 + rt)$

Substituting values, $S = 2500.00\left(1 + 0.05 \times \frac{6}{12}\right)$

$= \$2562.50$

Therefore, he has to make an equivalent payment of \$2562.50 in 6 months.

Example 8.3(b) **Equivalent Payment of a Single Payment being Received on an Earlier Date**

Grace is required to repay a matured loan amount of \$1500 in nine months. However, she realized that she can clear the loan amount in six months instead. How much would she have to pay to clear the loan in six months if the interest rate charged is 4.5% p.a. (simple interest)?

Solution

Page 326

$S = \$1500.00, \quad r = 4.5\% \text{ p.a.} = 0.045 \text{ p.a.}, \quad t = 3 \text{ months} = \frac{3}{12} \text{ years}$

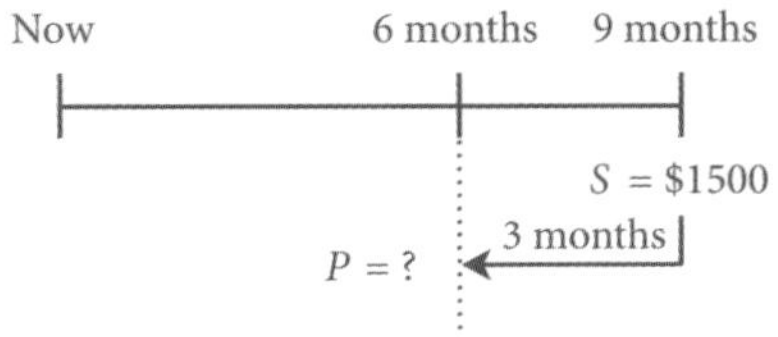

Using Formula 8.2(c), $P = S(1 + rt)^{-1}$

Substituting values, $P = 1500.00\left(1 + 0.045 \times \frac{3}{12}\right)^{-1}$

$= 1483.312732... = \$1483.31$

Therefore, she would have to pay \$1483.31 to clear the loan in 6 months.

Equivalent Payment of a Series of Payments

Since the value of money will be different at different points of time, equivalent payment calculations involving more than one payment will require a defined comparison point, known as the **focal date.** It is a reference date for calculating and equating the equivalent values of all payments. A timeline diagram will assist in calculating the equivalent value of a series of payments.

Note: *When working with equivalent payments in simple interest problems, the focal date should be defined. When the focal date changes, the value of the equivalent payment will be different.*

Example 8.3(c) **Single Equivalent Payment Replacing Two Payments with a Future Focal Date**

Abdul was supposed to pay \$500 six months ago and is supposed to pay \$900 in 10 months. He did not make the first payment as scheduled and will not make the scheduled payment in 10 months. Instead, he would like to clear the loan 18 months from now. What would the value of this single payment in 18 months be if the interest rate on the loan is 9% p.a.? Use 18 months from now as the focal date.

Solution

age 326

Let the single unknown payment in 18 months that is equivalent to the two payments be $x.

$x = *Equivalent value of $500 at the focal date* + *Equivalent value of $900 at the focal date*

$x = S_1 + S_2$

$S_1 = P_1(1 + rt_1)$

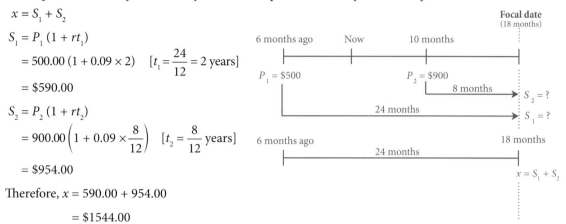

$= 500.00(1 + 0.09 \times 2) \quad [t_1 = \frac{24}{12} = 2 \text{ years}]$

$= \$590.00$

$S_2 = P_2(1 + rt_2)$

$= 900.00\left(1 + 0.09 \times \frac{8}{12}\right) \quad [t_2 = \frac{8}{12} \text{ years}]$

$= \$954.00$

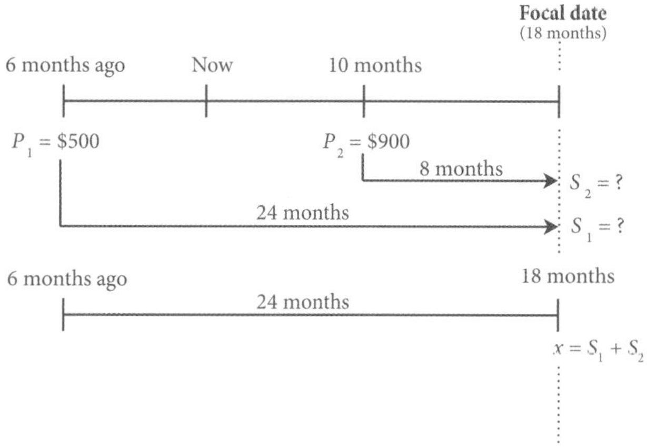

Therefore, $x = 590.00 + 954.00$

$= \$1544.00$

Therefore, the single equivalent payment in 18 months is $1544.00.

Example 8.3(d)

Single Equivalent Payment Replacing Two Payments with the Focal Date Falling Between the Two Payments

A payment of $5000 is due in three months and another payment of $8000 is due in nine months. Calculate the value of a single payment to be made in five months that is equivalent to these two payments if money earns 6% p.a. simple interest. Use five months from now as the focal date.

Solution

age 326

Let the single unknown payment in five months that is equivalent to the two payments be $x.

$x = *Equivalent value of $5000 at the focal date* + *Equivalent value of $8000 at the focal date*

$x = S_1 + P_2$

$S_1 = P_1(1 + rt_1)$

$= 5000.00\left(1 + 0.06 \times \frac{2}{12}\right) \quad [t_1 = \frac{2}{12} \text{ years}]$

$= \$5050.00$

$P_2 = S_2(1 + rt_2)^{-1}$

$= 8000.00\left(1 + 0.06 \times \frac{4}{12}\right)^{-1} \quad [t_2 = \frac{4}{12} \text{ years}]$

$= \$7843.137255...$

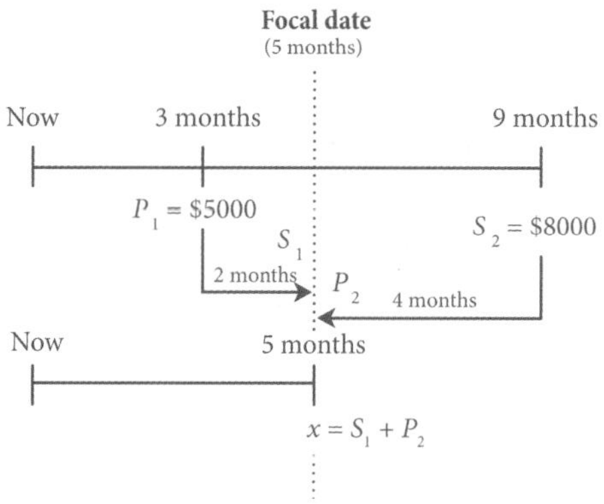

Therefore, $x = 5050.00 + 7843.137255...$

$= 12{,}893.13726... = \$12{,}893.14$

Therefore, the single payment to be made in five months is $12,893.14.

Example 8.3(e)

Comparing Two Different Payment Streams

A furniture supplier sold some furniture to a clothing store and provided them with two options to make a payment for the purchase:

Option (i): $4000 in two months and $1800 in six months.

Option (ii): $2150 in four months and $3732 in eight months.

If the rate of interest is 6% p.a. simple interest, calculate which option is economically better for the store. Use today as the focal date.

Page 327

Solution

We compare the equivalent values of the payments in Option (i) and Option (ii) at the focal date.

Equivalent value of payments using Option (i) at the focal date = $P_1 + P_2$

$$P_1 = S_1 (1 + rt_1)^{-1}$$
$$= 4000.00\left(1 + 0.06 \times \frac{2}{12}\right)^{-1}$$
$$= \$3960.396040...$$
$$P_2 = S_2 (1 + rt_2)^{-1}$$
$$= 1800.00\left(1 + 0.06 \times \frac{6}{12}\right)^{-1}$$
$$= \$1747.572816...$$
$$P_1 + P_2 = 3960.396040... + 1747.572816...$$
$$= 5707.968856...$$
$$= \$5707.97$$

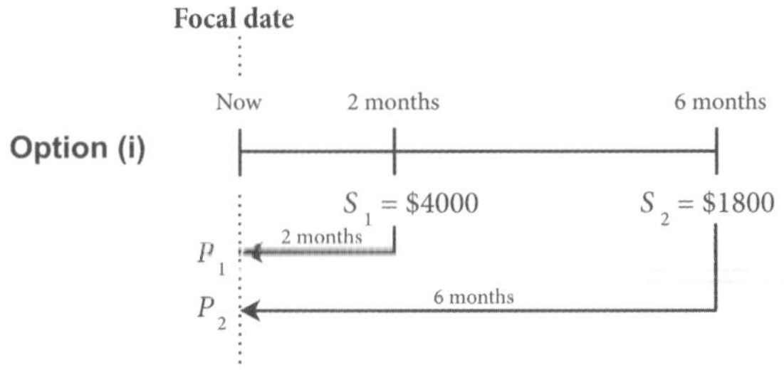

Therefore, the equivalent value of Option (i) at the focal date is \$5707.97.

Equivalent value of payments using Option (ii) at the focal date = $P_3 + P_4$

$$P_3 = S_3 (1 + rt_3)^{-1}$$
$$= 2150.00\left(1 + 0.06 \times \frac{4}{12}\right)^{-1}$$
$$= \$2107.843137...$$
$$P_4 = S_4 (1 + rt_4)^{-1}$$
$$= 3732.00\left(1 + 0.06 \times \frac{8}{12}\right)^{-1}$$
$$= \$3588.461538...$$
$$P_3 + P_4 = 2107.843137... + 3588.461538...$$
$$= 5696.304676...$$
$$= \$5696.30$$

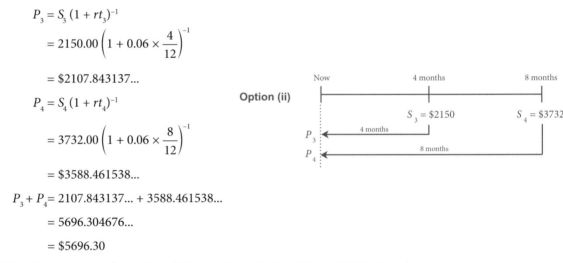

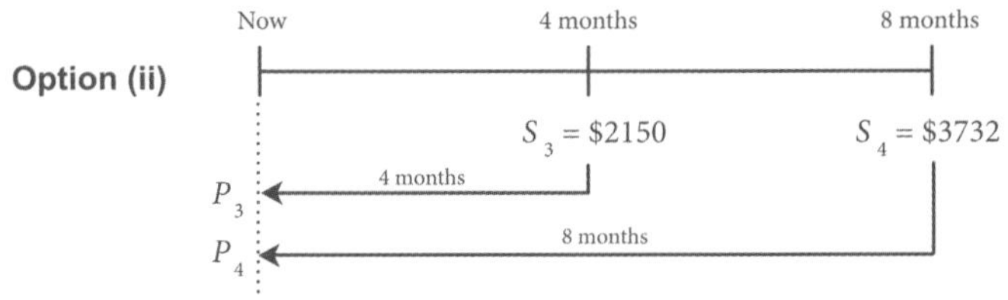

Therefore, the equivalent value of Option (ii) at the focal date is \$5696.30.

Comparing the equivalent value of Option (i) and Option (ii) at the focal date, the equivalent value of Option (ii) is economically better than that of Option (i).

Therefore, the store should choose Option (ii).

Example 8.3(f) **Two Equal Payments Replacing a Stream of Payments**

Cathleen has to repay a personal loan in two installments, one of \$1280 in 5 months and one of \$2193 in 15 months. If she wants to reschedule these payments with two equal payments, one in 8 months and the other in 12 months, what will be the amount of each of her new payments? Assume money is earning 8% p.a. simple interest and use 15 months from now as the focal date.

Page 327

Solution Let the two equal payment amounts be $x each.

Scheduled **Rescheduled**

Equivalent value of scheduled payments at the focal date = Equivalent value of rescheduled payments at the focal date

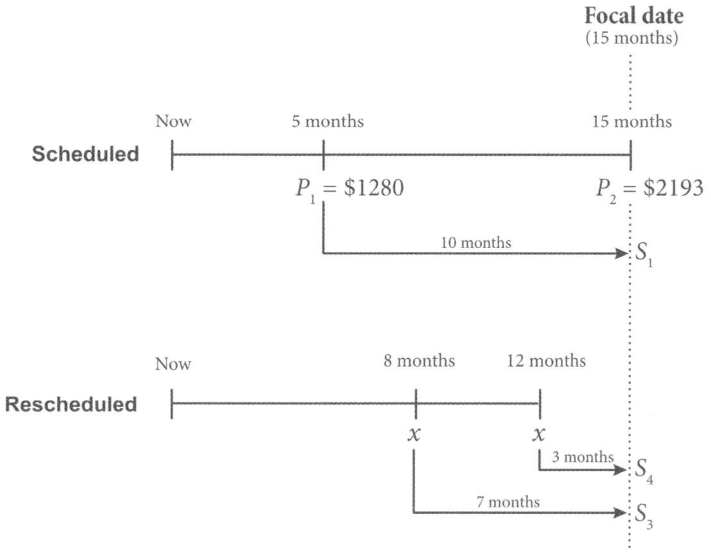

$$S_1 + P_2 = S_3 + S_4$$

Substituting values, $1280.00\,(1 + rt_1) + 2193.00 = x\,(1 + rt_3) + x\,(1 + rt_4)$

$$1280.00\left(1 + 0.08 \times \frac{10}{12}\right) + 2193.00 = x\left(1 + 0.08 \times \frac{7}{12}\right) + x\left(1 + 0.08 \times \frac{3}{12}\right)$$

Solving for x,

$$3558.333333\ldots = x(1.046666\ldots) + x(1.02)$$

$$3558.333333\ldots = x(2.066666\ldots)$$

$$x = 1721.774194\ldots = \$1721.77$$

> Remember to use the store and recall functions on the calculator as illustrated on Page 636.

Therefore, the two rescheduled equal payments that will replace her scheduled payments will be $1721.77 each.

8.3 | Exercises

Answers to the odd-numbered problems are available at the end of the textbook.

1. A company has two outstanding loans. The first one is for $20,000 at an interest rate of 15% p.a. and it was due six months ago and the second one is for $15,000 at an interest rate of 9.5% p.a. due today. The company re-negotiated to pay both loans with a single payment in four months. Calculate the repayment amount. Use four months from now as the focal date.

2. Sabir planned to make the following two investments: $7500 in 5 months at 10.8% p.a. and $5000 in 7 months at 6.5% p.a. Calculate the maturity value of both investments in 15 months. Use 15 months from now as the focal date.

3. Debt payments of $1250 and $1450 are due in four months and seven months, respectively. What single payment is required to settle both debts in one month? Assume an interest rate of 7.25% p.a. and use one month from now as the focal date.

4. A payment of $4500 was due three years ago and another payment of $2750 is due in four years. Determine the single payment that will settle both payments in two years. Assume an interest rate of 13.2% p.a. and use two years from now as the focal date.

5. A loan payment of $2900 was due 60 days ago and another payment of $3200 is due in 90 days. What single payment in 45 days is required to settle the two payments? Assume an interest rate of 4.2% p.a. and use 45 days from now as the focal date.

6. Saburi had to pay her landlord a payment of $750 that was due two months ago and another payment of $1250 in eight months. What single payment in three months will settle the amount that she owes the landlord, if the interest is 9% p.a.? Use three months from now as the focal date.

7. Natalia has to repay a loan in two installments: $10,000 in six months and $12,000 in ten months. Calculate the single equivalent payment that she can make in eight months that will replace these two payments if interest is 4% p.a. simple interest.
   a. Use eight months from now as the focal date.
   b. Use 'now' as the focal date.

8. Philip has two outstanding payments for a loan that he gave his friend: $7300, due two months ago, and another payment of $1800, due in eight months. If his friend promises to make one single payment in five months that would be equivalent to both these payments, what should be the size of the payment? Assume that money earns 3% p.a. simple interest.
   a. Use five months from now as the focal date.
   b. Use 'now' as the focal date.

9. You are given two options to settle a loan.
   - Option A: $600 now and $900 in one year.
   - Option B: $750 in six months and the balance in two years.

   If money earns 4.5% p.a. simple interest, calculate the payment required in two years under Option B. Use two years from now as the focal date.

10. You are given two options to settle a loan.
    - Option A: $750 now and $1250 in nine months.
    - Option B: $1000 in three months and the balance in one year.

    If money earns 4.8% p.a. simple interest, calculate the payment required in one year under Option B. Use one year from now as the focal date.

11. A supplier of doors provided a contractor with two options to make a payment for the supply of doors for a new condominium development project:
    - Option A: $120,500 immediately and another payment of $75,600 in six months.
    - Option B: $30,000 immediately and another payment of $165,500 in five months.

    If money earns 4% p.a. simple interest, calculate the option that would be economically better for the contractor and the amount by which he would benefit. Use today as the focal date.

12. Samantha won a lottery; however, the lottery company gave her the following two options to receive her prize money:
    - Option A: $10,000 in two months and $16,000 in eight months.
    - Option B: $5000 immediately and $22,000 in ten months.

    Which option would be economically better for Samantha and by how much, if money earns 7% p.a.? Use today as the focal date.

13. $1800 due two months ago and $700 due in three months are to be repaid by a payment of $1500 today and the balance payment in four months. Calculate the balance if the interest rate is 6% p.a. and the agreed focal date is four months from now.

14. Mee was supposed to pay $1350 that was due 150 days ago and is supposed to pay $450 that is due in 30 days to clear a loan that she borrowed from Yan. Instead, Mee promised to pay $1000 today and the balance in 60 days. Calculate the amount that she would have to pay in 60 days if the interest rate charged is 9% p.a. and the agreed focal date is 60 days from now.

15. The Director of Sales of a management consulting company was preparing a quotation for a potential client. He wanted to provide two payment options in the quote:
    - Payment Option A: $4500 in 4 months and another payment of $7630 in 13 months.
    - Payment Option B: Two equal payments, one in 6 months and the other in 12 months.

    If money earns 4% p.a., what must be the value of payments in Option B such that they are equivalent to the payments in Option A? Use now as the focal date.

16. What two equal payments, one on March 05, 2017 and the other on June 15, 2017, will be equivalent to the following two payments: $2400 on April 01, 2017 and $3500 on August 15, 2017? Assume that money earns 5% p.a. Use March 05, 2017 as the focal date.

- 17. The proprietor of Unica Hair Salon borrowed $9500 at 5% p.a. She agreed to settle the loan in two payments: one in six months and the other in nine months from the time of borrowing the loan. Calculate the amount of each payment, if the first payment is twice the amount of the second payment. Use nine months from now as the focal date.

- 18. Tiziana loaned $5000 to Jessica who settled the loan in two installments: one in three months and the other in ten months. If the second payment was three times the amount of the first payment, and Jessica was charged 4.5% p.a., calculate the value of each of the payments. Use ten months from now as the focal date.

- 19. Vijay borrowed $3000 that is to be settled in three installments as follows: first payment of $1000 in six months and two equal payments, one in nine months and the other in one year. Calculate the value of each of the equal payments if the interest charged was 7.5% p.a. Let the focal date be the end of one year.

- 20. A loan of $15,000 at 9% p.a. is to be settled in three installments as follows: first payment of $5000 in three months, and two equal payments, one in six months and the other in nine months. Calculate the size of each of the equal payments. Let the focal date be three months from now.

8.4 | Applications of Simple Interest

Some common applications of simple interest are seen in:

- Savings accounts, Term deposits, and Guaranteed Investment Certificates
- Demand loans and partial payments of demand loans
- Promissory notes
- Discounting and proceeds
- Treasury bills and Commercial papers

Savings Accounts, Term Deposits, and Guaranteed Investment Certificates

Financial institutions offer different types of investment options to investors. Some of the secure investment options are savings accounts, term deposits, and Guaranteed Investment Certificates. Investors are not charged any special fee to invest in these options. When they invest money in these options, the financial institution makes use of the money for a period of time, and therefore pays interest to the investors. At the same time, the financial institution charges a higher interest rate to those borrowing money from them. Even though there is no fee when money is invested in these accounts, financial institutions make money on the difference between the interest it pays investors and the interest it charges borrowers.

Savings Accounts

A savings account provides people with a safe place to deposit their money. It is an option where funds are usually easily accessible; i.e., people can deposit and withdraw money from a savings account at any convenient time.

In a savings account, the interest is often calculated on a daily balance and posted monthly.

For example, if you have invested $1000 in a savings account for the month of March at a bank that is offering you an interest rate of 1% p.a.,

$$\text{Interest rate per day} = \frac{1\%}{365}$$

$$\text{Interest amount per day} = \frac{0.01}{365} \times \$1000 = \$0.027397...$$

$$\text{Interest paid at the end of March} = \$0.027397... \times 31 \text{ days} = \$0.85$$

Term Deposits

Term deposits, also known as fixed deposits or time deposits, are investment options where money is invested for a fixed period of time. If investors want to withdraw their money from a term deposit prior to the end of the term, they may have to pay a penalty as determined by the financial institution. As this investment is fixed for a period of time, the interest rate is higher than that of a savings account.

Guaranteed Investment Certificates (GIC)

The interest earned from savings accounts, term deposits, and GICs is taxable income.

Purchasing a GIC refers to investing a sum of money for a specific period of time. It is similar to a term deposit or fixed deposit. The investor is guaranteed to receive the full principal investment plus interest at the end of the specified time period. The time period for a GIC can range from a few days to five years or even ten years. The interest rate for a longer investment period or a larger amount of investment will be higher than that of a shorter period or smaller amount of investment.

GICs can also be redeemable or non-redeemable. In a redeemable GIC, the deposit may be withdrawn in whole or in part before the maturity date. In a non-redeemable GIC, the deposit usually cannot be redeemed or withdrawn before the maturity date. As redeemable GICs offer the option to withdraw before maturity, their interest rate is less than that offered on non-redeemable GICs.

Example 8.4(a) **Comparing GICs**

A bank offers 1.75% p.a. on investments of \$5000 to \$99,999 and 1.95% on investments of \$100,000 to \$249,000 for three-year GICs. What additional amount will Harold earn from investing in a \$160,000 three-year GIC instead of two \$80,000, three-year GICs?

Solution

Page 327

Calculating the earnings from the \$160,000, three-year GIC

$$I = Prt = 160{,}000.00 \times 0.0195 \times 3 = \$9360.00$$

Calculating the earnings from two \$80,000, three-year GICs

$$I = Prt = 80{,}000.00 \times 0.0175 \times 3 = \$4200.00$$

Total earnings from two \$80,000.00, three-year GICs = 4200.00 × 2 = \$8400.00

Additional earnings = 9360.00 – 8400.00 = \$960.00

Therefore, Harold will earn \$960.00 more from the \$160,000.00 three-year GIC.

Demand Loans

A demand loan is a loan that is payable when it is demanded by the lender who issues the loan. The borrower signs a demand note agreeing to pay the interest and the principal on demand. Once the borrower signs the demand note, the lender has the right to ask for full payment at any time for any reason.

A demand loan requires no regular repayments of the principal amount, but the lender may request for regular payments to cover the interest on the loan. The borrower has an option to make a payment to settle the loan either in part (partial payment) or in full anytime without paying a penalty.

The interest rate on a demand loan is generally a few percent points above the prime rate. The prime rate is the lowest lending interest rate that is set by the Bank of Canada. The Bank of Canada changes the prime rate periodically. The rate on a demand loan will change when the prime rate changes. A demand loan is usually not a secured loan; i.e., no protection (collateral) is required with assets to obtain the loan. Therefore, it is a high risk loan and the borrower will pay a high interest rate for the loan.

Note: *Calculating the interest paid on a demand loan with a varying interest rate is similar to Example 8.2 (f).*

Partial Payments of Demand Loans

When partial payments (more than one payment) are made to reduce a loan, each payment amount is first used to reduce the interest on the loan and the remainder is used to reduce the amount of principal. This method of dealing with repayments is called the **declining balance method**.

Example 8.4(b) **Partial Payments Using the Declining Balance Method**

A demand loan of \$20,000 at 18% p.a. simple interest was settled by a payment of \$5000 in 2 months, another small payment of \$500 in 5 months, and the outstanding balance in 6 months. Using the declining balance method, calculate the amount of the last payment.

Page 327

Solution

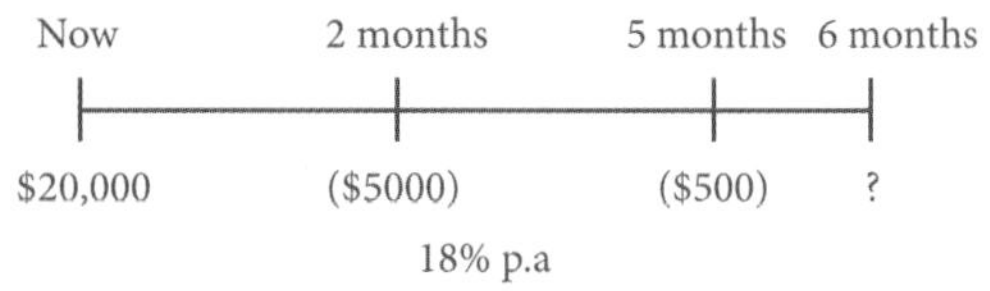

Calculating the balance after the first payment of $5000 in 2 months

The interest accumulated on the principal of $20,000.00 in the first two months at 18% p.a.:

Using the formula, $I = Prt$, $I = 20{,}000.00 \times 0.18 \times \frac{2}{12} = \$600.00$

The partial payment of $5000.00 is first used to clear the interest.

$$\textit{Amount left after clearing interest} = 5000.00 - 600.00 = \$4400.00$$

This balance amount from the partial payment is used to reduce the principal.

Therefore, $\textit{Principal Balance} = 20{,}000.00 - 4400.00 = \$15{,}600.00$

Calculating the balance after the second payment of $500.00 in 5 months

The interest accumulated on the principal of $15,600.00 since the last payment at 18% p.a.:

Using the formula, $I = Prt$, $I = 15{,}600.00 \times 0.18 \times \frac{3}{12} = \$702.00$

The partial payment of $500.00 is first used to clear the interest. Now, as the partial payment is less than the accumulated interest, there will be an interest balance.

$$\textit{Interest Balance} = 702.00 - 500.00 = \$202.00$$

Principal Balance will remain the same = $15,600.00

Last payment in 6 months

The interest accumulated on the principal of $15,600.00 since the last payment at 18% p.a.:

Using the formula, $I = Prt$, $I = 15{,}600.00 \times 0.18 \times \frac{1}{12} = \$234.00$

Calculating the balance to be paid in 6 months

Interest balance after the second payment = $202.00

Interest accumulated in the last month = $234.00

Principal amount remaining = $15,600.00

Total = 202.00 + 234.00 + 15,600.00 = $16,036.00

Therefore, the amount of the last payment is $16,036.00.

Note: *Partial payments can be greater or less than the interest that is due at the time of making the payment.*

- *If the partial payment is greater than the interest due at the time of the payment, the interest on the loan is first reduced. The remaining amount from the partial payment is then used to reduce the principal.*
- *If the payment is less than the interest due at the time of the payment, the payment is held (without interest) until another partial payment is made in an amount that exceeds the interest due at the time of the new partial payment.*

Promissory Notes

A promissory note is a written promise to repay a borrowed amount to the lender on an agreed date. The borrower of the amount is called the 'maker' of the note (as the borrower is making a promise to pay the amount) and the lender is called the 'payee' (as the borrower promises to pay the lender the amount). Promissory notes are generally used to record the financial details of personal loans:

- The amount shown on the promissory note is called the 'face value' of the note.
- The time period negotiated is known as the ‘term’ or the ‘maturity date', which may be in days, months, or years.

The interest period is the time period from the date of issue of the note to the legal due date. The maturity value is the amount payable on the legal due date.

As per Canadian Law (Bill of Exchange Act, Section 41), the legal due date is three days after the maturity date. This extension period is known as the 'grace period'. If a promissory note is issued with 'No Grace Period' marked on it, then the maturity date and the legal due date will be the same.

The interest period is the time period from the date of issue to the legal due date.

Note: *In the solved examples, we will assume that 'No Grace Period' is marked on all notes, so the legal due date and the maturity date will be the same.*

There are two types of promissory notes: interest-bearing notes and non-interest-bearing notes.

Interest-Bearing Promissory Note

The face value of the note is the amount of loan that must be repaid with the interest calculated based on the interest rate specified on the note. Therefore, the maturity value (S) is the amount to be repaid and is calculated using Formula 8.2(b): $S = P(1 + rt)$.

The face value of an interest-bearing promissory note is the principal amount.

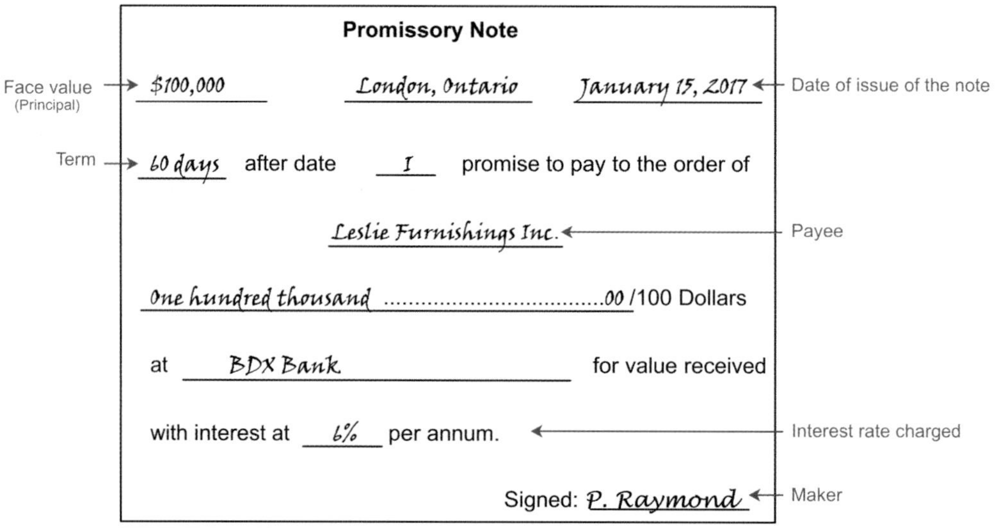
Promissory Note

Face value (Principal) → $100,000 London, Ontario January 15, 2017 ← Date of issue of the note

Term → 60 days after date I promise to pay to the order of

Leslie Furnishings Inc. ← Payee

One hundred thousand ....00 /100 Dollars

at BDX Bank for value received

with interest at 6% per annum. ← Interest rate charged

Signed: P. Raymond ← Maker

Exhibit 8.4(a): Sample Interest-Bearing Promissory Note

Example 8.4(c) Determining the Maturity Date and Maturity Value of an Interest-Bearing Promissory Note

Tony signs an interest-bearing promissory note for $100,000 at an interest rate of 6% p.a. The date of the note is April 15, 2017 and the term is 60 days. Determine the maturity date and the maturity value.

Solution

Page 327

Calculating the Maturity Date

Using the date worksheet on the financial calculator,

April 15, 2017 + 60 days = June 14, 2017

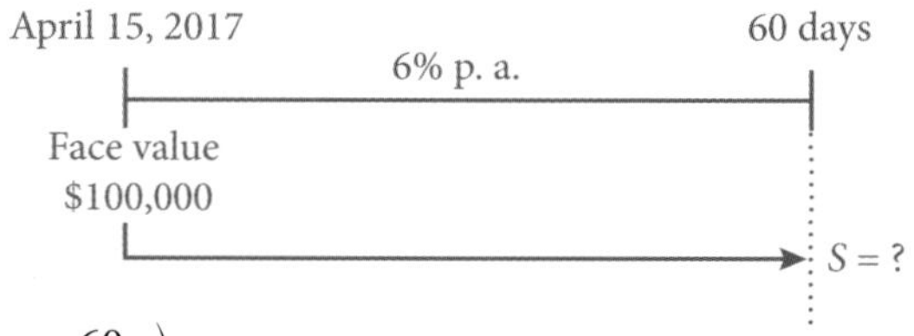

CALCULATOR METHOD

2ND DATE

4.1517 DT1 = 4-15-2017

ENTER ↓ ↓

DBD = 60

ENTER ↑

CPT

WED = 6-14-2017

Calculating the Maturity Value

$P = \$100,000.00$

Using Formula 8.2(b), $S = P(1 + rt)$

Substituting values, $S = 100,000.00\left(1 + 0.06 \times \frac{60}{365}\right)$

$= 100,986.3014... = \$100,986.30$

Therefore, the maturity value is $100,986.30.

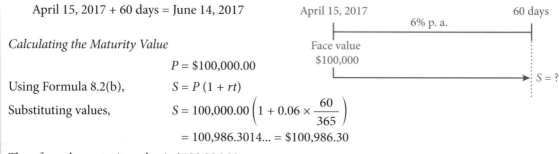

Example 8.4(d)

Calculating the Face Value of an Interest-Bearing Promissory Note

Compute the face value of a 90-day promissory note dated October 25, 2017 that has a maturity value of \$76,386.99 and an interest rate of 7.5% p.a.

Solution

Page 328

The face value is the principal amount of the maturity value.

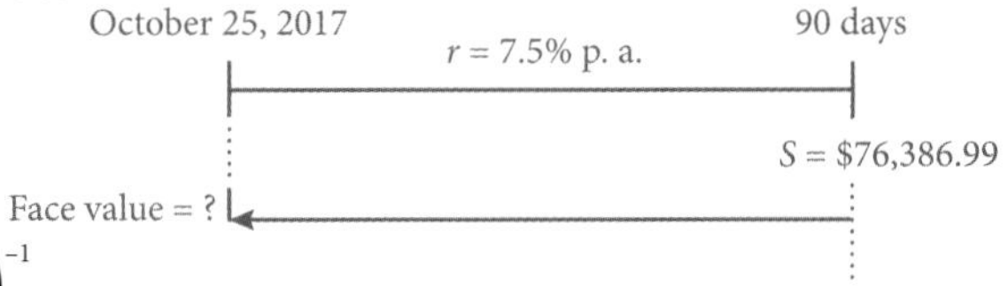

The maturity date is 90 days from October 25, 2017.

Using Formula 8.2(c), $P = S\,(1 + rt)^{-1}$

Substituting values, $P = 76{,}386.99\left(1 + 0.075 \times \dfrac{90}{365}\right)^{-1}$

$= 75{,}000.00363... = \$75{,}000.00$

Therefore, the face value of the promissory note is \$75,000.00.

Non-Interest-Bearing Promissory Note

The face value of a non-interest-bearing promissory note is the maturity value of the note; i.e., interest is calculated and included in the face value. The interest rate may not be specified on the note and the lender usually agrees on the interest rate on the loan. The loan amount is calculated using Formula 8.2(c): $P = S\,(1+ rt)^{-1}$.

The face value of a non-interest-bearing promissory note is the maturity value. Also observe that there is no interest rate given on the promissory note.

Note: *In cases when there is no interest charged on the loan (such as when lending to a friend or family member), non-interest-bearing promissory notes are used for record keeping purposes. In such cases, the face value will be the same as the loan amount.*

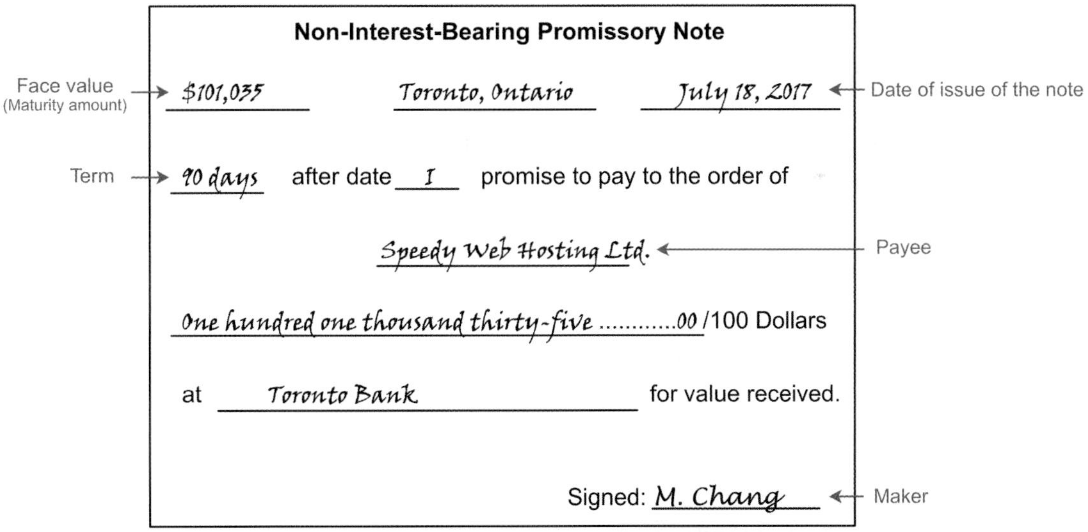
Non-Interest-Bearing Promissory Note

Face value (Maturity amount) → \$101,035 | Toronto, Ontario | July 18, 2017 ← Date of issue of the note

Term → 90 days after date I promise to pay to the order of

Speedy Web Hosting Ltd. ← Payee

One hundred one thousand thirty-five ....00 /100 Dollars

at Toronto Bank for value received.

Signed: M. Chang ← Maker

Exhibit 8.4(b): Sample Non-Interest-Bearing Promissory Note

Example 8.4(e)

Calculating the Loan Amount of a Non-Interest-Bearing Promissory Note

A 90-day non-interest-bearing promissory note dated March 25, 2017 has a face value of \$40,000. If the note is discounted at 5.5% p.a. on the date of issue, calculate the amount of the loan.

Solution

Page 328

The maturity date is 90 days from March 25, 2017.

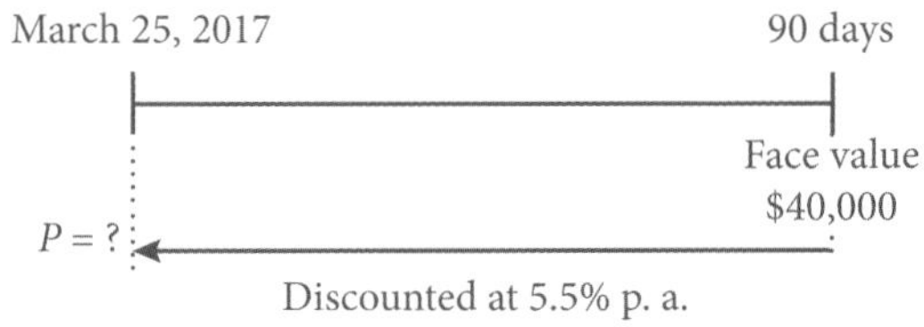

Using Formula 8.2(c), $P = S\,(1 + rt)^{-1}$

Substituting values, $P = 40{,}000.00\left(1 + 0.055 \times \dfrac{90}{365}\right)^{-1}$

$= 39{,}464.79254... = \$39{,}464.79$

Therefore, the amount of the loan is \$39,464.79.

Discounting and Proceeds

Discounting a promissory note refers to the process of finding the value of a note on a specific date before its specific legal due date. Sometimes notes and bills are resold before their maturity dates for various reasons. For example, the owner of the note may want to repay the loan earlier than the maturity date or the owner may require cash on the bill before its maturity date.

Proceeds: the amount for which a promissory note is bought or sold at the discounting date.

The amount received by the owner of the note at the time of the discount is called **proceeds** and the interest rate used or agreed to calculate the proceeds is called the **discount rate**. The discount rate may not be the same as the rate of interest on the note at the time of purchase.

The notes and bills are legal contracts. Therefore, it is necessary to find its maturity value first before calculating the proceeds.

For non-interest-bearing notes (T-bills and commercial papers), the face value is the maturity value. The maturity value is discounted using the discount rate to calculate the proceeds.

For interest-bearing notes, the face value is the amount of loan and the maturity value is to be calculated using $S = P(1 + rt)$. The maturity value is discounted using the discount rate to calculate the proceeds.

Example 8.4(f) **Calculating the Proceeds and Discount of a Non-Interest-Bearing Note**

A non-interest-bearing note with a face value of $30,000 is due in 120 days. If the note is discounted 30 days from the date of issue at a rate of 9% p.a., calculate the amount of proceeds and the amount of discount.

Solution

Page 328

Since it is a **non-interest-bearing note**, the face value is the maturity value. The maturity date is 120 days from the date of issue.

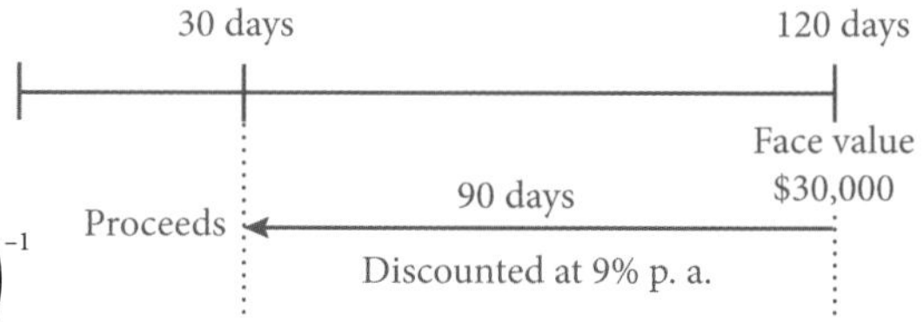

The time remaining is 120 – 30 = 90 days.

Using Formula 8.2(c), $P = S(1 + rt)^{-1}$

$$\text{Proceeds} = 30{,}000.00\left(1 + 0.09 \times \frac{90}{365}\right)^{-1}$$

$$= 29{,}348.70008... = \$29{,}348.70$$

The amount of proceeds is $29,348.70.

The amount of discount = 30,000.00 – 29,348.70 = $651.30.

Example 8.4(g) **Calculating the Proceeds and Discount of an Interest-Bearing Note**

An interest-bearing note for 90 days at 8% p.a. has a face value of $80,000. If the note is discounted 70 days from maturity at a rate of 10% p.a., calculate the amount of proceeds and the amount of discount.

Solution

Page 328

Since it is an **interest-bearing note**, the face value is the principal. The maturity date is 90 days from the date of issue.

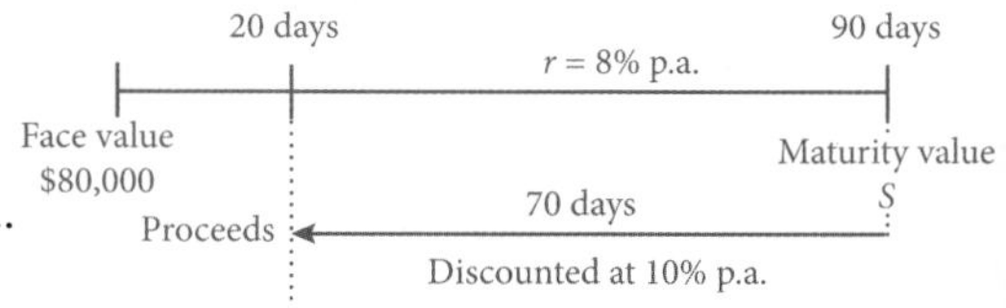

First calculate the maturity value of the note.

$$S = 80{,}000.00\left(1 + 0.08 \times \frac{90}{365}\right) = \$81{,}578.08219...$$

Now, since it is discounted 70 days from maturity,

$$t = 70 \text{ days} = \frac{70}{365} \text{ years}$$

Using Formula 8.2(c), $P = S(1 + rt)^{-1}$

$$\text{Proceeds} = 81{,}578.08219...\left(1 + 0.10 \times \frac{70}{365}\right)^{-1}$$

$$= 80{,}043.01075... = \$80{,}043.01$$

Therefore, the amount of proceeds will be $80,043.01.

The amount of discount = 81,578.08 – 80,043.01 = $1535.07.

Treasury Bills and Commercial Papers

Treasury bills, also known as T-bills, are written agreements or contracts issued to individuals, institutions, or corporate investors for a short term (less than a year) and are issued by the federal government on every other Tuesday through major financial institutions acting as their agents. The maturity period of T-bills is usually 13, 26, or 52 weeks (91, 182, or 364 days). Some provincial governments also issue T-bills, but on irregular dates or intervals. T-bills are generally available in denominations of $1000, $5000, $25,000, $100,000, and $1,000,000.

T-bills are considered very safe (risk-free) investments because they are fully guaranteed by the issuing government; however, they offer considerably lower returns than most other investments.

T-bills are similar to non-interest-bearing promissory notes. The face value of a T-bill is the amount shown on it and it is the maturity value that the government guarantees to pay on the maturity date. Therefore, the purchase price of a T-bill is calculated as a principal amount of the face value shown (maturity value) using the interest rate (called discount rate) offered at the time of purchase, which is based on market conditions.

T-bills are transferable and its value at the time of selling or buying is determined by the market rate for the time remaining until maturity.

Commercial papers are similar to T-bills, except that they are issued by large corporations. The maturity period of commercial papers is generally 1, 3, or 6 months (30, 90, or 180 days).

Example 8.4(h) **Calculating the Purchase Price of a T-bill**

Benjamin, an investor, purchased a 182-day T-bill that had an interest rate of 3.5% p.a. and face value of $25,000. Calculate the price he paid for the T-bill.

Solution

age 328

$S = \$25{,}000.00, \quad r = 0.035, \quad t = \frac{182}{365}$ years

Using Formula 8.2(c), $P = S(1 + rt)^{-1}$

Substituting values, $P = 25{,}000.00\left(1 + 0.035 \times \frac{182}{365}\right)^{-1}$

$= 24{,}571.18238... = \$24{,}571.18$

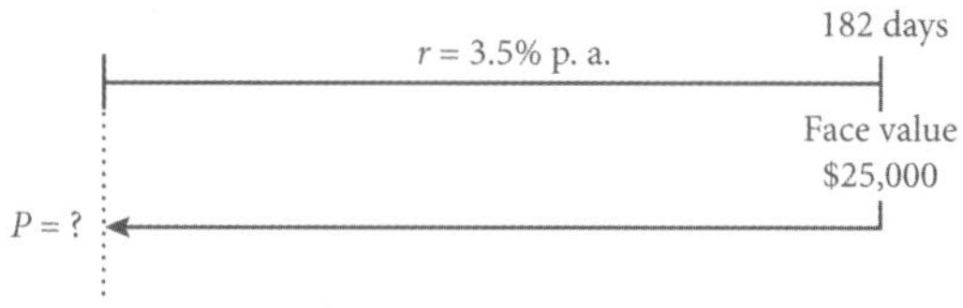

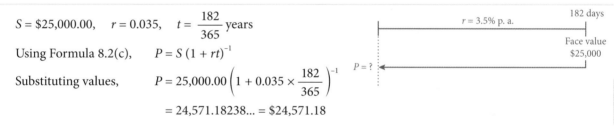

Therefore, he paid $24,571.18 for the T-bill.

Example 8.4(i) **Calculating the Purchase Price and Selling Price of a T-bill**

An investor purchased a 91-day T-bill with a face value of $5000 discounted at 3% p.a.

(i) Calculate the purchase price of the T-bill.

(ii) In 30 days, he needed the money, and therefore sold the T-bill to another investor. The rate for this investment in the market was 2.8% p.a at the time of the sale. Calculate his selling price and profit or loss on the transaction.

(iii) What annual rate of return did he realize while holding the T-bill?

Solution

ge 328

(i) $S = \$5000.00, \quad r = 0.03, \quad t = \frac{91}{365}$ years

Using Formula 8.2(c), $P = S(1 + rt)^{-1}$

Substituting values, $P = 5000.00\left(1 + 0.03 \times \frac{91}{365}\right)^{-1}$

$= 4962.880374... = \$4962.88$

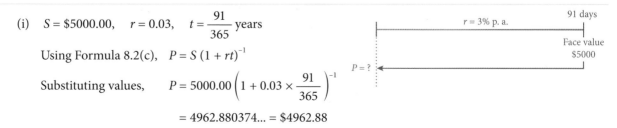

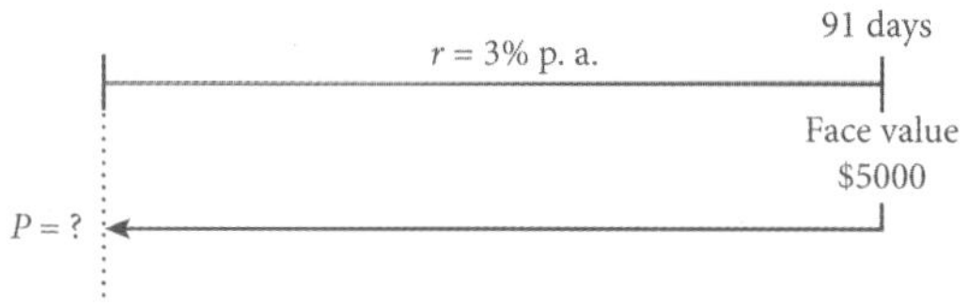

Therefore, the purchase price was $4962.88.

Solution *continued*

(ii) Days remaining on T-bill = 91 days – 30 days passed

= 61 days

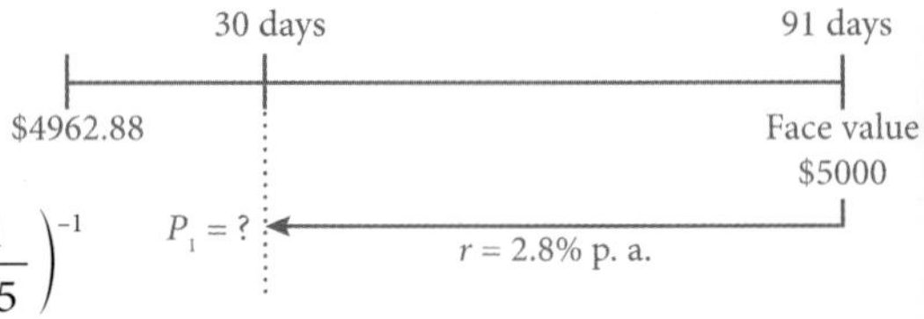

Using Formula 8.2(c), $P = S(1 + rt)^{-1}$

Substituting values, $P_1 = 5000.00\left(1 + 0.028 \times \frac{61}{365}\right)^{-1}$

$= 4976.711716... = \$4976.71$

Therefore, he sold it for $4976.71. He sold it for more; hence, he made a profit.

His profit on the sale of the T-Bill was $P_1 - P = 4976.71 - 4962.88 = \$13.83$

(iii) Since he held it for 30 days,

Rearranging Formula 8.1, $r = \frac{I}{Pt}$

Substituting values, $r = \frac{13.83}{4962.88\left(\frac{30}{365}\right)} = 0.033904... = 3.39\%$ p.a.

Therefore, he realized an annual rate of return of 3.39% p.a. while holding the T-bill.

8.4 | Exercises

Answers to the odd-numbered problems are available at the end of the textbook.

For the following problems, express answers rounded to two decimal places. Assume 'No Grace Period' is marked on all promissory notes.

1. Lea's bank offers interest rates of 1.50% p.a. for one-year GICs and 1.85% p.a. for two-year GICs for investments of $5000 to $99,000. Lea was considering the following two investment options:

   Option A: Invest $50,000 in a two-year GIC.

   Option B: Invest $50,000 in a one-year GIC, then invest the maturity amount in a second one-year GIC, assuming that the interest rate remains constant over the second one-year period.

   In which of the above two options will she earn more and by how much?

2. A bank offers interest rates of 1.25% p.a. for 60-day GICs and 1.50% p.a. for 120-day GICs for investments of $100,000 to $249,999. Chang was considering the following two investment options at this bank:

   Option A: Invest $150,000 in a 120-day GIC.

   Option B: Invest $150,000 in a 60-day GIC, then invest the maturity amount in a second 60-day GIC, assuming that the interest rate remains constant over the second 60-day period.

   In which of the above two options will he earn more and by how much?

3. Isabel received a demand loan from her bank for $8500 at 4% p.a. simple interest. Three months later, the prime rate increased and the rate on the loan changed to 4.25% p.a. If she repaid the loan in full in 8 months, calculate the total amount of interest that she paid on this loan.

4. On January 02, 2017, Chloe took a demand loan of $15,280 at 8.25% p.a. simple interest. On April 19, 2017, the prime rate decreased and the rate on the loan changed to 8% p.a. If Chloe cleared the loan on August 24, 2017, calculate the total amount of interest that she paid on this loan.

5. A 60-day interest-bearing promissory note for $37,500 has an interest rate of 2.25% p.a. and is dated December 20, 2016. Calculate the maturity date and the maturity value of the note.

6. On August 15, 2017, Sabina's Bakery loaned $100,000 to one of its suppliers for 90 days in return for a 6% p.a. interest-bearing promissory note. What is the maturity date and the maturity value of the note?

7. What is the face value of a 60-day interest-bearing promissory note dated April 18, 2017 with a maturity value of $10,078.08 and an interest rate of 4.75% p.a.?

8. What is the face value of a 90-day interest-bearing promissory note dated January 03, 2018 with a maturity value of $25,400.68 and interest rate of 6.50% p.a.?

9. What is the loan amount of a six-month, 3.4% p.a. non-interest-bearing promissory note that has a face value of $10,000?

10. How much did Owen pay for a two-month, non-interest-bearing note that had a face value of $5000 and an interest rate of 9% p.a.?

11. Calculate the amount of proceeds if a 90-day interest-bearing note that had a face value of $10,000 and an interest rate of 7% p.a. was sold in 30 days when the interest rate was 8% p.a.

12. Valentino purchased a 60-day interest-bearing note at 3% p.a. that had a face value of $12,000. If he settled the note in 30 days at a discounted rate of 4% p.a., calculate his proceeds.

13. Wesley purchased a 90-day interest-bearing promissory note that had a face value of $125,000 and an interest rate of 4.5% p.a. In 30 days, he sold the note for $125,500 to Walker. What rate of return did Walker earn on the note?

14. Paulina purchased a 120-day interest-bearing promissory note that had a face value of $50,000 and an interest rate of 4.75% p.a. In 100 days, she sold the note for $50,590 to Casey. What rate of return did Casey earn on the note?

15. Karim purchased a non-interest-bearing note that had a face value of $5000 and was due in 60 days. If he sold the note in 45 days to another investor when the rate was 4% p.a., calculate the amount of proceeds from the sale and amount of discount on the note.

16. Calculate the amount of proceeds and discount if a 90-day non-interest-bearing note that had a face value of $10,000 was sold in 30 days when the interest rate was 7% p.a.

17. How much did Kenneth pay for a 91-day T-bill that has an interest rate of 2.25% p.a. and a face value of $5000?

18. Rodney invested his savings by purchasing a 364-day T-bill that had a face value of $20,000 and an interest rate of 5.75% p.a. Calculate the amount that he paid for this T-bill.

19. Jonah took a demand loan of $10,000 at 11% p.a. simple interest to start a graphics design firm. In three months, he repaid $1000 towards the loan, and in six months, he repaid another $1000. He cleared the balance at the end of one year. Calculate the size of his last payment.

20. What is the final payment of a demand loan of $12,000 at 13% p.a. simple interest, if $2000 was repaid in 2 months, another $4000 was repaid in 6 months, and the final payment to clear the loan is due in 8 months?

21. Maya received a demand loan of $20,500 on January 15, 2017 from her bank at 12% p.a. simple interest. On April 12, 2017, she made a repayment of $5000 towards the loan and on July 16, 2017, she made a small repayment of $150. She cleared the rest of the loan on September 15, 2017. Calculate the size of her last repayment to clear the loan.

22. Sally received a demand loan of $17,500 on December 02, 2016 at 18% p.a. simple interest. She made a small repayment of $200 on December 31, 2016 towards the loan, and a larger repayment of $5000 on February 06, 2017. If she cleared the loan on April 13, 2017, what was the size of her final repayment?

• 23. A non-interest-bearing promissory note with a face value of $75,000 is sold at a discount of 4.5%, 30 days before maturity.

   a. Calculate the proceeds from the sale.

   b. What rate of return did the purchaser realize on the note?

• 24. Khalid purchased a non-interest-bearing promissory note with a face value of $27,500 and sold it to Sankara 60 days before maturity at a discount of 3% p.a.

   a. How much did Sankara pay for the note?

   b. What rate of return did Sankara earn on the note?

• 25. Kenneth bought a 182-day T-bill that had a face value of $1000 discounted at 2.3% p.a.

   a. How much did he pay for the T-bill?

   b. After 45 days, if he sold the T-bill to his friend when the interest rate for the T-bill in the market was 2% p.a., calculate his selling price and profit or loss on the transaction.

   c. What rate of return did he realize while holding the T-bill?

• 26. Yuan purchased a 364-day T-bill that had a face value of $5000 and an interest rate of 6% p.a.

   a. How much did he pay for the T-bill?

   b. After 180 days, he sold the T-bill to Liam when the interest rate for this T-bill in the market was 5% p.a. Calculate his selling price and profit or loss on the transaction.

   c. What rate of return did he realize while holding the T-bill?

8 | Review Exercises

Answers to the odd-numbered problems are available at the end of the textbook.

For the following problems, express the answers rounded to two decimal places and assume that 'No Grace Period' is marked on all promissory notes.

1. How long, in years and months, will it take for an investment of $1950 to accumulate to $2129.55 at 6.5% p.a. simple interest?

2. Blossom invested her savings of $2850 in an account that provided a simple interest rate of 4.25% p.a. How long, in years and months, will it take for her investment to grow to $3021.59?

3. Cristiano borrowed $4225 on June 04, 2017 from a money lender and agreed to repay the loan on April 03, 2018. What would be the repayment amount if the interest rate charged was 7.2% p.a.? How much of this is the interest?

4. Carlo loaned $5000 on December 18, 2017 to his business partner who agreed to repay the amount with simple interest on March 01, 2018. How much would Carlo receive at the end of the period if he charged his business partner an interest rate of 3.2% p.a.? How much of this amount is the interest?

5. The rate of return of a 182-day treasury bill with a face value of $20,000 is 5.25% p.a. Calculate the price on its issue date.

6. Felice purchased a 91-day T-Bill that has a face value of $5000 and an interest rate of 4% p.a. Calculate the price on its issue date.

7. Merilyn, the owner of a small internet hosting business, loaned $4000 to an employee who promised to repay her $4600 after eight months. Instead of loaning this money, if she had invested it in her local bank where the interest rate was $1\frac{1}{2}$% less than what she was offering her employee, how much would she have had in the bank at the end of eight months?

8. After ten months of investing $500 in a chequing account, Sarojin had a maturity amount of $680 in the account. Had she loaned this amount to her friend who was running a restaurant business, she would have received 2% more than what was being offered by her chequing account. Calculate the maturity amount after ten months if had she loaned the amount to her friend.

9. Marcello took a demand loan of $10,000 at 4% p.a. He paid $2500 at the end of 9 months and another $5000 at the end of 15 months. What amount at the end of 2 years would settle the loan?

10. Aarthi took a demand loan of $18,500 at 5% p.a. She paid $500 at the end of 3 months and another $6000 at the end of 8 months. How much would she have to pay at the end of 16 months to clear the balance?

11. Nikita owes $3500 in 6 months and another $2500 in 11 months. What single payment in 9 months would settle both payments? Assume an interest rate of 0.75% p.m. and choose 9 months from now as the focal date.

12. Trisha had to pay her friend $800 that was due two months ago and $200 in two months. If her friend was charging her an interest rate of 1.1% p.m., what single payment now would settle both payments? Choose now as the focal date.

13. An interest-bearing promissory note for $7500 is due in 180 days with simple interest at 6.25% p.a. If this note is sold after 70 days by discounting at a rate of 9% p.a., calculate the proceeds of the note.

14. Nicole purchased an interest-bearing promissory note for $5000 at 5% p.a., due in 90 days. If she sold the note in 30 days by discounting it at 6% p.a., calculate the proceeds of the note.

15. A six-month non-interest-bearing note was issued on August 08, 2017 for $1750. The note was discounted at 6.75% p.a. on October 30, 2017. Calculate the proceeds of the note.

16. Lee, a wealthy businessman, purchased a 120-day, $100,000 non-interest-bearing note on January 01, 2017. If he discounted the note at 8% p.a. on April 27, 2017, calculate the proceeds of the note.

• 17. Roanna borrowed $2500 at 7% p.a. She wanted to settle this loan with two equal payments, one in 5 months and another in 16 months. Determine the size of each of the payments using 'now' as the focal date.

• 18. Phoenix loaned $10,000 to a friend at 1.2% p.m. He wanted the amount to be paid in two equal payments, one in two months and the other in four months. Calculate the size of each of the payments using four months from now as the focal date.

• 19. Edna, a pottery designer, borrowed $12,800 at 6.5% p.a. to purchase pottery equipment. She agreed to settle the loan in two payments: one in five months and the other in ten months. Calculate the size of each payment if the first payment is half the second payment. Use ten months from now as the focal date.

• 20. Kassandra received a loan of $30,000 for her payroll payments. She settled this loan in two installments: one in 7 months and the other in 11 months. If the second payment was double the size of the first payment, and she was charged 5.5% p.a., calculate the size of each payment. Use 11 months from now as the focal date.

• 21. Ravindran borrowed $15,000 that is to be settled with the following three installments: the first payment of $10,000 in four months and two equal payments, one in six months and the other in one year. Calculate the size of each of the equal payments if the interest charged was 4.75% p.a. Let the focal date be one year from now.

• 22. A loan of $30,000 at 5% p.a. is to be settled with three equal installments in three months, six months, and nine months. Calculate the size of each of the equal payments. Let the focal date be six months from now.

• 23. A sum of money invested at a simple interest rate accumulates to $4590 after 6 months and to $4725 after 15 months. Calculate the simple interest rate per annum and the amount invested.

• 24. A sum of money invested at a simple interest rate accumulates to $6479 after 9 months and to $6758 after 18 months. Calculate the simple interest rate per annum and the amount invested.

8 | Self-Test Exercises

Answers to all the problems are available at the end of the textbook.

For the following problems, express the answers rounded to two decimal places and assume that 'No Grace Period' is marked on all promissory notes.

1. Rex invested his savings of $2000 in a savings account that was earning simple interest at 3% p.a. He also invested $1500 in his friend's business at 0.95% p.m. How much interest did he earn from both of these investments at the end of ten months?

2. On September 10, 2016, Zain received $5000 from his father. If he settled this amount on April 30, 2017 with an interest of $180, calculate the monthly rate of simple interest he was charged for this loan.

3. Angelina invested $200 for 16 months in a bank and received a maturity amount of $270.50. If she had invested the amount in a fund earning 2.5% p.a. more, how much would she have received at maturity?

4. Calculate the amount that Emilia invested in the savings account of her bank if it matured to $6740.75 at the end of 100 days. Assume that the simple interest rate was 3% p.a. How much of this amount was interest?

5. George had to make payments of $2000 and $3000 in 10 months and 18 months, respectively, to a raw material supplier. What single payment in five months would settle both these payments? Assume an interest rate of 6% p.a. and use five months as the focal date.

6. Thomas was supposed to pay Lenny $3800 six months ago and $1240 in five months. He wants to repay this with two payments: $3000 today and the balance amount in two months. Calculate the balance if the simple interest charged is 4% p.a. and the agreed focal date is two months from now.

7. Jolie received a demand loan for $8000 from her bank on February 16, 2017 at 6% p.a. simple interest. On May 23, 2017, the interest rate on the loan decreased to 5.75% p.a. and she settled the loan on July 14, 2017. Calculate the total interest paid on the loan.

8. Abbey bought a 182-day T-bill that has an interest rate of 4% p.a. and a face value of $25,000.
   a. How much did she pay for the T-bill?
   b. After 90 days, she sold the T-bill to her friend when the interest rate for this T-bill in the market increased to 4.25% p.a. What was her selling price and profit or loss on the transaction?
   c. What rate of return did she realize while holding the T-bill?

9. Oliver purchased a 90-day interest-bearing note at 5% p.a. that has a face value of $25,000. If he settles the note in 60 days at a discounted rate of 6% p.a., calculate his proceeds.

• 10. Brenda's lawyer gave her the following two options to settle her invoice:

Option A: $1800 in 1 month and the balance of $2100 in 3 months.

Option B: Two equal payments, one in 20 days and the other in 4 months.

If money earns 3.5% p.a., what is the value of each of the equal payments in Option B such that they are equivalent to the payments in Option A? Use now as the focal date for this question.

• 11. A bank offers interest rates of 1.50% p.a. for 60-day GICs and 1.75% p.a. for 120-day GICs. Roberto was considering the following two investment options at this bank:

Option A: Invest an amount in a 120-day GIC.

Option B: Invest an amount in a 60-day GIC then invest the maturity amount in a second 60-day GIC.

What interest rate should be offered on the second 60-day GIC for Roberto to earn the same amount from either option?

• 12. The total amount of simple interest earned from $6000 invested for 9 months and $4000 invested for 15 months, both at the same interest rate, was $570. Calculate the annual rate of interest.

CASE 8a

Borrowing and Investing Using Simple Interest

Shing and Benjamin, two classmates at a college, decided to use their free time after classes to create video games. On October 07, 2016, they received a loan of $3000 from a bank at 8.5% p.a. to start their small business. Two months later, they launched their first game in the community and it was highly successful. On March 02, 2017, a larger gaming company paid them $50,000 to purchase copyrights to their game. Shing and Benjamin used $5000 from this amount to settle the bank loan and to cover other miscellaneous expenses.

They then shared the balance of $45,000 equally between themselves.

Shing invested a portion of it in a 182-day T-bill that had an interest rate of 4% p.a. and a face value of $7500 and used the balance in a 270-day interest-bearing promissory note at 6% p.a.

Benjamin, on the other hand, invested a portion of it in a 270-day non-interest-bearing promissory note that had an interest rate of 5% p.a. and a face value of $9000, and loaned the balance to his friend, who was running a successful website-design business, for 182 days.

a. Calculate the total amount they paid to settle the bank loan.

b. i) Calculate the amounts that Shing invested in the T-bill and in the interest-bearing promissory note.

   ii) Calculate the amount that Benjamin invested in the non-interest-bearing promissory note and the amount that he loaned to his friend.

c. Shing decided to discount his interest-bearing promissory note at the time of maturity of his T-bill (182 days) and used the money to purchase a car for himself. Calculate the total proceeds from his investments if he discounted his interest-bearing promissory note at 6.50% p.a.

d. Benjamin wants to have the same amount as Shing in 182 days. If he discounts his non-interest-bearing promissory note at 7% p.a., what interest rate should he charge his friend for the loan?

e. If Benjamin invested his initial share at the interest rate that he loaned to his friend (determined from (d)), how long would it take for his investment to double?

CASE 8b

Investing in Bank of Canada Treasury Bills

Hameed learned that investing his money in T-bills would yield returns that are usually higher than that of a typical savings account but lower than those of other risky money market instruments like stocks and mutual funds.

In addition to being very safe investments (as they are guaranteed by the government), T-bills are also short-term investments. These features made the investment option very attractive for Hameed as he needed the money in a few months for a business opportunity.

On May 10, 2017 Hameed purchased a 91-day Bank of Canada T-bill that had a face value of $50,000. However, he sold the T-bill in 35 days as he urgently required the money for his business.

Answer the following questions using the information on the yield (return) of the T-bill at different times during the year provided in the graph.

a. How much did Hameed pay for the T-bill?

b. How much did he receive from the sale of the T-bill?

c. What rate of return did he finally earn on the T-bill?

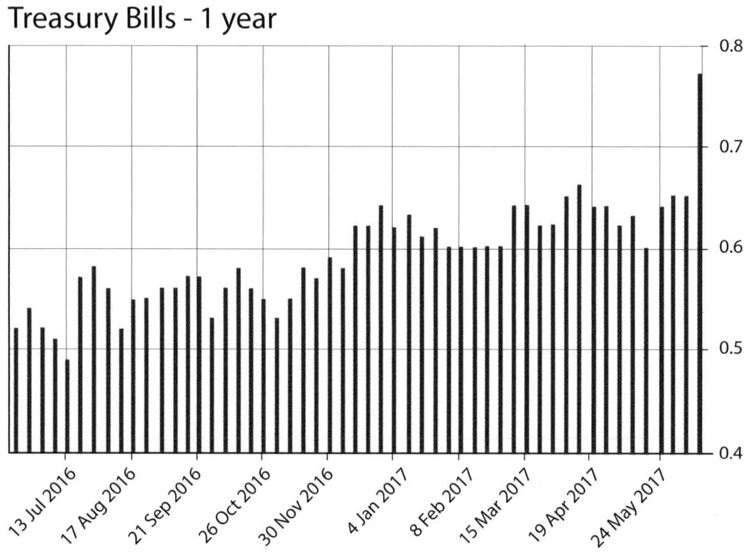

Date	Yield
2017-06-14	**0.77**
2017-06-07	**0.65**
2017-05-31	**0.65**
2017-05-24	**0.64**
2017-05-17	**0.60**
2017-05-10	**0.63**

http://www.bankofcanada.ca/rates/interest-rates/t-bill-yields

8 | Spreadsheet Solutions

Spreadsheet solutions to solved examples in the chapter.

8.1 Examples

Example 8.1(c)

	A	B	
1		Method 1	
2	***P***	$1,750.00	
3	***r***	4.50%	
4	***t***	0.75	= 9/12
5			
6	***I***	$59.06	= B2*B3*B4
7			
8		Method 2	
9	***P***	$1,750.00	
10	***r***	0.375%	= 4.50%/12
11	***t***	9	
12			
13	***I***	$59.06	= B9*B10*B11
14			

Example 8.1(d)

	A	B	
1		Calculating *I*	
2	***P***	$3,200.00	
3	***r***	6.00%	
4	***t***	0.342466	= 125/365
5			
6	***I***	$65.75	= B2*B3*B4
7			

Example 8.1(e)

	A	B	
1		Method 1	
2	***P***	$2,275.00	
3	***r***	0.75%	
4	***t***	2.958904	= (90/365)*12
5			
6	***I***	$50.49	= B2*B3*B4
7			
8		Method 2	
9	***P***	$2,275.00	
10	***r***	9.00%	= 0.75%*12
11	***t***	0.246575	= 90/365
12			
13	***I***	$50.49	= B9*B10*B11
14			

Example 8.1(f)

	A	B	
1		Method 1	
2	***P***	$5,680.00	
3	***r***	0.25%	
4	***t***	18	= 1.5*12
5			
6	***I***	$255.60	= B2*B3*B4
7			
8		Method 2	
9	***P***	$5,680.00	
10	***r***	3.00%	= 0.25%*12
11	***t***	1.5	
12			
13	***I***	$255.60	= B9*B10*B11
14			

Example 8.1(l)

	A	B	
1	**Day 1**	10/18/2017	= DATE(2017,10,18)
2	**Day 2**	4/5/2018	= DATE(2018,4,5) DATE(year, month, day)
3		Number of Days	
4		169	= DAYS(B2,B1) DAYS(end_date, start_date)
5			

8.2 Examples

Example 8.2(a)

	A	B	
1		Calculating *P*	
2	***P***	$5,142.86	= B6/(B3*B4)
3	***r***	3.50%	
4	***t***	0.416667	= 5/12
5			
6	***I***	$75.00	
7			

Example 8.2(b)

	A	B	
1		Calculating *t*	
2	***P***	$30,000.00	
3	***r***	9.50%	
4	***t***	0.666667	= B6/(B2*B3)
5			
6	***I***	$1,900.00	
7			
8		*t* in Months	
9		8	= B4*12
10		*t* in Days	
11		244	= ROUNDUP(B4*365,0) ROUNDUP (number, num_digits)
12			

Example 8.2(c)

	A	B	
1		Method 1	
2	***P***	$2,900.00	
3	***r***	8.79%	= B6/(B2*B4)
4	***t***	0.666667	= 8/12
5			
6	***I***	$170.00	
7			
8		Method 2	
9	***P***	$2,900.00	
10	***r***	8.79%	= B13/(B9*B11)*12
11	***t***	8	
12			
13	***I***	$170.00	
14			

Example 8.2(d)

	A	B	
1		Calculating *S*	
2	***P***	$700.00	
3	***r***	1.50%	
4	***t***	4	
5			
6	***I***	$42.00	= B7–B2
7	***S***	$742.00	= B2*(1 + B3*B4)
8			

Example 8.2(e)

	A	B	
1		Calculating *P*	
2	***P***	$2,122.97	= B7/(1 + B3*B4)
3	***r***	8.00%	
4	***t***	0.833333	= 10/12
5			
6	***I***	$141.53	= B7 – B2
7	***S***	$2,264.50	
8			

Example 8.2(f)

	A	B	
1	**Day 1**	4/13/2017	= DATE(2017,4,13)
2	**Day 2**	6/1/2017	= DATE(2017,6,1)
3	**Day 3**	7/15/2017	= DATE(2017,7,15)
4			DATE(year, month, day)
5		Calculating I_1	
6	***P***	$4,200.00	
7	***r***	4.10%	
8	***t***	0.134247	= DAYS(B2,B1)/365
9			DAYS(end_date, start_date)
10	***I***	$23.12	= B6*B7*B8
11			
12		Calculating I_2	
13	***P***	$4,200.00	
14	***r***	4.35%	
15	***t***	0.120548	= DAYS(B3,B2)/365
16			DAYS(end_date, start_date)
17	***I***	$22.02	= B13*B14*B15
18			
19	$I_1 + I_2$	$45.14	= B10 + B17
20	***S***	$4245.14	= B6 + B19
21			

8.3 Examples

Example 8.3(a)

	A	B	
1		Calculating *S*	
2	***P***	$2,500.00	
3	***r***	5.00%	
4	***t***	0.5	= 6/12
5			
6	***S***	$2,562.50	= B2*(1 + B3*B4)
7			

Example 8.3(b)

	A	B	
1		Calculating *P*	
2	***P***	$1,483.31	= B6/(1 + B3*B4)
3	***r***	4.50%	
4	***t***	0.25	= 3/12
5			
6	***S***	$1,500.00	
7			

Example 8.3(c)

	A	B	
1		Calculating S_1	
2	***P***	$500.00	
3	***r***	9.00%	
4	***t***	2	= (6 + 18)/12
5			
6	***S***	$590.00	= B2*(1 + B3*B4)
7			
8		Calculating S_2	
9	***P***	$900.00	
10	***r***	9.00%	
11	***t***	0.666667	= (18 – 10)/12
12			
13	***S***	$954.00	= B9*(1 + B10*B11)
14			
15		Equivalent Payment	
16		$1,544.00	= B6 + B13
17			

Example 8.3(d)

	A	B	
1		Calculating S_1	
2	***P***	$5,000.00	
3	***r***	6.00%	
4	***t***	0.166667	= (5 – 3)/12
5			
6	***S***	$5,050.00	= B2*(1 + B3*B4)
7			
8		Calculating P_2	
9	***P***	$7,843.14	= B13/(1 + B10*B11)
10	***r***	6.00%	
11	***t***	0.333333	= (9 – 5)/12
12			
13	***S***	$8,000.00	
14			
15		Equivalent Payment	
16		$12,893.14	= B6+B9
17			

Example 8.3(e)

	A	B	
1		Calculating P_1	
2	**P**	$3,960.40	= B6/(1+B3*B4)
3	**r**	6.00%	
4	**t**	0.166667	= 2/12
5			
6	**S**	$4,000.00	
7			
8		Calculating P_2	
9	**P**	$1,747.57	= B13/(1+B10*B11)
10	**r**	6.00%	
11	**t**	0.5	= 6/12
12			
13	**S**	$1,800.00	
14			
15		Equivalent Payment (i)	
16		$5,707.97	= B2 + B9
17			
18		Calculating P_3	
19	**P**	$2,107.84	= B23/(1 + B20*B21)
20	**r**	6.00%	
21	**t**	0.333333	= 4/12
22			
23	**S**	$2,150.00	
24			
25		Calculating P_4	
26	**P**	$3,588.46	= B30/(1 + B27*B28)
27	**r**	6.00%	
28	**t**	0.666667	= 8/12
29			
30	**S**	$3,732.00	
31			
32		Equivalent Payment (ii)	
33		$5,696.30	= B19 + B26
34			

Example 8.3(f)

	A	B	
1		Calculating S_1	
2	**P**	$1,280.00	
3	**r**	8.00%	
4	**t**	0.833333	= (15 – 5)/12
5			
6	**S**	$1,365.33	= B2*(1 + B3*B4)
7			
8		Calculating S_3	
9	**P**	$1.00	
10	**r**	8.00%	
11	**t**	0.583333	= (15 – 8)/12
12			
13	**S**	$1.046667	= B9*(1 + B10*B11)
14			
15		Calculating S_4	
16	**P**	$1.00	
17	**r**	8.00%	
18	**t**	0.25	= (15–12)/12
19			
20	**S**	$1.02	= B16*(1 + B17*B18)
21			
22		Equivalent Payment	
23		$1,721.77	= (B6 + 2193)/(B13 + B20)
24			

8.4 Examples

Example 8.4(a)

	A	B	
1		$160,000, 3-year GIC	
2	**P**	$160,000.00	
3	**r**	1.95%	
4	**t**	3	
5			
6	**I**	$9,360.00	= B2*B3*B4
7			
8		$80,000, 3-year GIC	
9	**P**	$80,000.00	
10	**r**	1.75%	
11	**t**	3	
12			
13	**I**	$4,200.00	= B9*B10*B11
14			

Example 8.4(b)

	A	B	
1		*I* after 1st Payment	
2	**P**	$20,000.00	
3	**r**	18.00%	
4	**t**	0.166667	= 2/12
5			
6	**I**	$600.00	= B2*B3*B4
7			
8		Amount Left after Interest	
9		$4,400.00	= 5000 – B6
10			
11		*I* after 2nd Payment	
12	**P**	$15,600.00	= B2 – B9
13	**r**	18.00%	
14	**t**	0.25	= 3/12
15			
16	**I**	$702.00	= B12*B13*B14
17			
18		Interest Balance	
19		$202.00	= B16 – 500
20			
21		*I* after 3rd Payment	
22	**P**	$15,600.00	= B12
23	**r**	18.00%	
24	**t**	0.083333	= 1/12
25			
26	**I**	$234.00	= B22*B23*B24
27			
28		Balance to be Paid	
29		$16,036.00	= B19 + B26 + B22
30			

Example 8.4(c)

	A	B	
1		Calculating *S*	
2	**P**	$100,000.00	
3	**r**	6.00%	
4	**t**	0.164384	= 60/365
5			
6	**S**	$100,986.30	= B2*(1 + B3*B4)
7			

Example 8.4(d)

	A	B	
1		Calculating *P*	
2	***P***	$75,000.00	= B6/(1 + B3*B4)
3	***r***	7.50%	
4	***t***	0.246575	= 90/365
5			
6	***S***	$76,386.99	
7			

Example 8.4(e)

	A	B	
1		Calculating *P*	
2	***P***	$39,464.79	= B6/(1 + B3*B4)
3	***r***	5.50%	
4	***t***	0.246575	= 90/365
5			
6	***S***	$40,000.00	
7			

Example 8.4(f)

	A	B	
1		Calculating *P*	
2	***P***	$29,348.70	= B6/(1+B3*B4)
3	***r***	9.00%	
4	***t***	0.246575	= (120 – 30)/365
5			
6	***S***	$30,000.00	
7			

Example 8.4(g)

	A	B	
1		Calculating *S*	
2	***P***	$80,000.00	
3	***r***	8.00%	
4	***t***	0.246575	= 90/365
5			
6	***S***	$81,578.08	= B2*(1 + B3*B4)
7			
8		Calculating *P*	
9	***P***	$80,043.01	= B6/(1 + B10*B11)
10	***r***	10.00%	
11	***t***	0.191781	= 70/365
12			

Example 8.4(h)

	A	B	
1		Calculating *P*	
2	***P***	$24,571.18	= B6/(1 + B3*B4)
3	***r***	3.50%	
4	***t***	0.498630	= 182/365
5			
6	***S***	$25,000.00	
7			

Example 8.4(i)

	A	B	
1	(i)	Calculating *P*	
2	***P***	$4,962.88	= B6/(1 + B3*B4)
3	***r***	3.00%	
4	***t***	0.249315	= 91/365
5			
6	***S***	$5,000.00	
7			
8	(ii)	Calculating P_1	
9	***P***	$4,976.71	= B13/(1 + B10*B11)
10	***r***	2.80%	
11	***t***	0.167123	= (91 – 30)/365
12			
13	***S***	$5,000.00	
14			
15	(iii)	Calculating *r*	
16	***P***	$4,962.88	= B2
17	***r***	3.39%	= B20/(B16*B18)
18	***t***	0.082192	= 30/365
19			
20	***I***	$13.83	= B9 – B2
21			

8 | Summary of Notation and Formulas

NOTATION

I = Amount of Interest

P = Principal

r = Simple Interest Rate

t = Time Period

S = Maturity Value

FORMULAS

Amount of Interest | 8.1

$I = Prt$

Maturity Value | 8.2(a)

$S = P + I$

Maturity Value | 8.2(b)

$S = P(1 + rt)$

Principal | 8.2(c)

$$P = \frac{S}{(1 + rt)} \quad \textbf{or} \quad P = S(1 + rt)^{-1}$$

Chapter

9

COMPOUND INTEREST

LEARNING OBJECTIVES

- Differentiate between the concepts of compound interest and simple interest.
- Calculate the future value and present value of investments and loans in compound interest applications using both the algebraic and financial calculator methods.
- Calculate equivalent payments that replace another payment or a set of payments.
- Calculate periodic and nominal interest rates.
- Calculate the number of compounding periods and time period of an investment or loan.
- Calculate the effective and equivalent interest rates for nominal interest rates.

CHAPTER OUTLINE

Introduction

Compound interest is a procedure where interest is added to the principal at the end of each compounding period to earn interest in the subsequent compounding periods.

In the previous chapter, you learned that money grows linearly when invested over a period of time at a simple interest rate. Have you ever wondered if money can grow exponentially? This chapter will teach you a method to have your money grow in leaps and bounds! It uses the concept of compound interest, where interest is earned upon interest. Compound interest is often remarked as being an extremely powerful force; it can either work for you when you invest, or against you when you borrow!

Difference Between Simple Interest and Compound Interest

Compound interest is a procedure where interest is calculated periodically (at regular intervals, known as compounding periods) and reinvested to earn interest at the end of each compounding period during the term; i.e., interest is added to the principal to earn interest. This is different from simple interest where interest is calculated only on the original amount (principal) for the entire term.

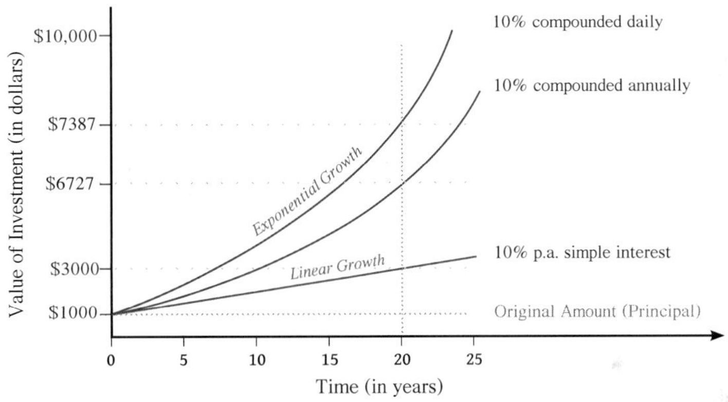

Exhibit 9: Difference Between Simple Interest and Compound Interest at Different Compounding Frequencies

9.1 | Compound Interest Terms

In compound interest, the interest earned in the previous compounding period also earns interest in subsequent compounding periods. For any given interest rate, the shorter the compounding period, the greater the interest earned, because the number of compoundings during the term will be greater. Generally, the compounding period can be one year (annually), six months (semi-annually), three months (quarterly), one month (monthly), or one day (daily).

Consider an example of $1000 invested or borrowed at 10% compounded annually for four years. Interest earned in the 1st year is added to the principal at the end of the 1st year. In the 2nd year, interest is calculated on the sum of the principal and interest earned. This is continued similarly at the end of each year.

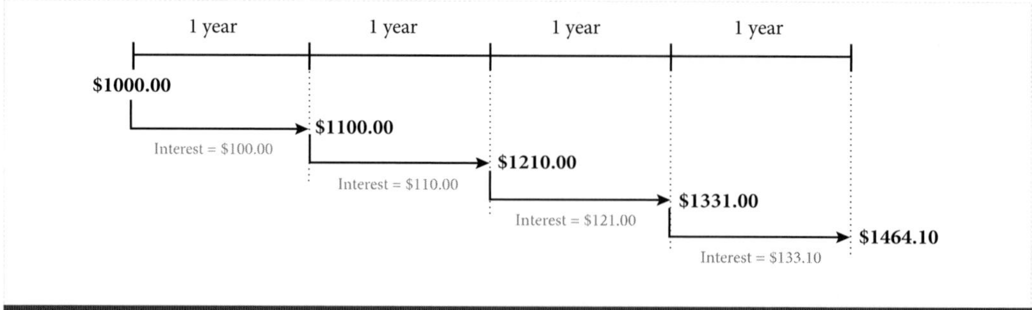

Exhibit 9.1: Interest Calculated Upon Interest

The value at the:

Beginning (initial value)	= $1000.00		
End of the 1st year	= $1000(1.10)	= $1100.00	
End of the 2nd year	= $1000(1.10)(1.10)	= $1000(1.10)^2$	= $1210.00
End of the 3rd year	= $1000(1.10)^2$ (1.10)	= $1000(1.10)^3$	= $1331.00
End of the 4th year	= $1000(1.10)^3$ (1.10)	= $1000(1.10)^4$	= $1464.10

Now consider an investment of 'PV' compounded 'n' times at the rate of 'i'.

The value of the initial investment	$= PV$
The value at the end of the 1st compounding period	$= PV(1+i)^1$
The value at the end of the 2nd compounding period	$= PV(1+i)^2$
The value at the end of the 3rd compounding period	$= PV(1+i)^3$
⋮	⋮
The value at the end of the nth compounding period	$= PV(1+i)^n$

If 'FV' is the value at the end of the nth compounding period, we obtain the formula for Future Value:

Formula 9.1(a)

Future Value (FV): the accumulated value or maturity value of an investment or loan.

Future Value

$$FV = PV(1+i)^n$$

Formula 9.1(a) is the basic compound interest formula where:

- 'FV' is the future value (accumulated value or maturity value)
- 'PV' is the present value (discounted value or principal amount)
- 'i' is the interest rate per compounding period
- 'n' is the total number of compounding periods during the term

Using Formula 9.1(a), $FV = PV(1+i)^n$ and dividing both sides by $(1+i)^n$ results in the formula for Present Value:

Formula 9.1(b)

Present Value (PV): the principal amount or discounted value of an investment or loan.

Present Value

$$PV = \frac{FV}{(1+i)^n} \quad \textbf{or} \quad PV = FV(1+i)^{-n}$$

Similar to simple interest, the amount of compound interest, 'I', is the difference between the Future Value and the Present Value:

Formula 9.1(c)

Amount of Compound Interest

$$I = FV - PV$$

Notation

Compounding period: the time interval between two successive interest calculation dates.

Compounding period (or interest period) is the period of time between the compounding of interest. For example, if the interest is compounded semi-annually, then the compounding period is 'semi-annual'. It usually appears after the word 'compounded' or 'compounding'.

Length of compounding period is the time interval between successive interest calculation dates. For example, if the interest is compounded monthly, then the length of the compounding period is every month.

Compounding frequency (m): the number of times interest is compounded every year.

m = **Compounding frequency** is the number of times interest is compounded every year.
That is, the number of compouding periods in one year.
For example, if the interest is compounded quarterly, then the compounding frequency (m) = 4.

Table 9.1

Compounding Frequencies for Common Compounding Periods

Compounding Period	Length of Compounding Period	Compounding Frequency (m)
Annually	Every year	1
Semi-annually	Every 6 months	2
Quarterly	Every 3 months	4
Monthly	Every month	12
Daily	Every day	365

If the compounding period is quarterly (every three months), then m = 4 because there are four 3-month periods in a year.

In this textbook, we will use a standard conversion rate of 365 days per year.

Note: *The length of the compounding period may be more often than 'every day' (daily compounding). For example, it may be every hour, every minute, every second, or continuous. With continuous compounding, the compounding frequency, 'm', becomes very large. In this textbook, we will only be using annual, semi-annual, quarterly, monthly, and daily compounding periods.*

***Nominal interest rate** (j): the quoted interest rate per annum.*

j – **Nominal interest rate** is the quoted or stated interest rate per annum on which the compound interest calculation is based for a given compounding period. It is the rate (expressed as a percent) that usually precedes the word *'compounding'* or *'compounded'*.

For example, **6%** compounded monthly: $j = 6\% = 0.06$

***Periodic interest rate** (i): the interest rate for a given compounding period.*

i = **Periodic interest rate** is the interest rate for a given compounding period and is calculated as follows:

$$\textit{Periodic Interest Rate} = \frac{\textit{Nominal Interest Rate}}{\textit{Compounding Frequency}}$$

Therefore, the formula for the periodic interest rate is,

Formula 9.1(d)

Periodic Interest Rate

$$i = \frac{j}{m}$$

The nominal interest rate (j) is always provided with a compounding frequency (m) and can easily be remembered as: 'j' compounded 'm' times.

For example, **6%** compounded **monthly**: $i = \frac{j}{m} = \frac{0.06}{12} = 0.005$

Time period (t): the period of time, in years, during which interest is calculated.

t = **Time period** is the period of time (in years) during which interest is calculated.

For example, 5% compounded quarterly for **18 months**: $t = 18 \text{ months} = \frac{18}{12} = 1.5 \text{ years}$

n = **Total number of compounding periods during the term** is calculated as follows:

Total Number of Compounding Periods = Compounding Frequency × Time in Years

Therefore, the formula for the total number of compounding periods during the term is,

Formula 9.1(e)

Number of Compounding Periods

$$n = m \times t$$

For example,

- 6% compounded **semi-annually** for **4 years**: $n = m \times t = 2 \times 4 = 8$
- 5% compounded **quarterly** for **18 months**: $n = m \times t = 4 \times \frac{18}{12} = 6$

Example 9.1(a)

Identifying and Calculating Compound Interest Terms

An investment is growing at 6% compounded monthly for ten years.

(i) Identify the nominal interest rate, compounding frequency, and time period.

(ii) Calculate the periodic interest rate and number of compounding periods.

Solution

(i) **6%** compounded **monthly** for **10 years**

$j = 0.06$ $m = 12$ $t = 10$

Therefore, the nominal interest rate is 6%, compounding frequency is 12, and time period is 10 years.

(ii) Periodic interest rate: $i = \frac{j}{m} = \frac{0.06}{12} = 0.005 = 0.5\%$

Number of compounding periods: $n = m \times t = 12 \times 10 = 120$ compounding periods

Therefore, the periodic interest rate is 0.5% per month and the number of compounding periods is 120.

Example 9.1(b)

Identifying and Calculating Compound Interest Terms When the Time Period is in Months

A loan is issued at 4.32% compounded quarterly for nine months.

(i) Identify the nominal interest rate, compounding frequency, and time period in years.

(ii) Calculate the periodic interest rate and number of compounding periods.

Solution

(i) **4.32%** compounded **quarterly** for **9 months**

$j = 0.0432$ $m = 4$ $t = \frac{9}{12}$ years

Therefore, the nominal interest rate is 4.32%, compounding frequency is 4, and time period is $\frac{9}{12}$ years.

Solution *continued*

(ii) Periodic interest rate: $i = \frac{j}{m} = \frac{0.0432}{4} = 0.0108 = 1.08\%$

Number of compounding periods: $n = m \times t = 4 \times \frac{9}{12} = 3$ compounding periods

Therefore, the periodic interest rate is 1.08% per quarter and the number of compounding periods is 3.

Example 9.1(c) **Identifying and Calculating Compound Interest Terms When the Time Period is in Years and Months**

An investment is earning 8.2% compounded semi-annually for 5 years and 6 months.

(i) Identify the nominal interest rate, compounding frequency, and time period in years.

(ii) Calculate the periodic interest rate and number of compounding periods.

Solution

(i) **8.2%** compounded **semi-annually** for **5 years and 6 months**

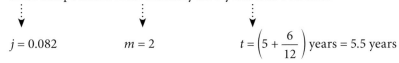

$j = 0.082$ $\quad m = 2$ $\quad t = \left(5 + \frac{6}{12}\right)$ years $= 5.5$ years

Therefore, the nominal interest rate is 8.2%, compounding frequency is 2, and time period is 5.5 years.

(ii) Periodic interest rate: $i = \frac{j}{m} = \frac{0.082}{2} = 0.041 = 4.10\%$

Number of compounding periods: $n = m \times t = 2 \times 5.5 = 11$ compounding periods

Therefore, the periodic interest rate is 4.10% per half-year and the number of compounding periods is 11.

9.1 | Exercises

Answers to the odd-numbered problems are available at the end of the textbook.

For the following problems, express the answers rounded to two decimal places, wherever applicable.
Calculate the missing values for Problems 1 and 2.

1.

	Nominal Interest Rate, Compounding Frequency, and Time Period	Number of Compounding Periods per Year (m)	Periodic Interest Rate (i)	Term (in years) (t)	Number of Compounding Periods for the Term (n)
a.	5% compounded semi-annually for 2 years	?	?	?	?
b.	11.4% compounded quarterly for 1 year and 6 months	?	?	?	?
c.	?% compounded monthly for 1 year and 6 months	?	0.70%	?	?
d.	?% compounded daily for 146 days	?	0.02%	?	?

2.

	Nominal Interest Rate, Compounding Frequency, and Time Period	Number of Compounding Periods per Year (m)	Periodic Interest Rate (i)	Term (in years) (t)	Number of Compounding Periods for the Term (n)
a.	11.40% compounded monthly for 15 months	?	?	?	?
b.	10.95% compounded daily for 292 days	?	?	?	?
c.	?% compounded semi-annually for $4\frac{1}{2}$ years	?	2.775%	?	?
d.	?% compounded quarterly for 1 year and 9 months	?	0.98%	?	?

3. A bank released a new credit card that charges interest at a rate of 1.35% p.m. Calculate the nominal interest rate compounded monthly for the credit card.

4. Calculate the nominal interest rate compounded monthly for a credit card that has a periodic interest rate of 1.1% p.m.

5. If the nominal interest rate of an investment is 5% and the periodic interest rate is 1.25%, calculate the compounding frequency.

6. If Rose invested her savings in a bank account that offered her a nominal interest rate of 2.86% and a periodic interest rate of 1.43%, what was the compounding frequency used?

7. Liana's investment has a time period of 3 years and 8 months and a monthly compounding frequency. Calculate the number of compounding periods during the term of her investment.

8. Jonathan received a mortgage that was compounded semi-annually for a period of 15 years. Calculate the number of compounding periods during the term of this mortgage.

9. Lila receives a personal loan that has 66 compoundings in a time period of 16 years and 6 months. Calculate the compounding frequency of the loan.

10. If Carrey invested money for 1 year and 3 months in a low-risk investment vehicle that had 15 compounding periods over the term, calculate the compounding frequency of the investment.

11. The periodic interest rate and nominal interest rate of a loan are 2.25% and 4.5%, respectively. Calculate the number of compounding periods if the loan is held for a period of 8 years.

12. Ramya deposits her savings in an investment that has nominal and periodic interest rates of 4.48% and 2.24%, respectively. If her investment was for a period of two years, what will be the number of compounding periods in the term?

• 13. Calculate the nominal interest rate of a loan that has 16 compounding periods over four years and a periodic interest rate of 0.5%.

• 14. George deposits his money for nine years in a savings account that has a periodic interest rate of 1.1%. Calculate the nominal interest rate of the account if there are 18 compounding periods during the period of investment.

9.2 | Calculating Future Value (FV)

The following examples will illustrate future value calculations using the future value formula, Formula 9.1(a) :

$$FV = PV(1 + i)^n$$

Example 9.2(a) **Calculating the Future Value and Interest Earned**

Hassan Furnishings Inc. invested $40,000 for two years at 3.5% compounded annually.

(i) Calculate the accumulated value of the investment at the end of two years.

(ii) Calculate the compound interest earned on this amount.

Solution

Although $42,849 is numerically different from $40,000, they are economically equal in value, considering the time value of money; i.e., money grows with interest over time.

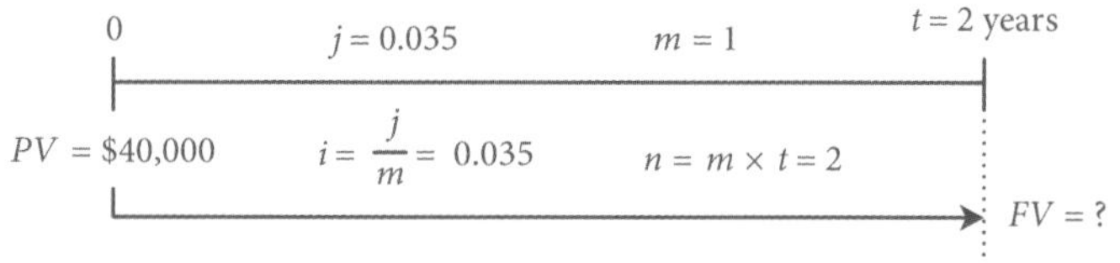

(i) $FV = PV(1 + i)^n = 40{,}000.00(1 + 0.035)^2 = 40{,}000.00(1.071225) = \$42{,}849.00$

Therefore, the accumulated value of the investment at the end of two years is $42,849.00.

(ii) Compound interest, $I = FV - PV = 42{,}849.00 - 40{,}000.00 = \$2849.00$

Therefore, the compound interest earned is $2849.00.

Using the Financial Calculator to Solve Problems

Solving problems algebraically will significantly improve your understanding of the subject; however, if you have to routinely solve financial problems and would like an easier and faster method to solve them, without having to remember formulas, financial calculators (that are pre-programmed) can be used. There are many financial calculators available, but we will use the Texas Instruments BA II Plus calculator to solve problems in this course.

We will be using the following function keys that are present in the 3rd row of your calculator (also known as the TVM row, or time value of money row) as shown:

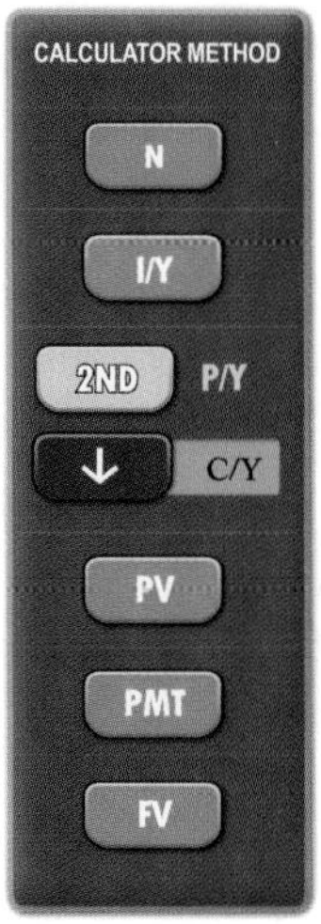

1. ***Number of compounding periods;*** represented by *'n'* in algebraic calculations.
2. ***Interest rate per year (nominal interest rate);*** represented by *'j'* in algebraic calculations. This is entered in percent form (without the % sign) directly and is not converted to a decimal. For example, 5% is entered as 5.
3. Pressing the **2ND** key then **I/Y** (to access the secondary key above the I/Y key) will open the P/Y-C/Y worksheet. P/Y stands for 'periodic payments per year' and is a concept that will be covered in the next chapter on annuities. Pressing the '**down arrow**' key will take you to C/Y which stands for ***'compoundings per year'***; represented by *'m'* in algebraic calculations. Pressing **2ND** then **Quit** will close the P/Y-C/Y worksheet.
4. ***Present value;*** represented by *'PV'* in algebraic calculations.
5. ***Periodic annuity payment;*** represented by *'PMT'*. This is a concept that will be covered in the next chapter on annuities.
6. ***Future value;*** represented by *'FV'* in algebraic calculations.

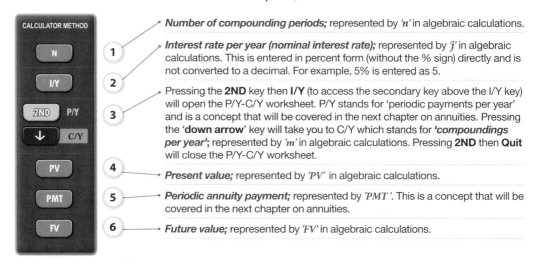

Before you start solving problems, you need to set the number of decimal places on your calculator to '9' to have a floating decimal. Follow these instructions on your calculator:

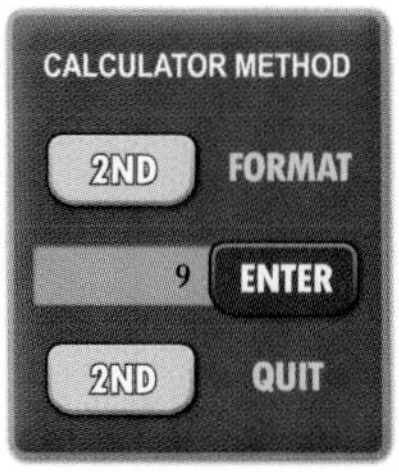

1. Press **2ND** then press **FORMAT** *(this is the secondary key above the decimal key).*
2. Enter **9** then press **ENTER** to have a floating decimal.
3. Press **2ND** and press **QUIT** (*this is the secondary key above* **CPT**).

Note: *Settings for other calculators can be viewed on page 636.*

Cash-Flow Sign Convention

When money is received, cash is flowing in and is called a cash-inflow. This amount has to be entered in your calculator as a positive amount. Similarly, when money is paid out, it is called a cash-outflow. This amount has to be entered as a negative amount. This cash-flow sign convention has to be followed in all calculators.

For example, if you make an investment in a bank, this is considered as a cash-outflow for you (money paid-out) and the value of the investment (PV) should be entered in your calculator as a negative amount. However, at the end of the time-period, when you receive your matured investment back from the bank, this is considered as a cash-inflow for you (money received) and the value of the amount received (FV) should be entered in your calculator as a positive amount.

Cash-Flow Sign Convention

Transaction	PV	FV
Investment	Outflow (–)	Inflow (+)
Loan	Inflow (+)	Outflow (–)

Let's look at another example: if you receive a loan, then the loan amount (PV) is considered as a cash-inflow, and therefore, has to be entered as a positive amount. When the loan is repaid, it is considered as a cash-outflow, and therefore, the amount paid (FV) has to be entered as a negative amount.

Solving Example 9.2(a) using the financial calculator is shown below:

Example 9.2(b) Using the Financial Calculator to Solve Example 9.2(a)

Hassan Furnishings Inc. invested $40,000 for two years at 3.5% compounded annually.

(i) Calculate the accumulated value of the investment at the end of two years.

(ii) Calculate the compound interest earned on this amount.

Solution

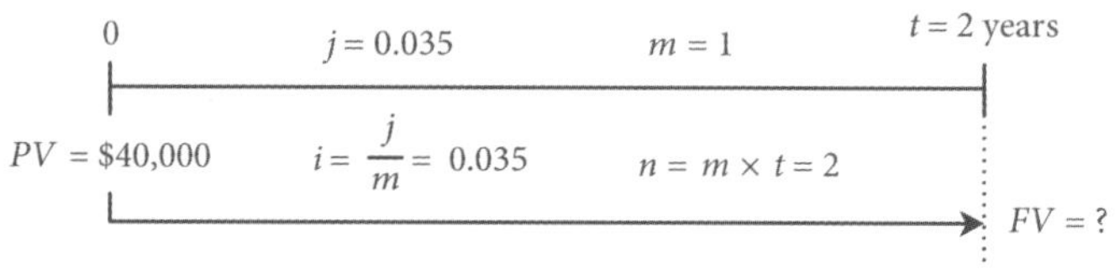

(i) In the example we have identified $PV = \$40,000$, $j = 3.5\%$, $m = 1$, and $n = 2$. We need to enter these values into the calculator and compute 'FV'.

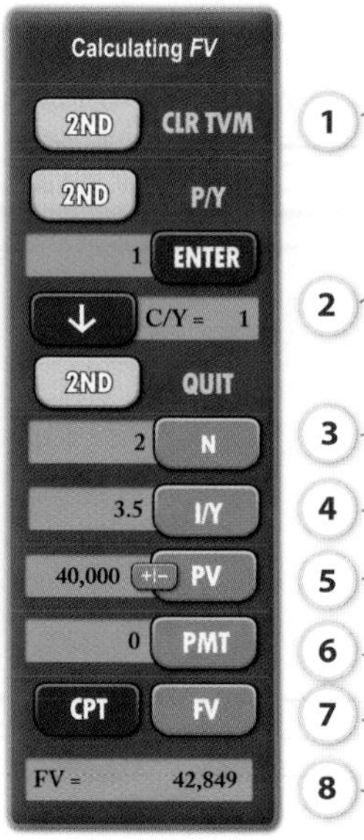

1. Press **2ND** then **CLR TVM** *(secondary function of the* **FV** *key)* to clear the memory of the TVM function keys.
2. As the calculation does not involve an annuity, we need to set ***payments per year*** *(P/Y)* to the same value as *the* ***number of compounding periods per year*** *(C/Y)*. To do this, press **2ND** then **P/Y** *(secondary function of the* **I/Y** *key)*, which opens the P/Y-C/Y worksheet. To set P/Y to 1 (as $m = 1$) enter **1** then press **ENTER**. When you scroll down (using the **down arrow key**), you will notice that C/Y will automatically be set to 1. Press **2ND** then press **QUIT** *(secondary function of the* **CPT** *key)* to close the P/Y-C/Y worksheet.
3. Enter the number of ***compounding periods, 'n'***, as **2** then press **N**.
4. Enter the ***interest per year, 'j'*** *(nominal rate)*, directly as **3.5** (*not as 3.5% or 0.035*) then press **I/Y**.
5. Enter the ***investment amount*** as a negative value, as it is a cash-outflow (cash paid/invested), by entering **40,000** and pressing the **+/– key**. Then press **PV**.
6. As the calculation does not involve annuity payments, enter '**0**' then press **PMT**.
7. To compute *FV*, press **CPT** then **FV**.
8. The calculator will display *42,849*. The value is positive as it is a cash-inflow (cash received).

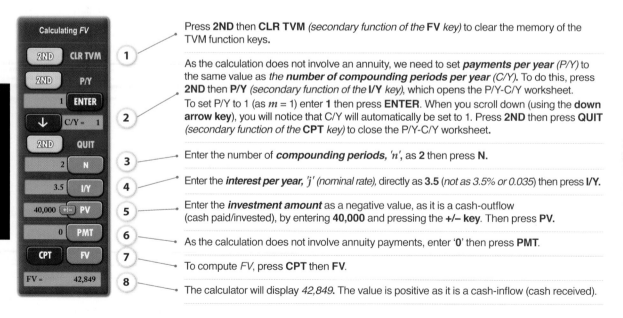

> We can view the value currently stored in any of the TVM function keys without changing the value by pressing RCL followed by the function key.

Therefore, the accumulated value of the investment at the end of two years is $42,849.00.

(ii) Compound interest, $I = FV - PV = 42,849.00 - 40,00.00 = \$2849.00$

Therefore, the compound interest earned is $2849.00.

Using Spreadsheets to Solve Problems

Similar to a financial calculator, spreadsheets are also valuable tools with built-in functions that we can use to solve financial problems. When solving compound interest questions, we will set up our spreadsheet as follows:

	A	B
1	Spreadsheet Method	
2	*j*	B2
3	*m*	B3
4	*t*	B4
5		
6	*i*	B6
7	*n*	B7
8	*PMT*	B8
9	*PV*	B9
10	*FV*	B10
11		

- In cell B2, enter the **nominal interest rate, *'j'***.
- In cell B3, enter the **compoundings per year, *'m'***.
- In cell B4, enter the **time period (in years), *'t'***.
- In cell B6, enter the **periodic interest rate, *'i'***; spreadsheets refer to this value as ***rate***.
- In cell B7, enter the **total number of compounding periods, *'n'***; spreadsheets refer to this value as ***nper***.
- In cell B8, enter the **periodic annuity payment, *'PMT'***; for compound interest questions, this value is always **0**.
- In cell B9, enter the **present value, *'PV'***.
- In cell B10, enter the **future value, *'FV'***.

When you call a built-in function on a spreadsheet, a guide will drop down to show you the required variables for the function, as well as the order in which they must be entered. For example, consider the following call to the future value function:

= FV(

FV(rate, nper, pmt, [pv], [type])

Note that the variables in brackets, [ ], are not always required for the function to operate. For example, we will not require the variable [type] in our future value function calls (until we discuss annuities in the next chapter).

Like a financial calculator, spreadsheets follow the cash-flow sign convention; cash-inflows must be entered as positive values, while cash-outflows must be entered as negative values.

Solving Example 9.2(a) using a spreadsheet is shown below:

Example 9.2(c)

Using a Spreadsheet to Solve Example 9.2(a)

Hassan Furnishings Inc. invested $40,000 for two years at 3.5% compounded annually.

(i) Calculate the accumulated value of the investment at the end of two years.

(ii) Calculate the compound interest earned on this amount.

Solution

(i) Set up your spreadsheet to include variables *j*, *m*, *t*, *i*, *n*, *PMT*, *PV*, and *FV* as shown.

	A	B
1		Calculating *FV*
2	*j*	3.50%
3	*m*	1
4	*t*	2
5		
6	*i*	3.50%
7	*n*	2
8	*PMT*	0
9	*PV*	($ 40,000.00)
10	*FV*	$42,849.00
11		

Future Value function call:

= FV(

FV(rate, nper, pmt, [pv], [type])

- To enter the **nominal interest rate**, **'*j*'**, select cell B2. Type **3.50%** and press **Enter**.
- To enter the **compoundings per year**, **'*m*'**, select cell B3. Type **1** and press **Enter**.
- To enter the **time period (in years)**, **'*t*'**, select cell B4. Type **2** and press **Enter**.
- To calculate the **periodic interest rate, '*i*'**, select cell B6. Type '=**B2/B3**' and press **Enter**. Alternatively, select B6 and type '=', select B2 and type '/', select B3 and press **Enter**. The periodic interest rate, '*i*', will be displayed in cell B6.
- To calculate the **total number of compounding periods, '*n*'**, select cell B7. Type '=**B3*B4**' and press **Enter**. Alternatively, select B7 and type '=', select B3 and type '*', select B4 and press Enter. The total number of compounding periods, '*n*', will be displayed in cell B7.
- Compound interest calculations do not involve periodic payments. Select cell B8, type **0**, and press **Enter**.
- To enter the **present value, '*PV*'**, as a negative value (cash-outflow) select cell B9. Type **–$40000.00** and press **Enter**.
- To calculate the **future value, '*FV*'**, using the built-in Future Value Function, select cell B10. Type '=**FV(B6,B7,B8,B9)**' and press **Enter**. Alternatively, type the function call and select each of the cells instead of typing their references. The future value, '*FV*', will be displayed in cell B10.

Therefore, the accumulated value of the investment at the end of two years is $42,849.00.

(ii) Compound interest, $I = FV - PV = 42{,}849.00 - 40{,}00.00 = \$2849.00$

Therefore, the compound interest earned is $2849.00.

Note: *Spreadsheet solutions to the examples are identified with an icon containing the page number and are available at the end of the chapter.*

Example 9.2(d) **Calculating the Future Value and Interest Earned When 'n' is a Fraction**

Executive International Inc. invested \$80,000 in an investment fund at 8% compounded quarterly for 3 years and 5 months.

(i) Calculate the accumulated value of this amount for this period.
(ii) Calculate the compound interest earned.

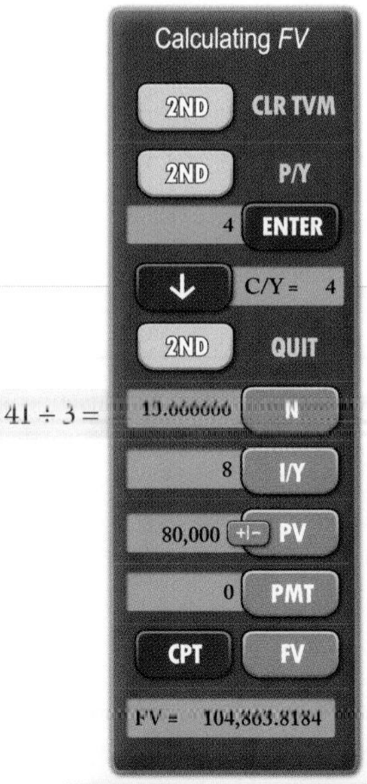

Solution

Page 379

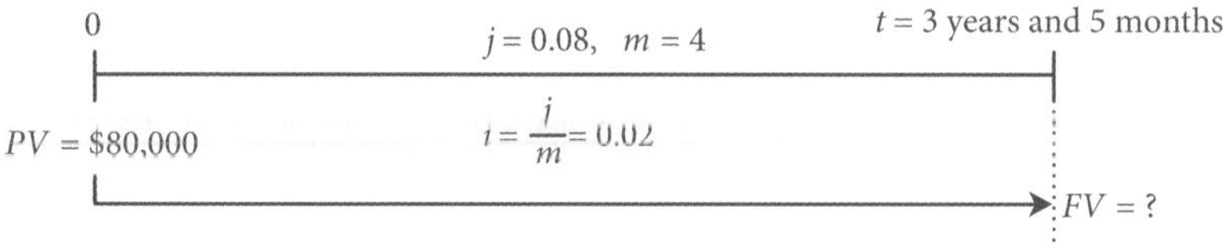

Do not round numbers in intermediate steps, such as 'n' in this case. However, round your final answer to two decimal places.

(i) $t = 3$ years and 5 months $= \left(3 + \frac{5}{12}\right)$ years $= 3\frac{5}{12}$ years

$n = m \times t = 4 \times 3\frac{5}{12} = 4 \times \frac{41}{12} = \frac{41}{3}$ compounding periods

$$FV = PV(1 + i)^n = 80{,}000.00\,(1 + 0.02)^{\frac{41}{3}}$$

$$= 104{,}863.8184... = \$104{,}863.82$$

Therefore, the accumulated amount at the end of the period is \$104,863.82.

(ii) Interest earned, $I = FV - PV = 104{,}863.82 - 80{,}000.00 = \$24{,}863.82$

Therefore, the compound interest earned on this amount is \$24,863.82.

Rounding n

$\left(\frac{41}{3} = 13.666666...\right)$ to 13.67 will give you an incorrect value of FV (\$104,870.74). Therefore, we use the exact value of n.

Example 9.2(e) **Calculating the Future Value and Interest Between Two Dates**

The bank lent Selena \$10,000 on August 11, 2017 at 4.25% compounded daily to assist her in starting her baking business.

(i) How much money did Selena pay the bank on May 29, 2018 to settle her entire loan?
(ii) How much did she pay in interest?

Solution

Page 379

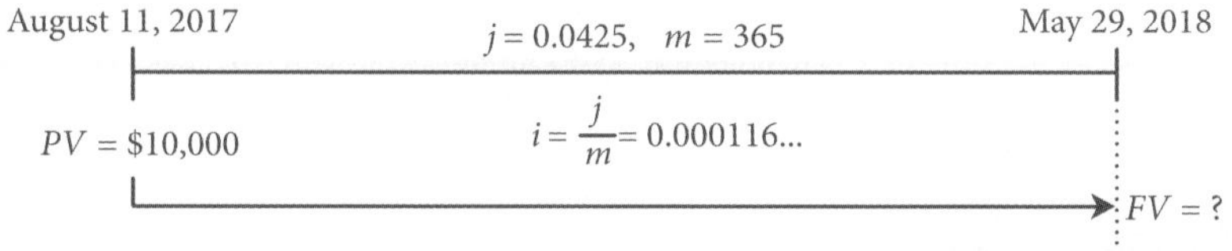

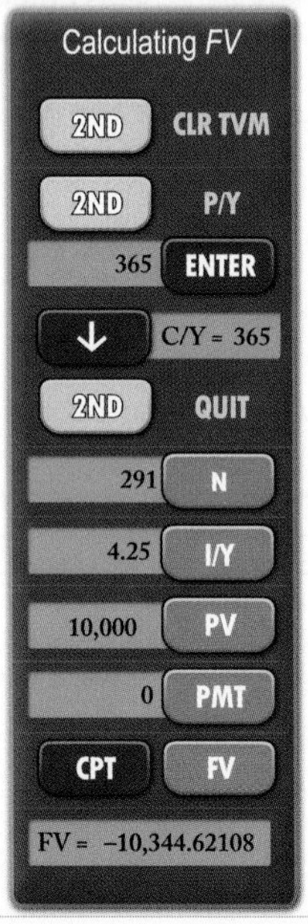

(i) The number of days between August 11, 2017 and May 29, 2018 is 291. The compounding frequency is daily.

Calculating the number of days between two dates is shown in Chapter 8.1.

Therefore, $n = 291$ compounding periods.

$$FV = PV(1 + i)^n = 10{,}000.00(1 + 0.000116...)^{291}$$

$$= 10{,}344.62108... = \$10{,}344.62$$

Therefore, Selena paid the bank \$10,344.62 on May 29, 2018 to settle her loan.

(ii) Interest paid, $I = FV - PV = 10{,}344.62 - 10{,}000.00 = \$344.62$

Therefore, she paid \$344.62 in interest.

Example 9.2(f) **Calculating the Future Value When Interest Rate Changes**

Amanda's consulting company deposited \$50,000 in a growth fund at 8% compounded semi-annually. After two years, the interest rate changed to 6% compounded annually. What is the value of the fund at the end of $5\frac{1}{2}$ years? Calculate the total interest her company earned over the entire period.

Solution

Page 379

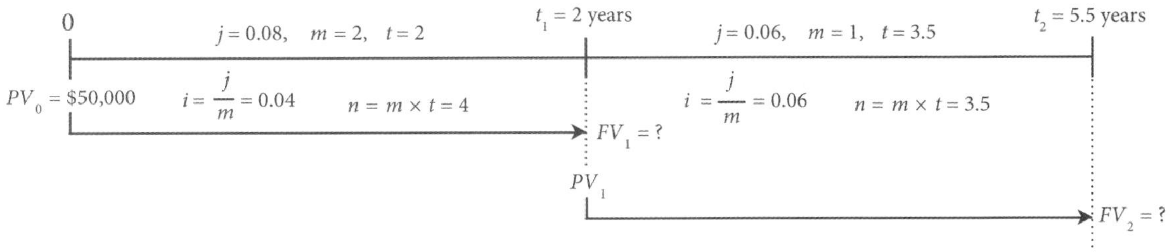

First, we need to determine the future value of the fund at the end of 2 years. The future value at the end of 2 years will become the present value in calculating the future value for the next $3\frac{1}{2}$ years.

The future value at the end of 2 years:

$$
\begin{aligned}
FV_1 &= PV_0(1 + i)^n \\
&= 50{,}000.00(1 + 0.04)^4 \\
&= \$58{,}492.928 = PV_1
\end{aligned}
$$

The future value at the end of $5\frac{1}{2}$ years:

$$
\begin{aligned}
FV_2 &= PV_1\,(1 + i)^n \\
&= 58{,}492.928(1 + 0.06)^{3.5} \\
&= 71{,}725.55046... = \$71{,}725.55
\end{aligned}
$$

Alternatively, you can calculate the future value at the end of $5\frac{1}{2}$ years in one step as follows:

$$
\begin{aligned}
FV_2 &= 50{,}000.00\,(1 + 0.04)^4(1 + 0.06)^{3.5} \\
&= 71{,}725.55046... = \$71{,}725.55
\end{aligned}
$$

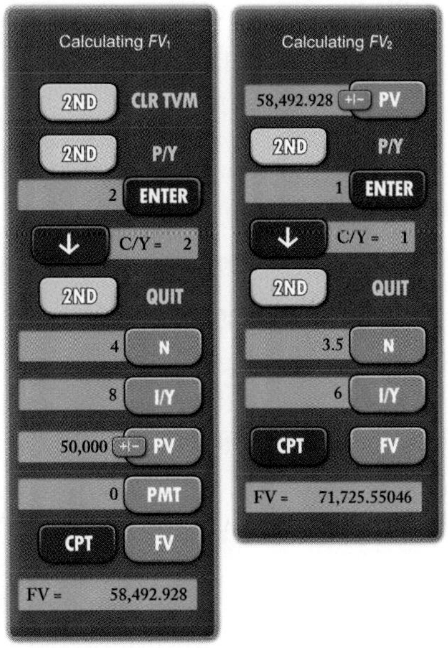

Therefore, the value of the fund at the end of $5\frac{1}{2}$ years is \$71,725.55.

The total interest earned = $FV_2 - PV_0$ = 71,725.55 – 50,000.00 = \$21,725.55

Therefore, the total interest earned over the entire period is \$21,725.55.

Example 9.2(g) **Calculating the Future Value When Principal Balance Declines**

Power Builders Inc. borrowed \$280,000 from the bank at 6.3% compounded monthly. It repaid \$120,000 at the end of the first year and another \$100,000 at the end of the second year. What amount at the end of the third year will settle this loan?

Solution

Page 379

$$j = 0.063, \quad m = 12, \quad i = \frac{j}{m} = 0.00525$$

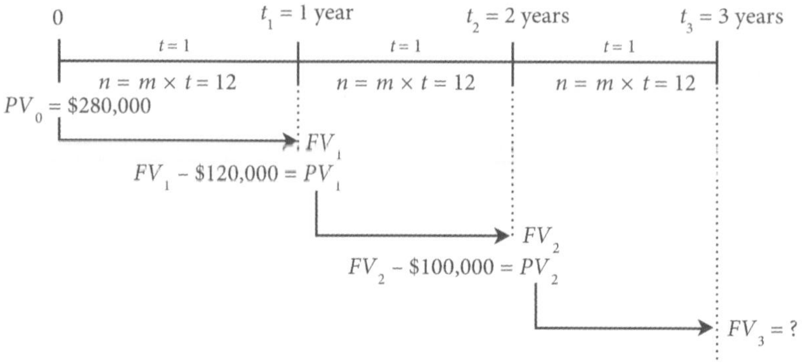

The future value at the end of the 1st year:

$$FV_1 = PV_0(1 + i)^n$$
$$= 280{,}000.00\ (1 + 0.00525)^{12}$$
$$= \$298{,}158.3749...$$

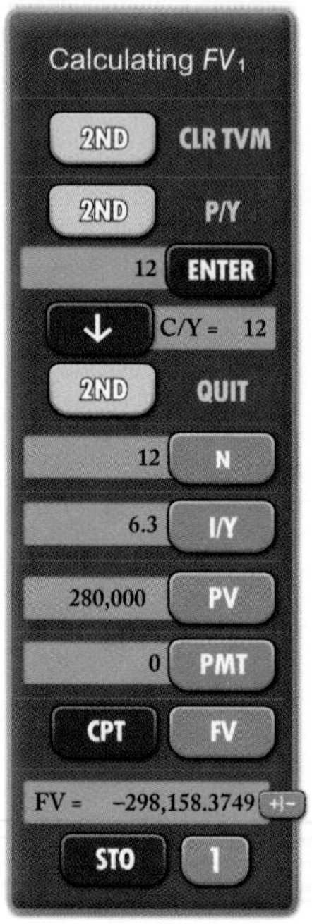

The future value at the end of the 1st year minus \$120,000 will become the present value for the 2nd year.

$$FV_1 - 120{,}000.00 = 298{,}158.3749... - 120{,}000.00$$
$$= 178{,}158.3749...$$
$$= PV_1$$

The future value at the end of the 2nd year:

$$FV_2 = PV_1(1 + i)^n$$
$$= 178{,}158.3749...(1 + 0.00525)^{12}$$
$$= \$189{,}712.1840...$$

Note:
If you do not clear the data stored in the TVM keys (2ND, CLR TVM), you need to enter only the values that are different.

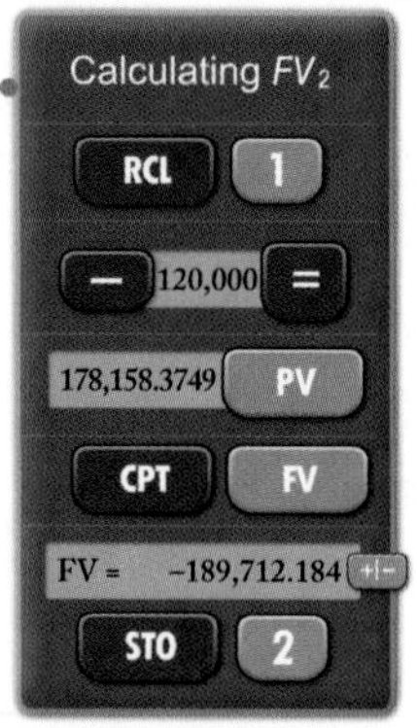

The future value at the end of the 2nd year minus \$100,000 will become the present value for the 3rd year.

$$FV_2 - 100{,}000.00 = 189{,}712.1840... - 100{,}000.00$$
$$= \$89{,}712.18405...$$
$$= PV_2$$

The future value at the end of the 3rd year:

$$FV_3 = PV_2(1 + i)^n$$
$$= 89{,}712.18405...(1 + 0.00525)^{12}$$
$$= 95{,}530.13930...$$
$$= \$95{,}530.14$$

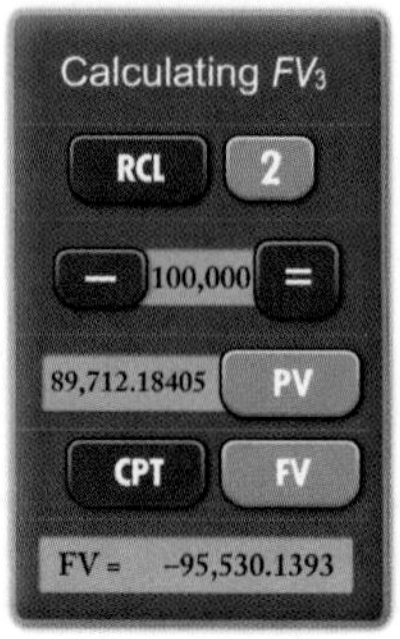

Therefore, \$95,530.14 at the end of the 3rd year will settle this loan.

Power of Compound Interest

Comparing Investment Growth when Money is Invested at Different Ages

Consider the following options where money is invested in a fund that is growing at 8% compounded annually:

Option 1: $5000 invested at the time of birth

Option 2: $5000 invested at age 15

Option 3: $5000 invested at age 30

There are no further contributions made to the fund and the money is left to grow up to the age of 65.

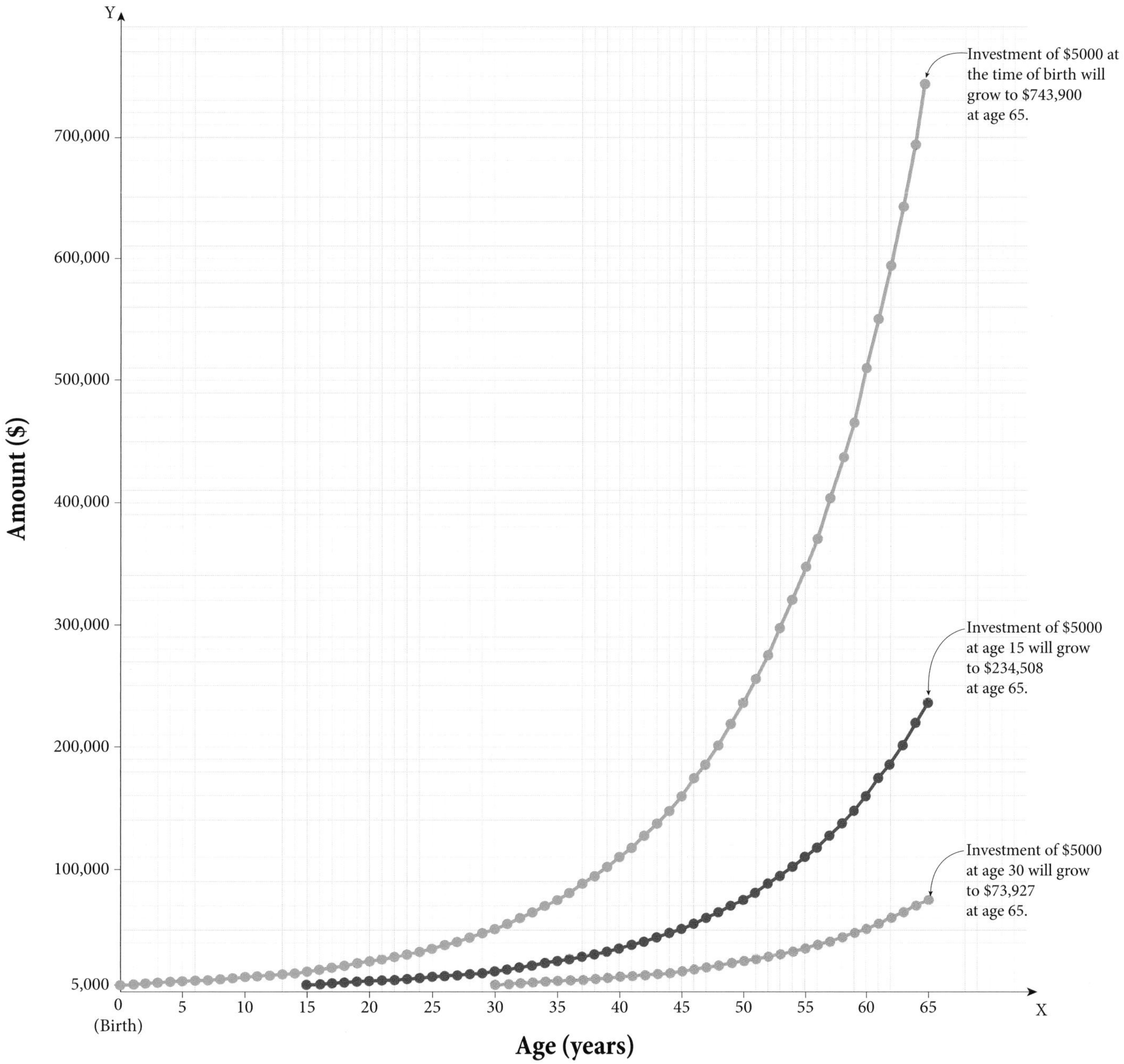
Y
Amount ($)
700,000
600,000
500,000
400,000
300,000
200,000
100,000
5,000
0
(Birth)
5
10
15
20
25
30
35
40
45
50
55
60
65
X
Age (years)
Investment of $5000 at the time of birth will grow to $743,900 at age 65.
Investment of $5000 at age 15 will grow to $234,508 at age 65.
Investment of $5000 at age 30 will grow to $73,927 at age 65.

Through the power of compound interest, you will see that the initial investment of $5000 grew to $743,900 by the age of 65 when the money was invested at the time of birth. This example illustrates the time value of money with compound interest.

9.2 | Exercises

Answers to the odd-numbered problems are available at the end of the textbook.

Calculate the missing values for Problems 1 and 2.

1.

	Present Value (*PV*)	Nominal Interest Rate (*j*)	Compounding Frequency (*m*)	Time Period (*t*)	Periodic Interest Rate (*i*)	Number of Compounding Periods (*n*)	Future Value (*FV*)
a.	$1000.00	5.11%	2	5 years and 6 months	?	?	?
b.	$3550.50	?	4	2 years and 3 months	1.1625%	?	?
c.	$16,500.00	6.30%	?	219 days	0.525%	?	?
d.	$9650.75	6.57%	1	? (in years and months)	?	11.25	?

2.

	Present Value (*PV*)	Nominal Interest Rate (*j*)	Compounding Frequency (*m*)	Time Period (*t*)	Periodic Interest Rate (*i*)	Number of Compounding Periods (*n*)	Future Value (*FV*)
a.	$12,450.50	4.95%	?	10 years	1.2375%	?	?
b.	$540.75	7.30%	365	292 days	?	?	?
c.	$16,400.00	5.84%	2	? (in years and months)	?	19.5	?
d.	$4500.00	?	12	3 years and 9 months	0.6050%	?	?

3. Shirley borrowed $3000 at 4.75% compounded annually. She repaid the loan in four years. Calculate the accumulated value of the loan at the end of the term and the interest charged during the period.

4. Ben invested $8450 for five years in his savings account that was earning 3.2% compounded annually. Calculate the future value of his investment at the end of the term and the amount of interest earned during the period.

5. If Shanta deposited $2800 in an investment fund that was earning 5.5% compounded semi-annually for a period of three years, calculate the accumulated value of the investment and the interest earned during the period.

6. Red Roses Florists received a loan of $7000 at 5.25% compounded daily. Calculate the accumulated value of the loan and the interest charged at the end of 200 days.

7. Robbie loaned $250,000 to a small business at 7.75% compounded semi-annually for 1 year and 2 months.
   a. How much would the business have to repay Robbie at the end of the period?
   b. How much interest did Robbie earn from this investment?

8. Power Printers received a loan of $25,000 from a bank at 5.15% compounded quarterly for 1 year and 5 months. Calculate the accumulated amount and the interest charged on this loan.

9. Carleen Corporation borrowed $20,000 for two years and six months at 5.5% compounded semi-annually.
   a. Calculate the accumulated value of the debt at the end of the time period.
   b. If the corporation kept the money for another two months (at the same interest rate), calculate the total repayment amount, total interest, and the amount of interest charged for the extended period.

10. Lee's real estate agency borrowed $10,000 from a credit union at 6.55% compounded monthly for 6 years and 9 months.
    a. How much should Lee's agency repay the credit union at the end of the time period?
    b. If the agency kept the money for another three months (at the same interest rate), calculate the total repayment amount and the amount of interest charged for the extended period.

11. Calculate the maturity value and the interest earned on an investment of $12,000 for four years if it was growing at 3.25% compounded semi-annually during the first year and 3.6% compounded monthly during the next three years.

12. Marcia invested $25,000 at 4.5% compounded monthly for the first two years and at 5% compounded daily for the third year. What is the maturity value of her investment and the amount of interest earned at the end of three years?

13. Top Tier Talent Inc., a successful recruitment agency in Montreal, loaned $30,000 to one of its partners for five years. If the interest rate for the first two years was 2% compounded monthly and for the next three years was 2.3% compounded semi-annually, how much should the partner repay the recruitment agency at the end of the period?

14. Brandon, an investment banker, took a risk and invested $350,000 in a fund that yielded 6.75% compounded daily. After one year, the rate dropped to 2.25% compounded monthly. What will be the accumulated amount in the fund at the end of 1 year and 8 months?

15. On May 16, 2014, Joseph invested $30,000 in a fund that was growing at 3.75% compounded semi-annually. On April 27, 2016, the interest rate on the fund changed to 4.25% compounded monthly and remained constant thereafter. What will be the accumulated value of the fund on December 29, 2020?

16. On April 11, 2014, Cynthia received a loan of $45,000 at 5.55% compounded monthly. On May 13, 2015, the interest rate on the loan changed to 5.75% compounded quarterly and remained constant thereafter. What will be the accumulated value of the loan on December 31, 2017?

17. Maxwell Servers Inc. wants to invest its net profits to gain the highest returns. Which of the following two options will yield the highest returns? (Hint: Assume $1000 for the present value and one year for the time period.) Show your calculations to support your answer.

    - Option A: A credit union that provides an interest rate of 6.09% compounded semi-annually.
    - Option B: A local business development bank that provides an interest rate of 6.05% compounded daily.

18. Roy was offered a choice between two interest rates for a loan: 5.13% compounded daily or 5.14% compounded monthly. Which one should he choose? (Hint: Assume $1000 for the present value and one year for the time period.) Show your calculations to support your answer.

19. The simple interest charged on a loan for two years at 4% p.a. is $375. Determine the compound interest amount on this loan for two years at 4% compounded quarterly.

20. The simple interest earned on an investment for one year at 5% p.a. is $250. Calculate the compound interest amount earned on the same amount for one year at 5% compounded daily.

21. How much more interest would you earn by investing $10,000 for six years at 5% compounded annually rather than at 5% p.a. simple interest?

22. How much more interest would you earn by investing $5850 for three months at 4% compounded semi-annually rather than at 4% p.a. simple interest?

23. Victor plans to invest $100,000 in a GIC for three years. A bank offers an increasing rate of interest on its three-year GICs that pay semi-annual compounded rates of 2.25%, 2.75%, and 3.25%, respectively, in each of the successive years. On the other hand, a trust company offers GICs that pay 2.80% compounded semi-annually for the three-year period. With which option would he earn more and by how much?

24. Lydia wanted to invest $80,000 in a GIC for three years. A bank offers an increasing rate of interest on its three-year GICs that pay semi-annual compounded rates of 2.75%, 3.00%, and 3.25%, respectively, in each of the successive years. A trust company offers GICs that pay 3.00% compounded semi-annually for the three-year period. With which option would she earn more and by how much?

25. Martha deposited $25,000 in her bank savings account that earns 2% compounded daily. At the end of one year, she deposited an additional $18,000 into this account. What was the balance in her account at the end of 450 days?

26. Ace Publishing Company invested $50,000 in an investment fund that was growing at a rate of 4% compounded monthly. After one year, the company deposited an additional $30,000 in the same fund. Calculate the balance in the fund at the end of three years (two years later).

27. Dylan invested his company's annual profits of $20,000 in an investment fund earning 4.75% compounded monthly. Next year, his company had a very profitable year, and he invested his company's profits of $32,000 in the same fund. What is the balance of the fund at the end of four years (three years after the last deposit)?

28. What is the accumulated value 500 days from now of \$8000 invested today and \$12,000 invested 180 days from now in a fund earning 3% compounded daily?

• 29. Harris Machinery received a demand loan of \$180,000. It repaid \$75,000 at the end of the first year, \$80,000 at the end of the second year, and the balance at the end of the third year. If the interest rate charged was 5.5% compounded semi-annually for the first year, 5.25% compounded quarterly for the second year, and 5.15% compounded monthly for the third year, calculate the final payment.

• 30. Sparco Medicals received a loan of \$285,000 from a Canadian financial institution. It repaid \$50,000 in one year, \$110,000 in two years, and the balance in three years. If the financial institution charged an interest rate of 7% compounded monthly for the first year, 6.5% compounded semi-annually for the second year, and 6% compounded daily for the third year, calculate the final payment.

• 31. Matthew received a personal loan from his local bank at an interest rate of 6.75% compounded semi-annually for one year. If the amount of interest charged at the end of the period was \$280.50, calculate the accumulated value of the loan.

• 32. The interest charged on a student loan that Hannah obtained from a bank for four years was \$1855. If the bank charged an interest rate of 4.35% compounded monthly, calculate the accumulated value of the loan at the end of the period.

9.3 | Calculating Present Value (PV)

As described in Section 9.1, present value (or discounted value or principal) can be calculated by rearranging the future value formula, Formula 9.1(a), $FV = PV(1 + i)^n$:

$$PV = \frac{FV}{(1+i)^n} \quad \text{or} \quad PV = FV(1+i)^{-n}$$

The following examples will illustrate present value calculations.

Example 9.3(a) Calculating the Present Value

Page 379

Calculate the present value of \$5000 due in three years at 5% compounded semi-annually.

When there is growth (i.e. interest rate is positive), the present value is always numerically smaller than the future value. For this reason, it is also known as the discounted value. The interest rate is known as the discount rate and the interest amount is known as the amount of discount.

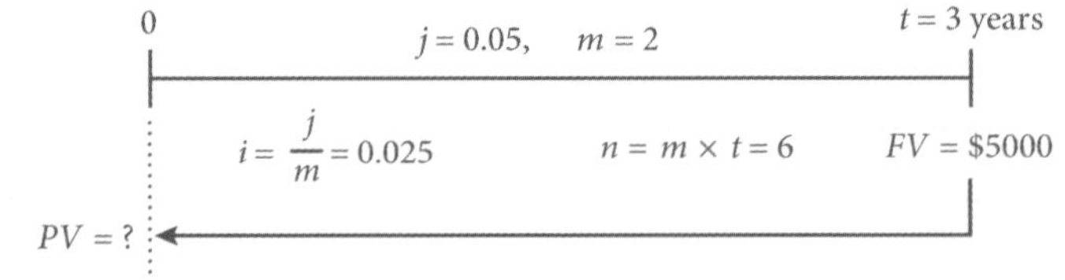

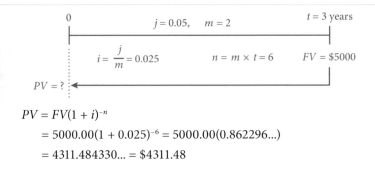

$$PV = FV(1 + i)^{-n}$$
$$= 5000.00(1 + 0.025)^{-6} = 5000.00(0.862296...)$$
$$= 4311.484330... = \$4311.48$$

Therefore, the present value of \$5000 due in three years is \$4311.48.

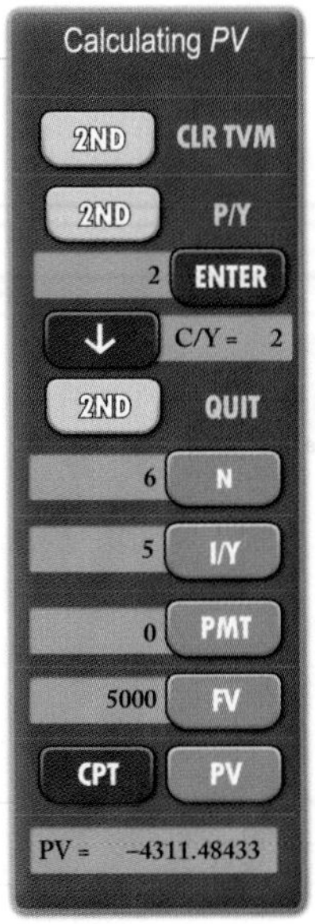

Example 9.3(b) Calculating the Present Value When 'n' is a Fraction and Interest Rate Changes

Orlandra Boutique wants $275,000 in 4 years and 7 months. How much should it invest now to meet this goal if the interest rate for the first year is 4% compounded semi-annually and 4% compounded quarterly thereafter?

Solution

Page 379

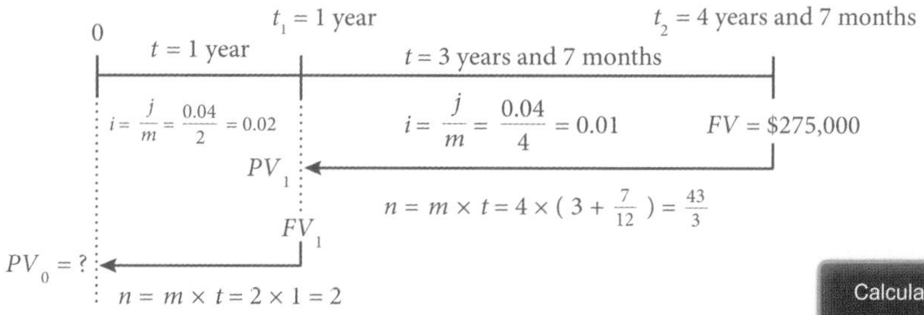

First, we need to determine the present value at the end of one year (PV_1).

PV_1 will become the future value (FV_1) in calculating the present value today (PV_0).

Calculating the present value at the end of year 1:

$$PV_1 = FV(1 + i)^{-n}$$
$$= 275{,}000.00(1 + 0.01)^{-\frac{43}{3}}$$
$$= 238{,}447.6260... = FV_1$$

Calculating the present value today:

$$PV_0 = FV_1(1 + i)^{-n}$$
$$= 238{,}447.6260...(1 + 0.02)^{-2}$$
$$= 229{,}188.4141... = \$229{,}188.41$$

Therefore, it should invest $229,188.41 now to meet its goal.

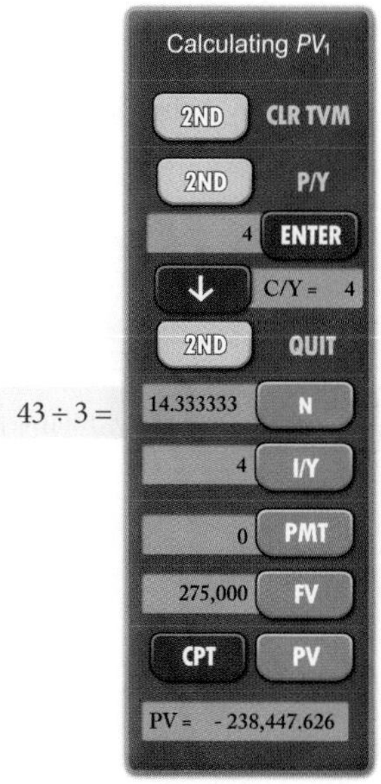

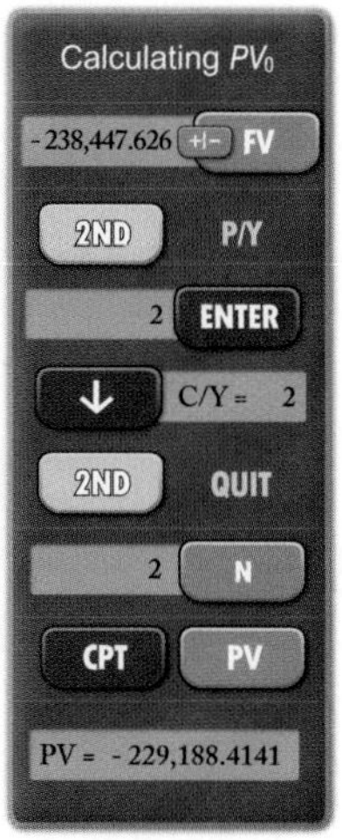

Example 9.3(c) Comparing Two Payment Options

RC Printers had the following two options to pay for printing supplies:

- Option A: A single payment of $650 at the beginning of the year.
- Option B: $200 at the beginning of the year and $480 at the end of the year.

If money can earn 8% compounded daily, which option is economically better (in current value).

Solution

Page 380

Comparing the Present Values of Both Options

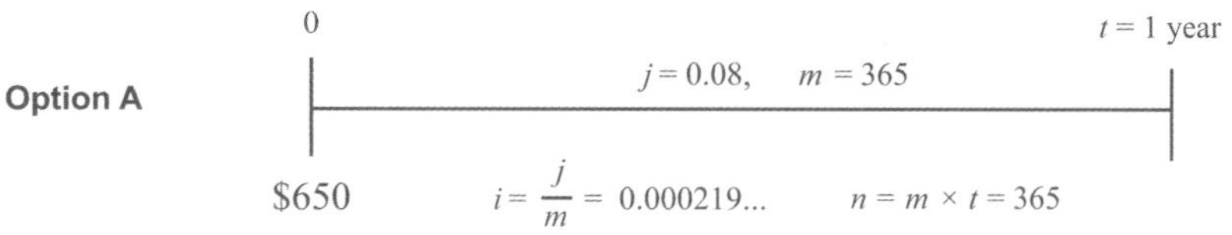

$$PV_{\text{Option A}} = \$650.00$$

The present value of Option A is $650.00.

Solution
continued

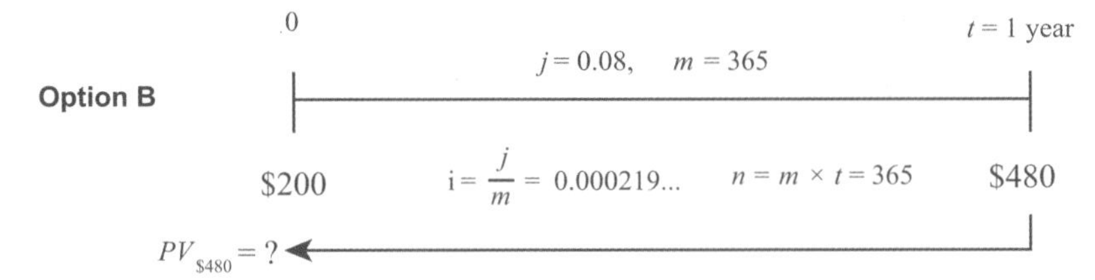

$$PV_{\$480} = 480.00(1 + 0.000219...)^{-365} = \$443.099730...$$

$$PV_{\text{Option B}} = 200.00 + 443.099730... = 643.099730... = \$643.10$$

The present value of Option B is $643.10.

Therefore, Option B is economically better, since in Option B, RC Printers will pay a smaller amount than in Option A.

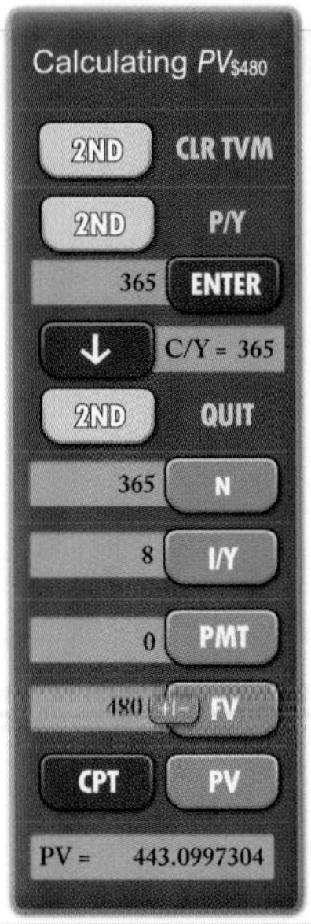

9.3 | Exercises

Answers to the odd numbered problems are available at the end of the textbook.

Calculate the missing values for Problems 1 and 2.

1.

	Present Value (*PV*)	Nominal Interest Rate (*j*)	Compounding Frequency (*m*)	Time Period (*t*)	Periodic Interest Rate (*i*)	Number of Compounding Periods (*n*)	Future Value (*FV*)
a.	?	5.38%	2	5 years	?	?	$6500.00
b.	?	?	4	10 years and 9 months	1.4550%	?	$16,000.00
c.	?	4.89%	?	7 years	0.4075%	?	$16,886.44
d.	?	7.42%	1	? (in years and months)	?	2.25	$8810.55

2.

	Present Value (*PV*)	Nominal Interest Rate (*j*)	Compounding Frequency (*m*)	Time Period (*t*)	Periodic Interest Rate (*i*)	Number of Compounding Periods (*n*)	Future Value (*FV*)
a.	?	6.90%	?	4 years	1.725%	?	$17,500.00
b.	?	10.95%	365	219 days	?	?	$12,450.00
c.	?	7.45%	2	? (in years and months)	?	13.5	$49,152.74
d.	?	?	12	30 months	0.670%	?	$19,856.11

3. Cheryl would like to accumulate $35,000 for her retirement in 10 years. If she is promised 4.75% compounded annually by her local bank, how much should she invest today?

4. If you wish to have $100,000 in five years, how much should you invest in an investment fund that earns 3.75% compounded annually?

5. Geoffrey wishes to have $20,800 saved in five years to use as a deposit for the purchase of a new home. How much money should he invest today at 3.25% compounded semi-annually in order to achieve this goal?

6. How much interest did Speedy Movers pay for a debt that accumulated to $58,556 in four years if the interest rate charged was 4.5% compounded quarterly?

7. The interest rate on a Guaranteed Investment Certificate (GIC) is 3.5% compounded daily. What was the purchase price if it has a maturity value of $38,430 in 300 days?

8. What amount deposited today would yield $50,000 in 4 years and 5 months if it were invested at 5.55% compounded semi-annually?

9. What is the discounted value of a loan that matured to $5000 in $5\frac{1}{2}$ years if the interest rate is 4% compounded monthly?

10. Samantha purchased a GIC that has a maturity value of $25,865 in 6 years and 4 months. What was the purchase price of the GIC if it earns 2.5% compounded quarterly?

11. What amount invested today will amount to $13,695.13 in two years if the interest rate is 4.2% compounded monthly for the first year and 5% compounded daily for the second year?

12. What amount invested today will accumulate to $18,613.77 in two years if the interest rate is 2.19% compounded daily during the first year and 4% compounded semi-annually during the second year?

13. A law firm invested its net profit into an investment fund that provided an initial interest rate of 4.55% compounded monthly. After six months, there was a boom in the market and the interest rate rose to 8.75% compounded monthly. If the accumulated value one year after the boom was $480,000, calculate the amount that was originally invested.

14. Kyle's investment in a Registered Retirement Savings Plan (RRSP) at an interest rate of 4.35% compounded semi-annually had grown to $24,000 at the end of one year. Thereafter, the interest rate on his RRSP dropped to 3.75% compounded monthly, and remained constant for the next two years. Calculate his original investment in the RRSP, and the accumulated amount at the end of three years (two years after the rate drop).

15. A loan accumulated to $25,050 in ten years at 5.5% compounded monthly. If this loan had been issued at 5.48% compounded quarterly instead of 5.5% compounded monthly, would there have been any savings? Show calculations to support your answer.

16. It was time for Bolder Cans Ltd. to repay its accumulated debt of $83,232. The original amount was received from a high net-worth individual at 5% compounded quarterly for five years. How much would have been saved if the loan had been received at 5% compounded semi-annually?

17. An amount of $30,500 is due to be paid on October 12, 2018. What equivalent payment should be made on August 16, 2016 to settle this amount, if money is worth 4.5% compounded daily?

18. What payment made on April 15, 2017 would be economically equivalent to a payment of $25,485 to be made on January 10, 2020, if money earns 5.75% compounded daily?

19. Karen has the following two options to receive a loan payment:

    Option A: receive $5000 today, or

    Option B: receive $3000 today and $2250 one year from now.

    If money is worth 3.45% compounded semi-annually, which option is more economical for her and by how much?

20. A company has the following payment options to settle a loan:

    Option A: pay $19,000 today, or

    Option B: pay $10,000 today and $9500 in one year.

    If money earns 4% compounded daily, which option is more economical for the company and by how much?

• 21. Brenda borrowed money to renovate her kitchen. She settled the loan in five years with a single payment of $55,021.80. If the interest rate charged on the loan was 3.8% compounded semi-annually for the first two years and 4.2% compounded monthly for the next three years, calculate the amount borrowed and the amount of interest paid on the loan.

• 22. The money that Susan invested in a mutual fund for four years matured to $20,961.47. If the fund was growing at 4.6% compounded semi-annually for the first year and 4.5% compounded monthly for the next three years, calculate the amount invested and the amount of interest earned from this investment.

• 23. Which option should Perfect Bookkeepers Inc. choose to invest its savings and why?

Option A: 5.02% compounded daily.

Option B: 5.50% compounded semi-annually.

(Hint: Assume either a future value or present value and a time period.)

• 24. Tao learned that he could save his money in a term deposit. Which ten-year term deposit should he choose if one is providing him with an interest rate of 6% compounded quarterly, and the other 6.5% compounded monthly? Show calculations to support your answer.

• 25. A bank offered a personal loan to George at an interest rate of 6.5% compounded semi-annually for two years. At the end of the period, if the amount of interest charged was \$880.50, calculate the present value of the loan.

• 26. The interest charged on a personal loan for two years was \$2450.75. If the interest rate charged on the loan was 5.95% compounded daily, calculate the present value of the loan.

9.4 | Calculating Equivalent Payments

A single payment or a set of payments, at a given interest rate, can be replaced by a single equivalent payment or an equivalent set of payments on any other date(s); this is accomplished using a **focal date**, as illustrated in the following examples.

Example 9.4(a) Calculating the Size of a Single Payment, Equivalent to Two Payments

What single payment in three years would be equivalent to \$1000 due one year ago (but not paid) and \$2000 in six years? Assume a rate of 5% compounded semi-annually during this period.

Solution

Page 380

First, create the timeline diagram showing the given payments and select a focal date. We will determine the value of all the payments on this date and equate them to determine the value of the unknown payment.

You can choose any date as the focal date. However, it is easier to choose the focal date on the date of one of the unknown payments.

Let the focal date be the date of the unknown payment, i.e., three years. We are asked to determine the payment on this focal date that is equivalent to the other two payments. To do so, we calculate the future value of the first payment (FV_1) on this focal date and the present value of the second payment (PV_2) on this focal date. Then,

$$\text{Equivalent payment} = FV_1 + PV_2$$

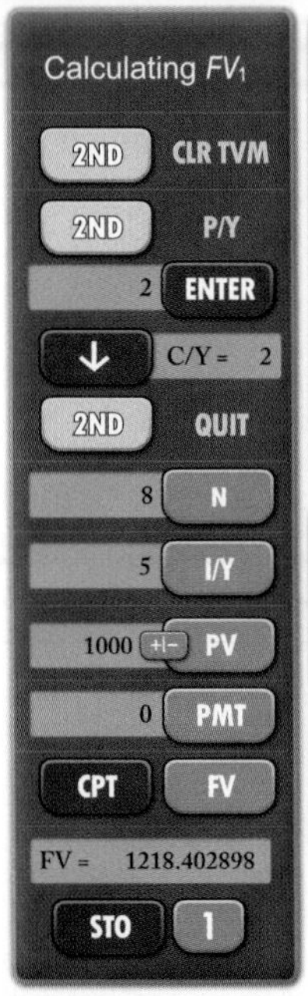

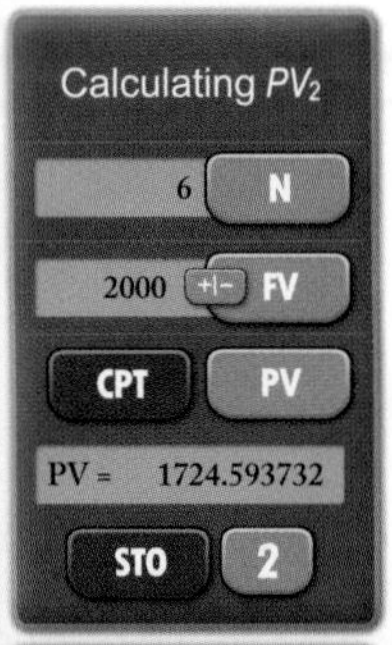

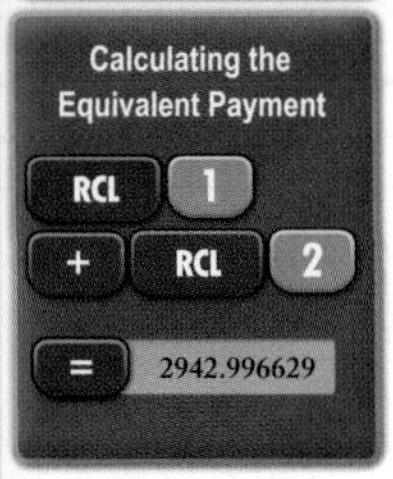

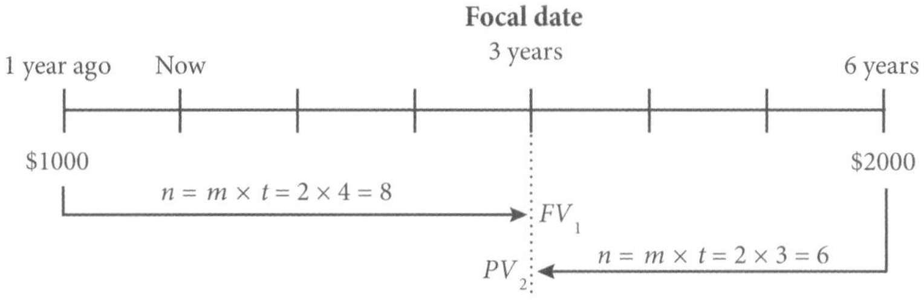

$$j = 0.05, \quad m = 2, \quad i = \frac{j}{m} = \frac{0.05}{2} = 0.025$$

$$FV_1 = 1000.00\,(1 + 0.025)^8 = \$1218.402898...$$

$$PV_2 = 2000.00\,(1 + 0.025)^{-6} = \$1724.593732...$$

Equivalent single payment in 3 years = 1218.402898... + 1724.593732...

= 2942.996629... = \$2943.00

Therefore, a single payment of \$2943.00 in three years would be equivalent to \$1000.00 due one year ago and \$2000.00 in 6 years.

Example 9.4(b) Calculating the Size of Two Equal Payments that would Replace a Single Payment, Using Different Focal Dates

A scheduled payment of $5000 due in three months is to be replaced by two equal payments. The first payment is due in one month and the second payment in six months. Calculate the size of each of the equal payments if money can earn 6% compounded monthly.

Solution

Page 380

Let '$\$x$' be the value of each equal payment.

This question can be solved by choosing different focal dates, as illustrated in Methods 1, 2, and 3 below:

Method 1: Let the focal date be in three months.

Note that in this example there will only be one unknown variable 'x', since the two unknown payments are of equal size.

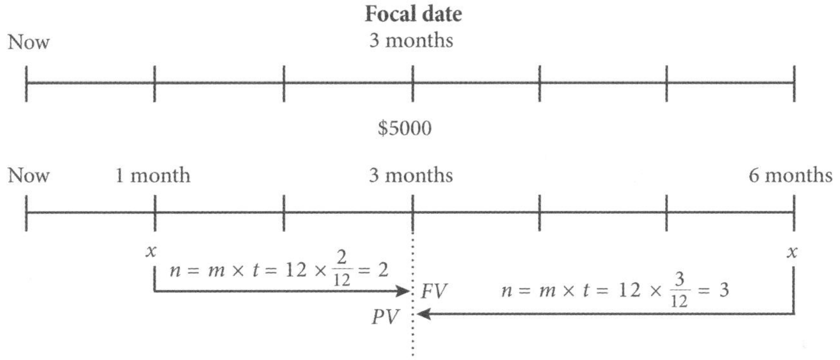

$$j = 0.06, \quad m = 12, \quad i = \frac{j}{m} = \frac{0.06}{12} = 0.005$$

$$\$5000.00 = FV_{\text{1st payment in 3 months}} + PV_{\text{2nd payment in 3 months}}$$

Substituting the values, $5000.00 = x(1 + 0.005)^2 + x(1 + 0.005)^{-3}$

Simplifying, $5000.00 = x(1.010025) + x(0.985148...)$

Solving for x, $5000.00 = x(1.995173...)$

$$x = 2506.047394... = \$2506.05$$

In the calculator method, assume that the equal payments are $1 each.

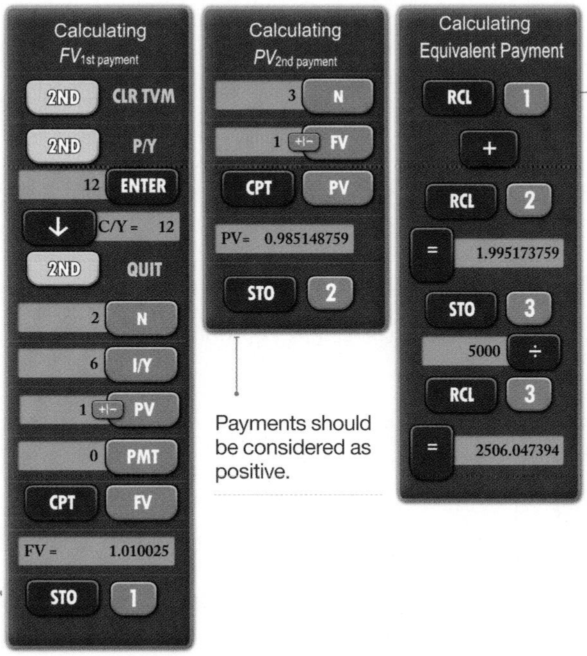

Recalls stored value under '**1**'

Payments should be considered as positive.

Stores value under '**1**'

Therefore, the size of each of the two equal payments is $2506.05.

Solution
continued

Method 2: Let the focal date be in six months.

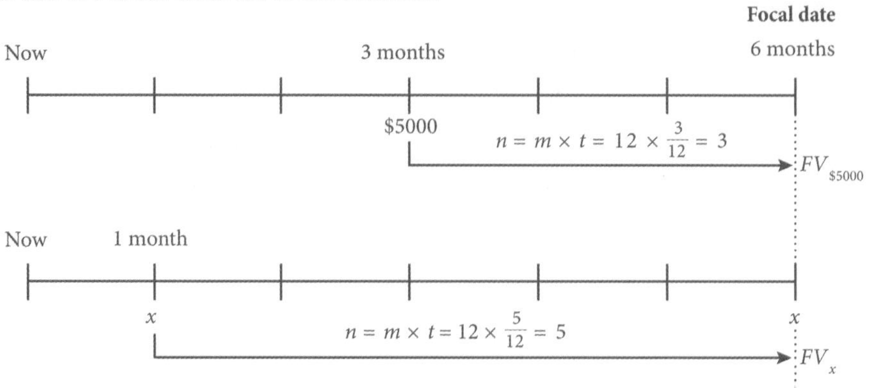

$$j = 0.06, \quad m = 12, \quad i = \frac{j}{m} = \frac{0.06}{12} = 0.005$$

$$FV_{\$5000 \text{ in 6 months}} = FV_{1^{st} \text{ payment in 6 months}} + \text{Value of } 2^{nd} \text{ payment } x$$

Substituting the values, $5000.00\,(1 + 0.005)^3 = x\,(1 + 0.005)^5 + x$

Simplifying, $5075.375625... = x\,(1.025251...) + x$

Solving for x, $5075.375625... = x\,(2.025251...)$

$$x = 2506.047394... = \$2506.05$$

Therefore, the size of each of the two equal payments is \$2506.05.

Method 3: Let the focal date be in one month.

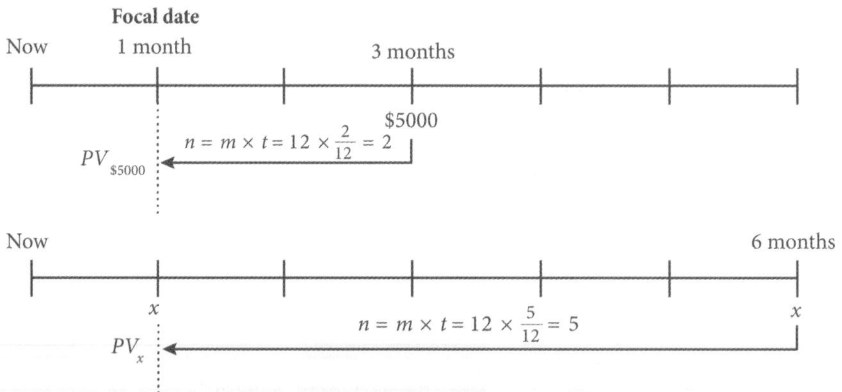

$$j = 0.06, \quad m = 12, \quad i = \frac{j}{m} = \frac{0.06}{12} = 0.005$$

You will notice that the choice of the focal date in solving compound interest problems (as shown in Methods 1, 2, and 3) has no bearing on the final answer.

$$PV_{\$5000 \text{ in 1 month}} = PV_{2nd \text{ payment in 1 month}} + \text{Value of } 1^{st} \text{ payment } x$$

Substituting the values, $5000.00\,(1 + 0.005)^{-2} = x\,(1 + 0.005)^{-5} + x$

Simplifying, $4950.372516... = x\,(0.975370...) + x$

Solving for x, $4950.372516... = x\,(1.975370...)$

$$x = 2506.047394... = \$2506.05$$

Therefore, the size of each of the two equal payments is \$2506.05.

Note: *The calculator method of solving the preceding problem has been omitted in Methods 2 and 3 and may be worked out as practice.*

Example 9.4(c) Calculating the Size of an Unknown Payment Given Two Equivalent Payment Streams

You are given two options to settle a loan:

Option 1: $2000 now and $3000 in two years.

Option 2: $2500 in six months and the balance in three years.

Calculate the payment required in three years under Option 2 if money earns 8% compounded quarterly.

Solution

Page 380

This question can be solved by choosing different focal dates. We will use three years as the focal date.

Option 1

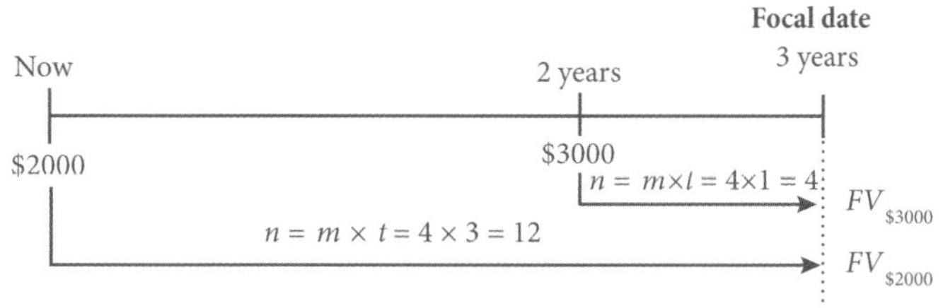

Option 2

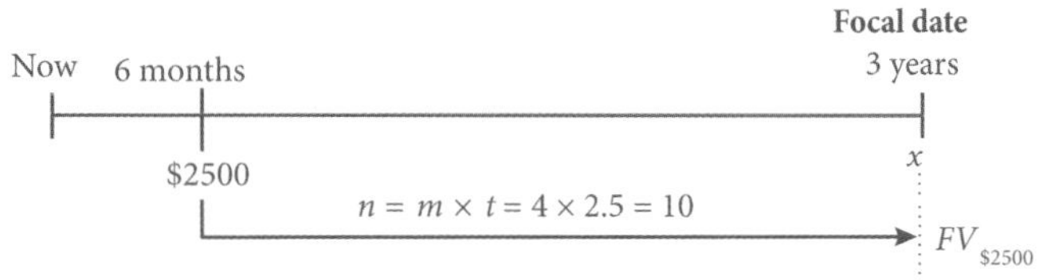

$j = 0.08, \quad m = 4, \quad i = \frac{j}{m} = \frac{0.08}{4} = 0.02$

Equating the values of Option 1 and Option 2 at the focal date,

$$FV_{\$2000} + FV_{\$3000} = FV_{\$2500} + x$$

$$2000.00\,(1 + 0.02)^{12} + 3000.00\,(1 + 0.02)^{4} = 2500.00(1 + 0.02)^{10} + x$$

$$2536.483589... + 3247.296480... = 3047.486050... + x$$

$$2536.483589... + 3247.296480... - 3047.486050... = x$$

$$x = 2736.294019... = \$2736.29$$

Therefore, the payment required in three years under Option 2 is $2736.29.

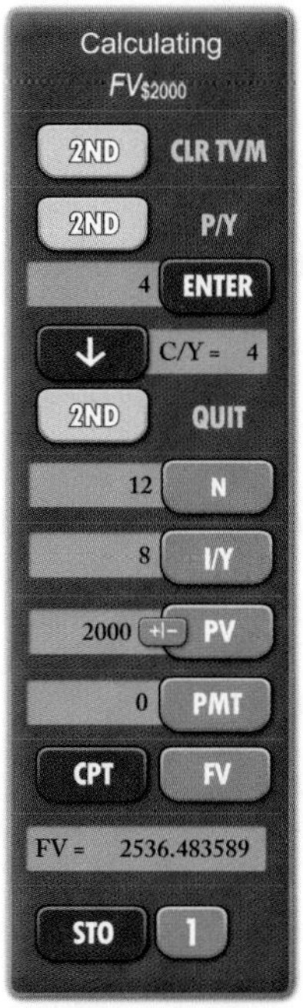

Note:
It is not necessary to re-enter I/Y, P/Y, and PMT as they have not changed and have not been cleared (by CLR TVM).

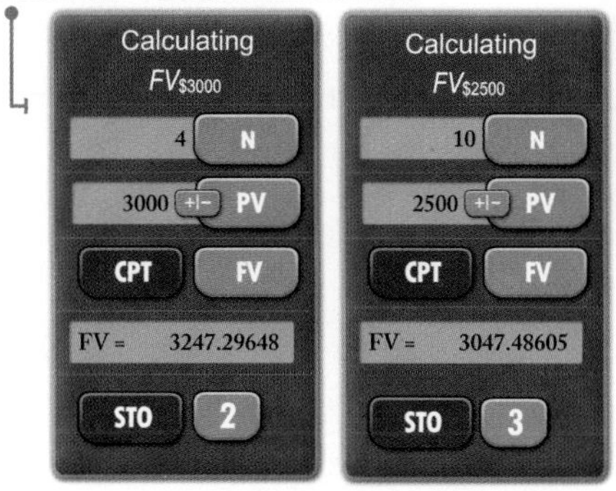

9.4 | Exercises

Answers to the odd-numbered problems are available at the end of the textbook.

For Problems 1 and 2, calculate the equivalent payment of the scheduled payment on the specified date.

1.

	Scheduled Payments	Date of Equivalent Payment	Interest Rate
a.	\$4000 due 3 years ago (but not paid) and \$2000 in 1 year	2 years from now	4.25% compounded semi-annually
b.	\$1500 in 2 years and \$2500 in 3 years	today	4.50% compounded quarterly
c.	\$750 due 1 year ago (but not paid) and \$1000 in 1 year	7 months from now	4.80% compounded monthly
d.	\$750 due 2 years ago (but not paid), \$1750 now, and \$1250 in 3 years	3 years from now	6.00% compounded annually

2.

	Scheduled Payments	Date of Equivalent Payment	Interest Rate
a.	\$1750 due 1 year ago (but not paid) and \$1500 in 1 year	3 years from now	4.20% compounded quarterly
b.	\$5000 in 1 year and \$4000 in 2 years	today	4.75% compounded semi-annually
c.	\$4000 due 3 years ago (but not paid) and \$2000 in 1 year	4 months from now	5.10% compounded monthly
d.	\$1000 due 1 year ago (but not paid), \$2500 now, and \$2000 in 4 years	1 year from now	4.80% compounded annually

3. If money earns 8.5% compounded monthly, what single payment in one year would be equivalent to:
   a. \$2340 due two years ago, but not paid, and \$500 today?
   b. \$880 due two years ago, but not paid, and \$850 in five years?
   Show your calculation with a timeline diagram, choosing one year from now as the focal date.
4. If money earns 6.25% compounded semi-annually, what single payment today would be equivalent to:
   a. \$300 in two years and \$780 in four years?
   b. \$8020 due six months ago, but not paid, and \$9050 in one year?
   Show your calculation with a timeline diagram, choosing today as the focal date.
5. If money earns 6.26% compounded daily, what two equal payments, one today and the other in one year, would be equivalent to:
   a. \$550 today and \$680 in 180 days?
   b. Two equal payments of \$5000: one due one year ago, but not paid, and the other due today?
6. If money earns 4% compounded semi-annually, what two equal payments, one in one year and the other in three years, would be equivalent to:
   a. \$8000 today?
   b. \$5650 due one year ago, but not paid, and \$6800 due two years ago, but not paid?
7. What single payment in two years would replace a payment of \$18,650 due one year ago and a payment of \$21,400 due two years and two months ago? Assume that both payments were not paid and that the interest rate is 4% compounded quarterly.

8. Mandy Industries was supposed to receive payments of $10,000 two years ago and $20,000 one year ago from a customer who could not make either payment as scheduled. If the customer would like to settle both payments today, what total amount would he have to pay Mandy Industries if an interest of 8% compounded daily is charged?

9. What three equal payments in one year, two years, and three years, would replace one single payment of $4000 today at an interest rate of 6% compounding monthly?

10. A year ago, Aisha loaned $12,000 to Chang at the rate of 4% compounded quarterly. Chang was required to repay this amount in three equal yearly installments, with payments starting from the end of the first year. How much interest did Aisha earn from this transaction?

11. What single payment today would replace a payment of $5000 in one year and $8000 in two years if the interest rate is 4% compounded monthly?

12. Calculate the single equivalent payment today that would replace three payments of $18,400, $21,065, and $12,560, in two years, four years, and five years, respectively, if money is earning interest at a rate of 3% compounded monthly.

13. Payments of $1500 in 1 year and $2500 in 2 years to settle a loan are to be rescheduled with a payment of $1000 in 6 months and the balance in 18 months. Calculate the payment required in 18 months to complete the transaction if money earns 4.25% compounded semi-annually.

14. Payments of $10,000 in one year and $25,000 in four years are to be rescheduled with a payment of $5000 today and the balance in three years. Calculate the payment required in three years to complete the transaction if money earns 5.2% compounded quarterly.

15. Nimmi invested $75,000 in an educational fund for her two granddaughters who are currently aged 3 years and 7 years, respectively. She planned that her granddaughters would receive equal amounts when each of them reached the age of 15 years. How much will each of them receive if the fund is earning 4.75% compounded semi-annually?

16. A father invested $125,000 at 4.8% compounded monthly so that his son and his daughter, aged 10 and 12, respectively, will receive equal amounts from this fund when each of them reach the age of 18. How much will each of them receive when they turn 18 years old?

17. You had an agreement to pay $6070 in 300 days and $10,500 in 500 days. What single payment 200 days earlier than the first scheduled payment would pay off this debt? Assume that money earns 3% compounded daily.

18. You are expected to settle a loan by making payments of $1200 in 180 days, $1560 in 365 days, and $3200 in 545 days. What single payment in 365 days would be equivalent to these scheduled payments if money is worth 6% compounded daily?

19. Jeremy had an agreement to repay payments of $6500 in four years and $11,225 in seven years. How much should he pay in five years in order to clear the debt if an interest rate of 5% compounded quarterly was charged?

20. What single payment in one year would be equivalent to $60,500 three years ago, but not paid, and $12,025 in four years? Assume an interest rate of 12% compounded monthly.

• 21. When Rutherford Steels bid for an infrastructure project, the company was offered the following two payment options:

Option A: A payment of $750,000 at the end of one year, which is the scheduled completion time for the project.

Option B: $100,000 advance payment on commencement of the project and the balance payment in two years.

If the two payments are economically equivalent and the interest rate is 3% compounded semi-annually, calculate the balance payment from Option B.

• 22. Thomas, an architect, is expected to make a first payment of $4000 in one year and a second payment in two years to a designer. Calculate his second payment if both these payments are economically equivalent to a single payment of $8000 today. Assume money can earn 6% compounded daily.

• 23. Calculate the two equal installments, one in one year and the other in two years, that would replace a payment of $2000 today and a payment of $8500 in five years. Assume money is worth 4% compounded semi-annually.

• 24. What equal payments, one in one year and the other in five years, would replace payments of $8000 and $10,000 in four and six years, respectively? Assume money can earn 8% compounded annually.

- 25. Niranjani was offered to settle her college tuition fee with two equal payments of $2500 in three months and nine months. She wanted to reschedule her payments with a payment of $1500 now and the balance in six months. Calculate the payment required in six months to settle the loan. Assume that money earns 3% compounded monthly.

- 26. Randy was offered the following equivalent payment options to settle his car loan:
    - Option A: A $7500 payment in 300 days and $10,000 in 450 days.
    - Option B: Two equal payments: one in 180 days and another in 365 days.

    Calculate the value of the equal payments under Option B assuming that money earns 4.2% compounded daily.

9.5 | Calculating Periodic Interest Rate (i) and Nominal Interest Rate (j)

We can calculate the periodic interest rate 'i' by rearranging Formula 9.1(a),

$$FV = PV(1 + i)^n$$ Dividing by 'PV' on both sides,

$$(1 + i)^n = \frac{FV}{PV}$$ Taking the nth root on both sides,

$$(1 + i) = \left(\frac{FV}{PV}\right)^{\frac{1}{n}}$$

Rearranging to isolate 'i' results in the following formula for periodic interest rate:

Formula 9.5(a) **Periodic Interest Rate**

$$i = \left(\frac{FV}{PV}\right)^{\frac{1}{n}} - 1$$

We can calculate the nominal interest rate 'j' by rearranging Formula 9.1(d),

$$i = \frac{j}{m}$$

Cross-multiplying the above results in the following formula for nominal interest rate:

Formula 9.5(b) **Nominal Interest Rate**

$$j = m \times i$$

Example 9.5(a) **Calculating the Nominal Interest Rate When 'FV' and 'PV' are Known**

At what rate compounded monthly will an investment of \$4500 grow to \$10,000 in four years?

Solution

Page 381

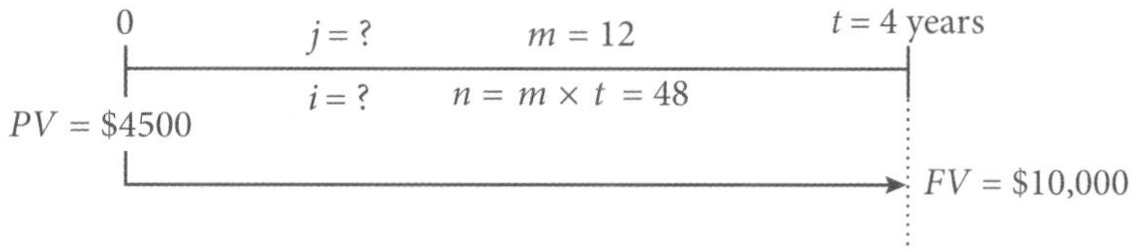

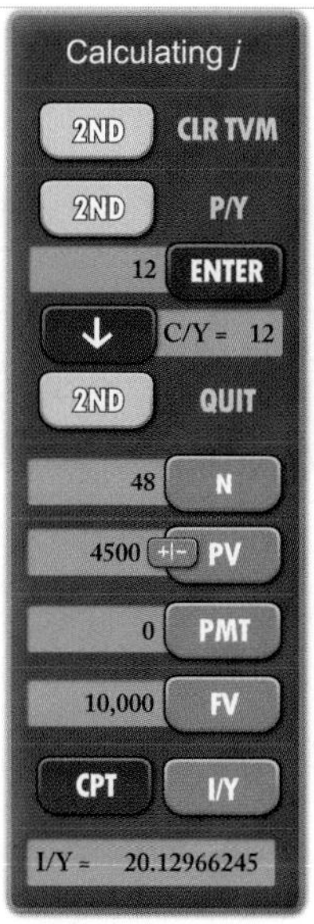

Using Formula 9.5(a), $i = \left(\frac{FV}{PV}\right)^{\frac{1}{n}} - 1$

$= \left(\frac{10,000.00}{4500.00}\right)^{\frac{1}{48}} - 1$

$= 0.016774...$

Using Formula 9.5(b), $j = m \times i$

$= 12 \times 0.016774...$

$= 0.201296...$

$= 20.13\%$

Do not round the value of i while calculating j as it is an intermediate step. Use the store and recall function in your calculator.

Therefore, the investment will grow to \$10,000 in four years at an interest rate of 20.13% compounded monthly.

Example 9.5(b) **Calculating the Nominal Interest Rate When 'PV' and 'I' are Known**

The interest on a three-year GIC is \$8269.17. If the GIC was purchased for \$180,000, what is the nominal interest rate of the GIC if interest is compounded quarterly?

Solution

Page 381

Note that FV is not directly provided, but the amount of interest is provided.

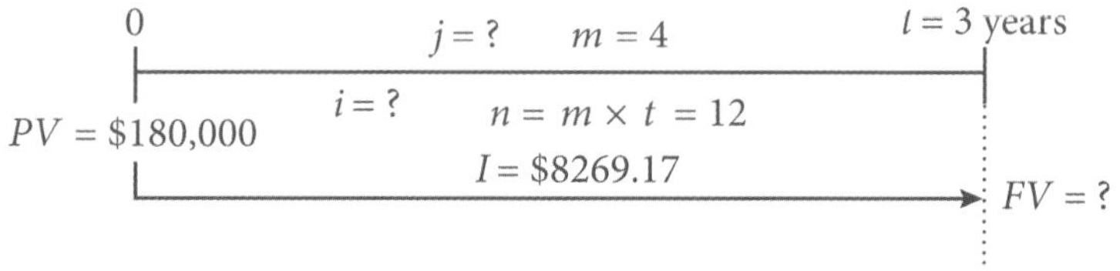

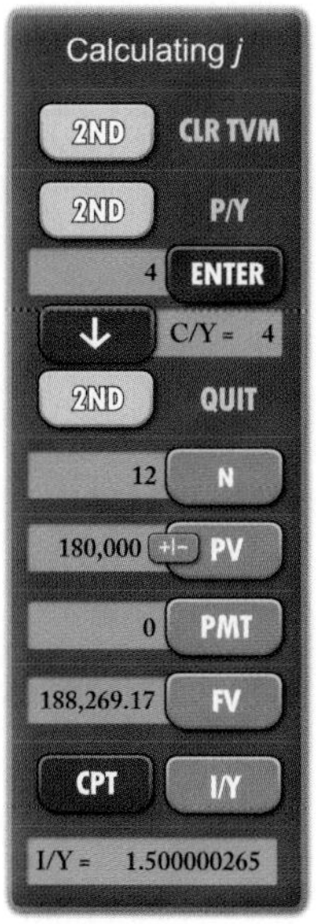

We know that $FV = PV + I$

$FV = 180,000.00 + 8269.17$

$= \$188,269.17$

Using Formula 9.5(a), $i = \left(\frac{FV}{PV}\right)^{\frac{1}{n}} - 1$

$= \left(\frac{188,269.17}{180,000.00}\right)^{\frac{1}{12}} - 1$

$= 0.003750...$

Using Formula 9.5(b), $j = m \times i$

$= 4 \times 0.003750...$

$= 0.015000...$

$= 1.50\%$

Therefore, the nominal interest rate of the GIC is 1.50% compounded quarterly.

Example 9.5(c) **Calculating the Nominal Interest Rate When an Investment Doubles**

At what nominal interest rate compounded semi-annually will an investment double in 12 years?

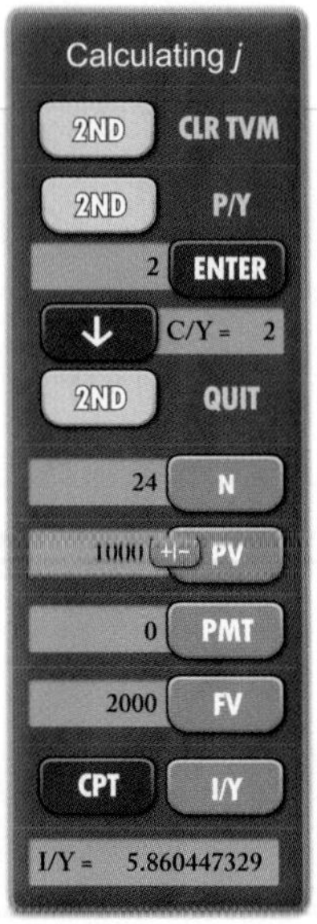

Solution

Page 381

When an investment doubles,

$$\frac{FV}{PV} = \frac{2}{1}$$

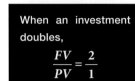

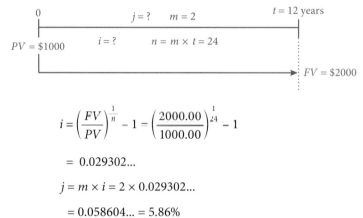

Assume $PV = \$1000$. If the investment doubles, $FV = \$2000$.

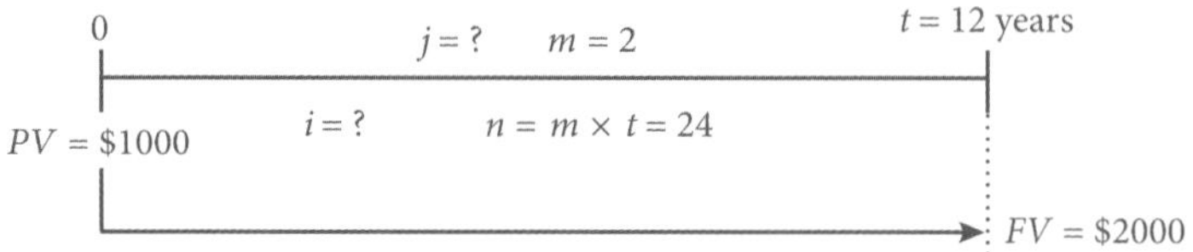

$$i = \left(\frac{FV}{PV}\right)^{\frac{1}{n}} - 1 = \left(\frac{2000.00}{1000.00}\right)^{\frac{1}{24}} - 1$$

$$= 0.029302...$$

$$j = m \times i = 2 \times 0.029302...$$

$$= 0.058604... = 5.86\%$$

Therefore, the investment will double at 5.86% compounded semi-annually.

9.5 | Exercises

Answers to the odd-numbered problems are available at the end of the textbook.

For the following problems, express the answers rounded to two decimal places, wherever applicable.

Calculate the missing values for Problems 1 and 2.

1.

	Present Value (*PV*)	Future Value (*FV*)	Term	Interest Rate
a.	$7000	$7975	2 years 9 months	?% compounded quarterly
b.	$2500	$2850	3 years 5 months	?% compounded monthly
c.	$3250	$3925	4 years 6 months	?% compounded semi-annually
d.	$5000	$5650	3 years	?% compounded daily

2.

	Present Value (*PV*)	Future Value (*FV*)	Term	Interest Rate
a.	$2000	$5000	5 years 2 months	?% compounded monthly
b.	$5250	$6000	3 years 6 months	?% compounded semi-annually
c.	$7500	$8600	2 years 3 months	?% compounded quarterly
d.	$4500	$5050	2 years	?% compounded daily

3. Calculate the nominal interest rate and periodic interest rate for an investment of $100,000 that matures to $200,000 in 10 years if interest is compounded monthly.

4. Canary Calendars Inc. invested this year's profits of $64,000 in a fund that matures to $84,500 in two years. Calculate the nominal interest rate compounded daily and the periodic interest rate of the fund.

5. A calculator distributor invested its net income of $35,000 in a mutual fund. Calculate the nominal interest rate compounded semi-annually if the accumulated value in 2 years and 7 months is $44,650.

6. Rose received an excellent interest rate for her car loan of $11,000. Calculate the nominal interest rate and periodic interest rate of her loan if it accumulated to $11,170 in five months and interest is compounded quarterly.

7. A computer assembling company received a loan of $30,000 to purchase a conveyer belt. If the debt accumulated to $45,850 in two years, calculate the nominal interest rate compounded daily.

8. If you have $250,000 in your savings account and wish to have it grow to $1,000,000 in 40 years, calculate the nominal interest rate compounded semi-annually.

9. Mark heard that he could triple his money in 15 years if he invested it in his friend's telecommunications business. What nominal interest rate compounded monthly does the business offer?

10. Anish wants to double his money in 15 years in a low-risk savings account. What nominal interest rate compounded monthly would allow this? What nominal interest rate compounded monthly would allow him to double his money in 10 years?

11. If an investment grew to $12,000 in two years and the interest earned was $800, calculate the nominal interest rate compounded daily.

12. Amex Industries Ltd. invested $30,000 in a mutual fund that earned an interest of $12,000 in 14 years. Calculate the nominal interest rate compounded quarterly for the fund.

• 13. The nominal interest rate on a car loan of $8000 that was compounded semi-annually changed at the end of one year. If the accumulated balance was $8656 at the end of the first year and $9100.50 at the end of the second year, calculate the nominal interest rates for each year.

• 14. An investment of $5000 in a TFSA (Tax Free Savings Account) accumulated to $5280 at the end of one year at a monthly compounding interest rate. However, the monthly compounding interest rate for the second year changed and the balance in the account at the end of the second year was $5875. Calculate the nominal interest rate for the first year and the nominal interest rate for the second year.

9.6 | Calculating Number of Compounding Periods (n) and Time Period (t)

We can calculate the number of compounding periods 'n' from Formula 9.1(a) as follows:

$$FV = PV(1 + i)^n \qquad \text{Dividing by 'PV' on both sides,}$$

$$\frac{FV}{PV} = (1 + i)^n \qquad \text{Taking the natural logarithm on both sides,}$$

$$\ln\left(\frac{FV}{PV}\right) = \ln(1 + i)^n \qquad \text{Using the power rule of logarithms, } \ln(A)^n = n\ln(A),$$

$$\ln\left(\frac{FV}{PV}\right) = n \times \ln(1+i)$$

Refer to Table 2.4 in Chapter 2 for Rules of Logarithms.

Rearranging to isolate 'n' results in the following formula for calculating the number of compounding periods:

Formula 9.6(a) **Number of Compounding Periods**

$$n = \frac{\ln\left(\frac{FV}{PV}\right)}{\ln(1 + i)}$$

We can calculate term 't' in years by rearranging Formula 9.1(e), $n = m \times t$.

Rearranging to isolate 't' results in the following formula for calculating the time period in years:

Formula 9.6(b) **Time Period in Years**

$$t = \frac{n}{m}$$

Note: *In determining the time period, 't', the value of 'n' is not to be rounded to the nearest (or rounded up to the next) compounding period.*

Example 9.6(a) Calculating the Time Period When 'PV' and 'FV' are Known

How long will it take for an investment of $32,000 in a mutual fund to mature to at least $100,000 if it is growing at the rate of 12% compounded semi-annually?

Express your answer in:

(i) years, rounded to two decimal places;

(ii) years and months;

(iii) years and days.

Solution

Page 381

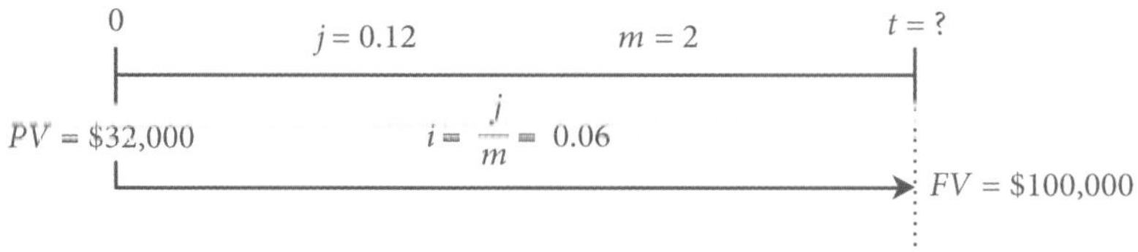

$$n = \frac{\ln\left(\frac{FV}{PV}\right)}{\ln(1+i)} = \frac{\ln\left(\frac{100{,}000.00}{32{,}000.00}\right)}{\ln(1+0.06)} = 19.554756\ldots \text{ compounding periods}$$

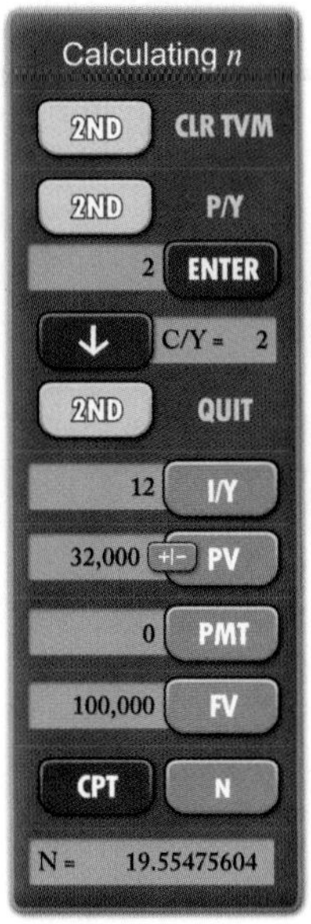

$$t = \frac{n}{m} = \frac{19.554756\ldots}{2} = 9.777378\ldots \text{ years}$$

(i) *Expressed in years, rounded to two decimal places*

$t = 9.777378\ldots$ years

Therefore, it will take 9.78 years for the investment to mature to at least $100,000.

(ii) *Expressed in years and months*

$t = 9.777378\ldots$ years

$= 9$ years $+ (0.777378\ldots \times 12)$ months

$= 9$ years $+ 9.328536\ldots$ months

$= 9$ years and 10 months

Therefore, it will take 9 years and 10 months for the investment to mature to at least $100,000.

> Since we want the fund to mature to *at least* $100,000, we round 9 years and 9.328536... months up to 9 years and 10 months.

(iii) *Expressed in years and days*

$t = 9.777378\ldots$ years

$= 9$ years $+ (0.777378\ldots \times 365)$ days

$= 9$ years $+ 283.742977\ldots$ days

$= 9$ years and 284 days

Therefore, it will take 9 years and 284 days for the investment to mature to at least $100,000.

Note: *In the above example, if the value of 'n', 19.554756... is rounded up to the next compounding period ($n = 20$), then the time period, t, will be $\frac{20}{2} = 10$ years. However, the investment of $32,000 will mature to $100,000 in 9 years and 10 months, or 9 years and 284 days, as calculated above. For this reason, we do not round the value of 'n' in compound interest calculations.*

Example 9.6(b) Calculating the Time Period When 'PV' and 'I' are Known

What is the term of an investment of $8000 that earns interest of at least $2000 at 4.80% compounded monthly?

Express your answer in:

(i) years, rounded to two decimal places;

(ii) years and months;

(iii) years and days.

Page 381

Solution

Note that FV is not directly provided but interest has been provided.

We know that $FV = PV + I$

$$FV = 8000.00 + 2000.00 = \$10{,}000.00$$

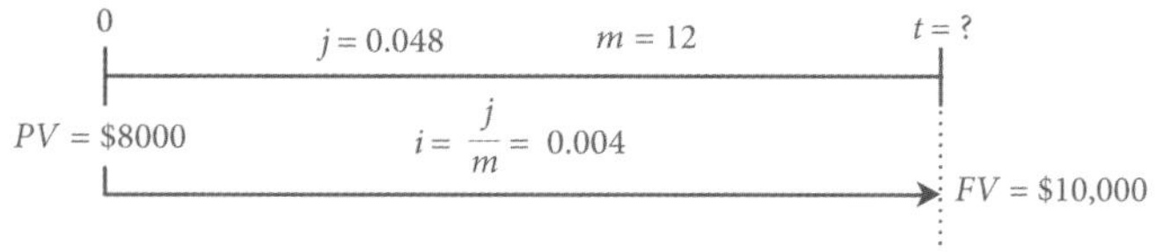

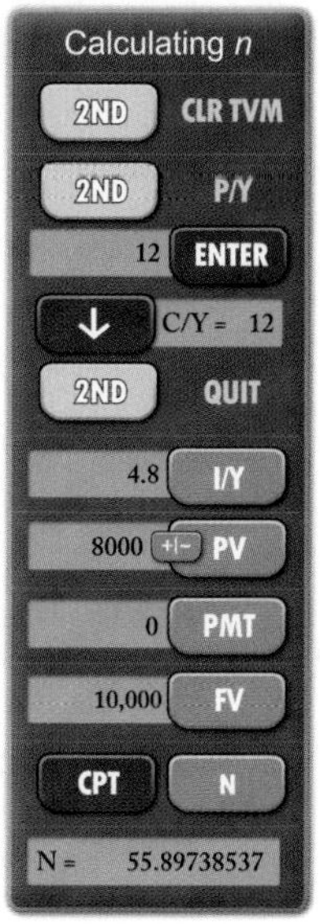

$$n = \frac{\ln\left(\frac{FV}{PV}\right)}{\ln(1+i)} = \frac{\ln\left(\frac{10{,}000.00}{8000.00}\right)}{\ln(1+0.004)} = 55.897385\text{... compounding periods}$$

$$t = \frac{n}{m} = \frac{55.897385...}{12} = 4.658115\text{... years}$$

(i) *Expressed in years, rounded to two decimal places*

$t = 4.658115...$ years

Therefore, the term for an investment of \$8000 that earns interest of at least \$2000 is 4.66 years.

(ii) *Expressed in years and months*

$t = 4.658115...$ years

= 4 years + (0.658115... × 12) months

= 4 years + 7.897385... months

= 4 years and 8 months

Therefore, the term for an investment of \$8000 that earns interest of at least \$2000 is 4 years and 8 months.

(iii) *Expressed in years and days*

$t = 4.658115...$ years

= 4 years + (0.658115... × 365) days

= 4 years + 240.212138... days

= 4 years and 241 days

> Since we want the fund to mature to *at least* \$10,000, we round 4 years and 240.212138... days up to 4 years and 241 days.

Therefore, the term for an investment of \$8000 that earns interest of at least \$2000 is 4 years and 241 days.

9.6 | Exercises

Answers to the odd-numbered problems are available at the end of the textbook.

For the following problems, round the term in years and months up to the next month, and the term in years and days up to the next day.

Calculate the missing values for Problems 1 and 2.

1.

	Present Value (PV)	Future Value (FV)	Interest Rate	Term in Years, Rounded to Two Decimal Places	Term in Years and Months	Term in Years and Days
a.	\$4500	\$5873.75	5.4% compounded semi-annually	?	?	?
b.	\$1250	\$1561.75	4.8% compounded quarterly	?	?	?
c.	\$2750	\$3255.14	5.2% compounded monthly	?	?	?
d.	\$7000	\$7800.17	4.2% compounded daily	?	?	?

2.

	Present Value (*PV*)	Future Value (*FV*)	Interest Rate	Term in Years, Rounded to Two Decimal Places	Term in Years and Months	Term in Years and Days
a.	$9000	$13,159.78	5.5% compounded quarterly	?	?	?
b.	$3750	$4195.63	4.5% compounded monthly	?	?	?
c.	$2500	$3475.34	5.2% compounded semi-annually	?	?	?
d.	$3000	$3780.16	3.9% compounded daily	?	?	?

For the following problems, express the term in years rounded to two decimal places, in years and months, and in years and days.

3. How long did it take for an investment of $25,000 to grow to at least $30,000 at 3.23% compounded annually?

4. How long did it take for a loan of $215,000 to accumulate to at least $271,825 at 5.27% compounded annually?

5. Rudolph invested $50,000 in an RRSP that was earning 4.52% compounded semi-annually. How long did it take for this investment to grow to at least $60,000?

6. A sugar processing factory invested its profits of $27,000 in a GIC at 6.25% compounded daily. How long did it take for this amount to grow to at least $30,000?

7. Hewlett Plastics Inc. received a loan of $860,000 at 8.75% compounded quarterly to purchase machinery for its factory. Calculate the time period of the loan if the interest accumulated was $355,801.96.

8. Your bank offers you a personal loan of $5000 at an interest rate of 6% compounded monthly. If the interest charged on the loan was $2160.22, calculate the term.

9. The accumulated value of a mutual fund is $23,371.10 and the interest earned is $5371.10. If it was growing at 7.25% compounded semi-annually, what is the time period of this investment?

10. The maturity value of an investment is $8455.45 and the interest earned is $455.45. Calculate the time period of the investment if the interest rate was 4.75% compounded daily.

11. How long would it take for an investment to at least double at 3.41% compounded semi-annually?

12. Apiscon Farms decided to invest its net profit in a fund that promised to double the investment at 7.03% compounded monthly. How long would it take for the investment to at least double?

13. How long would it take for an investment to at least triple at 2.51% compounded monthly?

14. Texas Equipments wanted to invest in a high-risk investment fund that promises to at least triple its investment at 14.92% compounded quarterly. How long would it take for the investment to mature?

• 15. A company was charged interest of $17,894.86 on a loan of $100,000 that was compounding monthly for three years. If the interest rate remains the same, how long will it take for the loan to accumulate additional interest of at least $20,000?

• 16. Interest of $6083.19 was charged on a student loan of $30,000 that was compounding semi-annually for three years. If the interest rate remains the same, how long will it take for the loan to accumulate additional interest of at least $6000?

9.7 | Calculating Effective Interest Rate (f)

Effective interest rate (f): *he annually compounding interest rate.*

Effective interest rate 'f' is the annually compounding interest rate of a given nominal interest rate 'j' at a different compounding frequency.

The effective interest rate 'f' is the annually compounding interest rate.

We have learned that the nominal interest rate 'j' (nominal meaning 'in name only') is the quoted or stated interest rate per annum on which the compound interest calculation is based for the given compounding period. The nominal interest rate is commonly used to express compounding periods that are annual, semi-annual, quarterly, monthly, or daily and is used to calculate the periodic interest rate 'i'.

When the nominal interest rate is compounded annually it is called the **effective interest rate.** The effective interest rate is used to compare the annual interest rate between loans and investments that have different compounding periods. By definition, the effective interest rate 'f' results in the same future value as a nominal rate with a given compounding frequency.

Therefore, the formula for calculating the effective interest rate can be derived by equating the following two equations:

a) The future value of an investment for one year at an effective rate 'f' (annually compounding rate with one compounding period per year).

Using, $FV = PV(1 + i)^n$ In this case, $n = m \times t = 1 \times 1 = 1$ and $i = \dfrac{j}{m} = \dfrac{f}{1} = f$

$FV = PV(1 + f)^1$ Equation (a)

b) The future value of the same investment for one year at a different compounding rate 'j' ($= m \times i$) with 'm' compoundings per year and a periodic interest rate of 'i'.

Using, $FV = PV(1 + i)^n$ In this case, $n = m \times t = m \times 1 = m$

$FV = PV(1 + i)^m$ Equation (b)

Equating equations (a) and (b),

$PV(1 + f)^1 = PV(1 + i)^m$ Dividing by 'PV' on both sides,

$(1 + f)^1 = (1 + i)^m$

Rearranging to solve for 'f' results in the following formula for calculating the effective interest rate:

Formula 9.7 **Effective Interest Rate**

$$f = (1 + i)^m - 1$$

Example 9.7(a) **Calculating the Effective Interest Rate When Nominal Rate is Given**

What is the effective interest rate that corresponds to:

(i) 9% compounded semi-annually? (ii) 9% compounded quarterly?
(iii) 9% compounded monthly? (iv) 9% compounded daily?

Page 381

Solution

(i) 9% compounded semi-annually: $j = 9\%$, $m = 2$, $i = \frac{j}{m} = \frac{0.09}{2} = 0.045$

$$f = (1 + i)^m - 1 = (1 + 0.045)^2 - 1 = 0.092025 = 9.20\%$$

Therefore, 9.20% compounded annually is the effective interest rate that corresponds to 9% compounded semi-annually.

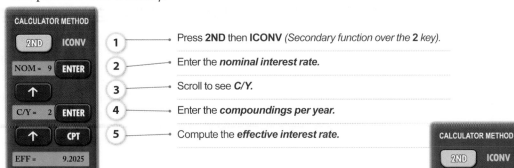

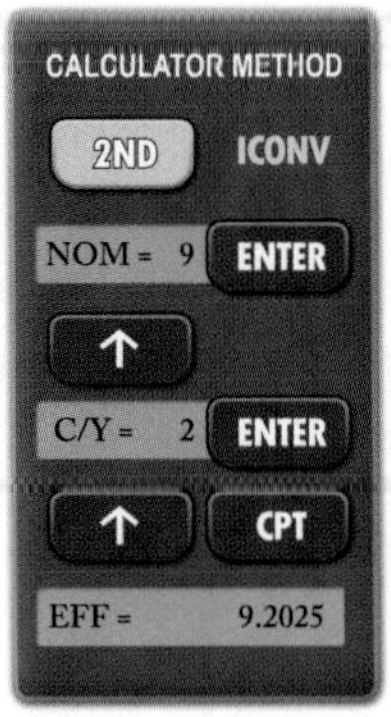

1. Press **2ND** then **ICONV** *(Secondary function over the* ***2*** *key).*
2. Enter the ***nominal interest rate.***
3. Scroll to see ***C/Y.***
4. Enter the ***compoundings per year.***
5. Compute the ***effective interest rate.***

(ii) 9% compounded quarterly: $j = 9\%$, $m = 4$, $i = \frac{j}{m} = \frac{0.09}{4} = 0.0225$

$$f = (1 + i)^m - 1 = (1 + 0.0225)^4 - 1$$

$$= 0.093083... = 9.31\%$$

Therefore, 9.31% compounded annually is the effective interest rate that corresponds to 9% compounded quarterly.

As the compounding frequency for the given nominal interest rate increases, so does the corresponding effective interest rate.

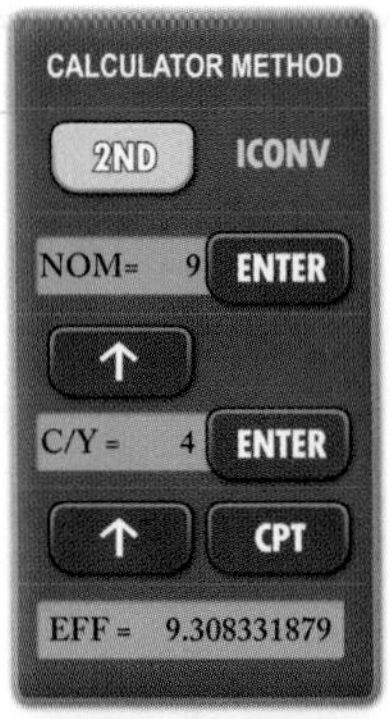

(iii) 9% compounded monthly: $j = 9\%$, $m = 12$, $i = \frac{j}{m} = \frac{0.09}{12} = 0.0075$

$$f = (1 + i)^m - 1 = (1 + 0.0075)^{12} - 1$$

$$= 0.093806... = 9.38\%$$

Therefore, 9.38% compounded annually is the effective interest rate that corresponds to 9% compounded monthly.

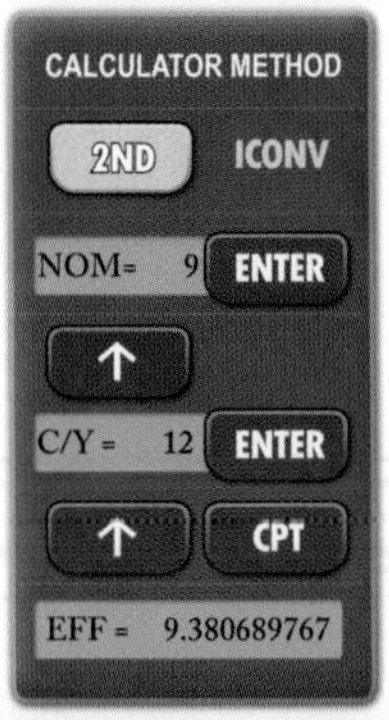

(iv) 9% compounded daily $j = 9\%$, $m = 365$, $i = \frac{j}{m} = \frac{0.09}{365} = 0.000246...$

$$f = (1 + i)^m - 1 = (1 + 0.000246...)^{365} - 1$$

$$= 0.094162... = 9.42\%$$

Therefore, 9.42% compounded annually is the effective interest rate that corresponds to 9% compounded daily.

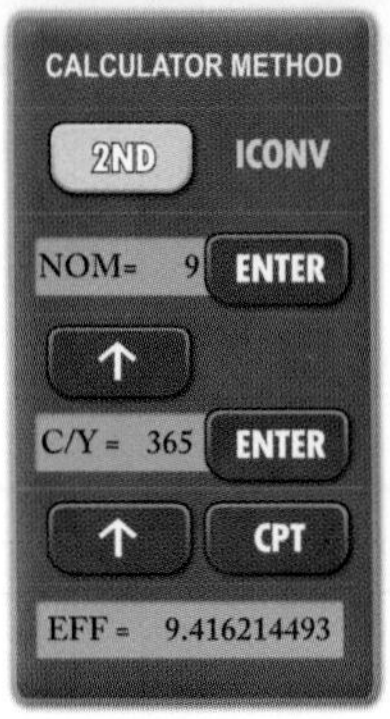

Example 9.7(b) Calculating the Effective Interest Rate When *'i'* is Given

If an interest rate of 1.2% per month is charged by a credit card company, what effective interest rate should be disclosed to the borrower?

Solution

age 381

$m = 12, i = 1.2\%$

$j = i \times m = 1.2 \times 12 = 14.4$

$f = (1 + i)^m - 1 = (1 + 0.012)^{12} - 1$

$= 0.153894... = 15.39\%$

"An interest rate of 1.2% per month" refers to the periodic interest rate *'i'* that is compounding monthly.

1.2% per month is effectively 15.39% compounded annually.

Therefore, 15.39% compounded annually should be disclosed to the borrower.

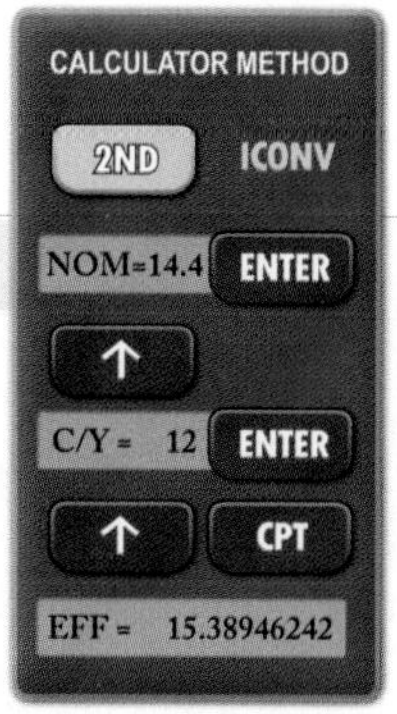

Example 9.7(c) Calculating the Effective Interest Rate When *'PV'*, *'FV'*, and *'t'* are Given

At what effective interest rate would $8000 grow to $13,663.19 in six years?

Solution

age 381

The effective interest rate is the annually compounding rate, so in this case, to calculate the effective interest rate, we can set $m = 1$ and calculate *'i'*.

$m = 1, \quad t = 6, \quad n = m \times t = 1 \times 6 = 6$

$$i = \left(\frac{FV}{PV}\right)^{\frac{1}{n}} - 1 = \left(\frac{13{,}663.19}{8000.00}\right)^{\frac{1}{6}} - 1 = 0.093310... = 9.33\%$$

Since the amount is compounded once a year, the periodic interest rate *'i'* will be equal to the effective interest rate *'f'*.

We can check this by using the formula:

$$f = (1 + i)^m - 1 = (1 + 0.093310...)^1 - 1 = 0.093310... = 9.33\%$$

Therefore, $8000 will grow to $13,663.19 at an effective interest rate of 9.33%.

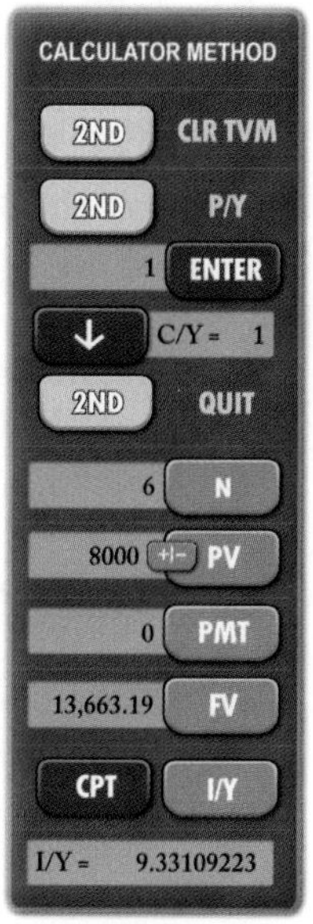

9.7 | Exercises

Answers to the odd-numbered problems are available at the end of the textbook.

For the following problems, express the answers rounded to two decimal places, wherever applicable.

1. Calculate the effective interest rate for each of the following nominal interest rates:
   a. 4.8% compounded semi-annually.
   b. 4.8% compounded quarterly.
   c. 4.8% compounded monthly.
   d. 4.8% compounded daily.

2. Calculate the effective interest rate for each of the following nominal interest rates:
   a. 6.75% compounded semi-annually.
   b. 6.75% compounded quarterly.
   c. 6.75% compounded monthly.
   d. 6.75% compounded daily.

3. Matthew invested $230,000 to purchase a home. After ten years, he sold the home for $340,000. Calculate the effective interest rate of growth of the value of the home.

4. If an $8000 investment grew to $13,000 in six years, what effective interest rate would have provided the same benefit?

5. Pierre invested $15,500 in shares of a blue chip company. After five years, he sold the shares at market price and earned a profit of $10,000. Calculate the effective interest rate of growth of the value of his shares.

6. A software development company lent $20,000 to an employee for two years. If interest of $880 was charged on this loan amount for the entire time period, calculate the effective interest rate of the loan.

7. Which of the following rates offers a higher rate of return:

   a. 10% compounded annually, **or** b. 9.7% compounded daily?

   Show calculations to support your answer.

8. Which of the following rates offers a higher rate of return:

   a. 7.55% compounded annually, **or** b. 7.30% compounded daily?

   Show calculations to support your answer.

9. Amanda's utility bill stated that interest would be charged at a rate of 2.5% per month on any outstanding payments on the invoice. What effective interest rate would be charged on outstanding payments?

10. If an interest rate of 1.75% per month is charged by a credit card company, what effective interest rate should be disclosed to the borrower?

11. At which of the following banks would you suggest that Best Electronics invest its savings of $200,000 for two years and why?

    a. The Bank of Kingston provides an interest rate of 4.5% compounded annually.

    b. The Bank of London provides an interest rate of 4.45% compounded monthly.

12. Ace Machinery wants to save an amount in an account that will give the company the highest return over a two-year period. The Bank of Halifax offers a rate of 2% compounded monthly whilst the Bank of Sarnia offers a rate of 2.1% compounded semi-annually. Which bank should Ace Machinery choose? Show calculations to support your answer.

13. The local bank in Edmonton decided to add 0.65% to the effective rate of interest on Mr. Smith's line of credit. If the current rate charged is 7.85% compounded quarterly, calculate the new nominal interest rate compounded quarterly.

14. First Choice offered its clients a credit card which had a rate of 18.55% compounded daily. If it added 0.5% to the effective rate of interest on this card, what would be the nominal interest rate compounded monthly?

15. Calculate the accumulated amount, compound interest, and effective interest rate on a three-year investment of $25,000. The rate of interest for the first two years was 6% compounded monthly and for the last year was 4.8% compounded daily.

16. Calculate the accumulated amount, compound interest, and effective interest rate on a four-year loan of $45,000. The rate of interest for the first year was 5% compounded semi-annually and for the next three years was 4.5% compounded quarterly.

17. Calculate the effective interest rate on a three-year investment of $15,000 if the successive interest rates for the three years are 4%, 4.5%, and 5% compounded quarterly, respectively.

18. Calculate the effective interest rate on a three-year, $9000 loan if the successive interest rates for the three years are 5%, 4.5%, and 4% compounded semi-annually, respectively.

19. Alyssa was in need of a personal loan urgently. She was offered a loan by her bank at an effective interest rate of 24%. However, she also had the option of obtaining the loan from her credit card company that charged her a simple interest rate of 1.8% p.m. Where would it be cheaper for her to take this loan?

20. If a credit card company is offering a loan at a simple interest rate of 1.55% p.m., what effective interest rate should a bank offer to match this rate?

• 21. What was the effective interest rate and the amount that was invested in a mutual fund for two years that grew to $20,000? The interest rates for the two successive years were 3.6% and 4.2% compounded monthly, respectively.

• 22. Calculate the effective interest rate and the amount invested today that will result in a maturity value of $35,000 in two years. The rates for the two successive years are 4.7% and 5.2% compounded daily, respectively.

9.8 | Calculating Equivalent Interest Rate

Equivalent interest rates are nominal interest rates with different compounding periods that result in the same future value of a given principal for any fixed period of time. Equivalent interest rates are used to compare the interest rates between loans and investments that have different compounding periods. Calculating the equivalent interest rate is a 2-step approach, as shown below:

Step I: Calculate the Equivalent Periodic Interest Rate

As the future values of two equal investments (PV) with equivalent interest rates are the same for a fixed period, for example, one year ($t = 1$), they can be equated:

$$FV = PV(1 + i_2)^{m_2}, \quad FV = PV(1 + i_1)^{m_1}$$

Equating FV from the above two equations,

$$PV(1 + i_2)^{m_2} = PV(1 + i_1)^{m_1}$$

Dividing both sides by PV,

$$(1 + i_2)^{m_2} = (1 + i_1)^{m_1}$$

Dividing the exponents on both sides by m_2,

$$(1 + i_2)^{m_2/m_2} = (1 + i_1)^{m_1/m_2}$$

$$1 + i_2 = (1 + i_1)^{m_1/m_2}$$

Rearranging to isolate 'i_2' results in the following formula for calculating the equivalent periodic interest rate:

Formula 9.8(a) **Equivalent Periodic Interest Rate**

$$i_2 = (1 + i_1)^{m_1/m_2} - 1$$

Equivalent interest rates *(j_2): nominal interest rates with different compounding periods that result in the same future value of a given principal at any fixed period of time.*

Step II: Calculate the Equivalent Nominal Interest Rate

We can multiply the equivalent periodic interest rate by the compounding frequency to calculate the equivalent nominal interest rate, using Formula 9.5(b),

$$j = m \times i$$

Using our values for 'j_2', 'i_2', and 'm_2' results in the following formula for calculating the equivalent nominal interest rate:

Formula 9.8(b) **Equivalent Nominal Interest Rate**

$$j_2 = m_2 \times i_2$$

Example 9.8 Calculating the Equivalent Nominal Interest Rate

(i) 8% compounded annually is equivalent to what nominal interest rate compounded semi-annually?

(ii) 16% compounded monthly is equivalent to what nominal interest rate compounded quarterly?

Solution

Page 382

(i) 8% compounded annually = ?% compounded semi-annually

$j_1 = 0.08, \quad m_1 = 1, \quad j_2 = ?, \quad m_2 = 2$

$$i_1 = \frac{0.08}{1}$$

$$i_2 = (1 + i_1)^{m_1/m_2} - 1$$

Note that 8% compounded annually is the effective interest rate.

Substituting the values, $i_2 = (1 + 0.08)^{1/2} - 1 = 0.039230...$

$$j_2 = m_2 \times i_2 = 2 \times 0.039230... = 0.078460... = 7.85\%$$

CALCULATOR METHOD

2ND ICONV

↓

EFF = 8 ENTER

↓

C/Y = 2 ENTER

↓ CPT

NOM = 7.846096908

Therefore, 8% compounded annually is equivalent to 7.85% compounded semi-annually.

(ii) 16% compounded monthly = ?% compounded quarterly

'm_1' is the compounding frequency of the known nominal interest rate 'j_1', and 'm_2' is the compounding frequency of the unknown nominal interest rate 'j_2'.

$j_1 = 0.16, \quad m_1 = 12, \quad j_2 = ?, \quad m_2 = 4$

$$i_1 = \frac{0.16}{12}$$

$$i_2 = (1 + i_1)^{m_1/m_2} - 1$$

Substituting the values, $i_2 = \left(1 + \frac{0.16}{12}\right)^{12/4} - 1$

$$= 0.040535...$$

$$j_2 = m_2 \times i_2 = 4 \times 0.040535... = 0.162142... = 16.21\%$$

Therefore, 16% compounded monthly is equivalent to 16.21% compounded quarterly.

Equivalent rates have the same effective rates (annually compounding rates). So, when we use the financial calculator, we start by calculating the effective rate corresponding to the given nominal rate. This effective rate is then converted to the required nominal rate.

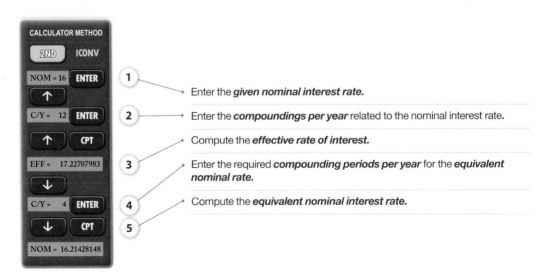

CALCULATOR METHOD

2ND ICONV

NOM = 16 ENTER — 1 — Enter the ***given nominal interest rate.***

↑

C/Y = 12 ENTER — 2 — Enter the ***compoundings per year*** related to the nominal interest rate.

↑ CPT — Compute the ***effective rate of interest.***

EFF = 17.22707983 — 3

↓

C/Y = 4 ENTER — 4 — Enter the required ***compounding periods per year*** for the ***equivalent nominal rate.***

↓ CPT — 5 — Compute the ***equivalent nominal interest rate.***

NOM = 16.21428148

9.8 | Exercises

Answers to the odd-numbered problems are available at the end of the textbook.

For the following problems, express the answers rounded to two decimal places, wherever applicable.

1. Determine the nominal interest rates compounded quarterly that are equivalent to the following:

   a. 7% compounded semi-annually b. 6.05% compounded monthly c. 8% compounded semi-annually

2. Determine the nominal interest rates compounded monthly that are equivalent to the following effective interest rates:

   a. 8% b. 12% c. 85.34%

3. A credit union pays 8% compounded annually on its five-year investments. What nominal interest rate compounded semi-annually would place investors in exactly the same financial position?

4. What nominal interest rate compounded semi-annually would place investors in exactly the same financial position as 8.25% compounded annually?

5. What nominal interest rate compounded quarterly would result in the same amount of interest earned as 12.13% compounded monthly?

6. What nominal interest rate compounded semi-annually would place you in the same financial position as 6.16% compounded quarterly?

7. A bank in Nova Scotia offers a return of 3.5% compounded quarterly on investments in savings accounts. What nominal interest rate compounded daily will provide the same financial benefit?

8. The ABC Bank offers five-year loans at 3.25% compounded semi-annually. What nominal interest rate compounded quarterly would a local bank have to offer you so that you would not be disadvantaged by choosing it?

9. By converting the following rates to their nominal interest rates compounded monthly, which is the best rate for a loan: (a) 6.15% compounded semi-annually, (b) 6.11% compounded quarterly, or (c) 6.09% compounded daily?

10. By converting the following rates to their nominal interest rates compounded quarterly, which is the best rate for an investment: (a) 4.68% compounded daily, (b) 4.72% compounded monthly, or (c) 4.74% compounded semi-annually?

11. Harold and Jeena were shopping around for a good interest rate and they received the following rates from three different banks: 5.84% compounded monthly, 5.92% compounded quarterly, and 6% compounded annually. Which interest rate is economically better for (a) an investment and (b) a loan?

12. Tom is offered a loan from Bank *A* at 8% compounded semi-annually. Bank *B* offers similar terms, but at a rate of 8.16% compounded annually. Which loan should he accept?

13. Francesca was offered rates of 1.2% p.m. or 14% compounded monthly for an upcoming investment. Which rate would earn the most interest?

14. Henry wanted a loan and was offered these two rates: 16% compounded quarterly or 1.5% p.m. Which rate would be most advantageous to him?

• 15. A credit card charges a periodic interest rate of 0.99% per month on the outstanding balance. Calculate the effective interest rate and its equivalent nominal interest rate compounded quarterly.

• 16. Calculate the effective interest rate and the nominal interest rate compounded daily that is equivalent to a periodic interest rate of 1.25% per month charged by a credit card company on the outstanding balance.

• 17. Calculate the nominal interest rate compounded monthly that provides the same benefit as 6% p.a. simple interest for an investment of $12,000 for nine months.

• 18. For a given simple interest rate of 7% p.a. for an investment of $25,000 for six months, calculate the nominal interest rate compounded monthly that provides the same benefit.

9 | Review Examples

Example 1

Compute the maturity value of $27,449.80 invested for ten years at 8% compounded semi-annually.

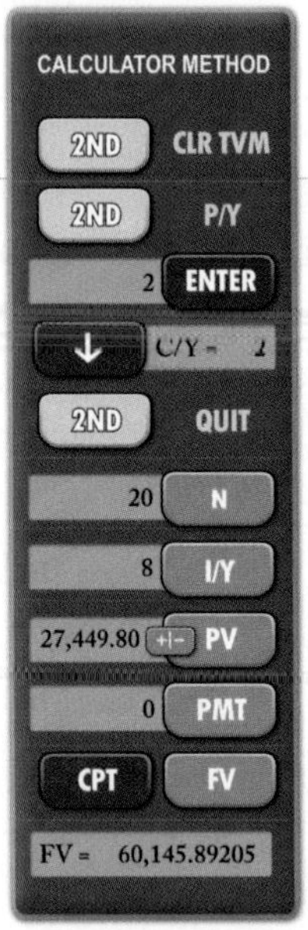

Solution

Page 382

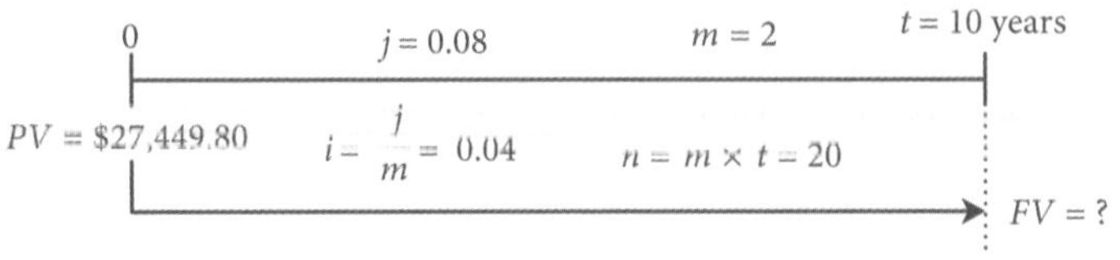

Using Formula 9.1(a), $FV = PV(1 + i)^n$

$$= 27{,}449.80(1 + 0.04)^{20}$$

$$= 60{,}145.89205... = \$60{,}145.89$$

Therefore, the maturity value is $60,145.89.

Example 2

What amount invested today would accumulate to $60,145.89 in ten years if it is invested at 8% compounded semi-annually?

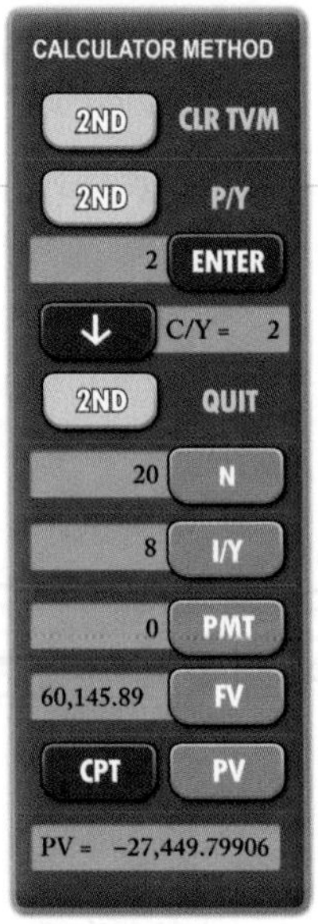

Solution

Page 382

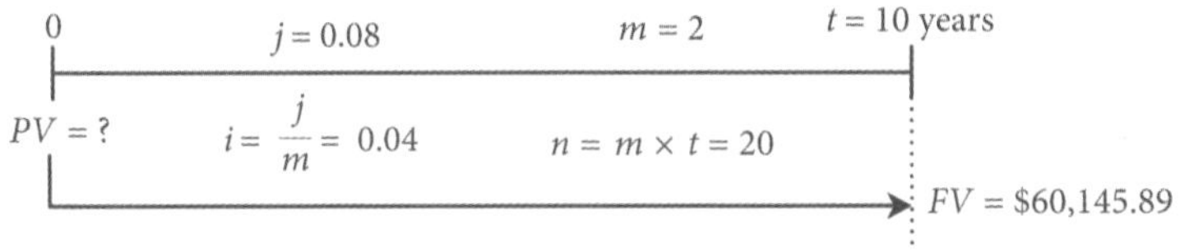

Using Formula 9.1(b), $PV = FV(1 + i)^{-n}$

$$= 60{,}145.89(1 + 0.04)^{-20}$$

$$= 27{,}449.79906... = \$27{,}449.80$$

Therefore, $27,449.80 invested today would accumulate to $60,145.89.

Example 3

At what rate compounded semi-annually will an investment of \$27,449.80 grow to \$60,145.89 in ten years?

Page 382

Solution

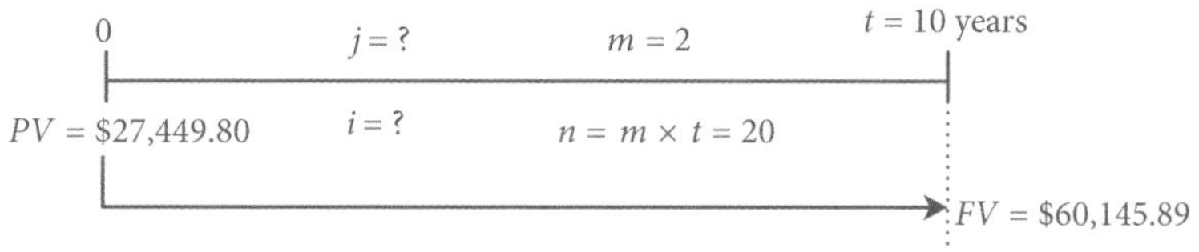

Using Formula 9.5(a), $i = \left(\frac{FV}{PV}\right)^{\frac{1}{n}} - 1 = \left(\frac{60{,}145.89}{27{,}449.80}\right)^{\frac{1}{20}} - 1 = 0.039999...$

Using Formula 9.5(b), $j = m \times i = 2 \times 0.039999... = 0.079999... = 8.00\%$

Therefore, \$27,449.80 will grow to \$60,145.89 at 8% compounded semi-annually.

Example 4

How long will it take for an investment of \$27,449.80 to grow to \$60,145.89 if it earns 8% compounded semi-annually?

Page 382

Solution

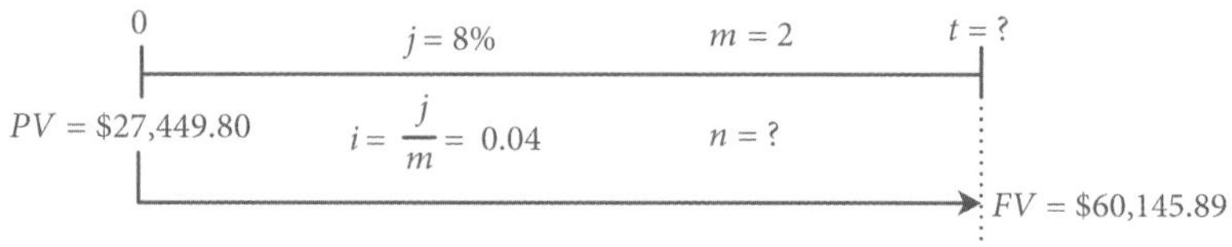

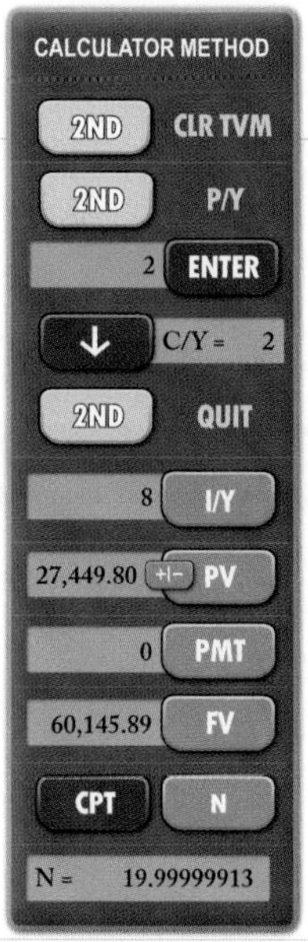

Using Formula 9.6(a), $n = \frac{\ln\left(\frac{FV}{PV}\right)}{\ln(1+i)} = \frac{\ln\left(\frac{60{,}145.89}{27{,}449.80}\right)}{\ln(1+0.04)}$

$= 19.999999...$ compounding periods

Using Formula 9.6(b), $t = \frac{n}{m} = \frac{19.999999...}{2} = 9.999999...$ years

Therefore, \$27,449.80 will grow to \$60,145.89 in ten years with an interest rate of 8% compounded semi-annually.

Example 5

What rate compounded monthly is equivalent to 7.5% compounded semi-annually?

Page 382

Solution

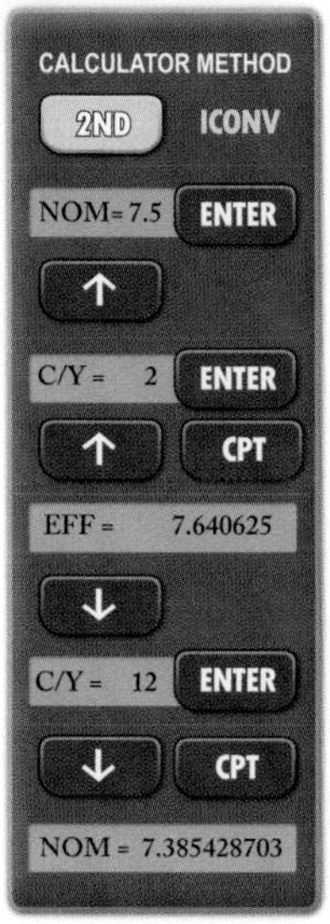

We can solve this using two different methods:

Method 1: Using an equivalent interest rate

7.5% compounded semi-annually

$j_1 = 0.075, m_1 = 2, i_1 = \frac{j_1}{m_1} = 0.0375$

? % compounded monthly

$j_2 = ?, m_2 = 12, i_2 = ?$

Using Formula 9.8(a), $i_2 = (1 + i_1)^{m_1/m_2} - 1$

$i_2 = (1 + 0.0375)^{2/12} - 1 = 0.006154...$

Using Formula 9.8(b), $j_2 = m_2 \times i_2 = 12 \times 0.006154... = 0.073854... = 7.39\%$

Therefore, 7.5% compounded semi-annually is equivalent to 7.39% compounded monthly.

Solution *continued*

Method 2: Assuming values for 'PV' and 't'

In this method, we assume PV = \$1000 and t = 1 year. We calculate 'FV' using the provided interest rate and then use this calculated 'FV' value to calculate the interest for the second case.

$PV = \$1000, \quad t = 1, \quad j = 0.075, \quad m = 2$

$i = \frac{j}{m} = \frac{0.075}{2} = 0.0375, \quad n = m \times t = 2 \times 1 = 2$

Using Formula 9.1(a), $FV = PV(1 + i)^n = 1000.00(1 + 0.0375)^2 = \$1076.40625$

Using the value of 'FV', we can now calculate the value for 'i' by using the second value of 'm'.

In this case: $n = m \times t = 12 \times 1 = 12$

Using Formula 9.5(a), $i = \left(\frac{FV}{PV}\right)^{\frac{1}{n}} - 1$

$$i = \left(\frac{1076.40625}{1000.00}\right)^{\frac{1}{12}} - 1 = 0.006154...$$

Using Formula 9.5(b), $j = m \times i = 12 \times 0.006154... = 0.073854... = 7.39\%$

Therefore, 7.5% compounded semi-annually is equivalent to 7.39% compounded monthly.

Note: *The calculator method of solving this problem has been omitted in Method 2 and may be worked out as practice.*

Example 6

A bank in Toronto offers John a loan at 8% compounded semi-annually. A bank in Montreal offers a similar loan for four years, but at a rate of 8.20% compounded annually. Which loan will be economically better for him?

Solution

Page 382

Method 1: Using effective interest rates

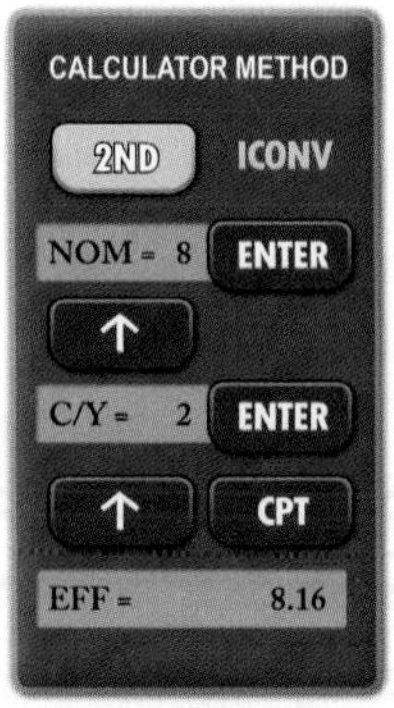

Calculate the effective interest rate that is equivalent to the 8% compounded semi-annually offered by the bank in Toronto.

Bank in Toronto:

$$j = 0.08, m = 2, i = \frac{j}{m} = 0.04$$

Using Formula 9.7, $f = (1 + i)^m - 1 = (1 + 0.04)^2 - 1 = 0.0816 = 8.16\%$

8% compounded semi-annually is equivalent to 8.16% compounded annually.

The bank in Montreal offers 8.20% compounded annually. This is the effective interest rate. As John is taking a loan, he should be looking for the lowest interest rate. The bank in Toronto is offering a lower interest rate of 8.16% compounded annually. Therefore, John should accept the loan offered by the bank in Toronto.

Solution *continued*

Method 2: Using equivalent interest rates

Calculate the nominal interest rate compounded semi-annually that is equivalent to the Montreal bank's offer of 8.20% compounded annually.

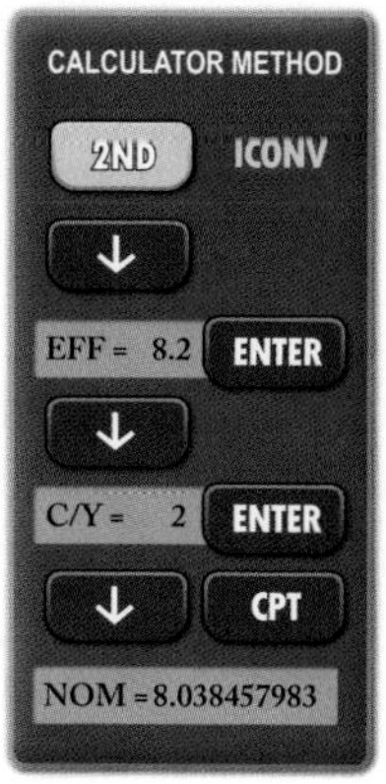

Bank in Montreal:

$$j_1 = 0.082,\ m_1 = 1,\ i_1 = \frac{j}{m} = 0.082$$

? % compounded semi-annually:

Using Formula 9.8(a), $i_2 = (1 + i_1)^{m_1/m_2} - 1 = (1 + 0.082)^{1/2} - 1 = 0.040192...$

Using Formula 9.8(b), $j_2 = m_2 \times i_2 = 2 \times 0.040192... = 0.080384... = 8.04\%$

Therefore, 8.20% compounded annually is equivalent to 8.04% compounded semi-annually.

As John is taking a loan, he should be looking for the lowest interest rate. The Toronto bank is offering a lower interest rate of 8% compounded semi-annually. Therefore, John should accept the loan offered by the Toronto bank.

Method 3: Using the Future Value

Assume: $PV = \$1000,\ t = 1$ year

Bank in Toronto: 8% compounded semi-annually

$$j = 0.08,\ m = 2,\ i = \frac{j}{m} = 0.04,\ n = m \times t = 2$$

Using Formula 9.1(a), $FV = PV(1 + i)^n = 1000.00(1 + 0.04)^2 = \$1081.60$

Bank in Montreal: 8.20% compounded annually

$$j = 0.082,\ m = 1,\ i = \frac{j}{m} = 0.082,\ n = m \times t = 1$$

Using Formula 9.1(a), $FV = PV(1 + i)^n = 1000.00(1 + 0.082)^1 = \$1082.00$

As John is obtaining a loan, he should choose a rate that results in the lowest accumulated value (i.e., 'FV') at the end of the time period. The rate offered by the bank in Toronto results in a lower accumulated value. Therefore, John should accept the loan offered by the bank in Toronto.

Note: *The calculator method of solving this problem has been omitted in Method 3 and may be worked out as practice.*

9 | Review Exercises

Answers to the odd-numbered problems are available at the end of the textbook.

For the following problems, express the answers rounded to two decimal places, wherever applicable.

1. A large software company deposited \$200,000 in a Swiss savings bank account at 8% compounded quarterly. Calculate the accumulated value of the investment at the end of 10 years and 6 months and the interest earned during the period.

2. Micropore LLP, a small law firm, borrowed \$280,000 for three years and two months at 12% compounded semi-annually. Calculate the amount the law firm would have to repay at the end of the period. What is the amount of interest charged on the loan?

3. Romba, a smart money lender, offers personal loans at an interest rate of 8.16% compounded annually for the first year and 8% compounded semi-annually thereafter. How much money did she lend Martha three years ago, if Martha owes her $45,450 today?

4. Westin Lord Braking Company invested $150,650 in a fund at an interest rate of 11% compounded daily. At the end of 150 days, the company's investment advisor transferred these funds to another investment that was yielding 13% compounded daily. Calculate the amount by which the fund grew at the end of 450 days from the initial investment.

5. How much more would an investment of $5000 be worth after five years if it was earning 10% compounded semi-annually instead of 10% compounded annually?

6. How much more would a loan of $11,860.50 accumulate to in two years if the interest rate charged was 4% compounded monthly instead of 4% compounded annually?

7. Determine the discounted value of an investment with a maturity value of $12,000, if it is discounted five years before maturity at 8% compounded quarterly. Also calculate the compound discount (amount by which the money is discounted).

8. Calculate the amount by which the money is discounted (compound discount) and the discounted value (present value) of an investment that has a maturity value of $22,450, if discounted two years before maturity at 4% compounded monthly.

9. Payments of $50,000 due in 200 days and $60,000 due in 600 days are to be replaced by payments of $75,000 today and the balance in 400 days. If money earns 8% compounded daily, calculate the value of the balance payment in 400 days.

10. Amanda won a lottery that would pay her $5000 in a year and $10,000 in two years. If the lottery company had another option where she could receive an upfront amount now and another $7000 in one year, calculate the upfront amount that she would receive now from the second option, assuming that money is worth 2% compounded daily.

11. What nominal interest rate compounded monthly is earned on an investment that doubles in eight years? What nominal interest rate compounded semi-annually will result in the same benefit?

12. What nominal interest rate compounded monthly is earned on an investment that triples in 20 years? What nominal interest rate compounded quarterly will result in the same benefit?

13. After ten years of semi-annual compounding, an $8000 investment in a GIC earns $3000 in interest. What are the periodic and nominal interest rates?

14. If Jackie wants to earn interest of $5000 on her $20,000 savings in two years, at what nominal interest rate compounded daily do you suggest she invest her money?

For Problems 15 and 16, express the term in years rounded to two decimal places, in years and months, and in years and days.

15. Calculate the term of a GIC you bought for $10,000 at 3.25% compounded quarterly to reach a maturity value of at least $18,000.

16. Calculate the time period for a $30,000 investment in a mutual fund to yield an interest of at least $13,600 at 6.65% compounded monthly.

17. Zack shopped around for a good interest rate to invest the prize amount that he received from a competition. He narrowed down his search to two banks: one was offering him 6% compounded semi-annually and the other 6.09% compounded annually. Which bank should he choose to save his prize money and why?

18. Which of the following interest rates would have a higher effective interest rate: 6.00% compounded daily or 6.09% compounded monthly?

19. What nominal interest rate compounded daily would place investors in exactly the same financial position as 6.55% compounded annually?

20. What nominal interest rate compounded monthly would place investors in exactly the same financial position as 8% compounded annually?

• 21. A mortgage has a nominal interest rate of 3.45% compounded semi-annually. If the bank that issued the mortgage added 1.5% to the effective interest rate, calculate the new mortgage rate compounded semi-annually.

• 22. Henrietta went to a bank and obtained a personal loan with an interest rate of 3.18% compounded monthly. If 1% was added to the effective interest rate, calculate the new nominal interest rate compounded monthly.

9 | Self-Test Exercises

Answers to all the problems are available at the end of the textbook.

For the following problems, express the answers rounded to two decimal places, wherever applicable.

1. A small telecommunications company invested its 2016 net income of $580,900 in a savings account for 2 years and 4 months. Calculate the amount it would have in this account at the end of the period and the interest earned if money was earning interest at a rate of 6.25% compounded quarterly.

2. Peter borrowed $28,000 from a local bank at 5% compounded monthly to start a cafe on a university campus. After two years, the interest rate on the debt changed to 5% compounded daily. What would be the accumulated amount of the debt in four years?

3. Rodney opened an RRSP account into which he deposited $4000. He then deposited $5000 in 180 days and $6000 in 365 days. If the RRSP was earning 4% compounded daily, calculate the accumulated value of his investments 730 days from the initial deposit.

4. The maturity value of a savings account that belonged to Paulo Window Manufacturing Ltd. was $30,223.50. If the money deposited earned 6% compounded semi-annually for the first three years and 4% compounded monthly for the next two years, calculate the amount deposited into this savings account.

5. How much more or less would you have to invest today to have $12,000 in four years at 4% compounded semi-annually instead of 4.04% compounded annually?

6. You wish to accumulate $12,000 in two years. How much should you deposit if your investment accumulates interest at a rate of 8% compounded daily?

7. If $18,850 is the interest earned on lending $82,400 for three years, calculate the nominal interest rate compounded monthly.

8. If Gaya invested $18,000 in an RRSP on her 21st birthday, how long would it take for the RRSP to earn interest of at least $6000 at 3.5% compounded quarterly? Express the term in years rounded to two decimal places, in years and months, or in years and days.

9. If the government invested $1,500,000 for ten years in international bonds, what was the effective rate of interest earned on the investment if the amount matured to $2,275,375?

10. Roxy obtained a loan of $100,000 four-and-a-half years ago. The interest rate on the loan was 4% compounded semi-annually for the first six months, 6% compounded semi-annually for the next one-and-a-half years, and 8% compounded semi-annually thereafter. Calculate the accumulated value of the loan today.

11. • A payment of $10,000 is due in one year and another payment of $5000 is due in two years. Calculate the size of two equal payments that would replace these payments in six months and three years if money is worth 8% compounded monthly.

CASE 9a

Investing for the Future

Martin, a 45-year-old shoe salesman, decided that it was time he started saving for retirement. He had money in his chequing account that was earning 1% compounded annually, and he decided to transfer this amount into an RRSP that invested in the bond market. The manager at his local bank assured him that the RRSP he chose would generate returns of 8% compounded quarterly. Martin learned Mathematics of Finance during his college days to be a well-informed investor and knew the right questions to ask the bank manager. What answers would the bank manager provide Martin for the following questions?

a. How long (rounded up to the next month) will it take for an investment to double while earning interest at the offered rate of 8% compounded quarterly?

b. If the offered rate was compounded daily instead of quarterly, how long (rounded up to the next month) would it take for an investment to double?

c. Martin wanted to triple his original investment in the RRSP before his retirement in 15 years. Is this achievable at the offered rate? Support your answer with an example.

d. At what rate compounded monthly would his investment triple in 15 years?

e. What is the effective rate of the monthly compounded rate calculated in part (d)?

f. He wanted to know if investing his money at 8% compounded monthly or at 8% compounded semi-annually would give him a higher accumulated value than the offered rate at the end of the same time period. Provide a suitable example with calculations to demonstrate the manager's approach to answering his question.

g. If he wants to withdraw an amount equal to 50% of the original amount invested at the end of 5 years and another amount equal to 50% of the original amount invested at the end of 10 years, what percent of his original investment would be available for withdrawal at the end of 15 years?

h. If he would like to make a deposit equal to 25% of the original investment in 5 years and another deposit equal to 75% of the original investment in 10 years, what percent of his original investment would be available for withdrawal at the end of 15 years?

CASE 9b

Borrowing to Start a Business

Enea, a budding entrepreneur, was excited that her presentation at her college annual entrepreneurial competition was voted the best by every judge. An angel investor in the audience was very impressed by her business plan and offered to help her start her designer clothing store by offering her a loan at 6% compounded semi-annually.

After two years, her business had savings of $80,654 and she used the entire amount to completely pay off her outstanding debt with the investor.

a. What was the loan amount provided to her by the angel investor and what was the accumulated interest over the two-year period?

b. What rate, compounded monthly, would have resulted in the same accumulated debt?

c. How long (rounded up to the next month) would it take for her debt to reach $100,000 if she does not repay any amount throughout the term? Assume the same interest rate of 6% compounded semi-annually throughout this extended period.

d. If she had obtained the same loan amount from a local bank, it would have accumulated to $80,654 in 18 months instead of two years. What is the interest rate compounded semi-annually charged by the local bank?

e. What would her savings be if the loan had been issued to her at an annually compounding frequency?

f. If her contract with the investor required that she settle all dues in two years, how much could she have borrowed initially if she was sure that she could repay $25,000 in one year and $40,000 at the end of two years?

g. What was the size of the loan provided by the investor if she was charged 6% compounded semi-annually for the first year, and 8% compounded quarterly for the second year and it accumulated to $80,654 in two years?

CASE 9c

Paying Off a Credit Card

Alana, a newly graduated student, just moved to a new city to start her first job. In order to assist her with moving expenses, she applied for a credit card. According to its terms, for any payment she makes within a month from the date of purchase, she will be charged no interest; however, if she does not pay off the full balance, interest will be charged daily on the remaining balance effective from the date of purchase. Every month she must make a minimum payment.

On May 01, Alana spent $1850 of her $2000 credit card limit buying furniture for her new apartment. She didn't make any other purchases in the month of May.

a. On June 01, Alana made the minimum payment of $35 that was charged on her credit card. After her payment, interest took effect, and her new balance was $1845.77. What is the nominal interest rate of her credit card compounded daily? Round your answer to two decimal places, and use this rounded value for the remainder of the case.

b. What annually-compounding rate is equivalent to her daily-compounding credit card rate?

c. Alana made no further purchases in the months of June and July, and made the minimum payments of $35 on July 01 and August 01. What will be her credit card balance on August 01, after her minimum payment? (*Hint: Create a timeline diagram showing the payment dates.*)

d. Alana was beginning to grow concerned about her growing debt, and wanted to fully pay off her credit card. What three equal payments, on September 01, October 01, and November 01, must she make in order to settle her debt?

e. After settling her debt on November 01, how much did Alana pay in interest towards her credit card since May 01?

9 | Spreadsheet Solutions

Spreadsheet solutions to solved examples in the chapter

9.2 Examples

Example 9.2(d)

	A	B	
1		Calculating *FV*	
2	*j*	8.00%	
3	*m*	4	
4	*t*	3.416667	= 3+5/12
5			
6	*i*	2.00%	= B2/B3
7	*n*	13.666667	= B3*B4
8	*PMT*	0	
9	*PV*	($80,000.00)	
10	*FV*	$104,863.82	= FV(B6, B7, B8, B9) FV(rate, nper, pmt, [pv], [type])
11			

Example 9.2(e)

	A	B	
1	Day 1	8/11/2017	= DATE(2017, 8, 11)
2	Day 2	5/29/2018	= DATE(2018, 5, 29) DATE(year, month, day)
3		Calculating *FV*	
4	*j*	4.25%	
5	*m*	365	
6	*t*	0.797260	= DAYS(B2, B1)/365 DAYS(end_date, start_date)
7			
8	*i*	0.0116%	= B4/B5
9	*n*	291	= B5*B6
10	*PMT*	0	
11	*PV*	$10,000.00	
12	*FV*	($10,344.62)	= FV(B8, B9, B10, B11) FV(rate, nper, pmt, [pv], [type])
13			

Example 9.2(f)

	A	B	
1		Calculating FV_1	
2	*j*	8.00%	
3	*m*	2	
4	*t*	2	
5			
6	*i*	4.00%	= B2/B3
7	*n*	4	= B3*B4
8	*PMT*	0	
9	*PV*	($50,000.00)	
10	*FV*	$58,492.93	= FV(B6, B7, B8, B9) FV(rate, nper, pmt, [pv], [type])
11			
12		Calculating FV_2	
13	*j*	6.00%	
14	*m*	1	
15	*t*	3.5	
16			
17	*i*	6.00%	= B13/B14
18	*n*	3.5	= B14*B15
19	*PMT*	0	
20	*PV*	($58,492.93)	= –B10
21	*FV*	$71,725.55	= FV(B17, B18, B19, B20) FV(rate, nper, pmt, [pv], [type])
22			

Example 9.2(g)

	A	B	
1		Calculating FV_1	
2	*j*	6.30%	
3	*m*	12	
4	*t*	1	
5			
6	*i*	0.525%	= B2/B3
7	*n*	12	= B3*B4
8	*PMT*	0	
9	*PV*	$280,000.00	
10	*FV*	($298,158.37)	= FV(B6, B7, B8, B9) FV(rate, nper, pmt, [pv], [type])
11			
12		Calculating FV_2	
13	*PV*	$178,158.37	= –B10 – 120000
14	*FV*	($189,712.18)	= FV(B6, B7, B8, B13) FV(rate, nper, pmt, [pv], [type])
15			
16		Calculating FV_3	
17	*PV*	$89,712.18	= –B14 – 100000
18	*FV*	($95,530.14)	= FV(B6, B7, B8, B17) FV(rate, nper, pmt, [pv], [type])
19			

9.3 Examples

Example 9.3(a)

	A	B	
1		Calculating *PV*	
2	*j*	5.00%	
3	*m*	2	
4	*t*	3	
5			
6	*i*	2.50%	= B2/B3
7	*n*	6	= B3*B4
8	*PMT*	0	
9	*PV*	($4,311.48)	= PV(B6, B7, B8, B10) PV(rate, nper, pmt, [fv], [type])
10	*FV*	$5,000.00	
11			

Example 9.3(b)

	A	B	
1		Calculating PV_1	
2	*j*	4.00%	
3	*m*	4	
4	*t*	3.583333	= 3 + 7/12
5			
6	*i*	1.00%	= B2/B3
7	*n*	14.333333	= B3*B4
8	*PMT*	0	
9	*PV*	($238,447.63)	= PV(B6, B7, B8, B10) PV(rate, nper, pmt, [fv], [type])
10	*FV*	$275,000.00	
11			
12		Calculating PV_0	
13	*j*	4.00%	
14	*m*	2	
15	*t*	1	
16			

Example 9.3(b) *Continued*

17	*i*	2.00%	= B13/B14
18	*n*	2	= B14*B15
19	*PMT*	0	
20	*PV*	($229,188.41)	= PV(B17, B18, B19, B21) PV(rate, nper, pmt, [fv], [type])
21	*FV*	$238,447.63	= –B9
22			

Example 9.3(c)

	A	B	
1		Calculating $PV_{\$480}$	
2	*j*	8.00%	
3	*m*	365	
4	*t*	1	
5			
6	*i*	0.0219%	= B2/B3
7	*n*	365	= B3*B4
8	*PMT*	0	
9	*PV*	$443.10	= PV(B6, B7, B8, B10) PV(rate, nper, pmt, [fv], [type])
10	*FV*	($480.00)	

9.4 Examples

Example 9.4(a)

	A	B	
1		Calculating FV_1	
2	*j*	5.00%	
3	*m*	2	
4	*t*	4	
5			
6	*i*	2.50%	= B2/B3
7	*n*	8	= B3*B4
8	*PMT*	0	
9	*PV*	($1,000.00)	
10	*FV*	$1,218.40	= FV(B6, B7, B8, B9) FV(rate, nper, pmt, [pv], [type])
11			
12		Calculating PV_2	
13	*j*	5.00%	
14	*m*	2	
15	*t*	3	
16			
17	*i*	2.50%	= B13/B14
18	*n*	6	= B14*B15
19	*PMT*	0	
20	*PV*	$1,724.59	= PV(B17, B18, B19, B21) PV(rate, nper, pmt, [fv], [type])
21	*FV*	($2,000.00)	
22			
23		Equivalent Payment	
24		$2,943.00	= B10 + B20
25			

Example 9.4(b)

	A	B	
1		Calculating FV_1	
2	*j*	6.00%	
3	*m*	12	
4	*t*	0.166667	= 2/12
5			
6	*i*	0.50%	= B2/B3
7	*n*	2	= B3*B4
8	*PMT*	0	
9	*PV*	($1.00)	
10	*FV*	$1.010025	= FV(B6, B7, B8, B9) FV(rate, nper, pmt, [pv], [type])
11			

Example 9.4(b) *Continued*

12		Calculating PV_2	
13	*j*	6.00%	
14	*m*	12	
15	*t*	0.25	= 3/12
16			
17	*i*	0.50%	= B13/B14
18	*n*	3	= B14*B15
19	*PMT*	0	
20	*PV*	$0.985149	= PV(B17, B18, B19, B21) PV(rate, nper, pmt, [fv], [type])
21	*FV*	($1.00)	
22			
23		Equivalent Payment	
24		$2,506.05	= 5000/(B10 + B20)
25			

Example 9.4(c)

	A	B	
1		Calculating $FV_{\$2000}$	
2	*j*	8.00%	
3	*m*	4	
4	*t*	3	
5			
6	*i*	2.00%	= B2/B3
7	*n*	12	= B3*B4
8	*PMT*	0	
9	*PV*	($2,000.00)	
10	*FV*	$2,536.48	= FV(B6, B7, B8, B9) FV(rate, nper, pmt, [pv], [type])
11			
12		Calculating $FV_{\$3000}$	
13	*j*	8.00%	
14	*m*	4	
15	*t*	1	
16			
17	*i*	2.00%	= B13/B14
18	*n*	4	= B14*B15
19	*PMT*	0	
20	*PV*	($3,000.00)	
21	*FV*	$3,247.30	= FV(B17, B18, B19, B20) FV(rate, nper, pmt, [pv], [type])
22			
23		Calculating $FV_{\$2500}$	
24	*j*	8.00%	
25	*m*	4	
26	*t*	2.5	
27			
28	*i*	2.00%	= B24/B25
29	*n*	10	= B25*B26
30	*PMT*	0	
31	*PV*	($2,500.00)	
32	*FV*	$3,047.49	= FV(B28, B29, B30, B31) FV(rate, nper, pmt, [pv], [type])
33			
34		Equivalent Payment	
35		$2,736.29	= B10 + B21 – B32
36			

9.5 Examples

Example 9.5(a)

	A	B	Formula
1		Calculating *j*	
2	*j*	20.13%	= B3*B6
3	*m*	12	
4	*t*	4	
5			
6	*i*	1.68%	= RATE (B7, B8, B9, B10) RATE(nper, pmt, pv, [fv], [type], [guess])
7	*n*	48	= B3*B4
8	*PMT*	0	
9	*PV*	($4,500.00)	
10	*FV*	$10,000.00	
11			

Example 9.5(b)

	A	B	Formula
1		Calculating *j*	
2	*j*	1.50%	= B3*B6
3	*m*	4	
4	*t*	3	
5			
6	*i*	0.38%	= RATE (B7, B8, B9, B10) RATE(nper, pmt, pv, [fv], [type], [guess])
7	*n*	12	= B3*B4
8	*PMT*	0	
9	*PV*	($180,000.00)	
10	*FV*	$188,269.17	= –B9 + 8269.17
11			

Example 9.5(c)

	A	B	Formula
1		Calculating *j*	
2	*j*	5.86%	= B3*B6
3	*m*	2	
4	*t*	12	
5			
6	*i*	2.93%	= RATE (B7, B8, B9, B10) RATE(nper, pmt, pv, [fv], [type], [guess])
7	*n*	24	= B3*B4
8	*PMT*	0	
9	*PV*	($1,000.00)	
10	*FV*	$2,000.00	
11			

9.6 Examples

Example 9.6(a)

	A	B	Formula
1		Calculating *t*	
2	*j*	12.00%	
3	*m*	2	
4	*t*	9.777378	= B7/B3
5			
6	*i*	6.00%	= B2/B3
7	*n*	19.554756	= NPER(B6, B8, B9, B10) NPER(rate, pmt, pv, [fv], [type])
8	*PMT*	0	
9	*PV*	($32,000.00)	
10	*FV*	$100,000.00	
11			

Example 9.6(b)

	A	B	Formula
1		Calculating *t*	
2	*j*	4.80%	
3	*m*	12	
4	*t*	4.658115	= B7/B3
5			
6	*i*	0.40%	= B2/B3
7	*n*	55.897385	= NPER(B6, B8, B9, B10) NPER(rate, pmt, pv, [fv], [type])
8	*PMT*	0	
9	*PV*	($8,000.00)	
10	*FV*	$10,000.00	= –B9 + 2000

9.7 Examples

Example 9.7(a)

	A	B	Formula
1		(i)	
2	*j*	9.00%	
3	*m*	2	
4	*f*	9.20%	= EFFECT(B2, B3) EFFECT(nominal_rate, npery)
5		(ii)	
6	*j*	9.00%	
7	*m*	4	
8	*f*	9.31%	= EFFECT(B6, B7) EFFECT(nominal_rate, npery)
9		(iii)	
10	*j*	9.00%	
11	*m*	12	
12	*f*	9.38%	= EFFECT(B10, B11) EFFECT(nominal_rate, npery)
13		(iv)	
14	*j*	9.00%	
15	*m*	365	
16	*f*	9.42%	= EFFECT(B14, B15) EFFECT(nominal_rate, npery)
17			

Example 9.7(b)

	A	B	Formula
1		Calculating *f*	
2	*j*	14.40%	= 1.2%*B3
3	*m*	12	
4	*f*	15.39%	= EFFECT(B2, B3) EFFECT(nominal_rate, npery)
5			

Example 9.7(c)

	A	B	Formula
1		Calculating *i*	
2	*j*	-	
3	*m*	1	
4	*t*	6	
5			
6	*i*	9.33%	= RATE (B7, B8, B9, B10) RATE(nper, pmt, pv, [fv], [type], [guess])
7	*n*	6	= B3*B4
8	*PMT*	0	
9	*PV*	($8,000.00)	
10	*FV*	$13,663.19	
11			

9.8 Examples

Example 9.8

	A	B	
1		(i)	
2	*j*	7.85%	= NOMINAL(B4, B3) NOMINAL(effect_rate, npery)
3	*m*	2	
4	*f*	8.00%	
5		(ii)	
6	*j*	16.00%	
7	*m*	12	
8	*f*	17.23%	= EFFECT(B6, B7) EFFECT(nominal_rate, npery)
9			
10	*i*	16.21%	= NOMINAL(B12, B11) NOMINAL(effect_rate, npery)
11	*m*	4	
12	*f*	17.23%	= B8
13			

Review Examples

Example 1

	A	B	
1		Calculating *FV*	
2	*j*	8.00%	
3	*m*	2	
4	*t*	10	
5			
6	*i*	4.00%	= B2/B3
7	*n*	20	= B3*B4
8	*PMT*	0	
9	*PV*	($27,449.80)	
10	*FV*	$60,145.89	= FV(B6, B7, B8, B9) FV(rate, nper, pmt, [pv], [type])
11			

Example 2

	A	B	
1		Calculating *PV*	
2	*j*	8.00%	
3	*m*	2	
4	*t*	10	
5			
6	*i*	4.00%	= B2/B3
7	*n*	20	= B3*B4
8	*PMT*	0	
9	*PV*	($27,449.80)	= PV(B6, B7, B8, B10) PV(rate, nper, pmt, [fv], [type])
10	*FV*	$60,145.89	
11			

Example 3

	A	B	
1		Calculating *j*	
2	*j*	8.00%	= B3*B6
3	*m*	2	
4	*t*	10	
5			
6	*i*	4.00%	= RATE (B7, B8, B9, B10) RATE(nper, pmt, pv, [fv], [type], [guess])
7	*n*	20	= B3*B4
8	*PMT*	0	
9	*PV*	($27,449.80)	
10	*FV*	$60,145.89	
11			

Example 4

	A	B	
1		Calculating *t*	
2	*j*	8.00%	
3	*m*	2	
4	*t*	10	= B7/B3
5			
6	*i*	4.00%	= B2/B3
7	*n*	20	= NPER (B6, B8, B9, B10) NPER(rate, pmt, pv, [fv], [type])
8	*PMT*	0	
9	*PV*	($27,449.80)	
10	*FV*	$60,145.89	
11			

Example 5

	A	B	
1		Calculating j_2	
2	*j*	7.50%	
3	*m*	2	
4	*f*	7.64%	= EFFECT(B2, B3) EFFECT(nominal_rate, npery)
5			
6	*j*	7.39%	= NOMINAL(B8, B7) NOMINAL(effect_rate, npery)
7	*m*	12	
8	*f*	7.64%	= B4
9			

Example 6

	A	B	
1		Calculating *f*	
2	*j*	8.00%	
3	*m*	2	
4	*f*	8.16%	= EFFECT(B2, B3) EFFECT(nominal_rate, npery)
5			

9 | Summary of Notation and Formulas

NOTATION

FV = Future value (maturity value or accumulated value) of a loan or investment

PV = Present value (discounted value or principal amount) of a loan or investment

I = Amount of compound interest of a loan or investment

j = Nominal (stated or quoted) annual interest rate

i = Periodic rate of interest (interest rate per compounding period)

m = Number of compounding periods per year (compounding frequency)

n = Number of compounding periods during the term

t = Time period or term in years

f = Effective interest rate (annually compounding rate)

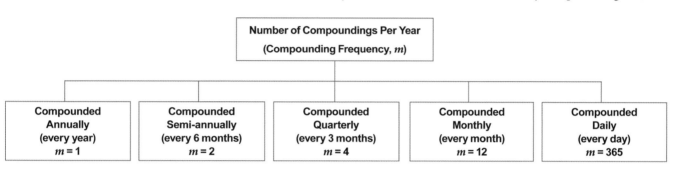

Number of Compoundings Per Year (Compounding Frequency, m)

Compounded Annually (every year) $m = 1$	Compounded Semi-annually (every 6 months) $m = 2$	Compounded Quarterly (every 3 months) $m = 4$	Compounded Monthly (every month) $m = 12$	Compounded Daily (every day) $m = 365$

FORMULAS

Future Value | 9.1(a)

$$FV = PV(1 + i)^n$$

Present Value | 9.1(b)

$$PV = \frac{FV}{(1 + i)^n} \quad \textbf{or} \quad PV = FV(1 + i)^{-n}$$

Amount of Compound Interest | 9.1(c)

$$I = FV - PV$$

Periodic Interest Rate | 9.1(d)

$$i = \frac{j}{m}$$

Number of Compounding Periods | 9.1(e)

$$n = m \times t$$

Periodic Interest Rate | 9.5(a)

$$i = \left(\frac{FV}{PV}\right)^{\frac{1}{n}} - 1$$

Nominal Interest Rate | 9.5(b)

$$j = m \times i$$

Number of Compounding Periods | 9.6(a)

$$n = \frac{\ln\left(\frac{FV}{PV}\right)}{\ln(1 + i)}$$

Time Period in Years | 9.6(b)

$$t = \frac{n}{m}$$

Effective Interest Rate | 9.7

$$f = (1 + i)^m - 1$$

Equivalent Periodic Interest Rate | 9.8(a)

$$i_2 = (1 + i_1)^{m_1/m_2} - 1$$

Equivalent Nominal Interest Rate | 9.8(b)

$$j_2 = m_2 \times i_2$$

Chapter

10 ANNUITIES

LEARNING OBJECTIVES

- Identify annuities based on a payment date and compounding period.
- Calculate the future value and present value of ordinary simple annuities.
- Calculate the future value and present value of ordinary general annuities.
- Calculate the future value and present value of simple annuities due and general annuities due.
- Calculate the size of the periodic payments (PMT), the number of payments (n), term (t), periodic interest rate (i), and nominal interest rate (j) of an annuity.

CHAPTER OUTLINE

Introduction

Many financial transactions involve investing or borrowing fixed amounts of money at regular intervals for a fixed period of time. Some examples from our day-to-day lives include regular contributions to an RRSP, RESP, or an investment fund; or making payments towards a mortgage, insurance, or student loan. Businesses and governments also save for future expansion projects by making regular deposits into investment funds. These regular payments and investments are called annuities.

Annuities are series of equal payments made at regular intervals for a period of time.

An **annuity** is a series of equal payments made at regular intervals for a fixed period of time. Consider an example where Melanie made regular deposits of \$100 at the end of every month for the past two years at an interest rate of 6% compounded monthly. This series of equal deposits that she made at regular intervals for a fixed period of time is called an annuity.

The timeline diagram below illustrates this annuity:

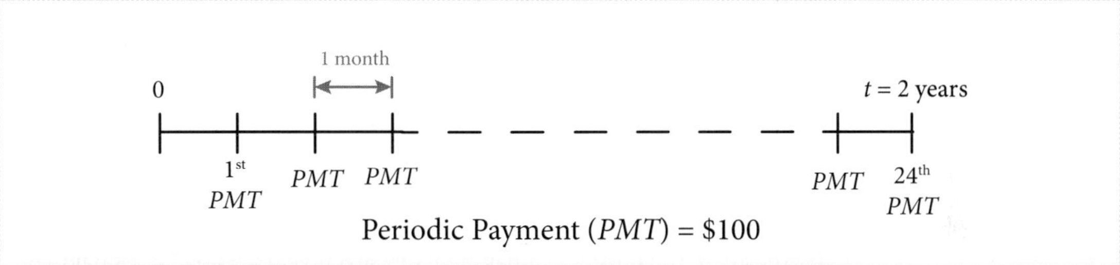

Exhibit 10: Annuity Payments

In this chapter, you will learn about the different types of annuities and their related calculations.

10.1 | Notation and Types of Annuities

Notation

Table 10.1: Number of Payments per Year for Different Payment Intervals	
Payment Interval	**Number of payments per year**
Daily (every day)	365
Monthly (every month)	12
Quarterly (every 3 months)	4
Semi-annually (every 6 months)	2
Annually (every year)	1

t is the **term** of an annuity. It is equal to the time from the beginning of the first payment interval to the end of the last payment interval.

PMT is the amount of the periodic payment of an annuity.

n is the total number of payments during the term of an annuity. It is equal to the number of payments per year × time period in years.

j is the nominal interest rate.

m is the compounding frequency (or number of compounding periods per year).

i is the periodic interest rate (or interest rate per compounding period).

Payment interval (or payment period) is the time between two successive payments.

FV is the accumulated value or future value of an annuity. It is the equivalent value of the series of payments at the **end of the term.**

PV is the discounted value or present value of an annuity. It is the equivalent value of the series of payments at the **beginning of the term.**

In the introductory example, where Melanie made regular deposits of $100 at the end of every month for two years at an interest rate of 6% compounded monthly,

$$t = 2 \text{ years, Payment interval} = 1 \text{ month}$$

$$PMT = \$100.00$$

$$n = 12 \text{ payments per year} \times 2 \text{ years} = 24 \text{ monthly payments}$$

$$j = 0.06$$

$$m = 12 \text{ compounding periods per year}$$

$$i = \frac{0.06}{12} = 0.005 \text{ per month}$$

In an annuity, 'n' is the number of payments during the term, *not* the number of compounding periods.

Periodic investments into a Registered Retirement Savings Plan (RRSP), Registered Education Savings Plan (RESP), Registered Retirement Income Fund (RRIF) are examples of annuities. Refer to pages 460 and 461 to learn more about investment options.

Example 10.1(a) **Calculating the Number of Payments During the Term of an Annuity**

Calculate the number of payments during the term for the following annuities:

(i) $500 deposited at the end of every three months for seven years.

(ii) $700 deposited at the end of every six months for 3 years and 6 months.

(iii) $100 received at the end of every month for the first five years and thereafter, $150 received at the end of every month for the next two years.

Solution

(i) The payment interval is three months. In one year, you would make $\frac{12}{3} = 4$ payments.

Therefore, n, the number of payments in seven years $= 4 \times 7 = 28$ payments.

(ii) The payment interval is six months. In one year, you would make $\frac{12}{6} = 2$ payments.

Therefore, n, the number of payments in 3 years and 6 months $= 2 \times 3.5 = 7$ payments.

(iii) The entire set of payments for the seven-year period is not one annuity. The periodic payment amount of $100 for the first five years forms one annuity with 60 payments and the periodic payment amount of $150 for the next two years forms another annuity with 24 payments, as shown in the timeline below:

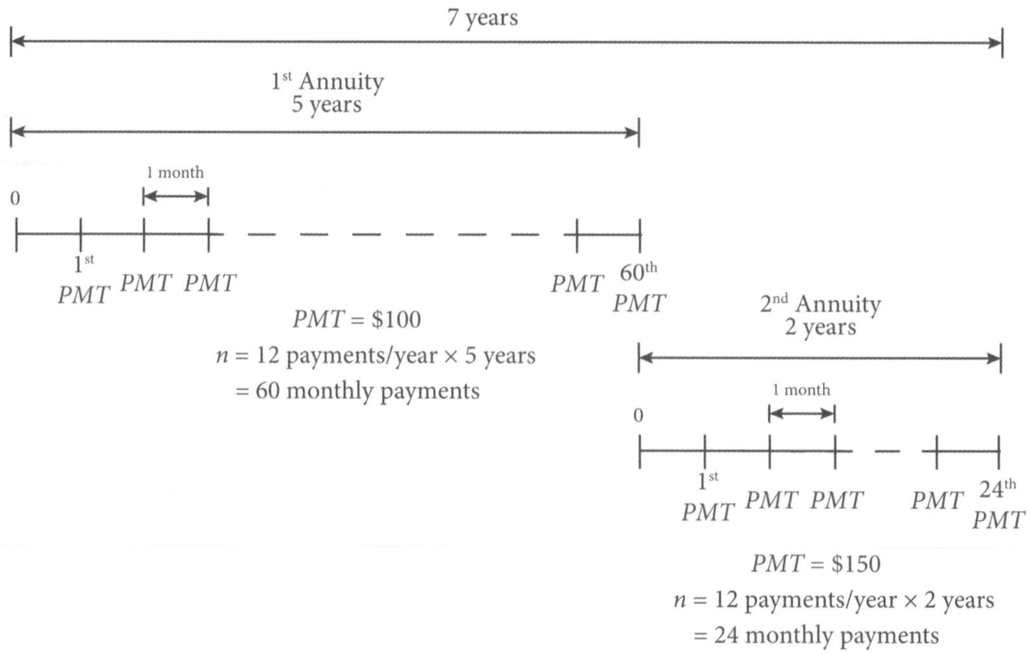

Types of Annuities Based on Payment Dates

When the payments are made at the **end of each payment period**, the annuity is referred to as an **ordinary annuity**. For example, mortgage payments and automobile loan payments are ordinary annuities.

When the payments are made at the **beginning of each payment period**, the annuity is referred to as an **annuity due**. For example, lease payments and automobile insurance payments are annuities due.

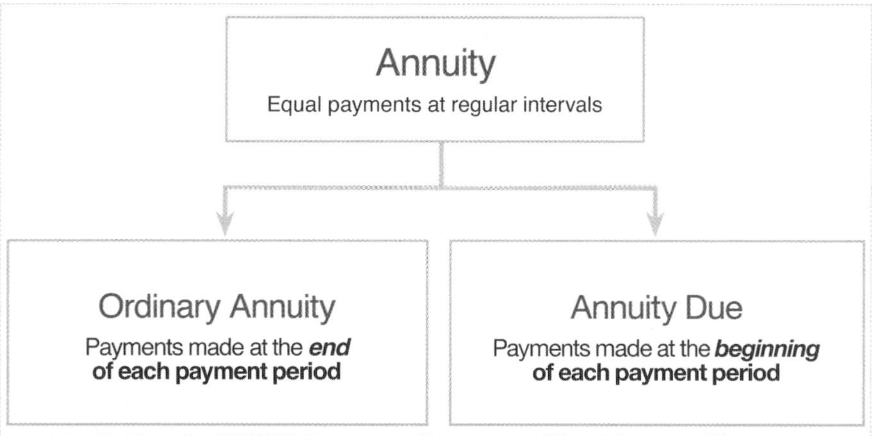

Exhibit 10.1(a): Types of Annuities Based on Payment Dates

Example 10.1(b) **Identifying the Types of Annuities Based on Payment Dates**

Maggie saves $750 in a bank account at the end of every month for one year. She also pays rent of $1200 at the beginning of every month for one year for her house. Identify the type of each of the annuity payments.

Solution

Both these payments are annuities of different types.

The savings of $750 are at the **end** of every month. Therefore, these payments form an **ordinary annuity**.

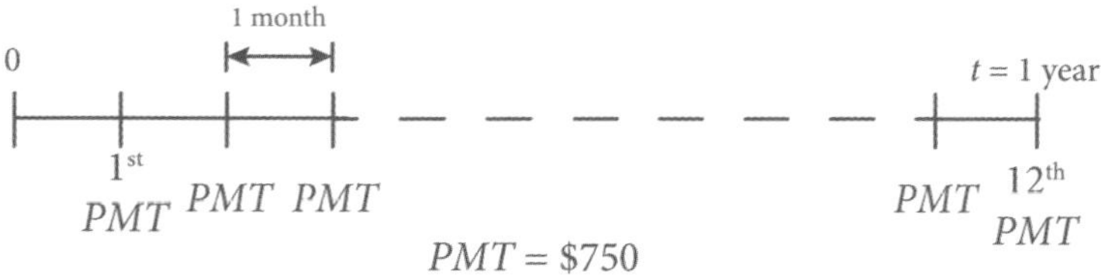

$PMT = \$750$

$n = 12$ payments/year $\times$ 1 year = 12 monthly payments

The rent payments of $1200 are payable at the **beginning** of every month. Therefore, these payments form an **annuity due**.

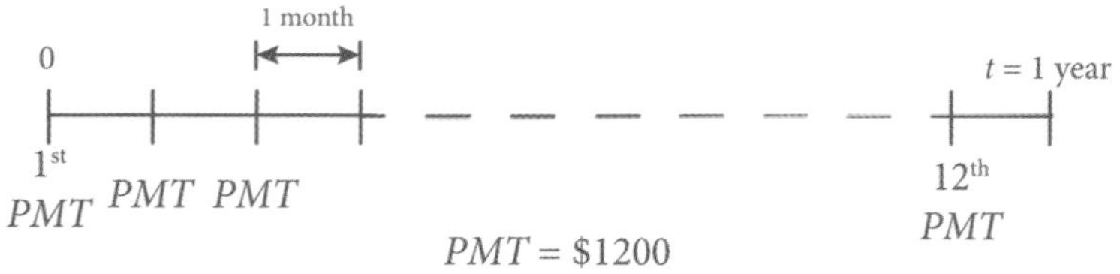

$PMT = \$1200$

$n = 12$ payments/year $\times$ 1 year = 12 monthly payments

Types of Annuities Based on Compounding Periods

When the **payment period** (or payment interval) and the interest **compounding period** (or compounding frequency) are the **same** (or equal), then the annuity is referred to as a **simple annuity**.

> In an annuity, if the compounding period is equal to the payment period, then it is a simple annuity; otherwise, it is a general annuity.

When the **payment period** (or payment interval) and the interest **compounding period** (or compounding frequency) are **not the same** (or not equal), then the annuity is referred to as a **general annuity**.

This applies to both ordinary annuities and annuities due:

In an **ordinary annuity** (where payments are made at the end of each payment period):

- If the compounding period and the payment period are the same, then it is referred to as an **ordinary simple annuity**.
- If the compounding period and the payment period are **not** the same, then it is referred to as an **ordinary general annuity**.

In an **annuity due** (where payments are made at the beginning of each payment period):

- If the compounding period and the payment period are the same, then it is referred to as a **simple annuity due**.
- If the compounding period and the payment period are **not** the same, then it is referred to as a **general annuity due**.

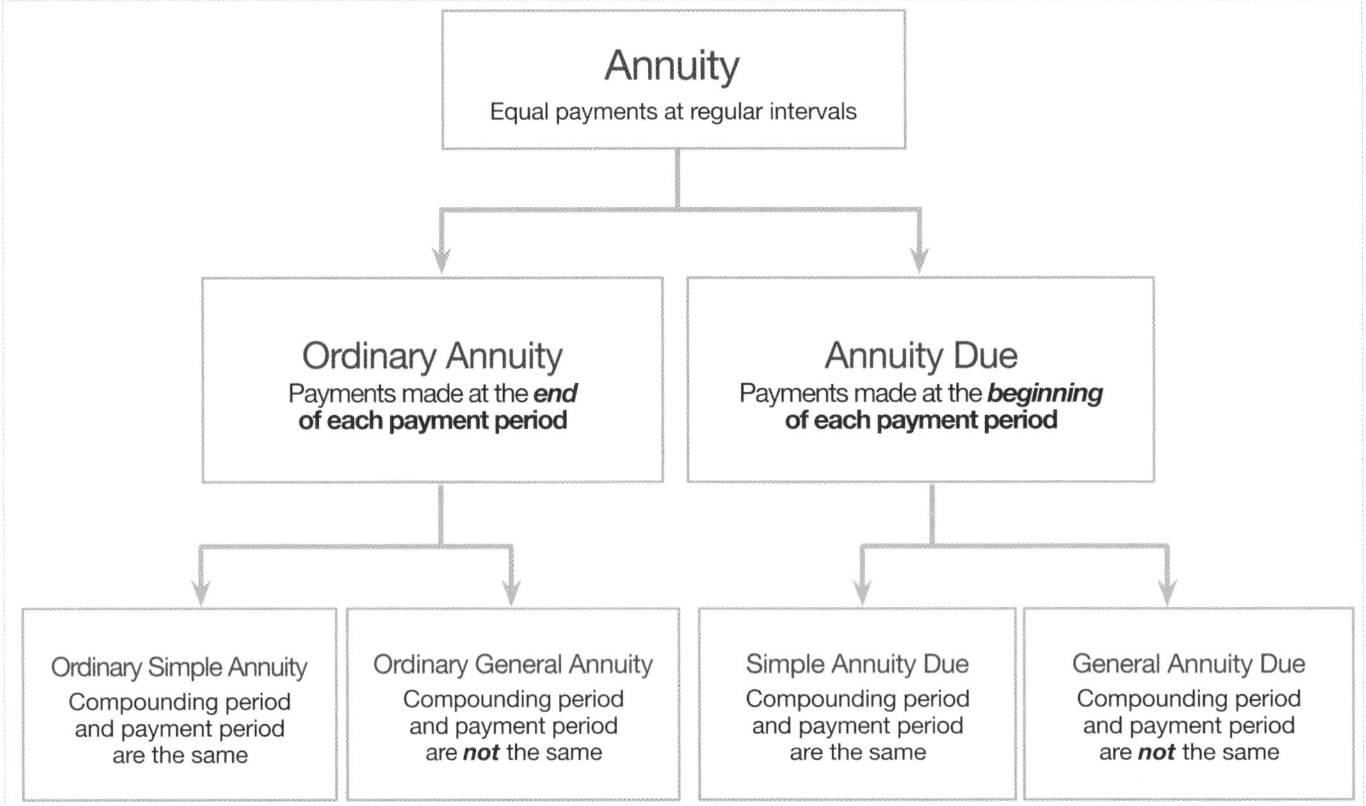
Annuity
Equal payments at regular intervals
Ordinary Annuity
Payments made at the end of each payment period
Annuity Due
Payments made at the beginning of each payment period
Ordinary Simple Annuity
Compounding period and payment period are the same
Ordinary General Annuity
Compounding period and payment period are not the same
Simple Annuity Due
Compounding period and payment period are the same
General Annuity Due
Compounding period and payment period are not the same

Exhibit 10.1(b): Types of Annuities Based on Compounding Periods

Example 10.1(c)

Identifying the Types of Annuities Based on Payment Dates and Compounding Periods

Identify the following types of annuities:

(i) Payments of $500 at the end of every month for ten years at 9% compounded monthly.

(ii) Payments of $500 at the end of every month for ten years at 9% compounded quarterly.

(iii) Payments of $500 at the beginning of every month for ten years at 9% compounded monthly.

(iv) Payments of $500 at the beginning of every month for ten years at 9% compounded quarterly.

Solution

(i) *Payments of $500 at the end of every month for ten years at 9% compounded monthly.*

- Payments are made at the **end** of every month
- Compounding period (monthly) = payment period (monthly)

Therefore, this is an ordinary simple annuity.

(ii) *Payments of $500 at the end of every month for ten years at 9% compounded quarterly.*

- Payments are made at the **end** of every month
- Compounding period (quarterly) ≠ payment period (monthly)

Therefore, this is an ordinary general annuity.

(iii) *Payments of $500 at the beginning of every month for ten years at 9% compounded monthly.*

- Payments are made at the **beginning** of every month
- Compounding period (monthly) = payment period (monthly)

Therefore, this is a simple annuity due.

(iv) *Payments of $500 at the beginning of every month for ten years at 9% compounded quarterly.*

- Payments are made at the **beginning** of every month
- Compounding period (quarterly) ≠ payment period (monthly)

Therefore, this is a general annuity due.

Example 10.1(d)

Identifying the Types of Annuities when Compounding Periods Change

An investor deposited $400 into a fund at the end of every month for six years. The interest rate for the first four years was 6% compounded monthly and for the next two years was 6% compounded quarterly. Identify the types of annuities in this scenario.

Solution

This forms two different annuities.

- First annuity is for four years with month-end payments (PMT = $400).
  Compounding period (monthly) = Payment period (monthly)
  Therefore, it is an ordinary simple annuity.
- Second annuity is for two years with month-end payments (PMT = $400).
  Compounding period (quarterly) ≠ Payment period (monthly)
  Therefore, it is an ordinary general annuity.

When the payment amount, interest rate, payment period, or compounding period changes, a new annuity is formed.

10.1 | Exercises

Answers to the odd-numbered problems are available at the end of the textbook.

Identify the type of annuity and calculate the number of payments during the term in the following problems:

1. Annie receives $2400 from an investment at the beginning of every month for 5 years and 11 months at 5% compounded semi-annually.

2. Karl pays $280 for a lease at the beginning of every month for 3 years and 6 months at 7% compounded annually.

3. Isabella receives $5000 at the end of every six months for 10 years and 6 months for money that she loaned to a friend at 7.50% compounded semi-annually.

4. Aida pays $1000 at the end of every three months for 5 years and 9 months towards her student loan at 4% compounded quarterly.

5. Michael pays $246.50 for a car lease at the beginning of every month for four years at 0.90% compounded monthly.

6. Melinda pays $1800 for a loan at the beginning of every quarter for two years at 7% compounded quarterly.

7. Afsoon deposits $800 at the end of every month for 20 years in a retirement fund at 2.5% compounded semi-annually.

8. Kapil receives $1500 at the end of every month for 15 years from a retirement fund at 4% compounded semi-annually.

• 9. Armas contributes $1000 at the beginning of every month into an RRSP (Registered Retirement Savings Plan) earning 4% compounded annually. After ten years, she converts the RRSP to a RRIF (Registered Retirement Income Fund) that earns 6.5% compounded semi-annually and withdraws $2850 at the end of every month from this fund for the next five years.

• 10. Marcie deposits $1850 at the beginning of every month into an RRSP earning 3.5% compounded semi-annually. After five years, she converts the RRSP to an RRIF that earns 3.75% compounded quarterly and withdraws $3560 at the end of every month from this fund for the next three years.

10.2 | Future Value and Present Value of an Ordinary Simple Annuity

In an ordinary simple annuity, payments are made at the end of each payment period and the compounding period is equal to the payment period. In this section, you will learn to calculate the future value and present value of an ordinary simple annuity.

Future Value of an Ordinary Simple Annuity

Consider an example where Abriella decides to invest $1000 at the end of every year for five years in a savings account that earns an interest rate of 10% compounded annually. She wants to determine the amount that she would have at the end of the five-year period. In other words, she wants to know the future value of her investments at the end of five years.

To calculate the future value of her investments at the end of five years, we could calculate the future value of each of her investments using the compound interest formula and then add all the future values.

From the compound interest Formula 9.1(a), we know that the future value of each payment is

$$FV = PV(1 + i)^n$$

where, FV = future value,

PV = present value,

i = interest rate for the compounding period (periodic interest rate), and

n = total number of compounding periods for each payment.

In this example:

In compound interest, *'n'* is the number of compounding periods during the term.

- *'PV'* for each payment is $1000.
- *'i'* for each payment is $i = \frac{j}{m} = \frac{0.10}{1} = 0.10$ per annum.
- *'n'* for each payment is not the same. *'n'* for each payment starting from the first payment is 4, 3, 2, 1, and 0.

The future value of an annuity is the sum of the accumulated value of each periodic payment.

ndividual future values alculated are in geometric eries with $'n'$ terms, where he first term is PMT and the ommon ratio is $(1 + i)$. By pplying the formula for the um of a geometric series, ou obtain the simplified FV' Formula 10.2 (a).

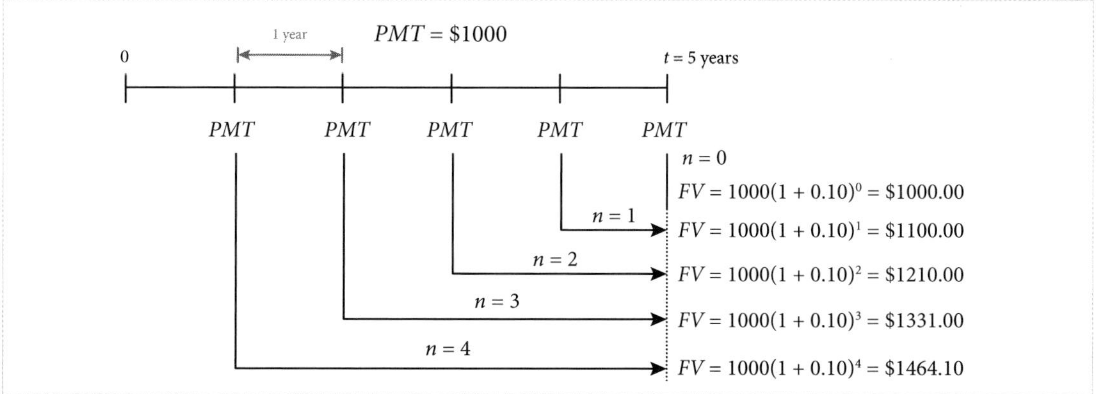

Exhibit 10.2(a): Future Value of Ordinary Simple Annuity Payments

Sum of the future values of her investment = 1464.10 + 1331.00 + 1210.00 +1100.00 + 1000.00
= $6105.10

Therefore, if she invests $1000 at the end of every year for five years at 10% compounded annually in a savings account, she would have a total of $6105.10 at the end of five years.

Now, if there were many payments for an annuity (e.g., she invested the same amount for 15 years, compounded annually), the above method would become too time-consuming.

A simplified formula to calculate the future value of an ordinary simple annuity is:

Formula 10.2(a) **Future Value of an Ordinary Simple Annuity**

$$FV = PMT\left[\frac{(1+i)^n - 1}{i}\right]$$

where $'n'$ is the number of payments during the term, $'PMT'$ is the amount of the periodic payment, and $'i'$ is the periodic interest rate.

Calculating the future value of her investment at the end of five years using this simplified formula,

In an annuity, $'n'$ is the number of payments during the term.

$$n = 1 \text{ payment/year} \times 5 \text{ years} = 5 \text{ annual payments}$$

$$i = \frac{j}{m} = \frac{0.10}{1} = 0.10$$

$$PMT = \$1000.00$$

$$FV = PMT\left[\frac{(1+i)^n - 1}{i}\right]$$

$$= 1000.00\left[\frac{(1+0.10)^5 - 1}{0.10}\right]$$

$$= 1000.00\,[6.1051]$$

$$= \$6105.10$$

Therefore, the future value of the investment is $6105.10.

In the calculation of the future value of annuities, the amount of interest is calculated as follows:

Amount of Interest Earned = Future Value of the Investments – Amount Invested Over the Term

$$I = FV - n(PMT)$$

In this example,

$$I = 6105.10 - 5(1000.00)$$

$$= 6105.10 - 5000.00$$

$$= \$1105.10$$

Therefore, she would earn $1105.10 from this investment.

Example 10.2(a) **Calculating the Future Value, Total Investment, and Interest Earned in an Ordinary Simple Annuity**

Rita invested $200 at the end of every month for 20 years into an RRSP. Assume that the interest rate was constant at 6% compounded monthly over the entire term.

(i) What was the accumulated value of the investment at the end of the term?

(ii) What was the total investment over the term?

(iii) What was the amount of interest earned?

Solution

This is an ordinary simple annuity as:

- Payments are made at the end of each payment period (monthly)
- Compounding period (monthly) = payment period (monthly)

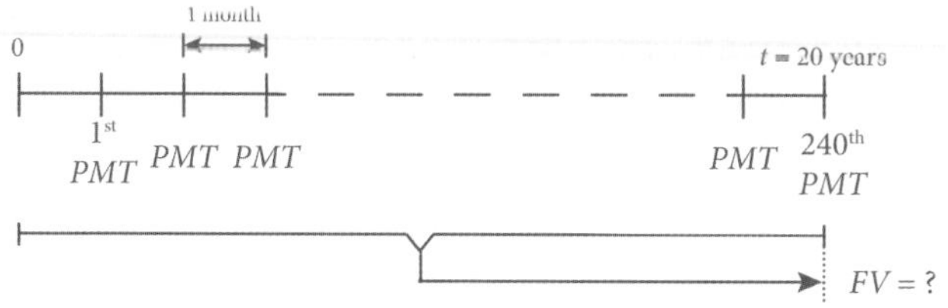

PMT = $200

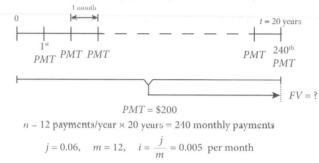

n = 12 payments/year × 20 years = 240 monthly payments

$$j = 0.06, \quad m = 12, \quad i = \frac{j}{m} = 0.005 \text{ per month}$$

(i) Using Formula 10.2(a),

$$FV = PMT\left[\frac{(1+i)^n - 1}{i}\right]$$

$$= 200.00\left[\frac{(1+0.005)^{240} - 1}{0.005}\right]$$

$$= 200.00\,[462.040895...]$$

$$= 92{,}408.17903... = \$92{,}408.18$$

Therefore, the accumulated value of the investment at the end of the term was $92,408.18.

(ii) *Total Investment* = $200 per month × 240 payments = $48,000.00

Therefore, the total investment over the term was $48,000.00.

(iii) *Interest Earned* = $92,408.18 – $48,000.00 = $44,408.18

Therefore, the amount of interest earned was $44,408.18.

Using the Financial Calculator to Solve Problems

Before you start solving problems, check and set the following in the Texas Instruments BA II Plus financial calculator:

1. Set the number of decimals to 9. (Set this only when you start using the calculator.)

1. Press **2ND** then press **FORMAT** (this is the secondary function of the **decimal key**).
2. Enter **9** then press **ENTER** to set the number of decimals to 9.
3. Press **2ND** then **QUIT** (this is the secondary key above **CPT**).

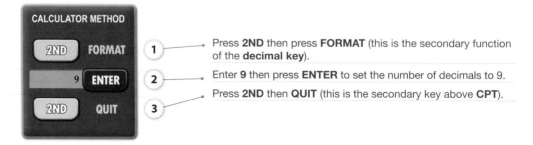

2. Check the settings for end-of-period (ordinary annuity) or beginning-of-period (annuity due) calculations. (You need to check this before you work out problems.)

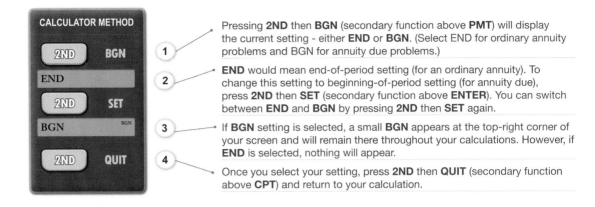

1. Pressing **2ND** then **BGN** (secondary function above **PMT**) will display the current setting - either **END** or **BGN**. (Select END for ordinary annuity problems and BGN for annuity due problems.)
2. **END** would mean end-of-period setting (for an ordinary annuity). To change this setting to beginning-of-period setting (for annuity due), press **2ND** then **SET** (secondary function above **ENTER**). You can switch between **END** and **BGN** by pressing **2ND** then **SET** again.
3. If **BGN** setting is selected, a small **BGN** appears at the top-right corner of your screen and will remain there throughout your calculations. However, if **END** is selected, nothing will appear.
4. Once you select your setting, press **2ND** then **QUIT** (secondary function above **CPT**) and return to your calculation.

Solution

Solving Example 10.2(a)(i) using the Texas Instruments BA II Plus calculator, to solve for *'FV'*

Where, P/Y = 12, C/Y = 12, N = 240, I/Y = 6, PMT = $200

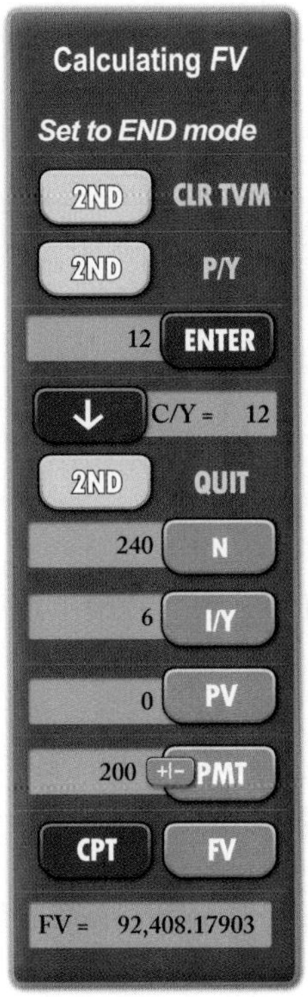

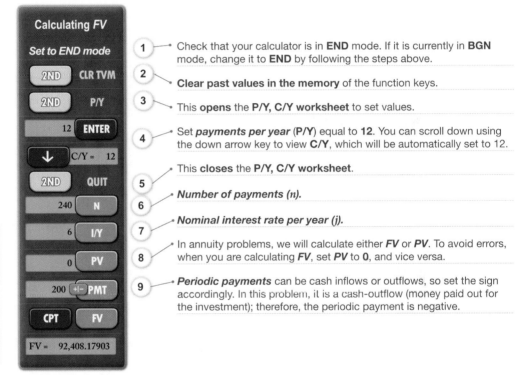

1. Check that your calculator is in **END** mode. If it is currently in **BGN** mode, change it to **END** by following the steps above.
2. **Clear past values in the memory** of the function keys.
3. This **opens** the **P/Y, C/Y worksheet** to set values.
4. Set ***payments per year*** (**P/Y**) equal to **12**. You can scroll down using the down arrow key to view **C/Y**, which will be automatically set to 12.
5. This **closes** the **P/Y, C/Y worksheet**.
6. ***Number of payments (n).***
7. ***Nominal interest rate per year (j).***
8. In annuity problems, we will calculate either ***FV*** or ***PV***. To avoid errors, when you are calculating ***FV***, set ***PV*** to **0**, and vice versa.
9. ***Periodic payments*** can be cash inflows or outflows, so set the sign accordingly. In this problem, it is a cash-outflow (money paid out for the investment); therefore, the periodic payment is negative.

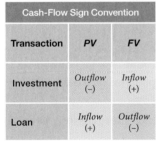

Cash-Flow Sign Convention

Transaction	*PV*	*FV*
Investment	*Outflow* (–)	*Inflow* (+)
Loan	*Inflow* (+)	*Outflow* (–)

Using Spreadsheets to Solve Problems

When using spreadsheets to solve annuity problems, the **type** of payment (end-of-period or beginning-of-period) is entered as a variable in the spreadsheet's built-in functions. For example, recall the following call to the future value function:

= FV(

FV(rate, nper, pmt, [pv], [type])

In our spreadsheets, we will call this variable ***BGN***. For end-of-period payments (ordinary annuities), ***BGN*** is set to 0; for beginning-of-period payments (annuities due), ***BGN*** is set to 1.

Solution

Solving Example 10.2(a)(i) using a spreadsheet, to solve for 'FV'

Where, $j = 6\%$, $m = 12$, payments/year = 12, $t = 20$, and $PMT = \$200.00$

	A	B
1		Calculating *FV*
2	*j*	6.00%
3	*m*	12
4	*P/Y*	12
5	*t*	20
6		
7	*i*	0.50%
8	*n*	240
9	*PMT*	($200.00)
10	*PV*	0
11	*FV*	$92,408.18
12	*BGN*	0
13		

Future Value function call:

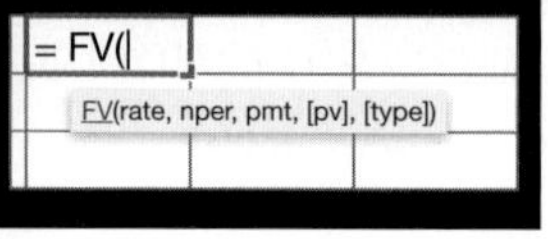

To enter the **nominal interest rate, '*j*'**, select cell B2. Type **6.00%** and press **Enter**.

To enter the **compoundings per year, '*m*'**, select cell B3. Type **12** and press **Enter**.

To enter the **payments per year, '*P/Y*'**, select cell B4. Type **12** and press **Enter**.

To enter the **time period (in years), '*t*'**, select cell B5. Type **20** and press **Enter**.

To calculate the **periodic interest rate, '*i*'**, select cell B7. Type '=**B2/B3**' and press **Enter**. Alternatively, select B7 and type '=', select B2 and type '**/**', select B3 and press **Enter**. The periodic interest rate, '*i*', will be displayed in cell B7.

To calculate the **total number of compounding periods, '*n*'**, select cell B8. Type '=**B4*B5**' and press **Enter**. Alternatively, select B8 and type '=', select B4 and type '*', select B5 and press **Enter**. The total number of compounding periods, '*n*', will be displayed in cell B8.

To enter the **periodic payment, '*PMT*'**, select cell B9. Type **–$200.00** (cash-outflow) and press **Enter**.

To enter the **present value, '*PV*'**, select cell B10. Type **0** and press **Enter**.

To calculate the **future value, '*FV*'**, using the built in Future Value Function, select cell B11. Type '=**FV(B7,B8,B9,B10,B12)**' and press **Enter**. Alternatively, type the function call and select each of the cells instead of typing their references. The future value, '*FV*', will be displayed in cell B11.

Select cell 12 to enter the **type** of payment, '***BGN***'. For end-of-period payments (ordinary annuity), we set ***BGN*** equal to 0; for beginning-of-period payments (annuity due), we set ***BGN*** equal to 1. Since this is an ordinary annuity, type **0** and press **Enter**.

Example 10.2(b)

Calculating the Future Value, Total Investment, and Interest Earned in an Ordinary Simple Annuity Combined with a Compound Interest Period

When the payment date of the investment is not stated, it is assumed to be at the end of the payment period.

Jack deposited $1500 into an account every three months for a period of four years. He then let the money grow for another six years without investing any more money into the account. The interest rate on the account was 6% compounded quarterly for the first four years and 9% compounded quarterly for the next six years.

(i) Calculate the accumulated amount of money in the account at the end of the ten-year period.

(ii) Calculate the total interest earned.

Solution

Page 452

This is an ordinary simple annuity as:

- Payments are assumed to be at the end of each payment period (quarterly)
- Compounding period (quarterly) = payment period (quarterly)

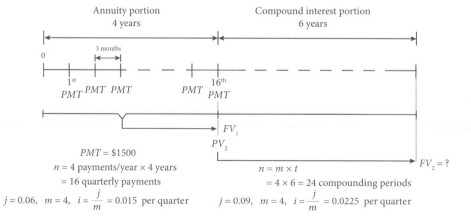

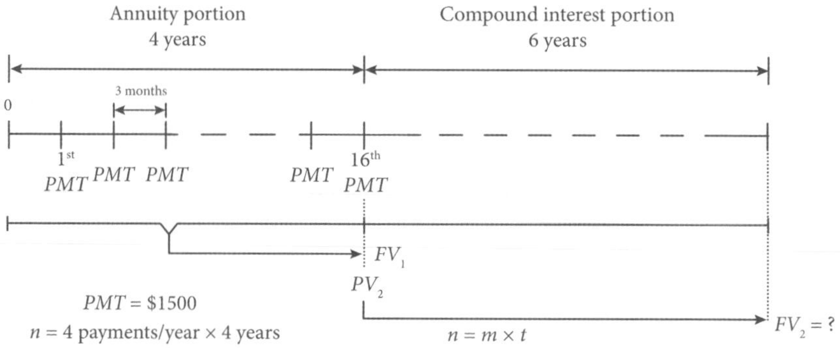

$PMT = \$1500$

$n = 4$ payments/year $\times$ 4 years

$= 16$ quarterly payments

$j = 0.06,\ m = 4,\ i = \frac{j}{m} = 0.015$ per quarter

$n = m \times t$

$= 4 \times 6 = 24$ compounding periods

$j = 0.09,\ m = 4,\ i = \frac{j}{m} = 0.0225$ per quarter

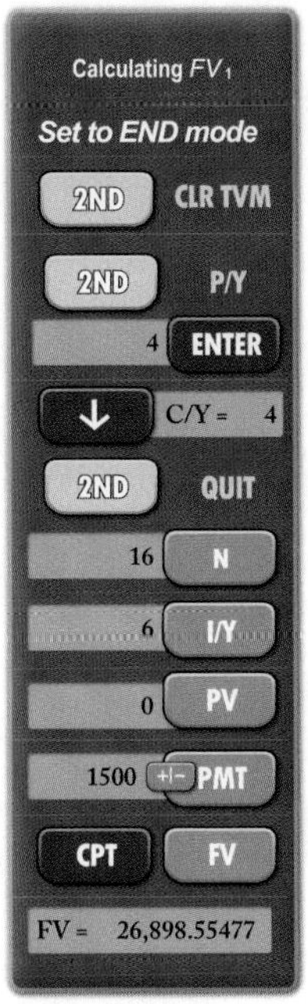

(i) Using Formula 10.2(a),

$$FV = PMT\left[\frac{(1+i)^n - 1}{i}\right]$$

$$FV_1 = 1500.00\left[\frac{(1+0.015)^{16} - 1}{0.015}\right]$$

$$= 1500.00\,[17.932369...] = \$26,898.55477...$$

We now need to calculate the future value of this amount at the end of the remaining six years using the compound interest formula (Formula 9.1(a)). FV_1 becomes the present value for the compounding period.

$$FV_2 = PV_2(1+i)^n$$

Here, 'n', the number of compounding periods = $m \times t = 24$

$$FV_2 = 26,898.55477...(1 + 0.0225)^{24}$$

$$= 45,882.65566... = \$45,882.66$$

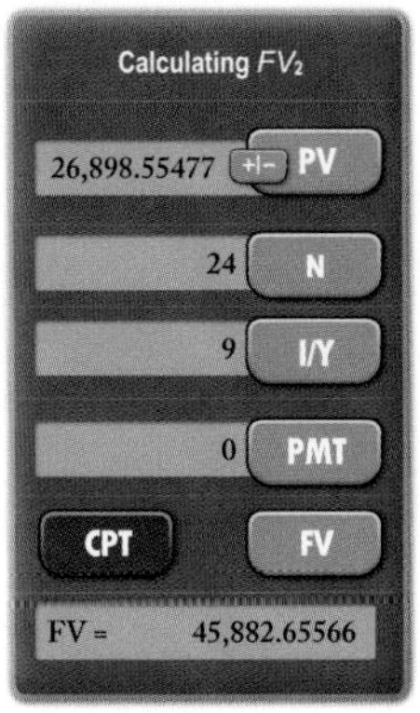

Therefore, the accumulated amount of money in the account at the end of the ten-year period was \$45,882.66.

(ii) *Total Invested* = $n(PMT)$

$$= 16 \times 1500.00 = \$24,000.00$$

Interest Earned = $FV - n(PMT)$

$$= 45,882.66 - 24,000.00 = \$21,882.66$$

Therefore, the total interest earned over the period was \$21,882.66.

Example 10.2(c) **Calculating the Future Value when Payment Changes**

Grace saved \$500 at the end of every month in an RRSP for five years and thereafter, \$600 at the end of every month for the next three years. If the investment was growing at 3% compounded monthly, calculate the maturity value of her RRSP at the end of eight years.

Solution

Page 452

This is an ordinary simple annuity as:

- Payments are made at the end of each payment period (monthly)
- Compounding period (monthly) = payment period (monthly)

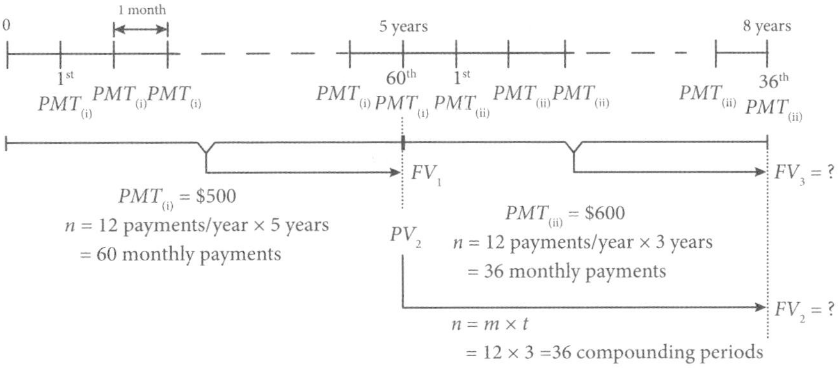

$$i = \frac{j}{m} = \frac{0.03}{12} = 0.0025 \text{ per month}$$

Solution *continued*

Calculating the future value of $PMT_{(i)}$ at the end of the term

Using Formula 10.2(a),

$$FV = PMT\left[\frac{(1+i)^n - 1}{i}\right]$$

$$FV_1 = 500.00\left[\frac{(1+0.0025)^{60} - 1}{0.0025}\right]$$

$$= 500.00\ [64.646712...]$$

$$= \$32{,}323.35631...$$

We now need to calculate the future value of this amount at the end of the remaining three years using the compound interest formula. FV_1 becomes the present value for the compounding period.

$$FV_2 = PV_2(1 + i)^n$$

Here 'n', the number of compounding periods = $m \times t = 36$

$$FV_2 = 32{,}323.35631...(1 + 0.0025)^{36}$$

$$= \$35{,}363.41325...$$

Calculating the future value of $PMT_{(ii)}$ at the end of the term

Using Formula 10.2(a),

$$FV = PMT\left[\frac{(1+i)^n - 1}{i}\right]$$

$$FV_3 = 600.00\left[\frac{(1+0.0025)^{36} - 1}{0.0025}\right]$$

$$= 600.00\ [37.620560...]$$

$$= \$22{,}572.33619...$$

Maturity value of investment at the end of the term:

$$= FV_2 + FV_3$$

$$= 35{,}363.41325... + 22{,}572.33619...$$

$$= 57{,}935.74944... = \$57{,}935.75$$

Therefore, the maturity value of her investment at the end of eight years is $57,935.75.

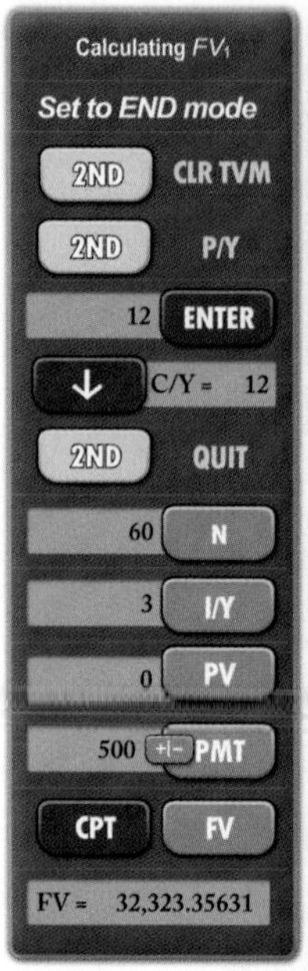

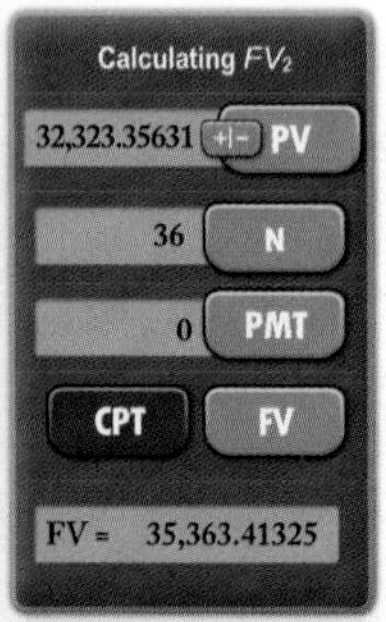

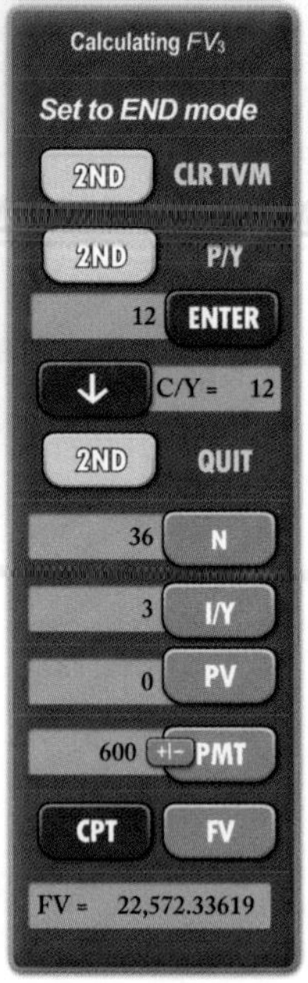

Present Value of an Ordinary Simple Annuity

Consider an example where Margaret wishes to withdraw $1000 at the end of every year for the next five years from an account that pays 10% compounded annually. How much money should she deposit into this account now?

To calculate the present value of all the payments at the beginning of the five-year period, we can calculate the present value of each payment and then add all the present values using the compound interest formula:

$$PV = \frac{FV}{(1+i)^n} = FV(1 + i)^{-n}$$

where 'n' is the number of compounding periods for each payment. 'n' for each payment starting from the first payment is 1, 2, 3, 4, and 5.

The present value of an annuity is the sum of the discounted values of each periodic payment.

Individual present values calculated are in geometric series with 'n' terms, where the first term is 'PMT' and the common ratio is $(1 + i)^{-1}$. By applying the formula for the sum of a geometric series, you obtain the simplified 'PV' Formula 10.2 (b).

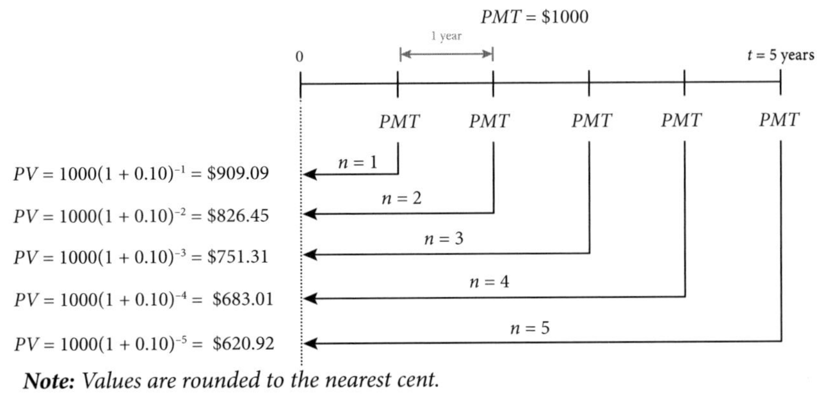

Exhibit 10.2(b): Present Value of Ordinary Simple Annuity Payments

$$\text{Sum of Present Values of her Investment} = 909.09 + 826.45 + 751.31 + 683.01 + 620.92$$
$$= \$3790.79$$

Now, similar to the simplified formula used in FV calculations, the simplified PV formula is:

Formula 10.2(b) **Present Value of an Ordinary Simple Annuity**

$$PV = PMT\left[\frac{1-(1+i)^{-n}}{i}\right]$$

where 'n' is the number of payments during the term, 'PMT' is the amount of the periodic payment, and 'i' is the periodic interest rate.

Calculating the present value of her payments using this simplified formula,

$$PV = 1000.00\left[\frac{1-(1+0.10)^{-5}}{0.10}\right]$$
$$= 1000.00\,[3.790786...]$$
$$= 3790.786770...$$
$$= \$3790.79$$

Therefore, she would have to deposit $3790.79 at the beginning of the five-year period to be able to withdraw $1000 at the end of each year for five years.

In calculating the present value of an annuity, the amount of interest is calculated as follows:

$$\text{Amount of Interest Earned} = \text{Amount Received over the Term} - \text{Present Value}$$
$$I = n(PMT) - PV$$

In this example, $I = 5(1000.00) - 3790.79 = 5000.00 - 3790.79 = \$1209.21$

Therefore, she would earn interest of $1209.21.

Example 10.2(d) **Calculating the Present Value and Interest Earned in an Ordinary Simple Annuity**

Zack purchased an annuity that provided him with payments of $1000 every month for 25 years at 5.4% compounded monthly.

(i) How much did he pay for the annuity?

(ii) What was the total amount received from the annuity and how much of this amount was the interest earned?

Solution

Page 452

This is an ordinary simple annuity as:

- Payments are assumed to be made at the end of each payment period (monthly)
- Compounding period (monthly) = payment period (monthly)

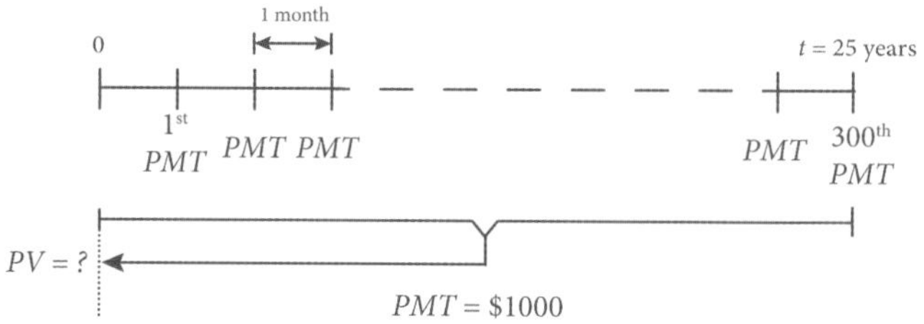

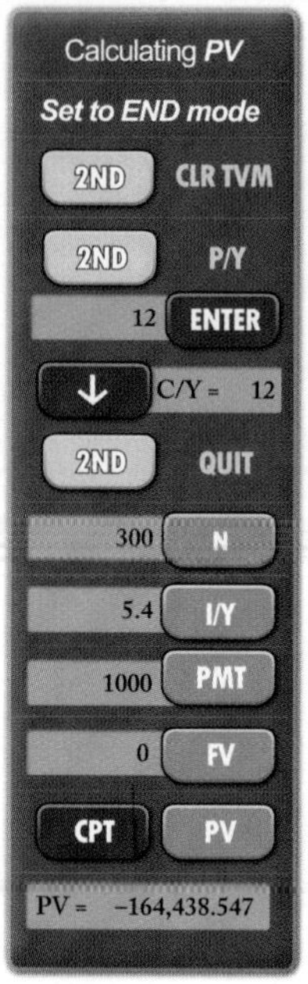

$PMT = \$1000$

$n = 12$ payments/year $\times$ 25 years = 300 monthly payments

$j = 0.054, \quad m = 12, \quad i = \frac{j}{m} = 0.0045$ per month

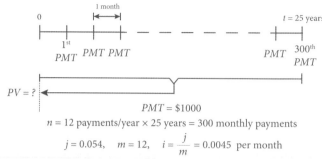

(i) Using Formula 10.2(b),

$$PV = PMT\left[\frac{1-(1+i)^{-n}}{i}\right]$$

$$= 1000.00\left[\frac{1-(1+0.0045)^{-300}}{0.0045}\right]$$

$$= 1000.00\,[164.438547...]$$

$$= 164{,}438.5470... = \$164{,}438.55$$

Therefore, he paid $164,438.55 for the annuity.

(ii) *Amount Received* $= n(PMT)$

$$= 300 \times 1000.00 = \$300{,}000.00$$

Interest Earned $= n(PMT) - PV$

$$= 300{,}000.00 - 164{,}438.55 = \$135{,}561.45$$

Therefore, the total amount received from the annuity was $300,000 and the amount of interest earned was $135,561.45.

Example 10.2(e) **Calculating the Present Value, Amount Invested, and Total Interest Charged in an Ordinary Simple Annuity**

Andrew paid $20,000 as a down payment towards the purchase of a machine and received a loan for the balance amount at an interest rate of 3% compounded monthly. He settled the loan in ten years by paying $1500 at the end of every month.

(i) What was the purchase price of the machine?

(ii) What was the total amount paid to settle the loan and what was the amount of interest charged?

Solution

Page 452

This is an ordinary simple annuity as:

- Payments are made at the end of each payment period (monthly)
- Compounding period (monthly) = payment period (monthly)

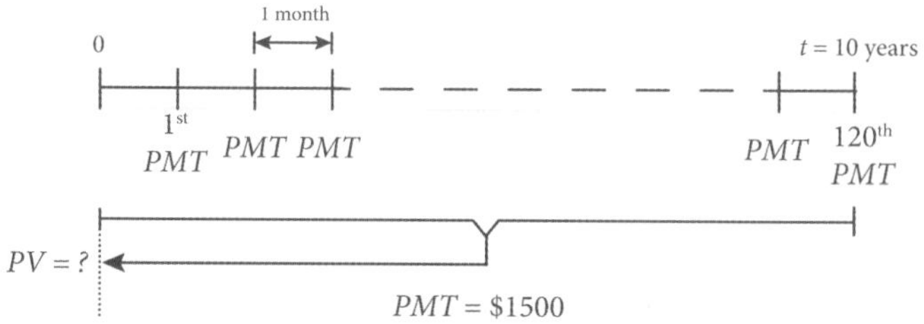

$PMT = \$1500$

$n = 12$ payments/year $\times$ 10 years = 120 monthly payments

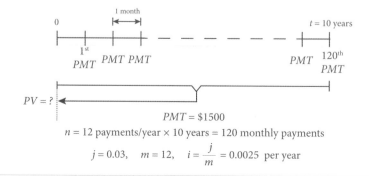

$j = 0.03, \quad m = 12, \quad i = \frac{j}{m} = 0.0025$ per year

Solution *continued*

(i) Using Formula 10.2(b),

$$PV = PMT\left[\frac{1-(1+i)^{-n}}{i}\right]$$

$$= 1500.00\left[\frac{1-(1+0.0025)^{-120}}{0.0025}\right]$$

$$= 1500.00\ [103.561753...]$$

$$= 155{,}342.6296... = \$155{,}342.63$$

As he paid $20,000 as down payment for the machine:

Purchase Price = Down Payment + PV of All Payments

= 20,000.00 + 155,342.63 = $175,342.63

Therefore, the purchase price of the machine was $175,342.63.

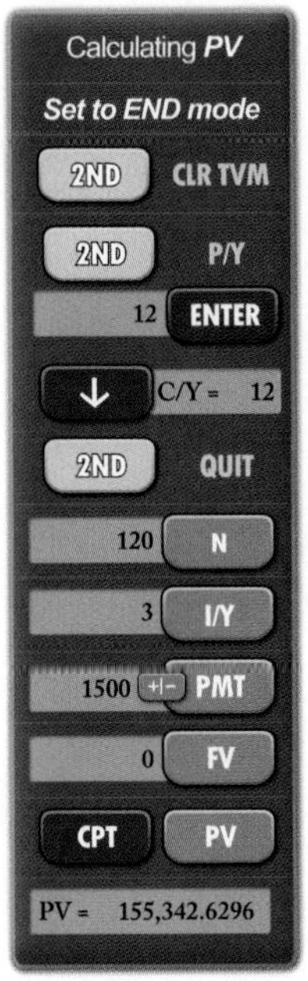

(ii) *Calculating the total amount paid and the interest amount*

Amount Paid = n(PMT)

= 120 × 1500.00 = $180,000.00

Interest Charged = n(PMT) – PV

= 180,000.00 – 155,342.63 = $24,657.37

Therefore, the total amount paid to settle the loan was $180,000 and the amount of interest charged was $24,657.37.

Example 10.2(f)

Calculating the Present Value when the Interest Rate Changes

How much should Halifax Steel Inc. invest today in a fund to be able to withdraw $15,000 at the end of every three months for a period of six years? The money in the fund is expected to grow at 4.8% compounded quarterly for the first two years and 5.6% compounded quarterly for the next four years.

Solution

Page 452

This is an ordinary simple annuity as:

- Withdrawals are made at the end of each payment period (quarterly)
- Compounding period (quarterly) = payment period (quarterly)

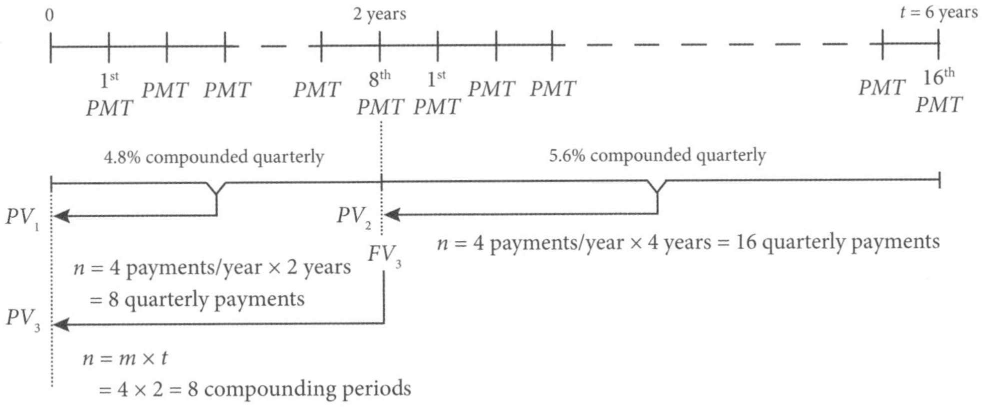

$PMT = \$15{,}000$

$i = \frac{j}{m} = \frac{0.048}{4} = 0.012$ per quarter

$i = \frac{j}{m} = \frac{0.056}{4} = 0.014$ per quarter

Solution
continued

Calculating PV when interest rate is 4.8% compounded quarterly

Using Formula 10.2(b),

$$PV = PMT\left[\frac{1-(1+i)^{-n}}{i}\right]$$

$$PV_1 = 15{,}000.00\left[\frac{1-(1+0.012)^{-8}}{0.012}\right]$$

$$= 15{,}000.00\,[7.584725...]$$

$$= \$113{,}770.8865...$$

Calculating PV when interest rate is 5.6% compounded quarterly

Using Formula 10.2(b),

$$PV = PMT\left[\frac{1-(1+i)^{-n}}{i}\right]$$

$$PV_2 = 15{,}000.00\left[\frac{1-(1+0.014)^{-16}}{0.014}\right]$$

$$= 15{,}000.00\,[14.245867...]$$

$$= \$213{,}668.0186...$$

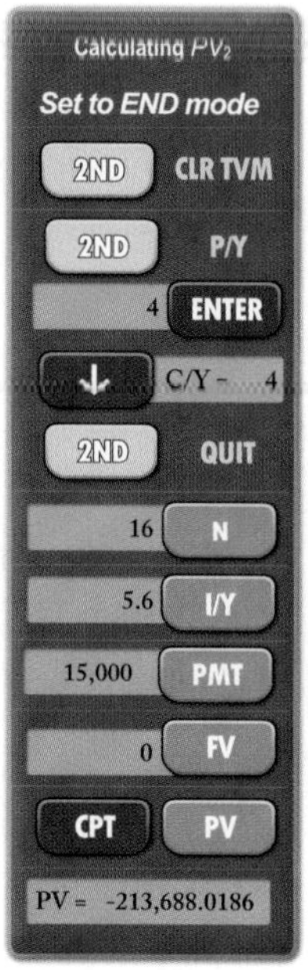

We now need to calculate the present value of this amount at the beginning of the remaining two years using the compound interest formula (Formula 9.1(b)). PV_2 becomes the future value for the compounding period.

$$PV_3 = FV_3(1+i)^{-n}$$

$$= 213{,}688.0186...(1+0.012)^{-8}$$

$$= \$194{,}238.8384...$$

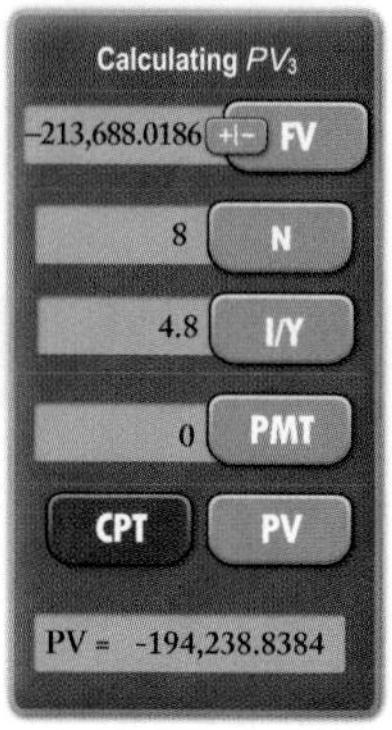

Initial value of the investment

$$= PV_1 + PV_3$$

$$= 113{,}770.8865... + 194{,}238.8384...$$

$$= 308{,}009.7249... = \$308{,}009.72$$

Therefore, in order to be able to withdraw \$15,000 at the end of every three months for six years, Halifax Steel Inc. should invest \$308,009.72 today.

10.2 | Exercises

Answers to the odd-numbered problems are available at the end of the textbook.

1. Calculate the future value of each of the following ordinary simple annuities:

	Periodic Payment	Payment Period	Term of Annuity	Interest Rate	Compounding Frequency
a.	$2500	Every year	10 years	4.50%	Annually
b.	$1750	Every 6 months	7.5 years	5.10%	Semi-annually
c.	$900	Every 3 months	5 years	4.60%	Quarterly
d.	$475	Every month	4.5 years	6.00%	Monthly

2. Calculate the future value of each of the following ordinary simple annuities:

	Periodic Payment	Payment Period	Term of Annuity	Interest Rate	Compounding Frequency
a.	$4500	Every year	12 years	4.75%	Annually
b.	$2250	Every 6 months	6 years	5.00%	Semi-annually
c.	$800	Every 3 months	8.5 years	4.80%	Quarterly
d.	$350	Every month	10 years 3 months	5.76%	Monthly

3. Calculate the present value of each of the ordinary simple annuities in Problem 1.

4. Calculate the present value of each of the ordinary simple annuities in Problem 2.

5. Aliana saved $600 at the end of every year in her savings account at 6% compounded annually for five years.
   a. What is the accumulated value of the money at the end of five years?
   b. What is the interest earned?

6. Sharleen contributed $400 towards an RRSP at the end of every month for four years at 2.5% compounded monthly.
   a. What is the accumulated value of the money at the end of four years?
   b. What is the interest amount earned?

7. Shanelle saves $600 at the end of every month in an RESP at 4.5% compounded monthly for 15 years for her child's education.
   a. How much will she have at the end of 15 years?
   b. If she leaves the accumulated money in the savings account for another two years, earning the same interest rate, how much will she have at the end of the period?

8. Lue makes deposits of $2000 at the end of every year for ten years in a savings account at 3.5% compounded annually.
   a. How much will he have at the end of ten years?
   b. If he plans to leave the accumulated amount in the account for another five years at the same interest rate, how much will he have at the end of the period?

9. Carrie saved $750 of her salary at the end of every month in an RRSP earning 4% compounded monthly for 20 years. How much more would she have earned if she had saved this amount in an RRSP that was earning 4.25% compounded monthly?

10. Adrian invests $500 at the end of every three months in a savings account at 6% compounded quarterly for 7 years and 9 months. How much more would he have earned if he had saved it in a fund that was providing an interest rate of 6.5% compounded quarterly?

11. If $3000 is received at the end of every 3 months for 10.5 years, what will be the discounted value? Assume that money is worth 3% compounded quarterly.

12. What is the discounted value of the following stream of payments: $1250 received at the end of every month for 3 years and 2 months? Assume that money is worth 2.75% compounded monthly.

13. How much should Cortland have in a savings account that is earning 4% compounded semi-annually if he plans to withdraw $9000 from the account at the end of every six months for ten years?

14. How much money should Eva deposit in an investment account that is growing at 6% compounded semi-annually to be able to withdraw $3300 at the end of every six months for four years?

15. Adler received a loan from his bank at 7% compounded monthly so that he could purchase a car. He was required to pay the bank $300 at the end of every month for the next three years. What was the cash price of the car?

16. What would be the purchase price of an annuity that provides $500 at the end of every month for five years and earns an interest rate of 4% compounded monthly?

17. What will be the accumulated value of an annuity if contributions of $500 are made at the end of every month for five years followed by contributions of $750 at the end of every month for the next four years? Assume that money is worth 4.2% compounded monthly.

18. Ali invested $1000 at the end of every six months for six years followed by $1250 at the end of every six months for three more years. If his investment was earning 3.25% compounded semi-annually, what will be the accumualted amount at the end of the nine-year period?

19. Estelle contributed $900 at the end of every three months for seven years into an RRSP fund that earned 3.9% compounded quarterly for the first four years and 3.8% compounded quarterly for the next three years. Calculate the accumulated value of her contributions for the seven-year period and the amount of interest earned.

20. An RESP fund, for a 12-year period, earned 3.75% compounded monthly for 7 years followed by 4.35% compounded monthly for the next 5 years. What will be the accumulated value of the fund and the interest earned if deposits of $125 were made at the end of every month?

21. Jordan invested $1500 at the end of every six months for four years and then $1750 at the end of every six months for the next two years. The investment earned 5% compounded semi-annually the first four years and 4.8% compounded semi-annually, thereafter. Calculate the accumulated value at the end of six years and the amount of interest earned.

22. Payments of $1500 are made at the end of every three months for three years at 4.1% compounded quarterly followed by payments of $1750 at the end of every three months for the next two years at 4.25% compounded quarterly. Calculate the accumulated value of the annuity.

23. Falco Inc. paid $25,000 as a down payment for a machine. The balance was financed with a loan at 3.25% compounded semi-annually and required payments of $9000 to be made at the end of every six months for five years to settle the debt.
    a. What was the purchase price of the machine?
    b. What was the total amount of interest charged?

24. Brandon purchased a computer-controlled machine for his machine shop by paying a down payment of $17,500. He financed the balance amount with a loan at 4.75% compounded semi-annually, which required a payment of $10,000 at the end of every six months for three years.
    a. What was the purchase price of the machine?
    b. What was the total amount of interest charged?

• 25. How much would you have to pay now for a retirement annuity that would provide $3000 at the end of every three months at 5% compounded quarterly for the first ten years and $2500 at the end of each month at 6% compounded monthly for the following five years?

• 26. How much should Drake pay today for a retirement annuity that would provide him with $4000 at the end of every month for five years at 3.5% compounded monthly and $20,000 every six months for the next ten years at 4% compounded semi-annually?

• 27. Kayla wanted to purchase a storage locker for $5000 at her apartment building. She could either pay the entire amount or take a loan from the bank at 6.5% compounded monthly. She would have to pay $150 every month to settle the loan in four years. Which option should she choose and why?

• 28. Ronald and Jill were wondering if they should pay $30,000 for a parking space in their condominium building or take a loan from the bank at 4% compounded monthly that required making monthly payments of $460 for five years. Which option should they choose and why?

10.3 | Future Value and Present Value of an Ordinary General Annuity

In an ordinary general annuity, payments are made at the end of each payment period and the compounding period is not equal to the payment period.

In this case, if we calculate the equivalent periodic rate, i_2, that matches the payment period, then using this equivalent periodic rate we can use the ordinary simple annuity formulas to calculate the future value and present value.

To calculate this, we first calculate the number of compounding periods per payment period (c) and then the equivalent periodic interest rate per payment period (i_2) using the following two formulas:

Formula 10.3(a)

Number of Compounding Periods per Payment Period

$$c = \frac{\textit{Number of compounding periods per year}}{\textit{Number of payments per year}}$$

Formula 10.3(b)

Equivalent Periodic Interest Rate per Payment Period

$$i_2 = (1 + i)^c - 1$$

Note: *The value of 'c' as calculated from Formula 10.3(a) is used in calculating 'i_2' in Formula 10.3(b).*

Substitute the value of 'i_2' for 'i' in the ordinary simple annuity formulas, Formula 10.2(a) and Formula 10.2(b), to solve for 'FV' and 'PV' of an ordinary general annuity:

$$FV = PMT\left[\frac{(1 + i_2)^n - 1}{i_2}\right] \text{ and } PV = PMT\left[\frac{1 - (1 + i_2)^{-n}}{i_2}\right]$$

Example 10.3(a)

Calculating the Compounding Periods per Payment Period (c) and the Equivalent Periodic Interest Rate (i_2) that Matches the Payment Period

Complete the table by calculating the number of compounding periods per payment period (c) and the equivalent periodic interest rate (i_2) that matches the payment period for the related interest rates:

Solution

Interest Rate	Payment Period	c	i_2
8% compounded quarterly	Monthly	$\frac{4}{12}$	$\left(1 + \frac{0.08}{4}\right)^{\frac{4}{12}} - 1 = 0.006622...$ per month
9% compounded semi-annually	Quarterly	$\frac{2}{4}$	$\left(1 + \frac{0.09}{2}\right)^{\frac{2}{4}} - 1 = 0.022252...$ per quarter
6% compounded monthly	Semi-annually	$\frac{12}{2}$	$\left(1 + \frac{0.06}{12}\right)^{\frac{12}{2}} - 1 = 0.030377...$ per half-year
5% compounded annually	Monthly	$\frac{1}{12}$	$\left(1 + \frac{0.05}{1}\right)^{\frac{1}{12}} - 1 = 0.004074...$ per month

The following two examples will demonstrate future value and present value calculations of an ordinary general annuity.

Example 10.3(b) **Calculating the Future Value of an Ordinary General Annuity**

Rachel would like to save \$100 every month for the next four years in a savings account at 2.92% compounded daily.

(i) What would be the accumulated value of the investments at the end of four years?

(ii) What would be the amount of interest earned?

Solution

Page 453

This is an ordinary general annuity as:

- Payments are made at the end of each payment period (monthly)
- Compounding period (daily) ≠ payment period (monthly)

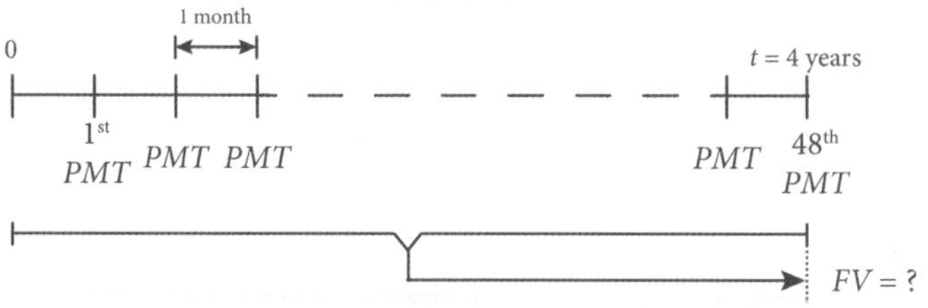

$$PMT = \$100$$

$$n = 12 \text{ payments/year} \times 4 \text{ years} = 48 \text{ monthly payments}$$

$$j = 0.0292, \quad m = 365, \quad i = \frac{j}{m} = 0.00008 \text{ per day}$$

(i) Using Formula 10.3(a),

$$c = \frac{\textit{Number of compounding periods per year}}{\textit{Number of payments per year}} = \frac{365}{12}$$

Using Formula 10.3(b),

$$i_2 = (1 + i)^c - 1 = (1 + 0.00008)^{(365/12)} - 1$$

$$= 0.002436\ldots \text{ per day}$$

Using Formula 10.2(a) and substituting i_2 for i,

$$FV = PMT\left[\frac{(1 + i_2)^n - 1}{i_2}\right]$$

$$= 100.00\left[\frac{(1 + 0.002436\ldots)^{48} - 1}{0.002436\ldots}\right]$$

$$= 100.00\,[50.853559\ldots]$$

$$= 5085.355985\ldots = \$5085.36$$

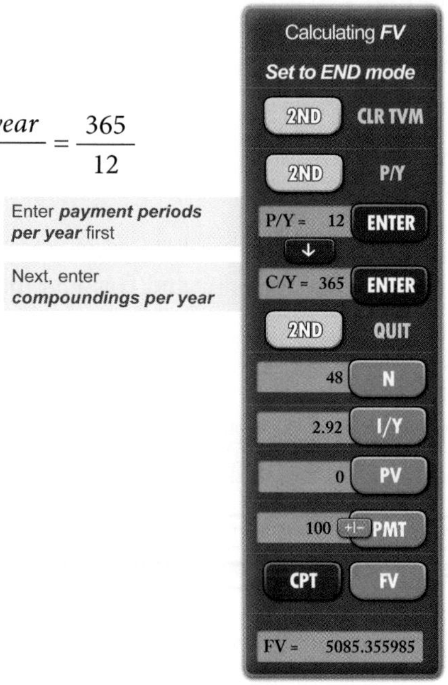

Therefore, the accumulated value of her investments at the end of four years would be \$5085.36.

(ii) *Interest Earned* = *FV* – *n*(*PMT*)

$$= 5085.36 - 48(100.00) = \$285.36$$

Therefore, the amount of interest earned over the time period would be \$285.36.

Example 10.3(c) **Calculating the Present Value of an Ordinary General Annuity**

Joseph borrowed money from a bank at 6% compounded annually. He settled the loan by repaying \$500 at the end of every month for six years.

(i) What was the loan amount received?

(ii) What was the amount of interest charged?

Page 453

Solution

This is an ordinary general annuity as:

- Payments are made at the end of each payment period (monthly)
- Compounding period (annually) ≠ payment period (monthly)

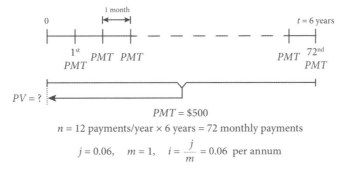

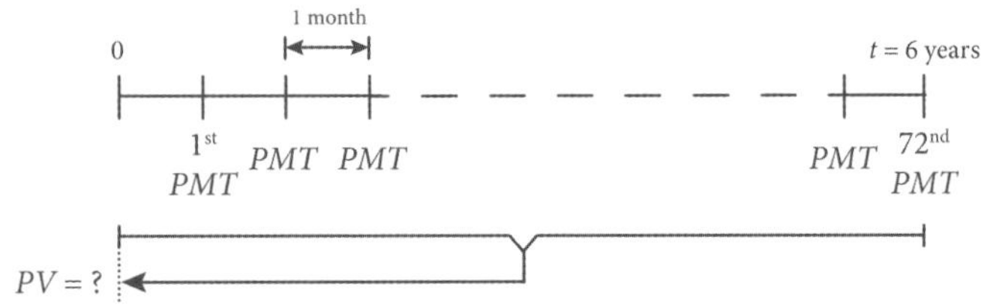

$$PMT = \$500$$

$$n = 12 \text{ payments/year} \times 6 \text{ years} = 72 \text{ monthly payments}$$

$$j = 0.06, \quad m = 1, \quad i = \frac{j}{m} = 0.06 \text{ per annum}$$

(i) Using Formula 10.3(a),

$$c = \frac{\textit{Number of compounding periods per year}}{\textit{Number of payments per year}} = \frac{1}{12}$$

Using Formula 10.3(b),

$$i_2 = (1 + i)^c - 1 = (1 + 0.06)^{(1/12)} - 1 = 0.004867... \text{ per month}$$

Using Formula 10.2(b) and substituting i_2 for i,

$$PV = PMT\left[\frac{1 - (1 + i_2)^{-n}}{i_2}\right]$$

$$= 500.00\left[\frac{1 - (1 + 0.004867...)^{-72}}{0.004867...}\right]$$

$$= 500.00\,[60.613537...]$$

$$= 30{,}306.76884... = \$30{,}306.77$$

Therefore, the loan amount received was \$30,306.77.

(ii) *Interest Charged* = $n(PMT) - PV$

$$= 72(500.00) - 30{,}306.77 = \$5693.23$$

Therefore, the amount of interest charged was \$5693.23

10.3 | Exercises

Answers to the odd-numbered problems are available at the end of the textbook.

1. Calculate the number of compounding periods per payment period (expressed as a fraction, wherever applicable) and the equivalent periodic interest rate per payment period (rounded to six decimal places, wherever applicable) that matches the payment period for each of the following:
   a. Interest rate is 5% compounded quarterly; payment period is semi-annually.
   b. Interest rate is 4.2% compounded daily; payment period is monthly.
   c. Interest rate is 4.8% compounded monthly; payment period is semi-annually.
   d. Interest rate is 4.9% compounded semi-annually; payment period is quarterly.

2. Calculate the number of compounding periods per payment period (expressed as a fraction, wherever applicable) and the equivalent periodic interest rate per payment period (rounded to six decimal places, wherever applicable) that matches the payment period for each of the following:
   a. Interest rate is 4% compounded daily; payment period is quarterly.
   b. Interest rate is 3.9% compounded quarterly; payment period is monthly.
   c. Interest rate is 5% compounded semi-annually; payment period is monthly.
   d. Interest rate is 4.9% compounded monthly; payment period is quarterly.

3. Calculate the future value of each of the following ordinary general annuities:

	Periodic Payment	Payment Period	Term of Annuity	Interest Rate	Compounding Frequency
a.	$2200	Every year	15 years	4.80%	Quarterly
b.	$1400	Every 6 months	16.5 years	4.00%	Monthly
c.	$1000	Every 3 months	11 years and 3 months	3.75%	Semi-annually
d.	$750	Every month	5 years 2 months	3.90%	Daily

4. Calculate the future value of each of the following ordinary general annuities:

	Periodic Payment	Payment Period	Term of Annuity	Interest Rate	Compounding Frequency
a.	$1200	Every 3 months	8 years and 6 months	3.20%	Monthly
b.	$400	Every month	15 years and 9 months	3.60%	Semi-annually
c.	$1850	Every 6 months	7.5 years	4.40%	Quarterly
d.	$3000	Every year	12 years	4.70%	Daily

5. Calculate the present value of each of the ordinary general annuities in Problem 3.

6. Calculate the present value of each of the ordinary general annuities in Problem 4.

7. Adrian invested $100 at the end of every month into an RRSP for five years. If the RRSP was providing an interest rate of 5% compounded daily, how much did he have in the RRSP at the end of the five years?

8. Bina saved $250 at the end of every month for two years in a savings account that earns 5% compounded daily. How much would she have in the account at the end of two years and how much of this is the interest earned?

9. Calculate the accumulated value of end-of-quarter payments of $800 made at the following interest rates for five years:

   a. 6.23% compounded quarterly.

   b. 6.24% compounded semi-annually.

10. Calculate the future value of month-end payments of $180 made at the following interest rates for ten years:

    a. 7.8% compounded monthly.

    b. 8% compounded quarterly.

11. Rose has been contributing $1000 at the end of every three months into a retirement fund for the past ten years. She decided to stop making payments and to allow her investment to grow for another five years. If money could earn 8% compounded semi-annually, how much interest would she have earned over the fifteen-year period?

12. Justin deposited $300 in a savings account at the end of every three months for five years. If the amount earned 5% compounded monthly, and if he left the accumulated money in the account to grow for another three years, calculate the balance in his savings account at the end of the period. What was his total deposit and total earnings?

13. Becca can afford to invest $400 at the end of every month in an RRSP for five years. By calculating the accumulated value of the payments in each of the following two investment options, identify the one that will give her the best return on her investment:

    RRSP 1: 3.55% compounded annually.

    RRSP 2: 3.50% compounded semi-annually.

14. An annuity pays $200 at the end of every month for five years. Compare the future values if the investment earns 4% compounded monthly, 4% compounded semi-annually, and 4% compounded annually.

15. A credit union offers an interest rate of 4.5% compounded monthly for all investments. Which of the following would result in a higher future value and by how much more, when invested at the credit union?

    Option A: $18,250 invested for ten years.

    Option B: Annuity payments of $475 at the end of every quarter for ten years.

16. Calculate the accumulated value of the following investment options if the bank offers an interest rate of 5% compounded semi-annually:

    a. A single amount of $5000 saved for five years.

    b. A series of payments of $100 at the end of every month for five years.

17. Alejandro has $25,000 in a savings account that yields 5.75% compounded daily. He intends to use these savings for his retirement in five years. In addition to these savings, he intends to deposit $1250 at the end of every month in a mutual fund that yields the same return. How much money will he have available for his retirement in five years?

18. Lily has accumulated $90,000 in a mutual fund. If she continues to deposit $500 at the end of every month from her salary into the fund for the next ten years, how much money will she have at the end of ten years if the fund earns 3.75% compounded daily?

19. Amanda invested $500 at the end of every month into an RRSP that had an interest rate of 3% compounded daily. Two years later, the interest rate on her RRSP increased to 3.25% compounded daily and remained the same, thereafter. What is the accumulated value of the RRSP in six years?

20. What will be the future value of a series of $1000 deposits made at the end of each quarter for ten years, if the interest rate is 5% compounded monthly for the first five years and 4% compounded annually for the next five years?

21. What is the discounted value of annuity payments of $2000 made at the end of every year for five years at 6% compounded semi-annually?

22. How much should Gilbert pay for a ten-year annuity that provides month-end payments of $1800 at 4.5% compounded quarterly?

23. A lottery winner is offered a choice between $100,000 now and another $100,000 in five years, or month-end payments of $2300 for eight years. If money can earn 3.75% compounded semi-annually, which alternative is economically better (in current value) for her and by how much?

24. You win a lottery that entitles you to receive either $250,000 now and another $125,000 in three years, or month-end payments of $8300 for five years. If money can earn 3.65% compounded daily, which offer is economically better (in current value) for you and by how much?

25. Troy has to make a down payment of $1000 at the time of purchase of a new car, and payments of $330 at the end of every month for 3 years and 3 months at an interest rate of 6% compounded semi-annually. What is the purchase price of the car and the total interest on the car loan?

26. Byron Manufacturing Inc. paid $30,000 as a down payment to purchase a machine. It received a loan for the remaining amount at 4.5% compounded daily. What is the purchase price of the machine and the total amount of interest paid if Bryon Manufacturing settled the loan with payments of $4500 made at the end of every month for five years?

27. Two annuities that provide end-of-quarter payments of $850 for a period of five years have the following interest rates:

    Annuity A: 9.45% compounded monthly.

    Annuity B: 9.50% compounded semi-annually.

    Which annuity would be less expensive to purchase, and by what amount?

28. Ellen wants to receive a retirement income of $3000 every month for 20 years from her savings. If a bank in London was offering 6% compounded semi-annually, how much would she have to invest to receive her planned retirement income? If a bank in Toronto was offering 5.98% compounded quarterly, how much cheaper would it be for Ellen to invest at this bank instead of investing at the bank in London?

29. What is the purchase price of an annuity that provides month-end payments of $500 for the first two years and $1000 for the next three years? Assume that the interest rate is 3% compounded daily throughout the time period.

30. How much should Emma pay for an annuity that would give her $5000 at the end of every year for the first seven years and $8000 at the end of every year for the next four years, if the interest rate is 6% compounded semi-annually throughout the time period?

- 31. Starting at age 35, Gabriella invested \$400 into an RRSP at the end of every month until her 45th birthday, and left the fund to grow under compound interest until her 65th birthday. Starting at age 50, Gerard deposited \$800 into a similar fund at the end of each month until his 65th birthday. Assume that both funds earned 6.4% compounded semi-annually.
  a. Who had more in his/her fund at age 65, and by what amount?
  b. Who earned more interest and by what amount?
- 32. Harry deposited \$1000 in a retirement account at the end of each quarter for 20 years until he reached the age of 55, and then made no further deposits. His wife deposited \$1000 in a retirement fund at the end of each quarter for 30 years until she reached the age of 65. Assume that both funds earned 4.65% compounded monthly.
  a. Who had more in his/her fund at age 65, and by what amount?
  b. Who earned more interest and by what amount?
- 33. A loan is settled by making payments of \$2000 at the end of every three months for four years, and then \$500 at the end of every month for the next six years. What was the amount of the loan if the interest rate was 4.5% compounded monthly?
- 34. Georgia borrowed money from a bank at 6% compounded quarterly. She settled the loan by repaying \$500 at the end of every month for the first two years, and \$2000 at the end of every three months for the next two years. What was the amount of the received loan?

10.4 | Future Value and Present Value of a Simple Annuity Due

In a simple annuity due, payments are made at the beginning of each payment period, and the compounding period is equal to the payment period. In this section, you will learn how to calculate the future value and present value of a simple annuity due.

Future Value of a Simple Annuity Due

In an annuity due, as each payment is made at the beginning of the payment period, you will notice that the future value (accumulated value) of each payment is a multiple of the future value (accumulated value) of each payment in an ordinary annuity by a factor of $(1 + i)$. Let us compare two examples of an annuity with five annual payments, where in the first example, payments are made at the beginning of each year (annuity due) and in the second example, payments are made at the end of each year (ordinary annuity).

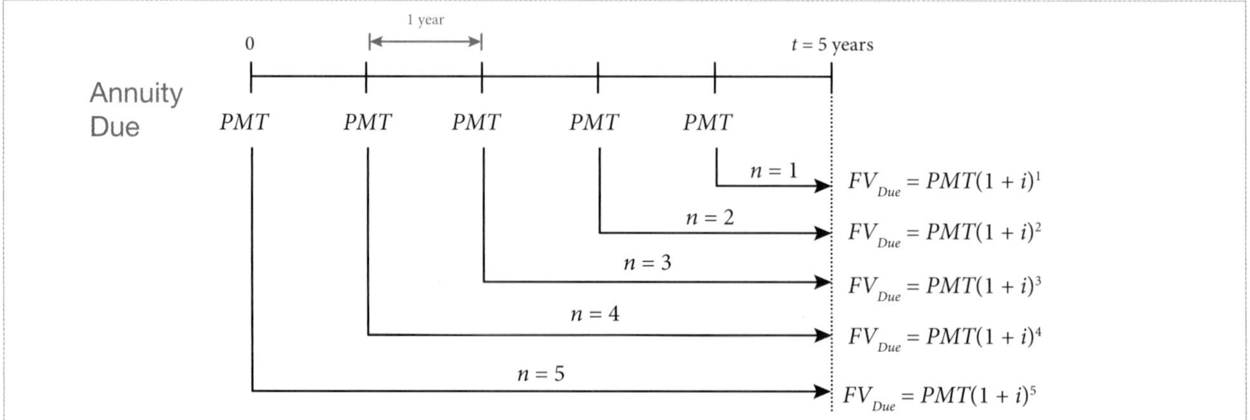

$$FV_{Due} = PMT(1 + i)^5 + PMT(1 + i)^4 + PMT(1 + i)^3 + PMT(1 + i)^2 + PMT(1 + i)^1$$

Exhibit 10.4(a): Future Value of Simple Annuity Due Payments (FV_{Due})

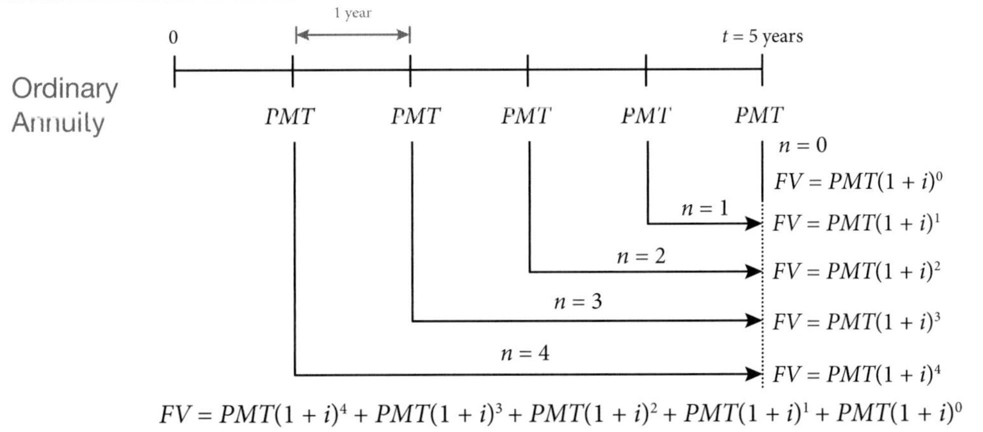

Exhibit 10.4(b): Future Value of Ordinary Simple Annuity Payments (FV)

Comparing the two equations in the preceding two diagrams:

$$FV_{Due} = PMT(1+i)^5 + PMT(1+i)^4 + PMT(1+i)^3 + PMT(1+i)^2 + PMT(1+i)^1$$
$$FV = PMT(1+i)^4 + PMT(1+i)^3 + PMT(1+i)^2 + PMT(1+i)^1 + PMT(1+i)^0$$

You will notice that each term in FV_{Due} is a multiple of the corresponding term in FV by a factor of $(1 + i)$.

Therefore, $FV_{Due} = FV(1 + i)$ and can be expressed by the following formula:

Formula 10.4(a) **Future Value of a Simple Annuity Due**

$$FV_{Due} = PMT\left[\frac{(1+i)^n - 1}{i}\right](1+i)$$

Present Value of a Simple Annuity Due

In an annuity due, as the payment is made at the beginning of the payment period, you will notice that the present value (discounted value) of each payment is a multiple of the present value (discounted value) of each payment in an ordinary annuity by a factor of $(1 + i)$. Let us compare two examples of an annuity with five annual payments, where in the first example, payments are made at the beginning of each year (annuity due) and in the second example, payments are made at the end of each year (ordinary annuity).

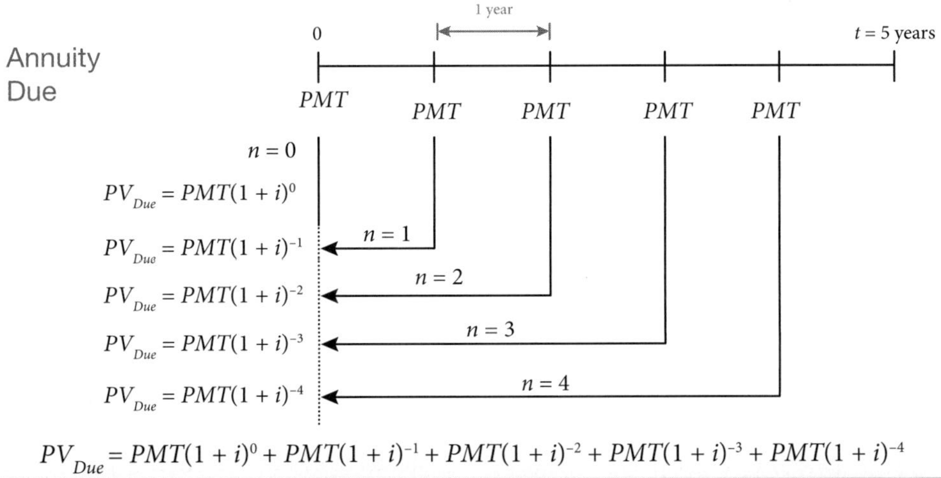

Exhibit 10.4(c): Present Value of Simple Annuity Due Payments (PV_{Due})

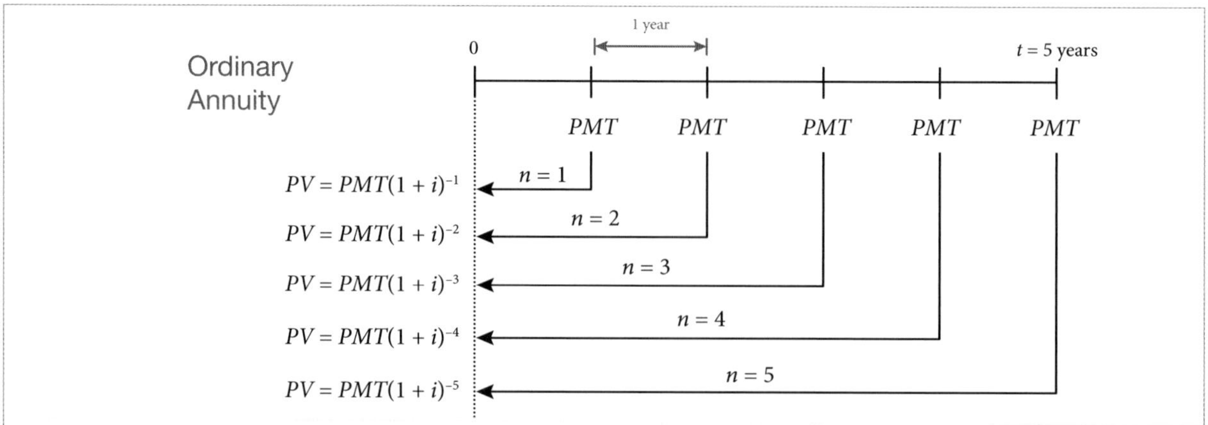

$$PV = PMT(1+i)^{-1} + PMT(1+i)^{-2} + PMT(1+i)^{-3} + PMT(1+i)^{-4} + PMT(1+i)^{-5}$$

Exhibit 10.4(d): Present Value of Ordinary Simple Annuity Payments (PV)

Comparing the two equations in the preceding two diagrams:

$$PV_{Due} = PMT(1+i)^{0} + PMT(1+i)^{-1} + PMT(1+i)^{-2} + PMT(1+i)^{-3} + PMT(1+i)^{-4}$$

$$PV = PMT(1+i)^{-1} + PMT(1+i)^{-2} + PMT(1+i)^{-3} + PMT(1+i)^{-4} + PMT(1+i)^{-5}$$

You will notice that each term in PV_{Due} is a multiple of the corresponding term in PV by a factor of $(1 + i)$.

Therefore, $PV_{Due} = PV(1 + i)$ and can be expressed by the following formula:

Formula 10.4(b) **Present Value of a Simple Annuity Due**

$$PV_{Due} = PMT\left[\frac{1-(1+i)^{-n}}{i}\right](1+i)$$

Example 10.4(a) **Calculating the Future Value of a Simple Annuity Due**

Madison makes contributions of \$500 at the beginning of every six months for ten years towards an RRSP. If the RRSP earns 5% compounded semi-annually, what would be the value of her RRSP at the end of the time period?

Solution

Page 453

This is a simple annuity due as:

- Payments are made at the beginning of each payment period (semi-annually)
- Compounding period (semi-annually) = payment period (semi-annually)

When using the financial calculator for annuity due calculations, set the calculator to beginning of period ('BGN' mode). This is described in Section 10.2

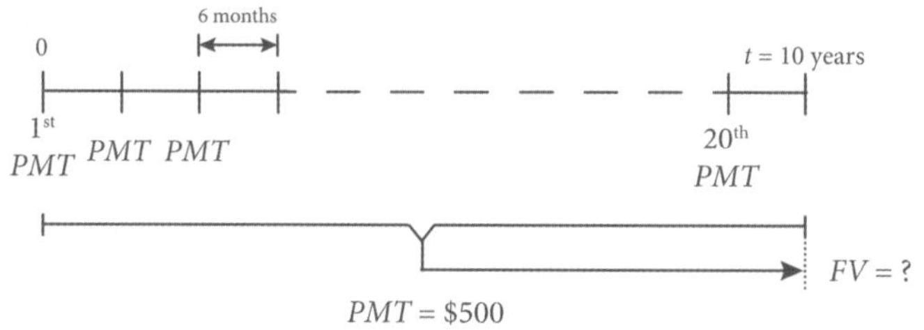

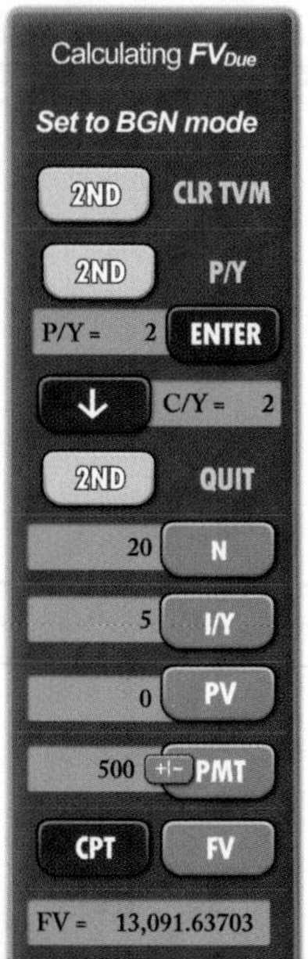

$PMT = \$500$

$n = 2$ payments/year × 10 years = 20 semi-annual payments

$j = 0.05, \quad m = 2, \quad i = \frac{j}{m} = 0.025$ per half-year

Using Formula 10.4(a), $FV_{Due} = PMT\left[\frac{(1+i)^{n}-1}{i}\right](1+i)$

$$= 500.00\left[\frac{(1+0.025)^{20}-1}{0.025}\right](1+0.025)$$

$$= 500.00\,[25.544657...]\,(1.025)$$

$$= 13{,}091.63703... = \$13{,}091.64$$

Therefore, the value of her RRSP would be \$13,091.64 at the end of the time period.

Example 10.4(b) **Calculating the Present Value of a Simple Annuity Due**

Louis purchases kitchen appliances for his new home. He sets up a payment plan where he pays $300 at the beginning of every three months for eight years, at a rate of 4% compounded quarterly. What is the cost of the kitchen appliances?

Page 453

Solution

This is a simple annuity due as:

- Payments are made at the beginning of each payment period (quarterly)
- Compounding period (quarterly) = payment period (quarterly)

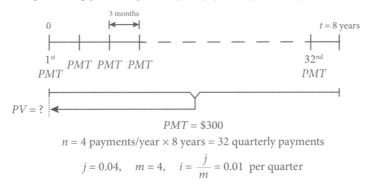

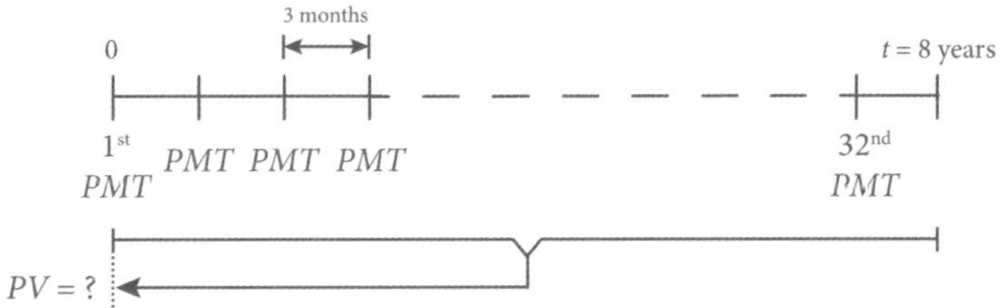

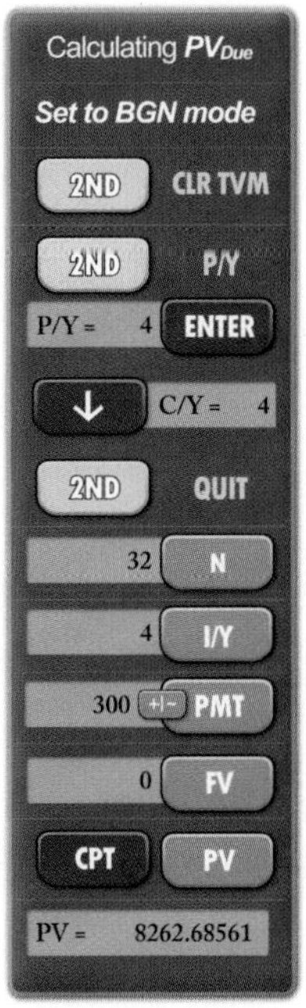

$$PMT = \$300$$

$$n = 4 \text{ payments/year} \times 8 \text{ years} = 32 \text{ quarterly payments}$$

$$j = 0.04, \quad m = 4, \quad i = \frac{j}{m} = 0.01 \text{ per quarter}$$

Using Formula 10.4(b),

$$PV_{Due} = PMT\left[\frac{1-(1+i)^{-n}}{i}\right](1+i)$$

$$= 300.00\left[\frac{1-(1+0.01)^{-32}}{0.01}\right](1+0.01)$$

$$= 300.00\,[27.269589...](1.01)$$

$$= 8262.685610... = \$8262.69$$

Therefore, the cost of the kitchen appliances is $8262.69.

Example 10.4(c) **Calculating the Future Value of a Simple Annuity Due when the Interest Rate Changes**

Stefani makes regular deposits of $200 at the beginning of every month into a savings account that earns 3% compounded monthly. After one year of deposits, the interest rate drops to 2.7% compounded monthly. How much money has accumulated in the savings account after five years of deposits?

Page 453

Solution

This is a simple annuity due as:

- Payments are made at the beginning of each payment period (monthly)
- Compounding period (monthly) = payment period (monthly)

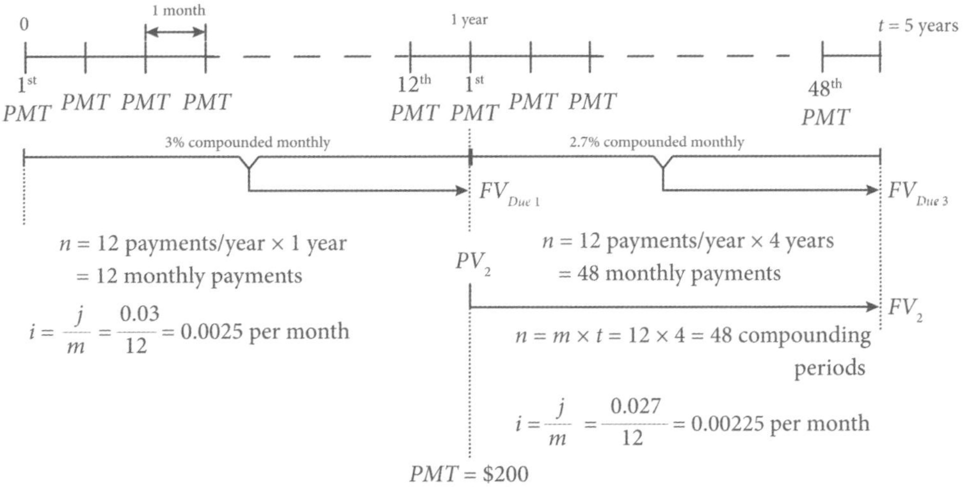

Solution *continued*

Calculating FV when interest rate is 3% compounded monthly

Using Formula 10.4(a),

$$FV_{Due} = PMT\left[\frac{(1+i)^n - 1}{i}\right](1+i)$$

$$FV_{Due\ 1} = 200.00\left[\frac{(1+0.0025)^{12} - 1}{0.0025}\right](1+0.0025)$$

$$= 200.00[12.166382...](1.0025)$$

$$= \$2439.359744...$$

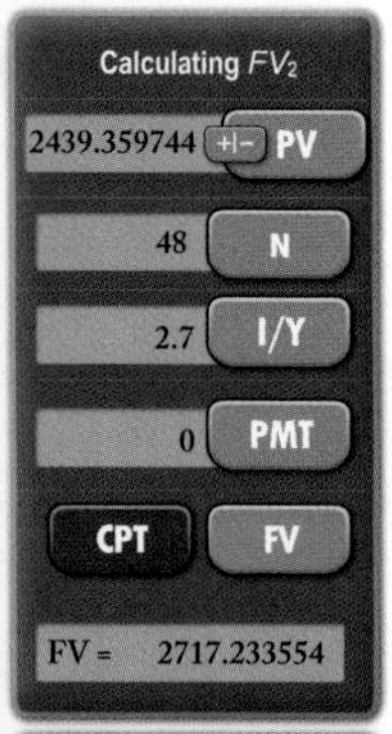

We now need to calculate the future value of this amount at the end of the remaining four years using the compound interest formula (Formula 9.1(a)). $FV_{Due\ 1}$ becomes the present value for the compounded period.

$$FV_2 = PV_2(1+i)^n$$

$$= 2439.359744...(1+0.00225)^{48}$$

$$= \$2717.233554...$$

Calculating FV when interest rate is 2.7% compounded monthly

Using Formula 10.4(a),

$$FV_{Due} = PMT\left[\frac{(1+i)^n - 1}{i}\right](1+i)$$

$$FV_{Due\ 3} = 200.00\left[\frac{(1+0.00225)^{48} - 1}{0.00225}\right](1+0.00225)$$

$$= 200.00[50.627821...](1.00225)$$

$$= \$10,148.34692...$$

Accumulated value of the investment

$$= FV_2 + FV_{Due\ 3}$$

$$= 2717.233554... + 10,148.34692...$$

$$= 12,865.58047... = \$12,865.58$$

Therefore, the savings account will have accumulated $12,865.58 in five years.

Leases

A **lease** presents an alternative to obtaining a loan to purchase an asset. With a lease, the **lessee** makes regular payments to essentially *borrow* an asset from the **lessor** (bank, company, etc.) throughout the term of the lease; the lessee does not own the asset during or after the term - the ownership remains with the lessor.

Vehicle leasing is a very common form of leasing. Vehicle lease payments generally occur at the beginning of a period (usually monthly), and therefore form an annuity due (simple or general).

Lease Terminology

The residual value on leases for vehicles is usually estimated by the lessor at the start of the lease as a percent of the manufacturer's suggested retail price (MSRP).

The **down payment** is a lump sum payment made at the start of a lease. For example, a 5% down payment on a \$35,000 vehicle is $35,000 \times 0.05 = \$1750$.

Not all leases require a down payment.

The **residual value** is the expected value of the asset at the end of the lease term. At the end of a lease term, the lessee often has the option to purchase the asset for the residual value, or return the asset to the lessor.

The **lease amount** is the value of the asset at the beginning of the lease term. This is calculated by adding the down payment, the present value of all the lease payments, and the present value of the residual value.

$$Lease\ Amount = Down\ Payment + PV_{Lease\ PMTs} + PV_{Residual}$$

The **buyback value** is the value of the asset on a specific date. This is calculated by adding the present value of the remaining lease payments and the present value of the residual value.

$$Buyback\ Value = PV_{Remaining\ PMTs} + PV_{Residual}$$

Example 10.4(d)

Choosing Between Lease and Buy Options and Calculating the Buyback Value

A car dealership provided Shelley with the following two options to buy or lease a vehicle:

- Buy Option: Pay $21,500 immediately to own the vehicle.
- Lease Option: Make a down payment of $2000, and lease payments of $230 at the beginning of every month for four years. At the end of four years, she has the option to buy the vehicle for the residual value of $10,000.

The cost of borrowing is 3% compounded monthly.

(i) Which option is economically better for Shelley?

(ii) In the lease option, what will be the buyback value of the vehicle at the end of three years?

Solution

Page 453

The lease payments form a simple annuity due as:

- Payments are made at the beginning of each payment period (monthly)
- Compounding period (monthly) = payment period (monthly)

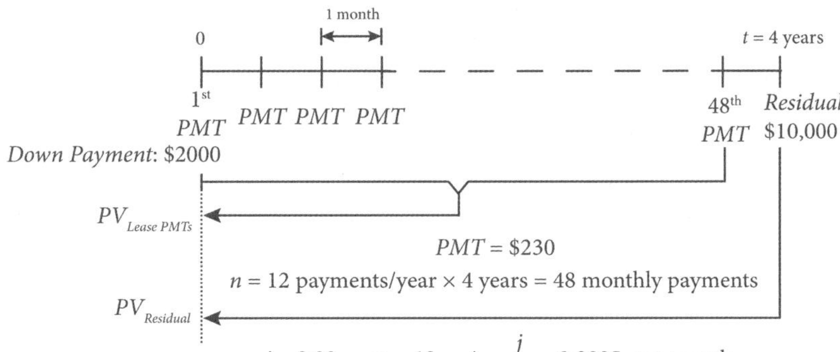

$$j = 0.03, \quad m = 12, \quad i = \frac{j}{m} = 0.0025 \text{ per month}$$

Using the financial calculator, you can either compute 'PV' separately and add the answers together, or you can do the entire calculation for the present values in one step as shown here.

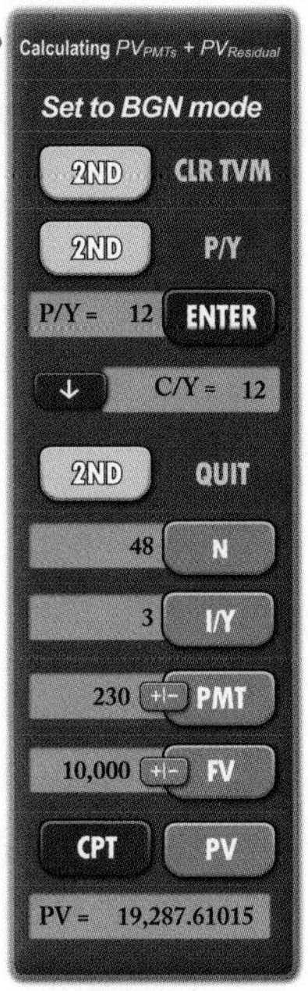

(i) *Calculating the Lease Amount*

$$Lease\ Amount = Down\ Payment + PV_{Lease\ PMTs} + PV_{Residual}$$

$$Down\ Payment = \$2000.00$$

Using Formula 10.4(b),

$$PV_{Due} = PMT\left[\frac{1-(1+i)^{-n}}{i}\right](1+i)$$

$$PV_{Lease\ PMTs} = 230.00\left[\frac{1-(1+0.0025)^{-48}}{0.0025}\right](1+0.0025)$$

$$= 230.00[45.178694...](1.0025)$$

$$= \$10{,}417.07751...$$

Using Formula 9.1(b),

$$PV = FV(1+i)^{-n}$$

$$PV_{Residual} = 10{,}000.00(1+0.0025)^{-48}$$

$$= 10{,}000.00(0.887053...)$$

$$= \$8870.532634...$$

Solution *continued*

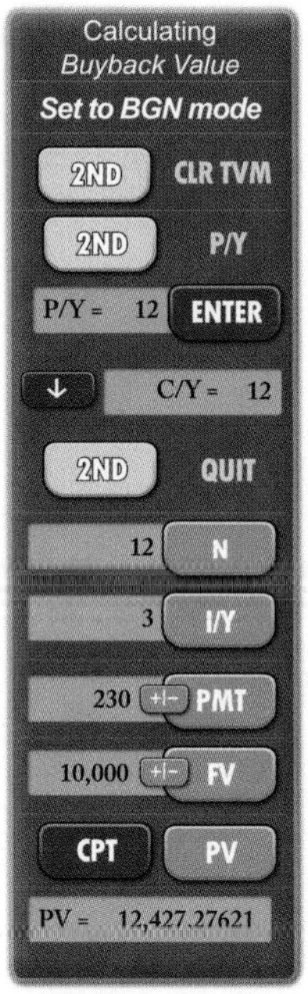

Therefore, $\textit{Lease Amount} = 2000.00 + 10{,}417.07751\ldots + 8870.532634\ldots$

$$= 21{,}287.61015\ldots = \$21{,}287.61$$

The lease amount is less than the buy option of $21,500. Therefore, the lease option is economically better for Shelley.

(ii) *Calculating the buyback value at the end of three years*

n = Remaining lease payments = 12 monthly payments

$$\textit{Buyback Value} = PV_{\textit{Remaining PMTs}} + PV_{\textit{Residual}}$$

$$= 230.00\left[\frac{1-(1+0.0025)^{-12}}{0.0025}\right](1+0.0025) + 10{,}000.00(1+0.0025)^{-12}$$

$$= 2722.457554\ldots + 9704.818654\ldots$$

$$= 12{,}427.27621\ldots = \$12{,}427.28$$

Therefore, in the lease option, the buyback value of the vehicle at the end of three years will be $12,427.28.

10.4 | Exercises

Answers to the odd-numbered problems are available at the end of the textbook.

1. Calculate the future value of each of the following simple annuities due:

	Periodic Payment	Payment Period	Term of Annuity	Interest Rate	Compounding Frequency
a.	$4750	Every year	9 years	5%	Annually
b.	$1500	Every 6 months	12.5 years	4.75%	Semi-annually
c.	$675	Every 3 months	7 years and 3 months	4.25%	Quarterly
d.	$300	Every month	5 years 2 months	3.6%	Monthly

2. Calculate the future value of each of the following simple annuities due:

	Periodic Payment	Payment Period	Term of Annuity	Interest Rate	Compounding Frequency
a.	$4500	Every year	16 years	4.8%	Annually
b.	$2225	Every 6 months	12 years and 6 months	4%	Semi-annually
c.	$1100	Every 3 months	11 years and 3 months	3.75%	Quarterly
d.	$850	Every month	4 years 7 months	3.9%	Monthly

3. Calculate the present value of each of the simple annuities due in Problem 1.

4. Calculate the present value of each of the simple annuities due in Problem 2.

5. What is the accumulated value of periodic deposits of $3000 at the beginning of every six months for four years if the interest rate is 6% compounded semi-annually?

6. Sean contributes $200 at the beginning of every month into an account that earns 7.25% compounded monthly. What is the accumulated value of the fund after ten years of contributions?

7. From the day Donald was born, his grandmother saved $150 every month for 15 years in an account at 3.5% compounded monthly. On his 15th birthday, she did not make a deposit into this account.
   a. How much did he have in this account on his 15th birthday?
   b. What was the total investment?
   c. What was the interest earned?

8. Rodney plans to retire on his 50th birthday and has saved $10,000 every year since his 30th birthday in a fund that earns 4.5% compounded annually. He did not make an investment on his 50th birthday.
   a. How much did he have in this account on his 50th birthday?
   b. What was the total investment?
   c. What was the interest earned?

9. Amanda deposits $1500 into her retirement fund at the beginning of every month for ten years. If the fund had an initial balance of $50,000 before her first deposit was made, what will be the accumulated value of the fund at the end of the time period if it was earning 6.15% compounded monthly?

10. Solomon has accumulated $12,500 in his savings account. In addition, he plans to deposit $500 at the beginning of every six months into the account for three years. If the account earns 3.9% compounded semi-annually, what will be the balance after three years?

11. Jonathan made contributions of $200 at the beginning of each month to an RRSP for ten years. It earned 5% compounded monthly for the first five years and 6% compounded monthly for the next five years. Calculate (a) the accumulated value of her investment and (b) the interest earned.

12. Karen invested $1850 at the beginning of every 3 months in an RRSP for 20 years. For the first 9 years it earned 6% compounded quarterly and for the next 11 years it earned 6.75% compounded quarterly. Calculate (a) the accumulated value of her investment and (b) the interest earned.

13. Anette made deposits of $2000 at the beginning of every six months for seven years in an investment fund that was earning 7.25% compounded semi-annually. She then left the money in the fund for another three years to accumulate interest. If the fund was earning the same interest rate during the entire time period, what is the amount of interest earned on her investment during the term?

14. Judy saved $150 at the beginning of every month in a savings account for ten years. After this period, she stopped making periodic deposits and left the accumulated amount to grow for another four years. How much interest did she earn if the interest rate on the account was 3.55% compounded monthly?

15. How much should Kyle invest today at 4% compounded monthly in order to pay his son's rent of $500 at the beginning of each month for the next four years?

16. Tom wants to make 6 payments of $2250 at the beginning of every six months from his account. What amount must he have in this account if it is earning 3% compounded semi-annually?

17. Ruba saved $1200 of her salary at the beginning of every month in an RRSP earning 3.5% compounded monthly for 30 years. How much more would she have saved if she had put this amount in an RRSP that was earning 4.5% compounded monthly?

18. Calvin invested $3000 at the beginning of every three months in a savings account at 6% compounded quarterly for 9 years and 9 months. How much more would he have earned if he had invested it in a mutual fund that was growing at 6.5% compounded quarterly?

CFA Prep.

19. What is the maximum an investor should be willing to pay for an annuity that will pay $10,000 at the beginning of each year for the next ten years, given that the investor wants to earn 5.75% compounded annually?

20. What is the purchase price of an annuity that will provide payments of $100 at the beginning of every month for 3 years and 6 months? The annuity has an interest rate of 5.75% compounded monthly.

21. Mala can purchase a vehicle for $16,000. Alternatively, she can pay $1500 as a down payment to lease the vehicle, and pay $250 at the beginning of every month for three years. The vehicle has a residual value of $8000. Assume that the cost of borrowing is 6.75% compounded monthly.

    a. Which option is economically better for Mala?

    b. In the lease option, what will be the buyback value of the vehicle at the end of two years?

22. Rita can purchase a new car for $30,000. Alternatively, in addition to a down payment of $1000, Rita can make lease payments of $500 at the beginning of each month for three years to lease the car. The car has a residual value of $15,000. Assume that the cost of borrowing is 4.25% compounded monthly.

    a. Which option is economically better for Rita?

    b. In the lease option, what will be the buyback value of the vehicle at the end of two years?

• 23. Calculate the accumulated value and the amount of interest earned by deposits made by an investor for eight years at 7.3% compounded semi-annually. The investor deposited $2500 at the beginning of every six months for three years, followed by $3000 at the beginning of every six months for the next five years.

• 24. Samuel deposited $750 at the beginning of every six months into an investment fund for the first two years followed by $1000 at the beginning of every six months for the next three years. Calculate the accumulated value and the amount of interest earned at the end of five years if the fund earned 5% compounded semi-annually.

• 25. Thomas converted his RRSP into an RRIF that earns 3.85% compounded monthly. It will pay $1500 at the beginning of every month for three years followed by $2000 at the beginning of every month for the next five years. What was the value of the RRIF?

• 26. Josephine is considering purchasing an annuity with a rate of return of 6% compounded semi-annually. If the annuity will pay 20 equal payments of $1000 at the beginning of every six months, followed by another 20 equal payments of $1500 at the beginning of every six months, how much should she pay for the annuity?

• 27. Estelle leases a car worth $24,000 at 2.99% compounded monthly. She agrees to make 36 lease payments of $330 each at the beginning of every month. What is the residual value of the car at the end of the lease? What is the buyback value of the car at the end of two years?

• 28. Valcina agrees to make 48 lease payments of $450 each at the beginning of every month for a $28,000 car. If the rate charged was 4.75% compounded monthly, what is the residual value of the car at the end of the lease? What is the buyback value of the car at the end of three years?

10.5 | Future Value and Present Value of a General Annuity Due

In a general annuity due, payments are made at the beginning of each payment period, and the compounding period is not equal to the payment period. In this section, you will learn how to calculate the future value and present value of a general annuity due.

Similar to the ordinary general annuities, we first need to calculate the equivalent periodic interest rate per payment period (i_2) using Formulas 10.3(a) and 10.3(b):

$$c = \frac{\textit{Number of compounding periods per year}}{\textit{Number of payments per year}}$$

$$i_2 = (1 + i)^c - 1$$

Then, substituting the value of 'i_2' for 'i' in the simple annuity due Formula 10.4(a) and Formula 10.4(b), we solve for 'FV_{Due}' and 'PV_{Due}' as follows:

$$FV_{Due} = PMT\left[\frac{(1+i_2)^n - 1}{i_2}\right](1+i_2) \quad \text{and} \quad PV_{Due} = PMT\left[\frac{1-(1+i_2)^{-n}}{i_2}\right](1+i_2)$$

Note: *In using the Texas Instruments BA II Plus calculator for annuity due calculations, set the calculator to beginning of period calculations ('BGN' mode) as described in Section 10.2.*

Example 10.5(a) **Calculating the Future Value, Amount Invested, and Total Interest of a General Annuity Due**

Tao invested $5000 in a fund at the beginning of every three months for five years. The fund was earning 5% compounded monthly.

(i) What was the total amount invested?

(ii) What was the accumulated value of the investment?

(iii) What was the interest earned over the period?

Solution

Page 454

This is a general annuity due as:

- Payments are made at the beginning of each payment period (quarterly)
- Compounding period (monthly) ≠ payment period (quarterly)

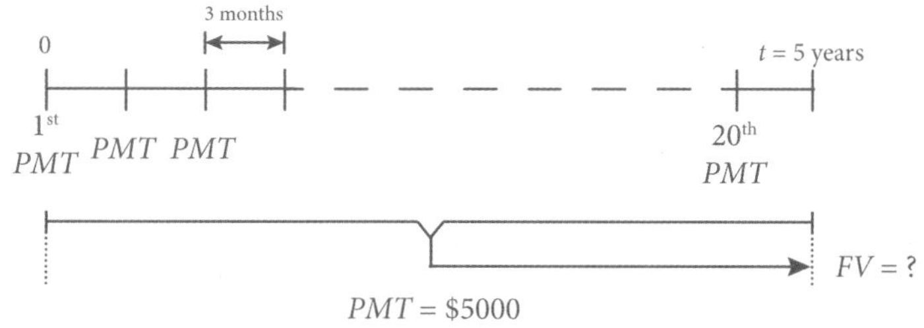

n = 4 payments/year × 5 years = 20 quarterly payments

$$j = 0.05, \quad m = 12, \quad i = \frac{j}{m} = 0.004166... \text{ per month}$$

(i) The total amount invested in the fund = $n(PMT)$ = 20 × 5000.00 = $100,000.00

(ii) *Calculating the accumulated value of the investment*

$$c = \frac{\textit{Number of compounding periods per year}}{\textit{Number of payments per year}} = \frac{12}{4}$$

$$i_2 = (1+i)^c - 1 = (1+0.004166...)^{(12/4)} - 1 = 0.012552... \text{ per quarter}$$

Using Formula 10.4(a) and substituting i_2 for i,

$$FV_{Due} = PMT\left[\frac{(1+i_2)^n - 1}{i_2}\right](1+i_2)$$

$$= 5000.00\left[\frac{(1+0.012552...)^{20} - 1}{0.012552...}\right](1+0.012552...)$$

$$= 5000.00\,[22.574503...]\,(1.012552...)$$

$$= 114{,}289.3094... = \$114{,}289.31$$

Therefore, the accumulated value of his investment would be $114,289.31.

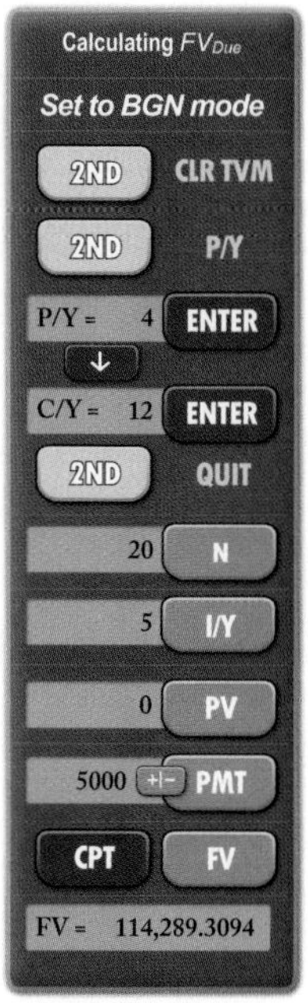

(iii) The interest earned over the period = $FV_{Due} - n(PMT)$

= 114,289.31 – 100,000.00 = $14,289.31

Therefore, the interest earned over the period is $14,289.31.

Example 10.5(b)

Calculating the Present Value of a General Annuity Due

Alexandria inherited money that was invested in an account which provided her with $4500 at the beginning of every month for 30 years. If the interest rate on the savings account was 4% compounded semi-annually, what was the amount of the inheritance? Round your answer to the nearest hundred dollars.

Page 454

Solution

This is a general annuity due as:

- Payments are made at the beginning of each payment period (monthly)
- Compounding period (semi-annually) ≠ payment period (monthly)

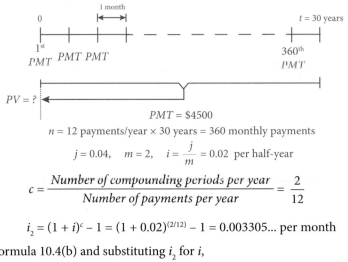

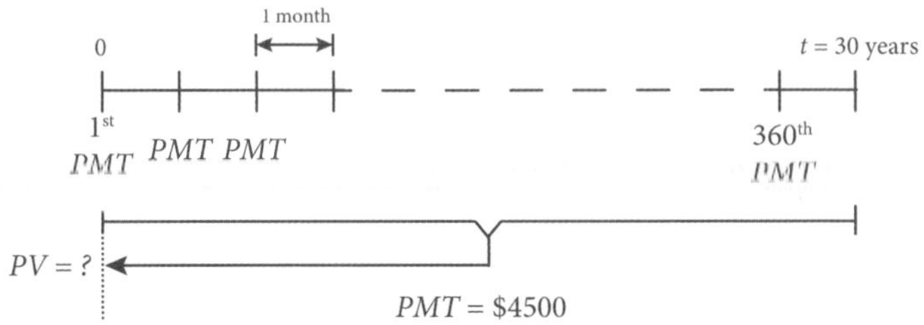

$PMT = \$4500$

$n = 12$ payments/year × 30 years = 360 monthly payments

$j = 0.04, \quad m = 2, \quad i = \frac{j}{m} = 0.02$ per half-year

$$c = \frac{\textit{Number of compounding periods per year}}{\textit{Number of payments per year}} = \frac{2}{12}$$

$$i_2 = (1 + i)^c - 1 = (1 + 0.02)^{(2/12)} - 1 = 0.003305... \text{ per month}$$

Using Formula 10.4(b) and substituting i_2 for i,

$$PV_{Due} = PMT\left[\frac{1 - (1 + i_2)^{-n}}{i_2}\right](1 + i_2)$$

$$= 4500.00\left[\frac{1 - (1 + 0.003305...)^{-360}}{0.003305...}\right](1 + 0.003305...)$$

$$= 4500.00\,[210.296672...](1.003305...)$$

$$= 949{,}463.5042... = \$949{,}463.50$$

Therefore, she inherited $949,500.00 (rounded to the nearest $100).

Example 10.5(c)

Comparing RRSP Contribution Plans

Ariana contributed $100 from her paycheque at the beginning of every month from age 18 to 65 into an RRSP account (no contribution in the month of her 65th birthday). Macy contributed $4000 at the beginning of every year from age 35 to 55 into a similar RRSP account, then left the money in the fund to accumulate for another 10 years (no contribution in the year of her 55th birthday). Money earned 4.8% compounded daily in both RRSP accounts.

(i) Who had a greater accumulated value, and by how much, when they retired at age 65?

(ii) Calculate how much interest both Ariana and Macy earned in their RRSP accounts, respectively.

Page 454

Solution

(i) *Calculating Ariana's accumulated value*

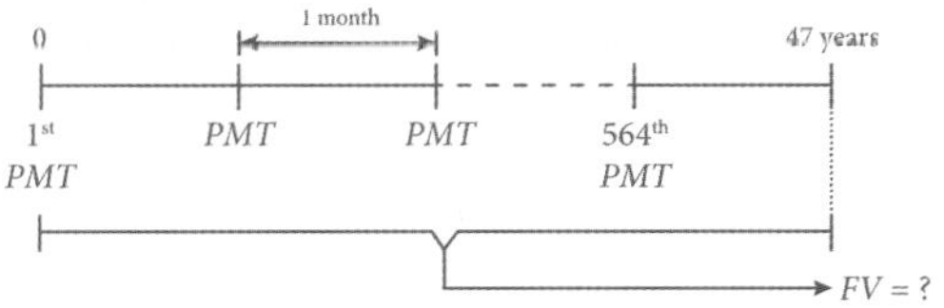

$PMT = \$100$

$n = 12$ payments/year × 47 years = 564 monthly payments

$j = 0.048, \quad m = 365, \quad i = \frac{j}{m} = 0.000131...$ per day

$$c = \frac{\text{Number of compounding periods per year}}{\text{Number of payments per year}}$$

$$= \frac{365}{12}$$

$$i_2 = (1 + i)^c - 1 = (1 + 0.000131...)^{(365/12)} - 1$$

$$= 0.004007...$$

Using Formula 10.4(a) and substituting i_2 for i,

$$FV_{Due} = PMT\left[\frac{(1 + i_2)^n - 1}{i_2}\right](1 + i_2)$$

$$= 100.00\left[\frac{(1 + 0.004007...)^{564} - 1}{0.004007...}\right](1 + 0.004007...)$$

$$= 100.00[2131.725999...](1.004007...)$$

$$= 214{,}026.9424... = \$214{,}026.94$$

Calculating Macy's accumulated value

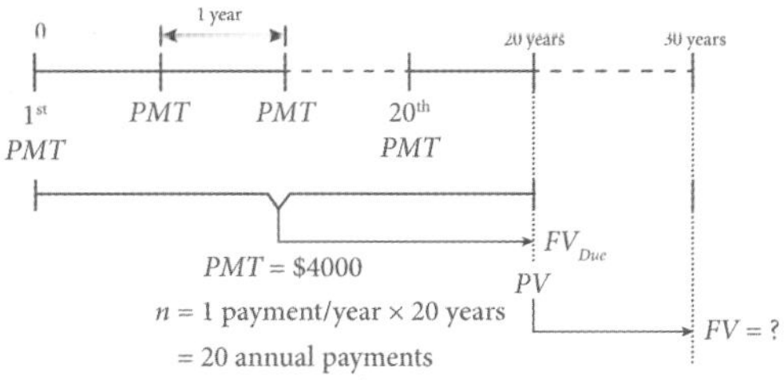

$PMT = \$4000$

$n = 1$ payment/year × 20 years = 20 annual payments

$j = 0.048, \quad m = 365, \quad i = \frac{j}{m} = 0.000131...$ per day

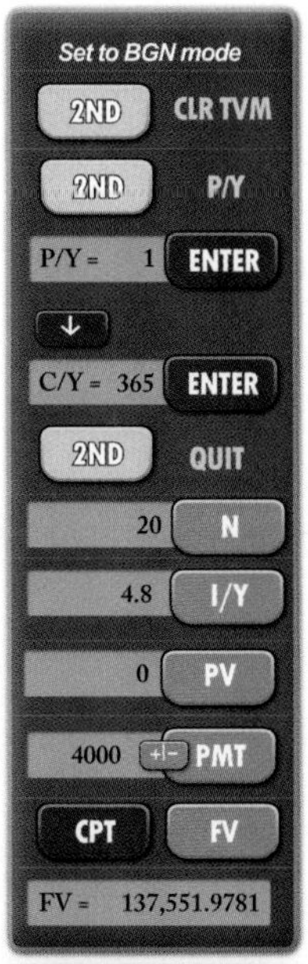

$$c = \frac{\text{Number of compounding periods per year}}{\text{Number of payments per year}}$$

$$= \frac{365}{1}$$

$$i_2 = (1 + i)^c - 1 = (1 + 0.000131...)^{365} - 1$$

$$= 0.049167...$$

Using Formula 10.4(a) and substituting i_2 for i,

$$FV_{Due} = PMT\left[\frac{(1 + i_2)^n - 1}{i_2}\right](1 + i_2)$$

$$= 4000.00\left[\frac{(1 + 0.049167...)^{20} - 1}{0.049167...}\right](1 + 0.049167...)$$

$$= 4000.00[32.776462...](1.049167...)$$

$$= \$137{,}551.9781...$$

Using Formula 9.1(a),

$$FV = PV(1 + i)^n$$

$$= 137{,}551.9781...(1 + 0.000131...)^{(365 \times 10)}$$

$$= 222{,}287.2155... = \$222{,}287.22$$

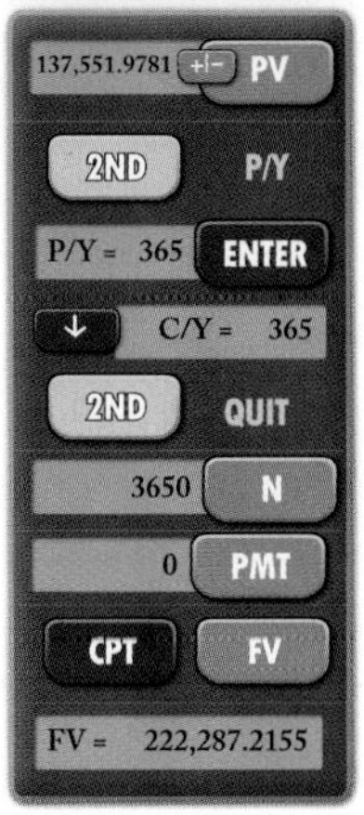

Therefore, when they retired at age 65, Macy's RRSP had a greater accumulated value, by 222,287.22 – 214,026.94 = \$8260.28.

(ii) Ariana's Interest Earned $= FV_{Due} - n(PMT)$

$$= 214{,}026.94 - 564(100.00) = \$157{,}626.94$$

Macy's Interest Earned $= FV_{Due} - n(PMT)$

$$= 222{,}287.22 - 20(4000.00) = \$142{,}287.22$$

Therefore, even though Macy's RRSP had a greater accumulated value, Ariana earned 157,626.94 – 142,287.22 = \$15,339.72 more interest.

In Example 10.5(c), we saw that even though Ariana contributed less total money to her RRSP than Macy, she earned more interest by retirement than Macy did. This important concept is further explored in the following illustration.

Planning Ahead

Comparing RRSP Contribution Plans

You are considering two RRSP investment plans for your retirement:

Plan 1: Contribute $150 at the end of every month for 10 years, starting at age 20.

Plan 2: Contribute $150 at the end of every month for 35 years, starting at age 30.

Which plan will result in a higher return at the time of your retirement at age 65?

On first glance, it may look like Plan 2 will result in a higher return at the time of your retirement as you are making investments for 35 years, as compared to Plan 1 where the investments are only made for 10 years. However, due to the time value of money, the illustration below shows that when making regular contributions to a savings account, such as an RRSP, starting your contributions early will dramatically affect the accumulated value over time.

For this illustration, we assume that the RRSP earns 8% compounded annually.

CONTRIBUTION PLAN 1		
Age	Total Investments ($)	Accumulated Value (nearest $)
20	1800	1,865
21	1800	3,879
22	1800	6,055
23	1800	8,404
24	1800	10,942
25	1800	13,682
26	1800	16,642
27	1800	19,838
28	1800	23,290
29	1800	27,019
30	-	29,180
31	-	31,515
32	-	34,036
33	-	36,759
34	-	39,699
35	-	42,875
36	-	46,305
37	-	50,010
38	-	54,010
39	-	58,331
40	-	62,998
↓	↓	↓
60	-	293,630
61	-	317,120
62	-	342,490
63	-	369,889
64	-	**$399,480**
TOTAL	**$18,000**	-

10 years of monthly PMTs of $150

Total Interest Earned: 399,480 – 18,000 = $381,480

CONTRIBUTION PLAN 2		
Age	Total Investments ($)	Accumulated Value (nearest $)
20	-	-
21	-	-
22	-	-
23	-	-
24	-	-
25	-	-
26	-	-
27	-	-
28	-	-
29	-	-
30	1800	1,865
31	1800	3,879
32	1800	6,055
33	1800	8,404
34	1800	10,942
35	1800	13,682
36	1800	16,642
37	1800	19,838
38	1800	23,290
39	1800	27,019
40	1800	31,045
↓	↓	↓
60	1800	230,050
61	1800	250,319
62	1800	272,210
63	1800	295,852
64	1800	**$321,385**
TOTAL	**$63,000**	-

35 years of monthly PMTs of $150

Total Interest Earned: 321,385 – 63,000 = $258,385

The above illustration shows that a periodic investment of $150 per month for 10 years starting at age 20 results in a higher accumulated value on retirement than a periodic investment of $150 per month for 35 years starting at age 30.

10.5 | Exercises

Answers to the odd-numbered problems are available at the end of the textbook.

1. Calculate the future value of the following general annuities due:

	Periodic Payment	Payment Period	Term of Annuity	Interest Rate	Compounding Frequency
a.	$3750	Every year	16 years	4.80%	Monthly
b.	$1950	Every 6 months	12.5 years	4.00%	Quarterly
c.	$1500	Every 3 months	9 years and 9 months	3.75%	Daily
d.	$1200	Every month	6 years 7 months	3.90%	Semi annually

2. Calculate the future value of the following general annuities due:

	Periodic Payment	Payment Period	Term of Annuity	Interest Rate	Compounding Frequency
a.	$3600	Every year	6 years	4.50%	Daily
b.	$1250	Every 6 months	9.5 years	5.10%	Quarterly
c.	$2750	Every 3 months	5 years and 9 months	4.60%	Monthly
d.	$1950	Every month	12 years 8 months	6.00%	Semi-annually

3. Calculate the present value of each of the general annuities due in Problem 1.

4. Calculate the present value of each of the general annuities due in Problem 2.

5. Deposits of $2500 are made into a fund at the beginning of every three months for 2 years and 9 months. What would be the accumulated value if the fund was earning 2.85% compounded monthly?

CFA Prep.

6. As part of his New Year's resolution, Clive committed to save $500 per month in a mutual fund account. He deposited the money at the beginning of every month and projected that he would earn 8.5% compounded annually on the funds. At the end of 12 months, how much did Clive accumulate?

7. At the beginning of every 3 months, $450 is deposited into a savings account for 15 years. The money remained in the account for another 5 years and earned an average of 3.45% compounded monthly during the 20-year period. Calculate the accumulated amount and the interest earned in the account.

8. A grandmother opened a savings account for her granddaughter on the day she was born and deposited $1000. Each year on her birthday, she deposited $1000 until her granddaughter's 16th birthday (she did not make a deposit on the 16th birthday). If the account earned 4.38% compounded daily, how much was in the account on her granddaughter's 21st birthday and what was the interest earned?

9. What is the value of a lease contract if it requires you to make lease payments of $450 at the beginning of each month for five years? Assume an interest rate of 6% compounded semi-annually.

10. Tom converts his RRSP that was earning 5.5% compounded daily into an RRIF. What was in his RRSP that will enable him to receive $3000 at the beginning of every month for ten years?

11. Marlin secured a lease amount on a machine by paying $4500 as a down payment and lease payments of $750 at the beginning of every month for a period of five years. At the end of five years, he would have to pay $5000 to own the machine. If money is worth 5.55% compounded quarterly, calculate the lease amount of the machine.

12. Nina leased a car for four years by making a down payment of $1500 and lease payments of $180 at the beginning of every month for four years. She could own the car by paying $4000 at the end of the lease. If money is worth 4% compounded daily, calculate the lease amount of the car.

13. Lydia deposited $10,000 into a savings account at the beginning of every year for ten years. The account was growing at 3% compounded monthly. After the ten-year period, she left the accumulated money in the account to grow for another year.
    a. What was the balance in the account at the end of 11 years?
    b. What was the total interest earned?

14. Chase has been contributing $1500 into a retirement fund at the beginning of each quarter for the past 15 years. He decided to stop making payments and to allow his investment to grow for another 5 years. If money can earn 8% compounded monthly, how much interest would he have earned over the 20-year period?

15. Alan's retirement fund currently has a balance of $40,000. He decides to deposit $400 into this fund at the beginning of every month starting from today for the next 15 years. Calculate the accumulated value of the fund and the amount of interest earned if the fund earns 4.25% compounded quarterly.

16. Margie deposits $25,000 into a savings account yielding 3.5% compounded semi-annually. In addition, she plans to deposit $1000 at the beginning of every three months for ten years into this account. Determine the total amount she will have at the end of ten years and the interest earned.

17. A contract requires lease payments of $400 at the beginning of every month for ten years.
    a. What is the value of the contract if the cost of borrowing is 4.5% compounded annually?
    b. What is the value of the contract if the cost of borrowing is 4.5% compounded daily?

18. Soong decided to retire in Canada and wants to receive a retirement income of $4000 at the beginning of every month for 15 years from her savings. If a bank in Vancouver is offering her an interest rate of 5% compounded annually, how much would she have to invest to receive her planned retirement income? What is the financial benefit for her to invest in a bank in Niagara Falls if they are offering her an interest rate of 5% compounded quarterly?

19. How much less will the value of an RRSP account be at the end of ten years if you contribute $200 at the beginning of every month instead of $2400 at the beginning of every year? Assume the account earns an interest rate of 5.2% compounded semi-annually in both cases.

20. Nathan deposited $500 at the beginning of each month into a fund. His wife deposited $1500 at the beginning of every three months into a similar fund. If they continue these deposits, which fund will have a larger balance at the end of 15 years? Both funds earn 6.2% compounded semi-annually.

21. How much should Main Corp. pay for an annuity that would give it $20,000 at the beginning of every year for the first five years and $30,000 at the beginning of every year for the next three years, if the interest rate is 7% compounded monthly throughout the term?

22. What is the purchase price of an annuity that provides beginning-of-month payments of $400 for the first three years and $600 for the next two years? Assume that the interest rate is 4% compounded daily throughout the time period.

23. The monthly rent on an apartment is $1750 per month, payable at the beginning of each month. What single payment in advance on the first day of rental would be equal to three years' rent? Assume an interest rate of 4.38% compounded daily.

24. Machinery can be leased for your manufacturing plant with a payment of $4500 at the beginning of every three months. What single payment in advance on the first day of the lease would be equal to four years of lease payments? Assume an interest rate of 4.4% compounded monthly.

25. Jasmine, an office administrator, was evaluating the following quotation that she received for the purchase of a printing machine for her company:

    Lease Option: Make a down payment of $1000, and lease payments of $750 at the beginning of every month for two years. At the end of two years, pay $3000 to own the printer.

    Purchase Option: Make a payment of $20,500 immediately.

    The cost of borrowing is 6% compounded semi-annually.
    a. Which option is economically better for the company?
    b. In the lease option, what will be the buyback value of the printer at the end of one year?

26. Madison can purchase a sports car for \$68,000, or she can lease it for four years with a down payment of \$3500 and payments of \$1200 at the beginning of every month followed by a \$20,000 payout at the end of the lease in order to own it. The cost of borrowing money is 7% compounded daily.
    a. Which option is economically better for her?
    b. In the lease option, what will be the buyback value of the sports car at the end of three years?

• 27. Ryder invested \$1000 at the beginning of every three months into his RRSP account from age 35 to 45 and left the money to grow until his retirement at the age of 65. Bill invested \$1000 at the beginning of every three months into a similar RRSP account from age 45 until his retirement at the age of 65. Assuming money earns 5.8% compounded annually in both RRSP accounts, calculate who had the greater accumulated value, and by how much, when they retired.

• 28. Chan made deposits of \$250 into a fund at the beginning of every month from age 40 to 48. He left the money to accumulate in the fund until he reached the age of 60. David made deposits of \$250 at the beginning of every month into an RRSP from age 48 until he reached the age of 60. Assuming money earns 6.25% compounded semi-annually in both cases, calculate who had the greater accumulated value, and by how much, when they reached 60 years of age.

• 29. A lottery winner is offered a choice of either receiving \$20,500 at the beginning of every year for ten years or receiving \$18,000 at the beginning of every six months for five years. If the interest rate is 4.4% compounded quarterly, which choice is economically better (in current value), and by what amount?

• 30. You have a choice of either receiving \$15,000 at the beginning of every year for ten years or receiving \$2250 at the beginning of every month for five years. If the interest rate is 4.8% compounded semi-annually, which choice is economically better (in current value), and by what amount?

10.6 | Calculating Periodic Payment (PMT)

If the future value of an annuity, 'FV', the periodic interest rate, 'i', and the number of payment periods, 'n', are known, we can use the future value formula to solve for the unknown 'PMT'.

Similarly, if the present value of an annuity, 'PV', the periodic interest rate, 'i', and the number of payment periods, 'n', are known, we can use the present value formula to solve for the unknown 'PMT'.

Example 10.6(a) Calculating the Periodic Payment of an Ordinary Simple Annuity, Given Present Value

Rodney received a \$35,000 home improvement loan from his bank at an interest rate of 6% compounded monthly.

(i) How much would he need to pay every month to settle the loan in ten years?

(ii) What was the amount of interest charged?

Solution

Page 454

This is an ordinary simple annuity as:

- Payments are made at the end of each payment period (monthly)
- Compounding period (monthly) = payment period (monthly)

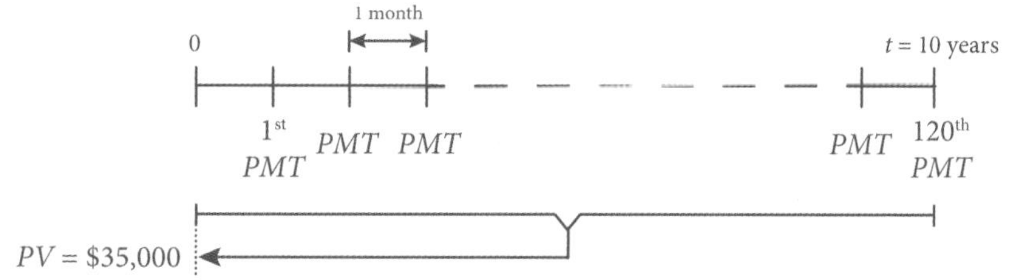

$PMT = ?$

n = 12 payments/year × 10 years = 120 monthly payments

$j = 0.06, \quad m = 12, \quad i = \frac{j}{m} = 0.005$ per month

Solution *continued*

(i) Using Formula 10.2(b),

$$PV = PMT\left[\frac{1-(1+i)^{-n}}{i}\right]$$

$$35{,}000.00 = PMT\left[\frac{1-(1+0.005)^{-120}}{0.005}\right] \quad \text{Solving for 'PMT',}$$

$$PMT = \frac{35{,}000.00}{\left[\frac{1-(1+0.005)^{-120}}{0.005}\right]} = \frac{35{,}000.00}{[90.073453...]}$$

$$= 388.571756... = \$388.57$$

Therefore, he would need to pay \$388.57 every month to settle the loan in ten years.

(ii) $Interest\ Charged = n(PMT) - PV$

$$= 120(388.57) - 35{,}000.00$$

$$= \$11{,}628.40$$

Therefore, the amount of interest charged during the period of the loan would be \$11,628.40.

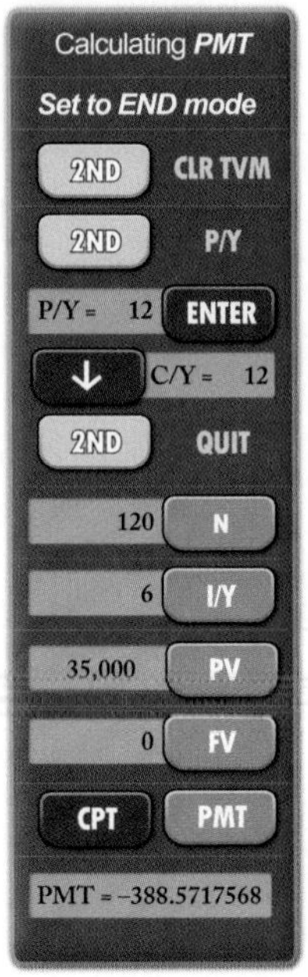

Example 10.6(b) **Calculating the Periodic Payment of an Ordinary General Annuity, Given Future Value**

What quarterly payments should Ben make in order to save \$60,000 in ten years if money can earn 8% compounded semi-annually?

Solution

Page 454

This is an ordinary general annuity as:

- Payments are made at the end of each payment period (quarterly)
- Compounding period (semi-annually) ≠ payment period (quarterly)

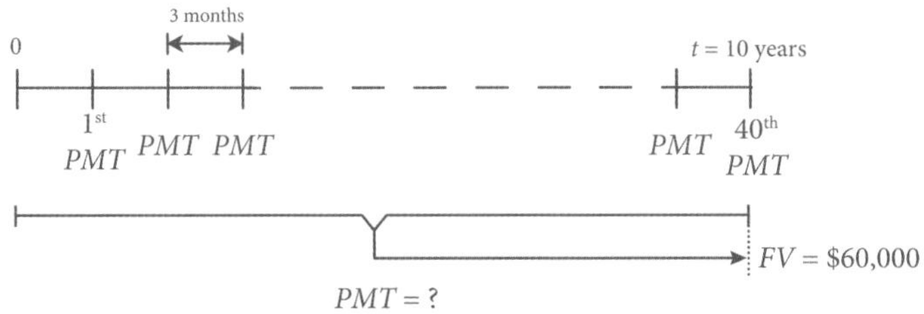

n = 4 payments/year × 10 years = 40 quarterly payments

$$j = 0.08, \quad m = 2, \quad i = \frac{j}{m} = 0.04 \text{ per half-year}$$

$$c = \frac{\textit{Number of compounding periods per year}}{\textit{Number of payments per year}} = \frac{2}{4}$$

$$i_2 = (1+i)^c - 1 = (1+0.04)^{(2/4)} - 1 = 0.019803\ldots \text{ per quarter}$$

Using Formula 10.2(a), and substituting i_2 for i,

$$FV = PMT\left[\frac{(1+i_2)^n - 1}{i_2}\right]$$

$$60{,}000.00 = PMT\left[\frac{(1+0.019803...)^{40} - 1}{0.019803...}\right] \quad \text{Solving for } PMT,$$

$$PMT = \frac{60{,}000.00}{\left[\frac{(1+0.019803...)^{40} - 1}{0.019803...}\right]} = \frac{60{,}000.00}{[60.145879...]}$$

$$= 997.574574... = \$997.57$$

Therefore, Ben should pay quarterly payments of \$997.57.

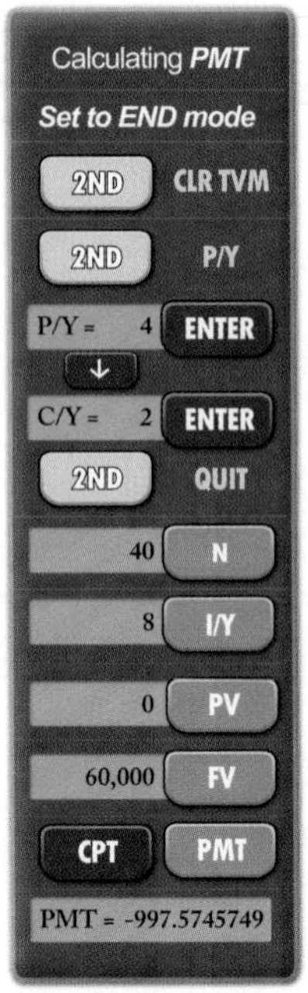

Example 10.6(c) **Calculating the Periodic Payment of a General Annuity Due, Given Present Value**

An amount of $10,000 is deposited into an account earning 4% compounded annually. What is the largest withdrawal that can be made at the beginning of each month from this account for the next five years?

age 455

Solution

This is a general annuity due as:

- Withdrawals are made at the beginning of each payment period (monthly)
- Compounding period (annually) ≠ payment period (monthly)

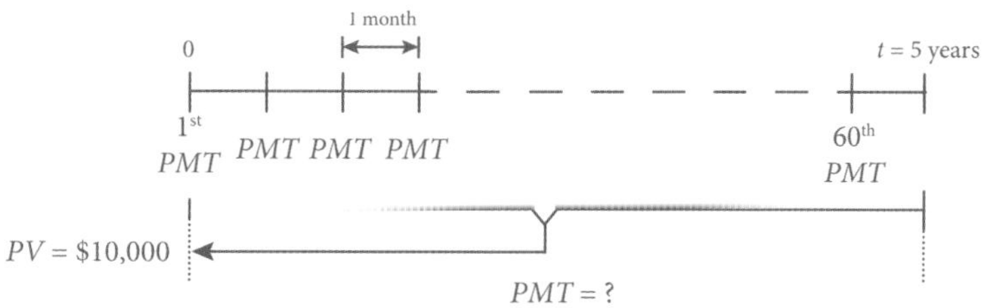

$PMT = ?$

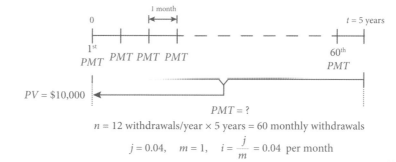

$n = 12$ withdrawals/year × 5 years = 60 monthly withdrawals

$j = 0.04, \quad m = 1, \quad i = \frac{j}{m} = 0.04$ per month

$$c = \frac{\textit{Number of compounding periods per year}}{\textit{Number of payments per year}} = \frac{1}{12}$$

$$i_2 = (1+i)^c - 1 = (1+0.04)^{(1/12)} - 1 = 0.003273\ldots \text{ per month}$$

While using the financial calculator for annuity due calculations, set the calculator to the beginning of period calculations ('BGN' mode) as described in Section 10.2.

Using Formula 10.4(b) and substituting i_2 for i,

$$PV_{Due} = PMT\left[\frac{1-(1+i_2)^{-n}}{i_2}\right](1+i_2)$$

$$10{,}000.00 = PMT\left[\frac{1-(1+0.003273\ldots)^{-60}}{0.003273\ldots}\right](1+0.003273\ldots) \quad \text{Solving for } PMT,$$

$$PMT = \frac{10{,}000.00}{\left[\frac{1-(1+0.003273\ldots)^{-60}}{0.003273\ldots}\right](1+0.003273\ldots)} = \frac{10{,}000.00}{[54.394333\ldots](1.003273\ldots)}$$

$$= 183.242790\ldots = \$183.24$$

Therefore, the largest withdrawal which could be made is $183.24.

Example 10.6(d) **Calculating a Periodic Lease Payment**

A car with a manufacturer's suggested retail price (MSRP) of $38,000 is estimated to have a residual value of $15,960 in four years. If the car is leased for four years at the MSRP, with a down payment of 10%, what is the size of each of the beginning-of-month lease payments? Assume an interest rate of 3.6% compounded monthly.

ge 455

Solution

The lease payments form a simple annuity due as:

- Payments are made at the beginning of each payment period (monthly)
- Compounding period (monthly) = payment period (monthly)

$\textit{Down Payment} = 38{,}000.00 \times 0.10 = \$3800.00$

Solution
continued

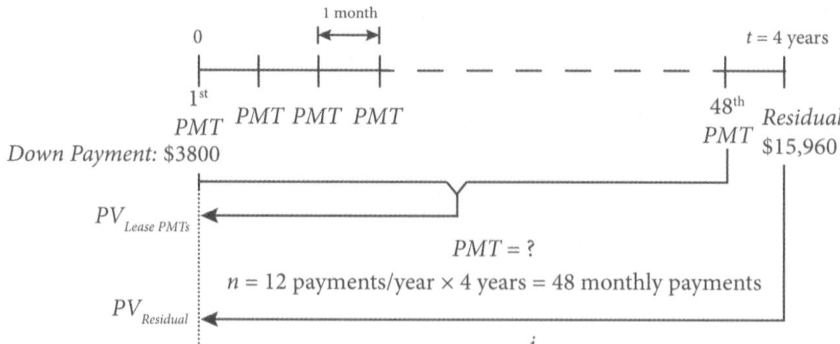

$j = 0.036, \quad m = 12, \quad i = \frac{j}{m} = 0.003$ per month

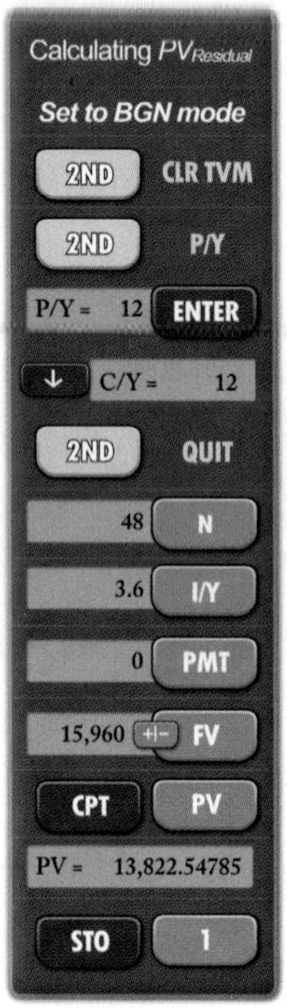

Using Formula 9.1(b), $PV = FV(1 + i)^{-n}$

$$PV_{Residual} = 15{,}960.00(1 + 0.003)^{-48}$$

$$= 15{,}960.00(0.866074...)$$

$$= \$13{,}822.54785...$$

$$Lease\ Amount = Down\ Payment + PV_{Lease\ PMTs} + PV_{Residual}$$

Therefore, $PV_{Lease\ PMTs} = Lease\ Amount - Down\ Payment - PV_{Residual}$

$$= 38{,}000.00 - 3800.00 - 13{,}822.54785...$$

$$= \$20{,}377.45215...$$

Substituting this value for PV_{Due} in Formula 10.4(b),

$$PV_{Due} = PMT\left[\frac{1 - (1 + i)^{-n}}{i}\right](1 + i)$$

$$20{,}377.45215... = PMT\left[\frac{1 - (1 + 0.003)^{-48}}{0.003}\right](1 + 0.003)$$

Solving for PMT,

$$PMT = \frac{20{,}377.45215...}{\left[\frac{1 - (1 + 0.003)^{-48}}{0.003}\right](1 + 0.003)} = \frac{20{,}377.45215...}{[44.641857...](1.003)}$$

$$PMT = 455.099847... = \$455.10$$

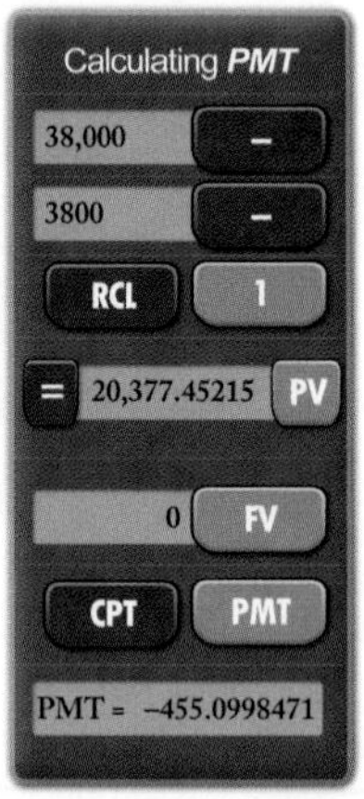

Therefore, the size of each of the beginning-of-month lease payments is \$455.10.

10.6 | Exercises

Answers to the odd-numbered problems are available at the end of the textbook.

1. An investment fund growing at 9% compounded monthly has an accumulated value of \$50,000. The fund has been receiving equal payments at the end of each month for the past two years. Calculate the size of the payment.

CFA Prep.
2. At an expected rate of return of 7% compounded annually, how much must be deposited at the end of each year for the next 15 years to accumulate \$300,000?

CFA Prep.
3. If you are considering applying for a \$2000 loan that will be repaid with equal end-of-year payments over the next 13 years, what will be the size of the payment? Assume that the interest rate for the loan is 6% compounded annually.

4. Jordan purchased a car for \$30,000. He paid 10% of the cost as a down payment and financed the balance amount at 7% compounded monthly for five years. What is the size of the payment made at the end of each month to settle the loan?

5. What is the size of the periodic payment made at the end of every month into a fund that is growing at 4.5% compounded daily, if the accumulated value at the end of five years is \$420,000?

6. An investment fund grew to $30,000 after month-end payments for ten years. If the fund was earning 5% compounded semi-annually throughout the time period, what was the size of these payments?

7. Marcia sold her $2 million business and invested the money in a fund that will allow her to withdraw regular monthly payments for 20 years. If the fund is earning 4% compounded annually, how much will she be able to withdraw at the end of every month?

8. Cyrus purchased a networking system for his office for $20,000 using a five-year loan at 6.5% compounded daily. If the first payment was made a month from when he purchased the system, what is the size of the monthly payment?

9. Metal Equipment Co. has an investment fund that has accumulated $180,500 in three years. If the fund was earning 9% compounded daily, what was the size of the payment that was deposited into this fund at the beginning of each month throughout the term?

10. Martha's retirement fund has an accumulated amount of $45,000. If it has been earning 5% compounded semi-annually, calculate the size of the payment that she deposited at the beginning of each month in this fund for the past 20 years.

11. Chase leased equipment for five years that was valued at $23,000. If the cost of borrowing is 5.75% compounded monthly, calculate the size of the lease payment that is required to be made at the beginning of each month.

12. Vaughan had a $650,000 surplus in property tax collections for 2017 and decided to use the money for a parks renewal project. The city can earn 4% compounded quarterly in an investment fund. How much money can be taken out of the fund at the beginning of each month to sustain the renewal project from the beginning of 2018 until the end of 2022?

13. How much should Tyler save at the beginning of each month in order to have one million dollars in 30 years if money earns 6.5% compounded monthly?

14. What amount saved at the beginning of every six months will accumulate to $100,000 in ten years if money earns 4.2% compounded semi-annually?

15. Quincy made equal deposits at the end of every month for five years into an investment fund. He then left the money in the fund to grow for another four years. If the fund earned 4% compounded monthly for the entire period and the accumulated amount at the end of the term was $100,000, calculate the size of the periodic deposit.

16. Ivan made equal deposits at the end of every three months into a savings account for 12 years. After this period, he stopped making deposits and left the accumulated amount to grow for another five years. What was the size of the periodic deposit if the accumulated amount at the end of the term was $37,450? Assume that the fund was earning 2.85% compounded quarterly for the entire period.

17. You deposited $75,000 into an account paying 3.75% compounded semi-annually so that it will pay you equal payments at the end of every six months over the next four years. What is the size of the semi-annual payment?

18. What periodic payment at the end of each month will settle a student loan of $45,000 in seven years? Assume that the interest rate of the loan is 6.75% compounded monthly.

19. An RESP account earns 4.38% compounded daily. How much must be contributed at the end of each month in order to accumulate $250,000 in 18 years?

20. The interest rate for a five year RRSP is 4.7% compounded monthly. How much must Andrew deposit at the end of every six months in order to accumulate $60,000?

21. A loan of $200,000 is to be repaid by payments at the end of every 3 months over a period of 25 years. If the effective interest rate on the loan is 5%, what is the size of the payment due at the end of every 3 months?

22. A company has borrowed $50,000 from a bank at an effective rate of interest of 7%. Calculate the size of the payment at the end of every six months that will settle the loan in five years.

23. A car worth $26,000 is being leased with a down payment of $1500 and equal payments at the beginning of every month for five years. If the residual value is $11,500 and the interest rate is 5.4% compounded monthly, what is the size of each monthly payment?

24. Joan is leasing a vehicle worth $20,000, with a down payment of $1000 and equal payments at the beginning of every month for three years. What is the size of each lease payment if the cost of borrowing is 6.75% compounded monthly and the residual value is $10,500?

25. Tom has a retirement fund of $500,000. If the fund is earning 3.75% compounded monthly, how much can he withdraw at the beginning of each month for the next 20 years?

26. Zachary accumulated $250,000 in his RRSP and decided to convert it to an RRIF that will earn 5% compounded monthly. What payment can he receive at the beginning of each month for the next 20 years?

27. Brooke plans to accumulate $150,000 in ten years by making deposits at the beginning of every three months into a fund. If the fund is earning 6% compounded semi-annually, what will be the size of each deposit?

28. Carlos accumulated $85,000 in seven years by making regular deposits at the beginning of every month into a fund. If the fund was earning 3.75% compounded quarterly, what was the size of each deposit?

29. The value of a lease contract is $5000. It requires eight equal lease payments to be made at the beginning of every three months. If the cost of borrowing is 2.8% compounded daily, what is the size of the lease payment?

30. Harrison, an insurance salesman, offers an insurance policy that provides a benefit of $45,000 five years from now. Alternatively, he offers 60 equal payments that can be received at the beginning of each month. What is the size of the payment if the interest rate is 3.3% compounded semi-annually?

• 31. Lillian is leasing a new car worth $36,000. She will receive $4500 to use as a down payment for trading in her old car, and her lease is for five years at 3% compounded monthly. The residual value is $13,000.

   a. What is the size of the lease payment at the beginning of every month?

   b. How much lower would the month-beginning payment be if the interest rate was 3% compounded quarterly?

• 32. Wang leased a vehicle worth $27,500 by paying $5000 as a down payment and making lease payments for four years at 6.75% compounded monthly. The residual value is $12,000.

   a. What is the size of the lease payment at the beginning of every month?

   b. How much lower would the month-beginning payment be if the interest rate was 6.75% compounded semi-annually?

• 33. Dominic wants to save equal amounts at the beginning of every six months for the next five years so that he can retire eight years from now. Upon retirement, he will withdraw $25,000 at the end of every six months for ten years. How much must he set aside every six months if interest is 4% compounded semi-annually during the eighteen-year period?

• 34. A father wants to save equal amounts at the beginning of every month for the next 6 years so that his son will be able to withdraw $1500 per month for 4 years for his university education. If the first withdrawal is 11 years from now, how much must the father set aside every month if money earns an average of 4% compounded monthly?

10.7 | Calculating Number of Payments (n) and Time Period (t)

If the periodic payment (PMT), periodic interest rate (i), and either present value (PV) or future value (FV) of an annuity are known, then we can calculate the number of payments, 'n', and the time period, 't', as follows.

Ordinary Annuity

If 'FV' is known, we can calculate the number of payments, 'n', using Formula 10.2(a),

$$FV = PMT\left[\frac{(1+i)^n - 1}{i}\right]$$

Rearranging and isolating 'n' using natural logarithms (ln) results in the following formula:

Formula 10.7(a)

Number of Payments, Given 'FV'

$$n = \frac{\ln\left[1 + \frac{i \times FV}{PMT}\right]}{\ln(1 + i)}$$

If 'PV' is known, using Formula 10.2(b),

$$PV = PMT\left[\frac{1 - (1 + i)^{-n}}{i}\right]$$

In annuity calculations, n is the number of payments during the term and its value is rounded up to the next whole number of payments. Whereas, in compound interest calculations, n is the number of compounding periods during the term and its exact value is used.

Rearranging and isolating 'n' using natural logarithms (ln) results in the following formula:

Formula 10.7(b)

Number of Payments, Given 'PV'

$$n = -\frac{\ln\left[1 - \frac{i \times PV}{PMT}\right]}{\ln(1 + i)}$$

Note: *The value of 'n' is rounded up to the next whole number of payments. In such situations, the last payment will be of a smaller value than the other payments.*

We know that the number of payments during the term of an annuity, 'n', is:

$$n = \text{number of payments per year} \times \text{number of years } (t)$$

Rearranging to isolate 't' results in the following formula for the time period:

Formula 10.7(c)

Time Period (in years)

$$t = \frac{n}{\textit{Number of payments per year}}$$

Annuity Due

If 'FV_{Due}' is known, using Formula 10.4(a),

$$FV_{Due} = PMT\left[\frac{(1 + i)^n - 1}{i}\right](1 + i)$$

Rearranging and isolating 'n' using natural logarithms (ln) results in the following formula:

Formula 10.7(d)

Number of Payments, Given 'FV_{Due}'

$$n = \frac{\ln\left[1 + \frac{i \times FV_{Due}}{PMT(1 + i)}\right]}{\ln(1 + i)}$$

If 'PV_{Due}' is known, using Formula 10.4(b),

$$PV_{Due} = PMT\left[\frac{1-(1+i)^{-n}}{i}\right](1+i)$$

Rearranging and isolating 'n' using natural logarithms (ln) results in the following formula:

Formula 10.7(e) **Number of Payments, Given 'PV_{Due}'**

$$n = -\frac{\ln\left[1 - \frac{i \times PV_{Due}}{PMT(1+i)}\right]}{\ln(1+i)}$$

Knowing the number of payments, 'n', from above, we can calculate the time period using Formula 10.7(c).

Example 10.7(a) **Calculating the Time Period of an Ordinary General Annuity, Given Future Value**

Steve was planning for retirement and invested \$5000 at the end of every year into an RRSP that was earning 12% compounded monthly. How long will it take for his RRSP fund to grow to \$500,000?

Solution

Page 455

This is an ordinary general annuity as:

- Payments are made at the end of each payment period (annually)
- Compounding period (monthly) ≠ payment period (annually)

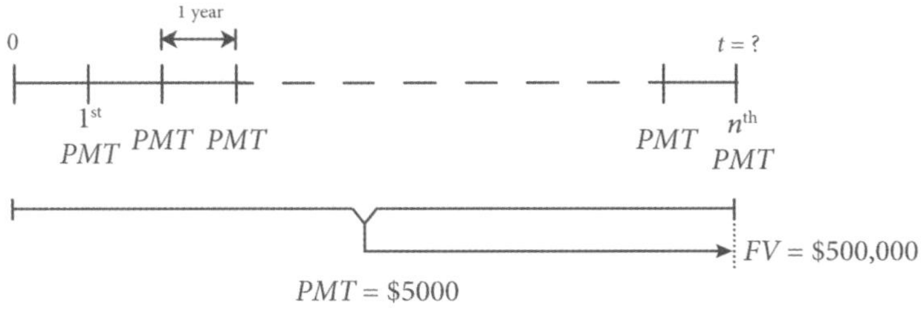

$n = ?,\quad j = 0.12,\quad m = 12,\quad i = \frac{j}{m} = 0.01$ per month

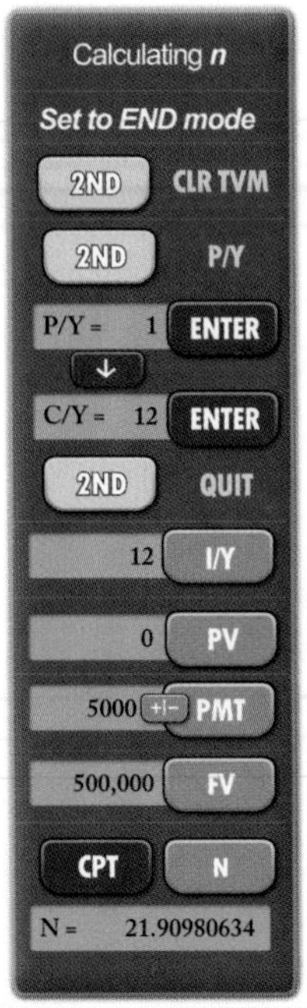

$$c = \frac{\text{Number of compounding periods per year}}{\text{Number of payments per year}} = \frac{12}{1} = 12$$

For an ordinary general annuity or a general annuity due, use 'i_2' in place of 'i'.

$$i_2 = (1+i)^c - 1 = (1+0.01)^{12} - 1 = 0.126825\ldots \text{ per year}$$

Using Formula 10.7(a) and substituting 'i_2' for 'i',

$$n = \frac{\ln\left[1 + \frac{i_2 \times FV}{PMT}\right]}{\ln(1+i_2)} = \frac{\ln\left[1 + \frac{0.126825\ldots \times 500{,}000.00}{5000.00}\right]}{\ln(1+0.126825\ldots)}$$

$= 21.909806\ldots$ Round up to the next payment period.

$= 22$ contributions The 22nd contribution will be smaller than \$5000.

Time period, $t = \frac{n}{\text{Number of payments per year}} = \frac{22}{1} = 22$ years

Therefore, it will take 22 years for the funds in the RRSP to grow to \$500,000.

Example 10.7(b) Calculating the Time Period of an Ordinary General Annuity, Given Present Value

Trent won a lottery of $50,000 and he deposited the money in an investment fund earning 6% compounded semi-annually. If he withdraws $5000 at the end of every three months, how long will the money last?

Solution

Page 455

This is an ordinary general annuity as:

- Payments are made at the end of each payment period (quarterly)
- Compounding period (semi-annually) ≠ payment period (quarterly)

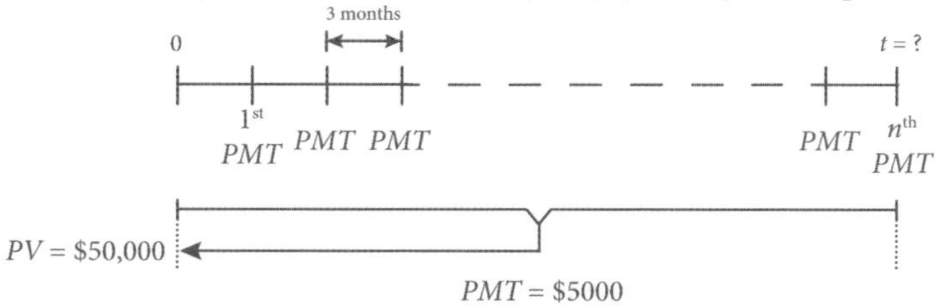

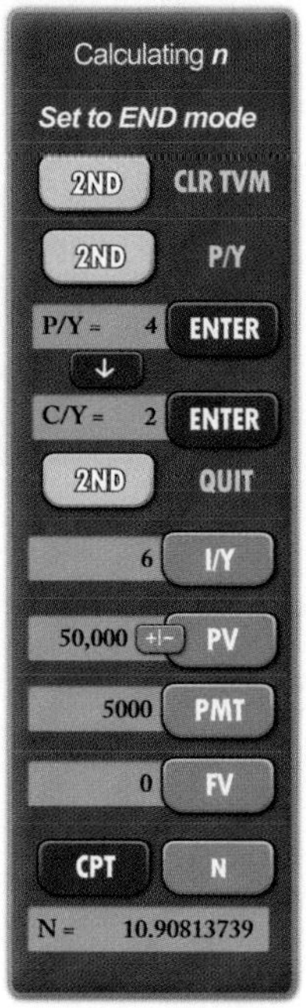

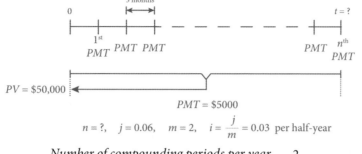

$n = ?,\quad j = 0.06,\quad m = 2,\quad i = \frac{j}{m} = 0.03$ per half-year

$$c = \frac{\textit{Number of compounding periods per year}}{\textit{Number of payments per year}} = \frac{2}{4}$$

$i_2 = (1 + i)^c - 1 = (1 + 0.03)^{(2/4)} - 1 = 0.014889...$ per quarter

Using Formula 10.7(b) and substituting 'i_2' for 'i',

$$n = -\frac{\ln\left[1 - \frac{i_2 \times PV}{PMT}\right]}{\ln(1 + i_2)} = -\frac{\ln\left[1 - \frac{0.014889... \times 50{,}000.00}{5000.00}\right]}{\ln(1 + 0.014889...)}$$

$= 10.908137...$ Round up to the next payment period.

$= 11$ withdrawals The 11th withdrawal will be smaller than $5000.

$$t = \frac{n}{\textit{Number of payments per year}} = \frac{11}{4}$$

$= 2.75$ years $= 2$ years and (0.75×12) months $= 2$ years and 9 months

Therefore, the money will last for 2 years and 9 months.

Example 10.7(c) Calculating the Time Period of a General Annuity Due, Given Future Value

Bentley plans to save $250,000 in his RRSP that is growing at 3.5% compounded semi-annually. He deposits $2500 into this fund at the beginning of every month. How long will it take for him to save this amount?

Solution

Page 455

This is a general annuity due as:

- Payments are made at the beginning of each payment period (monthly)
- Compounding period (semi-annually) ≠ payment period (monthly)

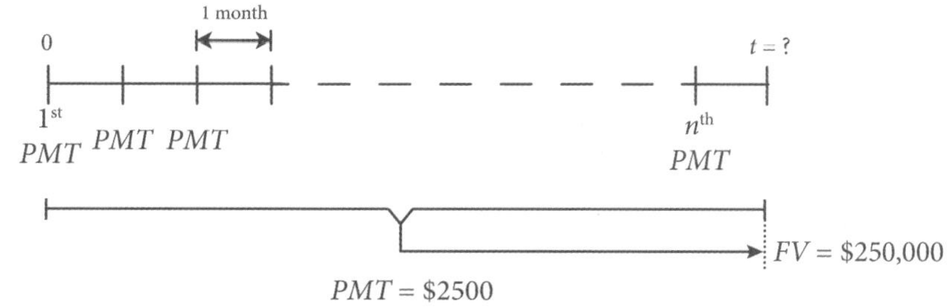

$n = ?,\quad j = 0.035,\quad m = 2,\quad i = \frac{j}{m} = 0.0175$ per half-year

Solution *continued*

$$c = \frac{\textit{Number of compounding periods per year}}{\textit{Number of payments per year}} = \frac{2}{12}$$

$$i_2 = (1 + i)^c - 1 = (1 + 0.0175)^{(2/12)} - 1 = 0.002895\ldots \text{ per month}$$

Using Formula 10.7(d) and substituting 'i_2' for 'i',

$$n = \frac{\ln\left[1 + \dfrac{i_2 \times FV_{Due}}{PMT(1 + i_2)}\right]}{\ln(1 + i_2)} = \frac{\ln\left[1 + \dfrac{0.002895\ldots \times 250{,}000.00}{2500.00(1 + 0.002895\ldots)}\right]}{\ln(1 + 0.002895\ldots)}$$

$= 87.725988\ldots$ Round up to the next payment period.

$= 88$ contributions The 88th contribution will be smaller than \$2500.

$$t = \frac{n}{\textit{Number of payments per year}} = \frac{88}{12}$$

$= 7.333333\ldots = 7$ years and $(0.333333\ldots \times 12)$ months $= 7$ years and 4 months

Therefore, it will take 7 years and 4 months to save this amount.

Example 10.7(d) Calculating the Time Period of a Simple Annuity Due, Given Present Value

Kayla saved \$100,000 in a retirement investment fund earning 4% compounded quarterly. She plans to withdraw \$2000 at the beginning of every three months.

(i) After how many withdrawals will the fund be depleted?

(ii) How long will it take for the fund to be depleted?

Solution

Page 455

This is a simple annuity due as:

- Withdrawals are made at the beginning of each payment period (quarterly)
- Compounding period (quarterly) = payment period (quarterly)

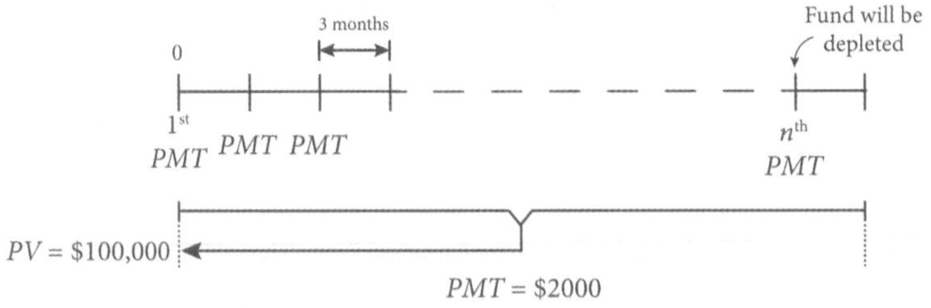

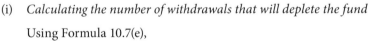

$$n = ?,\quad j = 0.04,\quad m = 4,\quad i = \frac{j}{m} = 0.01 \text{ per quarter}$$

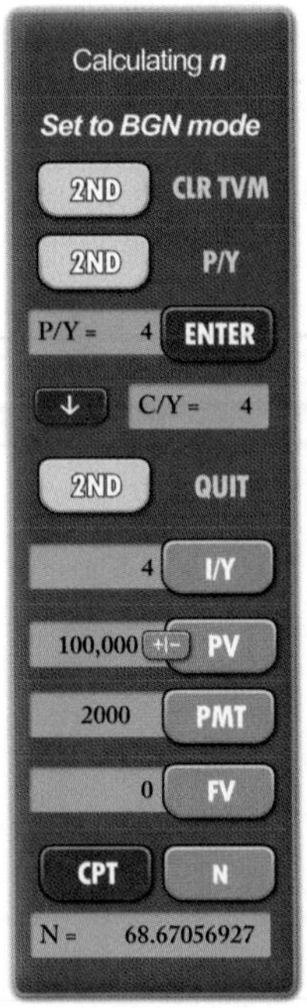

(i) *Calculating the number of withdrawals that will deplete the fund*

Using Formula 10.7(e),

$$n = -\frac{\ln\left[1 - \dfrac{i \times PV_{Due}}{PMT(1 + i)}\right]}{\ln(1 + i)} = -\frac{\ln\left[1 - \dfrac{0.01 \times 100{,}000.00}{2000.00(1 + 0.01)}\right]}{\ln(1 + 0.01)}$$

$= 68.670569\ldots$ Round up to the next payment period.

$= 69$ withdrawals The 69th withdrawal will be smaller than \$2000.

Therefore, the fund will be depleted after 69 withdrawals.

Solution *continued*

(ii) *Calculating the time taken to deplete the fund*

We will first calculate the term of the annuity due. Using Formula 10.7(c),

$$t = \frac{n}{\textit{Number of payments per year}} = \frac{69}{4}$$

$$= 17.25 \text{ years} = 17 \text{ years and } (0.25 \times 12) \text{ months} = 17 \text{ years and } 3 \text{ months}$$

From the time line diagram, notice that the term of the annuity due extends one period (three months) after the last withdrawal. Since we are only concerned with the time until the last withdrawal, we subtract one period from the term of the annuity due.

Time taken to deplete the fund = 17 years and 3 months – 3 months = 17 years

Therefore, the fund will be depleted in 17 years.

10.7 | Exercises

Answers to the odd-numbered problems are available at the end of the textbook.

For the following problems, express the time period in years and months rounded up to the next payment period, wherever applicable.

1. Adrian deposits $3000 at the end of every month into a savings account at 4.75% compounded monthly. How long will it take for the savings to grow to $49,200?

2. Lucy deposited $900 at the end of every month into her RRSP account that had an interest rate of 3.35% compounded monthly. How long will it take for the balance on the account to grow to $30,000?

3. (CFA Prep.) Payments of $10,000 are made at the end of each year into a fund that is earning 4.5% compounded annually. How long will it take to accumulate $92,000 in this fund?

4. Bridgette has been depositing $400 at the end of every month into a savings account with a goal of accumulating $25,000. If her account earns 4% compounded monthly, how many deposits will she have to make to reach her goal?

5. Longcore Technologies has to settle a business loan of $80,000, which has an interest rate of 12% compounded semi-annually. The settlement will consist of semi-annual payments of $20,000 (with the first payment being made six months from now). How many payments will it take to settle the loan?

6. (CFA Prep.) Justine purchased a $100,000 annuity that is earning 8% compounded annually. It will provide her with payments of $15,000 at the end of every year. How many payments will she receive from this annuity?

7. You plan to save money for a down payment of $50,000 to purchase an apartment. You can only afford to save $1000 at the end of every month in an account that has an interest rate of 2.29% compounded quarterly. How long will it take you to save the amount?

8. Daryl's goal is to save $24,000 in an investment fund that is growing at 5.15% compounded monthly. How long will it take to reach his goal if he deposits $1020 at the end of every three months into this fund?

9. Lilly has been depositing $2000 into an RESP at the end of every three months to save for her daughter's education. If the RESP earns 6% compounded monthly, how long will it take for the investment to grow to $20,000?

10. Ashton deposits $1000 at the end of every month into an RRSP. If the RRSP is earning 5% compounded daily, how long will it take for his investment to accumulate to $40,000?

11. Lush Gardens Co. bought a new truck for $45,000. It paid 10% of this amount as a down payment and financed the balance at 5.75% compounded semi-annually. If the company makes payments of $1500 at the end of every month, how long will it take to settle the loan?

12. Clara purchased a machine for $14,000. She paid 15% of the purchase price as a down payment and financed the balance at 4.25% compounded daily. If she paid $500 at the end of every month, how long did it take to settle the loan?

13. Liam has $30,000 in his RRSP account and wants this to accumulate to $250,000. The account is earning 6.1% compounded semi-annually and he plans to deposit $2500 at the beginning of every six months into this account. How long will it take to achieve his goal?

14. Dao-ming has $5000 in his savings account and wants this to accumulate to $25,000 for a condominium down payment. He plans to deposit $2000 at the beginning of every three months into the account. If the account pays 5.8% compounded quarterly, how long will it take to accumulate the amount?

15. Julie's RRSP savings of $250,000 is converted to an RRIF at 3.86% compounded monthly. It pays her $1750 at the beginning of every month. How many payments will it take to deplete the fund?

16. A company withdraws $36,000 at the beginning of every six months from a $400,000 fund that is growing at 2.25% compounded semi-annually. After how many withdrawals will the fund be depleted?

17. Elijah had $75,000 in an investment fund that was growing at 6.1% compounded semi-annually. He plans to withdraw $2500 from this fund at the beginning of every six months.

    a. After how many withdrawals will the fund be depleted?

    b. How long will it take for the fund to be depleted?

18. Amber has an investment account of $150,000 that is earning 4.25% compounded monthly. She wants to withdraw $5000 at the beginning of every month from this fund.

    a. After how many withdrawals will the fund be depleted?

    b. How long will it take for the fund to be depleted?

19. A credit card company charges an effective interest rate of 18%. If Claude's current balance is $5000 and she makes the minimum payment of $150 at the beginning of each month, calculate the number of payments that she will have to make to settle the debt.

20. A credit card charges an effective rate of 19% for Joanne's credit card bill of $7500. Joanne decides to stop using her card and make the minimum payment of $175 at the beginning of each month. How many payments will it take for Joanne to settle her debt?

• 21. Samantha made regular, equal deposits into a savings account at the end of every month for three years. Her investments were earning 5% compounded quarterly and grew to $12,800 at the end of three years. Calculate the size of her month-end deposits. After the above period, if she continues making the same month-end deposits, how long will it take to accumulate to $45,000?

• 22. Mario made regular, equal deposits into an RRSP at the end of every month for two years. His investments were earning 4.75% compounded daily and grew to $18,435 at the end of two years. Calculate the size of the month-end deposits. After the above period, if he continues making the same month-end deposits, how long will it take to accumulate to $35,000?

10.8 | Calculating Periodic Interest Rate (i) and Nominal Interest Rate (j)

Calculating the periodic interest rate 'i' using algebraic methods is difficult as 'i' cannot be isolated easily from the present value and future value formulas. Thus, there is no formula to calculate 'i', although the value for 'i' can be calculated using a trial-and-error method – a time-consuming procedure with some 'guessing'. However, the financial calculator can be used to calculate the value of 'j'. Therefore, in this section you will learn only the financial calculator method to calculate 'j'. Once 'j' is calculated, the periodic interest rate (i) can be calculated using the formula $i = \frac{j}{m}$.

Example 10.8(a) **Calculating the Nominal and Periodic Interest Rates of an Ordinary Simple Annuity, Given Present Value**

What is the nominal interest rate compounded monthly and the periodic interest rate per month of a \$25,000 loan that can be settled by making payments of \$240 at the end of every month for ten years?

Solution

Page 456

Calculating the nominal interest rate

$$PV = PMT\left[\frac{1-(1+i)^{-n}}{i}\right]$$

$$25{,}000.00 = 240.00\left[\frac{1-(1+i)^{-120}}{i}\right]$$

Inputting these values into the calculator and computing I/Y, we obtain the nominal interest rate, j, compounded monthly = 0.028783...

Therefore, the nominal interest rate compounded monthly is 2.88%.

Calculating the periodic interest rate

$$i = \frac{j}{m}$$

Substituting values, $i = \frac{0.028783...}{12}$

$= 0.002398...$

$= 0.24\%$ per month.

Do not round the value of j while calculating i.

Therefore, the periodic interest rate per month is 0.24%.

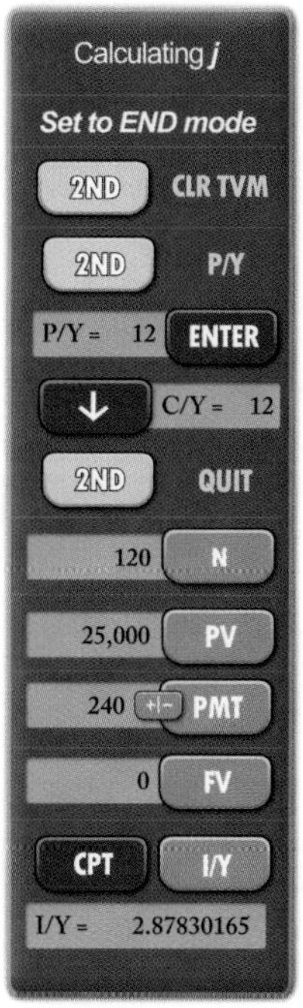

Example 10.8(b) Calculating the Nominal and Periodic Interest Rates of a General Annuity Due, Given Future Value

At what nominal interest rate compounded quarterly would payments of $1500 towards an RRSP at the beginning of every 6 months result in a maturity value of $50,000 in 12 years? Also, determine the corresponding periodic interest rate per quarter.

Solution

Page 456

Calculating the nominal interest rate

$$c = \frac{\text{Number of compounding periods per year}}{\text{Number of payments per year}} = \frac{4}{2}$$

$$i_2 = (1 + i)^c - 1 = (1 + i)^{(4/2)} - 1$$

$$FV_{Due} = PMT\left[\frac{(1 + i_2)^n - 1}{i_2}\right](1 + i_2)$$

$$50{,}000.00 = 1500.00\left[\frac{(1 + i_2)^{24} - 1}{i_2}\right](1 + i_2)$$

For all annuity due calculations, remember to set your calculator to 'BGN' mode.

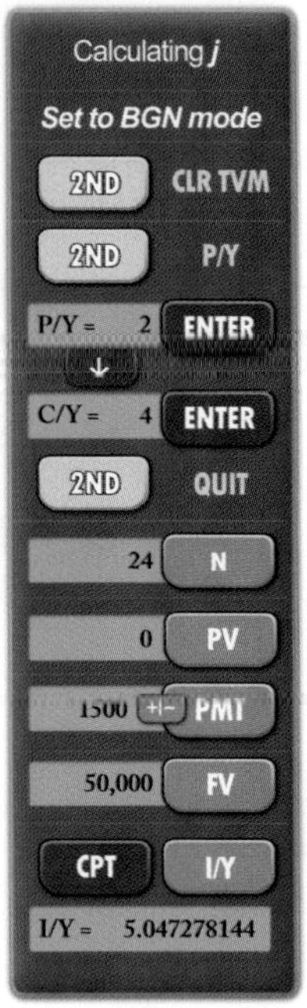

Inputting these values into the calculator and computing I/Y, we obtain the nominal interest rate, *j*, compounded quarterly = 0.050472...

Therefore, the nominal interest rate compounded quarterly is 5.05%.

Calculating the periodic interest rate

$$i = \frac{j}{m}$$

Substituting values, $i = \frac{0.050472...}{4}$

$= 0.012618...$

$= 1.26\%$ per quarter

Therefore, the periodic interest rate per quarter is 1.26%.

Example 10.8(c) Calculating and Comparing Effective Interest Rates of Annuities

Camila wishes to renovate her home, and is comparing two loan options. Bank *A* is offering a loan of $30,000, to be settled with payments of $12,000 at the end of every year for three years. Bank *B* is offering a loan of $30,000, to be settled with payments of $1150 at the end of every month for two-and-a-half years. By calculating the effective interest rate of both options, determine which bank is offering Camila a more economical rate.

Solution

Page 456

Calculating Bank A's effective interest rate

This is an ordinary simple annuity as:

- Payments are made at the end of each payment period (annually)
- Compounding period (annually) = payment period (annually)

Recall: the effective interest rate is the nominal interest rate compounded *annually*. Therefore, the number of compounding periods per year will be 1.

$$PV = PMT\left[\frac{1 - (1 + i)^{-n}}{i}\right]$$

$$30{,}000.00 = 12{,}000.00\left[\frac{1 - (1 + i)^{-3}}{i}\right]$$

Inputting these values into the calculator and computing I/Y, we obtain the effective interest rate, *f*, of 9.70%.

Solution *continued*

Calculating Bank B's effective interest rate

This is an ordinary general annuity as:

- Payments are made at the end of each payment period (monthly)
- Compounding period (annually) ≠ payment period (monthly)

$$c = \frac{\textit{Number of compounding periods per year}}{\textit{Number of payments per year}} = \frac{1}{12}$$

$$i_2 = (1 + i)^c - 1 = (1 + i)^{(1/12)} - 1$$

$$PV = PMT\left[\frac{1 - (1 + i_2)^{-n}}{i_2}\right]$$

$$30{,}000.00 = 1150.00\left[\frac{1 - (1 + i_2)^{-30}}{i_2}\right]$$

Inputting these values into the calculator and computing I/Y, we obtain the effective interest rate, *f*, of 11.70%.

The effective interest rate for Bank *A* is lower than the effective interest rate for Bank *B*. Therefore, Bank *A* is offering Camila a more economical rate.

Example 10.8(d)

Calculating the Nominal Interest Rate of a Lease

Dylan leases a new car by making a down payment of $2000 and beginning-of-month payments of $275 for four years. If the lease amount of the car is $23,500 and Dylan has the option of buying it for $11,250 at the end of the lease, what nominal interest rate compounded monthly is he paying?

ge 456

Solution

The lease payments form a simple annuity due as:

- Payments are made at the beginning of each payment period (monthly)
- Compounding period (monthly) = payment period (monthly)

n = 12 payments/year × 4 years = 48 monthly payments, PMT = $275.00

PV = *Lease Amount* – *Down Payment* = 23,500.00 – 2000.00 = $21,500.00

FV = *Residual Value* = $11,250.00

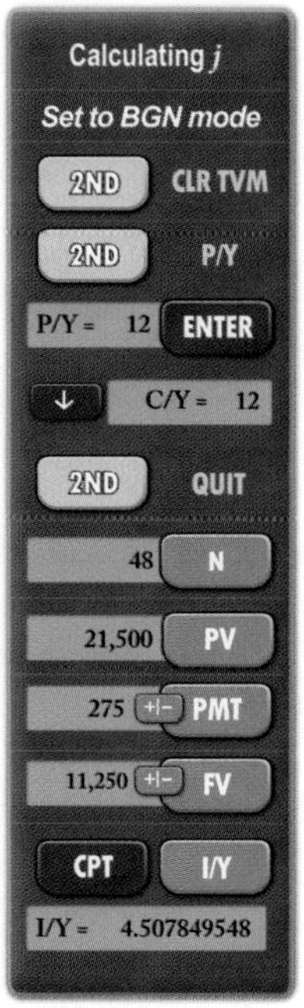

Inputting these values into the calculator and computing I/Y, we obtain the nominal interest rate, *j*, compounded monthly of 4.51%.

10.8 | Exercises

Answers to the odd-numbered problems are available at the end of the textbook.

For the following problems, express the answers rounded to two decimal places, wherever applicable.

CFA Prep.
1. You invested $10,000 at the end of each year for five years in an investment fund. At the end of the fifth year, if the balance in the fund was $55,000, what was the nominal interest rate compounded annually?

2. Oliver deposits $300 in his savings account at the end of every month for 3 years and 6 months. What is the nominal interest rate compounded monthly if the accumulated amount at the end of the period is $13,600?

CFA Prep.
3. What is the nominal interest rate compounded annually that you will earn on an annuity that requires a deposit of $75,000 today and promises to pay $10,000 at the end of every year for the next ten years?

4. You have the opportunity to make an investment of $100,000 today and receive $1250 at the end of every month for the next ten years. Calculate the nominal interest rate compounded monthly on this investment.

5. An amount of $150,000 is invested in an annuity that pays $6000 at the end of every six months for twenty years. What is the nominal interest rate compounded semi-annually that is required to support the payments?

6. You have $70,000 in a savings account and you plan to withdraw $2250 at the end of every three months from this account for ten years. What is the nominal interest rate compounded quarterly that is required to support the withdrawals?

7. A five-year lease requires payments of $750 at the beginning of every month. Calculate the nominal interest rate compounded monthly if the value of the lease contract is $40,750.

8. A lease agreement requires that the lease holder pays $2800 at the beginning of every quarter for three years. If the value of the lease contract is $31,000, what is the nominal interest rate compounded quarterly?

9. At the end of 25 years, Christopher wishes to have accumulated $500,000 in his RRSP fund. He plans to accumulate this amount by making monthly deposits of $750 into the fund. All deposits will be made at the beginning of each month. What nominal interest rate compounded monthly must the fund earn?

10. Deposits of $200 were made to an investment at the beginning of every three months for a period of ten years. If the accumulated value of the investment was $10,000, what nominal interest rate compounded quarterly was being earned?

11. Raga Steel Corporation leased a furnace for $80,000 for ten years. Calculate the nominal interest rate compounded semi-annually if $1000 was paid at the beginning of every month and the residual value is $5000.

12. Hudson's lease contract had a value of $18,000 and he made lease payments of $300 at the beginning of every month. What is the nominal interest rate compounded quarterly if the lease was for 5 years and 9 months and the residual value is $3500?

13. Nailah's retirement fund grew to $40,000 following $200 payments at the end of every three months for 20 years.
    a. What nominal interest rate compounded quarterly was she earning? (Assume that the rate remained constant throughout the 20-year term.)
    b. What nominal interest rate compounded quarterly would produce the same accumulated amount in 15 years? (Assume that the same payments are being made at the end of every three months.)

14. Standard Co. makes deposits of $5000 at the end of every month into an investment fund which will accumulate to $1.5 million in 15 years.
    a. At what nominal interest rate compounded monthly is Standard Co. earning interest in the fund? (Assume that the rate remains constant throughout the 15-year term.)
    b. At what nominal interest rate compounded monthly would the fund accumulate to $1.5 million in 14 years, rather than 15 years? (Assume that the same month-end payments are being made.)

15. Nicky's goal is to have $75,000 in 15 years for her university education. She sets up an investment fund and contributes $250 at the end of every month for the time period. What effective interest rate is required to achieve this goal?

16. Sabrina wishes to accumulate $25,000 in a savings account at the end of ten years. She plans to deposit $500 at the end of every three months. What effective interest rate must the savings account pay for her to reach her goal?

17. Month-end payments of $1550 are required to settle a loan of $142,000 in ten years. What is the effective rate of interest?

18. A principal of $80,000 generates income of $4000 at the end of every six months for fifteen years. What is the effective rate of interest?

19. Cameron's parents deposited $400 at the beginning of every three months into his RESP account. The accumulated value of the account at the end of six years is $11,000. Calculate the effective rate of interest of this investment.

20. Determine the effective interest rate at which an investment of $1100 at the beginning of every three months will accumulate to $20,000 in four years.

• 21. A company has the following two options to purchase a machine:

- Option A: Pay $33,500.
- Option B: Lease for seven years with a down payment of $1000, payments of $1400 at the beginning of every three months, and purchase the machine for $3000 at the end of the lease term.

Calculate the nominal interest rate compounded quarterly if both of these options are economically equal.

• 22. To purchase a car, Henry was provided the following two options:

- Option A: Pay $27,500.
- Option B: Lease for five years with a down payment of $2000, payments of $335 at the beginning of every month, and purchase the car for $10,000 at the end of the lease term.

Calculate the nominal interest rate compounded monthly if both of these options are economically equal.

• 23. You wish to buy a used car priced at $27,000. The car dealer's offer is for you to pay $825 at the beginning of each month for the next three years. At the same time, a bank offers you a loan of $27,000 which is to be settled in five years with month-end payments of $525. By calculating the effective interest rate of both options, determine the option that is more economical.

• 24. For the purchase of $7500 worth of home appliances, a store's offer is for you to pay $1000 at the beginning of every three months for two years. A financial institution offers you a loan of $7500 which is to be settled in three years with payments of $725 at the end of every three months. By calculating the effective interest rate of both options, determine the option that is more economical.

10 | Review Examples

Example 1

Determine the maturity value of $1000 invested at the end of every three months for ten years at 8% compounded semi-annually.

Page 456

Solution

This is an ordinary general annuity as:

- Payments are made at the end of each payment period (quarterly)
- Compounding period (semi-annually) ≠ payment period (quarterly)

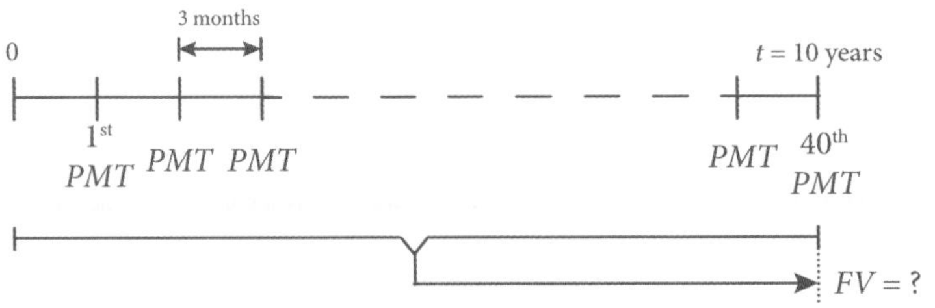

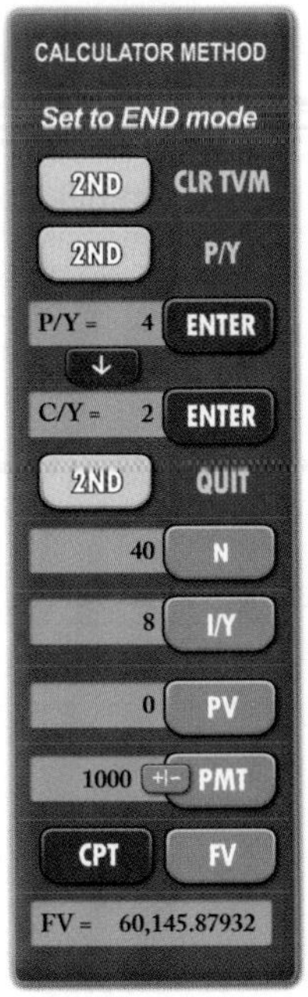

$$PMT = \$1000$$

$$n = 4 \text{ payments/year} \times 10 \text{ years} = 40 \text{ quarterly payments}$$

$$j = 0.08, \quad m = 2, \quad i = \frac{j}{m} = 0.04 \text{ per half-year}$$

$$c = \frac{\textit{Number of compounding periods per year}}{\textit{Number of payments per year}} = \frac{2}{4}$$

$$i_2 = (1 + i)^c - 1 = (1 + 0.04)^{(2/4)} - 1 = 0.019803... \text{ per quarter}$$

Using Formula 10.2(a) and substituting 'i_2' for 'i',

$$FV = PMT\left[\frac{(1 + i_2)^n - 1}{i_2}\right]$$

$$= 1000.00\left[\frac{(1 + 0.019803...)^{40} - 1}{0.019803...}\right]$$

$$= 1000.00[60.145879...]$$

$$= 60{,}145.87932... = \$60{,}145.88$$

Therefore, the maturity value is $60,145.88.

Example 2

What amount of loan at 8% compounded semi-annually can be repaid in ten years with payments of $1000 at the end of every three months?

Page 456

Solution

This is an ordinary general annuity as:

- Payments are made at the end of each payment period (quarterly)
- Compounding period (semi-annually) ≠ payment period (quarterly)

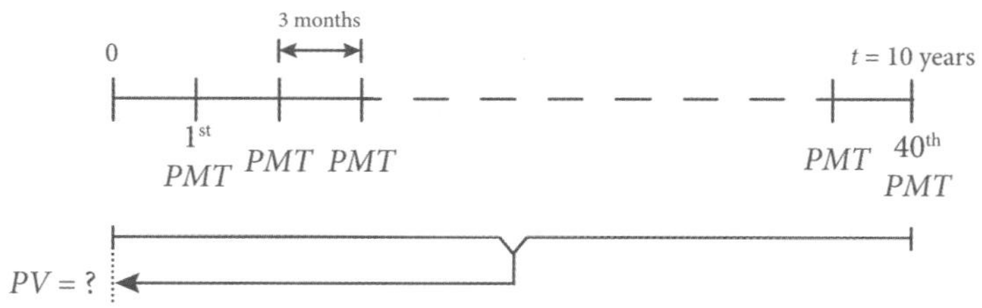

$PMT = \$1000$

$n = 4$ payments/year × 10 years = 40 quarterly payments

$j = 0.08, \quad m = 2, \quad i = \frac{j}{m} = 0.04$ per half-year

$$c = \frac{\textit{Number of compounding periods per year}}{\textit{Number of payments per year}} = \frac{2}{4}$$

$$i_2 = (1 + i)^c - 1 = (1 + 0.04)^{(2/4)} - 1 = 0.019803... \text{ per quarter}$$

Using Formula 10.2(b) and substituting 'i_2' for 'i',

$$PV = PMT\left[\frac{1 - (1 + i_2)^{-n}}{i_2}\right]$$

$$= 1000.00\left[\frac{1 - (1 + 0.019803...)^{-40}}{0.019803...}\right]$$

$$= 1000.00[27.449794...]$$

$$= 27{,}449.79419... = \$27{,}449.79$$

Therefore, a loan of $27,449.79 can be repaid in ten years.

Example 3

What payments at the end of every three months at 8% compounded semi-annually will accumulate to $60,145.88 in ten years?

Page 457

Solution

This is an ordinary general annuity as:

- Payments are made at the end of each payment period (quarterly)
- Compounding period (semi-annually) ≠ payment period (quarterly)

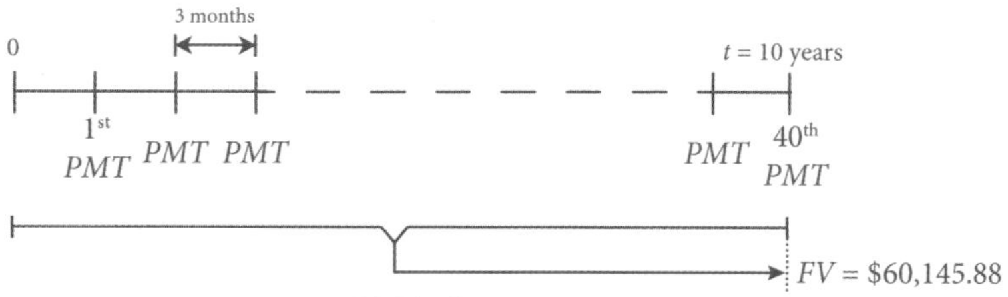

$PMT = ?$

$n = 4$ payments/year × 10 years = 40 quarterly payments

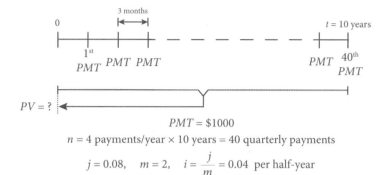

$j = 0.08, \quad m = 2, \quad i = \frac{j}{m} = 0.04$ per half-year

Solution *continued*

$$c = \frac{\textit{Number of compounding periods per year}}{\textit{Number of payments per year}} = \frac{2}{4}$$

$$i_2 = (1 + i)^c - 1 = (1 + 0.04)^{(2/4)} - 1 = 0.019803... \text{ per quarter}$$

Using Formula 10.2(a) and substituting 'i_2' for 'i',

$$FV = PMT\left[\frac{(1 + i_2)^n - 1}{i_2}\right]$$

$$60{,}145.88 = PMT\left[\frac{(1 + 0.019803...)^{40} - 1}{0.019803...}\right] \quad \text{Solving for } PMT,$$

$$PMT = \frac{60{,}145.88}{\left[\dfrac{(1 + 0.019803...)^{40} - 1}{0.019803...}\right]} = \frac{60{,}145.88}{[60.145879...]}$$

$$= 1000.000011... = \$1000.00$$

Therefore, payments of $1000 at the end of every three months will accumulate to $60,145.88 in ten years.

Example 4

What payments at the end of every quarter will pay off a loan of $27,449.79 in ten years at 8% compounded semi-annually?

Solution

Page 457

This is an ordinary general annuity as:

- Payments are made at the end of each payment period (quarterly)
- Compounding period (semi-annually) ≠ payment period (quarterly)

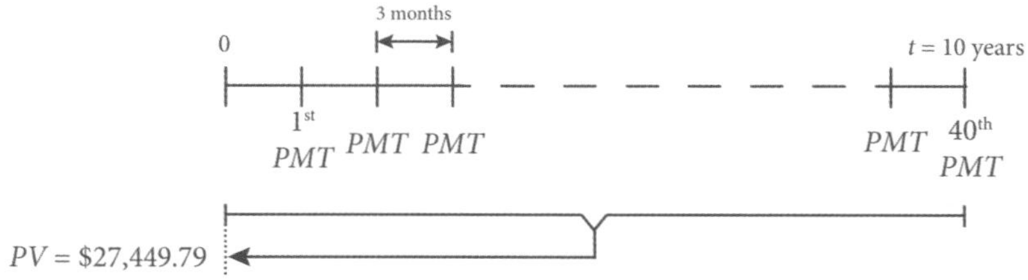

$PMT = ?$

$n = 4 \text{ payments/year} \times 10 \text{ years} = 40 \text{ quarterly payments}$

$j = 0.08, \quad m = 2, \quad i = \frac{j}{m} = 0.04 \text{ per half-year}$

$$c = \frac{\textit{Number of compounding periods per year}}{\textit{Number of payments per year}} = \frac{2}{4}$$

$$i_2 = (1 + i)^c - 1 = (1 + 0.04)^{(2/4)} - 1 = 0.019803... \text{ per quarter}$$

Using Formula 10.2(b) and substituting 'i_2' for 'i',

$$PV = PMT\left[\frac{1 - (1 + i_2)^{-n}}{i_2}\right]$$

$$27{,}449.79 = PMT\left[\frac{1 - (1 + 0.019803...)^{-40}}{0.019803...}\right] \quad \text{Solving for } PMT,$$

$$PMT = \frac{27{,}449.79}{\left[\dfrac{1 - (1 + 0.019803...)^{-40}}{0.019803...}\right]} = \frac{27{,}449.79}{[27.449794...]}$$

$$PMT = 999.999847... = \$1000.00$$

Therefore, payments of $1000 at the end of every quarter will settle a loan of $27,449.79 in ten years.

Example 5

How long would it take to accumulate \$60,145.88 with \$1000 payments at the end of every three months if invested at 8% compounded semi-annually?

Page 457

Solution

This is an ordinary general annuity as:

- Payments are made at the end of each payment period (quarterly)
- Compounding period (semi-annually) ≠ payment period (quarterly)

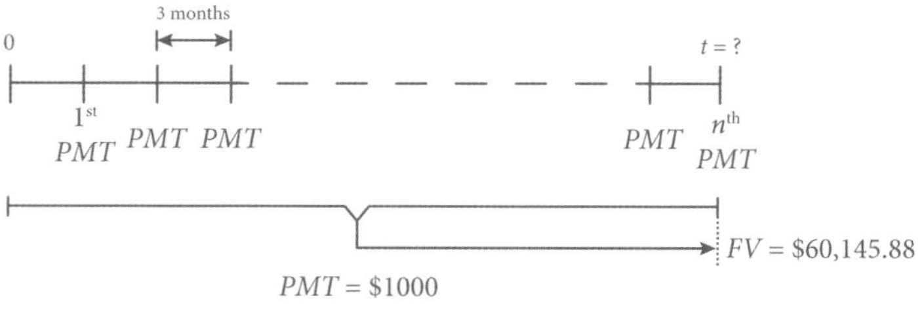

$j = 0.08, \quad m = 2, \quad i = \frac{j}{m} = 0.04$ per half-year

$$c = \frac{\textit{Number of compounding periods per year}}{\textit{Number of payments per year}} = \frac{2}{4}$$

$$i_2 = (1+i)^c - 1 = (1+0.04)^{(2/4)} - 1 = 0.019803... \text{ per quarter}$$

Using Formula 10.7(a) and substituting 'i_2' for 'i',

$$n = \frac{\ln\left(1 + \frac{i_2 \times FV}{PMT}\right)}{\ln(1+i_2)}$$

$$= \frac{\ln\left(1 + \frac{0.019803... \times 60{,}145.88}{1000.00}\right)}{\ln(1+0.019803...)}$$

$$= 40 \text{ payments}$$

Time period, $t = \frac{n}{\textit{Number of payments per year}} = \frac{40}{4} = 10$ years

Therefore, it would take ten years for the payments to accumulate to \$60,145.88.

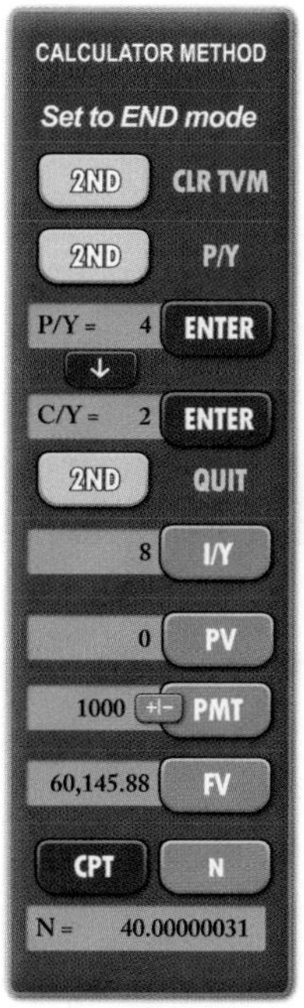

Example 6

How long would it take to settle a loan of \$27,449.79 with \$1000 payments at the end of every three months at 8% compounded semi-annually?

Page 457

Solution

This is an ordinary general annuity as:

- Payments are made at the end of each payment period (quarterly)
- Compounding period (semi-annually) ≠ payment period (quarterly)

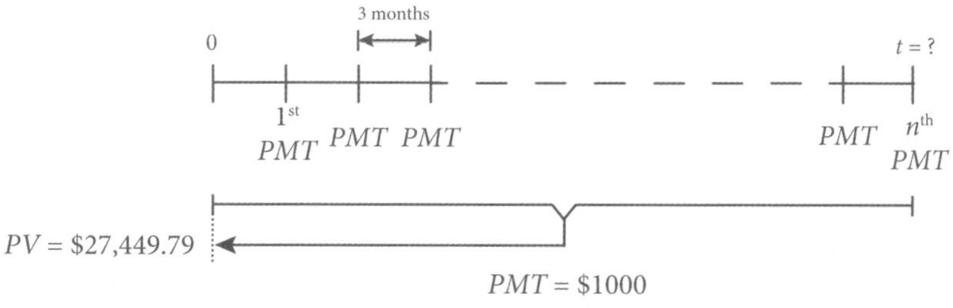

$j = 0.08, \quad m = 2, \quad i = \frac{j}{m} = 0.04$ per half-year

Solution *continued*

$$c = \frac{\textit{Number of compounding periods per year}}{\textit{Number of payments per year}} = \frac{2}{4}$$

$$i_2 = (1 + i)^c - 1 = (1 + 0.04)^{(2/4)} - 1 = 0.019803... \text{ per quarter}$$

Using Formula 10.7(b) and substituting 'i_2' for 'i',

$$n = -\frac{\ln\left(1 - \frac{i_2 \times PV}{PMT}\right)}{\ln(1 + i_2)}$$

$$= -\frac{\ln\left(1 - \frac{0.019803... \times 27{,}449.79}{1000.00}\right)}{\ln(1 + 0.019803...)}$$

$$= 40 \text{ payments}$$

Time period, $t = \frac{n}{\textit{Number of payments per year}} = \frac{40}{4} = 10$ years

Therefore, it would take ten years to settle the loan.

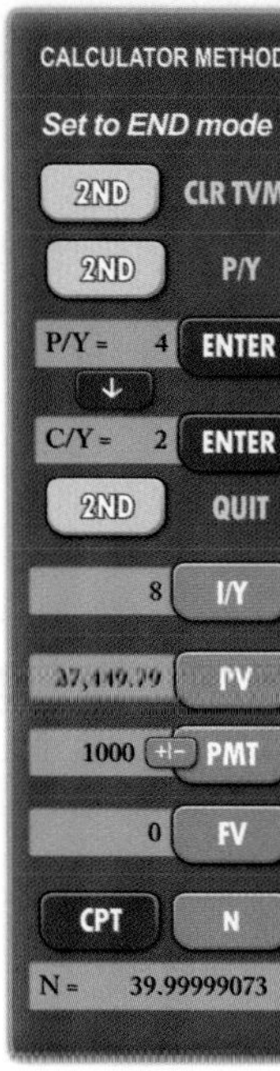

Example 7 At what nominal interest rate compounded semi-annually can you accumulate $60,145.88 in ten years with payments of $1000 at the end of every three months?

Page 457

Solution This is an ordinary general annuity as:

- Payments are made at the end of each payment period (quarterly)
- Compounding period (semi-annually) ≠ payment period (quarterly)

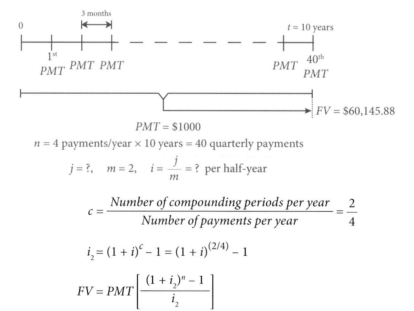

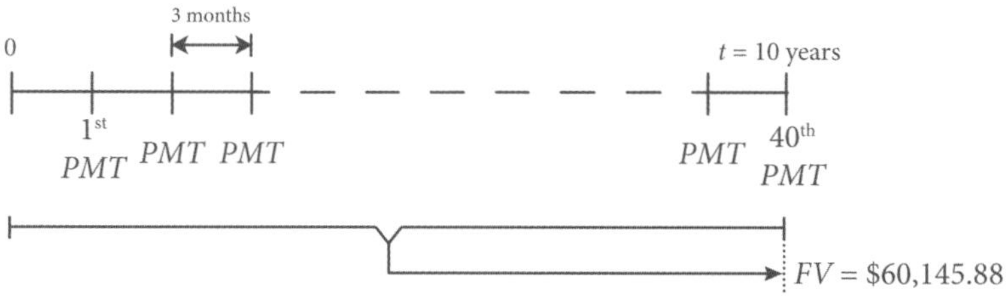

$PMT = \$1000$

$n = 4$ payments/year × 10 years = 40 quarterly payments

$j = ?,\quad m = 2,\quad i = \frac{j}{m} = ?$ per half-year

$$c = \frac{\textit{Number of compounding periods per year}}{\textit{Number of payments per year}} = \frac{2}{4}$$

$$i_2 = (1 + i)^c - 1 = (1 + i)^{(2/4)} - 1$$

$$FV = PMT\left[\frac{(1 + i_2)^n - 1}{i_2}\right]$$

$$60{,}145.88 = 1000.00\left[\frac{(1 + i_2)^{40} - 1}{i_2}\right]$$

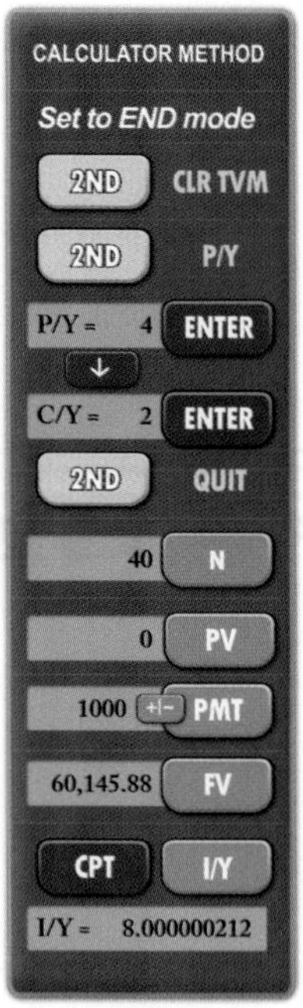

Inputting these values into the calculator and computing I/Y, we obtain the nominal interest rate, j, compounded semi-annually of 8%.

Example 8

At what periodic interest rate compounded semi-annually can you settle a loan of $27,449.79 in ten years with $1000 payments made at the beginning of every three months?

Solution

Page 457

This is a general annuity due as:

- Payments are made at the beginning of each payment period (quarterly)
- Compounding period (semi-annually) ≠ payment period (quarterly)

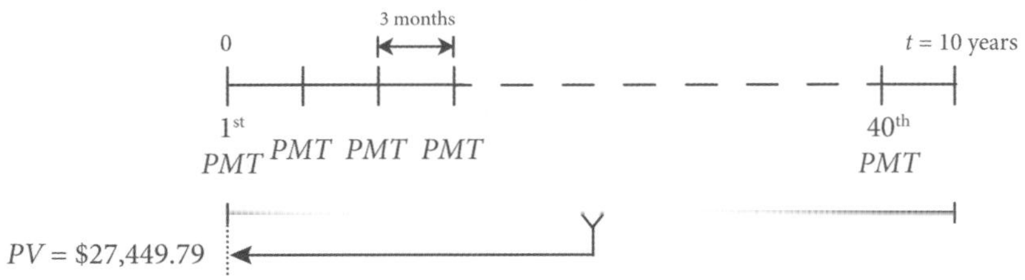

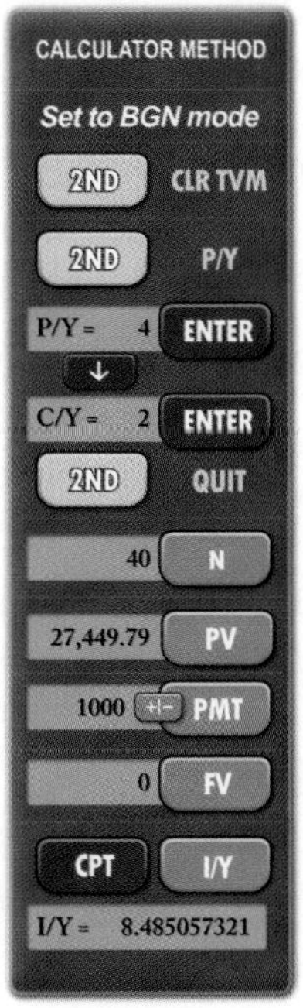

$$PMT = \$1000$$

$$n = 4 \text{ payments/year} \times 10 \text{ years} = 40 \text{ quarterly payments}$$

$$j = ?, \quad m = 2, \quad i = \frac{j}{m} = ? \text{ per half-year}$$

Calculating the nominal interest rate

$$c = \frac{\textit{Number of compounding periods per year}}{\textit{Number of payments per year}} = \frac{2}{4}$$

$$i_2 = (1 + i)^c - 1 = (1 + i)^{(2/4)} - 1$$

$$PV_{Due} = PMT\left[\frac{1 - (1 + i_2)^{-n}}{i_2}\right](1 + i_2)$$

$$27{,}449.79 = 1000.00\left[\frac{1 - (1 + i_2)^{-40}}{i_2}\right](1 + i_2)$$

Inputting these values into the calculator and computing I/Y, we obtain the nominal interest rate, j, compounded semi-annually of 8.49%.

Calculating the periodic interest rate

$$i = \frac{j}{m}$$

Substituting values,

$$i = \frac{0.084850\ldots}{2}$$

$$= 0.042425\ldots$$

$$= 4.24\% \text{ per half-year}$$

Therefore, you can settle the loan at a periodic interest rate of 4.24% per half-year.

10 | Review Exercises

Answers to the odd-numbered problems are available at the end of the textbook.

For the following problems, express the answers rounded to two decimal places, wherever applicable.

1. How much interest would be earned if $800 is invested at the end of every six months for five years at 6% compounded semi-annually?

2. Nicholas contributed $1250 at the end of every six months for fifteen years to an RRSP fund earning 5% compounded semi-annually. Calculate the amount of interest earned over this period.

3. What single payment now is equivalent to month-end payments of $1000 for ten years? Assume money earns 9% compounded monthly.

4. Calculate the amount of a loan that can be settled by payments of $750 at the end of every three months for three years if money earns 6% compounded quarterly.

5. Evelyn saved $1000 at the end of every six months for five years in a savings account that earned 4% compounded semi-annually. At the end of the five years, she left her money to earn 6% compounded daily for the next five years. Calculate the balance in her savings account at the end of ten years and the total interest earned over this term.

6. Schmidt invested $5540 at the end of every three months in an investment that was earning 9% compounded quarterly. He stopped making regular deposits at the end of five years when the interest rate changed to 8.75% compounded monthly. However, he let the money grow in this investment account for the next two years. Calculate the accumulated balance in his investment account at the end of the seven-year period and the total interest earned.

7. Deposits of $1500 are made to an investment fund at the end of each month for eight years. What will be the accumulated value of the fund if the interest earned is 6% compounded annually for the first half of the term and 3% compounded daily for the second half of the term?

8. Zoe started investing $700 at the end of every month into an RRSP that has an interest rate of 4% compounded semi-annually. Three years later, the interest rate on her RRSP increased to 5% compounded monthly and remained the same, thereafter. What is the accumulated value of the RRSP after seven years?

9. Nigel purchased a property by making a down payment of $50,000 and month-end payments of $1500 for 15 years. What was the value of the property if money is worth 6% compounded semi-annually?

10. Lina wants to receive $5000 at the end of every six months for the next seven years. How much money should she invest now at 3.75% compounded monthly?

11. For the past ten years, Anton has been depositing $1000 into an RRSP at the beginning of each year. The interest rate for the first four years was 6% compounded annually and 6.5% compounded annually for the next six years. Calculate the accumulated value of his investment at the end of the ten years. How much of this was earned from interest?

12. Since the birth of her daughters 16 years ago, Solange has deposited $50 at the beginning of every month into an RESP. The interest rate on the plan was 4.8% compounded monthly for the first eight years and 4.2% compounded monthly for the next eight years. Calculate the value of the fund today (the end of a 16-year term). How much of this is interest?

13. Henry wants to accumulate $25,000 in eight years by making equal deposits into an investment fund at the end of every six months. What is the size of each deposit if the fund earns 5% compounded semi-annually?

14. How much did Alexis deposit every month into her savings account if she has $15,000 after 24 month-end deposits? The money in her account was growing at 4.8% compounded monthly.

15. Melia received a $30,000 loan at an interest rate of 9.5% compounded monthly to renovate her basement. What is the size of the month-end payment required to clear the loan in six years?

16. Marblestone, a retail appliance store, sold a $1600 refrigerator with a three-year financing plan at an interest rate of 5.5% compounded monthly. If a customer made a down payment of $350, what should be the size of the loan payment at the end of each month?

17. Harris leased a vehicle by making a down payment of $1000 and lease payments of $500 at the beginning of each month for three years. The residual value is $10,000 and cost of borrowing is 5.5% compounded monthly. What is the lease amount of the printing machine?

18. A car was leased with a down payment of $4000 and monthly lease payments of $360 payable at the beginning of each month for five years. If the interest rate is 5% compounded annually and the residual value is $12,000, calculate the lease amount of the car.

19. Crystal purchased a scooter for her grandmother by making payments of $70 at the beginning of every three months for four years. If the cost of borrowing is 8% compounded quarterly, what is the cash price of the scooter?

20. Edwin wants to set up a fund for his son's education so that he would be able to withdraw $2000 at the beginning of every three months for the next five years. If the fund earns 3.6% compounded daily, what amount must he deposit today?

21. Karina is charged an interest rate of 6% compounded monthly for her $25,000 student loan. How long (in years and months) will it take her to settle the debt if she makes end-of-month payments of $500?

22. Bilal has a $55,000 loan that has an interest rate of 12% compounded quarterly. How long (in years and months) will it take him to clear the loan if he makes end-of-quarter payments of $10,000 each?

23. The interest rate charged on a $30,000 student loan is 5.4% compounded daily. How long (in years and months) will it take to repay the loan if payments of $500 are made at the end of every month?

24. A $325,000 loan is to be repaid by monthly payments of $1750. If the interest rate on the loan is 4.5% compounded semi-annually, what is the term of the loan (in years and months)?

25. Jerry and Jill planned to save $25,000 to purchase a machine for their bakery. They achieved this target by depositing $2000 at the end of every month into an investment fund for one year. What was the nominal interest rate compounded monthly at which the fund was growing?

26. Shortboard Inc. is investing in a new manufacturing process which will cost $220,000. To accumulate this amount, $26,500 is deposited at the end of every three months for two years in an investment fund. Calculate the nominal interest rate compounding quarterly.

27. A loan of $20,000 was settled in four years with payments of $2000 made at the end of every three months. Calculate the nominal interest rate compounded monthly.

28. Month-end contributions of $150 were made to an RESP fund for ten years. If the accumulated value of the fund at the end of the last contribution was $25,000, calculate the effective interest rate at which the fund was growing.

• 29. Rosy wanted to have savings of $100,000 in ten years so she made equal deposits at the end of every six months into a savings account at 5% compounded semi-annually. If the interest rate offered was 5% compounded daily instead of 5% compounded semi-annually, by how much would the size of her deposits reduce to ensure that she would have the same accumulated amount at the end of ten years?

• 30. Amanda's bank offers her an interest rate of 7% compounded monthly on her investments. How much more money would she have to deposit at the end of every month for her fund to accumulate to $30,000 in eight years if the interest rate was 7% compounded semi-annually?

10 | Self-Test Exercises

Answers to all the problems are available at the end of the textbook.

For the following problems, express the answers rounded to two decimal places, wherever applicable.

1. Ronny had a balance of $2000 in his RRSP. In addition to this, he invested $1000 at the end of every six months for 5 years and 6 months. If his RRSP earned 4% compounded semi-annually for the first two years and 4.25% compounded semi-annually for the rest of the period, how much did he have in the RRSP at the end of the time period? What were his total earnings?

2. Andrew won a lottery and must decide among the following options:

   Option A: $50,000 cash today.

   Option B: $1250 at the end of every 3 months for 20 years.

   Option C: $400 at the end of every month for 20 years.

   If money is worth 9% compounded annually, calculate the present value of each option. Which option is economically best?

3. Hurd Corporation wants to save $10,000 at the end of every year for five years. Bank *A* offers an interest rate of 6% compounded daily and Bank *B* offers an interest rate of 6% compounded monthly. Hurd Corporation is considering the following two options:

   - Option A: Save $4000 annually in Bank *A* and $6000 annually in Bank *B*.
   - Option B: Save $6000 annually in Bank *A* and $4000 annually in Bank *B*.

   Calculate the present value of each option and determine which option is economically better.

4. A 20-year loan is amortized by payments of $1200 made at the end of each month. If the interest rate is 4% compounded semi-annually, what is the loan principal?

5. A savings account is earning 3.5% compounded semi-annually. How long (in years and months) would it take to save at least $50,000 by making month-end deposits of $500?

6. How many more payments would be required to be able to accumulate at least $200,000 by saving $1500 at the end of every three months instead of $1500 at the beginning of every month? Assume an interest rate of 6% compounded quarterly.

7. How much more money should be invested now in order to receive $900 at the beginning of each month for ten months instead of $300 at the beginning of each month for 30 months? Assume an interest rate of 6% compounded semi-annually.

8. Nuben obtained a business loan of $300,000 at 4.5% compounded semi-annually.

   a. What is the size of the semi-annual payments to be made over 20 years in order to pay off the loan?

   b. Calculate the amount of interest paid on the loan.

9. Bella obtained a loan of $50,000 at 3.6% compounded monthly. How long (in years and months) will it take to settle the loan with month-end payments of $500?

10. Bethany paid off her student loan in five years by making payments of $750 at the beginning of every month. If the interest rate on her loan was 6% compounded monthly, calculate the size of the original loan and the amount of interest paid on the loan.

11. Atif plans to retire on his 40th birthday. He has been saving $1200 every month since his 22nd birthday in a fund that earns 7.5% compounded annually. What would the balance be in the fund on his 40th birthday, assuming that he did not make any investment on his 40th birthday? What was his contribution and interest earned through the years?

12. The interest rate on a five-year, $100,000 loan is 4% compounded daily. Calculate the amount of interest saved if the loan was settled with month-end payments in three years instead of month-end payments in five years.

13. Tobin has $35,000 in an RRSP that is growing at 3.6% compounded monthly. He wants to withdraw $650 at the beginning of every month from this RRSP. After how many withdrawals will the fund be completely depleted?

• 14. How much more money should be deposited at the end of every month to accumulate $50,000 in ten years at 6.2% compounded quarterly instead of 6.2% compounded monthly?

• 15. A loan of $190,000 was settled in seven years with payments of $8000 at the end of every three months.

   a. What nominal interest rate compounded monthly was charged on the loan?

   b. At this rate (use the full un-rounded interest rate), what month-end payments would have settled the loan in five years?

CASE 10a

Saving for Retirement

At the age of 30, Morgan decided to create a financial plan to retire in 25 years. He had the following retirement objectives:

- Home purchase objective: Own a home worth at least $1,200,000 with no mortgage.
- Vacation objective: Have an amount of $45,000 for a European tour.
- Monthly allowance objective: Receive a month-beginning allowance of $2000 for 20 years after retirement.

He created the following financial plans to achieve the above retirement objectives. Answer the questions related to each plan.

Plan to achieve his home purchase objective

Assuming that the value of a property in a Toronto suburb would double over 25 years, Morgan would purchase a house worth $600,000 by making a down-payment of $30,000 and obtaining a mortgage for the balance amount from a local bank at an interest rate of 4% compounded semi-annually for 25 years.

a. If the interest rate is constant over the 25-year period, calculate the month-end payments for the mortgage. What would be his total investment in the house over the term?

Plan to achieve his vacation objective

Deposit $150 at the end of every month for ten years into a savings account that earns 3% compounded monthly. At the end of the ten years, transfer the accumulated money into an investment fund that earns 6% compounded quarterly, and allow the money to grow in this fund until retirement.

b. How long (in years and months) would it take to accumulate the required amount of $45,000 to pay for his vacation?

c. To ensure that the amount accumulates to only $45,000 at the time of retirement, by how much should he change his monthly deposit?

Plan to achieve his monthly allowance objective

He will save $500 at the beginning of every month until retirement in an RRSP that has an interest rate of 5.4% compounded monthly.

d. What would be the accumulated value of the RRSP at the time of retirement?

e. For Morgan to be able to withdraw $2000 from the RRSP at the beginning of every month during his planned 20-year retirement period, what does the nominal interest rate, compounded monthly, need to change to, assuming the interest rate during the 25-year savings period remains unchanged at 5.4% compounded monthly?

CASE 10b

Lease or Finance Option

Henry graduated from college and found a job as an online marketing specialist in a social networking company. Within a year, he saved $2000 and was determined to buy a new car. However, he was unsure as to whether he should lease it or buy it by financing the amount from a bank.

A car salesman at the showroom gave him the following table illustrating the comparison of the lease vs. finance options for the car he liked.

Description	Leasing the car	Financing the car
Manufacturer's Suggested Retail Price (MSRP)	$21,500.00	$21,500.00
Additional purchase costs*	$1,817.00	$1,817.00
13% HST	-	$3031.21
Net price	$23,317.00	$26,348.21
Down payment	$2000.00	$2000.00
Term in months	48	48
Monthly payments	$250.00 + 13% HST (month-beginning payments)	$562.13 (month-end payments)
Residual payment to own	$12,453.56 + 13% HST	Nil

**Additional purchase costs include freight & PDI, Air Conditioner Tax, Tire Tax, and registration fees.*

Assume that money is worth 5.5% compounded annually.

a. Which option would be economically better for Henry?

b. Which option would be economically better if the residual value was $15,500 (including HST) for the lease option?

c. What size of equal, beginning-of-month lease payments (including HST) would make the lease option economically equivalent to the finance option? Assume the original residual value and the term is still 48 months.

CASE 10c

Paying Off a Credit Card with Payments that Form an Annuity

After spending too much money on credit card interest last year, Alana applied for a new credit card that had a lower interest rate of 16.9% compounded daily. The terms of her new credit card are similar to her old one:

- For any payment she makes within a month from the date of purchase, she will be charged no interest.
- However, if she does not pay off the full balance, interest is charged daily on the remaining balance effective from the date of purchase.
- Every month she must make a minimum payment.

On November 30, Alana completed all of her Christmas shopping using her new credit card. Also, she did not make any other purchases in the following months.

a. On December 31, Alana made a payment of $100, and on the last days of January to May, respectively, she made the minimum payment of $20 that was charged on her credit card. After the May 31 payment, the balance on her card was $610.06. What was the value of all the purchases she made on November 30? (*Hint: Remember, interest is not charged on any payments she made within the first month.*)

b. How much longer would it take Alana to pay off her debt if she continued to only make the minimum payment of $20 at the end of each month? Round your answer up to the next month.

c. How much quicker could she pay off her debt by making payments of $40 at the end of each month instead? Round your answer up to the next month.

d. Alana was shocked by how long it would take for her to pay off her debt if she continued to only make the minimum payment of $20, and so she made a plan to be debt-free in six months. What equal payments would she have to make at the end of each month (starting on June 30) in order to achieve this goal?

e. If she followed her payment plan laid out in (d), what would the balance be on Alana's credit card after her third payment (halfway through her repayment plan)?

f. If on November 30, after making her final payment, her credit card balance is $0, how much interest did she pay towards her credit card since November 30 the previous year?

10 | Spreadsheet Solutions

Spreadsheet solutions to solved examples in the chapter.

10.2 Examples

Example 10.2(b)

	A	B	
1		Calculating FV_1	
2	***j***	6.00%	
3	***m***	4	
4	***P/Y***	4	
5	***t***	4	
6			
7	***i***	1.50%	= B2/B3
8	***n***	16	= B4*B5
9	***PMT***	($1,500.00)	
10	***PV***	0	
11	***FV***	$26,898.55	= FV(B7, B8, B9, B10, B12) FV(rate, nper, pmt, [pv], [type])
12	***BGN***	0	
13			
14		Calculating FV_2	
15	***j***	9.00%	
16	***m***	4	
17	***t***	6	
18			
19	***i***	2.25%	= B15/B16
20	***n***	24	= B16*B17
21	***PMT***	0	
22	***PV***	($26,898.55)	= –B11
23	***FV***	$45,882.66	= FV(B19, B20, B21, B22) FV(rate, nper, pmt, [pv], [type])
24			

Example 10.2(c)

	A	B	
1		Calculating FV_1	
2	***j***	3.00%	
3	***m***	12	
4	***P/Y***	12	
5	***t***	5	
6			
7	***i***	0.25%	= B2/B3
8	***n***	60	= B4*B5
9	***PMT***	($500.00)	
10	***PV***	0	
11	***FV***	$32,323.36	= FV(B7, B8, B9, B10, B12) FV(rate, nper, pmt, [pv], [type])
12	***BGN***	0	
13			
14		Calculating $FV_2 + FV_3$	
15	***j***	3.00%	
16	***m***	12	
17	***P/Y***	12	
18	***t***	3	
19			
20	***i***	0.25%	= B15/B16
21	***n***	36	= B17*B18
22	***PMT***	($600.00)	
23	***PV***	($32,323.36)	= –B11
24	***FV***	$57,935.75	= FV(B20, B21, B22, B23, B25) FV(rate, nper, pmt, [pv], [type])
25	***BGN***	0	
26			

Example 10.2(d)

	A	B	
1		Calculating *PV*	
2	***j***	5.40%	
3	***m***	12	
4	***P/Y***	12	
5	***t***	25	
6			
7	***i***	0.45%	= B2/B3
8	***n***	300	= B4*B5
9	***PMT***	$1,000.00	
10	***PV***	($164,438.55)	= PV(B7, B8, B9, B11, B12) PV(rate, nper, pmt, [fv], [type])
11	***FV***	0	
12	***BGN***	0	

Example 10.2(e)

	A	B	
1		Calculating *PV*	
2	***j***	3.00%	
3	***m***	12	
4	***P/Y***	12	
5	***t***	10	
6			
7	***i***	0.25%	= B2/B3
8	***n***	120	= B4*B5
9	***PMT***	($1,500.00)	
10	***PV***	$155,342.63	= PV(B7, B8, B9, B11, B12) PV(rate, nper, pmt, [fv], [type])
11	***FV***	0	
12	***BGN***	0	
13			

Example 10.2(f)

	A	B	
1		Calculating PV_1	
2	***j***	4.80%	
3	***m***	4	
4	***P/Y***	4	
5	***t***	2	
6			
7	***i***	1.20%	= B2/B3
8	***n***	8	= B4*B5
9	***PMT***	$15,000.00	
10	***PV***	($113,770.89)	= PV(B7, B8, B9, B11, B12) PV(rate, nper, pmt, [fv], [type])
11	***FV***	0	
12	***BGN***	0	
13			
14		Calculating PV_2	
15	***j***	5.60%	
16	***m***	4	
17	***P/Y***	4	
18	***t***	4	
19			
20	***i***	1.40%	= B15/B16
21	***n***	16	= B17*B18
22	***PMT***	$15,000.00	
23	***PV***	($213,688.02)	= PV(B20, B21, B22, B24, B25) PV(rate, nper, pmt, [fv], [type])
24	***FV***	0	
25	***BGN***	0	
26			

Example 10.2(f) *Continued*

27		Calculating PV_3	
28	*i*	1.20%	= B2/B3
29	*n*	8	= B3*B5
30	*PMT*	0	
31	*PV*	($194,238.84)	= PV(B28, B29, B30, B32) PV(rate, nper, pmt, [fv], [type])
32	*FV*	$213,688.02	= –B23
33			

10.3 Examples

Example 10.3(b)

	A	B	
1		Calculating *FV*	
2	*j*	2.92%	
3	*m*	365	
4	*P/Y*	12	
5	*t*	4	
6			
7	*i*	0.008%	= B2/B3
8	*c*	30.416667	= B3/B4
9	i_2	0.2436%	= (1 + B7)^B8 – 1
10	*n*	48	= B4*B5
11	*PMT*	($100.00)	
12	*PV*	0	
13	*FV*	$5085.36	= FV(B9, B10, B11, B12, B14) FV(rate, nper, pmt, [pv], [type])
14	*BGN*	0	
15			

Example 10.3(c)

	A	B	
1		Calculating *PV*	
2	*j*	6.00%	
3	*m*	1	
4	*P/Y*	12	
5	*t*	6	
6			
7	*i*	6.00%	= B2/B3
8	*c*	0.083333	= B3/B4
9	i_2	0.4868%	= (1 + B7)^B8 – 1
10	*n*	72	= B4*B5
11	*PMT*	($500.00)	
12	*PV*	$30,306.77	= PV(B9, B10, B11, B13, B14) PV(rate, nper, pmt, [fv], [type])
13	*FV*	0	
14	*BGN*	0	
15			

10.4 Examples

Example 10.4(a)

	A	B	
1		Calculating FV_{Due}	
2	*j*	5.00%	
3	*m*	2	
4	*P/Y*	2	
5	*t*	10	
6			
7	*i*	2.50%	= B2/B3
8	*n*	20	= B4*B5
9	*PMT*	($500.00)	
10	*PV*	0	
11	*FV*	$13,091.64	= FV(B7, B8, B9, B10, B12) FV(rate, nper, pmt, [pv], [type])
12	*BGN*	1	
13			

Example 10.4(b)

	A	B	
1		Calculating PV_{Due}	
2	*j*	4.00%	
3	*m*	4	
4	*P/Y*	4	
5	*t*	8	
6			
7	*i*	1.00%	= B2/B3
8	*n*	32	= B4*B5
9	*PMT*	($300.00)	
10	*PV*	$8,262.69	= PV(B7, B8, B9, B11, B12) PV(rate, nper, pmt, [fv], [type])
11	*FV*	0	
12	*BGN*	1	
13			

Example 10.4(c)

	A	B	
1		Calculating $FV_{Due\ 1}$	
2	*j*	3.00%	
3	*m*	12	
4	*P/Y*	12	
5	*t*	1	
6			
7	*i*	0.25%	= B2/B3
8	*n*	12	= B4*B5
9	*PMT*	($200.00)	
10	*PV*	0	
11	*FV*	$2,439.36	= FV(B7, B8, B9, B10, B12) FV(rate, nper, pmt, [pv], [type])
12	*BGN*	1	
13			
14		Calculating $FV_2 + FV_{Due\ 3}$	
15	*j*	2.70%	
16	*m*	12	
17	*P/Y*	12	
18	*t*	4	
19			
20	*i*	0.225%	= B15/B16
21	*n*	48	= B17*B18
22	*PMT*	($200.00)	
23	*PV*	($2,439.36)	= –B11
24	*FV*	$12,865.58	= FV(B20, B21, B22, B23, B25) FV(rate, nper, pmt, [pv], [type])
25	*BGN*	1	
26			

Example 10.4(d)

	A	B	
1	Calculating *Lease Amount*		
2	*j*	3.00%	
3	*m*	12	
4	*P/Y*	12	
5	*t*	4	
6			
7	*i*	0.25%	= B2/B3
8	*n*	48	= B4*B5
9	*PMT*	($230.00)	
10	*PV*	$21,287.61	= PV(B7, B8, B9, B11, B12) + 2000 PV(rate, nper, pmt, [fv], [type])
11	*FV*	($10,000.00)	
12	*BGN*	1	
13			
14	Calculating *Buyback Value*		
15	*j*	3.00%	
16	*m*	12	
17	*P/Y*	12	
18	*t*	1	
19			

Example 10.4(d) *Continued*

20	*i*	0.25%	= B15/B16
21	*n*	12	= B17*B18
22	*PMT*	($230.00)	
23	*PV*	$12,427.28	= PV(B20, B21, B22, B24, B25) PV(rate, nper, pmt, [fv], [type])
24	*FV*	($10,000.00)	
25	*BGN*	1	
26			

10.5 Examples

Example 10.5(a)

	A	B	
1		Calculating FV_{Due}	
2	*j*	5.00%	
3	*m*	12	
4	*P/Y*	4	
5	*t*	5	
6			
7	*i*	0.4167%	= B2/B3
8	*c*	3	= B3/B4
9	i_2	1.2552%	= (1 + B7)^B8 – 1
10	*n*	20	= B4*B5
11	*PMT*	($5,000.00)	
12	*PV*	0	
13	*FV*	$114,289.31	= FV(B9, B10, B11, B12, B14) FV(rate, nper, pmt, [pv], [type])
14	*BGN*	1	
15			

Example 10.5(b)

	A	B	
1		Calculating PV_{Due}	
2	*j*	4.00%	
3	*m*	2	
4	*P/Y*	12	
5	*t*	30	
6			
7	*i*	2.00%	= B2/B3
8	*c*	0.166667	= B3/B4
9	i_2	0.3306%	= (1 + B7)^B8 – 1
10	*n*	360	= B4*B5
11	*PMT*	$4,500.00	
12	*PV*	($949,463.50)	= PV(B9, B10, B11, B13, B14) PV(rate, nper, pmt, [fv], [type])
13	*FV*	0	
14	*BGN*	1	
15			

Example 10.5(c)

	A	B	
1	Calculating FV_{Ariana}		
2	*j*	4.80%	
3	*m*	365	
4	*P/Y*	12	
5	*t*	47	
6			
7	*i*	0.0132%	= B2/B3
8	*c*	30.416667	= B3/B4
9	i_2	0.4008%	= (1 + B7)^B8 – 1
10	*n*	564	= B4*B5
11	*PMT*	($100.00)	
12	*PV*	0	
13	*FV*	$214,026.94	= FV(B9, B10, B11, B12, B14) FV(rate, nper, pmt, [pv], [type])
14	*BGN*	1	
15			

Example 10.5(c) *Continued*

16	Calculating FV_{Macy}		
17	*j*	4.80%	
18	*m*	365	
19	*P/Y*	1	
20	*t*	20	
21			
22	*i*	0.0132%	= B17/B18
23	*c*	365	= B18/B19
24	i_2	4.9167%	= (1 + B22)^B23 – 1
25	*n*	20	= B19*B20
26	*PMT*	($4,000.00)	
27	*PV*	0	
28	*FV*	$137,551.98	= FV(B24, B25, B26, B27, B29) FV(rate, nper, pmt, [pv], [type])
29	*BGN*	1	
30			
31	*j*	4.80%	
32	*m*	365	
33	*t*	10	
34			
35	*i*	0.0132%	= B31/B32
36	*n*	3650	= B32*B33
37	*PMT*	0	
38	*PV*	($137,551.98)	= –B28
39	*FV*	$222,287.22	= FV(B35, B36, B37, B38) FV(rate, nper, pmt, [pv], [type])
40			

10.6 Examples

Example 10.6(a)

	A	B	
1		Calculating *PMT*	
2	*j*	6.00%	
3	*m*	12	
4	*P/Y*	12	
5	*t*	10	
6			
7	*i*	0.50%	= B2/B3
8	*n*	120	= B4*B5
9	*PMT*	($388.57)	= PMT(B7, B8, B10, B11, B12) PMT(rate, nper, pv, [fv], [type])
10	*PV*	$35,000.00	
11	*FV*	0	
12	*BGN*	0	
13			

Example 10.6(b)

	A	B	
1		Calculating *PMT*	
2	*j*	8.00%	
3	*m*	2	
4	*P/Y*	4	
5	*t*	10	
6			
7	*i*	4.00%	= B2/B3
8	*c*	0.5	= B3/B4
9	i_2	1.9804%	= (1 + B7)^B8 – 1
10	*n*	40	= B4*B5
11	*PMT*	($997.57)	= PMT(B9, B10, B12, B13, B14) PMT(rate, nper, pv, [fv], [type])
12	*PV*	0	
13	*FV*	$60,000.00	
14	*BGN*	0	
15			

Example 10.6(c)

	A	B	
1		Calculating *PMT*	
2	*j*	4.00%	
3	*m*	1	
4	*P/Y*	12	
5	*t*	5	
6			
7	*i*	4.00%	= B2/B3
8	*c*	0.083333	= B3/B4
9	i_2	0.3274%	= (1 + B7)^B8 – 1
10	*n*	60	= B4*B5
11	*PMT*	$183.24	= PMT(B9, B10, B12, B13, B14) PMT(rate, nper, pv, [fv], [type])
12	*PV*	($10,000.00)	
13	*FV*	0	
14	*BGN*	1	
15			

Example 10.6(d)

	A	B	
1	Calculating $PV_{Residual}$		
2	*j*	3.60%	
3	*m*	12	
4	*P/Y*	12	
5	*t*	4	
6			
7	*i*	0.30%	= B2/B3
8	*n*	48	= B3*B5
9	*PMT*	0	
10	*PV*	($13,822.55)	= PV(B7, B8, B9, B11) PV(rate, nper, pv, [fv], [type])
11	*FV*	$15,960.00	
12			
13	Calculating *PMT*		
14	*i*	0.30%	= B2/B3
15	*n*	48	= B4*B5
16	*PMT*	($455.10)	= PMT(B14, B15, B17, B18, B19) PMT(rate, nper, pv, [fv], [type])
17	*PV*	$20,377.45	= 38000 – 3800 + B10
18	*FV*	0	
19	*BGN*	1	
20			

10.7 Examples

Example 10.7(a)

	A	B	
1		Calculating *t*	
2	*j*	12.00%	
3	*m*	12	
4	*P/Y*	1	
5	*t*	22	= ROUNDUP(B10,0)/B4 ROUNDUP(number, num_digits)
6			
7	*i*	1.00%	= B2/B3
8	*c*	12	= B3/B4
9	i_2	12.6825%	= (1 + B7)^B8 – 1
10	*n*	21.909806	= NPER(B9, B11, B12, B13, B14) NPER(rate, pmt, pv, [fv], [type])
11	*PMT*	($5,000.00)	
12	*PV*	0	
13	*FV*	$500,000.00	
14	*BGN*	0	
15			

Example 10.7(b)

	A	B	
1		Calculating *t*	
2	*j*	6.00%	
3	*m*	2	
4	*P/Y*	4	
5	*t*	2.75	= ROUNDUP(B10,0)/B4 ROUNDUP(number, num_digits)
6			
7	*i*	3.00%	= B2/B3
8	*c*	0.5	= B3/B4
9	i_2	1.4889%	= (1 + B7)^B8 – 1
10	*n*	10.908137	= NPER(B9, B11, B12, B13, B14) NPER(rate, pmt, pv, [fv], [type])
11	*PMT*	$5,000.00	
12	*PV*	($50,000.00)	
13	*FV*	0	
14	*BGN*	0	
15			

Example 10.7(c)

	A	B	
1		Calculating *t*	
2	*j*	3.50%	
3	*m*	2	
4	*P/Y*	12	
5	*t*	7.33	= ROUNDUP(B10,0)/B4 ROUNDUP(number, num_digits)
6			
7	*i*	1.75%	= B2/B3
8	*c*	0.166667	= B3/B4
9	i_2	0.2896%	= (1 + B7)^B8 – 1
10	*n*	87.725989	= NPER(B9, B11, B12, B13, B14) NPER(rate, pmt, pv, [fv], [type])
11	*PMT*	($2,500.00)	
12	*PV*	0	
13	*FV*	$250,000.00	
14	*BGN*	1	
15			

Example 10.7(d)

	A	B	
1		Calculating *t*	
2	*j*	4.00%	
3	*m*	4	
4	*P/Y*	4	
5	*t*	17.25	= ROUNDUP(B8,0)/B4 ROUNDUP(number, num_digits)
6			
7	*i*	1.00%	= B2/B3
8	*n*	68.670569	= NPER(B7, B9, B10, B11, B12) NPER(rate, pmt, pv, [fv], [type])
9	*PMT*	$2,000.00	
10	*PV*	($100,000.00)	
11	*FV*	0	
12	*BGN*	1	
13			

10.8 Examples

Example 10.8(a)

	A	B	
1		Calculating *j*	
2	*j*	2.88%	= B7*B3
3	*m*	12	
4	*P/Y*	12	
5	*t*	10	
6			
7	*i*	0.24%	= RATE(B8, B9, B10, B11, B12) (RATE(nper, pmt, pv, [fv], [type], [guess]))
8	*n*	120	= B4*B5
9	*PMT*	($240.00)	
10	*PV*	$25,000.00	
11	*FV*	0	
12	*BGN*	0	
13			

Example 10.8(b)

	A	B	
1		Calculating *j*	
2	*j*	5.05%	= B7*B3
3	*m*	4	
4	*P/Y*	2	
5	*t*	12	
6			
7	*i*	1.26%	= (1 + B9)^(1/B8) – 1
8	*c*	2	= B3/B4
9	i_2	2.5396%	= RATE(B10, B11, B12, B13, B14) (RATE(nper, pmt, pv, [fv], [type], [guess]))
10	*n*	24	= B4*B5
11	*PMT*	($1,500.00)	
12	*PV*	0	
13	*FV*	$50,000.00	
14	*BGN*	1	
15			

Example 10.8(c)

	A	B	
1	Calculating *f* - Bank *A*		
2	*j*	-	
3	*m*	1	
4	*P/Y*	1	
5	*t*	3	
6			
7	*i*	9.70%	= RATE(B8, B9, B10, B11, B12) (RATE(nper, pmt, pv, [fv], [type], [guess]))
8	*n*	3	= B4*B5
9	*PMT*	($12,000.00)	
10	*PV*	$30,000.00	
11	*FV*	0	
12	*BGN*	0	
13			
14	Calculating *f* - Bank *B*		
15	*j*	-	
16	*m*	1	
17	*P/Y*	12	
18	*t*	2.5	
19			
20	*i*	11.70%	= (1 + B22)^(1/B21) – 1
21	*c*	0.083333	= B16/B17
22	i_2	0.9265%	= RATE(B23, B24, B25, B26, B27) (RATE(nper, pmt, pv, [fv], [type], [guess]))
23	*n*	30	= B17*B18
24	*PMT*	($1,150.00)	
25	*PV*	$30,000.00	
26	*FV*	0	
27	*BGN*	0	
28			

Example 10.8(d)

	A	B	
1		Calculating *j*	
2	*j*	4.51%	= B7*B3
3	*m*	12	
4	*P/Y*	12	
5	*t*	4	
6			
7	*i*	0.38%	= RATE(B8, B9, B10, B11, B12) (RATE(nper, pmt, pv, [fv], [type], [guess]))
8	*n*	48	= B4*B5
9	*PMT*	($275.00)	
10	*PV*	$21,500.00	= 23500 – 2000
11	*FV*	($11,250.00)	
12	*BGN*	1	
13			

Review Examples

Example 1

	A	B	
1		Calculating *FV*	
2	*j*	8.00%	
3	*m*	2	
4	*P/Y*	4	
5	*t*	10	
6			
7	*i*	4.00%	= B2/B3
8	*c*	0.5	= B3/B4
9	i_2	1.9804%	= (1 + B7)^B8 – 1
10	*n*	40	= B4*B5
11	*PMT*	($1,000.00)	
12	*PV*	0	
13	*FV*	$60,145.88	= FV(B9, B10, B11, B12, B14) (FV(rate, nper, pmt, [pv], [type]))
14	*BGN*	0	
15			

Example 2

	A	B	
1		Calculating *PV*	
2	*j*	8.00%	
3	*m*	2	
4	*P/Y*	4	
5	*t*	10	
6			
7	*i*	4.00%	= B2/B3
8	*c*	0.5	= B3/B4
9	i_2	1.9804%	= (1 + B7)^B8 – 1
10	*n*	40	= B4*B5
11	*PMT*	($1,000.00)	
12	*PV*	$27,449.79	= PV(B9, B10, B11, B13, B14) (PV(rate, nper, pmt, [fv], [type]))
13	*FV*	0	
14	*BGN*	0	
15			

Example 3

	A	B	Formula
1		Calculating *PMT*	
2	***j***	8.00%	
3	***m***	2	
4	***P/Y***	4	
5	***t***	10	
6			
7	***i***	4.00%	= B2/B3
8	***c***	0.5	= B3/B4
9	i_2	1.9804%	= (1 + B7)^B8 – 1
10	***n***	40	= B4*B5
11	***PMT***	($1,000.00)	= PMT(B9, B10, B12, B13, B14) PMT(rate, nper, pv, [fv], [type])
12	***PV***	0	
13	***FV***	$60,145.88	
14	***BGN***	0	
15			

Example 4

	A	B	Formula
1		Calculating *PMT*	
2	***j***	8.00%	
3	***m***	2	
4	***P/Y***	4	
5	***t***	10	
6			
7	***i***	4.00%	= B2/B3
8	***c***	0.5	= B3/B4
9	i_2	1.9804%	= (1 + B7)^B8 – 1
10	***n***	40	= B4*B5
11	***PMT***	($1,000.00)	= PMT(B9, B10, B12, B13, B14) PMT(rate, nper, pv, [fv], [type])
12	***PV***	$27,449.79	
13	***FV***	0	
14	***BGN***	0	
15			

Example 5

	A	B	Formula
1		Calculating *t*	
2	***j***	8.00%	
3	***m***	2	
4	***P/Y***	4	
5	***t***	10	= ROUNDUP(B10,0)/B4 ROUNDUP(number, num_digits)
6			
7	***i***	4.00%	= B2/B3
8	***c***	0.5	= B3/B4
9	i_2	1.9804%	= (1 + B7)^B8 – 1
10	***n***	40	= NPER(B9, B11, B12, B13, B14) NPER(rate, pmt, pv, [fv], [type])
11	***PMT***	($1,000.00)	
12	***PV***	0	
13	***FV***	$60,145.88	
14	***BGN***	0	
15			

Example 6

	A	B	Formula
1		Calculating *t*	
2	***j***	8.00%	
3	***m***	2	
4	***P/Y***	4	
5	***t***	10	= ROUNDUP(B10,0)/B4 ROUNDUP(number, num_digits)
6			
7	***i***	4.00%	= B2/B3
8	***c***	0.5	= B3/B4
9	i_2	1.9804%	= (1 + B7)^B8 – 1
10	***n***	40	= NPER(B9, B11, B12, B13, B14) NPER(rate, pmt, pv, [fv], [type])
11	***PMT***	($1,000.00)	
12	***PV***	$27,449.79	
13	***FV***	0	
14	***BGN***	0	
15			

Example 7

	A	B	Formula
1		Calculating *j*	
2	***j***	8.00%	= B7*B3
3	***m***	2	
4	***P/Y***	4	
5	***t***	10	
6			
7	***i***	4.00%	= (1 + B9)^(1/B8) – 1
8	***c***	0.5	= B3/B4
9	i_2	1.9804%	= RATE(B10, B11, B12, B13, B14) RATE(nper, pmt, pv, [fv], [type], [guess])
10	***n***	40	= B4*B5
11	***PMT***	($1,000.00)	
12	***PV***	0	
13	***FV***	$60,145.88	
14	***BGN***	0	
15			

Example 8

	A	B	Formula
1		Calculating *i*	
2	***j***	8.49%	= B7*B3
3	***m***	2	
4	***P/Y***	4	
5	***t***	10	
6			
7	***i***	4.24%	= (1 + B9)^(1/B8) – 1
8	***c***	0.5	= B3/B4
9	i_2	2.0992%	= RATE(B10, B11, B12, B13, B14) RATE(nper, pmt, pv, [fv], [type], [guess])
10	***n***	40	– B4*B5
11	***PMT***	($1,000.00)	
12	***PV***	$27,449.79	
13	***FV***	0	
14	***BGN***	1	
15			

Summary of Types of Annuities and Formulas

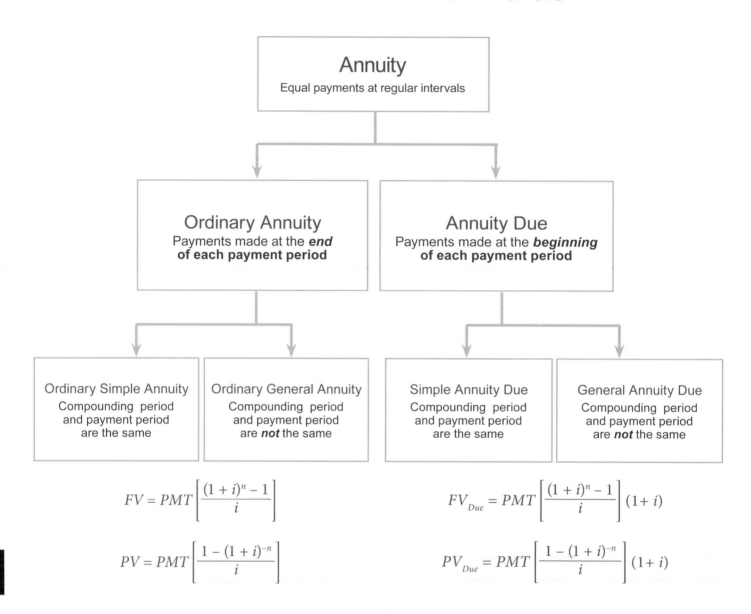

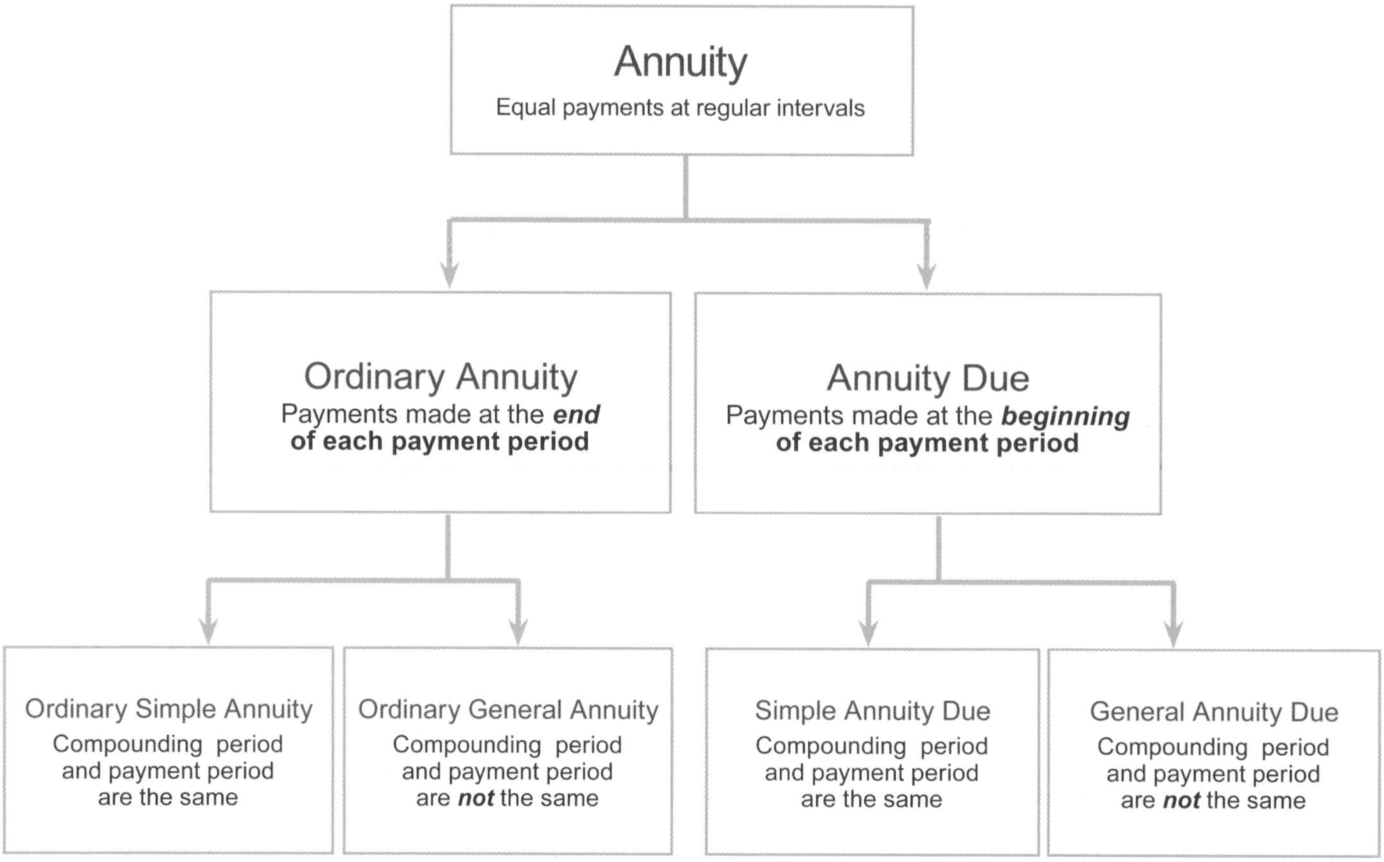
Annuity
Equal payments at regular intervals
Ordinary Annuity
Payments made at the end of each payment period
Annuity Due
Payments made at the beginning of each payment period
Ordinary Simple Annuity
Compounding period and payment period are the same
Ordinary General Annuity
Compounding period and payment period are not the same
Simple Annuity Due
Compounding period and payment period are the same
General Annuity Due
Compounding period and payment period are not the same

$$FV = PMT\left[\frac{(1+i)^n - 1}{i}\right]$$

$$FV_{Due} = PMT\left[\frac{(1+i)^n - 1}{i}\right](1+i)$$

$$PV = PMT\left[\frac{1-(1+i)^{-n}}{i}\right]$$

$$PV_{Due} = PMT\left[\frac{1-(1+i)^{-n}}{i}\right](1+i)$$

In the case of ordinary general annuity and general annuity due, substitute 'i_2' for 'i' in the annuity formulas.

$$c = \frac{\text{Number of compounding periods per year}}{\text{Number of payments per year}}$$

$$i_2 = (1+i)^c - 1$$

10 | Summary of Notation and Formulas

NOTATION

PMT = Amount of periodic payment in an annuity

n = Total number of payments during the term of an annuity
= Number of compounding periods during the term of a single payment in compound interest

i = Interest rate per compounding period (periodic interest rate)

c = Number of compounding periods per payment period

i_2 = Equivalent interest rate per payment period

j = Nominal interest rate

t = Time period or Term

FV = Accumulated value or future value of an ordinary annuity

FV_{Due} = Accumulated value or future value of an annuity due

PV = Discounted value or present value of an ordinary annuity

PV_{Due} = Discounted value or present value of an annuity due

FORMULAS

Future Value of an Ordinary Simple Annuity | 10.2(a)

$$FV = PMT\left[\frac{(1+i)^n - 1}{i}\right]$$

Present Value of an Ordinary Simple Annuity | 10.2(b)

$$PV = PMT\left[\frac{1-(1+i)^{-n}}{i}\right]$$

Number of Compounding Periods per Payment Period | 10.3(a)

$$c = \frac{\textit{Number of compounding periods per year}}{\textit{Number of payments per year}}$$

Equivalent Periodic Interest Rate per Payment Period | 10.3(b)

$$i_2 = (1+i)^c - 1$$

In the case of ordinary general annuity and general annuity due, substitute 'i_2' for 'i' in the formulas.

Future Value of a Simple Annuity Due | 10.4(a)

$$FV_{Due} = PMT\left[\frac{(1+i)^n - 1}{i}\right](1+i)$$

Present Value of a Simple Annuity Due | 10.4(b)

$$PV_{Due} = PMT\left[\frac{1-(1+i)^{-n}}{i}\right](1+i)$$

Number of Payments, Given 'FV' | 10.7(a)

$$n = \frac{\ln\left[1 + \frac{i \times FV}{PMT}\right]}{\ln(1+i)}$$

Number of Payments, Given 'PV' | 10.7(b)

$$n = -\frac{\ln\left[1 - \frac{i \times PV}{PMT}\right]}{\ln(1+i)}$$

Time Period (in years) | 10.7(c)

$$t = \frac{n}{\textit{Number of payments per year}}$$

Number of Payments, Given 'FV_{Due}' | 10.7(d)

$$n = \frac{\ln\left[1 + \frac{i \times FV_{Due}}{PMT(1+i)}\right]}{\ln(1+i)}$$

Number of Payments, Given 'PV_{Due}' | 10.7(e)

$$n = -\frac{\ln\left[1 - \frac{i \times PV_{Due}}{PMT(1+i)}\right]}{\ln(1+i)}$$

Expert Advice

Understanding Your Investment Options

Armed with the knowledge of annuities, it is important to know the different investment options that are available in Canada

The Canadian investment landscape is structured to cater to the needs of individuals with low-, medium-, and high-risk tolerance. Low-risk investments yield low returns, whereas high-risk investments yield high returns. The appropriate investment for individuals is determined by three things: investment objective, risk profile, and time period of investment. Investments can be made directly into investment vehicles such as bonds, shares, T-bills, etc., or through investment plans such as RRSPs, RESPs, etc., which have particular tax benefits.

Investment vehicles are differentiated based on their risk and return. If you are not able to assume high risk or liability, you can invest in debt instruments, which are low-risk and provide low returns. However, if you have a higher threshold for risk, you can invest in the equity market, which has a higher risk, but also higher returns.

HIGH RISK, HIGH RETURN

Equity Investments

Shares (or stocks): In order to raise money, companies offer ownership of their business either to the public or a select, private group of people in the form of shares or stock.

Mutual Funds: Investment vehicles that contain a portfolio of investments that are managed to provide the required rate of return.

Treasury Bills (T-Bills): Investment offered and guaranteed by the Government of Canada.

Guaranteed Investment Certificate (GIC): Investment where the principal and return are guaranteed. These investments are offered by banks, credit unions, and trust companies.

Bonds: Investment where you lend money to a bond-issuer (who may be the government or a corporation) who gives you a bond that promises to pay you a specified interest during the bond's life and the face value (principal) on maturity.

Debt Investments

LOW RISK, LOW RETURN

> *"Buy when everyone else is selling and hold until everyone else is buying. That's not just a catchy slogan. It's the very essence of successful investing."*
>
> J. Paul Getty, Industrialist

Investment Plans are methods of investing in investment vehicles. Investment plans are non-registered when you directly invest in an investment vehicle, or registered when they are approved by the Federal Government and may have special tax advantages to the investor. Registered plans contain a mix of one or many investment vehicles in different proportions. The rate of return of the plan is the average of the individual rates of returns of each investment vehicle in the plan. The four most popular investment plans are described below.

REGISTERED RETIREMENT SAVINGS PLAN

Initiated by the Federal Government to encourage people to invest towards their retirement with a tax deduction as incentive. Anyone who has earned income, has a social insurance number, and has filed a tax return can contribute to an RRSP until the end of the year in which they reach age 71. Contributions to RRSPs are deductible from total income, reducing income tax payable for the year in which the contributions are claimed. No income earned in the account is taxed, but withdrawals are taxed as income when they are withdrawn. The contribution limit for current year (tax year 2017) is 18% of the earned income from the previous year, up to the maximum annual contribution limit of $26,230.

RRSP

REGISTERED EDUCATION SAVINGS PLAN

Initiated by the Federal Government to encourage parents to save for the post-secondary education of their children. RESP has a current maximum lifetime contribution limit of $50,000. The contributions are, or have already been, taxed at the contributor's tax rate, while the investment growth is taxed on withdrawal at the recipient's tax rate. An RESP recipient is typically a post-secondary student who generally pays little or no federal income tax. RESP contributions can only be made until the beneficiary reaches 31 years of age and has a maximum life of 35 years. Canada Education Savings Grant (CESG) complement 20% of the annual RESP contributions up to $500 per year to a lifetime maximum of $7200.

RESP

TAX FREE SAVINGS ACCOUNT

Initiated by the Federal Government in year 2009 to provide any Canadian resident of 18 years of age or older with tax-free savings throughout their lifetime. TFSA is a flexible investment account that can help to meet both short- and long-term goals. Contributions to a TFSA are not deductible for income tax purposes. Income earned or withdrawals made from a TFSA account are not taxed. The annual contribution limit for current year (tax year 2017) is $5500.

TFSA

REGISTERED RETIREMENT INCOME FUND

A plan to convert RRSPs to grow tax-free while giving access to the money saved in RRSP in the form of retirement income. There is no age minimum to starting an RRIF, but no later than the end of the year you turn 71. A minimum amount must be withdrawn every year starting from the following year the RRIF is opened and continue for your entire life. For ages below 71, the minimum withdrawal amount is based on a percentage of the value of RRIF calculated using the formula: $1 \div (90 - \textit{age})$. After age 71, the government puts out a set schedule for the minimum withdrawal amount. There is no maximum withdrawal limit. All withdrawals from an RRIF are taxable and considered income.

RRIF

Chapter

11 OTHER TYPES OF ANNUITIES

LEARNING OBJECTIVES

- Calculate the present value, number of payments, term, and size of periodic payments of a deferred annuity.
- Calculate the present value and size of periodic payments of a perpetuity.
- Calculate the future value and present value of a constant-growth annuity.

CHAPTER OUTLINE

11.1 Deferred Annuities
11.2 Perpetuities
11.3 Constant-Growth Annuities

Introduction

In the previous chapter, we learned how to analyze situations where series of equal payments are made towards an investment or loan at regular intervals for a fixed period of time. However, there are many practical situations when an annuity may need to be treated slightly differently.

Other types of annuities include deferred annuities, perpetuities, and constant-growth annuities.

Consider a situation where a business has to make monthly payments towards the purchase of new equipment, starting six months from now (after a certain time interval). Or, a college that wishes to offer an annual scholarship to the business student with the highest average indefinitely (no fixed period of time). Finally, consider a woman who wants to make semi-annual contributions to her RRSP, increasing each contribution by 2.5% (payment increasing by a constant growth rate).

This chapter deals with these three different types of annuities, which, respectively, are called **deferred annuities**, **perpetuities**, and **constant-growth annuities**.

11.1 | Deferred Annuities

A deferred annuity is an annuity in which the first periodic payment is made after a certain interval of time, known as the **deferral period**. The deferral period is the time interval from 'now' to the beginning of the annuity period.

Ordinary Deferred Annuity

If the deferral period ends one payment interval before the first periodic payment, then it is an ordinary deferred annuity.

Deferred Annuity Due

If the deferral period ends at the beginning of the first periodic payment, then it is a deferred annuity due.

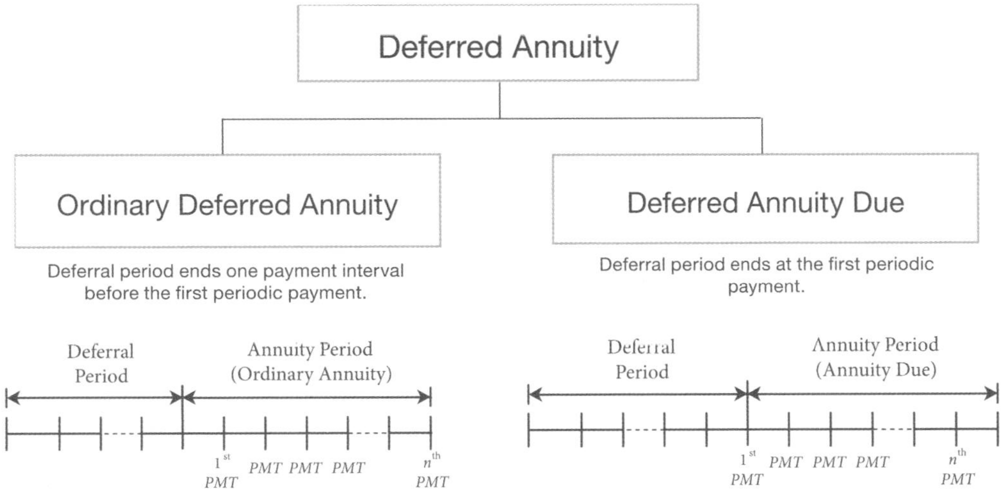

The ordinary deferred annuity or the deferred annuity due can be simple or general based on the payment period and the compounding period.

A **deferred annuity due** can be modified to become an **ordinary deferred annuity** by shortening the deferral period by one payment period. By doing this, the payments made at the beginning of each payment period can be accommodated by making them into payments made at the end of each payment period, as shown below:

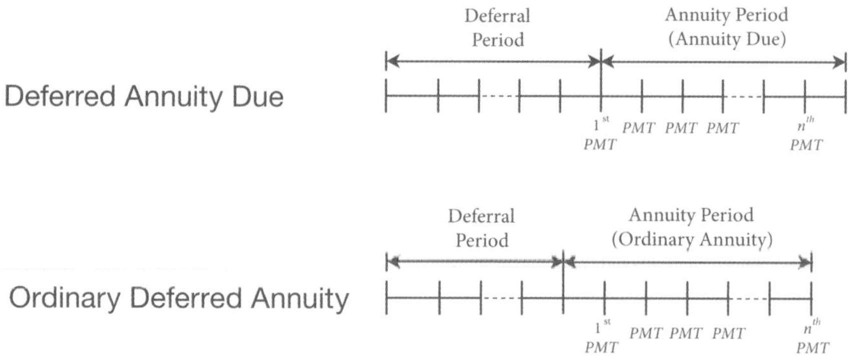

Example 11.1(a) **Identifying the Deferral Period and Annuity Period in an Annuity**

Payments of $1000 are made at the beginning of each year for ten years with the first payment being made three years from now.

(i) Assuming the annuity is a deferred annuity due, identify the deferral period and the annuity period.

(ii) Assuming the annuity is an ordinary deferred annuity, identify the deferral period and the annuity period.

Solution

(i) *Deferred annuity due*

- Deferral period ends at the first periodic payment.
- Payments start 3 years from now.

When considered as a deferred annuity due, the annuity due term starts three years from now. Therefore, the deferral period is 3 years.

The annuity period is 10 years.

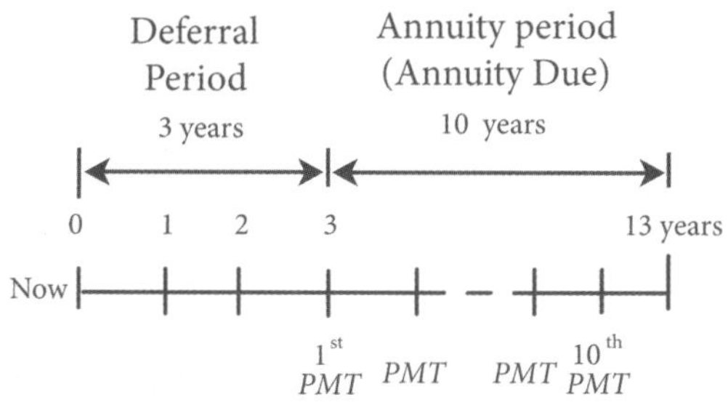

n = 1 payment/year × 10 years
= 10 annual payments

(ii) *Ordinary deferred annuity*

- Deferral period ends one payment interval before the first periodic payment.
- Payments start 3 years from now.

When considered as an ordinary deferred annuity, the ordinary annuity term starts two years from now; i.e., one payment interval before the first periodic payment. Therefore, the deferral period is 2 years.

The annuity period is 10 years.

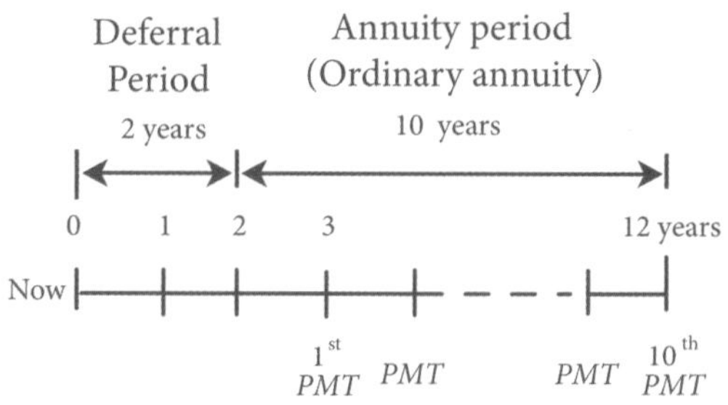

n = 1 payment/year × 10 years
= 10 annual payments

Calculating Future Value and Present Value of a Deferred Annuity

The future value of a deferred annuity (FV_{Def}) is the accumulated value of the stream of payments at the end of the annuity period. This is the same procedure as calculating the future value of any annuity that you have learned in Chapter 10.

The present value of a deferred annuity (PV_{Def}) is the discounted value of the stream of payments at the beginning of the deferral period. This follows a two-step procedure and the following examples will illustrate these calculations.

Example 11.1(b) Calculating the Present Value of a Deferred Annuity

What amount should you invest now if you want to receive payments of $1000 every year for ten years with the first payment to be received three years from now? Assume that money earns 5% compounded annually.

Page 486

Solution

We can treat the annuity as either an ordinary deferred annuity **or** a deferred annuity due.

Method 1: Treating the annuity as an ordinary deferred annuity

- Deferral period ends one payment interval before the first periodic payment
- Compounding period (annually) = payment period (annually)
- Payments start 3 years from now

When calculated as an ordinary simple deferred annuity, the ordinary annuity term starts two years from now; i.e., one payment interval before the first periodic payment. Therefore, the deferral period is 2 years.

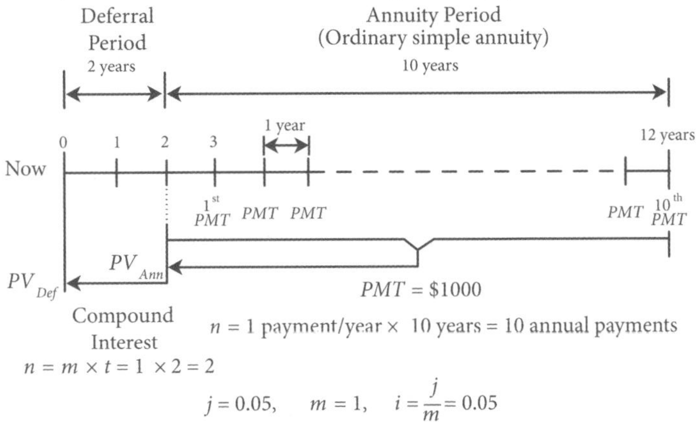

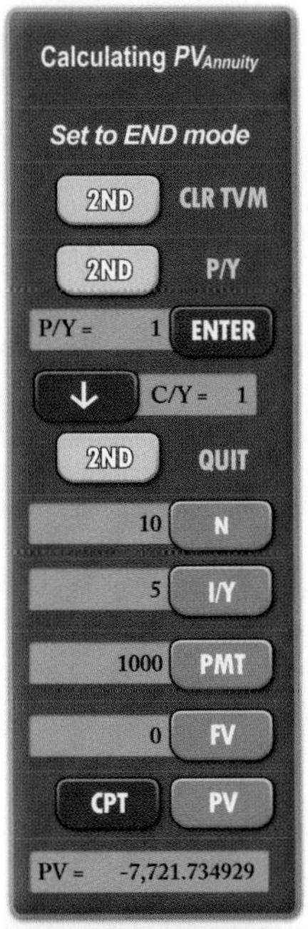

As you can see in the time line diagram, there is a deferral period of 2 years followed by an annuity period of 10 years. We are required to calculate the present value of the deferred annuity (PV_{Def}).

Step 1: Calculating the present value of the ordinary simple annuity ($PV_{Annuity}$)

Using Formula 10.2(b), $PV_{Annuity} = PMT\left[\dfrac{1-(1+i)^{-n}}{i}\right]$

$$= 1000.00\left[\dfrac{1-(1+0.05)^{-10}}{0.05}\right]$$

$$= \$7721.734929\ldots$$

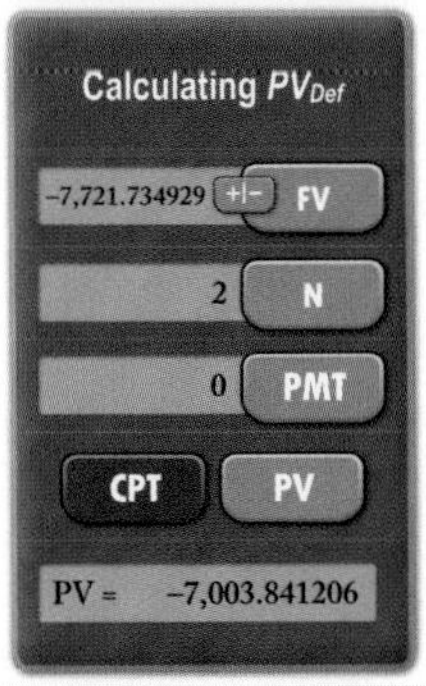

Step 2: Calculating the present value of this amount at the beginning of the deferral period (PV_{Def})

Using Formula 9.1(b), $PV = FV(1+i)^{-n}$

$$PV_{Def} = PV_{Annuity}(1+i)^{-n}$$

$$= 7721.734929\ldots(1+0.05)^{-2}$$

$$= 7003.841206\ldots = \$7003.84$$

Therefore, you should invest $7003.84 in the fund now.

Page 486

Solution *continued*

Method 2: Treating the annuity as a deferred annuity due

- Deferral period ends at the first periodic payment
- Compounding period (annually) = payment period (annually)
- Payments start 3 years from now

When calculated as a simple deferred annuity due, the ordinary annuity term starts three years from now. Therefore, the deferral period is 3 years.

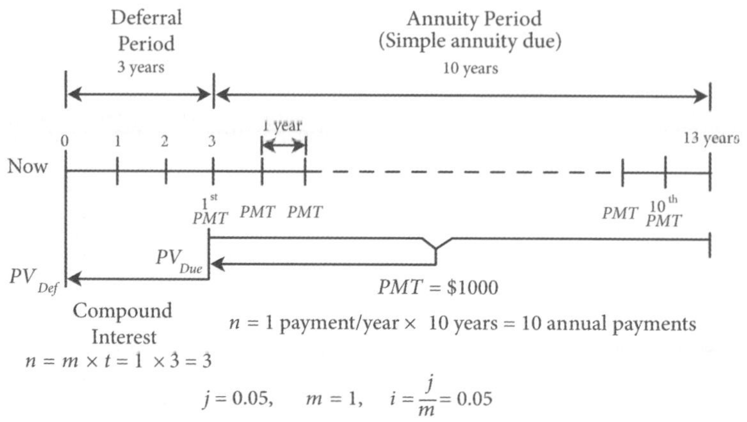

As you can see in the time line diagram, there is a deferral period of 3 years followed by an annuity period of 10 years. We are required to calculate the present value of the deferred annuity (PV_{Def}).

Step 1: Calculating the present value of the simple annuity due (PV_{Due})

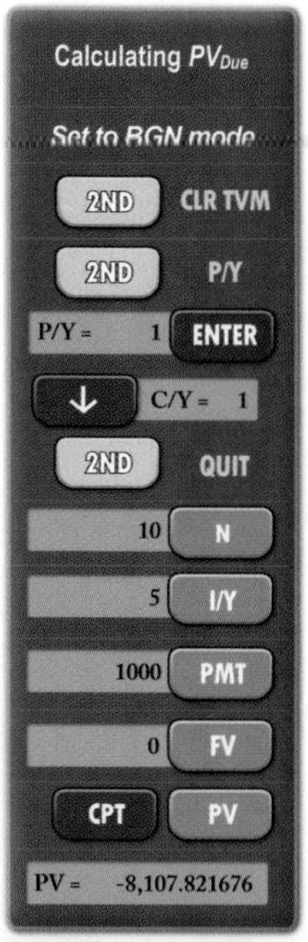

Using Formula 10.4(b),

$$PV_{Due} = PMT\left[\frac{1-(1+i)^{-n}}{i}\right](1+i)$$

$$= 1000.00\left[\frac{1-(1+0.05)^{-10}}{0.05}\right](1+0.05)$$

$$= \$8107.821676...$$

Step 2: Calculating the present value of this amount at the beginning of the deferral period (PV_{Def})

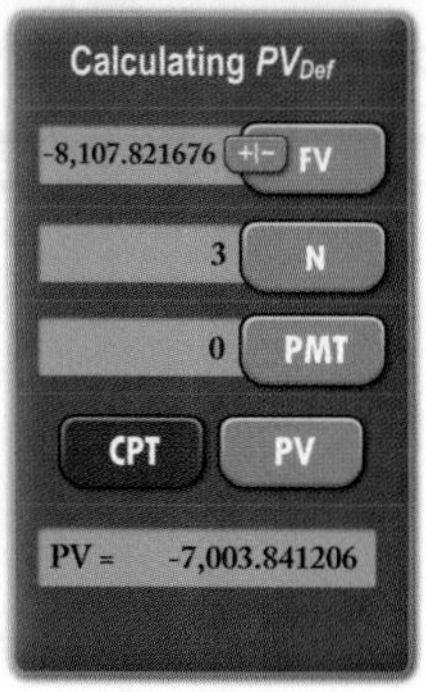

Using Formula 9.1(b),

$$PV = FV(1+i)^{-n}$$

$$PV_{Def} = PV_{Due}(1+i)^{-n}$$

$$= 8107.821676...(1+0.05)^{-3}$$

$$= 7003.841206... = \$7003.84$$

Therefore, you should invest $7003.84 in the fund now.

You will notice that treating the annuity as an ordinary deferred annuity (Method 1) or as a deferred annuity due (Method 2) has no bearing on the final answer.

In the solved examples and exercise problems in this section, whenever the periodic payment is specified to occur at the *end* of the payment interval, we will treat the annuity as an ordinary deferred annuity; whenever the periodic payment is specified to occur at the *beginning* of the payment interval, we will treat the annuity as a deferred annuity due. However, any deferred annuity can be treated as either an ordinary deferred annuity or a deferred annuity due.

Example 11.1(c) **Calculating the Present Value of a General Deferred Annuity Due**

Calculate the amount of money an investment banker would have to deposit in an investment fund that will provide him with \$1000 at the beginning of each month for eleven years. He is to receive his first payment two years from now and the interest rate is 6% compounded semi-annually.

Solution

Page 486

- Payments are made at the beginning of each payment period (monthly)
- Compounding period (semi-annually) ≠ payment period (monthly)
- Payments start 2 years from now

When calculated as a general deferred annuity due, the annuity due term starts two years from now. Therefore, the deferral period is 2 years.

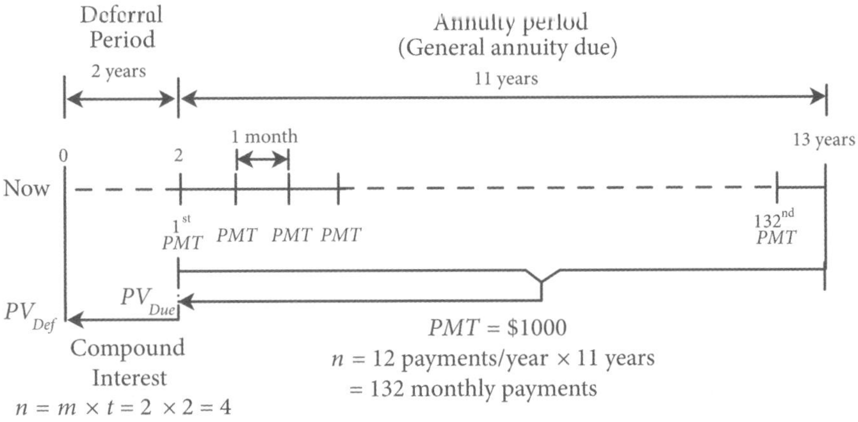

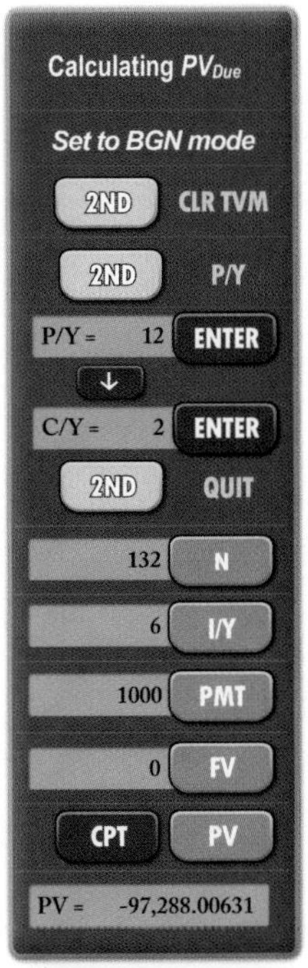

$$j = 0.06, \quad m = 2, \quad i = \frac{j}{m} = 0.03$$

We are required to calculate the present value of the deferral period (PV_{Def}).

Step 1: Calculating the present value of the general annuity due (PV_{Due})

$$c = \frac{\text{Number of compounding periods per year}}{\text{Number of payments per year}} = \frac{2}{12}$$

$$i_2 = (1 + i)^c - 1 = (1 + 0.03)^{(2/12)} - 1 = 0.004938...$$

Using Formula 10.4(b) and substituting i_2 for i,

$$PV_{Due} = PMT\left[\frac{1 - (1 + i_2)^{-n}}{i_2}\right](1 + i_2)$$

$$= 1000.00\left[\frac{1 - (1 + 0.004938...)^{-132}}{0.004938...}\right](1 + 0.004938...)$$

$$= \$97{,}288.00631...$$

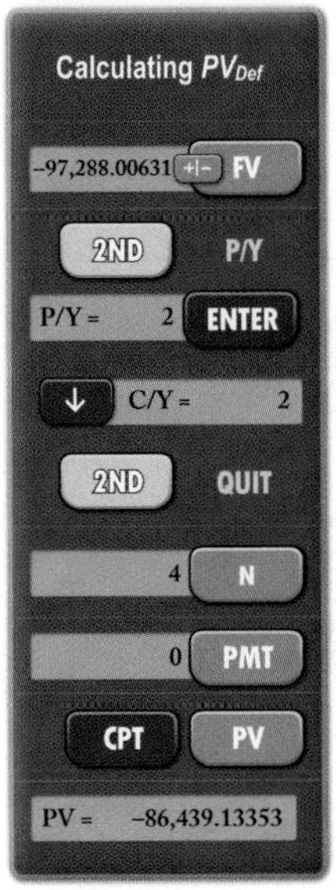

Step 2: Calculating the present value of this amount at the beginning of the deferral period (PV_{Def})

Using Formula 9.1(b), $PV = FV(1 + i)^{-n}$

$$PV_{Def} = PV_{Due}(1 + i)^{-n}$$

$$= 97{,}288.00631... (1 + 0.03)^{-4}$$

$$= 86{,}439.13353... = \$86{,}439.13$$

Or,

$$PV_{Def} = PV_{Due}(1 + i_2)^{-n}$$

$$= 97{,}288.00631... (1 + 0.004938...)^{-(12 \times 2)}$$

$$= 86{,}439.13353... = \$86{,}439.13$$

Therefore, the investment banker would have to deposit \$86,439.13 in the investment fund.

Example 11.1(d) **Calculating the Periodic Payments of an Ordinary General Deferred Annuity**

The owner of a business borrowed $7500 to purchase a new machine for his factory. The interest rate charged on the loan is 4% compounded semi-annually and he is required to settle the loan by making equal monthly payments at the end of each month for five years, with the first payment to be made 1 year and 1 month from now. Calculate the size of the monthly payments that are required to settle the loan.

Solution

Page 486

- Payments are made at the end of each payment period (monthly)
- Compounding period (semi-annually) ≠ payment period (monthly)
- Payments start 1 year and 1 month from now

When calculated as an ordinary general deferred annuity, the ordinary annuity term starts one year from now; i.e., one payment interval before the first periodic payment. Therefore, the deferral period is 1 year.

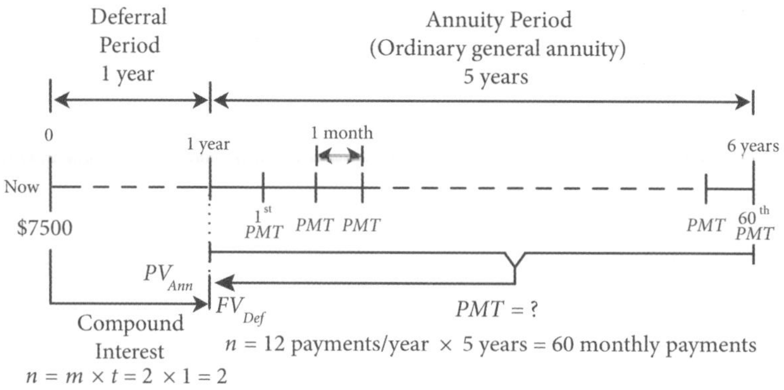

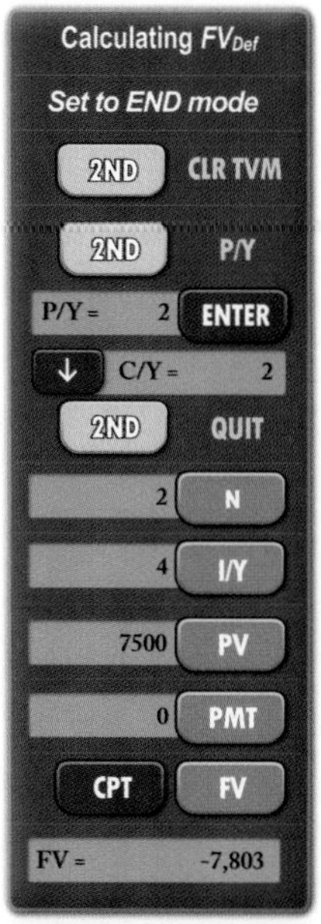

$$j = 0.04, \quad m = 2, \quad i = \frac{j}{m} = 0.02$$

Step 1: Calculating the future value of the investment at the end of the deferral period (FV_{Def})

Using Formula 9.1(a), $FV_{Def} = PV_{Def}(1 + i)^n$

$$= 7500.00(1 + 0.02)^2 = \$7803.00$$

This amount becomes the present value for the ordinary general deferred annuity (PV_{Ann}).

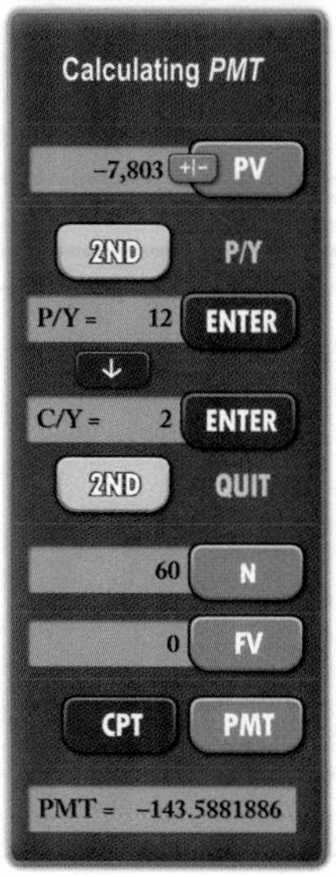

Step 2: Calculating PMT of the general deferred annuity

$$c = \frac{\textit{Number of compounding periods per year}}{\textit{Number of payments per year}} = \frac{2}{12}$$

$$i_2 = (1 + i)^c - 1 = (1 + 0.02)^{(2/12)} - 1 = 0.003305...$$

Using Formula 10.2(b) and substituting i_2 for i, to solve for PMT,

$$PV = PMT\left[\frac{1 - (1 + i_2)^{-n}}{i_2}\right]$$

$$7803.00 = PMT\left[\frac{1 - (1 + 0.003305...)^{-60}}{0.003305...}\right]$$

$$PMT = 143.588188... = \$143.59$$

Therefore, the size of the monthly payments required to settle the loan are $143.59.

Example 11.1(e) **Calculating the Number of Payments and Term of a General Deferred Annuity Due**

Neelima Glassware Corporation invested its annual net profits of $500,000 in a fixed deposit at 8% compounded quarterly. It wants to withdraw $90,000 at the beginning of every year, with the first withdrawal to be made three years from now. Calculate the time period of the annuity. Round your answer up to the next payment period.

Page 487

Solution

- Withdrawals are made at the beginning of each payment period (annually)
- Compounding period (quarterly) ≠ payment period (annually)
- Withdrawals start 3 years from now

When calculated as a general deferred annuity due, the annuity due term starts three years from now. Therefore, the deferral period is 3 years.

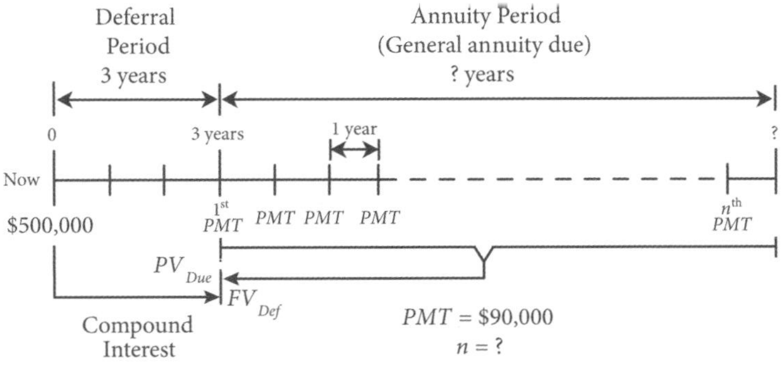

$n = m \times t = 4 \times 3 = 12$

$j = 0.08, \quad m = 4, \quad i = \frac{j}{m} = 0.02$

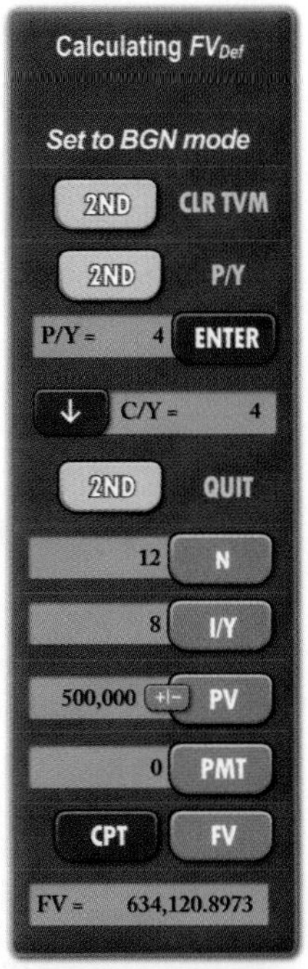

Step 1: Calculating the future value of the investment at the end of the deferral period (FV_{Def})

Using Formula 9.1(a), $FV_{Def} = PV_{Def}(1 + i)^n$

$= 500{,}000.00(1 + 0.02)^{12} = \$634{,}120.8973...$

This amount becomes the present value for the general annuity due (PV_{Due}).

Step 2: Calculating 'n' for for the general annuity due

$$c = \frac{\textit{Number of compounding periods per year}}{\textit{Number of payments per year}} = \frac{4}{1}$$

$$i_2 = (1 + i)^c - 1 = (1 + 0.02)^4 - 1 = 0.082432...$$

Using Formula 10.7(e) and substituting i_2 for i,

$$n = -\frac{\ln\left[1 - \frac{i_2 \times PV_{Due}}{PMT(1 + i_2)}\right]}{\ln(1 + i_2)}$$

$$= -\frac{\ln\left[1 - \frac{0.082432... \times 634{,}120.8973...}{90{,}000.00(1 + 0.082432...)}\right]}{\ln(1 + 0.082432...)}$$

$= 9.709541...$ Round up to the next payment period.

$= 10$ withdrawals The 10th withdrawal will be smaller than $90,000.

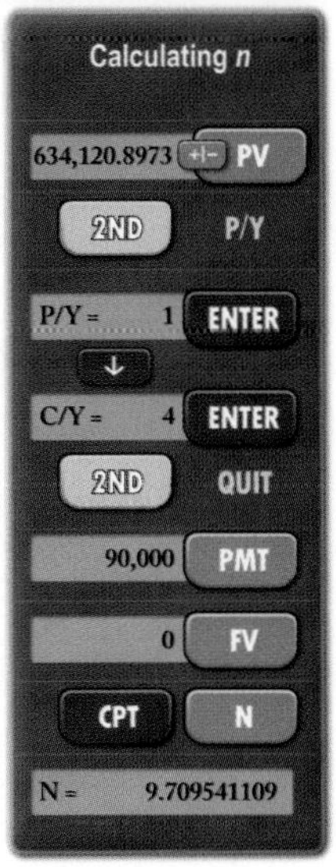

$$t = \frac{n}{\textit{Number of payments per year}} = \frac{10}{1}$$

$= 10$ years

Therefore, the time period of the annuity is 10 years.

11.1 | Exercises

Answers to the odd-numbered problems are available at the end of the textbook.

1. $500 is deposited into a savings account at the end of each month for three years and the first deposit is to be made five months from now.
   a. Assuming the annuity is an ordinary deferred annuity, identify the deferral period and the annuity period.
   b. Assuming the annuity is a deferred annuity due, identify the deferral period and the annuity period.

2. A certain amount is deposited into a GIC today and payments of $10,000 are withdrawn at the beginning of every quarter for five years. The first payment is to be received two years from now.
   a. Assuming the annuity is an ordinary deferred annuity, identify the deferral period and the annuity period
   b. Assuming the annuity is a deferred annuity due, identify the deferral period and the annuity period.

3. How much would a business have to invest in a high-growth fund to receive $10,000 at the end of every quarter for five years? The first payment is to be received two years from now and the investment has an interest rate of 12% compounded quarterly.

4. How much should a company borrow at 6% compounded monthly in order to repay $2800 at the end of every month for ten years? The first payment is to be received two years from now.

5. Keira is planning to retire in seven years and would like to receive $3000 from her RRSP at the end of every month for ten years during her retirement. She would like to receive her first periodic payment on the day she retires. How much would she have to invest in an RRSP that has an interest rate of 8% compounded quarterly?

6. Tasty Pastries Inc. wants to purchase a deferred annuity that would provide the company annuity payments of $20,000 at the end of every six months for seven years. Calculate the purchase price of the deferred annuity if the first payment is to be received in 2 years and 6 months and the interest rate is 6% compounded monthly.

7. An investment banker would like to receive $1000 at the beginning of every month from her investment fund for a period of 10 years. The fund is earning 6% compounded monthly. Calculate the amount of money she should deposit if the first payment is to be received in 3 years and 6 months.

8. A restaurant owner wants to invest in GICs that have an interest rate of 3.25% compounded semi-annually. Calculate the amount he should invest in order to receive annuity payments of $2000 at the beginning of every 6 months for a period of 5 years. The first GIC payment is to be received in 2 years and 6 months.

9. On the day Cecilia was born, her grandmother made an investment in a fund that was growing at 6.75% compounded quarterly. How much was invested in the fund to enable annual withdrawals of $10,000 for five years starting from Cecilia's 18th birthday?

10. Jemi purchased a deferred annuity with his 2017 earnings. The annuity will pay him $1200 at the beginning of every month for five years and the first payment will be received in one year. Calculate the purchase price of the deferred annuity assuming an interest rate of 8% compounded semi-annually.

11. Yuan invested $10,000 in a fund earning 8% compounded monthly. He wishes to withdraw $800 from the fund at the end of every quarter, with the first withdrawal to be made three years from now. How long will it take for the fund to be depleted?

12. Ardiana has a $280,000 business loan at an interest rate of 3.45% compounded semi-annually. The mortgage requires that she makes equal month-end payments of $1500. If her first payment is to be made six months from now, how long will it take her to settle the loan?

13. Russ Inc. invested its annual net profits of $25,000 into a fund at 8% compounded quarterly. The company wants to withdraw $2500 at the beginning of every six months, with the first withdrawal to be made two years from now. For how long can withdrawals be made?

14. Samantha deposited her sales commission of $15,500 in an investment that was growing at 7% compounded monthly. If she wanted to withdraw $2500 at the beginning of every quarter, with the first withdrawal to be made four years from now, how long will she be able to make withdrawals?

15. Jehona took an $8000 loan at 11% compounded quarterly in order to purchase equipment for her hair salon. Calculate the month-end payments required to settle the loan in 5 years, if her first payment is made 1 year and 4 months from now.

16. A small business invested its profits of $20,850 in an annuity at an interest rate of 8% compounded monthly. The annuity will pay equal amounts at the end of every quarter for five years. If the first payment is to be received two years from now, what will be the size of the payments?

17. A software company took a loan of $85,000 from a bank at a rate of 8.5% compounded semi-annually. The company was required to pay equal payment amounts at the beginning of every month for ten years. The first payment will be made one year from now.
    a. What will be the size of the monthly payments?
    b. What will be the total interest charged?

18. Amanda obtained a student loan of $55,000 for her two-year MBA program. The loan agreement states that she would have to make equal payments at the beginning of each month to settle the loan over ten years upon graduation two years from now. The interest rate on the loan is 6% compounded quarterly.
    a. What will be the size of the monthly payments?
    b. What will be the total interest charged?

• 19. Leigha invested $35,000 in a retirement fund and withdrew equal amounts at the end of each month for 20 years. She made her first withdrawal 5 years after she made the initial investment. Calculate the size of the withdrawals if the fund was earning 9.5% compounded quarterly during the deferral period and 8% compounded quarterly during the annuity period.

• 20. Five years ago, a bank offered an interest rate of 4% compounded semi-annually on a $20,000 investment. Now, one month before the first withdrawal is to be made, the rate has been changed to 4% compounded quarterly. Calculate the size of the equal withdrawals at the end of each month that would ensure that the investment will last for ten years.

• 21. A company invested $380,000 in a fixed deposit at 5.75% compounded quarterly. After a deferral period, it withdrew $11,100.21 at the beginning of the month for four years. How long was the deferral period? Express your answer in years rounded to two decimal places.

• 22. Beyonce received a student loan of $56,000 at 6.55% compounded semi-annually. She was required to settle the loan by making payments of $1409.07 at the beginning of every month for a period of five years from the date of graduation. How long is the deferral period? Express your answer in years rounded to two decimal places.

• 23. Ada is planning to retire in 15 years and would like to receive $2500 from her RRSP at the end of every month for 20 years during her retirement. At the end of this 20-year period, she would like to have $20,000 in the RRSP after receiving her last payment. If she receives the first periodic payment one month after she retires, how much would she have to invest in an RRSP that has an interest rate of 4.5% compounded semi-annually?

• 24. A company purchased a deferred annuity that provided it with annuity payments of $15,000 at the end of every three months for ten years. At the end of this ten-year period, the account would have a balance of $10,000 after the last payment has been withdrawn. Calculate the purchase price of the deferred annuity if the first payment is to be received in 4 years and 3 months, and the interest rate is 5.75% compounded monthly.

11.2 | Perpetuities

A perpetuity is an annuity in which the periodic payments begin on a fixed date and continue indefinitely. Therefore, it is not possible to calculate its future value. However, there is a definite present value for a perpetuity.

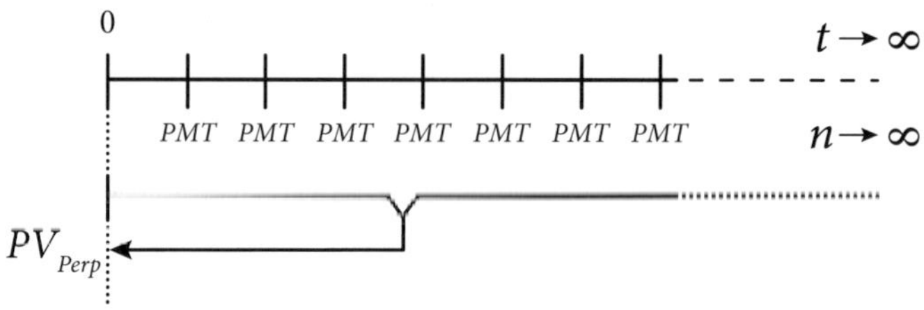

The formula for the present value of an ordinary perpetuity is derived using Formula 10.2(b),

$$PV = PMT\left[\frac{1 - (1 + i)^{-n}}{i}\right]$$

As the number of payments, n, in an annuity increases, the value of $(1 + i)^{-n}$ (which is a ratio of $\frac{1}{(1 + i)^n}$) becomes smaller. Therefore, as n approaches infinity, as in the case of a perpetuity, the value of $(1 + i)^{-n}$ approaches zero.

$$PV_{Perp} = PMT\left[\frac{1 - (0)}{i}\right] = \frac{PMT}{i}$$

Therefore, the formula for the present value of an ordinary perpetuity can be expressed as follows:

Formula 11.2(a) **Present Value of an Ordinary Perpetuity**

$$PV_{Perp} = \frac{PMT}{i}$$

Similar to annuities, perpetuities can be classified as:

- Ordinary perpetuity or perpetuity due.
- Ordinary deferred perpetuity or deferred perpetuity due.

Each of the above can be simple or general.

If the periodic payment in a perpetuity is at the beginning of the payment period, then it is a perpetuity due.

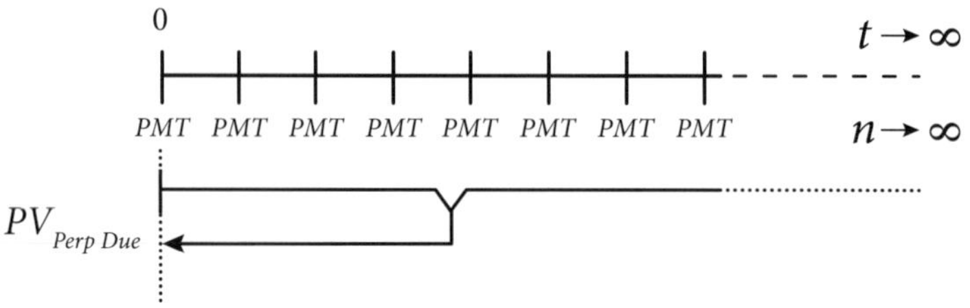

In a perpetuity due, the factor $(1 + i)^{-n}$ in the present value of an annuity due formula (Formula 10.4(b)) approaches zero.

$$PV_{Due} = PMT\left[\frac{1-(1+i)^{-n}}{i}\right](1+i)$$

$$PV_{Perp\ Due} = PMT\left[\frac{1-(0)}{i}\right](1+i)$$

$$= \left[\frac{PMT}{i}\right](1+i) = \frac{PMT}{i} + PMT$$

$$= PV_{Perp} + PMT$$

Therefore, the present value of a perpetuity due can be expressed as follows.

Formula 11.2(b)

Present Value of a Perpetuity Due

$$PV_{Perp\ Due} = \frac{PMT}{i}(1+i) \quad \text{or} \quad PV_{Perp\ Due} = \frac{PMT}{i} + PMT$$

In the case of an ordinary general perpetuity (or a general perpetuity due), where the compounding period is not equal to the payment period, we would carry out the same procedure by first calculating the equivalent periodic interest rate, 'i_2', and substituting this in place of 'i' in the PV_{Perp} (or $PV_{Perp\ Due}$) formula.

A few examples of perpetuities include:

- Continuous interest payments from a lump sum of money invested at a fixed interest rate.
- A scholarship to students paid from an endowment fund on a perpetual basis.
- A charity fund established to provide regular payments indefinitely to needy children.

Example 11.2(a)

Calculating the Present Value of an Ordinary Simple Perpetuity

A college wants to provide students with a perpetual scholarship of $10,000 at the end of every three months. How large should its endowment fund be if the money is growing at 8% compounded quarterly?

Solution

Page 487

This is an ordinary simple perpetuity as:

- Payments are made at the end of each payment period (quarterly)
- Compounding period (quarterly) = payment period (quarterly)

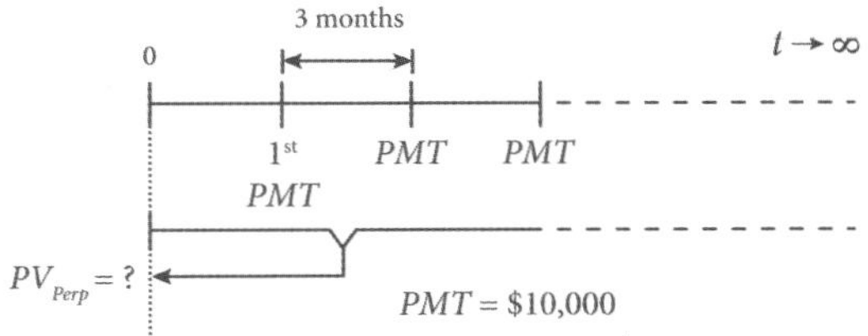

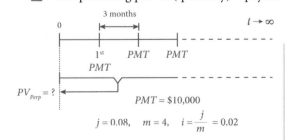

$j = 0.08, \quad m = 4, \quad i = \frac{j}{m} = 0.02$

Endowment Amount = PV = ?

Using Formula 11.2(a),

$$PV_{Perp} = \frac{PMT}{i} = \frac{10{,}000.00}{0.02} = \$500{,}000.00$$

The endowment fund required is $500,000.

While solving perpetuity problems using the financial calculator (or spreadsheet), we will have to assume the number of periodic payments, **N**, to be a very large number. However, if **N** is too large for the computational power of the device, an error message will be displayed. In the examples and exercises, we will assume **N** = 10,000 payments, i.e., enter **N** = 10,000 in the calculator (or spreadsheet).
In cases when an error message is displayed, decrease the value of **N** but keep it as large as possible.

Example 11.2(b) Calculating the Present Value of a General Perpetuity Due

A wealthy donor sponsors an endowment fund that provides a hospital with $5000 at the beginning of every month in perpetuity. What was the sponsorship amount if the fund is growing at 8% compounded quarterly?

Solution

Page 487

This is a general perpetuity due as:

- Payments are made at the beginning of each payment period (monthly)
- Compounding period (quarterly) ≠ payment period (monthly)

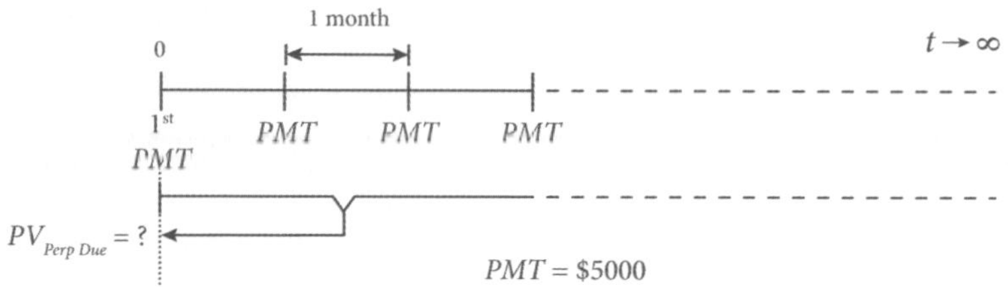

$PMT = \$5000$

$$j = 0.08, \quad m = 4, \quad i = \frac{j}{m} = 0.02$$

$$c = \frac{\textit{Number of compounding periods per year}}{\textit{Number of payments per year}} = \frac{4}{12}$$

$$i_2 = (1 + i)^c - 1 = (1 + 0.02)^{(4/12)} - 1 = 0.006622\ldots$$

Using Formula 11.2(b) and substituting i_2 for i,

$$PV_{Perp\ Due} = \frac{PMT}{i_2}(1 + i_2) = \frac{5000.00}{0.006622\ldots}(1 + 0.006622\ldots)$$

$$= 759{,}977.9972\ldots = \$759{,}978.00$$

Therefore, the sponsorship amount is $759,978.00.

Example 11.2(c) Calculating the Periodic Payment of an Ordinary General Perpetuity

A large telecommunications business purchases a perpetual bond at $500,000 that earns interest of 5.75% compounded monthly. Calculate the end-of-quarter payments that will be received from the bond.

Solution

Page 487

This is an ordinary general perpetuity as:

- Payments are made at the end of each payment period (quarterly)
- Compounding period (monthly) ≠ payment period (quarterly)

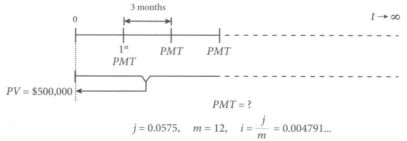

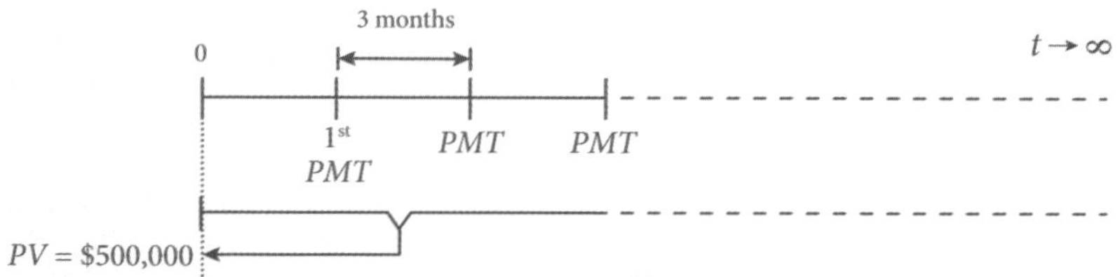

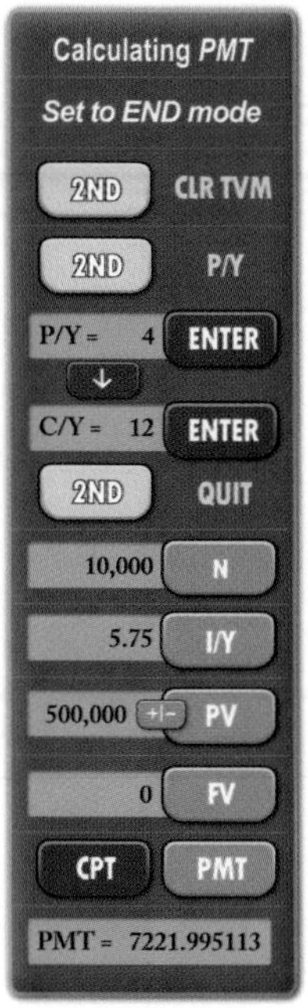

$PMT = ?$

$$j = 0.0575, \quad m = 12, \quad i = \frac{j}{m} = 0.004791\ldots$$

$$c = \frac{\textit{Number of compounding periods per year}}{\textit{Number of payments per year}} = \frac{12}{4}$$

$$i_2 = (1 + i)^c - 1 = (1.004791\ldots)^{(12/4)} - 1 = 0.014443\ldots$$

Rearranging Formula 11.2(a),

$$PMT = PV_{Perp} \times i_2 = 500{,}000.00\ (0.014443\ldots) = 7221.995113\ldots = \$7222.00$$

Therefore, the end-of-quarter payments will be $7222.00.

Example 11.2(d) **Calculating the Present Value of a Deferred Perpetuity Due**

Green Splash Publishers invested a lump sum amount in a fund growing at 6% compounded monthly. It plans to withdraw $2000 at the beginning of every month from the fund with the first withdrawal to be made two years from now. How much should it invest in the fund?

Page 487

Solution

This is a simple deferred perpetuity due as:

- Payments are made at the beginning of each payment period (monthly)
- Compounding period (monthly) = payment period (monthly)
- Payments start 2 years from now

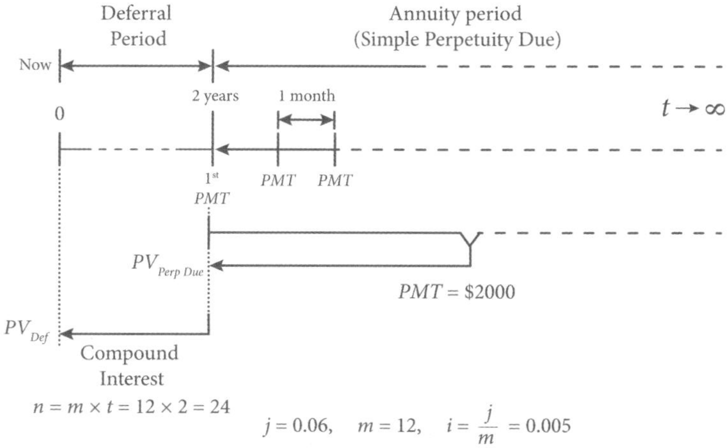

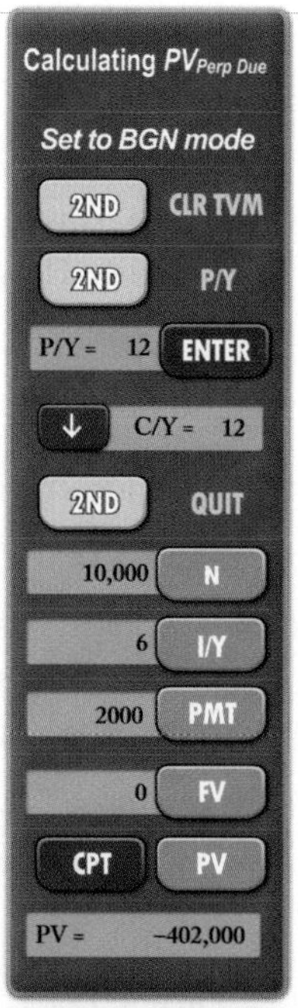

Step 1: Calculating $PV_{Perp\ Due}$

$$PV_{Perp\ Due} = \frac{PMT}{i}(1 + i) = \frac{2000.00}{0.005}(1+ 0.005) = \$402{,}000.00$$

Step 2: Calculating PV_{Def}

$$PV_{Def} = PV_{Perp\ Due}(1 + i)^{-n}$$

$$= 402{,}000.00(1 + 0.005)^{-24}$$

$$= 356{,}648.6389... = \$356{,}648.64$$

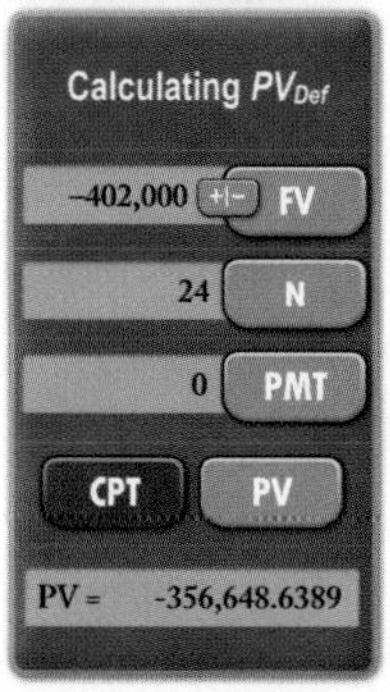

Therefore, it should invest $356,648.64 in the fund.

11.2 | Exercises

Answers to the odd-numbered problems are available at the end of the textbook.

1. A college wants to provide students with a perpetual scholarship of $5000 at the end of every three months. How large should its endowment fund be if money can earn 12% compounded quarterly?

2. Ayes Inc., an e-learning company, wants to create a fund that pays $500 at the end of every month in perpetuity. If money earns 6% compounded monthly, calculate the initial investment into this fund.

3. How much money is required to fund a perpetuity that pays $1000 at the end of every three months and earns 6% compounded semi-annually?

4. Henry, a retired businessman, owns a perpetuity that pays him $200 at the end of every month and earns 8% compounded quarterly. For how much did he purchase this perpetuity?

5. If Webcom Inc. pays dividends of $2.50 per share at the beginning of each quarter, calculate the market price per share assuming that money earns 5% compounded quarterly.

6. A college was raising funds for a $5000 scholarship that it wanted to provide to its first semester students at the beginning of every six months. If money is worth 3.5% compounded semi-annually, how much money should the college raise for this endowment fund?

7. Alba was receiving rental payments of $3000 at the beginning of each month from the tenants of her commercial property. What would be the value of her property on the market if she wants to sell it, assuming money earns 9% compounded semi-annually?

8. A condominium was leased for $1200 per month with payments being made at the beginning of each month. Calculate the market price of the condominium, assuming that money is worth 4% compounded quarterly.

9. $700,000 is invested in an endowment fund at 4.5% compounded semi-annually in order to support scholarship payments at a college. What will be the size of the payments that students will receive at the end of every six months?

10. Roger runs a successful publishing business and invests his 2016 profits of $400,000 in a bank at 2% compounded monthly. How much money can he withdraw from this account at the end of every month in perpetuity?

11. A $110,540 endowment fund was set up to provide month-end scholarships of $600 in perpetuity. What nominal interest rate compounded quarterly was the fund earning?

12. An endowment fund is providing scholarships of $7500 at the end of every year in perpetuity. If the investment in the fund is $200,000, calculate the nominal interest rate compounded annually.

13. Anna purchased a perpetuity that was paying her $12,500 at the end of every six months and that had an interest rate of 8% compounded semi-annually. How much less would it cost Anna if the perpetuity had an interest rate of 8% compounded quarterly instead of 8% compounded semi-annually?

14. A college endowment fund provides year-end scholarships of $7500 at 2.85% compounded semi-annually. If the fund was set up to earn 2.85% compounded monthly instead, how much less money would be required to start the fund?

15. A fund was established to provide scholarship payments of $11,500 at the beginning of every six months. If money can earn 4.55% compounded monthly instead of 4.55% compounded semi-annually, how much less would be needed to ensure these payments in perpetuity?

16. An investment is required to pay $1000 at the beginning of every three months for a scholarship. If money is worth 6% compounded annually instead of 6% compounded quarterly, how much more will be required to maintain these payments in perpetuity?

- 17. Calculate the purchase price of a perpetuity that provides month-end payments of $1000, with the first payment to be received in three years. The interest on the perpetuity is 2.25% compounded quarterly.

- 18. Yara purchased a perpetuity that pays her $3000 at the end of every quarter, with the first payment to be received in five years. If the perpetuity had an interest rate of 4% compounded quarterly, calculate its purchase price.

- 19. A technology company deposited $62,580 into an account for yearly scholarships to be awarded to business students in Canada. The scholarship will be given at the beginning of every year forever, with the first scholarship to be awarded four years after the amount was deposited. What will be the size of these annual scholarships if the interest rate is 6.6% compounded semi-annually?

- 20. The alumni of the Department of Engineering at a university collected $28,200 to set up a fund that will provide yearly scholarships to first-year graduate students. The scholarship will be awarded at the beginning of every year forever, with the first scholarship to be awarded five years after the amount is deposited. What will be the size of the scholarship if the fund is earning 7.8% compounded quarterly?

- 21. Toby invested $200,000 in a fund that will provide scholarship amounts in perpetuity. The fund earns 6% compounded monthly. What is the monthly scholarship amount if:

    a. the first payment starts at the end of the first month?

    b. the first payment starts at the beginning of the first month?

    c. the first payment starts five years from now?

    d. the first payment starts at the end of the first month and the interest rate is 6% compounded semi-annually instead of 6% compounded monthly?

• 22. A company invested \$880,450 in an account that was providing monthly payments in perpetuity to the community hospital. The account earns 4.75% compounded monthly. What is the monthly payment amount if:

a. the first payment starts at the end of the first month?

b. the first payment starts at the beginning of the first month?

c. the first payment starts three years from now?

d. the first payment starts at the end of the first month and the interest rate is 4.75% compounded quarterly instead of 4.75% compounded monthly?

11.3 | Constant-Growth Annuities

A constant-growth annuity is an annuity where the periodic payment amount (PMT) increases by a constant rate (g) over the preceding payment amount. A few examples of constant-growth annuities may include retirement annuity contracts, insurance policies, leases, installment purchases, and court-awarded payments.

Consider an example where you plan to deposit regular payments into your RRSP at the end of every month for 3 years, starting with an initial investment of \$100, and increasing the amount by 2% every month.

1st payment would be:	$PMT_1 = \$100.00$
2nd payment:	$PMT_2 = 100 + (2\% \text{ of } 100) = \$102.00$
This is the same as:	$PMT_2 = PMT + g(PMT) = PMT(1 + g)$
3rd payment:	$PMT_3 = 102 + (2\% \text{ of } 102) = \$104.04$
This is the same as:	$PMT_3 = PMT_2(1 + g) = PMT(1 + g)(1 + g) = PMT(1 + g)^2$

Notice that each payment amount increases by a factor of $(1 + g)$, in relation to the previous payment.

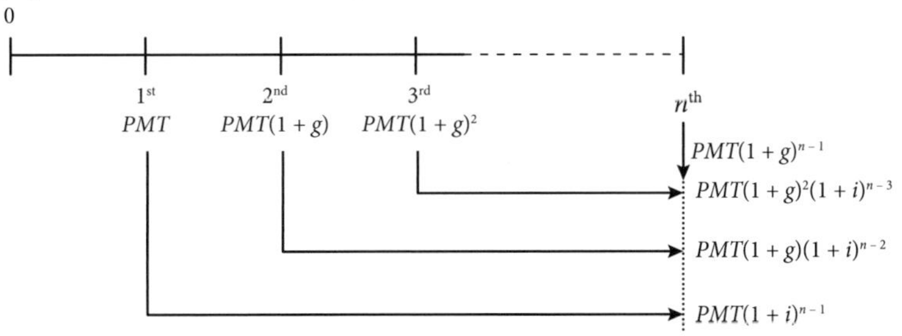

To calculate the future value of these payments at the end of the period:

$$FV = FV_{1^{st}\,PMT} + FV_{2^{nd}\,PMT} + FV_{3^{rd}\,PMT} + \dots + FV_{n^{th}\,PMT}$$

$$FV = PMT(1 + i)^{n-1} + PMT(1 + g)(1 + i)^{n-2} + PMT(1 + g)^2(1 + i)^{n-3} + \dots + PMT(1 + g)^{n-1}$$

This is a geometric series [first term = $PMT\,(1 + i)^{n-1}$, common ratio = $(1 + g)(1 + i)^{-1}$, number of terms = n] and the sum of this is expressed as follows:

Formula 11.3(a) **Future Value of an Ordinary Simple Constant-Growth Annuity**

$$FV = PMT\left[\frac{(1 + i)^n - (1 + g)^n}{(i - g)}\right]$$

Notice that if 'g' is zero (i.e., there is no growth in the payment), the formula reduces back to the 'FV' of an ordinary annuity:

$$FV = PMT\left[\frac{(1 + i)^n - 1}{i}\right]$$

Similarly, the present value for a constant growth annuity is calculated as follows:

Formula 11.3(b) **Present Value of an Ordinary Simple Constant-Growth Annuity**

$$PV = PMT\left[\frac{1-(1+g)^{n}(1+i)^{-n}}{(i-g)}\right]$$

Notice that if 'g' is zero (i.e., there is no growth in the payment), the formula reduces back to the 'PV' of an ordinary annuity:

$$PV = PMT\left[\frac{1-(1+i)^{-n}}{i}\right]$$

We can also calculate the sum of all the payments in a constant growth annuity:

$$Sum\ of\ Constant\ Growth\ Payments = PMT + PMT(1+g) + PMT(1+g)^2 + \ldots + PMT(1+g)^{n-1}$$

This is a geometric series [first term = PMT, common ratio $(1+g)$, number of terms = n] and the sum of this can be expressed as follows:

Formula 11.3(c) **Sum of Constant-Growth Payments**

$$\begin{matrix}Sum\ of\ Constant\text{-}\\Growth\ Payments\end{matrix} = PMT\left[\frac{(1+g)^{n}-1}{g}\right]$$

The Sum of Constant-Growth Payments formula is the same as the Future Value of an Ordinary Simple Annuity formula, replacing i with g.

Example 11.3(a) **Calculating the Future Value of an Ordinary Simple Constant-Growth Annuity**

A business made end-of-month investments in a high-growth fund starting at $500 and increased it by 1.5% per month thereafter, for 15 years. The fund has an interest rate of 12% compounded monthly.

(i) What was the accumulated amount in the fund at the end of the period?

(ii) What was the total interest earned?

Solution

Page 488

This is an ordinary simple constant-growth annuity as:

- Payments are made at the end of the payment period (monthly)
- Compounding period (monthly) = payment period (monthly)
- Constant-growth rate is 1.5%

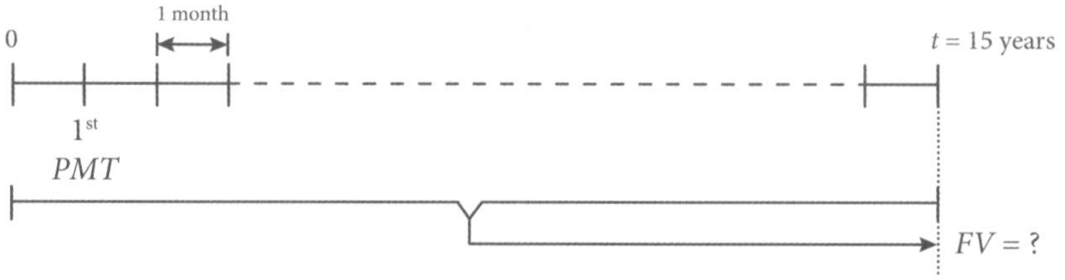

When using the Texas Instruments BAII Plus financial calculator for constant growth annuity, there is no direct input for I/Y. This should be calculated separately then entered in the calculator. These solutions have been omitted from this section.

1st PMT = $500

n = 12 payments/year × 15 years = 180 monthly payments

$$j = 0.12,\quad m = 12,\quad i = \frac{j}{m} = 0.01,\quad g = 0.015$$

(i) *Calculating the accumulated value of the fund*

Using Formula 11.3(a), $FV = PMT\left[\frac{(1+i)^{n}-(1+g)^{n}}{(i-g)}\right]$

$$= 500.00\left[\frac{(1+0.01)^{180}-(1+0.015)^{180}}{(0.01-0.015)}\right] = 500.00[1717.713143\ldots]$$

$$= 858{,}856.5714\ldots = \$858{,}856.57$$

Therefore, the accumulated value in the fund at the end of the period would be $858,856.57.

Solution *continued*

(ii) *Calculating the amount of interest earned*

Using Formula 11.3(c),

$$\text{Sum of Constant-Growth Payments} = PMT\left[\frac{(1+g)^n - 1}{g}\right] = 500.00\left[\frac{(1+0.015)^{180} - 1}{0.015}\right]$$

$$= 452{,}812.2563... = \$452{,}812.26$$

$$\text{Total interest earned} = FV - \textit{Sum of Constant-Growth Payments}$$

$$= 858{,}856.57 - 452{,}812.26 = \$406{,}044.31$$

Therefore, the amount of interest earned was $406,044.31.

Example 11.3(b) **Calculating the Present Value of an Ordinary Simple Constant-Growth Annuity**

Abel purchased a ten-year annuity that has an interest rate of 5% compounded semi-annually and which will provide him with payments at the end of every six months. The first payment received is $1000 and it increases by 2% thereafter, every six months.

(i) How much did he pay for the annuity?

(ii) What was the total interest earned?

Solution

Page 488

This is an ordinary simple constant-growth annuity as:

- Payments are made at the end of each payment period (semi-annually)
- Compounding period (semi-annually) = payment period (semi-annually)
- Constant-growth rate is 2%

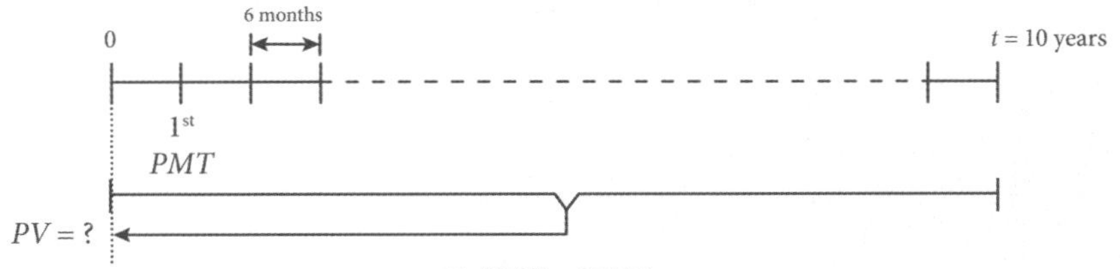

1st $PMT = \$1000$

$n = 2$ payments/year × 10 years = 20 semi-annual payments

$$j = 0.05, \quad m = 2, \quad i = \frac{j}{m} = 0.025, \quad g = 0.02$$

(i) *Calculating the present value of the fund*

Using Formula 11.3(b), $PV = PMT\left[\frac{1-(1+g)^n(1+i)^{-n}}{(i-g)}\right]$

$$= 1000.00\left[\frac{1-(1+0.02)^{20}(1+0.025)^{-20}}{(0.025-0.02)}\right] = 1000.00[18.633896...]$$

$$= 18{,}633.89632... = \$18{,}633.90$$

Therefore, he paid $18,633.90 for the annuity.

(ii) *Calculating the amount of interest earned*

Using Formula 11.3(c),

$$\text{Sum of Constant-Growth Payments} = PMT\left[\frac{(1+g)^n - 1}{g}\right] = 1000.00\left[\frac{(1+0.02)^{20} - 1}{0.02}\right]$$

$$= 24{,}297.36980... = \$24{,}297.37$$

$$\text{Total interest earned} = \textit{Sum of Constant-Growth Payments} - PV$$

$$= 24{,}297.37 - 18{,}633.90 = \$5663.47$$

Therefore, the amount of interest earned was $5663.47.

Example 11.3(c) **Calculating the Size of the Initial Payment of an Ordinary Simple Constant-Growth Annuity**

Adam made contributions growing at 2.25% at the end of every 3 months to his RRSP that was earning 8% compounded quarterly. In 30 years, his RRSP savings had accumulated to $147,034.45.

(i) What was the size of the first contribution?

(ii) What was the total interest earned?

Solution

Page 488

This is an ordinary simple constant-growth annuity as:

- Payments are made at the end of each payment period (quarterly)
- Compounding period (quarterly) = payment period (quarterly)
- Constant-growth rate is 2.25%

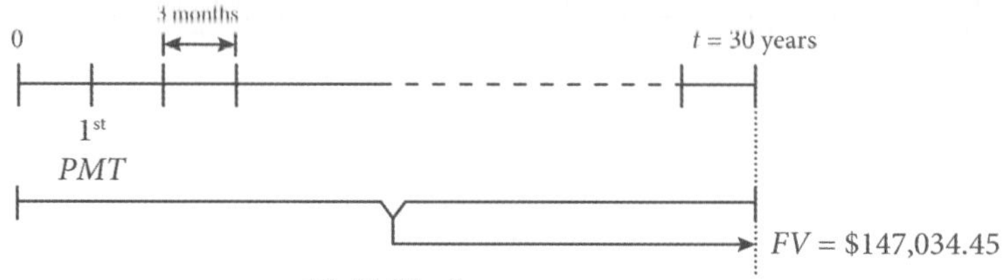

1st $PMT = ?$

n = 4 payments/year × 30 years = 120 quarterly payments

$$j = 0.08, \quad m = 4, \quad i = \frac{j}{m} = 0.02, \quad g = 0.0225$$

(i) *Calculating the size of the first contribution*

Using Formula 11.3(a),

$$FV = PMT\left[\frac{(1+i)^n - (1+g)^n}{(i-g)}\right]$$

$$147{,}034.45 = PMT\left[\frac{(1+0.02)^{120} - (1+0.0225)^{120}}{(0.02-0.0225)}\right]$$

Rearranging and solving for PMT,

$$PMT = 99.999997... = \$100.00$$

Therefore, the size of the first contribution was $100.00.

(ii) *Calculating the total interest earned*

Using Formula 11.3(c),

$$\text{Sum of Constant-Growth Payments} = PMT\left[\frac{(1+g)^n - 1}{g}\right] = 100.00\left[\frac{(1+0.0225)^{120} - 1}{0.0225}\right]$$

$$= 59{,}737.88618... = \$59{,}737.89$$

Total interest earned = FV – *Sum of Constant-Growth Payments*

= 147,034.45 – 59,737.89 = $87,296.56

Therefore, the amount of interest earned was $87,296.56.

11.3 | Exercises

Answers to the odd-numbered problems are available at the end of the textbook.

1. Investments were made at the end of every six months for five years in a fund that had an interest rate of 5% compounded semi-annually.

   a. If the investment amount was $1000, calculate the accumulated amount in the fund.

   b. If the starting investment amount was $1000 and it was increased by 1% thereafter every six months, calculate the accumulated amount in the fund.

   c. What was the total amount of interest earned in the constant-growth fund?

2. An amount of $850 was invested in a savings account at the end of every three months for ten years. The interest rate on the account was 4.5% compounded quarterly.
   a. Calculate the accumulated amount in the account.
   b. After the first investment of $850, if the amount was increased by 1% thereafter every three months for the time period, calculate the accumulated amount in the account.
   c. What was the total amount of interest earned in the constant-growth account?

3. Harold Petrochemicals made its first deposit of $1000 into an investment fund and thereafter, increased the size of the payments by 2% every month. The deposits are made at the end of every month for five years and the investment fund was growing at 6% compounded semi-annually.
   a. What was the accumulated value in the fund at the end of the annuity term?
   b. What was the total amount of interest earned?

4. Micro-Fibres Inc. deposited $10,000 at the end of the first year and increased this amount by 3% every year for the next ten years. The deposits were made into an overseas investment fund that was growing at 12% compounded semi-annually.
   a. What was the accumulated value in the fund at the end of the term?
   b. What was the total amount of interest earned?

5. A five-year annuity provides payments at the end of every three months starting at $2800, and growing by 2% with every payment. The annuity earns 6% compounded quarterly.
   a. What is the purchase price of the annuity?
   b. What is the total amount of interest earned?

6. Janet secured a job that is paying her $35,000 per annum. She intends to work for 40 years, with her income growing by 5% every year. Calculate the discounted value of her income stream if money earns 4% compounded annually.

7. The City of Oshawa wants to accumulate $2,000,000 in a savings account by the end of ten years. It will be making deposits at the end of every three months and will increase the deposit amount by 3% every three months. If the account earns 6% compounded semi-annually, what is the size of the first deposit?

8. The Harold family makes month-end payments to repay their mortgage of $825,000. They plan to increase their payment by 1.2% every month in order to clear their mortgage in seven years. Calculate the size of their first payment, if the mortgage has an interest rate of 3.5% compounded semi-annually.

9. Peter wishes to save $50,000 in ten years. He makes a deposit at the end of every year and increases the savings amount by 6% every year. Calculate his first year-end deposit. Assume that money earns 4.8% compounded monthly.

10. Lucy wants to save $60,000 in four years. She makes a deposit at the end of every month and increases the savings amount by 2% every month. Calculate her first month-end deposit. Assume money earns 4% compounded quarterly.

11. You wish to receive payments at the end of every year for the next five years, starting at $5000 per year. Your payment amount is expected to increase by 6% every year. If money is worth 6% compounded semi-annually, how much should you invest now?

12. You wish to receive increasing month-end payments with a 3% growth-rate per month for the next two years. If your first monthly payment was $750, how much should you invest now? Assume that money is worth 4.2% compounded semi-annually.

11 | Review Exercises

Answers to the odd-numbered problems are available at the end of the textbook.

1. How much would a vegetable oil business have to invest in a high-growth fund to receive $50,000 at the end of every quarter for seven years, with the first payment to be received in 4 years and 3 months? Money is worth 6% compounded quarterly.

2. An investment firm will receive $120,000 at the end of every month for four years with the first payment to be received two years from now. For how much did it purchase this deferred annuity if money is worth 9.5% compounded monthly?

3. Ivan purchased a deferred annuity with his 2016 earnings. If it will pay $800 at the beginning of every quarter for eight years with the first payment to be received in two years, calculate the purchase price of the deferred annuity. Assume an interest rate of 7.5% compounded semi-annually.

4. Armery Inc. purchased a deferred annuity which pays $50,000 at the beginning of every quarter for five years, with the first payment to be received in three years. Calculate the expected purchase price of the annuity if money is worth 6% compounded monthly.

5. Tashoido Inc. invested its annual net profit of $60,000 in a fixed deposit at 6% compounded annually. If the company wants to withdraw $2000 at the beginning of every month starting two years from now, for how long can withdrawals be made?

6. Pickles Inc. sold a plant and invested the proceeds of $200,000 into an investment earning interest at 8% compounded quarterly. If the company wants to withdraw $5000 at the beginning of every month starting one year from now, for how long can withdrawals be made?

7. A tool-die shop obtained a loan of $120,000 from a bank. The shop is required to make equal payments at the beginning of every month for 8 years, starting 18 months from now. Calculate the size of the monthly payments if the interest rate charged is 8% compounded semi-annually.

8. The Mitchell family is planning on taking on a $400,000 mortgage. The mortgage would be accumulating interest at a rate of 3.5% compounded quarterly and would have a term of 20 years. What would be the size of their beginning-of-month payments if the bank allows them to make the first payment in nine months?

9. What would be the size of the scholarship payments that students at a college would receive at the end of every quarter in perpetuity if $1 million is invested in an endowment fund that is earning 3% compounded quarterly?

10. A perpetuity earning 6% compounded monthly is started with a $100,000 investment. What is the size of the periodic withdrawals taken from the investment at the end of every month in perpetuity?

11. A perpetuity that is earning 7% compounded quarterly is to pay $30,000 at the end of every quarter. How much less money would be required to fund the perpetuity if the money could be invested to earn 7% compounded monthly instead of 7% compounded quarterly?

12. Nikia started a fund earning 3% compounded monthly, which would pay out $500 at the end of every month. How much more money is required to set up the fund if the interest rate was 3% compounded semi-annually instead of 3% compounded monthly?

13. How much more should a college raise for its endowment fund to provide scholarships of $7500 at the beginning of every six months if the money was invested at 8.5% compounded semi-annually rather than 8.5% compounded monthly?

14. A perpetuity that is earning 6% compounded quarterly is to pay $10,000 at the beginning of every year. How much less money would be required to fund the perpetuity if the money could only earn 6% compounded monthly instead of 6% compounded quarterly?

15. Petreas Fine Leather has made its first deposit of $1000 at the end of the month into an investment fund, and the company plans to increase the payments thereafter by 0.5% every month. If the deposits are made at the end of every month for 25 years and if the investment fund has an interest rate of 11% compounded semi-annually, calculate the accumulated value in the fund at the end of the annuity term.

16. At the end of last month, Elmough Bed & Breakfast decided to invest $500 monthly into an investment fund earning 6% compounded monthly. It plans on continuing these deposits on a regular monthly basis, increasing the deposit amount by 0.75% each time. If these payments continue for 15 years, what would be the accumulated value of the fund at the end of the term?

17. Calculate the purchase price of a seven-year annuity that provides end-of-quarter payments that start at $2800 and grow by 2% every quarter. Assume that money earns 6% compounded quarterly.

18. Calculate the purchase price of a ten-year annuity that provides payments at the end of every month starting at $500, growing by 1% every month. Assume that money earns 5% compounded quarterly.

19. The Gauche Institute makes month-end payments to repay its outstanding loans of $825,000. If it plans to increase the payment by 1% every month to clear the loan in seven years, calculate the size of the first payment. The loan has an interest rate of 5.5% compounded annually.

20. Cleverson Industries took a $50,000 loan, which is being repaid with increasing month-end payments, growing by 0.5% every month. If it plans on settling the loan in five years and is being charged interest of 12% compounded quarterly, what should be the size of the first payment?

11 | Self-Test Exercises

Answers to all the problems are available at the end of the textbook.

1. Aleks received 60 annuity payments of $1000 each at the end of every month, with the first payment received after 3 years and 1 month. The interest rate for the deferral period was 4% compounded monthly, and 5.4% compounded monthly for the annuity period. Calculate the present value of this deferred annuity.

2. If you invested $350,000 in a business that would pay you monthly payments at the beginning of every month for 25 years, with the first payment being made in 5 years, calculate the size of the periodic payments. Assume that the interest rate is 6% compounded quarterly throughout the period.

3. A deferred annuity with a present value of $25,000 will pay $500 at the end of every month, and the first payment is received in four years. If the interest rate is 3.6% compounded monthly, calculate the term of the annuity.

4. Ben has $150,000 in his RRSP which earns 4% compounded semi-annually. How much more could he withdraw at the end of every month for a ten-year period if the first withdrawal is made in 5 years and 1 month instead of 3 years and 1 month?

5. A perpetual scholarship fund is to be set up to pay $10,000 at the end of every month. How much more would be required to fund the scholarship if the money invested were to earn 4.5% compounded semi-annually instead of 4.5% compounded monthly?

6. If money earns 6% compounded annually, how much more would be required to fund an ordinary perpetuity paying $1000 every year than to fund an annuity paying $1000 at the end of every year for 30 years?

7. A college alumnus donated $150,000 to start an annual perpetual scholarship for the best student in his college's business program. If the fund earns 5% compounded semi-annually, what will be the amount of the year-end scholarship?

8. James wants to retire in five years and has started to save for his retirement with month-end contributions into a fund for five years, which earns 6.8% compounded semi-annually. His initial contribution was $1000. The contribution will be increased by 2% each month. Calculate his retirement fund at the end of his last contribution.

9. Nadia wanted to convert her RRSP into an annuity for ten years, so that she would be able to withdraw money at the end of every year, with an increasing withdrawal of 10% annually. If the first withdrawal amount is to be $5000, what amount should she have now if money earns 5.4% compounded quarterly?

10. Andrew has $40,000 in his RESP account and wants to withdraw annually from this account, with withdrawals increasing by 6% annually to pay for his higher education for the next five years. If money earns 4.8% compounded monthly, determine the size of his first withdrawal.

CASE 11a

Financial Planning for a Secure Future

Elijah and his wife, Carol, had their first child on Elijah's 30th birthday. They decided that it was time to meet their financial advisor, Cheng, and request that he create a sound financial plan for their future.

Cheng commenced his analysis by understanding their current situation. Through a few questions, he gathered the following information: Elijah had a stable job as a college professor and had plans to retire at the age of 65. He would like to receive a pension amount of $36,000 every year when he retires. Both of them would also like to create a fund that would support their child through his university education.

Recently, Elijah received a lump sum amount of $50,000 from the will of a wealthy uncle who had recently died. At the end of the discussion, Elijah also added that he had a vision of donating some money to his college when he retires. His hope is that the college would create an endowment fund that would provide a suitable scholarship for the college's business students.

With this information, Cheng, created the following financial plan for Elijah and Carol:

1. Make month-end deposits into an RESP starting at $50 and increase the deposits by 1.25% every month for 14 years. 17 years from now, their son will be able to withdraw money at the beginning of every year from the RESP for his university education and increase his withdrawals by 2% every year (to cover for any inflation in the economy) for five years. During the first 17 years, their money will be growing at 9% compounded monthly, and thereafter, they will move the RESP to a fund that earns 10% compounded annually for the next five years.
2. Save the lump sum amount of $50,000 in an RRSP at 6% compounded quarterly. When Elijah is 65-years-old, withdraw one-fourth of the accumulated amount and donate it to his college to create the endowment fund.
3. Convert the balance amount in the RRSP to an annuity paying $36,000 annually.

Elijah and Carol were excited that they had a financial plan in place for their future. However, they needed a few clarifications and sent Cheng an email with their questions. Assist Cheng in providing Elijah with answers to the following questions:

a. What would be their son's first withdrawal amount for his five-year university education?

b. How long would they receive their pension amount?

c. What would be the scholarship that students receive at the beginning of every six months in perpetuity if the college creates an endowment fund on Elijah's 65th birthday, and the fund earns 8% compounded quarterly?

CASE 11b

RBC Students Leading Change Scholarship

The Royal Bank of Canada offers scholarships to recognize Canadian students who have made meaningful contributions to better their communities.

> *"As students across Canada continue to invest in their education, many are taking the time to invest in their communities as well. In recognition of the growing number of Canadian students showing a passion to lead and inspire positive change in their community, we have created the RBC Students Leading Change Scholarship."*
>
> \- scholarships.rbc.com

The RBC Students Leading Change Scholarship is awarded to eight students graduating high school and seven students currently enrolled in a post-secondary program each year. Each of the fifteen scholarships is worth $10,000, totaling $150,000 worth of scholarships.

Consider the following hypothetical scenario:

In order to continue to offer these scholarships every year in perpetuity, RBC was looking into setting up an endowment fund, growing at 4.75% daily. The first set of scholarships is to be offered today.

a. What should be the size of the endowment fund set up by RBC today in order to fully cover the costs of offering the scholarships every year in perpetuity?

b. RBC currently has $2,600,000 that they are able to invest in the endowment fund. If RBC invested this amount in the fund today, what is the maximum amount that may be withdrawn every year to put towards the scholarships?

c. What should be the size of the endowment fund set up by RBC today in order to fully cover the costs of offering the scholarships every year in perpetuity, if the first set of scholarships is offered in five years instead of today?

d. Instead of investing in an endowment fund today, RBC contemplated setting up a high-growth fund using their monthly profits to save up for the cost of the endowment fund. If they make payments at the end of every month, with payments increasing by 2.5% per month, what would be the size of RBC's first monthly payment in order to accumulate to the value calculated in (a) in five years? The fund has an interest rate of 10.5% compounded monthly.

e. Does RBC earn more interest if it follows the payment plan laid out in (c) or (d)? By how much?

11 | Spreadsheet Solutions

Spreadsheet solutions to solved examples in the chapter.

11.1 Examples

Example 11.1(b): Method 1

	A	B	
1		Calculating $PV_{Annuity}$	
2	j	5.00%	
3	m	1	
4	P/Y	1	
5	t	10	
6			
7	i	5.00%	= B2/B3
8	n	10	= B4*B5
9	**PMT**	$1,000.00	
10	**PV**	($7,721.73)	= PV(B7, B8, B9, B11, B12) PV(rate, nper, pmt, [fv], [type])
11	**FV**	0	
12	**BGN**	0	
13			
14	Calculating PV_{Def}		
15	j	5.00%	
16	m	1	
17	t	2	
18			
19	i	5.00%	= B15/B16
20	n	2	= B16*B17
21	**PMT**	0	
22	**PV**	($7,003.84)	= PV(B19, B20, B21, B23) PV(rate, nper, pmt, [fv], [type])
23	**FV**	$7,721.73	= –B10
24			

Example 11.1(b): Method 2

	A	B	
1		Calculating PV_{Due}	
2	j	5.00%	
3	m	1	
4	P/Y	1	
5	t	10	
6			
7	i	5.00%	= B2/B3
8	n	10	= B4*B5
9	**PMT**	$1,000.00	
10	**PV**	($8,107.82)	= PV(B7, B8, B9, B11, B12) PV(rate, nper, pmt, [fv], [type])
11	**FV**	0	
12	**BGN**	1	
13			
14		Calculating PV_{Def}	
15	j	5.00%	
16	m	1	
17	t	3	
18			
19	i	5.00%	= B15/B16
20	n	3	= B16*B17
21	**PMT**	0	
22	**PV**	($7,003.84)	= PV(B19, B20, B21, B23) PV(rate, nper, pmt, [fv], [type])
23	**FV**	$8,107.82	= –B10
24			

Example 11.1(c)

	A	B	
1	Calculating PV_{Due}		
2	j	6.00%	
3	m	2	
4	P/Y	12	
5	t	11	
6			
7	i	3.00%	= B2/B3
8	c	0.166667	= B3/B4
9	i_2	0.4939%	= (1 + B7)^B8 – 1
10	n	132	= B4*B5
11	**PMT**	$1,000.00	
12	**PV**	($97,288.01)	= PV(B9, B10, B11, B13, B14) PV(rate, nper, pmt, [fv], [type])
13	**FV**	0	
14	**BGN**	1	
15			
16	Calculating PV_{Def}		
17	j	6.00%	
18	m	2	
19	t	2	
20			
21	i	3.00%	= B17/B18
22	n	4	= B18*B19
23	**PMT**	0	
24	**PV**	($86,439.13)	= PV(B21, B22, B23, B25) PV(rate, nper, pmt, [fv], [type])
25	**FV**	$97,288.01	= –B12
26			

Example 11.1(d)

	A	B	
1	Calculating FV_{Def}		
2	j	4.00%	
3	m	2	
4	t	1	
5			
6	i	2.00%	= B2/B3
7	n	2	= B3*B4
8	**PMT**	0	
9	**PV**	$7,500.00	
10	**FV**	($7,803.00)	= FV(B6, B7, B8, B9) FV(rate, nper, pmt, [pv], [type])
11			
12	Calculating PMT		
13	j	4.00%	
14	m	2	
15	P/Y	12	
16	t	5	
17			
18	i	2.00%	= B13/B14
19	c	0.166667	= B14/B15
20	i_2	0.3306%	= (1 + B18)^B19 – 1
21	n	60	= B15*B16
22	**PMT**	($143.59)	= PMT(B20, B21, B23, B24, B25) PMT(rate, nper, pv, [fv], [type])
23	**PV**	$7,803.00	= –B10
24	**FV**	0	
25	**BGN**	0	
26			

Example 11.1(e)

	A	B	Formula
1	Calculating FV_{Def}		
2	*j*	8.00%	
3	*m*	4	
4	*t*	3	
5			
6	*i*	2.00%	= B2/B3
7	*n*	12	= B3*B4
8	*PMT*	0	
9	*PV*	($500,000.00)	
10	*FV*	$634,120.90	= FV(B6, B7, B8, B9) FV(rate, nper, pmt, [pv], [type])
11			
12	Calculating *t*		
13	*j*	8.00%	
14	*m*	4	
15	*P/Y*	1	
16	*t*	10	= ROUNDUP(B21,0)/B15 ROUNDUP(number, num_digits)
17			
18	*i*	2.00%	= B13/B14
19	*c*	4	= B14/B15
20	i_2	8.2432%	= (1 + B18)^B19 – 1
21	*n*	9.709541	= NPER(B20, B22, B23, B24, B25) NPER(rate, pmt, pv, [fv], [type])
22	*PMT*	$90,000.00	
23	*PV*	($634,120.90)	= –B10
24	*FV*	0	
25	*BGN*	1	
26			

11.2 Examples

Example 11.2(a)

	A	B	Formula
1	Calculating PV_{Perp}		
2	*j*	8.00%	
3	*m*	4	
4	*P/Y*	4	
5	*t*	-	
6			
7	*i*	2.00%	= B2/B3
8	*n*	10,000	
9	*PMT*	($10,000.00)	
10	*PV*	$500,000.00	= PV(B7, B8, B9, B11, B12) PV(rate, nper, pmt, [fv], [type])
11	*FV*	0	
12	*BGN*	0	
13			

Example 11.2(b)

	A	B	Formula
1	Calculating $PV_{Perp\ Due}$		
2	*j*	8.00%	
3	*m*	4	
4	*P/Y*	12	
5	*t*	-	
6			
7	*i*	2.00%	= B2/B3
8	*c*	0.333333	= B3/B4
9	i_2	0.6623%	= (1 + B7)^B8 – 1
10	*n*	10,000	
11	*PMT*	($5,000.00)	
12	*PV*	$759,978.00	= PV(B9, B10, B11, B13, B14) PV(rate, nper, pmt, [fv], [type])
13	*FV*	0	
14	*BGN*	1	
15			

Example 11.2(c)

	A	B	Formula
1	Calculating *PMT*		
2	*j*	5.75%	
3	*m*	12	
4	*P/Y*	4	
5	*t*	-	
6			
7	*i*	0.4792%	= B2/B3
8	*c*	3	= B3/B4
9	i_2	1.4444%	= (1 + B7)^B8 – 1
10	*n*	10,000	
11	*PMT*	$7,222.00	= PMT(B9, B10, B12, B13, B14) PMT(rate, nper, pv, [fv], [type])
12	*PV*	($500,000.00)	
13	*FV*	0	
14	*BGN*	0	
15			

Example 11.2(d)

	A	B	Formula
1	Calculating $PV_{Perp\ Due}$		
2	*j*	6.00%	
3	*m*	12	
4	*P/Y*	12	
5	*t*	-	
6			
7	*i*	0.50%	= B2/B3
8	*n*	10,000	
9	*PMT*	$2,000.00	
10	*PV*	($402,000.00)	= PV(B7, B8, B9, B11, B12) PV(rate, nper, pmt, [fv], [type])
11	*FV*	0	
12	*BGN*	1	
13			
14	Calculating PV_{Def}		
15	*j*	6.00%	
16	*m*	12	
17	*t*	2	
18			
19	*i*	0.50%	= B15/B16
20	*n*	24	= B16*B17
21	*PMT*	0	
22	*PV*	($356,648.64)	= PV(B19, B20, B21, B23) PV(rate, nper, pmt, [fv], [type])
23	*FV*	$402,000.00	= –B10
24			

11.3 Examples

Example 11.3(a)

	A	B	
1	(i)	Calculating *FV*	
2	***j***	12.00%	
3	***m***	12	
4	***P/Y***	12	
5	***t***	15	
6			
7	***i***	1.00%	= B2/B3
8	***g***	1.50%	
9	***n***	180	= B4*B5
10	***PMT***	$500.00	
11			
12	$(1+i)^n$	5.995802	= (1 + B7)^B9
13	$(1+g)^n$	14.584368	= (1 + B8)^B9
14	$(i-g)$	-0.50%	= B7 – B8
15	***FV***	$858,856.57	= B10*((B12 – B13)/B14)
16			
17	(ii)	Sum of Payments	
18		$452,812.26	= FV(B8, B9, –B10,0) FV(rate, nper, pmt, [pv], [type])
19			

Example 11.3(b)

	A	B	
1	(i)	Calculating *PV*	
2	***j***	5.00%	
3	***m***	2	
4	***P/Y***	2	
5	***t***	10	
6			
7	***i***	2.50%	= B2/B3
8	***g***	2.00%	
9	***n***	20	= B4*B5
10	***PMT***	$1,000.00	
11			
12	$(1+g)^n$	1.485947	= (1 + B8)^B9
13	$(1+i)^{-n}$	0.610271	= (1 + B7)^–B9
14	$(i-g)$	0.50%	= B7 – B8
15	***PV***	$18,633.90	= B10*((1 – B12*B13)/B14)
16			
17	(ii)	Sum of Payments	
18		$24,297.37	= FV(B8, B9, –B10,0) FV(rate, nper, pmt, [pv], [type])
19			

Example 11.3(c)

	A	B	
1	(i)	Calculating *PMT*	
2	***j***	8.00%	
3	***m***	4	
4	***P/Y***	4	
5	***t***	30	
6			
7	***i***	2.00%	= B2/B3
8	***g***	2.25%	
9	***n***	120	= B4*B5
10	***FV***	$147,034.45	
11			
12	$(1+i)^n$	10.765163	= (1 + B7)^B9
13	$(1+g)^n$	14.441024	= (1 + B8)^B9
14	$(i-g)$	-0.25%	= B7 – B8
15	***PMT***	$100.00	= B10/((B12–B13)/B14)
16			
17	(ii)	Sum of Payments	
18		$59,737.88	= FV(B8, B9, –B15,0) FV(rate, nper, pmt, [pv], [type])
19			

11 | Summary of Notation and Formulas

NOTATION

g = Constant growth rate

PMT = Periodic payment of the annuity

n = Number of payments during the term of an annuity

FV = Accumulated value or future value of an annuity

FV_{Due} = Future value of an annuity due

FV_{Def} = Future value of a deferred annuity

PV_{Perp} = Present value of an ordinary perpetuity

i = Interest rate per conversion period (periodic interest rate)

j = Nominal interest rate

t = Time period

PV = Discounted value or present value of an annuity

PV_{Due} = Present value of an annuity due

PV_{Def} = Present value of a deferred annuity

$PV_{Perp\ Due}$ = Present value of a perpetuity due

FORMULAS

Present Value of an Ordinary Perpetuity | 11.2(a)

$$PV_{Perp} = \frac{PMT}{i}$$

Present Value of a Perpetuity Due | 11.2(b)

$$PV_{Perp\ Due} = \frac{PMT}{i}(1 + i) \quad \textbf{or} \quad PV_{Perp\ Due} = \frac{PMT}{i} + PMT$$

Future Value of an Ordinary Simple Constant-Growth Annuity | 11.3(a)

$$FV = PMT\left[\frac{(1 + i)^n - (1 + g)^n}{(i - g)}\right]$$

Present Value of an Ordinary Simple Constant-Growth Annuity | 11.3(b)

$$PV = PMT\left[\frac{1 - (1 + g)^n (1 + i)^{-n}}{(i - g)}\right]$$

Sum of Constant-Growth Payments | 11.3(c)

$$\textit{Sum of Constant-Growth Payments} = PMT\left[\frac{(1 + g)^n - 1}{g}\right]$$

Chapter

12 AMORTIZATION OF LOANS AND MORTGAGES

LEARNING OBJECTIVES

- Apply the principle of amortization of loans in constructing an amortization schedule.
- Calculate the principal balance.
- Calculate the final payment.
- Calculate the interest portion, principal portion, and principal balance after any payment.
- Construct a partial amortization schedule.
- Compare different types of mortgages.
- Calculate mortgage payments for the initial term and renewal term.
- Examine the requirement to qualify for a mortgage and the different options available to prepay a mortgage, and the effect of prepayment on the amortization period.

CHAPTER OUTLINE

Introduction

People borrow money from financial institutions for various reasons. You may require a loan in order to start a business, go to school, purchase a car, or renovate your home. As we have learned in previous chapters, when you borrow money, you need to pay back the principal amount, plus the interest acquired over the time of the loan. The process of repaying a compound interest bearing loan by periodic payments over a period of time is called **amortization**.

Amortization is the reduction of a debt through periodic repayments, usually of equal amounts, over a period of time.

One of the largest amounts for which one often borrows money is for the purchase of a property; this is a special type of loan referred to as a **mortgage**. Since the principal of a mortgage is generally quite high, in exchange for lending money at a specific interest rate for a period of time, a financial institution has claim over the purchased property.

In this chapter, we will use many of the terms and procedures that we learned in the previous chapters dealing with compound interest and annuities to examine applications involving amortization of loans and mortgages.

12.1 | Amortization of Loans

The **amortization of a loan** is the gradual reduction in the loan amount through periodic repayments, usually of equal amounts, over a predetermined length of time. The time period set to repay the loan is called the **amortization period**. Each repayment amount is first used to pay off the interest charged during that period and the rest of the repayment amount is used to reduce a portion of the principal of the loan. Therefore, after every repayment, the interest for the next period is calculated on the reduced principal. Examples of loans that are amortized include car loans and mortgages on properties.

Amortization of loans is primarily considered as an *ordinary annuity* because loan repayments are usually made at the end of the payment period.

Therefore, if the compounding period is equal to the payment period, the present value of a loan (which is the principal) is calculated by the ordinary simple annuity formula, Formula 10.2(b):

$$PV = PMT\left[\frac{1-(1+i)^{-n}}{i}\right]$$

If the compounding period is not equal to the payment period, the present value of the loan is calculated by substituting the equivalent periodic interest rate per payment period (i_2) for 'i' in the above formula:

$$PV = PMT\left[\frac{1-(1+i_2)^{-n}}{i_2}\right]$$

The equivalent periodic interest rate per payment period (i_2) is calculated using Formula 10.3(a) and Formula 10.3(b), as follows:

From Formula 10.3(a), $$c = \frac{\text{Number of compounding periods per year}}{\text{Number of payments per year}}$$

From Formula 10.3(b), $$i_2 = (1+i)^c - 1$$

Note that most of the notations and formulas in this section make use of those from the compound interest and annuity chapters.

Amortization Schedule

An amortization schedule is a detailed table that breaks down each loan repayment amount into its interest portion and principal portion. It also shows the amount of principal balance after each payment is made.

Amortization schedules are created and used by financial institutions to provide customers with the exact amount of the loan that is outstanding after each payment. Amortization schedules are most frequently used for mortgages.

An amortization schedule typically contains the following information:

- Payment number (or payment date)
- Payment amount (PMT)
- Interest portion of the payment amount (INT)
- Principal portion of the payment amount (PRN)
- Principal balance (or outstanding balance or outstanding principal balance) after each payment (BAL)

At the beginning of the amortization schedule, a larger portion of the periodic payment goes towards the interest portion. However, later on in the schedule, a larger portion of the periodic payment goes towards the principal portion.

Constructing an Amortization Schedule

Table 12.1 and the steps that follow illustrate the construction of a typical amortization schedule:

Table 12.1 **Constructing an Amortization Schedule**

Payment Number	Amount Paid (Periodic Payment) PMT (\$)	Interest Portion (Previous Balance) INT (\$)	Principal Portion ($PMT - INT$) PRN (\$)	Principal Balance (Previous Balance − PRN) BAL (\$)
0	-	-	-	Loan amount: PV
1	PMT	INT_1 $(= PV \times i)$	PRN_1 $(= PMT - INT_1)$	BAL_1 $(= PV - PRN_1)$
2	PMT	INT_2 $(= BAL_1 \times i)$	PRN_2 $(= PMT - INT_2)$	BAL_2 $(= BAL_1 - PRN_2)$
3	PMT	INT_3 $(=BAL_2 \times i)$	PRN_3 $(= PMT - INT_3)$	BAL_3 $(= BAL_2 - PRN_3)$
.	.	.	.	.
.	.	.	.	.
$n-1$	PMT	$INT_{(n-1)}$ $(=BAL_{(n-2)} \times i)$	$PRN_{(n-1)}$ $(= PMT - INT_{(n-1)})$	$BAL_{(n-1)}$ $(= BAL_{(n-2)} - PRN_{(n-1)})$
n	PMT_n $(= BAL_{(n-1)} + BAL_{(n-1)} \times i)$	INT_n $(= BAL_{(n-1)} \times i)$	PRN_n $(=BAL_{(n-1)})$	0
Total	Total Amount Paid	Total Interest Portion	Total Principal Portion	

Step 1: Calculate the periodic interest rate (i).

Step 2: Enter '0' as the first payment number in the first row and enter the original loan amount, PV, as the principal balance in this row.

Step 3: Enter the periodic payment, PMT, in a new row against its respective payment number. The periodic payment amount is generally a rounded amount. Therefore, the final payment will be different from the other periodic payments as it will carry the difference resulting from having rounded the previous payments. The calculation for the final payment amount is explained in Step 8.

Step 4: Enter the interest portion, INT, of the payment in the 3rd column. This is the previous principal balance multiplied by the periodic interest rate.

Step 5: Enter the principal portion, PRN, of the payment in the 4th column. This is the difference between the periodic payment amount and the interest portion.

Step 6: Enter the principal balance, BAL, in the 5th column. This is the difference between the previous principal balance and the principal portion.

Step 7: Construct the remaining rows of the amortization schedule by performing the calculations in Steps 3–6 until the final payment number, where the principal balance will be zero.

Step 8: The final payment amount is calculated by adding the previous principal balance and the interest charged on the previous principal balance.

Step 9: The last row contains all the totals and can be used to cross-check if the calculations are correct:

Total Principal Portion = Original loan amount

Total Amount Paid = Total Interest Portion + Total Principal Portion

Example 12.1(a) Constructing an Amortization Schedule, Given the Term

Shiela received a loan of $7500 at 9% compounded quarterly to purchase a machine for her small business. She settled the loan by making payments at the end of every three months for one year.

(i) Calculate the size of the payments.

(ii) Construct an amortization schedule for the loan.

Solution

The loan is in the form of an ordinary simple annuity as:

- Payments are made at the end of each payment period (quarterly)
- Compounding period (quarterly) = payment period (quarterly)

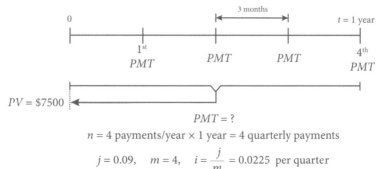

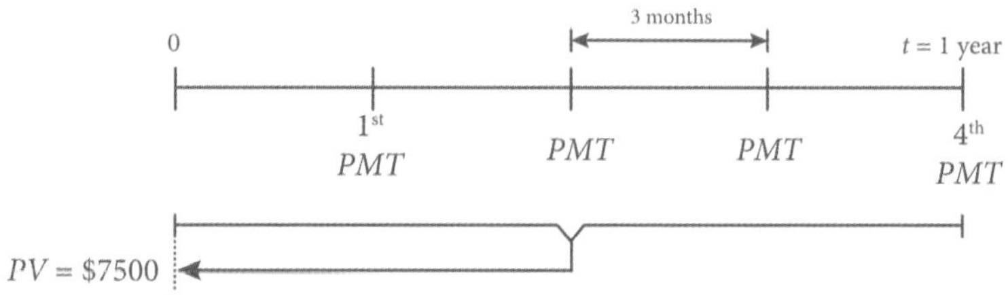

$$PMT = ?$$

$$n = 4 \text{ payments/year} \times 1 \text{ year} = 4 \text{ quarterly payments}$$

$$j = 0.09, \quad m = 4, \quad i = \frac{j}{m} = 0.0225 \text{ per quarter}$$

(i) *Calculating the size of the payments*

Using Formula 10.2(b),
$$PV = PMT\left[\frac{1-(1+i)^{-n}}{i}\right]$$

$$7500.00 = PMT\left[\frac{1-(1+0.0225)^{-4}}{0.0225}\right]$$

$$PMT = 1981.641957... = \$1981.64$$

When the periodic payments, PMT, are rounded, the last payment amount will be different from the PMT.

Therefore, the size of the end-of-quarter payments was $1981.64 (rounded to the nearest cent).

Solution *continued*

(ii) *Constructing an amortization schedule*

Payment Number	Amount Paid (Periodic Payment) *PMT* ($)	Interest Portion (Previous Balance) *INT* ($)	Principal Portion (*PMT* – *INT*) *PRN* ($)	Principal Balance (Previous Balance – *PRN*) *BAL* ($)
0	-	-	-	$7500.00
1	$1981.64	$168.75 (=7500.00 × 0.0225)	$1812.89 (=1981.64 – 168.75)	5687.11 (= 7500.00 – 1812.89)
2	1981.64	127.96 (=5687.11 × 0.0225)	1853.68 (=1981.64 – 127.96)	3833.43 (= 5687.11 – 1853.68)
3	1981.64	86.25 (=3833.43 × 0.0225)	1895.39 (=1981.64 – 86.25)	1938.04 (= 3833.43 – 1895.39)
4	1981.65 (=1938.04+1938.04 × 0.0225)	43.61 (=1938.04 × 0.0225)	1938.04	$0.00
Total	$7926.57	$426.57	$7500.00	

Cross-checking the above totals:

Total Principal Portion = *Original loan amount* = $7500.00

Total Amount Paid = *Total Interest Portion* + *Total Principal Portion*

= $426.57 + $7500.00 = $7926.57

Using Spreadsheets to Construct Amortization Schedules

When constructing amortization schedules, spreadsheets can aid us with repeated calculations.

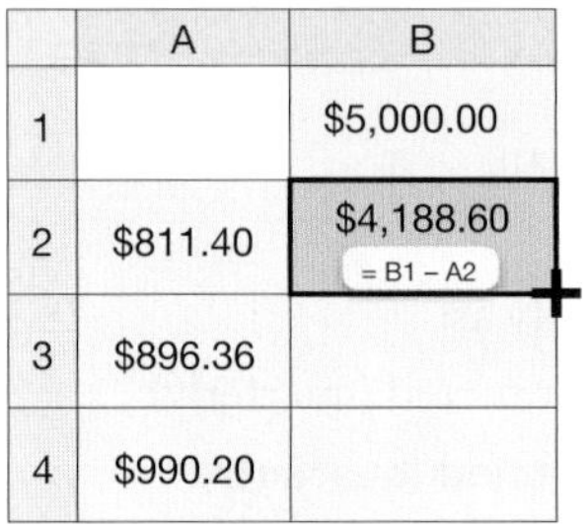
A
B
1
$5,000.00
2
$811.40
$4,188.60
= B1 – A2
3
$896.36
4
$990.20

Step 1: Select a cell containing a formula, and hover your mouse cursor over the bottom-right corner of the cell. A black + will appear.

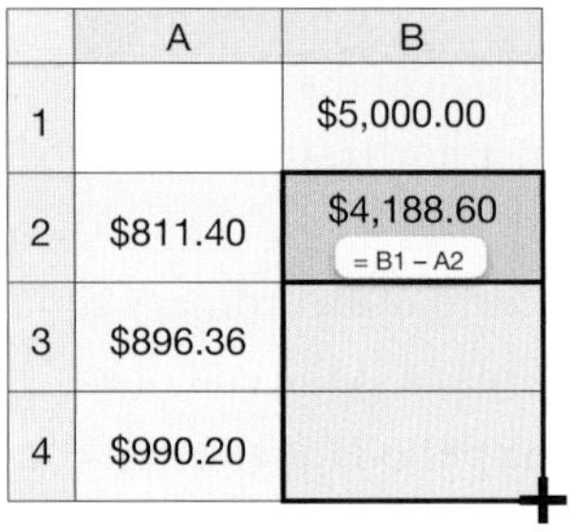
A
B
1
$5,000.00
2
$811.40
$4,188.60
= B1 – A2
3
$896.36
4
$990.20

Step 2: Click and drag the + symbol down as many cells as you want to perform the same calculation.

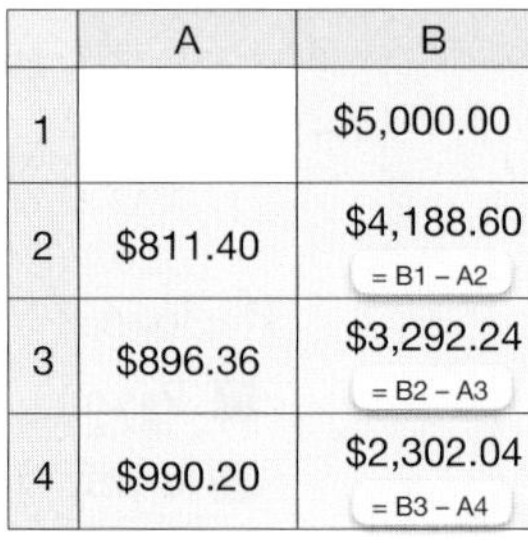
A
B
1
$5,000.00
2
$811.40
$4,188.60
= B1 – A2
3
$896.36
$3,292.24
= B2 – A3
4
$990.20
$2,302.04
= B3 – A4

Step 3: When you release your mouse cursor, the spreadsheet will automatically perform the calculations in each of the cells you highlighted with the updated cell references.

Note in the example above that the spreadsheet automatically updated the formula in cell B3 to be 'B2 – A3' and the formula in cell B4 to be 'B3 – A4'. If you do not want your spreadsheet to automatically update a specific cell reference when using the drag-and-drop formula feature, type a $ between the letter and number in the cell's reference. This is called an *absolute cell reference.*

For example, if the formula in cell B2 was instead 'B$1 – A2', then the spreadsheet would automatically update the formula in cell B3 to be 'B$1 – A3' and the formula in cell B4 to be 'B$1 – A4'.

Note: *Microsoft Excel and other spreadsheet software offer built in templates for creating loan and mortgage amortization schedules. However, we will construct our own schedule for the spreadsheet method solutions to the solved examples in the text.*

Solving Example 12.1(a) using a spreadsheet is shown below:

Example 12.1(b) **Using a Spreadsheet to Solve Example 12.1(a)**

Shiela received a loan of $7500 at 9% compounded quarterly to purchase a machine for her small business. She settled the loan by making payments at the end of every three months for one year.

(i) Calculate the size of the payments.
(ii) Construct an amortization schedule for the loan.

Solution We will use a spreadsheet's drag-and-drop formula feature to help us create our amortization schedule.

	A	B	C	D	E	F	G	H	I
1	Calculating *PMT*								
2	***j***	9.00%							
3	***m***	4		Amortization Schedule					
4	***P/Y***	4		**Payment Number**	**Amount Paid**	**Interest Portion**	**Principal Portion**	**Principal Balance**	
5	***t***	1		0	-	-	-	$7,500.00 (= B10)	
6				1	$1,981.64 (= ROUND(–B$9, 2))	$168.75 (= ROUND(H5*B$7, 2))	$1,812.89 (= E6 – F6)	$5,687.11 (= H5 – G6)	
7	***i***	2.25% (= B2/B3)		2	$1,981.64	$127.96	$1,853.68	$3,833.43	
8	***n***	4 (= B4*B5)		3	$1,981.64	$86.25	$1,895.39	$1,938.04	
9	***PMT***	($1,981.64) (= PMT(B7, B8, B10, B11, B12))		4	$1,981.65 (= H8 + H8*B7)	$43.61	$1,938.04	$0.00	
10	***PV***	$7,500.00		**Total**	$7,926.57 (= SUM(E6 : E9))	$426.57 (= SUM(F6 : F9))	$7,500.00 (= SUM(G6 : G9))		
11	***FV***	0							
12	***BGN***	0							
13									

The formula in cell H7 is H6–G7.

The formula in cell F9 is ROUND(H8*B$7,2).

***Note:** Although PMT in cell B9 is displayed as a rounded value, the cell holds the **exact** PMT value of –$1981.641957... Since the periodic payment amount is generally rounded, we must use the built-in function **ROUND** to round PMT to two decimal places in our amortization schedule (cells E6, E7, and E8), so that the rounded PMT is used in calculations. Similarly, ROUND is also used when calculating Interest Portion in our amortization schedule.*

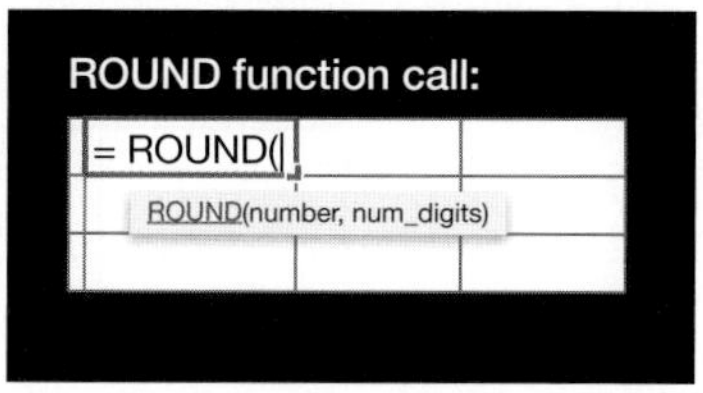

Example 12.1(c) Constructing an Amortization Schedule, Given the Payment

A manufacturer received a loan of $12,450 at 12% compounded monthly to purchase equipment for his factory. He paid $3000 at the end of every three months to settle the loan.

(i) Calculate the number of payments required.

(ii) Construct an amortization schedule for the loan.

ge 528

Solution This loan is in the form of an ordinary general annuity as:

- Payments are made at the end of each payment period (quarterly)
- Compounding period (monthly) ≠ payment period (quarterly)

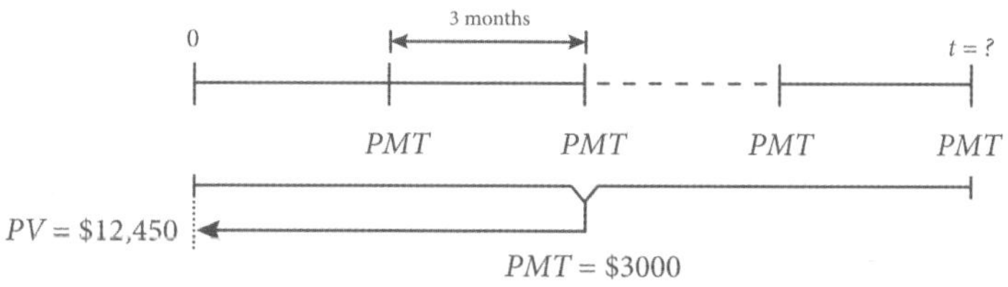

$j = 0.12,\quad m = 12,\quad i = \frac{j}{m} = 0.01$ per month

Using Formula 10.3(a), $c = \frac{\textit{Number of compounding periods per year}}{\textit{Number of payments per year}} = \frac{12}{4}$

Using Formula 10.3(b), $i_2 = (1 + i)^c - 1 = (1 + 0.01)^{(12/4)} - 1 = 0.030301$ per quarter

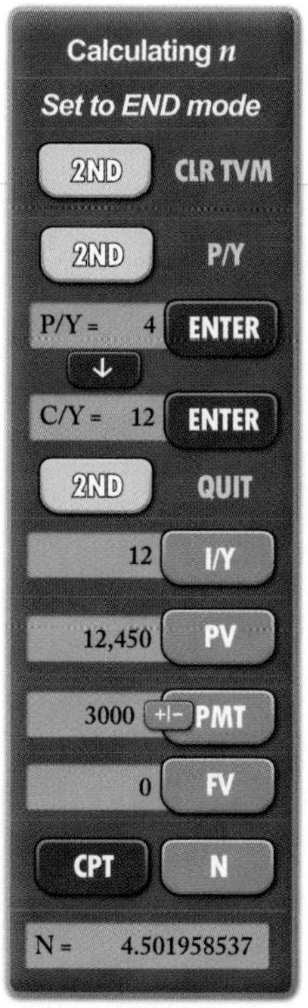

Solution *continued*

(i) *Calculating the number of payments*

Using Formula 10.7(b), $$n = -\frac{\ln\left[1 - \frac{i_2 \times PV}{PMT}\right]}{\ln(1 + i_2)} = -\frac{\ln\left[1 - \frac{0.030301 \times 12{,}450.00}{3000.00}\right]}{\ln(1 + 0.030301)}$$

$= 4.501958...$ Round up to the next payment period.

$= 5$ The 5th payment will be smaller in size.

In this problem, we have been given a specific rounded payment amount of $3000 that has to be made at the end of every three months. Therefore, the last payment amount will be different from this amount. The following amortization schedule will illustrate this.

(ii) *Constructing an amortization schedule*

Payment Number	Amount Paid (Periodic Payment) *PMT* ($)	Interest Portion (Previous Balance) *INT* ($)	Principal Portion (*PMT* - *INT*) *PRN* ($)	Principal Balance (Previous Balance - *PRN*) *BAL* ($)
0	-	-	-	$12,450.00
1	$3000.00	$377.25 (=12,450.00 × 0.030301)	$2622.75 (=3000.00 – 377.25)	9827.25 (=12,450.00 – 2622.75)
2	3000.00	297.78 (=9827.25 × 0.030301)	2702.22 (=3000.00 – 297.78)	7125.03 (=9827.25 – 2702.22)
3	3000.00	215.90 (=7125.03 × 0.030301)	2784.10 (=3000.00 – 215.90)	4340.93 (=7125.03 – 2784.10)
4	3000.00	131.53 (=4340.93 × 0.030301)	2868.47 (=3000.00 – 131.53)	1472.46 (=4340.93 – 2868.47)
5	1517.08 (=1472.46 + 1472.46 × 0.030301)	44.62 (=1472.46 × 0.030301)	1472.46	$0.00
Total	$13,517.08	$1067.08	$12,450.00	

Cross-checking the above totals:

Total Principal Portion = *Original loan amount* = $12,450.00

Total Amount Paid = *Total Interest Portion* + *Total Principal Portion*

= $1067.08 + $12,450.00 = $13,517.08

Calculating the Principal Balance

It may be necessary to know the principal balance at an earlier time than at the end of the loan period in order to settle the loan earlier or make a partial repayment. This may be done by creating an amortization schedule and calculating the principal balance at the required date or by directly using any of the following three methods:

Method 1: Prospective Method (considering payments that are yet to be made)

The principal balance at the focal date can be calculated by determining the present value of all the outstanding payments on that focal date. This method is also known as the Present Value approach.

$$BAL_{\text{Focal Date}} = PV_{\text{Outstanding Payments on the Focal Date}}$$

When *PMT* is known, calculate the exact (non-rounded) number for *n*. The principal balance on the focal date is the *PV* of the payments on the focal date using the non-rounded value of *n*.

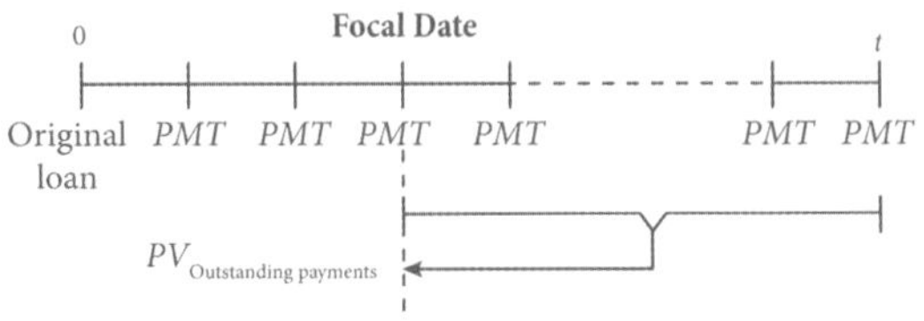

When the term is known, first calculate *PMT*, which is usually rounded to the nearest cent (or nearest dollar). The final payment will be slightly different from the periodic *PMT* and is calculated as explained at the end of this section. The principal balance on the focal date is the sum of the *PV* of all outstanding payments (including the final payment) on the focal date.

Method 2: Retrospective Method (considering payments that have already been made)

The principal balance at the focal date can also be calculated by deducting the future value of all the payments that have been made until the focal date from the future value of the original loan amount on the focal date. This method is also known as the Future Value approach.

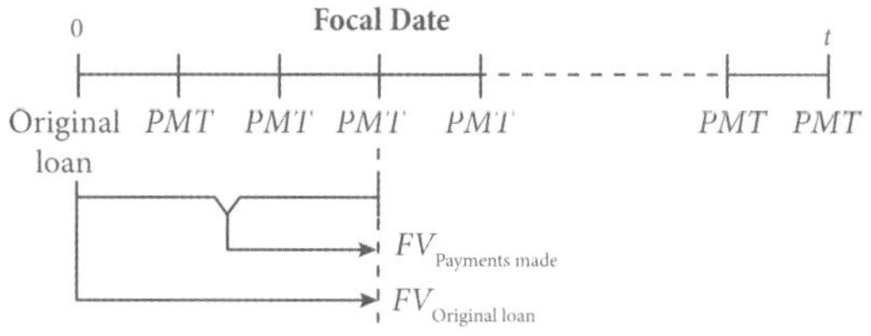

$$BAL_{Focal\ Date} = FV_{Original\ Loan} - FV_{Payments\ Made\ until\ the\ Focal\ Date}$$

Method 3: Using the Amortization Worksheet in a Preprogrammed Financial Calculator

If the size of the payment is not provided, compute its value and **re-enter *PMT* rounded to two decimal places**. Then follow these instructions using the calculator's amortization worksheet:

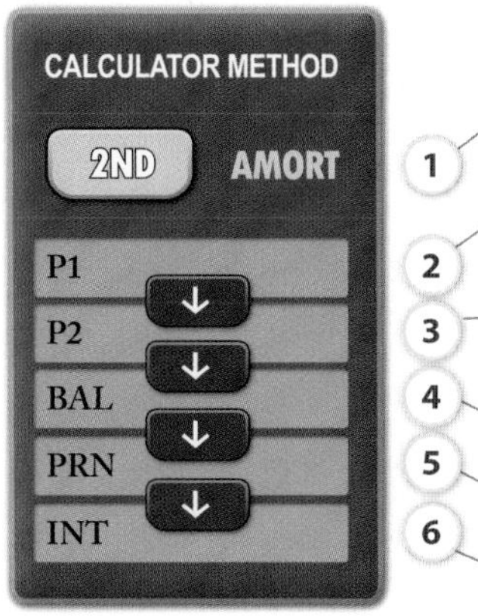

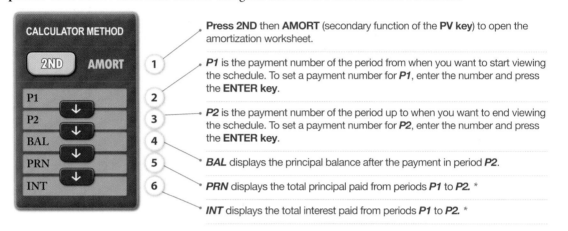

1. **Press 2ND** then **AMORT** (secondary function of the **PV key**) to open the amortization worksheet.
2. ***P1*** is the payment number of the period from when you want to start viewing the schedule. To set a payment number for ***P1***, enter the number and press the **ENTER key**.
3. ***P2*** is the payment number of the period up to when you want to end viewing the schedule. To set a payment number for ***P2***, enter the number and press the **ENTER key**.
4. ***BAL*** displays the principal balance after the payment in period ***P2***.
5. ***PRN*** displays the total principal paid from periods ***P1*** to ***P2***. *
6. ***INT*** displays the total interest paid from periods ***P1*** to ***P2***. *

* *To obtain the principal portion and interest portion of a particular payment number, set P1 and P2 to that payment number. For example, when P1 = 5 and P2 = 5, PRN displays the principal portion of the 5th payment and INT displays the interest portion of the 5th payment. BAL displays the principal balance after the 5th payment.*

Note: *In the prospective method, calculating the final payment and using it to calculate the principal balance at the focal date becomes lengthy. For this reason, in the examples and exercises of this section, we only use the retrospective method and amortization worksheet methods to calculate the principal balance.*

Example 12.1(d) Calculating the Principal Balance, Given the Term

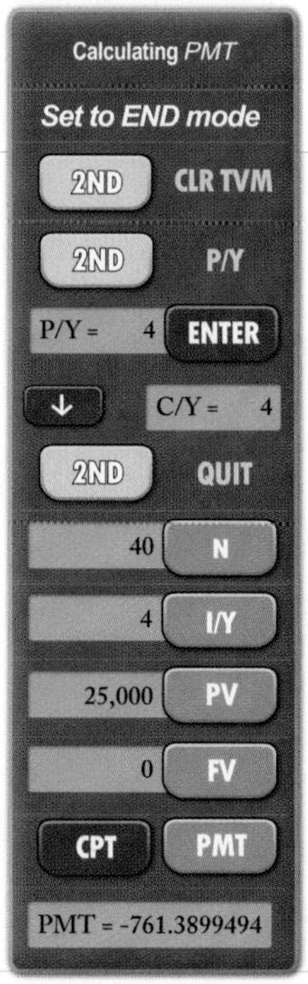

age 529

Samantha received a loan of $25,000 at 4% compounded quarterly. If the loan is amortized over ten years with payments made at the end of every three months, what was the balance on her loan after one year?

This loan is in the form of an ordinary simple annuity as:

- Payments are made at the end of each payment period (quarterly)
- Compounding period (quarterly) = payment period (quarterly)

$n = 4$ payments/year × 10 years = 40 quarterly payments, $j = 0.04$, $m = 4$, $i = \frac{j}{m} = 0.01$ per quarter

Calculating the payment amount

Using Formula 10.2(b), $$PV = PMT\left[\frac{1 - (1 + i)^{-n}}{i}\right]$$

$$25{,}000.00 = PMT\left[\frac{1 - (1 + 0.01)^{-40}}{0.01}\right]$$

$$PMT = 761.389949... = \$761.39$$

Solution *continued*

Using the Retrospective Method

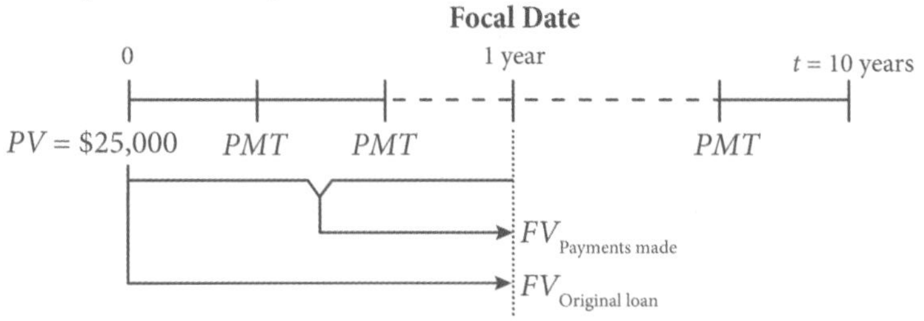

It is not necessary to re-enter I/Y, P/Y, and PV as they have not changed and have not been cleared (by CLR TVM).

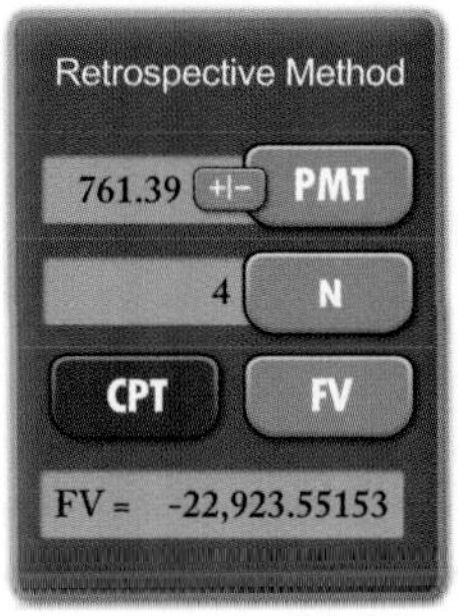

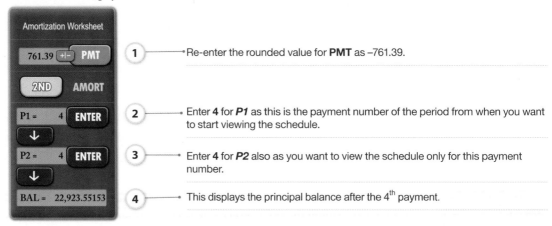

Since we need to determine the balance of her loan after one year, we will use n = 4 payments/year × 1 year = 4 quarterly payments.

$$BAL_{\text{Focal Date}} = FV_{\text{Original Loan}} - FV_{\text{Payments Made until the Focal Date}}$$

Using Formula 9.1(a) and Formula 10.2(a),

$$BAL_{\text{1 year}} = PV(1+i)^n - PMT\left[\frac{(1+i)^n - 1}{i}\right]$$

$$= 25{,}000.00(1+0.01)^4 - 761.39\left[\frac{(1+0.01)^4 - 1}{0.01}\right] = 26{,}015.10025... - 3091.548717...$$

$$= 22{,}923.55153... = \$22{,}923.55$$

Using the Amortization Worksheet

First re-enter the rounded value for PMT as –761.39 in the TVM worksheet.

After one year, four payments were made. Therefore, we need to determine the principal balance at the end of the fourth payment as illustrated below:

1. Re-enter the rounded value for **PMT** as –761.39.
2. Enter **4** for ***P1*** as this is the payment number of the period from when you want to start viewing the schedule.
3. Enter **4** for ***P2*** also as you want to view the schedule only for this payment number.
4. This displays the principal balance after the 4th payment.

Therefore, the principal balance on the loan after one year was $22,923.55.

Example 12.1(e) Calculating the Principal Balance, Given the Payment

Andrew received a student loan of $45,000 at 6% compounded monthly. If he has to repay $500 at the end of every month, what was his principal balance at the end of two years?

Page 529

The loan is in the form of an ordinary simple annuity as:

- Payments are made at the end of each payment period (monthly)
- Compounding period (monthly) = payment period (monthly)

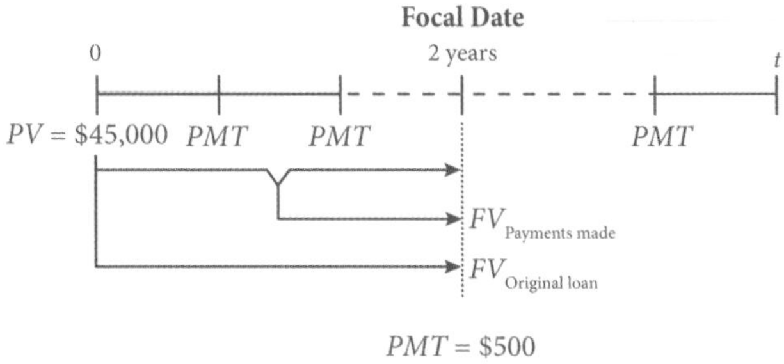

$$i = \frac{j}{m} = \frac{0.06}{12} = 0.005$$

Solution *continued*

Calculating the principal balance using the retrospective method and the amortization worksheet

Since we need to determine the principal balance at the end of 2 years, we will use n = 12 payments/year × 2 years = 24 monthly payments.

$$BAL_{Focal\ Date} = FV_{Original\ Loan} - FV_{Payments\ Made\ until\ the\ Focal\ Date}$$

Using Formula 9.1(a) and Formula 10.2(a),

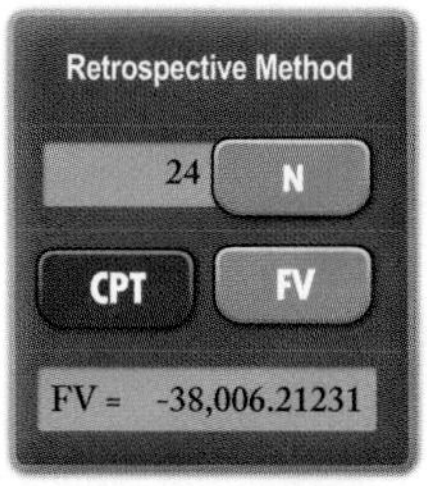

$$BAL_{2\ years} = PV(1+i)^n - PMT\left[\frac{(1+i)^n - 1}{i}\right]$$

$$= 45{,}000.00(1 + 0.005)^{24} - 500.00\left[\frac{(1 + 0.005)^{24} - 1}{0.005}\right]$$

$$= 50{,}722.18993... - 12{,}715.97762...$$

$$= 38{,}006.21231... = \$38{,}006.21$$

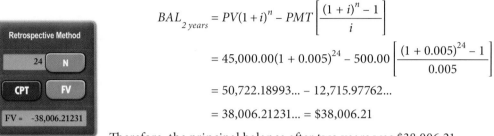

Therefore, the principal balance after two years was $38,006.21.

Calculating the Final Payment

The final payment can be calculated using either of the following methods:

Method 1: Direct Method

From Table 12.1, we know that the final payment is the sum of the principal balance before the final payment and the interest charged on that principal balance.

$$PMT_{Final} = BAL_{Before\ Final\ Payment} + BAL_{Before\ Final\ Payment} \times i$$

$$= BAL_{Before\ Final\ Payment}(1 + i)$$

Method 2: Overpayment Method

By rounding 'n' up to a whole number, the calculator assumes that the final payment is the same amount as all of the other payments. Thus, when you calculate the future value, the result will represent the overpayment that resulted from the final payment being larger than it should be. To find the correct amount for the final payment, subtract the amount of overpayment from the regular payment amount as shown:

$$PMT_{Final} = PMT - Overpayment$$

Example 12.1(f) **Calculating the Final Payment of an Ordinary General Annuity**

A loan of $750,000 at 12% compounded quarterly was settled by making payments of $50,000 at the end of every six months.

(i) How many payments were required to settle the loan?

(ii) What was the final payment on the loan?

Solution

Page 529

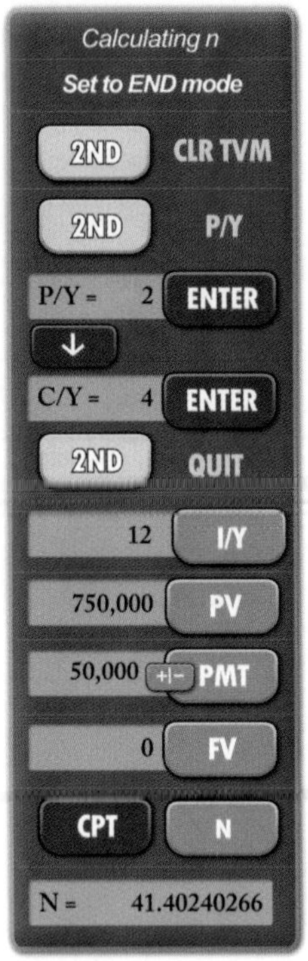

This loan is in the form of an ordinary general annuity as:

- Payments are made at the end of each payment period (semi-annually)
- Compounding period (quarterly) ≠ payment period (semi-annually)

$$i = \frac{j}{m} = \frac{0.12}{4} = 0.03 \text{ per quarter}$$

From Formula 10.3(a), $c = \dfrac{\textit{Number of compounding periods per year}}{\textit{Number of payments per year}} = \dfrac{4}{2}$

From Formula 10.3(b), $i_2 = (1 + i)^c - 1 = (1 + 0.03)^{(4/2)} - 1 = 0.0609$ per half-year

(i) *Calculating the number of payments*

From Formula 10.7(b), $n = -\dfrac{\ln\left[1 - \dfrac{i \times PV}{PMT}\right]}{\ln(1+i)} = -\dfrac{\ln\left[1 - \dfrac{0.0609 \times 750{,}000.00}{50{,}000.00}\right]}{\ln(1 + 0.0609)}$

$= 41.402402...$ Round to the next payment period,

$= 42$ payments The 42nd payment will be of a smaller size.

Therefore, 42 payments were required to settle the loan.

(ii) *Calculating the final payment on the loan*

Method 1: Direct Method

Using the retrospective method to calculate the principal balance after 41 payments are made:

$$BAL_{\textit{Focal Date}} = FV_{\textit{Original Loan}} - FV_{\textit{Payments Made until the Focal Date}}$$

Using Formula 9.1(a) and Formula 10.2(a),

$$BAL_{\textit{Focal Date}} = PV(1+i)^n - PMT\left[\frac{(1+i)^n - 1}{i}\right]$$

$$BAL_{41} = 750{,}000.00(1 + 0.0609)^{41} - 50{,}000.00\left[\frac{(1 + 0.0609)^{41} - 1}{0.0609}\right]$$

$= 8{,}466{,}690.593... - 8{,}447{,}389.812...$

$= 19{,}300.78124...$

$$PMT_{\textit{Final}} = BAL_{41}(1 + i)$$

$= 19{,}300.78124...(1 + 0.0609) = 20{,}476.19882... = \$20{,}476.20$

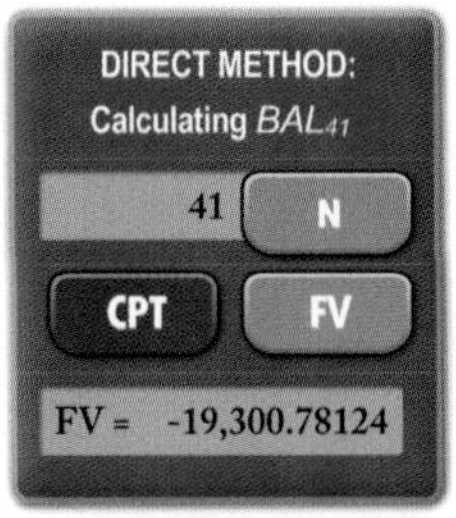

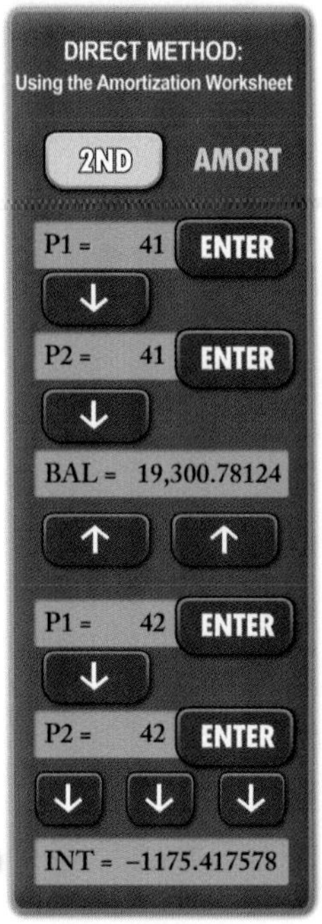

Final Payment = 1 + 2
= 19,300.78 + 1175.42
= $20,476.20

Method 2: Overpayment Method

Using the overpayment method, we assume that each of the 42 payments were of equal size. Then the future value after the 42nd payment is equal to the overpayment.

$$PMT_{\textit{Final}} = PMT - \textit{Overpayment}$$

$= 50{,}000.00 - 29{,}523.80118...$

$= 20{,}476.19882... = \$20{,}476.20$

Therefore, the final payment was $20,476.20.

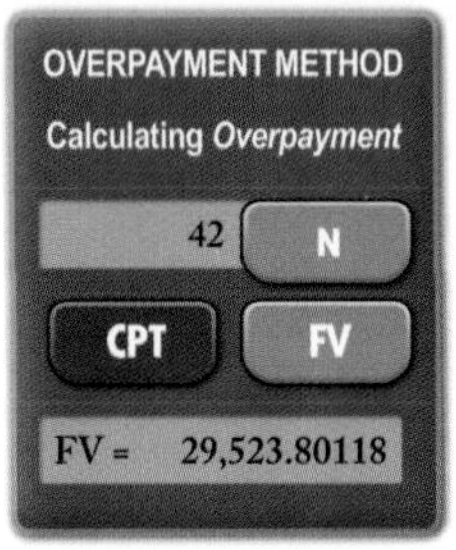

Example 12.1(g) Calculating the Final Payment of a Simple Annuity Due

Jia's student loan had accumulated to $16,550 at the time of her graduation. She had to start making payments of $273 at the beginning of every month to settle the loan. The interest rate charged was 6% compounded monthly.

(i) How many payments are required to settle the loan?

(ii) What is the final payment?

Page 529

Solution

Calculating n
Set to BGN mode
2ND CLR TVM
2ND P/Y
P/Y = 12 ENTER
↓ C/Y = 12
2ND QUIT
6 I/Y
16,550 PV
273 +|- PMT
0 FV
CPT N
N = 71.97357362

The loan is in the form of a simple annuity due as:

- Payments are made at the beginning of each period (monthly)
- Compounding period (monthly) – payment period (monthly)

$$i = \frac{j}{m} = \frac{0.06}{12} = 0.005 \text{ per month}$$

(i) *Calculating the number of payments*

From Formula 10.7(e), $n = -\dfrac{\ln\left[1 - \dfrac{i \times PV_{Due}}{PMT(1+i)}\right]}{\ln(1+i)} = -\dfrac{\ln\left[1 - \dfrac{0.005 \times 16{,}550.00}{273.00(1+0.005)}\right]}{\ln(1+0.005)}$

$= 71.973573...$ Round to the next payment period,

$= 72$ payments The 72nd payment will be of a smaller size.

Therefore, 72 payments are required to settle the loan.

(ii) *Calculating the final payment*

Using the retrospective method to calculate the principal balance after 71 payments are made,

$$BAL_{Focal\ Date} = FV_{Original\ Loan} - FV_{Payments\ Made\ until\ Focal\ Date}$$

Using Formula 9.1(a) and Formula 10.4(a),

DIRECT METHOD
Calculating BAL_{71}
71 N
CPT FV
FV = −265.8030999

$$BAL_{Focal\ Date} = PV(1+i)^n - PMT\left[\frac{(1+i)^n - 1}{i}\right](1+i)$$

$$BAL_{71} = 16{,}550.00(1+0.005)^{71} - 273.00\left[\frac{(1+0.005)^{71} - 1}{0.005}\right](1+0.005)$$

$$= 23{,}582.42071... - 23{,}316.61761... = 265.803099... = \$265.80$$

The principal balance of \$265.80 at the end of the 71st payment will be the final 72nd payment as it is at the beginning of the payment period.

Alternatively, using the overpayment method:
P1 = 72, P2 = 72, BAL = −7.20
Final Payment = 273.00 − 7.20 = \$265.80

DIRECT METHOD:
Using the Amortization Worksheet
2ND AMORT
P1 = 71 ENTER
↓
P2 = 71 ENTER
↓
1 BAL = 264.4806964
↑ ↑
P1 = 72 ENTER
↓
P2 = 72 ENTER
↓ ↓ ↓
2 INT = −1.322403482

Final Payment = 1 + 2
= 264.48 + 1.32
= \$265.80

Calculating the Interest and Principal Portions of a Payment

In addition to determining the principal balance at a given time, it may be necessary to determine the interest portion and principal portion of a payment at any given time. The interest portion at any given time is calculated on the previous principal balance. The principal portion can then be determined by subtracting the calculated interest portion from the payment amount of the loan.

Example 12.1(h) **Calculating the Interest Portion and Principal Portion of a Single Payment**

Clear Circuits Inc., an electrical contracting company, receives a loan of \$130,000 at 6% compounded monthly to purchase some heavy equipment. It must make payments of \$5000 at the end of every month to settle the loan.

(i) What is the interest portion of the 19th payment?

(ii) What is the principal portion of the 19th payment?

Page 529

Solution

Inputting Initial Values
Set to END mode
2ND CLR TVM
2ND P/Y
P/Y = 12 ENTER
↓ C/Y = 12
2ND QUIT
6 I/Y
130,000 PV
5000 +/- PMT

This loan is in the form of an ordinary simple annuity as:

- Payments are made at the end of each payment period (monthly)
- Compounding period (monthly) = payment period (monthly)

$$i = \frac{j}{m} = \frac{0.06}{12} = 0.005 \text{ per month}$$

(i) The **interest portion** of a payment is calculated on the previous principal balance.

Therefore, to calculate the interest portion of the 19th payment, we need to calculate the principal balance after 18 payments.

Using the retrospective method,

$$BAL_{\text{Focal Date}} = FV_{\text{Original loan}} - FV_{\text{Payments made until the focal date}}$$

Using Formula 9.1(a) and Formula 10.2(a),

$$BAL_{\text{Focal Date}} = PV(1+i)^n - PMT\left[\frac{(1+i)^n - 1}{i}\right]$$

Calculating BAL_{18}
18 N
CPT FV
FV = -48,281.82258

$$BAL_{18} = 130{,}000.00(1+0.005)^{18} - 5000.00\left[\frac{(1+0.005)^{18} - 1}{0.005}\right]$$

$$= 142{,}210.7621... - 93{,}928.93955... = \$48{,}281.82258...$$

$$INT_{19} = BAL_{18} \times i = 48{,}281.82258... \times 0.005$$

$$= 241.409112... = \$241.41$$

Therefore, the interest portion of the 19th payment is \$241.41.

(ii) The **principal portion** of the 19th payment = *Payment Amount – Interest Portion*

$$= 5000.00 - 241.41 = \$4758.59$$

Therefore, the principal portion of the 19th payment is \$4758.59.

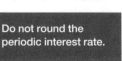

Amortization Worksheet
2ND AMORT
P1 = 19 ENTER
↓
P2 = 19 ENTER
↓
BAL = 43,523.23169
↓
PRN = -4758.590887
↓
INT = -241.4091129

Example 12.1(i) **Calculating the Total Principal Portion and Interest Portion of Payments Made During a Period**

Harold Consulting was paying \$1500 at the end of every month to settle a loan of \$300,000 at 5.45% compounded quarterly.

(i) What was the total principal repaid in the 12th year?
(ii) What was the total interest paid in the 12th year?

Page 530

Inputting Initial Values
Set to END mode
2ND CLR TVM
2ND P/Y
P/Y = 12 ENTER
↓
C/Y = 4 ENTER
2ND QUIT
5.45 I/Y
300,000 PV
1500 +/- PMT

The loan is in the form of an ordinary general annuity as:

- Payments are made at the end of each payment period (monthly)
- Compounding period (quarterly) ≠ payment period (monthly)

$$i = \frac{j}{m} = \frac{0.0545}{4} = 0.013625$$

$$c = \frac{\text{Number of compounding periods per year}}{\text{Number of payments per year}} = \frac{4}{12}$$

$$i_2 = (1+i)^c - 1 = (1+0.013625)^{(4/12)} - 1 = 0.004521... \text{ per month}$$

Do not round the periodic interest rate.

(i) *Total principal repaid in the 12th year*

$$= BAL_{11^{th}\text{ year}} - BAL_{12^{th}\text{ year}}$$

$$= BAL_{12 \text{ payments per year} \times 11 \text{ years}} - BAL_{12 \text{ payments per year} \times 12 \text{ years}}$$

$$= BAL_{132} - BAL_{144}$$

Solution *continued*

Using the retrospective method,

$$BAL_{Focal\ Date} = PV(1 + i)^n - PMT\left[\frac{(1 + i)^n - 1}{i}\right]$$

$$BAL_{132} = 300{,}000.00(1 + 0.004521...)^{132} - 1500.00\left[\frac{(1 + 0.004521...)^{132} - 1}{0.004521...}\right]$$

$$= 544{,}155.5280... - 270{,}012.1831... = \$274{,}143.3449...$$

$$BAL_{144} = 300{,}000.00(1 + 0.004521...)^{144} - 1500.00\left[\frac{(1 + 0.004521...)^{144} - 1}{0.004521...}\right]$$

$$= 574{,}423.6327... - 303{,}485.7526... = \$270{,}937.8802...$$

Therefore, total principal repaid in the 12th year = 274,143.3449... – 270,937.8802...

= 3205.464768... = \$3205.46

(ii) *Total interest paid in the 12th year*

= Total amount paid in the 12th year – Total principal repaid in the 12th year

= (12 payments × \$1500.00) – \$3205.46 = \$14,794.54

Therefore, the total interest paid in the 12th year was \$14,794.54.

Calculating BAL_{132}

132 N

CPT FV

FV = –274,143.3449

Calculating BAL_{144}

144 N

CPT FV

FV = –270,937.8802

Amortization Worksheet

2ND AMORT

P1 = 133 ENTER

↓

P2 = 144 ENTER

↓

BAL = 270,937.8802

↓

PRN = –3205.464768

↓

INT = –14,794.53523

Example 12.1(j) Calculating the Principal Reduction and Interest Paid during a Period

Sheela received an \$18,000 loan at 5.25% compounded monthly that was to be repaid by payments of \$500 made at the end of every month. Just when she completed making the first 12 payments, she lost her job. However, her father helped her pay the payments in the second year of the loan.

(i) How much of the loan did her father settle?

(ii) How much interest did her father pay?

Solution

age 530

The loan is in the form of an ordinary simple annuity as:

- Payments are made at the end of each payment period (monthly)
- Compounding period (monthly) = payment period (monthly)

$$i = \frac{j}{m} = \frac{0.0525}{12} = 0.004375 \text{ per month}$$

(i) Principal reduced by the 2nd year payments = $BAL_{12^{th}\ Payment} - BAL_{24^{th}\ Payment}$

Using the retrospective method,

$$BAL_{Focal\ Date} = PV(1 + i)^n - PMT\left[\frac{(1 + i)^n - 1}{i}\right]$$

$$BAL_{12} = 18{,}000.00(1 + 0.004375)^{12} - 500.00\left[\frac{(1 + 0.004375)^{12} - 1}{0.004375}\right]$$

$$= 18{,}968.07396... - 6146.501340...$$

$$= \$12{,}821.57262...$$

$$BAL_{24} = 18{,}000.00(1 + 0.004375)^{24} - 500.00\left[\frac{(1 + 0.004375)^{24} - 1}{0.004375}\right]$$

$$= 19{,}988.21277... - 12{,}623.57312...$$

$$= \$7364.639647...$$

Principal Reduction = \$12,821.57262... – 7364.639647...

= 5456.932974 ... = \$5456.93

Therefore, her father settled \$5456.93 of the loan.

Inputting Initial Values

Set to END mode

2ND CLR TVM

2ND P/Y

P/Y = 12 ENTER

↓ C/Y = 12

2ND QUIT

5.25 I/Y

18,000 PV

500 +/– PMT

Calculating BAL_{12}

12 N

CPT FV

FV = –12,821.57262

Calculating BAL_{24}

24 N

CPT FV

FV = –7364.639647

Amortization Worksheet

2ND AMORT

P1 = 13 ENTER

↓

P2 = 24 ENTER

↓

BAL = 7364.639647

↓

PRN = –5456.932974

↓

INT = –543.0670261

Solution *continued*

(ii) Total Interest paid = Total Payment – Total Principal paid

$$= (12 \text{ payments} \times 500.00) - 5456.93$$
$$= \$543.07$$

Therefore, her father paid $543.07 in interest.

Constructing a Partial Amortization Schedule

There may be instances when it is necessary to determine the amortization details of a portion of the schedule, such as the last five payments, the first five payments, or the interest and principal portions of a particular payment. It is for this reason that we determine all the payment details and create a partial amortization schedule.

Example 12.1(k) **Constructing a Partial Amortization Schedule for Example 12.1(h)**

Clear Circuits Inc., an electrical contracting company, receives a loan of $130,000 at 6% compounded monthly to purchase some heavy equipment. It must make payments of $5000 at the end of every month to settle the loan. Construct the partial amortization details and schedule for the:

(i) first two payments.
(ii) last two payments.
(iii) total payment made and interest paid.

Page 530

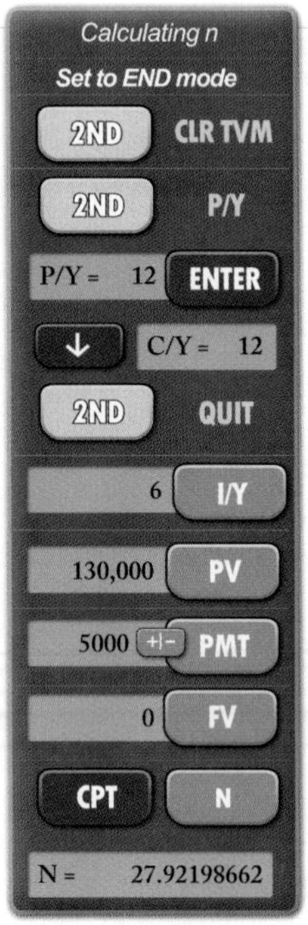

This loan is in the form of an ordinary simple annuity as:

- Payments are made at the end of each payment period (monthly)
- Compounding period (monthly) = payment period (monthly)

$$i = \frac{j}{m} = \frac{0.06}{12} = 0.005 \text{ per month}$$

We need to calculate the number of payments, 'n',

$$\text{From Formula 10.7(b), } n = -\frac{\ln\left[1 - \frac{i \times PV}{PMT}\right]}{\ln(1+i)} = -\frac{\ln\left[1 - \frac{0.005 \times 130{,}000.00}{5000.00}\right]}{\ln(1+0.005)}$$

$= 27.921986...$ Round up to the next payment period.

$n = 28$ payments The 28th payment will be of a smaller size.

(i) *Amortization details of the 1st payment*

$$INT_1 = \textit{Original Loan Amount} \times i$$
$$= 130{,}000.00 \times 0.005 = \$650.00$$
$$PRN_1 = PMT - INT_1$$
$$= 5000.00 - 650.00 = \$4350.00$$
$$BAL_1 = \textit{Original Loan Amount} - PRN_1$$
$$= 130{,}000.00 - 4350.00 = \$125{,}650.00$$

Amortization details of the 2nd payment

$$INT_2 = BAL_1 \times i$$
$$= 125{,}650.00 \times 0.005 = \$628.25$$
$$PRN_2 = PMT - INT_2$$
$$= 5000.00 - 628.25 = \$4371.75$$

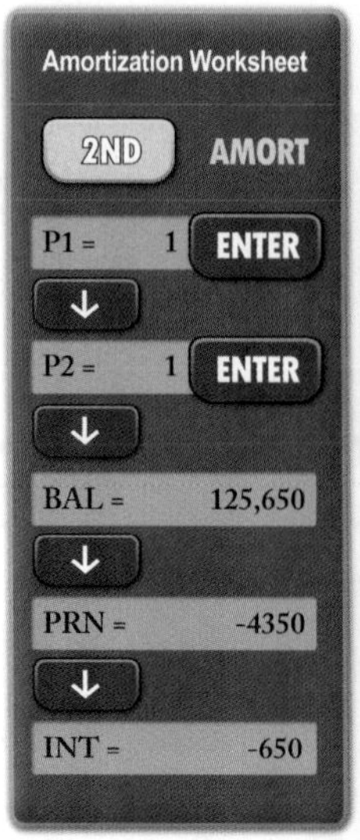

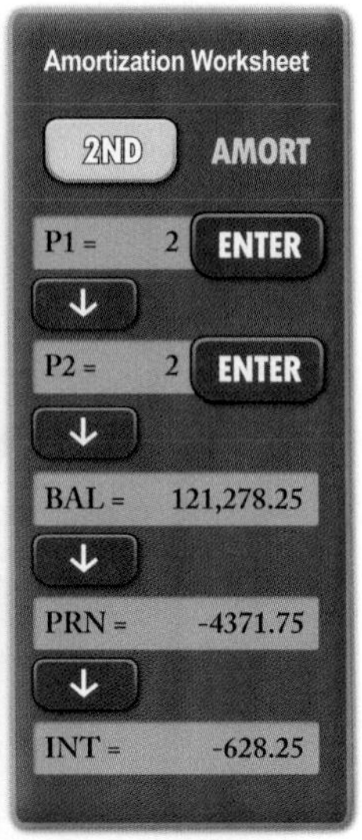

Solution *continued*

$$BAL_2 = BAL_1 - PRN_2$$

$$= 125{,}650.00 - 4371.75 = \$121{,}278.25$$

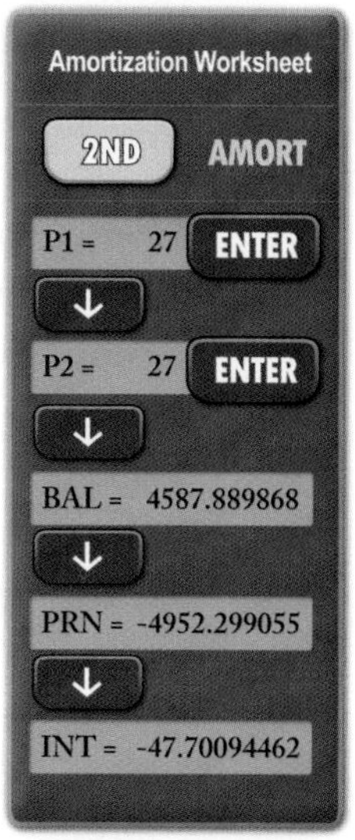

(ii) *Amortization details of the 27th payment*

To calculate the amortization details of the 27th payment, we need to determine the principal balance after the 26th payment.

Using the retrospective method,

$$BAL_{26} = FV_{Original\ Loan} - FV_{Payments\ Made\ until\ the\ 26th\ Payment}$$

Using Formula 9.1(a) and Formula 10.2(a),

$$BAL_{Focal\ Date} = PV(1+i)^n - PMT\left[\frac{(1+i)^n - 1}{i}\right]$$

$$BAL_{26} = 130{,}000.00(1+0.005)^{26} - 5000.00\left[\frac{(1+0.005)^{26} - 1}{0.005}\right]$$

$$= 147{,}999.7419... - 138{,}459.5529... = \$9540.19$$

$$INT_{27} = BAL_{26} \times i = 9540.19 \times 0.005 = \$47.70$$

$$PRN_{27} = PMT - INT_{27} = 5000.00 - 47.70 = \$4952.30$$

$$BAL_{27} = BAL_{26} - PRN_{27} = 9540.19 - 4952.30 = \$4587.89$$

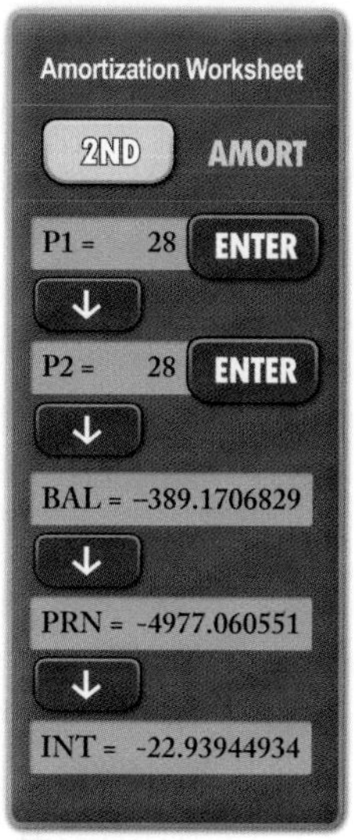

Amortization details of the 28th payment (last payment)

$$INT_{28} = BAL_{27} \times i = 4587.89 \times 0.005 = \$22.94 \quad *$$

$$PRN_{28} = BAL_{27} = \$4587.89 \quad **$$

$$PMT_{28} = INT_{28} + PRN_{28} = 22.94 + 4587.89 = \$4610.83$$

$$BAL_{28} = 0$$

* *If the last payment was \$5000, an excess of \$389.17 would be paid.*

** *If the last payment was \$5000, the principal portion of the payment would be \$4977.06.*

(iii) *Total Payment Made* $= (n - 1)PMT + Final\ Payment$

$$= (27 \times 5000.00) + 4610.83$$

$$= \$139{,}610.83$$

Total Interest Paid = Total Payment Made − Total Principal Paid

$$= 139{,}610.83 - 130{,}000.00$$

$$= \$9610.83$$

Using the amortization details calculated in (i), (ii), and (iii), construct the partial amortization schedule as shown below:

Payment Number	Amount Paid (Periodic Payment) *PMT* (\$)	Interest Portion (Previous Balance) *INT* (\$)	Principal Portion (*PMT - INT*) *PRN* (\$)	Principal Balance (Previous Balance - *PRN*) *BAL* (\$)
0	-	-	-	\$130,000.00
1	\$5000.00	\$650.00	\$4350.00	125,650.00
2	5000.00	628.25	4371.75	121,278.25
.	.	.	.	.
26	.	.	.	9540.19
27	5000.00	47.70	4952.30	4587.89
28	4610.83	22.94	4587.89	\$0.00
Total	\$139,610.83	\$9610.83	\$130,000.00	-

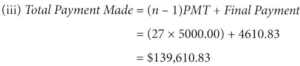

12.1 | Exercises

Answers to the odd-numbered problems are available at the end of the textbook.

1. Alberto received a loan of $10,000 at 4% compounded quarterly from a credit union to use as working capital for his business. He had to make payments at the end of every three months for a period of one year to settle the loan.
   a. What was the size of the quarterly payments?
   b. Construct an amortization schedule for the loan.
   c. What was the total amount paid to amortize the loan?
   d. What was the cost of financing (total interest paid)?

2. Aiden and Abbey received a small business loan of $81,500 at 9% compounded semi-annually. They received the loan for two years and had to make payments at the end of every six months to settle the loan.
   a. What was the size of the semi-annual payments?
   b. Construct an amortization schedule for the loan.
   c. What was the total amount paid to amortize the loan?
   d. What was the cost of financing (total interest paid)?

3. General Computers Inc. purchased a computer server for $75,400. It paid 40% of the value as a down payment and received a loan for the balance at 7.55% compounded monthly. It made payments of $2098.25 at the end of every three months to settle the loan.
   a. What was the amortization period?
   b. Construct an amortization schedule for the loan.
   c. What was the cost of financing?

4. Bella purchased a machine for $350,000. She paid 30% of the value as a down payment and received a loan for the balance at 5.75% compounded semi-annually. She had to make payments of $8081.40 at the end of every three months to settle the loan.
   a. What was the amortization period?
   b. Construct an amortization schedule for the loan.
   c. What was the cost of financing?

5. Cooper's student loan of $24,500 at 5.75% compounded daily was amortized over three years with payments made at the end of every month. What was the principal balance on the loan after one year?

6. Herbert's loan of $225,000 at 4.25% compounded semi-annually was amortized over 15 years with payments made at the end of every month. Calculate the outstanding balance on the loan after 10 years.

7. Rex had a loan of $40,000 and made payments of $3000 at the end of every three months to settle it. If he received the loan at 7.25% compounded quarterly, what was the balance on the loan at the end of two years?

8. Sheng-Li and Tai received a $5000 loan from a bank at 4.75% compounded monthly. If they had to make payments of $100 at the end of every month, what will be the balance on their loan at the end of three years?

9. A design studio received a loan of $300,000 at 6% compounded monthly to use as working capital for the business. It was required to settle the loan with payments of $2500 at the end of every month.
   a. How many payments are required to settle the loan?
   b. What is the size of the final payment?

10. Leslie borrowed $25,000 at 7.85% compounded quarterly. He paid $1170 at the end of every three months to settle the loan.
    a. How many payments were required to settle the loan?
    b. What was the size of the final payment?

11. A student loan that had grown to $22,600 had to be repaid with payments of $350 at the beginning of every month. The interest rate charged was 5.75% compounded monthly.
    a. How many payments are required to settle the loan?
    b. What is the final payment?

12. An $18,500 lease had to be repaid with lease payments of $500 at the beginning of every month. The cost of borrowing was 6.25% compounded monthly.
    a. How many lease payments are required to settle the lease liability?
    b. What is the final lease payment?

13. A company borrowed $500,000 at 8.5% compounded daily. It settled the loan by paying $6200 at the end of every month.
    a. How many payments were required to settle the loan?
    b. What was the outstanding balance on the loan at the end of nine years?
    c. What was the size of the final payment?
    d. What was the total interest paid?

14. Britney Distributors was repaying a loan of $37,500 with payments of $1000 made at the end of every month. The interest rate on the loan is 6.75% compounded semi-annually.
    a. How many payments were required to settle the loan?
    b. What was the outstanding balance on the loan at the end of three years?
    c. What was the size of the final payment?
    d. What was the total interest paid?

15. Usman purchased a machine for $12,000 for his company. He paid 10% of this amount as a down payment and financed the rest at 4.5% compounded monthly. He paid $1600 at the end of every month to settle the loan.
    a. What was the principal portion of the 6th payment?
    b. What was the interest portion of the 6th payment?

16. Alexandria renovated her kitchen for $13,860. She paid 15% of this amount as a down payment and financed the rest at 5% compounded monthly. She paid $250 at the end of every month to settle the loan.
    a. What was the principal portion of the 30th payment?
    b. What was the interest portion of the 30th payment?

17. For Problem 15, calculate the size of the final payment.

18. For Problem 16, calculate the size of the final payment.

19. A loan of $100,000 at 5% compounded daily was amortized over ten years with payments made at the end of every month.
    a. What was the principal portion of the 24th payment?
    b. What was the interest portion of the 24th payment?
    c. What was the balance on the loan at the end of two years?

20. Martha received a student loan of $20,000 at 6.25% compounded monthly for five years. She made payments at the end of every three months to settle the loan.
    a. What was the principal portion of the 16th payment?
    b. What was the interest portion of the 16th payment?
    c. What was the balance on the loan at the end of four years?

21. For Problem 19, construct a partial amortization schedule showing details of the first two payments, last two payments, total payment made, and interest paid.

22. For Problem 20, construct a partial amortization schedule showing details of the first two payments, last two payments, total payment made, and interest paid.

23. Hank was paying $550 at the end of every month to settle a loan of $18,750 at 5.45% compounded quarterly.
    a. What was the total principal repaid in the 2nd year?
    b. What was the total interest paid in the 2nd year?

24. Darren Associates borrowed $200,500 at 7.85% compounded semi-annually. It repaid this loan by making payments of $4000 at the end of every month.
    a. What was the total principal repaid in the 4th year?
    b. What was the total interest paid in the 4th year?

25. For Problem 23, construct a partial amortization schedule showing details of the first two payments, last two payments, total payment made, and interest paid.

26. For Problem 24, construct a partial amortization schedule showing details of the first two payments, last two payments, total payment made, and interest paid.

27. Davis purchased a machine with a loan of $75,000 at 8.75% compounded daily. He settled the loan by making payments of $1300 at the end of every month.
    a. What was the reduction in the loan amount during the 13th to the 21st payments, both inclusive?
    b. What was the interest amount paid during the 13th to the 21st payments, both inclusive?

28. Ming received a $15,000 loan at 7.75% compounded semi-annually that was to be repaid by payments of $550 at the end of every month. Upon completing the first 7 payments, he lost his job. However, his father helped him pay the 8th to the 12th payments.
    a. What was the reduction in the loan amount during the 8th to the 12th payments, both inclusive?
    b. What was the interest amount paid during the 8th to the 12th payments, both inclusive?

29. For Problem 27, construct a partial amortization schedule showing details of the first two payments, last two payments, total payment made, and total interest paid.

30. For Problem 28, construct a partial amortization schedule showing details of the first two payments, last two payments, total payment made, and total interest paid.

12.2 | Mortgages

Mortgage: loan issued by a financial institution to purchase real estate.

A **mortgage** is a loan that is issued by a financial lending institution to a borrower, to purchase real estate (commercial or residential property) at a specific interest rate for a specific time period. As the principal amount of mortgages is high, the borrower (mortgagor) generally provides the lender (mortgagee) with legal claim over the property (called collateral), as per the mortgage contract, until the mortgage loan has been completely amortized.

Amortization Period: length of time it takes to pay off the entire amount borrowed based on the original mortgage contract.

The **amortization period** is the length of time it takes to pay off the entire amount borrowed based on the original mortgage contract. Mortgages can have varying amortization periods and they generally do not exceed 25 years. A shorter amortization period would mean that the borrower would repay the mortgage sooner, so the mortgage payments would be larger and the total amount of interest on the mortgage would be less. Longer amortization periods spread the repayment across several years and allow for smaller mortgage payments, but also result in more interest over the total life of the mortgage.

Mortgage Term: length of time for which the mortgage agreement will be in effect.

The **mortgage term** is the length of time for which the mortgage agreement (a specific interest rate) will be in effect, for example, 3.5% compounded semi-annually for three years. The mortgage term usually varies from six months to ten years. At the end of each term, the mortgage agreement is re-negotiated unless the mortgage is paid off completely. Mortgage agreements are generally negotiated several times during the amortization period. Choosing a mortgage term depends on the borrower's expectation of how interest rates may fluctuate in the future. A shorter term is better if the interest rate decreases at the time the borrower renews his or her mortgage; however, a longer term is better if the interest rate increases, as the borrower will still be paying the older, lower rate.

Types of Mortgages

Lenders offer two types of mortgages: fixed rate and variable rate mortgages.

Fixed rate mortgages have a fixed interest rate for a specific period of time (mortgage term). When the term expires, the lender may renew the term for another fixed period depending on the market interest rate.

Variable rate mortgages have rates that are dependent on changes in the market, such as the change in the Bank of Canada's prime lending rate. Mortgages with variable interest rates are also referred to as floating rate mortgages.

Fixed or variable rate mortgages can be open or closed.

Sample Mortgage Rates (as of June 2017)

	Closed	Open
Fixed	2.69%	4.20%*
Variable	2.60%	3.90%

** Fixed, open mortgage rates are generally only offered as 6-month to 1-year terms.*

An **Open Mortgage** allows borrowers to prepay any amount at any time, close the entire mortgage, or transfer from one lender to another without being charged an additional fee or penalty. Open mortgage rates are generally higher than closed mortgage rates.

A **Closed Mortgage** is for a specific term and borrowers would have to pay a penalty for prepaying a large amount, closing the loan, or transferring to another lender.

Calculating Mortgage Payments and Principal Balance

As per Canadian law, fixed mortgage rates are compounded semi-annually and payments are made at the end of the payment period. Payments are generally paid monthly. However, lenders may also agree to receive payments semi-monthly, bi-weekly, or even weekly.

As the compounding frequency (semi-annually) is usually different from the payment period (monthly, bi-weekly, or weekly), mortgages in Canada usually form an ordinary general annuity.

Example 12.2(a) **Calculating Mortgage Payments for the First Term and Renewal Term**

A $250,000 mortgage for a house was issued with an amortization period of 25 years and payments had to be made monthly. The interest rate on the mortgage was 3.4% compounded semi-annually for a term of three years.

(i) What was the size of the monthly payment?

(ii) What was the principal balance at the end of the three-year term?

(iii) What would be the size of the monthly payment if the mortgage is renewed for another three-year term at 3.8% compounded semi-annually?

Solution

Page 531

Calculating *PMT*

Set to END mode

2ND CLR TVM

2ND P/Y

P/Y = 12 ENTER

↓

C/Y = 2 ENTER

2ND QUIT

300 N

3.4 I/Y

250,000 PV

0 FV

CPT PMT

PMT = -1235.016702

These mortgage payments represent an ordinary general annuity.

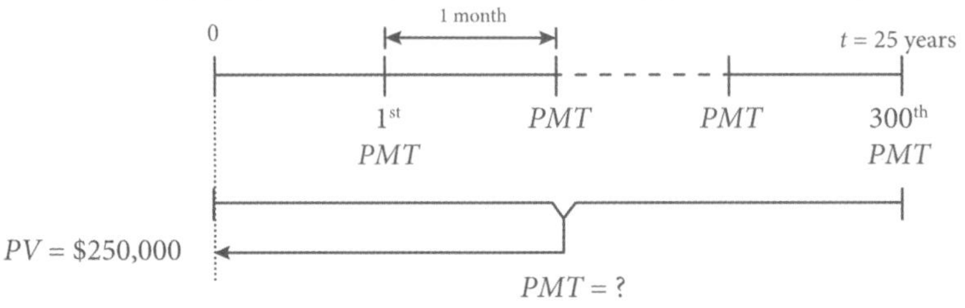

n = 12 payments/year × 25 years = 300 monthly payments

$j = 0.034, \quad m = 2, \quad i = \frac{j}{m} = 0.017$ per half-year

From Formula 10.3(a), $c = \frac{\textit{Number of compounding periods per year}}{\textit{Number of payments per year}} = \frac{2}{12}$

From Formula 10.3(b), $i_2 = (1 + i)^c - 1 = (1 + 0.017)^{(2/12)} - 1 = 0.002813...$ per month

(i) *Calculating the size of the monthly payment*

Using Formula 10.2(b),

$$PV = PMT\left[\frac{1 - (1 + i)^{-n}}{i}\right]$$

$$250{,}000.00 = PMT\left[\frac{1 - (1 + 0.002813...)^{-300}}{0.002813...}\right]$$

$$PMT = 1235.016702... = \$1235.02$$

Therefore, the monthly payment amount would be $1235.02

Solution *continued*

(ii) *Calculating the principal balance at the end of the three-year term*

Number of payments made by the end of the three-year term:

$$\textit{Number of Payments} = \textit{Payments Per Year} \times \textit{Number of Years}$$

$$= 12 \times 3 = 36 \text{ payments}$$

Calculating the principal balance at the end of 36 payments using the retrospective method,

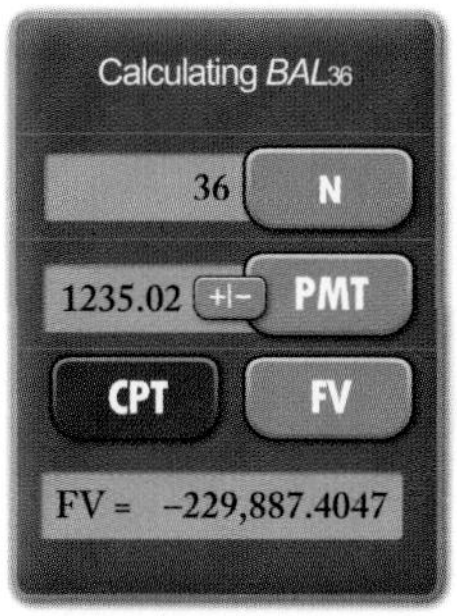

$$BAL_{36} = FV_{\textit{Original Loan}} - FV_{\textit{Payments Made until the } 36^{th} \textit{ payment}}$$

Using Formula 9.1(a) and Formula 10.2(a),

$$BAL_{\textit{Focal Date}} = PV(1+i)^n - PMT\left[\frac{(1+i)^n - 1}{i}\right]$$

$$BAL_{36} = 250{,}000.00(1 + 0.002813...)^{36} - 1235.02\left[\frac{(1 + 0.002813...)^{36} - 1}{0.002813...}\right]$$

$$= 276{,}608.6303... - 46{,}721.22567... = 229{,}887.4047... = \$229{,}887.40$$

Therefore, the principal balance at the end of the three-year term was $229,887.40.

(iii) *Calculating the size of the monthly payment if the mortgage is renewed for another three-year term at 3.8% compounded semi-annually*

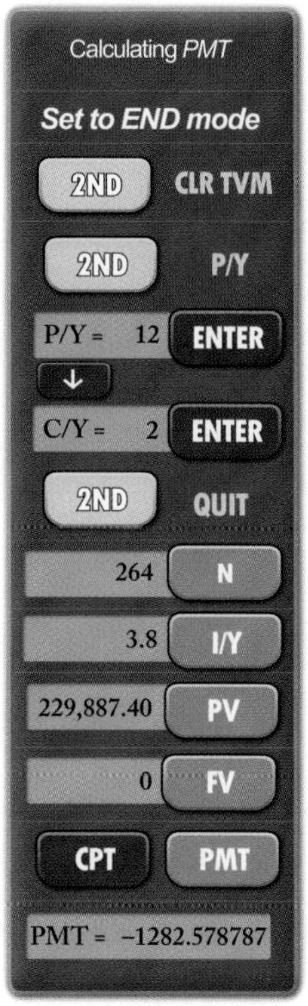

The renewed term will have a new periodic payment as the interest rate has changed.

$$\textit{Amortization Period} = 25 \text{ years} - 3 \text{ years} = 22 \text{ years}$$

From (ii),

$$\textit{Principal} = BAL_{\textit{three-year term}} = \$229{,}887.40$$

$$n = 12 \text{ payments per year} \times 22 \text{ years} = 264 \text{ payments}$$

$$i = \frac{j}{m} = \frac{0.038}{2} = 0.019 \text{ per half-year}$$

From Formula 10.3(a),

$$c = \frac{\textit{Number of compounding periods per year}}{\textit{Number of payments per year}} = \frac{2}{12}$$

From Formula 10.3(b),

$$i_2 = (1 + i)^c - 1 = (1 + 0.019)^{(2/12)} - 1 = 0.003141... \text{ per month}$$

Using Formula 10.2(b),

$$PV = PMT\left[\frac{1 - (1+i)^{-n}}{i}\right]$$

$$229{,}887.40 = PMT\left[\frac{1 - (1 + 0.003141...)^{-264}}{0.003141...}\right]$$

$$PMT = 1282.578787... = \$1282.58$$

Therefore, if the mortgage is renewed for another three-year term at 3.8% compounded semi-annually, the size of the monthly payment would be $1282.58.

Example 12.2(b) Mortgage Calculations when Payments are Rounded Up

Cindy received a $60,000 mortgage that is amortized over four years. She negotiated a fixed interest rate of 4% compounded semi-annually for the term. Payments had to be made on a monthly basis.

(i) Calculate the size of the monthly payments if they are rounded up to the next $100.

(ii) Calculate the size of the final payment on the mortgage.

Solution

Page 531

These mortgage payments represent an ordinary general annuity.

(i) *Calculating the size of the monthly payments, rounded up to the next $100*

$$n = 12 \text{ payments per year} \times 4 \text{ years} = 48 \text{ payments}$$

$$i = \frac{j}{m} = \frac{0.04}{2} = 0.02 \text{ per half-year}$$

From Formula 10.3(a), $c = \dfrac{\textit{Number of compounding periods per year}}{\textit{Number of payments per year}} = \dfrac{2}{12}$

From Formula 10.3(b), $i_2 = (1 + i)^c - 1 = (1 + 0.02)^{(2/12)} - 1 = 0.003305\ldots$ per month

Using Formula 10.2(b), $PV = PMT\left[\dfrac{1 - (1 + i)^{-n}}{i}\right]$

$$60{,}000.00 = PMT\left[\frac{1 - (1 + 0.003305\ldots)^{-48}}{0.003305\ldots}\right]$$

$$PMT = \$1353.859273\ldots$$

Therefore, rounding up to the next $100, the monthly payments are $1400.00.

(ii) *Calculating the size of the final payment*

By rounding the mortgage payments up to the next $100, the mortgage payments are higher, so there will be fewer than 48 payments required to settle the mortgage.

We need to calculate the number of payments left to amortize the mortgage.

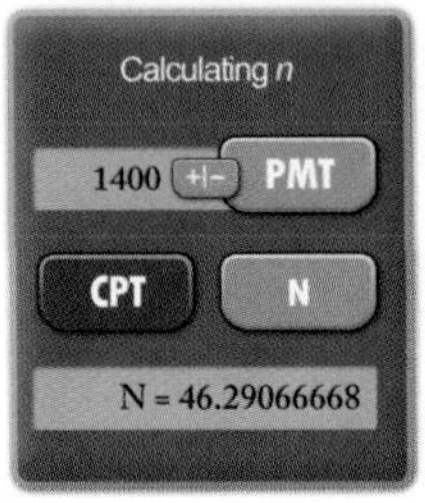

From Formula 10.7(b), $n = -\dfrac{\ln\left[1 - \dfrac{i \times PV}{PMT}\right]}{\ln(1 + i)} = -\dfrac{\ln\left[1 - \dfrac{0.003305\ldots \times 60{,}000.00}{1400.00}\right]}{\ln(1 + 0.003305\ldots)}$

$= 46.290666\ldots$ Round up to the next payment period.

$= 47$ payments The 47th payment will be of a smaller size.

Therefore, the number of payments has reduced from 48 payments to 47 payments by rounding the mortgage payment up to the next $100.

We need to calculate the size of the final payment.

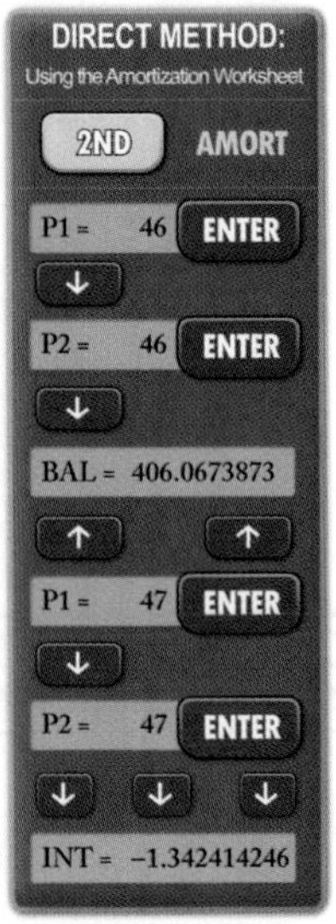

Final Payment = 1 + 2
= 406.07 + 1.34 = $407.41

Method 1: Direct Method

We know that the final payment amount = $BAL_{n-1}(1 + i)$

Using the retrospective method to calculate the principal balance after 46 payments are made:

$$BAL_{46} = FV_{\textit{Original Loan}} - FV_{\textit{Payments Made until the } 46^{th} \textit{ Payment}}$$

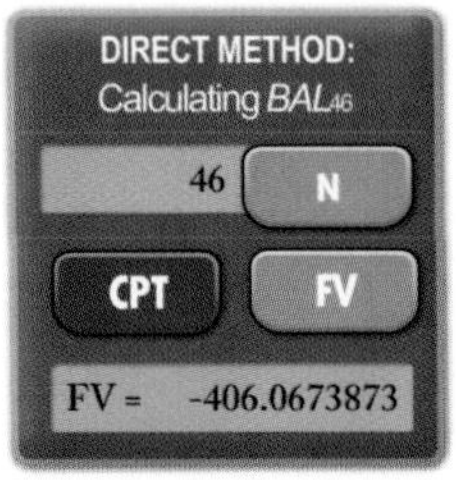

Using Formula 9.1(a) and Formula 10.2(a),

$$BAL_{\textit{Focal Date}} = PV(1 + i)^n - PMT\left[\frac{(1 + i)^n - 1}{i}\right]$$

$$BAL_{46} = 60{,}000.00(1 + 0.003305\ldots)^{46} - 1400.00\left[\frac{(1 + 0.003305\ldots)^{46} - 1}{0.003305\ldots}\right]$$

$$= 69{,}837.05235\ldots - 69{,}430.98496\ldots = \$406.067387\ldots$$

$$PMT_{\textit{Final}} = BAL_{n-1}(1 + i)$$

$$= 406.067387\ldots(1 + 0.003305\ldots) = 407.409801\ldots = \$407.41$$

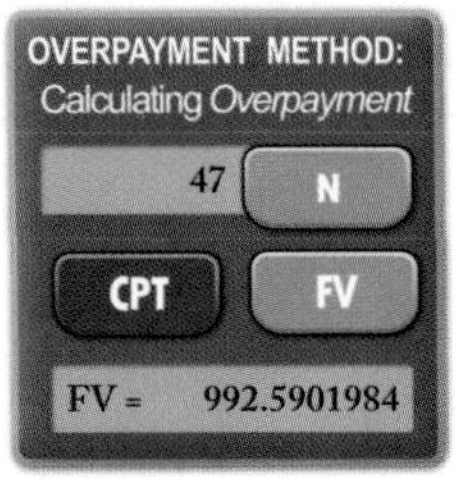

Method 2: Overpayment Method

Using the overpayment method, we assume that each of the 47 payments were of equal size. Then the future value after the 47th payment is equal to the overpayment.

$$PMT_{\textit{Final}} = PMT - \textit{Overpayment}$$

$$= 1400.00 - 992.590198\ldots = 407.409801\ldots = \$407.41$$

Therefore, the size of the final payment on the mortgage is $407.41.

Example 12.2(c) **Constructing a Partial Mortgage Schedule for Example 12.2(b)**

Cindy received a $60,000 mortgage that is amortized over four years. She negotiated a fixed interest rate of 4% compounded semi-annually for the term. Payments had to be made on a monthly basis. If payments are rounded up to the next $100, construct the partial mortgage schedule for the:

(i) first two payments.

(ii) last two payments.

(iii) total payment made and interest paid.

Solution

Page 531

These mortgage payments represent an ordinary general annuity.

$$i = \frac{j}{m} = \frac{0.04}{2} = 0.02 \text{ per half-year}$$

From Formula 10.3(a), $c = \dfrac{\textit{Number of compounding periods per year}}{\textit{Number of payments per year}} = \dfrac{2}{12}$

From Formula 10.3(b), $i_2 = (1 + i)^c - 1 = (1 + 0.02)^{(2/12)} - 1 = 0.003305\ldots$ per month

From Example 12.2(b), $PMT = \$1400.00$, $PMT_{Final} = \$407.41$, $n = 47$ payments

Constructing a mortgage schedule

Payment Number	Amount Paid (Periodic Payment) *PMT* ($)	Interest Portion (Previous Balance) *INT* ($)	Principal Portion (*PMT – INT*) *PRN* ($)	Principal Balance (Previous Balance – *PRN*) *BAL* ($)
0	-	-	-	$60,000.00
1	$1400.00	$198.35 (= 60,000.00 × 0.003305…)	$1201.65 (= 1400.00 – 198.35)	58,798.35 (= 60,000.00 – 1201.65)
2	1400.00	194.38 (= 58,798.35 × 0.003305…)	1205.62 (= 1400.00 – 194.38)	57,592.73 (= 58,798.35 – 1205.62)
.	.	.	.	.
45	.	.	.	1800.12 *
46	1400.00	5.95 (= 1800.12 × 0.003305...)	1394.05 (= 1400.00 – 5.95)	406.07 (= 1800.12 – 1394.05)
47	407.41 (= 406.07 + 406.07 × 0.003305...)	1.34 (= 406.07 × 0.003305...)	406.07	$0.00
Total	$64,807.41 (= 1400.00 × 46 + 407.41)	$4807.41 (= 64,807.41 – 60,000.00)	$60,000.00	-

*Calculating BAL_{45}:

$$BAL_{45} = PV(1+i)^n - PMT\left[\frac{(1+i)^n - 1}{i}\right]$$

$$= 60{,}000.00(1 + 0.003305\ldots)^{45} - 1400.00\left[\frac{(1 + 0.003305\ldots)^{45} - 1}{0.003305\ldots}\right]$$

$$= 69{,}606.93944\ldots - 67{,}806.82304\ldots$$

$$= 1800.116400\ldots = \$1800.12$$

Qualifying for a Mortgage

Before planning to purchase a new house, it is important that the buyer finds out if he or she qualifies for a mortgage to purchase the house.

There are two parameters that need to be calculated to determine how much mortgage the borrower can afford.

1. **Gross Debt Service Ratio (GDS)** measures the borrower's costs of owning the new house (such as mortgage payments, taxes, costs of utilities, etc.). Generally, this amount should not be more than 32% of the gross monthly income.

   For example, if your gross monthly income is $5000, you should not be spending more than $1600 in monthly housing expenses.

2. **Total Debt Service Ratio (TDS)** measures the borrower's total debt obligations (such as housing costs, personal loans, car payments, credit card bills, etc.). Generally, this should not be more than 40% of your gross monthly income.

   For example, if your gross monthly income is $5000, your total debt obligation for a month should not be more than $2000.

In addition to the above two qualifiers, most lenders also look at the borrower's annual income, employment history, and credit history while determining whether a borrower qualifies for a mortgage.

If the purchase price is less than $500,000, the minimum down payment is 5%. If the purchase price is between $500,000 and $999,999, the minimum down payment is 5% of the first $500,000, and 10% of any amount over $500,000.

Buyers are also required to pay an amount towards the purchase of the house. This amount is called the down payment. The mortgage covers the rest of the purchase price of the house. In Canada, a minimum down payment of 5% of the purchase price of the house is required.

If the down payment is less than 20% of the purchase price, the mortgage is required to be insured by the **Canadian Mortgage and Housing Corporation (CMHC)**. CMHC operates Canada's Housing Insurance Fund, which assists borrowers who cannot afford the entire down payment by insuring the property for 95% of its value, thereby providing the buyer with the option to pay only 5% of the amount. There is a fee to insure the house, which may also be included in the mortgage.

The maximum amortization period allowed in Canada is 25 years if the down payment is less than 20% of the value of the house. If the down payment is 20% or greater, the maximum amortization period allowed is 30 years.

For first-time home buyers, the Home Buyers' Plan (HBP) administered by the Canada Revenue Agency (CRA) allows a buyer to withdraw money from their **Registered Retirement Savings Plan (RRSP)**, tax-free, to make the down payment. A maximum of $25,000 (or $50,000 for a couple) can be withdrawn from the RRSP and no tax is deducted from the money that is withdrawn. The withdrawal from the RRSP account should be repaid within 15 years by making RRSP deposits every year, starting from the second year following the withdrawal.

A good understanding of how the interest rate and the term of the mortgage affects the cost of borrowing can help us to make wise decisions regarding the terms or lender. Choosing the shortest amortization period for a mortgage with the largest periodic payment that the buyer can afford, will save the buyer thousands or even tens of thousands of dollars in interest over the life of the mortgage.

Prepaying a Mortgage

A mortgage can be settled sooner if the borrower pays an extra amount over the periodic payment towards the mortgage. This is known as prepaying a mortgage. Some popular prepayment methods are listed below:

- **Making a lump-sum payment:** Lenders may permit the borrower to make a lump-sum payment towards settling the mortgage. For example, the lump-sum payment could be 15% of the original mortgage amount every year.
- **Increasing the periodic payment amount:** Lenders may allow borrowers to increase their payments by up to 100% of their periodic payments. In fact, by simply increasing the periodic payment by 10-15%, the borrower can save significant costs and can settle the mortgage sooner.

- **Increasing the frequency of payments:** Borrowers have an option to pay half their monthly payment on a bi-weekly basis (accelerated bi-weekly) or even a quarter of their monthly payment on a weekly basis (accelerated weekly). These changes will help the borrower clear the mortgage sooner.
- **Combination of methods:** Lenders offer a situation where borrowers can take advantage of all the above strategies at the same time; i.e., switching to a higher frequency of payments, increasing the size of the periodic payment, and making a lump-sum payment every year. Savings are considerable in this case.
- **Reducing the amortization period:** Most mortgages are issued out for a 25-year period; however, the borrower has the option to choose a shorter period with increased periodic payments to settle the mortgage sooner.

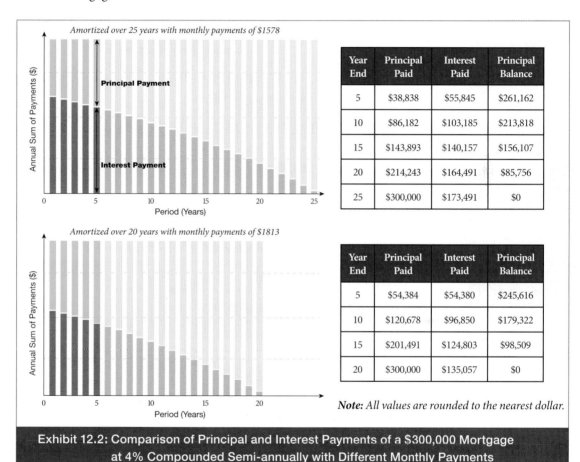

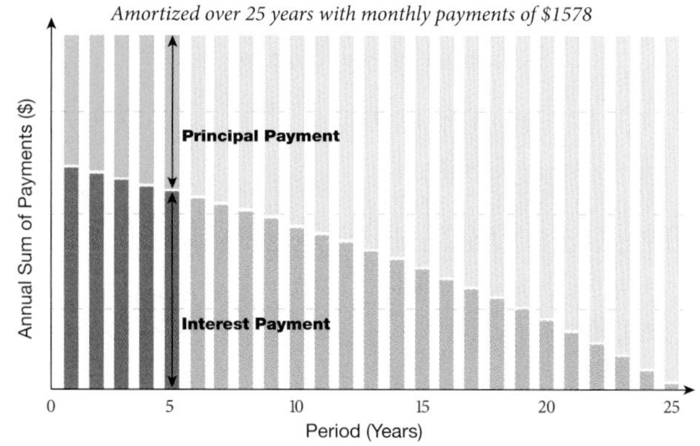

Year End	Principal Paid	Interest Paid	Principal Balance
5	$38,838	$55,845	$261,162
10	$86,182	$103,185	$213,818
15	$143,893	$140,157	$156,107
20	$214,243	$164,491	$85,756
25	$300,000	$173,491	$0

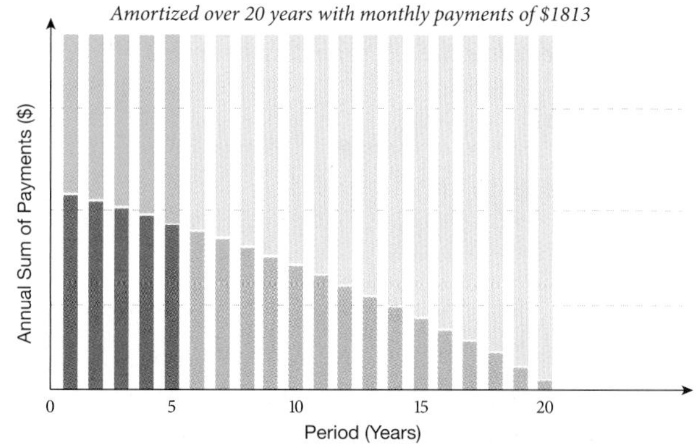

Year End	Principal Paid	Interest Paid	Principal Balance
5	$54,384	$54,380	$245,616
10	$120,678	$96,850	$179,322
15	$201,491	$124,803	$98,509
20	$300,000	$135,057	$0

***Note:** All values are rounded to the nearest dollar.*

Exhibit 12.2: Comparison of Principal and Interest Payments of a $300,000 Mortgage at 4% Compounded Semi-annually with Different Monthly Payments

Example 12.2(d) **Calculating the Effect of a Lump-Sum Payment on the Amortization Period**

Benjamin and Hailey purchased a $250,000 apartment in Calgary. They paid 20% of the amount as a down payment and secured a 25-year mortgage for the balance. They negotiated a fixed interest rate of 3.6% compounded semi-annually for a five-year term with repayments made at the end of every month. Their mortgage contract also stated that they may prepay up to 10% of the original principal every year without an interest penalty. At the end of the first year, in addition to the regular monthly payment, they made a lump-sum payment of $15,000.

(i) What was the size of the monthly payment?

(ii) What was the principal balance after the 12th monthly payment (before they made the lump-sum payment)?

(iii) By how much did the amortization period shorten after they made the lump-sum payment at the end of the first year?

Solution

Page 532

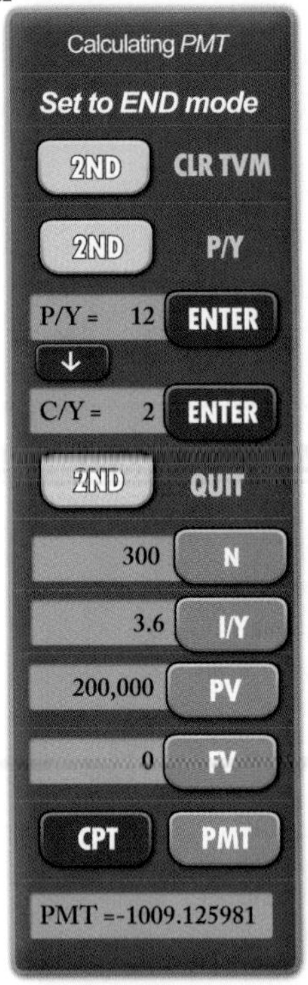

Mortgage amount = 0.80(250,000.00) = \$200,000.00

The mortgage payments represent an ordinary general annuity.

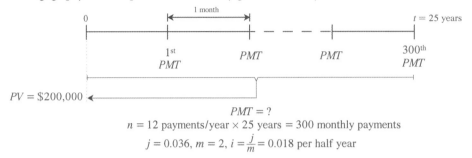

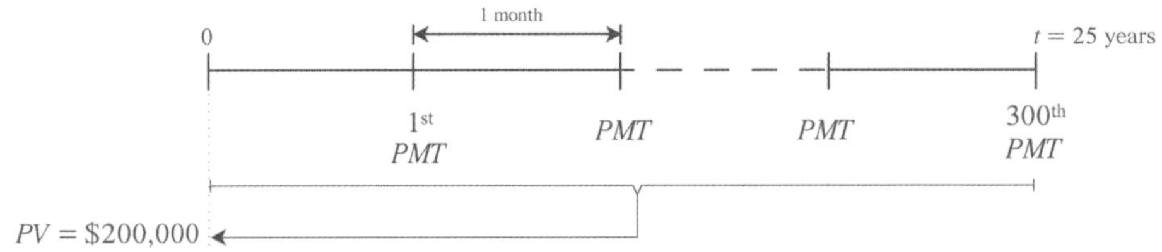

$PMT = ?$

$n = 12$ payments/year × 25 years = 300 monthly payments

$j = 0.036,\ m = 2,\ i = \frac{j}{m} = 0.018$ per half year

From Formula 10.3(a), $c = \frac{\text{Number of compounding periods per year}}{\text{Number of payments per year}} = \frac{2}{12}$

From Formula 10.3(b), $i_2 = (1 + i)^c - 1 = (1 + 0.018)^{(2/12)} - 1 = 0.002977...$ per month

(i) *Calculating the size of the monthly payment*

Using Formula 10.2(b), $PV = PMT\left[\frac{1 - (1 + i)^{-n}}{i}\right]$

$$200{,}000.00 = PMT\left[\frac{1 - (1 + 0.002977...)^{-300}}{0.002977...}\right]$$

$$PMT = 1009.125981... = \$1009.13$$

Therefore, the size of the monthly payment was \$1009.13.

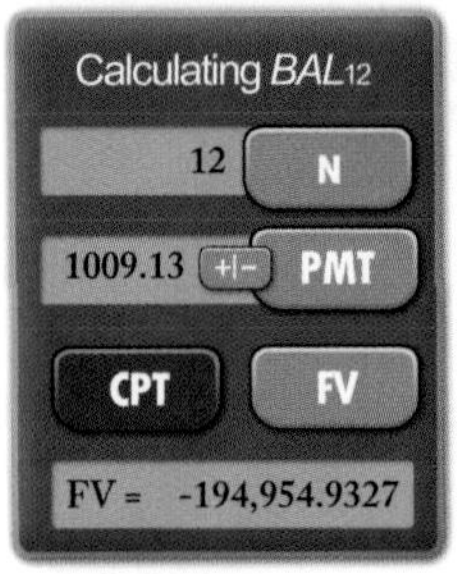

(ii) *Calculating the principal balance after the 12th monthly payment*

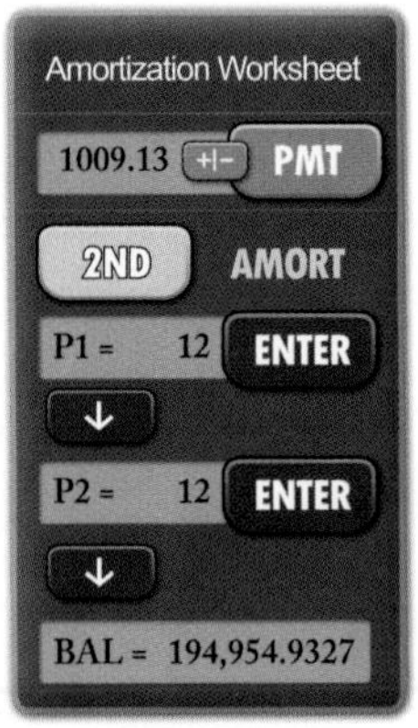

$$BAL_{12} = FV_{\text{Original Loan}} - FV_{\text{Payments Made until the 12}^{th}\text{ Payment}}$$

Using Formula 9.1(a) and Formula 10.2(a),

$$BAL_{\text{Focal Date}} = PV(1 + i)^n - PMT\left[\frac{(1 + i)^n - 1}{i}\right]$$

$$BAL_{12} = 200{,}000.00(1 + 0.002977...)^{12} - 1009.13\left[\frac{(1 + 0.002977...)^{12} - 1}{0.002977...}\right]$$

$$= 207{,}264.80 - 12{,}309.86725... = 194{,}954.9327... = \$194{,}954.93$$

Therefore, the principal balance after the 12th monthly payment was \$194,954.93.

(iii) *Calculating the effect of the lump-sum payment on the amortization period*

As they made a lump-sum payment of \$15,000 at the end of the first year, BAL_{12} will reduce by \$15,000.

$$New\ BAL_{12} = 194{,}954.93 - 15{,}000.00 = \$179{,}954.93$$

Therefore, the principal balance at the end of the first year after making the lump-sum payment was \$179,954.93.

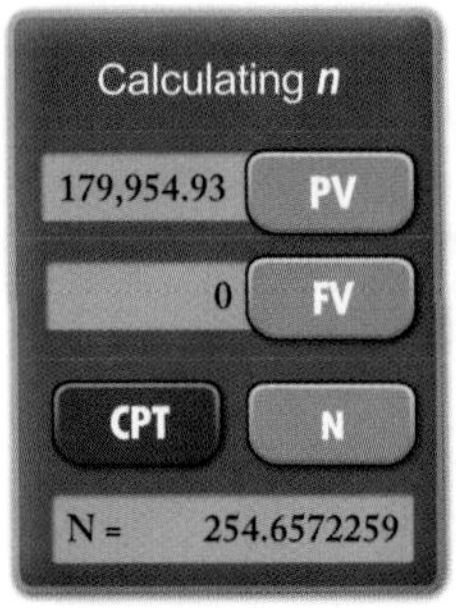

Calculating the new number of payments

From Formula 10.7(b), $n = -\frac{\ln\left[1 - \frac{i \times PV}{PMT}\right]}{\ln(1 + i)} = -\frac{\ln\left[1 - \frac{0.002977... \times 179{,}954.93}{1009.13}\right]}{\ln(1 + 0.002977...)}$

= 254.657225... Round up to the next payment period.

= 255 payments The 255th payment will be of a smaller size.

Solution *continued*

Therefore, the lump-sum payment reduced the number of payments from 288 (12 payments per year × 24 years) to 255.

$$\text{Time Period} = \frac{\text{Number of Payments}}{\text{Payments Per Year}} = \frac{255}{12}\text{ years} = 21.25\text{ years} = 21\text{ years and }(0.25 \times 12)\text{ months}$$

$$= 21\text{ years and 3 months}$$

Therefore, by making the lump-sum payment of $15,000 at the end of the first year, the amortization period was shortened by: 24 years – (21 years and 3 months) = 2 years and 9 months.

Example 12.2(e) Calculating the Effect of an Increase in the Payment on the Amortization Period

A $450,000 condominium in downtown Vancouver was purchased with a down payment of 20% of the amount. A 20-year mortgage was obtained for the balance. The negotiated fixed interest rate was 4.25% compounded semi-annually for a three-year term with repayments made at the end of every month.

(i) What is the size of the monthly payment?

(ii) What was the principal balance at the end of the three-year term?

(iii) By how much did the amortization period shorten if the size of the periodic payments were increased by 15% starting from the 37th payment? Assume the same interest rate.

Solution

Page 532

Mortgage amount = 0.80(450,000.00) = $360,000.00

The mortgage payments represent an ordinary general annuity.

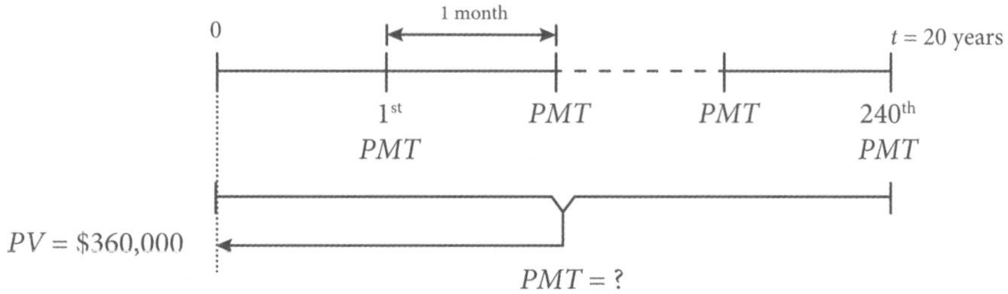

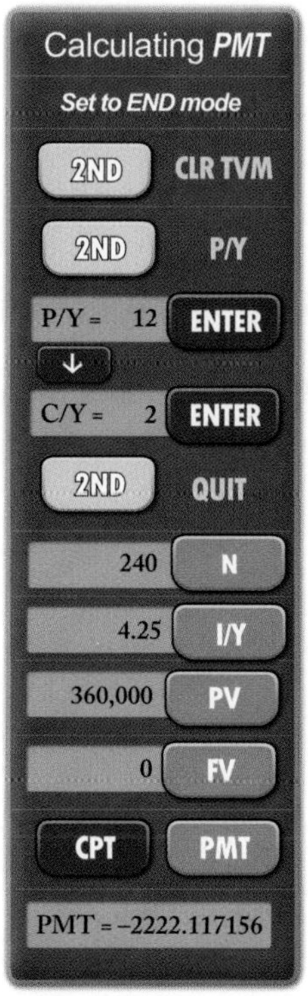

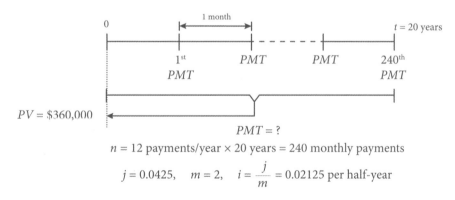

n = 12 payments/year × 20 years = 240 monthly payments

$$j = 0.0425, \quad m = 2, \quad i = \frac{j}{m} = 0.02125 \text{ per half-year}$$

From Formula 10.3(a), $c = \dfrac{\text{Number of compounding periods per year}}{\text{Number of payments per year}} = \dfrac{2}{12}$

From Formula 10.3(b), $i_2 = (1 + i)^c - 1 = (1 + 0.02125)^{(2/12)} - 1 = 0.003510...$

(i) *Calculating the size of the monthly payment*

From Formula 10.2(b), $PV = PMT\left[\dfrac{1-(1+i)^{-n}}{i}\right]$

$$360{,}000.00 = PMT\left[\frac{1-(1+0.003510...)^{-240}}{0.003510...}\right]$$

$$PMT = 2222.117156... = \$2222.12$$

Therefore, the size of the monthly payment is $2222.12.

Solution *continued*

(ii) *Calculating the principal balance at the end of the three-year term*

$$BAL_{36} = FV_{\text{Original Loan}} - FV_{\text{Payments made until the } 36^{th} \text{ Payment}}$$

Calculating BAL_{36}

36 N
2222.12 +|- PMT
CPT FV
FV = -323,296.2078

Using Formula 9.1(a) and Formula 10.2(a),

$$BAL_{\text{Focal Date}} = PV(1 + i)^n - PMT\left[\frac{(1 + i)^n - 1}{i}\right]$$

$$BAL_{36} = 360{,}000.00(1 + 0.003510...)^{36} - 2222.12\left[\frac{(1 + 0.003510...)^{36} - 1}{0.003510...}\right]$$

$$= 408{,}408.6371... - 85{,}112.42930...$$

$$= 323{,}296.2078... = \$323{,}296.21$$

Amortization Worksheet

2222.12 +|- PMT
2ND AMORT
P1 = 36 ENTER
↓
P2 = 36 ENTER
↓
BAL = 323,296.2078

Therefore, the principal balance at the end of the three-year term was $323,296.21.

(iii) *Increasing the periodic payment by 15% starting from the 37th payment*

From the calculation in (ii), we know that the BAL_{36} = $323,296.21

New monthly payment, $PMT = 2222.12 \times 1.15 = 2555.438 = \$2555.44$

Using Formula 10.7(b),

Calculating *n*

323,296.21 PV
2555.44 +|- PMT
0 FV
CPT N
N = 167.5693532

$$n = -\frac{\ln\left[1 - \frac{i \times PV}{PMT}\right]}{\ln(1 + i)} = -\frac{\ln\left[1 - \frac{0.003510... \times 323{,}296.21}{2555.44}\right]}{\ln(1 + 0.003510...)}$$

$= 167.569353...$ Round up to the next payment period.

$= 168$ payments The 168th payment will be of a smaller size.

Therefore, the number of payments reduced from 204 payments (12 payments per year × 17 years) to 168 payments.

$$\text{Time Period} = \frac{\textit{Number of Payments}}{\textit{Payments Per Year}} = \frac{168}{12} \text{ years} = 14 \text{ years}$$

Therefore, by increasing the periodic payment by 15% starting from the 37th payment, the amortization period was shortened by: 17 years – 14 years = 3 years.

Example 12.2(f) **Calculating the Effect of an Increase in the Frequency of Payments on the Amortization Period**

A $300,000 mortgage at 4% compounded semi-annually is settled with monthly payments of $1578.09.

(i) What is the amortization period?

(ii) Instead of monthly payments, if accelerated bi-weekly payments of $789.05 are made, what will be the amortization period?

(iii) How much interest will be saved if accelerated bi-weekly payments are made, as in (ii), instead of monthly payments?

When the monthly payment is divided by two and is paid every two weeks, it is called an accelerated bi-weekly payment.

Solution

Page 532

(i) *Monthly payments*

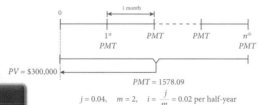

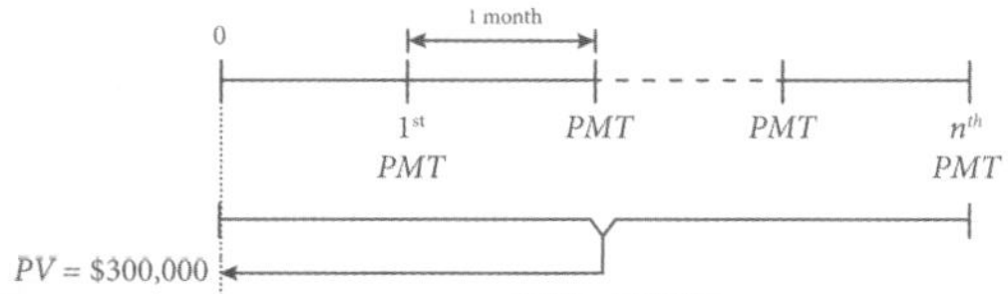

$PMT = 1578.09$

$j = 0.04, \quad m = 2, \quad i = \frac{j}{m} = 0.02$ per half-year

$$c = \frac{2}{12}$$

$$i_2 = (1 + i)^c - 1 = (1 + 0.02)^{(2/12)} - 1$$

$$= 0.003305\ldots \text{ per month}$$

$$n = -\frac{\ln\left[1 - \frac{i \times PV}{PMT}\right]}{\ln(1 + i)}$$

$$= -\frac{\ln\left[1 - \frac{0.003305\ldots \times 300{,}000.00}{1578.09}\right]}{\ln(1 + 0.003305\ldots)}$$

$$= 299.990456\ldots$$

$$= 300 \text{ payments}$$

$$t = \frac{\textit{Number of Payments}}{\textit{Payments Per Year}}$$

$$= \frac{300}{12}$$

$$= 25 \text{ years}$$

Therefore, with monthly payments, the amortization period is 25 years.

(ii) *Accelerated bi-weekly payments*

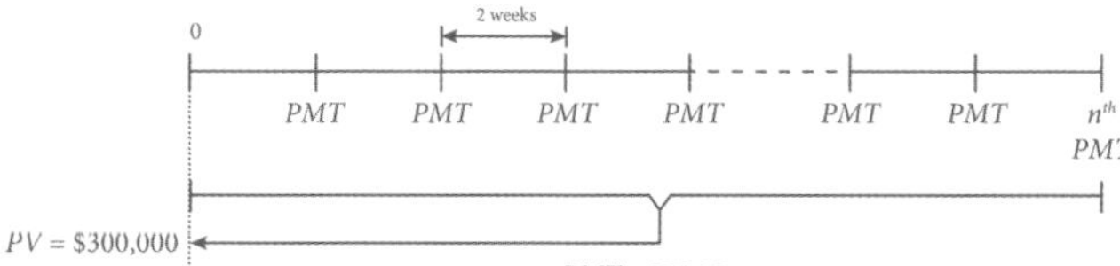

$PMT = 789.05$

$j = 0.04, \quad m = 2, \quad i = \frac{j}{m} = 0.02$ per half-year

$$c = \frac{2}{26}$$

$$i_2 = (1 + i)^c - 1 = (1 + 0.02)^{(2/26)} - 1$$

$$= 0.001524\ldots \text{ per two weeks}$$

$$n = -\frac{\ln\left[1 - \frac{i \times PV}{PMT}\right]}{\ln(1 + i)}$$

$$= -\frac{\ln\left[1 - \frac{0.001524\ldots \times 300{,}000.00}{789.05}\right]}{\ln(1 + 0.001524\ldots)}$$

$$= 568.867743\ldots$$

$$= 569 \text{ payments}$$

$$t = \frac{\textit{Number of Payments}}{\textit{Payments Per Year}}$$

$$= \frac{569}{26} = 21.884615\ldots\text{years}$$

$$= 21 \text{ years and } (0.884615\ldots \times 52 \text{ weeks})$$

$$= 21 \text{ years and } 46 \text{ weeks}$$

Therefore, with accelerated bi-weekly payments, the amortization period will be 21 years and 46 weeks.

(iii) *Comparing the interest charged*

Interest = *Total Paid* – *Original Loan*

= [299(1578.09) + 1563.05] – 300,000.00

= $173,411.96

Final Payment = (1) + (2)

= 1557.90 + 5.15 = $1563.05

Interest = *Total Paid* – *Original Loan*

= [568(789.05) + 684.76] – 300,000.00

= $148,865.16

Final Payment = (1) + (2)

= 683.72 + 1.04 = $684.76

Difference in interest charged, $173,411.96 – $148,865.16 = $24,546.80

Therefore, an interest amount of $24,546.80 will be saved when accelerated bi-weekly payments are made instead of monthly payments.

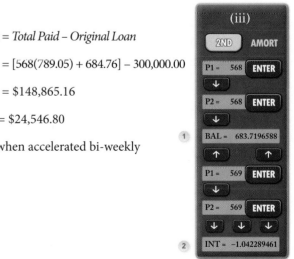

12.2 | Exercises

Answers to the odd-numbered problems are available at the end of the textbook.

1. Amanda purchased a townhouse for $320,000. She made a down payment of 10% of the value of the house and received a mortgage for the rest of the amount at 3.5% compounded semi-annually for 25 years. The interest rate was fixed for a five-year period.
   a. Calculate the monthly payment amount.
   b. Calculate the principal balance at the end of the five-year term.
   c. Calculate the monthly payment amount if the mortgage was renewed for another five-year fixed term at 3.7% compounded semi-annually.

2. The Drew family purchased a villa on the outskirts of the city for $1,250,000. They made a down payment of 20% of the value and received a mortgage for the balance for a period of 25 years. The interest rate was fixed at 4.25% compounded semi-annually for a three-year period.
   a. Calculate the monthly payment amount.
   b. Calculate the principal balance at the end of the three-year term.
   c. Calculate the size of the monthly payment if the mortgage is renewed for another three-year fixed term at 4.75% compounded semi-annually.

3. A $100,000 mortgage was amortized over ten years by monthly payments. The interest rate on the mortgage was fixed at 5.5% compounded semi-annually for the entire period.
   a. Calculate the size of the payments if they are rounded up to the next $100.
   b. Calculate the size of the final payment.

4. Henry received a mortgage of $80,000 that was amortized over three years and fixed at an interest rate of 2.75% compounded semi-annually.
   a. What was the size of the monthly payments if they were rounded up to the next $500?
   b. What was the size of the final payment?

5. Construct a partial mortgage schedule for Problem 3, showing the first two payments, last two payments, and total payment made and interest paid.

6. Construct a partial mortgage schedule for Problem 4, showing the first two payments, last two payments, and total payment made and interest paid.

7. A mortgage for a condominium had a principal balance of $44,910 that had to be amortized over the remaining period of four years. The interest rate was fixed at 4.5% compounded semi-annually and payments were made monthly.
   a. Calculate the size of the monthly payments if they are rounded up to the next $50.
   b. If the monthly payments were set at $1200, by how much would the time period of the mortgage shorten?
   c. If the monthly payments were set at $1200, what is the size of the final payment?

8. Bradley had five years left to clear the mortgage on his house. The balance on the mortgage was $12,545.50 and the interest rate was fixed at 3.45% compounded semi-annually for the remaining five years. He was settling the mortgage with monthly payments.
   a. Calculate the size of the monthly payments if they are rounded up to the next $50.
   b. If the monthly payments were set at $300, by how much would the time period of the mortgage shorten?
   c. If the monthly payments were set at $300, what would be the size of the final payment?

9. William received a ten-year mortgage of $150,000 at an interest rate of 4.5% compounded semi-annually for the first five years.

   a. During the first five years, what was the size of the monthly payments, rounded up to the next $10?

   b. What was the balance on the mortgage at the end of 5 years?

   c. During the last five years, if the interest rate remained the same, what was the size of the monthly payments, rounded up to the next $10? What was the size of the final payment?

10. A mortgage of $105,400 was to be amortized over seven years. The interest rate was a variable, closed rate of 2.35% compounded semi-annually. Three years after the mortgage was issued, the Bank of Canada increased its prime lending rate. Therefore, the variable interest rate on the mortgage increased to 2.85% compounded semi-annually and remained the same for the rest of the term.

    a. During the first three years, what was the size of the monthly payments, rounded up to the next $10?

    b. What was the balance on the mortgage at the end of three years?

    c. During the last four years, what was the size of the monthly payments, rounded up to the next $10? What was the size of the final payment?

11. Ashi planned to obtain a mortgage to purchase a house but could only afford to pay a maximum amount of $1550 every month as mortgage payments. Assuming an average interest rate of 4.5% compounded semi-annually on mortgages amortized over 25 years, calculate the maximum amount of the mortgage.

12. Aden and his fiancée were planning to purchase an apartment in Calgary. They could afford to pay a maximum amount of $1000 every month as mortgage payments. Assuming an average interest rate of 2.5% compounded semi-annually on mortgages amortized over 20 years, calculate the maximum amount of the mortgage.

13. Earl purchased a house for $380,000 by paying 20% of the amount as a down payment and he received a 25-year mortgage for the balance. The interest rate was fixed at 4.5% compounded semi-annually for a term of five years and he was allowed to make prepayments of up to 20% of the original principal every year without any penalty.

    a. What is the size of the monthly payment?

    b. What is the principal balance at the end of the five-year term?

    c. By how much did the amortization period shorten if he made a lump-sum payment of $40,000, in addition to the monthly payment, at the end of the five-year term of the mortgage?

14. Munroe purchased a house for $400,000. He paid 30% of the purchase price as a down payment and received a mortgage for the balance. The amortization period was for 25 years and he negotiated a fixed interest rate of 3.75% compounded semi-annually for a term of three years.

    a. What is the size of the monthly payment?

    b. What is the principal balance at the end of the three-year term?

    c. By how much did the amortization period shorten if he made a lump-sum payment of $15,000, in addition to the monthly payment, at the end of the three-year term of the mortgage? Assume that the mortgage contract does not charge him a penalty for making this lump-sum payment.

15. Kim purchased a $250,000 condominium in Halifax with a down payment of 25% of the amount. She received a 20-year mortgage for the balance at a fixed interest rate of 4.75% compounded semi-annually for a three-year term. Payments were to be made at the end of every month.

    a. What is the size of the monthly payment?

    b. What was the principal balance at the end of the three-year term?

    c. By how much did the amortization period shorten if the size of the periodic payments were increased by 10% starting from the 37th payment?

16. A $300,000 apartment in Edmonton was purchased with a down payment of 20% of the amount. A 25-year mortgage was obtained for the balance. The negotiated fixed interest rate was 5.50% compounded semi-annually for a five-year term with repayments made at the end of every month.
    a. What is the size of the monthly payment?
    b. What was the principal balance at the end of the five-year term?
    c. By how much did the amortization period shorten if the size of the periodic payments was increased by 5% starting from the 61st payment?

17. A $280,000 mortgage at 5.75% compounded semi-annually was settled with monthly payments of $1955.03.
    a. What is the amortization period?
    b. Instead of monthly payments, if accelerated bi-weekly payments of $977.50 were made, what will be the amortization period?
    c. How much interest will be saved if accelerated bi-weekly payments are made, as in (b), instead of monthly payments?

18. A $420,000 mortgage at 4.75% compounded semi-annually was settled with monthly payments of $2435.73.
    a. What is the amortization period?
    b. Instead of monthly payments, if accelerated bi-weekly payments of $1217.50 were made, what will be the amortization period?
    c. How much interest will be saved if accelerated bi-weekly payments are made, as in (b), instead of monthly payments?

12 | Review Exercises

Answers to the odd-numbered problems are available at the end of the textbook.

1. Aiden received a loan of $17,500 at 5.25% compounded quarterly to purchase a printer for his office. If he made equal payments at the end of every three months to settle the loan, calculate the size of his periodic payments and the total interest paid if he settled the loan in three years. Construct a partial amortization schedule showing details of the first two payments and the last two payments for his loan.

2. Sturdy Metals Inc. received a loan of $800,000 from the Small Business Banking Association to purchase additional factory space. It received the loan at 7.75% compounded monthly and had to make equal month-end payments for 20 years to amortize the loan. What was the size of the periodic payment and how much did it pay in interest over the period of the loan? Construct a partial amortization schedule showing details of the first two payments and the last two payments of the loan.

3. If $500 was paid every month to amortize a $16,850 student loan that was issued at 4.45% compounded daily, calculate the balance on the loan at the end of 2 years and 7 months and the size of the final payment.

4. Henry could afford to pay only $1400 a month towards repayment of his student loan of $50,000 that he received at 8.55% compounded semi-annually. If he made these payments, what was the balance on his loan at the end of two years and what was his final payment to clear the loan?

5. For Problem 3, calculate the interest portion and principal portion of the 30th payment.

6. For Problem 4, calculate the interest portion and principal portion of the 40th payment.

7. For Problem 3, construct a partial amortization schedule showing details of the first two payments, last two payments, total payment made, and total interest paid.

8. For Problem 4, construct a partial amortization schedule showing details of the first three payments, last three payments, total payment made, and total interest paid.

9. A Calgary based mining company received a loan of $1,250,000 at 4.55% compounded semi-annually to purchase an industrial boiler. It paid off the loan in five years by making annual payments. Construct an amortization schedule providing details of its loan payments.

10. Cranes Limited obtained a loan of $450,000 at 4% compounded monthly from its bank to train all its employees on new safety measures. If it made semi-annual payments to amortize the loan in four years, construct the amortization schedule for its loan.

11. Abha purchased a new line of clothing for her designer boutique for $12,680. She paid 20% of this amount as a down payment and obtained a loan for the balance at 11% compounded monthly. If she amortized this loan over five years by making semi-annual payments, calculate the size of her payments and the principal balance at the end of two years.

12. Adapt Developers, a leading construction development company in Vancouver, purchased land for $1,000,000 in the city. It paid 35% of this amount as a down payment and received a loan for the balance at 10.45% compounded semi-annually. If its loan was amortized over ten years by making payments every three months, calculate the size of the payments and the principal outstanding at the end of seven years.

13. In Problem 11, calculate the size of her final payment and the interest portion and principal portion of her 5th payment.

14. In Problem 12, calculate the size of the final payment and the interest portion and principal portion of the 18th payment.

15. Maada and his wife purchased a house for $447,000 in Edmonton. They made a down payment of 20% of the value of the house and received a mortgage at 3.85% compounded semi-annually for the balance for 20 years. The interest rate was fixed for a period of five years.

    a. What is the monthly payment amount?

    b. What is the principal balance at the end of the five-year term?

    c. What is the monthly payment amount if the mortgage was renewed for another five-year fixed term at 4.25% compounded semi-annually?

16. Grace recently graduated from college and purchased an apartment for $210,000 in London. She paid 10% of this amount as a down payment and received a mortgage for the rest of the amount for 25 years. The interest rate on the mortgage was fixed at 4.5% compounded semi-annually for the first five years.

    a. What is the monthly payment amount?

    b. What is the principal balance at the end of the five-year term?

    c. What is the monthly payment amount if the mortgage was renewed for another five-year fixed term at 5.05% compounded semi-annually?

17. A $25,000 mortgage was amortized over three years by monthly repayments. The interest rate on the mortgage was fixed at 3.28% compounded semi-annually.

    a. What is the size of the payments if they are rounded up to the next $100?

    b. What is the size of the final payment?

18. Bernard obtained a mortgage to purchase a parking spot at his condominium for $40,000. The mortgage was amortized over four years at 4.5% compounded semi-annually for the entire period.

    a. What is the size of the monthly payments if they are rounded up to the next $100?

    b. What is the size of the final payment?

19. Patricia and her husband were planning to purchase an apartment in British Columbia. They could afford to pay $800 every month towards mortgage payments. Their mortgage broker was offering them a variable, open interest rate of 3.75% compounded semi-annually amortized over 25 years. Calculate the maximum mortgage amount they can afford.

20. Nikita received a mortgage to purchase a town-house and paid $1200 every month as mortgage payments. The variable, open interest rate on the mortgage was 2.85% compounded semi-annually and it was amortized over 25 years. What was the mortgage amount received?

12 | Self-Test Exercises

Answers to all the problems are available at the end of the textbook.

1. An automobile financing company was offering loans of $20,000 at 1.2% compounded monthly to purchase a specific model of its cars. If Alana received this loan and purchased the car, how much would she have to pay every month to amortize the loan in ten years? Construct a partial amortization schedule showing details of the first two payments and the last two payments of the loan.

2. If Nancy can pay only $350 a month towards her student loan of $18,400 that she received at 7.45% compounded quarterly, what would be the balance on the loan at the end of four years and what would be her final payment to settle the entire amount?

3. In Problem 2, calculate the interest portion and principal portion of the 50th payment.

4. In Problem 2, construct a partial amortization schedule showing details of the first three payments, last three payments, total payment made, and total interest paid.

5. Hair & Care, a salon in Edmonton, purchased chairs for $25,000. It paid 10% of this amount as a down payment and received a loan for the rest at 8.25% compounded semi-annually. Its loan was amortized over five years by making monthly payments. Calculate the size of the payments and the principal outstanding at the end of three years.

6. In Problem 5, calculate the size of the final payment and the interest portion and principal portion of the 12th payment.

7. Thema just qualified to receive a mortgage from her bank at 3.5% compounded semi-annually for a five-year term. She purchased an apartment worth $220,000 and paid 10% as a down payment. The amortization period for the mortgage was 25 years and she was required to make monthly payments to settle the mortgage.
   a. What is the monthly payment amount?
   b. What is the principal balance at the end of the five-year term?
   c. What is the monthly payment amount if the mortgage was renewed for another five-year fixed term at 4.5% compounded semi-annually?

8. Martin received a loan to purchase a locker at his condominium for $4000. The loan was amortized over two years at 3.26% compounded semi annually for the entire period.
   a. What is the size of the monthly payments if they are rounded up to the next $10?
   b. What is the size of the final payment?

9. Natalie received a sales commission of $15,000 and decided to use this amount as a lump-sum payment towards her mortgage of $250,000 which was for 25 years at 2.88% compounded semi-annually. If she made the lump-sum payment at the time of the 15th payment, in addition to the regular monthly payment, calculate the reduction in the amortization period.

10. In Problem 9, by how much would her amortization period have decreased if she had increased her periodic payment by 15% from her 15th payment onwards, instead of making the lump-sum payment?

CASE 12a

Financing a Growing Business

Jane, Georgia, and Melody started a cupcake business in their final year in college, registering the company as 'Sugary Bites'. They needed measuring cups, mixers, a food processor, and other baking equipment to prepare for production. This equipment cost a total of $1500, which the entrepreneurs financed through a loan from a bank at 12.5% compounded monthly, amortized over two years. Within a week, they started making cupcakes and delivering them to their college cafeteria.

Within two months, Sugary Bites cupcakes was the talk of the college campus and the bakery business was making modest profits. After graduating, the three budding entrepreneurs decided to expand their operation. They rented a retail store in the city and added ten new cupcake flavours to their product line. They also hired an assistant to run the store and a delivery person to handle personal orders.

After two years of successfully managing Sugary Bites, they saved enough money to use as a down payment to purchase a small shop where they could make their cupcakes, and a delivery truck to deliver them. They identified a $108,000 commercial property and secured a mortgage for 80% of its value to purchase it. The fixed interest rate on the mortgage was 3.4% compounded semi-annually for an amortization period of five years. They also purchased a delivery truck for the business at a cost of $18,500 and financed 80% of it at 7% compounded monthly. They made monthly payments of $300 towards this loan.

Answer the following questions related to each of their debts:

Startup Loan

a. What were their monthly payments to settle this loan?
b. What was the principal balance on the loan after one year?
c. Construct an amortization schedule for this loan.

Mortgage

d. Calculate the size of their monthly payments rounded to the nearest $10.
e. By how much would their amortization period have shortened if they had made a lump-sum payment of $30,000 at the end of the 3rd year of the mortgage and increased their periodic payment by 30% after the 40th payment?

Delivery Truck Loan

f. How long would it take to settle this loan with regular monthly payments of $300?
g. On their 20th payment, what will be the interest portion and what will be the principal portion?
h. Construct a partial amortization schedule showing details of the first two payments, last two payments, total payment made, and the total interest paid towards this loan.

CASE 12b

Securing a Mortgage

Claude and Mike are a young couple of working professionals living in Thunder Bay, Ontario. Together, they have a combined gross monthly income of $5500. They currently pay $280 per month towards a lease on their car and Claude makes a payment of $200 per month towards her school debt. They have also developed a high credit score, by keeping their credit card balances low and paying off all bills and debts on time.

Claude and Mike have been putting money aside from each of their paycheques to save up for a down payment of 20% on a $200,000 condo. Once they saved up enough money, they began researching different mortgage options online.

Through their research, Claude and Mike discovered that in addition to big banks, there are mortgage brokers who can assist them with their mortgage. A mortgage broker will negotiate terms with multiple different potential lenders, and as such, can often find the lowest interest rate offered by a financial lending institution. In addition to this, a mortgage broker is paid commission by the lender, and therefore, the service would not be of cost to Claude and Mike.

Intrigued by this, the couple contacted a Canadian mortgage broker company, that has access to over 30 of the top mortgage lenders in Canada.

a. What size of mortgage do the couple require?
b. If the mortgage broker is able to secure them with a ten-year mortgage with a fixed rate of 2.44% compounded semi-annually for a term of five years, what would be the size of their monthly payment?
c. Claude and Mike are informed that the utilities and taxes on their condo will be approximately $215 per month. Assuming the mortgage terms outlined in (b), is it advisable for the lender to qualify the couple for their mortgage? Explain your answer.

The couple accepted the mortgage terms, and made monthly payments for five years. At the end of the term, a new term of five years with a fixed rate of 2.74% compounded semi-annually was negotiated.

d. What is the new monthly payment that Claude and Mike must make?
e. Instead of making monthly payments, the mortgage broker presented an option of accelerated bi-weekly payments, in which the couple must make a payment of half the amount calculated in (d) every two weeks. What are the pros and cons of Claude and Mike accepting this accelerated bi-weekly payment schedule?
f. Claude and Mike opted for the accelerated bi-weekly payment schedule. By how many weeks did they shorten their amortization period?
g. Construct a partial mortgage schedule the mortgage broker can present to the couple, showing:

    (i) the first two payments of the first term,

    (ii) the last two payments of the first term,

    (iii) the first two payments of the second term,

    (iv) the last two payments of the second term, and,

    (v) the total payment made and interest paid.

CASE 12c

Business and Property Spreadsheet Project

The spreadsheet calculations should be set up in a systematic manner. Your set-up should contain a list of the given values, and as many calculated values as possible. Make your spreadsheet as 'active' as possible by using cell references (so that if one value is changed, subsequent calculations will automatically update). Use absolute cell references in special situations.

Bob and Angelique Mackenzie bought a property valued at $84,000 for $15,000 down with the balance amortized over 20 years. The terms of the mortgage require equal payments at the end of each month. Interest on the mortgage is 3.4% compounded semi-annually and the mortgage is renewable after five years.

a. What is the size of each monthly payment?
b. Prepare an amortization schedule for the first five-year term. Make sure your values are rounded to the nearest cent. Express totals at the bottom of each column as currency.
c. What is the cost of the debt during the first five-year term?
d. If the mortgage is renewed for a further five years at 4.2% compounded semi-annually, what will be the size of each monthly payment?

The Mackenzie's also bought a business for $90,000. They borrowed the money to buy the business at 6.9% compounded semi-annually and are to repay the debt by making quarterly payments of $3645.

e. How many payments are required to repay the loan?
f. What is the term of the loan in years and months?
g. Prepare a complete amortization schedule for the loan. Make sure your values are rounded to the nearest cent. Express totals at the bottom of each column as currency.
h. What is the principal reduction in the 6th year?
i. What is the total cost of financing the debt?
j. If Angelique makes a lump sum payment of $10,000 at the end of the fourth year, by how much is the amortization period shortened?

12 | Spreadsheet Solutions

Spreadsheet solutions to solved examples in the chapter.

12.1 Examples

Example 12.1(c)

	A	B	C	D	E	F	G	H	I
1	Calculating *n*								
2	*j*	12.00%							
3	*m*	12		Amortization Schedule					
4	*P/Y*	4		**Payment Number**	**Amount Paid**	**Interest Portion**	**Principal Portion**	**Principal Balance**	
5	*t*	-		0	-	-	-	$12,450.00 = B12	
6				1	$3,000.00 = –B$11	$377.25 = ROUND(H5*B$9, 2)	$2,622.75 = E6 – F6	$9,827.25 = H5 – G6	
7	*i*	1.00% = B2/B3		2	$3,000.00	$297.78	$2,702.22	$7,125.03	
8	*c*	3 = B3/B4		3	$3,000.00	$215.90	$2,784.10	$4,340.93	
9	i_2	3.0301% = (1+B7)^B8 – 1		4	$3,000.00	$131.53	$2,868.47	$1,472.46	
10	*n*	4.501959 = NPER(B9, B11, B12, B13, B14)		5	$1,517.08 = H9 + H9*B9	$44.62	$1,472.46	$0.00	
11	*PMT*	($3,000.00)		**Total**	$13,517.08 = SUM(E6 : E10)	$1,067.08 = SUM(F6 : F10)	$12,450.00 = SUM(G6 : G10)		
12	*PV*	$12,450.00							
13	*FV*	0							
14	*BGN*	0							
15									

Example 12.1(d)

	A	B	
1	Calculating *PMT*		
2	*j*	4.00%	
3	*m*	4	
4	*P/Y*	4	
5	*t*	10	
6			
7	*i*	1.00%	= B2/B3
8	*n*	40	= B4*B5
9	*PMT*	($761.39)	= PMT(B7, B8, B10, B11, B12) PMT(rate, nper, pv, [fv], [type])
10	*PV*	$25,000.00	
11	*FV*	0	
12	*BGN*	0	
13			
14	Calculating $BAL_{1\ year}$		
15	*j*	4.00%	
16	*m*	4	
17	*P/Y*	4	
18	*t*	1	
19			
20	*i*	1.00%	= B15/B16
21	*n*	4	= B17*B18
22	*PMT*	($761.39)	= ROUND(B9, 2) ROUND(number, num_digits)
23	*PV*	$25,000.00	
24	*FV*	($22,923.55)	= FV(B20, B21, B22, B23, B25) FV(rate, nper, pmt, [pv], [type])
25	*BGN*	0	
26			

Example 12.1(e)

	A	B	
1	Calculating $BAL_{2\ years}$		
2	*j*	6.00%	
3	*m*	12	
4	*P/Y*	12	
5	*t*	2	
6			
7	*i*	0.50%	= B2/B3
8	*n*	24	= B4*B5
9	*PMT*	($500.00)	
10	*PV*	$45,000.00	
11	*FV*	($38,006.21)	= FV(B7, B8, B9, B10, B12) FV(rate, nper, pmt, [pv], [type])
12	*BGN*	0	
13			

Example 12.1(f)

	A	B	
1		Calculating *n*	
2	*j*	12.00%	
3	*m*	4	
4	*P/Y*	2	
5	*t*	-	
6			
7	*i*	3.00%	= B2/B3
8	*c*	2	= B3/B4
9	i_2	6.09%	= (1 + B7)^B8 – 1
10	*n*	41.402403	= NPER(B9, B11, B12, B13, B14) NPER(rate, pmt, pv, [fv], [type])
11	*PMT*	($50,000.00)	
12	*PV*	$750,000.00	
13	*FV*	0	
14	*BGN*	0	
15			

Example 12.1(f) *Continued*

16	PMT_{Final}: Method 1		
17	*n*	41	= ROUNDDOWN(B10, 0) ROUNDDOWN(number, num_digits)
18	*FV*	($19,300.78)	= FV(B9, B17, B11, B12, B14) FV(rate, nper, pmt, [pv], [type])
19			
20	PMT_F	($20,476.20)	= B18*(1 + B9)
21			
22	PMT_{Final}: Method 2		
23	*n*	42	= ROUNDUP(B10, 0) ROUNDUP(number, num_digits)
24	*FV*	$29,523.80	= FV(B9, B23, B11, B12, B14) FV(rate, nper, pmt, [pv], [type])
25			
26	PMT_F	($20,476.20)	= B11 + B24
27			

Example 12.1(g)

	A	B	
1	Calculating *n*		
2	*j*	6.00%	
3	*m*	12	
4	*P/Y*	12	
5	*t*	-	
6			
7	*i*	0.50%	= B2/B3
8	*n*	71.973574	= NPER(B7, B9, B10, B11, B12) NPER(rate, pmt, pv, [fv], [type])
9	*PMT*	($273.00)	
10	*PV*	$16,550.00	
11	*FV*	0	
12	*BGN*	1	
13			
14		Calculating BAL_{71}	
15	*n*	71	= ROUNDDOWN(B8, 0) ROUNDDOWN(number, num_digits)
16	*FV*	($265.80)	= FV(B7, B15, B9, B10, B12) FV(rate, nper, pmt, [pv], [type])
17			

Example 12.1(h)

	A	B	
1	Calculating BAL_{18}		
2	*j*	6.00%	
3	*m*	12	
4	*P/Y*	12	
5	*t*	-	
6			
7	*i*	0.50%	= B2/B3
8	*n*	18	
9	*PMT*	($5,000.00)	
10	*PV*	$130,000.00	
11	*FV*	($48,281.82)	= FV(B7, B8, B9, B10, B12) FV(rate, nper, pmt, [pv], [type])
12	*BGN*	0	
13			
14	INT_{19}	($241.41)	= B11*B7
15	PRN_{19}	($4,758.59)	= B9 – B14
16			

Example 12.1(i)

	A	B	Formula
1		Calculating BAL_{132}	
2	**j**	5.45%	
3	**m**	4	
4	**P/Y**	12	
5	**t**	-	
6			
7	**i**	1.3625%	= B2/B3
8	**c**	0.333333	= B3/B4
9	**i_2**	0.4521%	= (1 + B7)^B8 – 1
10	**n**	132	
11	**PMT**	($1,500.00)	
12	**PV**	$300,000.00	
13	**FV**	($274,143.34)	= FV(B9, B10, B11, B12, B14) FV(rate, nper, pmt, [pv], [type])
14	**BGN**	0	
15			
16		Calculating BAL_{144}	
17	**n**	144	
18	**FV**	($270,937.88)	= FV(B9, B17, B11, B12, B14) FV(rate, nper, pmt, [pv], [type])
19			
20		Total Principal	
21		($3,205.46)	= B13 – B18
22			
23		Total Interest	
24		($14,794.54)	= B11*12 – B21
25			

Example 12.1(j)

	A	B	Formula
1		Calculating BAL_{12}	
2	**j**	5.25%	
3	**m**	12	
4	**P/Y**	12	
5	**t**	-	
6			
7	**i**	0.4375%	= B2/B3
8	**n**	12	
9	**PMT**	($500.00)	
10	**PV**	$18,000.00	
11	**FV**	($12,821.57)	= FV(B7, B8, B9, B10, B12) FV(rate, nper, pmt, [pv], [type])
12	**BGN**	0	
13			
14		Calculating DAL_{24}	
15	**n**	24	
16	**FV**	($7,364.64)	= FV(B7, B15, B9, B10, B12) FV(rate, nper, pmt, [pv], [type])
17			
18		Total Principal	
19		($5,456.93)	= B11 – B16
20			
21		Total Interest	
22		($543.07)	= B9*12 – B19
23			

Example 12.1(k)

	A	B	C	D	E	F	G	H	I
1	Calculating *n*								
2	**j**	6.00%		Amortization Schedule					
3	**m**	12		**Payment Number**	**Amount Paid**	**Interest Portion**	**Principal Portion**	**Principal Balance**	
4	**P/Y**	12		0	-	-	-	$130,000.00 = B10	
5	**t**	-		1	$5,000.00 = –B$9	$650.00 = ROUND(H4*B$7, 2)	$4,350.00 = E5 – F5	$125,650.00 = H4 – G5	
6				2	$5,000.00	$628.25	$4,371.75	$121,278.25	
7	**i**	0.50% = B2/B3		-	-	-	-	-	
8	**n**	27.921987 = NPER(B7, B9, B10, B11, B12)		26	-	-	-	$9,540.19 = –FV(B7, 26, B9, B10, B12)	
9	**PMT**	($5,000.00)		27	$5,000.00 = –B9	$47.70 = ROUND(H8*B$7, 2)	$4,952.30 = E9 – F9	$4,587.89 = H8 – G9	
10	**PV**	$130,000.00		28	$4,610.83 = H9 + H9*B7	$22.94	$4,587.89	$0.00	
11	**FV**	0		**Total**	$139,610.83 = –B9*27 + E10	$9,610.83 = E11 – G11	$130,000.00 = B10		
12	**BGN**	0							
13									

12.2 Examples

Example 12.2(a)

	A	B	Formula
1	(i)	Calculating *PMT*	
2	*j*	3.40%	
3	*m*	2	
4	*P/Y*	12	
5	*t*	25	
6			
7	*i*	1.70%	= B2/B3
8	*c*	0.166667	= B3/B4
9	i_2	0.2813%	= (1 + B7)^B8 – 1
10	*n*	300	= B4*B5
11	*PMT*	($1235.02)	= PMT(B9, B10, B12, B13, B14) PMT(rate, nper, pv, [fv], [type])
12	*PV*	$250,000.00	
13	*FV*	0	
14	*BGN*	0	
15			
16	(ii)	Calculating BAL_{36}	
17	*n*	36	
18	*FV*	($229,887.40)	= FV(B9, B17, ROUND(B11, 2), B12, B14) FV(rate, nper, pmt, [pv], [type]) ROUND(number, num_digits)
19			
20	(iii)	Calculating *PMT*	
21	*j*	3.80%	
22	*m*	2	
23	*P/Y*	12	
24	*t*	22	= 25 – 3
25			
26	*i*	1.90%	= B21/B22
27	*c*	0.166667	= B22/B23
28	i_2	0.3142%	= (1 + B26)^B27 – 1
29	*n*	264	= B23*B24
30	*PMT*	($1,282.58)	= PMT(B28, B29, B31, B32, B33) PMT(rate, nper, pv, [fv], [type])
31	*PV*	$229,887.40	= –B18
32	*FV*	0	
33	*BGN*	0	
34			

Example 12.2(b)

	A	B	Formula
1	(i)	Calculating *PMT*	
2	*j*	4.00%	
3	*m*	2	
4	*P/Y*	12	
5	*t*	4	
6			
7	*i*	2.00%	= B2/B3
8	*c*	0.166667	= B3/B4
9	i_2	0.3306%	= (1 + B7)^B8 – 1
10	*n*	48	= B4*B5
11	*PMT*	($1,353.86)	= PMT(B9, B10, B12, B13, B14) PMT(rate, nper, pv, [fv], [type])
12	*PV*	$60,000.00	
13	*FV*	0	
14	*BGN*	0	
15			
16	(ii)	Calculating *n*	
17	*n*	46.290667	= NPER(B9, B18, B12, B13, B14) NPER(rate, pmt, pv, [fv], [type])
18	*PMT*	($1,400.00)	= ROUNDUP(B11, –2) ROUNDUP(number, num_digits)
19			
20	PMT_{Final}: Method 1		
21	*n*	46	= ROUNDDOWN(B17, 0) ROUNDDOWN(number, num_digits)
22	*FV*	($406.07)	= FV(B9, B21, B18, B12, B14) FV(rate, nper, pmt, [pv], [type])
23			
24	PMT_F	($407.41)	= B22*(1 + B9)
25			
26	PMT_{Final}: Method 2		
27	*n*	47	= ROUNDUP(B17, 0) ROUNDUP(number, num_digits)
28	*FV*	$992.59	= FV(B9, B27, B18, B12, B14) FV(rate, nper, pmt, [pv], [type])
29			
30	PMT_F	($407.41)	= B18 + B28
31			

Example 12.2(c)

	A	B	C	D	E	F	G	H	I
1	*Inputting Initial Values*								
2	*j*	4.00%							
3	*m*	2		Amortization Schedule					
4	*P/Y*	12		**Payment Number**	**Amount Paid**	**Interest Portion**	**Principal Portion**	**Principal Balance**	
5	*t*	-		0	-	-	-	$60,000.00 = B12	
6				1	$1,400.00 = –B$11	$198.35 = ROUND(H5*B$9, 2)	$1,201.65 = E6 – F6	$58,798.35 = H5 – G6	
7	*i*	2.00% = B2/B3		2	$1,400.00	$194.38	$1,205.62	$57,592.73	
8	*c*	0.166667 = B3/B4		-	-	-	-	-	
9	i_2	0.3306% = (1 + B7)^B8 –1		45	-	-	-	$1,800.12 = –FV(B9, 45, B11, B12, B14)	
10	*n*	47		46	$1,400.00 = –B11	$5.95 = ROUND(H9*B$9, 2)	$1,394.05 = E10 – F10	$406.07 = H9 – G10	
11	*PMT*	($1,400.00)		47	$407.41 = H10 + H10*B9	$1.34	$406.07	$0.00	
12	*PV*	$60,000.00		**Total**	$64,807.41 = –B11*46 + E11	$4,807.41 = E12 – G12	$60,000.00 = B12		
13	*FV*	0							
14	*BGN*	0							

Example 12.2(d)

	A	B	Formula
1	(i)	Calculating *PMT*	
2	***j***	3.60%	
3	***m***	2	
4	***P/Y***	12	
5	***t***	25	
6			
7	***i***	1.80%	= B2/B3
8	***c***	0.166667	= B3/B4
9	i_2	0.2978%	= (1 + B7)^B8 – 1
10	***n***	300	= B4*B5
11	***PMT***	($1,009.13)	= PMT(B9, B10, B12, B13, B14) PMT(rate, nper, pv, [fv], [type])
12	***PV***	$200,000.00	= 0.8*250000
13	***FV***	0	
14	***BGN***	0	
15			
16	(ii)	Calculating BAL_{12}	
17	***n***	12	
18	***FV***	($194,954.93)	= FV(B9, B17, ROUND(B11, 2), B12, B14) FV(rate, nper, pmt, [pv], [type]) ROUND(number, num_digits)
19			
20	(iii)	Calculating *n*	
21	***n***	254.657232	= NPER(B9, ROUND(B11, 2), B22, B13, B14) NPER(rate, pmt, pv, [fv], [type]) ROUND(number, num_digits)
22	***PV***	$179,954.93	= –B18 – 15000
23			

Example 12.2(e)

	A	B	Formula
1	(i)	Calculating *PMT*	
2	***j***	4.25%	
3	***m***	2	
4	***P/Y***	12	
5	***t***	20	
6			
7	***i***	2.1250%	= B2/B3
8	***c***	0.166667	= B3/B4
9	i_2	0.3511%	= (1 + B7)^B8 – 1
10	***n***	240	= B4*B5
11	***PMT***	($2,222.12)	= PMT(B9, B10, B12, B13, B14) PMT(rate, nper, pv, [fv], [type])
12	***PV***	$360,000.00	= 0.8*450000
13	***FV***	0	
14	***BGN***	0	
15			
16	(ii)	Calculating BAL_{36}	
17	***n***	36	
18	***FV***	($323,296.21)	= FV(B9, B17, ROUND(B11, 2), B12, B14) FV(rate, nper, pmt, [pv], [type]) ROUND(number, num_digits)
19			
20	(iii)	Calculating *n*	
21	***n***	167.569352	= NPER(B9, ROUND(B22, 2), B23, B13, B14) NPER(rate, pmt, pv, [fv], [type])
22	***PMT***	($2,555.44)	= ROUND(B11, 2)*1.15 ROUND(number, num_digits)
23	***PV***	$323,296.21	= –B18
24			

Example 12.2(f)

	A	B	Formula
1	(i)	Calculating *t*	
2	***j***	4.00%	
3	***m***	2	
4	***P/Y***	12	
5	***t***	25	= ROUNDUP(B10, 0)/B4 ROUNDUP(number, num_digits)
6			
7	***i***	2.00%	= B2/B3
8	***c***	0.166667	= B3/B4
9	i_2	0.3306%	= (1 + B7)^B8 – 1
10	***n***	299.990457	= NPER(B9, B11, B12, B13, B14) NPER(rate, pmt, pv, [fv], [type])
11	***PMT***	($1,578.09)	
12	***PV***	$300,000.00	
13	***FV***	0	
14	***BGN***	0	
15			
16	(ii)	Calculating *n*	
17	***j***	4.00%	
18	***m***	2	
19	***P/Y***	26	
20	***t***	21.884615	= ROUNDUP(B25, 0)/B19 ROUNDUP(number, num_digits)
21			
22	***i***	2.00%	= B17/B18
23	***c***	0.076923	= B18/B19
24	i_2	0.1524%	= (1 + B22)^B23 – 1
25	***n***	568.867743	= NPER(B24, B26, B27, B28, B29) NPER(rate, pmt, pv, [fv], [type])
26	***PMT***	($789.05)	
27	***PV***	$300,000.00	
28	***FV***	0	
29	***BGN***	0	
30			
31	(iii)	*Monthly PMTs*	
32	***n***	299	= ROUNDDOWN(B10, 0) ROUNDDOWN(number, num_digits)
33	***FV***	($1,557.90)	= FV(B9, B32, B11, B12, B14) FV(rate, nper, pmt, [pv], [type])
34			
35	PMT_F	($1,563.05)	= B33*(1 + B9)
36			
37		Total Interest	
38		($173,411.96)	= (B11*B32 + B35) + B12
39			
40		*Bi-weekly PMTs*	
41	***n***	568	= ROUNDDOWN(B25, 0) ROUNDDOWN(number, num_digits)
42	***FV***	($683.72)	= FV(B24, B41, B26, B27, B29) FV(rate, nper, pmt, [pv], [type])
43			
44	PMT_F	($684.76)	= B42*(1 + B24)
45			
46		Total Interest	
47		($148,865.16)	= (B26*B41 + B44) + B27
48			
49		Difference in Interest	
50		($24,546.80)	= B38 – B47
51			

12 | Summary of Notation

PMT = Periodic payment

INT = Interest portion of a payment

PRN = Principal portion of a payment

BAL = Principal balance

Chapter

13 BONDS AND SINKING FUNDS

LEARNING OBJECTIVES

- Understand terminology used in bonds.
- Calculate the purchase price of a bond on an interest payment date.
- Calculate the purchase price of a bond between interest payment dates.
- Calculate the yield rate.
- Use the quoted price of a bond in calculations.
- Construct a schedule of bond payments.
- Perform sinking fund calculations and construct a sinking fund schedule.

CHAPTER OUTLINE

Introduction

Bonds
are certificates or contracts that borrowers issue, promising to repay a loan with interest payments periodically, and principal repayment on maturity.

When a government agency or a corporation borrows money from people for a long term, they issue a printed contract or certificate to the lender, promising to repay the loan with periodic interest payments, with the principal to be repaid upon maturity. This certificate or contract is called a **bond** or **debenture**.

Bonds are issued by governments or corporations as a method of raising money for new projects that they undertake or to expand their facilities. Canada Savings Bonds (CSB) are examples of bonds that are issued by the federal government and sold to investors through financial institutions.

Bonds are similar to term loans, except that in term loans, each payment has an interest portion that pays for the interest on the previous balance and a principal portion that reduces the outstanding balance (debt); however, a bond requires only periodic payments for the interest. The issuer of the bond (the borrower) agrees to repay the principal amount of the loan when the bond reaches maturity and to pay only the interest periodically, as specified in the contract.

The borrower of the money is the **issuer** of the bond, the lender of the money is the **holder** of the bond, the interest rate charged is the **coupon rate**, and the interest payments paid by the issuer to the holder are known as **coupons**.

Since a bond is generally secured (by some underlying asset), the risk of default is low, whereas a debenture is unsecured, and therefore the risk of default is high. This is why debentures generally have a higher rate of return than bonds. However, the term 'bond' is often used to refer to both secured and unsecured debts.

For example, the Bank of Canada and provincial governments issue bonds that are unsecured but are considered very safe because they are backed by good credibility and are guaranteed by the federal or provincial governments.

Exhibit 13: Time-line Diagram Illustrating Bond Payments

In this chapter, we will study the terms and calculations that are necessary in determining the price of a bond, the rate of return expected by investors, etc. The calculations are based on the topics that you have learned in previous chapters.

13.1 | Bond Terminology

- **Face value** (also called **par value**, or **denomination**) is the value that is assigned to the bond by the issuer. It is the principal amount that is owed to the bond holder at the end of the debt period. Bonds are generally issued in specific denominations (multiples of $100). The most commonly used denominations are $1000, $5000, $10,000, $25,000, or $100,000. The smallest corporate bond denomination is usually $1000. Interest payments (coupons) made to the holder are calculated on the face value of the bond.

- **Redemption value** (also called **maturity value**) is the amount to be repaid by the issuer of the bond to the holder when the bond is redeemed or surrendered. Bonds are usually redeemed at par (redeemed for their face value) at the time of maturity. However, there may be situations when bonds are redeemed before the maturity date for a value higher than the face value (redemption at a premium) or less than the face value (redemption at a discount).

  Note: *In this chapter, we only deal with bonds that are redeemed for their face value (redemption at par) at the time of maturity. Therefore, the redemption value will be the face value of the bond.*

- **Coupon rate** (also called the **bond rate** or **contract rate**) is the interest rate of the bond. The coupon rate is used to calculate the periodic interest payments (coupons) of a bond. This rate is assigned by the issuer of the bond and is fixed for the entire time period of the bond. Coupon rates are generally compounded semi-annually, and in Canada, bonds typically pay interest every six months, although other payment frequencies are possible.

- **Maturity** (also called **term-to-maturity**) is the length of time before the principal is returned on a bond (it varies from a few months to 30+ years for a few corporate bonds).

  - **Short-term bond** is a bond that matures in one year or less.
  - **Intermediate-term bond** is a bond that matures in more than one year but less than or equal to ten.
  - **Long-term bond** is a bond that matures in more than ten years.

The holder of the bond will receive periodic interest payments throughout the life of the bond and the redemption value of the bond when it is redeemed.

- **Maturity date** (also called **redemption date**) is the date on which the bond expires (or matures). On this date, the issuer must repay the redemption value and the final interest payment to the holder of the bond.

- **Balloon payment** is the final payment on the maturity date encompassing the redemption value and the final interest payment.

- **Purchase price** is the price that the holder pays to purchase a bond. The redemption value that is repaid on maturity and the periodic interest payments (coupons) usually remain fixed. However, the price of a bond fluctuates in the market depending on various market conditions. Although a bond has a specific face value and coupon rate assigned by the issuer, the price at which it is actually purchased in the market may not be the face value of the bond. A bond can be sold at its face value (at par), above its face value (above par), or below its face value (below par) depending on various market conditions, such as the market interest rate for a similar type of bond (called the bond's yield rate) and the credit-worthiness (trustworthiness to repay debt) of the issuer.

Bond purchased at par:
Purchase price = Face Value
Bond purchased at premium:
Purchase price > Face Value
Bond purchased at discount:
Purchase price < Face Value

- **Yield rate** (also called **yield-to-maturity (YTM)** or **bond yield**) is the market rate of return that the purchaser of the bond will earn if the bond is purchased at its current market price and held until maturity. It represents the discount rate which equates the discounted value of a bond's future cash flow to its current market price.

  The price of the bond in the market depends on the yield rate.

  - **If the yield rate of the bond is the same as its coupon rate**, it signifies that the bond is providing the same rate of return as an investment in the market that has similar risk. Such a bond is said to be selling **at par**.
  - **If the yield rate of the bond is higher than its coupon rate**, it signifies that the bond is providing a lower rate of return than an investment in the market that has similar risk. Therefore, the bond will not be in demand in the market and it will be traded at a price that is lower than its face value. Such a bond is said to be selling **below par** or at a **discount**. The amount of discount on the bond is the difference between its face value and purchase price.
  - **If the yield rate of the bond is lower than its coupon rate**, it signifies that the bond is providing a higher rate of return than an investment in the market that has similar risk. Therefore, the bond will be in demand in the market and will be traded at a price that is higher than its face value. Such a bond is said to be selling **above par** or at a **premium**. The amount of premium on the bond is the difference between its purchase price and face value.

Bonds trade at par when their coupon rate is the same as the market rate of interest.

Note: *The price of the bond changes inversely to the yield rate (market interest rate); i.e., when the yield rate increases, the price of the bond decreases, and vice versa, as shown in Exhibit 13.1.*

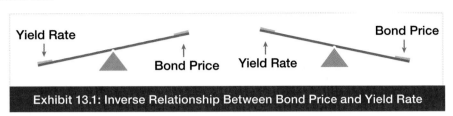

Exhibit 13.1: Inverse Relationship Between Bond Price and Yield Rate

Example 13.1 **Understanding Bond Terminology**

The Bank of Canada issues a $10,000 bond on January 01, 2017 that is redeemable at par in ten years. The bond has a coupon rate of 5%. What is the face value, redemption value, and maturity date of the bond? Will the bond be sold at par, discount, or premium if its yield rate is:

(i) 5% compounded semi-annually?

(ii) 7% compounded semi-annually?

(iii) 4% compounded semi-annually?

Solution

The coupon rate is compounded semi-annually and the coupon payments are made every six months, unless otherwise stated.

Face value = $10,000

Redemption value = *Face value (as it is redeemed at par at the time of maturity)* = $10,000

Maturity date (redemption date) = January 01, 2027

(i) *Yield rate: 5% compounded semi-annually.*

As the yield rate is the same as the coupon rate, the bond is providing the same rate of return as any other investment of similar risk.

Therefore, the bond will be sold at par on the purchase date.

(ii) *Yield rate: 7% compounded semi-annually.*

As the yield rate is higher than the coupon rate, the bond is providing a lower rate of return than any other investment of similar risk.

Therefore, the bond will be sold at a discount on the purchase date.

(iii) *Yield rate: 4% compounded semi-annually.*

As the yield rate is lower than the coupon rate, the bond is providing a higher rate of return than any other investment of similar risk.

Therefore, the bond will be sold at a premium on the purchase date.

13.1 | Exercises

Answers to the odd-numbered problems are available at the end of the textbook.

In the following problems, assume that the coupon rate is compounded semi-annually, and bonds are redeemable at par on maturity, unless otherwise stated.

Calculate the missing values for Problems 1 and 2.

1.

	Face Value	Redemption Value	Coupon Rate	Yield Rate	Purchase Date	Redemption Date	Maturity	Sold at Par/ at a Discount/ at a Premium
a.	$5000.00	?	5.75%	6.00%	January 01, 2017	January 01, 2029	?	?
b.	$30,000.00	?	3.10%	2.85%	March 15, 2018	?	5 years	?
c.	?	$10,000.00	4.15%	4.15%	?	February 10, 2020	8 months	?

2.

	Face Value	Redemption Value	Coupon Rate	Yield Rate	Purchase Date	Redemption Date	Maturity	Sold at Par/ at a Discount/ at a Premium
a.	$1000.00	?	7.10%	7.10%	April 01, 2018	October 01, 2018	?	?
b.	$10,000.00	?	4.65%	3.80%	July 06, 2017	?	2.5 years	?
c.	?	$20,000.00	2.30%	3.30%	?	October 20, 2029	10 years	?

For Problems 3 to 10, determine the face value, maturity date, and whether the bond was sold at par, discount, or premium.

3. A $1000 bond with a coupon rate of 4.30% is purchased on November 01, 2020 when the yield rate was 5.25% compounded semi-annually. It is redeemable in one year.

4. A $12,000 bond with a coupon rate of 4% is redeemable in seven years. It was purchased on April 13, 2017 when the yield rate was 4.50% compounded semi-annually.

5. A bond with a coupon rate of 3.25% is redeemed on December 15, 2026 for $5000. It was purchased three years ago, when the yield rate was 3.25% compounded semi-annually.

6. The coupon rate and yield rate of a $15,000 bond are both 4.60% compounded semi-annually on the purchase date of September 10, 2018, six years before its maturity date.

7. Michael purchased a bond with a coupon rate of 5% three years ago, when the yield rate was 4.25% compounded semi-annually. He redeemed the bond for $3000 on March 14, 2022.

8. Jamie purchased a $6000 bond on January 01, 2018 with a yield rate of 2.25% compounded semi-annually. The bond has a coupon rate of 2.75% and is redeemable in 3.5 years.

• 9. A $10,000 bond with a coupon rate of 6% is redeemable in five years. It was purchased on March 31, 2017 when the yield rate was 6% compounded annually.

• 10. A bond bearing a coupon rate of 3.17% is redeemed on June 20, 2021 for $5000. It was purchased four years ago with a yield rate of 3.10% compounded daily.

13.2 | Calculating Purchase Price and Yield Rate of Bonds

Calculating the Purchase Price

As described earlier, bonds can be purchased and sold on any date prior to the maturity date. It can be sold either on an interest payment date (i.e., a date when interest on the bond is to be paid) or a date between interest payments. The procedure for determining the purchase price of a bond differs depending on whether it is purchased on an interest payment date or between interest payment dates.

Purchase Price on an Interest Payment Date

Assume that interest on the bond is paid semi-annually and that it is sold on an interest payment date (shown as 'Purchase date' in the line-diagrams below).

The purchase price of the bond on the interest payment date is the sum of the present value of all the remaining interest payments on the bond (PV_{PMT}) on this date, and the present value of the redemption value of the bond ($PV_{Redemption\ Value}$) on this date, discounted at the bond's yield rate, 'i'.

This is illustrated as follows:

PV_{PMT} on the date the bond is sold

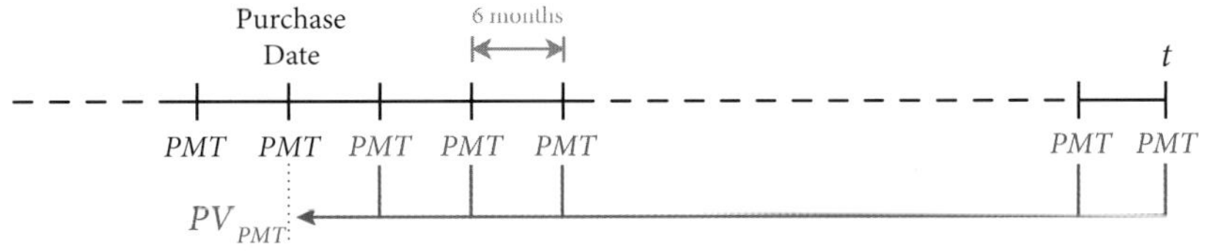

$PV_{Redemption\ Value}$ on the date the bond is sold

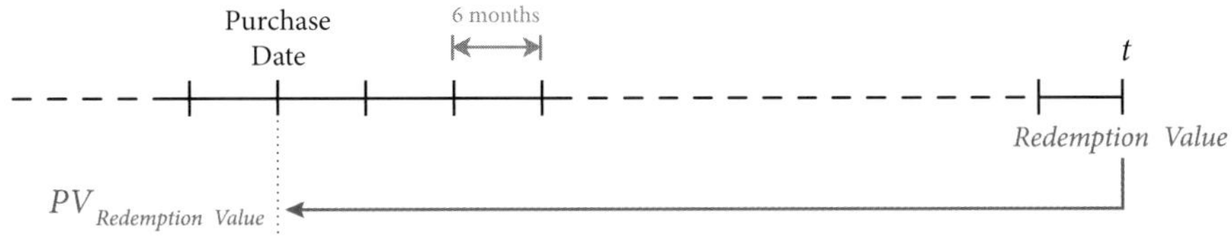

Therefore, the formula for the purchase price of a bond on an interest payment date is:

Formula 13.2(a)

Purchase Price of a Bond

$$Purchase\ Price = PV_{PMT} + PV_{Redemption\ Value}$$

The holder of the bond will receive periodic interest payments throughout the life of the bond and the redemption value of the bond when it is redeemed.

Note: *Interest payment on the date of purchase (which is an interest payment date) goes to the seller of the bond and not the buyer. Interest payments to the buyer starts only on the first interest payment date after the purchase.*

Notation

In this chapter, we only deal with bonds that are redeemed for their face value (redemption at par) at the time of maturity. Therefore, the redemption value will be the face value of the bond.

- b = Periodic **coupon** rate is used to calculate the periodic interest payment (coupon), where $b = \frac{j}{m}$ (From Formula 9.1(d) for the periodic interest rate)
- i = Periodic **yield** rate, where $i = \frac{j}{m}$ (From Formula 9.1(d) for the periodic interest rate)
- FV = Redemption value is the face value of a bond when it is redeemed at par at the time of maturity.
- PMT = Periodic interest payment (or coupon) is as follows:

Formula 13.2(b)

Periodic Interest Payment of a Bond

$$PMT = FV \times b$$

Example 13.2(a)

Calculating the Purchase Price of a Bond at Different Yield Rates

A bond has a face value of $1000, coupon rate of 10%, and will mature in six years.

(i) Calculate the purchase price when the yield rate is 10% compounded semi-annually.

(ii) Calculate the purchase price and the amount of discount when the yield rate is 12% compounded semi-annually.

(iii) Calculate the purchase price and the amount of premium when the yield rate is 8% compounded semi-annually.

Page 571

Solution

Using the financial calculator, you can either compute *'PV'* seperately and add the answers together, or you can complete the entire calculation in one step as shown here.

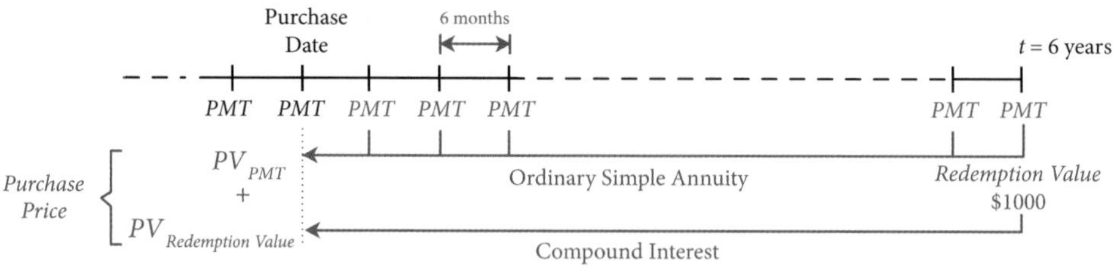

(i) Calculating *Purchase Price*

Set to END mode

2ND CLR TVM

2ND P/Y

P/Y = 2 ENTER

↓ C/Y = 2

2ND QUIT

12 N

10 I/Y

50 PMT

1000 FV

CPT PV

PV= -1000

Note: *In this chapter, we assume that the bond is redeemed for its face value at maturity. Therefore, the redemption value is the face value of the bond.*

$FV = \$1000.00, \quad n = 2 \times 6 = 12, \quad \text{Coupon rate, } b = \frac{j}{m} = \frac{0.10}{2} = 0.05 \text{ per half-year}$

Using Formula 13.2(b), $PMT = FV \times b = 1000.00 \times 0.05 = \$50.00$

(i) *Bond purchased when the yield rate is equal to the coupon rate*

Periodic yield rate, $i = \frac{j}{m} = \frac{0.10}{2} = 0.05$ per half-year

Using the Ordinary Simple Annuity Formula 10.2(b),

$$PV = PMT\left[\frac{1-(1+i)^{-n}}{i}\right]$$

$$PV_{PMT} = 50.00\left[\frac{1-(1+0.05)^{-12}}{0.05}\right]$$

$$= 50.00[8.863251...] = \$443.162581...$$

Using the Compound Interest Formula 9.1(b),

$$PV = FV(1+i)^{-n}$$

$$PV_{Redemption\ Value} = 1000.00(1+0.05)^{-12}$$

$$= 1000.00(0.556837...)$$

$$= \$556.837418...$$

Using Formula 13.2(a), $\quad Purchase\ Price = PV_{PMT} + PV_{Redemption\ Value}$

$$= 443.162581... + 556.837418... = \$1000.00$$

Therefore, the purchase price of the bond when the yield rate is the same as the coupon rate is \$1000.00. As the purchase price is the same as the face value, the bond is sold at par.

It is not necessary to re-enter N, P/Y, C/Y, PMT, and FV as they have not changed and have not been cleared (by CLR TVM).

(ii) Calculating *Purchase Price*

12 I/Y

CPT PV

PV= -916.1615606

(ii) *Bond purchased when the yield rate is higher than the coupon rate*

Periodic yield rate, $i = \frac{j}{m} = \frac{0.12}{2} = 0.06$ per half-year

$$PV_{PMT} = 50.00\left[\frac{1-(1+0.06)^{-12}}{0.06}\right]$$

$$= 50.00[8.383843...] = \$419.192197...$$

$$PV_{Redemption\ Value} = 1000.00(1+0.06)^{-12}$$

$$= 1000.00(0.496969...)$$

$$= \$496.969363...$$

Using Formula 13.2(a), $\quad Purchase\ Price = PV_{PMT} + PV_{Redemption\ Value}$

$$= 419.192197... + 496.969363...$$

$$= 916.161560... = \$916.16$$

Therefore, the purchase price of the bond when the yield rate is higher than the coupon rate is \$916.16. As the purchase price is less than the face value, the bond is sold below par or at a discount.

When the market interest rate (yield rate) increases, the price of the bond decreases.

$Amount\ of\ Discount = Redemption\ Value - Purchase\ Price = 1000.00 - 916.16 = \$83.84$

Therefore, the amount of discount on the bond is \$83.84.

Solution *continued*

(iii) Calculating *Purchase Price*

8 I/Y

CPT PV

PV= -1093.850738

When the market interest rate (yield rate) decreases, the price of the bond increases.

(iii) *Bond purchased when the yield rate is less than the coupon rate*

Periodic yield rate, $i = \frac{j}{m} = \frac{0.08}{2} = 0.04$ per half-year

$$PV_{PMT} = 50.00\left[\frac{1-(1+0.04)^{-12}}{0.04}\right]$$

$$= 50.00[9.385073...] = \$469.253688...$$

$$PV_{Redemption\ Value} = 1000.00(1+0.04)^{-12}$$

$$= 1000.00(0.624597...)$$

$$= \$624.597049...$$

Using Formula 13.2(a), $\quad Purchase\ Price = PV_{PMT} + PV_{Redemption\ Value}$

$$= 469.253688... + 624.597049...$$

$$= 1093.850738... = \$1093.85$$

Therefore, the purchase price of the bond when the yield rate is less than the coupon rate is \$1093.85.

As the purchase price is higher than the face value, the bond is sold above par or at a premium.

$$Amount\ of\ Premium = Purchase\ Price - Redemption\ Value = 1093.85 - 1000.00 = \$93.85$$

Therefore, the amount of premium on the bond is \$93.85.

Example 13.2(b) Calculating the Purchase Price of a Bond when the Yield Rate is at a Different Compounding Frequency than the Bond's Coupon Rate

A \$25,000 bond that carries a 4.6% coupon rate is purchased five years before maturity when the yield rate was 5% compounded annually. Calculate the purchase price and amount of discount on the bond.

Solution

Page 571

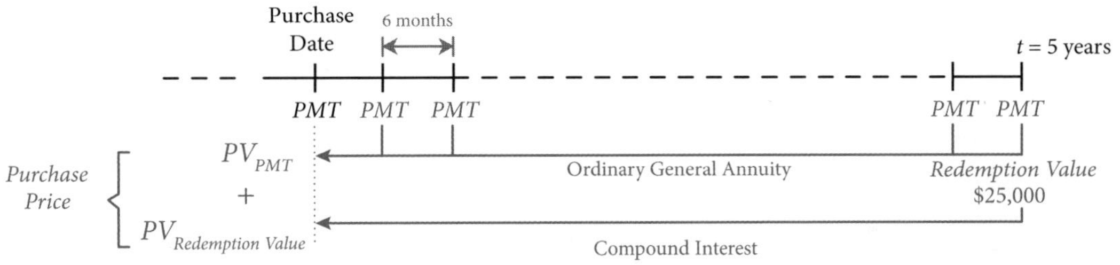

Calculating *Purchase Price*

Set to END mode

2ND CLR TVM

2ND P/Y

P/Y = 2 ENTER

↓

C/Y = 1 ENTER

2ND QUIT

10 N

5 I/Y

575 PMT

25,000 FV

CPT PV

PV= -24,628.52947

$FV = \$25,000.00$

$n = 2 \times 5 = 10 \qquad (t = 5$ since there are 5 years left on the bond)

Coupon rate, $b = \frac{j}{m} = \frac{0.046}{2} = 0.023$ per half-year

Using Formula 13.2(b), $PMT = FV \times b = 25{,}000.00 \times 0.023 = \$575.00$

Periodic yield rate, $i = \frac{j}{m} = \frac{0.05}{1} = 0.05$ per year

Since the yield rate is compounded annually and the coupon rate is compounded semi-annually, PV_{PMT} is calculated as an ordinary general annuity.

Using Formula 10.3(a), $c = \frac{Number\ of\ compounding\ periods\ per\ year}{Number\ of\ payments\ per\ year} = \frac{1}{2}$

Using Formula 10.3(b), $i_2 = (1+i)^c - 1 = (1+0.05)^{(1/2)} - 1 = 0.024695...$ per half-year

$$PV_{PMT} = 575.00\left[\frac{1-(1+0.024695...)^{-10}}{0.024695...}\right]$$

$$= 575.00(8.765870...)$$

$$= \$5040.375307...$$

$$PV_{Redemption\ Value} = 25{,}000.00(1+0.024695...)^{-10}$$

$$= 25{,}000.00(0.783526...)$$

$$= \$19{,}588.15416...$$

Solution *continued*

Using Formula 13.2(a), $\textit{Purchase Price} = PV_{PMT} + PV_{\textit{Redemption Value}}$

$$= 5040.375307... + 19{,}588.15416...$$

$$= 24{,}628.52947... = \$24{,}628.53$$

Therefore, the purchase price of the bond is $24,628.53. The bond is sold below par or at a discount.

$$\textit{Amount of Discount} = \textit{Redemption Value} - \textit{Purchase Price}$$

$$= 25{,}000.00 - 24{,}628.53$$

$$= \$371.47$$

Therefore, the amount of discount on the bond is $371.47.

Example 13.2(c) Calculating the Gain or Loss from Purchasing Bonds

A $20,000 bond has a 6% coupon rate and matures on June 01, 2024. Suzanne purchased it on June 01, 2014 when the interest rate in the market was 7% compounded semi-annually. On June 01, 2018, she sold the bond when the interest rate in the market was 5% compounded semi-annually.

(i) What was the purchase price of the bond?
(ii) What was the selling price of the bond?
(iii) How much did she gain or lose on this investment?
(iv) What is the percent gain or loss on this investment?

Solution

Page 571

Face value, $FV = \$20{,}000.00$, Coupon rate, $b = \frac{j}{m} = \frac{0.06}{2} = 0.03$ per half-year

Using Formula 13.2(b), $PMT = FV \times b = 20{,}000.00 \times 0.03 = \$600.00$

(i) *Purchase price of the bond when yield rate was 7% compounded semi-annually*

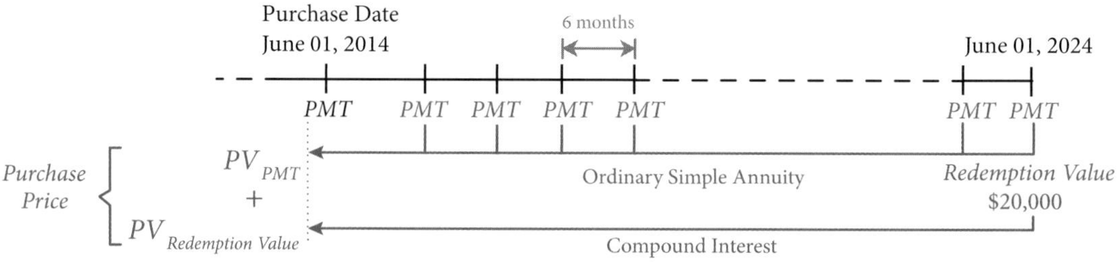

$n = 2 \times 10 = 20$, Periodic yield rate, $i = \frac{j}{m} = \frac{0.07}{2} = 0.035$ per half-year

Using Formula 13.2(a), $\textit{Purchase Price} = PV_{PMT} + PV_{\textit{Redemption Value}}$

$$= 600.00\left[\frac{1-(1+0.035)^{-20}}{0.035}\right] + 20{,}000.00(1+0.035)^{-20}$$

$$= 8527.441981... + 10{,}051.31769...$$

$$= 18{,}578.75967... = \$18{,}578.76$$

Therefore, the purchase price of the bond was $18,578.76.

(ii) *Selling price of the bond when yield rate was 5% compounded semi-annually*

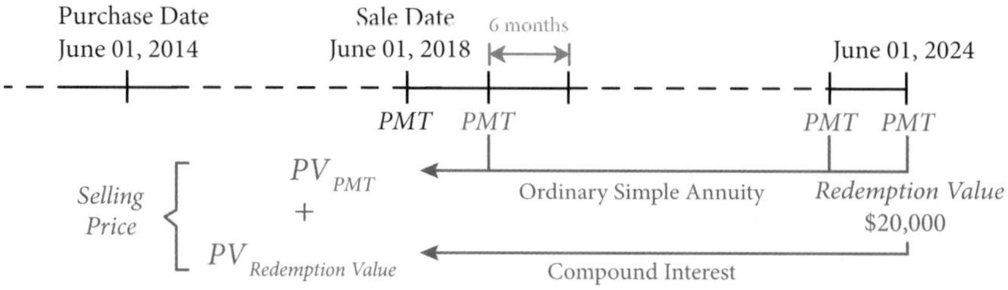

Solution
continued

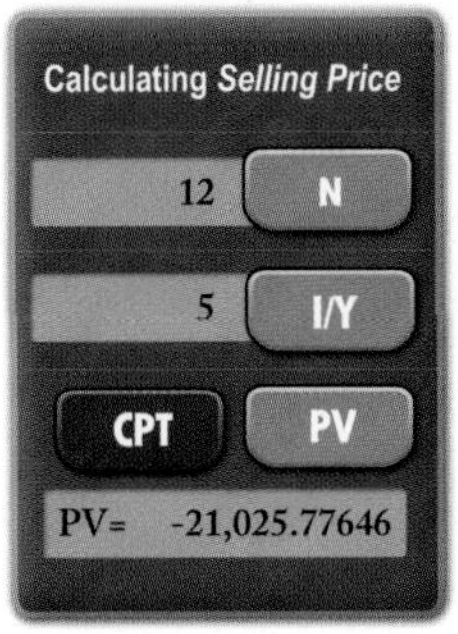

$n = 2 \times 6 = 12$ ($t = 6$ since there are 6 years left on the bond)

Periodic yield rate, $i = \dfrac{j}{m} = \dfrac{0.05}{2} = 0.025$ per half-year

Using Formula 13.2(a), $Purchase\ Price = PV_{PMT} + PV_{Redemption\ Value}$

$$Selling\ Price\ (Buyer's\ Purchase\ Price) = 600.00\left[\frac{1-(1+0.025)^{-12}}{0.025}\right] + 20{,}000.00(1+0.025)^{-12}$$

$$= 6154.658759... + 14{,}871.11770...$$

$$= 21{,}025.77646... = \$21{,}025.78$$

Therefore, the selling price of the bond was $21,025.78.

(iii) $Amount\ of\ gain\ on\ the\ investment = 21{,}025.78 - 18{,}578.76 = \$2447.02$

Therefore, she gained $2447.02 on this investment.

(iv) $Percent\ gain\ on\ the\ investment = \dfrac{21{,}025.78 - 18{,}578.76}{18{,}578.76} \times 100\% = 0.131710... \times 100\% = 13.17\%$

Therefore, the percent gain on the investment is 13.17%.

Purchase Price Between Interest Payment Dates

In the previous section, we learned to calculate the purchase price of a bond when the bond is sold on an interest payment date. However, bonds are commonly sold on any date, and the date may be between interest payment dates. In this section, we will learn to calculate the purchase price of a bond when it is sold between interest payment dates.

When a bond is purchased between interest payment dates, the buyer and the seller split the interest payment (coupon) at the time of the purchase based on the fractional part of the interest period during which each of them holds ownership of the bond. The interest part received by the seller (called **accrued interest**) is the interest that has accumulated on a bond since the last interest payment up to, but not including, the settlement date. This accrued interest is included in the purchase price.

The following steps are followed for calculating the purchase price of the bond between interest payment dates:

Step 1: Identifying the Interest Payment Dates

Start by identifying the redemption date, purchase date, previous interest payment date, and the next interest payment date.

Step 2: Calculating the Purchase Price on the Previous Interest Payment Date

The purchase price on the previous interest payment date is the sum of the present value of all the remaining interest payments on the bond (PV_{PMT}) on this date, and the present value of the redemption value of the bond ($PV_{Redemption\ Value}$) on this date discounted at the yield rate, 'i'.

Using Formula 13.2(a), $Purchase\ Price_{Previous\ Interest\ Payment\ Date} = PV_{PMT} + PV_{Redemption\ Value}$

Step 3: Calculating the Purchase Price on the Purchase Date

The purchase price of the bond is the future value of the price calculated in Step 2, on the purchase date. This is calculated using the compound interest formula.

Using Formula 9.1(a), $Purchase\ Price_{Purchase\ Date} = Purchase\ Price_{Previous\ Interest\ Payment\ Date}(1+i)^n$

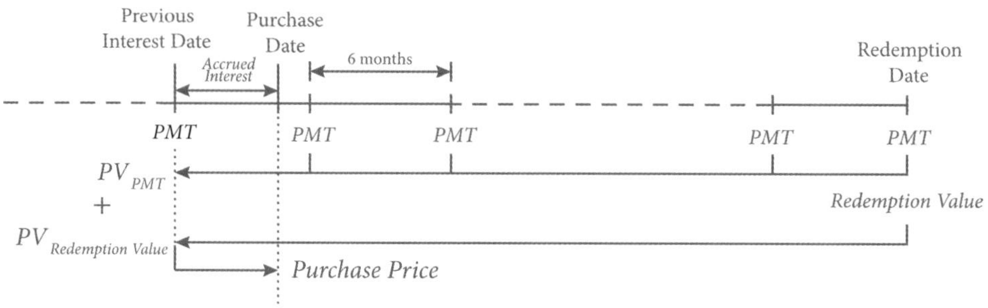

The fractional compounding period "n" on the purchase date is:

$$n = \frac{\textit{Number of days from previous interest date to purchase date}}{\textit{Number of days from previous interest date to next interest date}}$$

Example 13.2(d) **Calculating the Purchase Price of a Bond when it is Sold Between Interest Payment Dates**

A company issued a \$1000 bond with a coupon rate of 10% and redeemable on January 01, 2023. If Henry wanted to purchase this bond on April 16, 2016 when the yield rate was 7% compounded semi-annually, calculate the purchase price of the bond.

Page 572

Solution

Step 1: Identifying the Interest Payment Dates

Redemption date: January 01, 2023

As the redemption date is January 01, semi-annual interest payment dates would be January 01 and July 01 of every year.

Purchase date: April 16, 2016

Previous interest payment date: January 01, 2016

Next interest payment date: July 01, 2016

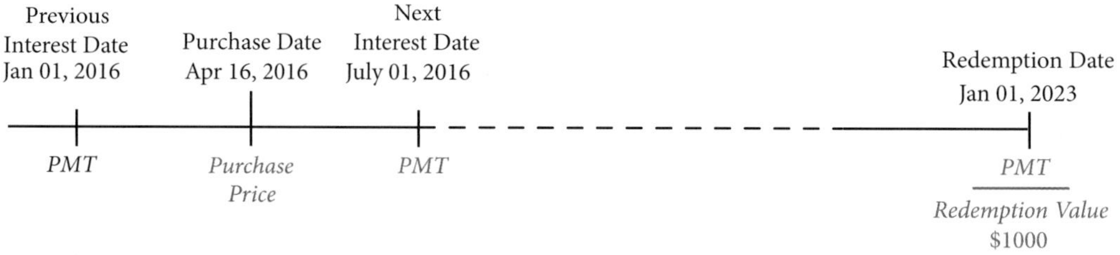

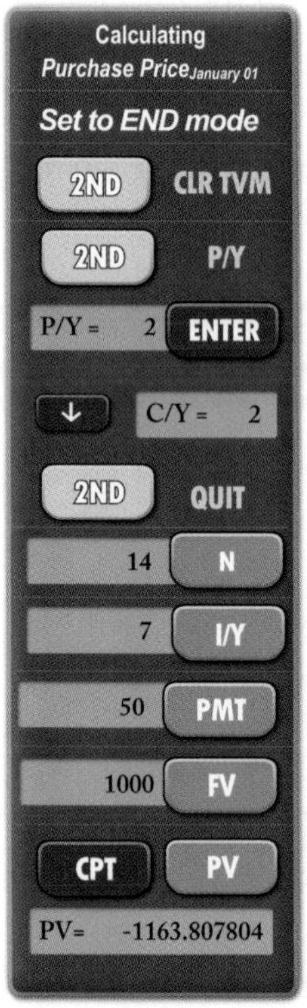

Step 2: Calculating the Purchase Price on the Previous Interest Payment Date

Time from previous interest date to redemption date = January 01, 2016 to January 01, 2023 = 7 years

$n = 2 \times 7 = 14$

Coupon rate, $b = \frac{j}{m} = \frac{0.10}{2} = 0.05$ per half-year

Using Formula 13.2(b), $PMT = FV \times b = 1000.00 \times 0.05 = \$50.00$

Periodic yield rate, $i = \frac{j}{m} = \frac{0.07}{2} = 0.035$ per half-year

Using Formula 13.2(a), $\textit{Purchase Price} = PV_{PMT} + PV_{\textit{Redemption Value}}$

$$\textit{Purchase Price}_{\text{January 01, 2016}} = 50.00\left[\frac{1-(1+0.035)^{-14}}{0.035}\right] + 1000.00(1+0.035)^{-14}$$

$$= 546.026013... + 617.781790... = \$1163.807804...$$

Solution *continued*

Step 3: Calculating the Purchase Price on the Purchase Date

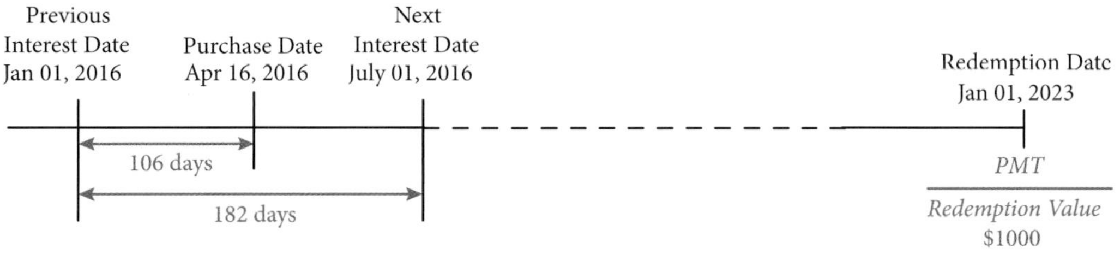

The fractional compounding period "n" on the purchase date is:

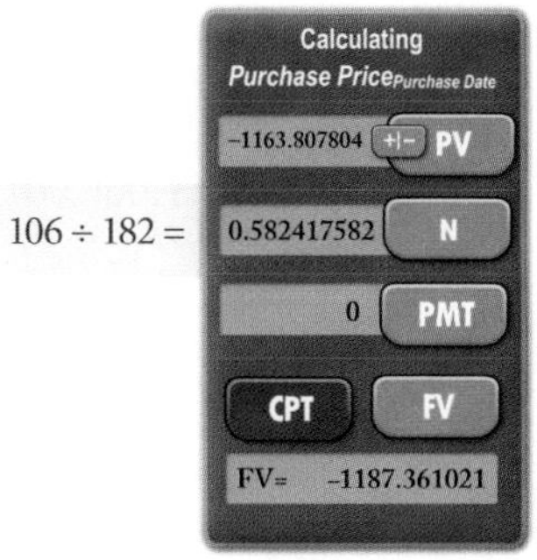

$$n = \frac{\textit{Number of days from previous interest date to purchase date}}{\textit{Number of days from previous interest date to next interest date}}$$

$$= \frac{\text{January 01, 2016 to April 16, 2016}}{\text{January 01, 2016 to July 01, 2016}} = \frac{106}{182}$$

$$\textit{Purchase Price}_{\textit{Purchase Date}} = \textit{Purchase Price}_{\textit{Previous Interest Payment Date}} (1 + i)^n$$

$$= 1163.807804...(1 + 0.035)^{(106/182)}$$

$$= 1187.361021... = \$1187.36$$

Therefore, the purchase price of the bond is \$1187.36.

Calculating the Yield Rate

As explained in Section 13.1, the yield rate is the market rate of return that the purchaser of the bond will earn if the bond is purchased at its current market price and held until maturity. It represents the discount rate, which equates the discounted value of a bond's future cash flow to its current market price.

The yield rate can be calculated using Formulas 13.2(a) and 13.2(b). However, the simplest method for finding the yield rate is by using the financial calculator. The calculator method to solve for yield rate is shown in the following example.

Example 13.2(e) **Calculating the Yield Rate**

A \$10,000 bond has a coupon rate of 12% and is redeemable in five years. What is the yield rate of the bond if it was purchased for \$9640?

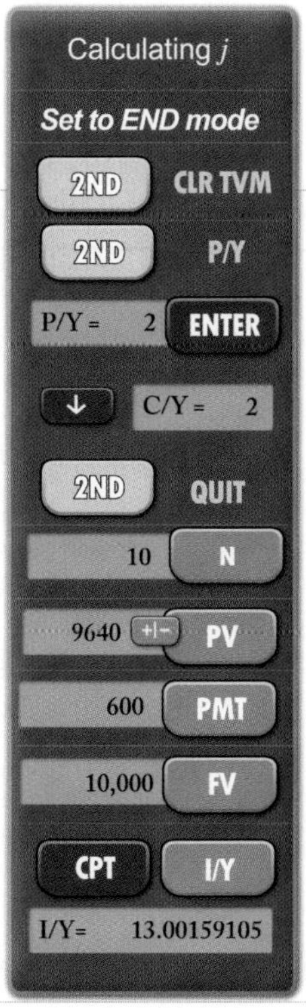

Solution

Page 572

$FV = \$10{,}000.00$, $\quad \textit{Purchase Price} = \$9640.00$, $\quad n = 2 \times 5 = 10$, $\quad b = \frac{0.12}{2} = 0.06$

Using Formula 13.2(b),

$$PMT = FV \times b = 10{,}000.00 \times 0.06 = \$600.00$$

Using Formula 13.2(a),

$$\textit{Purchase Price} = PV_{PMT} + PV_{\textit{Redemption Value}}$$

$$9640.00 = 600.00\left[\frac{1 - (1 + i)^{-10}}{i}\right] + 10{,}000.00(1 + i)^{-10}$$

Inputting these values into the calculator and computing I/Y, we determine that the yield rate of the bond, $j = 13.00\%$.

13.2 | Exercises

Answers to the odd-numbered problems are available at the end of the textbook.

In the following problems, assume that the coupon rate is compounded semi-annually, the coupons are paid every six months, and bonds are redeemed at par (for their face value) on maturity, unless otherwise stated.

Express the answers rounded to two decimal places, wherever applicable.

For Problems 1 and 2, determine the purchase price and the amount of premium/discount of the given bonds.

1.

	Face Value	Coupon Rate	Yield Rate	Redemption Date	Purchase Date	Purchase Price	Amount of Premium/Discount
a.	$1000.00	5.25%	5.25%	January 01, 2024	January 01, 2019	?	?
b.	$5000.00	4.75%	6.75%	October 20, 2028	October 20, 2018	?	?
c.	$10,000.00	7.85%	4.15%	August 16, 2034	August 16, 2014	?	?

2.

	Face Value	Coupon Rate	Yield Rate	Redemption Date	Purchase Date	Purchase Price	Amount of Premium/Discount
a.	$25,000.00	4.35%	4.35%	February 12, 2022	February 12, 2015	?	?
b.	$1000.00	5.75%	7.25%	April 22, 2027	April 22, 2018	?	?
c.	$20,000.00	7.85%	6.35%	June 13, 2031	June 13, 2017	?	?

3. A $1000 bond with a coupon rate of 5% is redeemable in twenty years.
    a. Calculate the purchase price when the yield rate is 5% compounded semi-annually.
    b. Calculate the purchase price and the amount of discount when the yield rate is 7% compounded semi-annually.
    c. Calculate the purchase price and the amount of premium when the yield rate is 4% compounded semi-annually.

4. A $5000 bond with a coupon rate of 7% is redeemable in ten years.
    a. Calculate the purchase price when the yield rate is 7% compounded semi-annually.
    b. Calculate the purchase price and the amount of discount when the yield rate is 8% compounded semi-annually.
    c. Calculate the purchase price and the amount of premium when the yield rate is 5% compounded semi-annually.

5. Abigail purchased a $100,000 corporate bond that has a coupon rate of 4.25% and is redeemable in ten years. The yield rate at the time of purchase was 6.75% compounded semi-annually.
    a. What was the purchase price of the bond?
    b. What was the amount of discount or premium on the bond?

6. William purchased a $10,000 corporate bond with a 5% coupon rate which is redeemable in twenty years. The yield rate at the time of purchase was 6.25% compounded semi-annually.
    a. What was the purchase price of the bond?
    b. What was the amount of discount or premium on the bond?

7. Mia purchased a $50,000 bond with a coupon rate of 6.25% and six years to maturity. She sold the bond, after holding it for two years, when the yield rate was 5.35% compounded semi-annually.
    a. What was the selling price of the bond?
    b. What was the discount or premium on the bond at the time of sale?

8. Liam purchased a $25,000 bond with a coupon rate of 7.15% and eight years to maturity. He sold the bond, after holding it for six years, when the yield rate was 6.25% compounded semi-annually.

   a. What was the selling price of the bond?

   b. What was the discount or premium on the bond at the time of sale?

9. A $10,000 bond with a coupon rate of 3.5% is redeemable in ten years. It was purchased three years before maturity when the yield rate was 4.5% compounded quarterly.

   a. What was the purchase price of the bond?

   b. What was the amount of discount or premium on the bond?

10. Sabena purchased a $5000, 5.15% bond when it had two years to maturity and the yield rate was 6.50% compounded monthly.

    a. What was the purchase price of the bond?

    b. What was the amount of discount or premium on the bond?

11. A $1000 bond has a coupon rate of 5%. Ria purchased this bond when there were five years left to maturity and when the yield rate was 5.5% compounded semi-annually. She held the bond for two years then sold it when the yield rate was 4.5% compounded semi-annually.

    a. At what price did she purchase the bond?

    b. At what price did she sell the bond?

    c. What was her gain or loss on the investment?

    d. What was her percent gain or loss on the investment?

12. A company issued a $50,000 bond paying a 4% coupon rate. An investor purchased this bond when the yield rate was 3.5% compounded semi-annually and the bond had seven years left to maturity. Three years later, the investor sold the bond when the yield rate was 5% compounded semi-annually.

    a. At what price did the investor purchase the bond?

    b. At what price did the investor sell the bond?

    c. What was the investor's gain or loss on the investment?

    d. What was the investor's percent gain or loss on the investment?

For Problems 13 and 14, determine the missing values.

13.

	Face Value	Coupon Rate	Yield Rate	Redemption Date	Purchase Date	Purchase Price	Amount of Premium/Discount
a.	$10,000.00	8.00%	5.25%	March 15, 2023	July 12, 2018	?	?
b.	$20,000.00	7.25%	6.75%	May 26, 2029	August 12, 2019	?	?
c.	$1000.00	4.55%	?	November 12, 2031	November 12, 2016	$1024.00	?
d.	$5000.00	6.65%	?	May 15, 2024	May 15, 2016	$3998.50	?

14.

	Face Value	Coupon Rate	Yield Rate	Redemption Date	Purchase Date	Purchase Price	Amount of Premium/Discount
a.	$5000.00	6.75%	4.35%	January 06, 2025	May 11, 2019	?	?
b.	$25,000.00	4.25%	7.25%	June 13, 2029	April 11, 2020	?	?
c.	$1000.00	5.65%	?	May 26, 2024	May 26, 2017	$1027.75	?
d.	$100,000.00	7.75%	?	July 27, 2032	July 27, 2012	$94,708.00	?

15. A $10,000 bond with a coupon rate of 4.65% was redeemable on July 01, 2020. It was purchased on September 10, 2015 when the yield rate was 5.50% compounded semi-annually.
    a. What was the purchase price of the bond?
    b. What was the amount of discount or premium on the bond?

16. Martha purchased a $1000 bond on November 19, 2015 when the yield-to-maturity was 4.85% compounded semi-annually. The bond had a coupon rate of 5.35% and was redeemable on December 31, 2019.
    a. What was the purchase price of the bond?
    b. What was the amount of discount or premium on the bond?

17. A ten-year, $1000 bond paying an 8.5% coupon rate was purchased at $991. Calculate the yield rate at the time of purchase.

18. What is the yield rate on a $25,000, five-year, 6% bond that was purchased at $25,850?

19. Nathan bought a $100,000 bond that has a coupon rate of 4.75% and is redeemable in ten years. If he paid $104,800 for the bond, what was the market rate of return at the time of purchase?

20. Brianna paid $24,780 for a $25,000 bond that has a coupon rate of 5.25% and is redeemable in seven years. What was the market rate of return at the time of purchase?

13.3 | Quotation of Bonds

In our previous examples, we have been calculating the price of the bond that includes any interest that has accrued since the most recent coupon (interest payment). This is the amount that the buyer of the bond would actually pay when the bond is purchased. This price is called the **full price** (also called purchase price, invoice price, dirty price, or flat price) of the bond.

Bond prices fluctuate in the market for the following reasons:

- **Change in market interest rate:** The market interest rate keeps fluctuating, leading to a higher or lower yield rate. A high yield rate reduces the present value of the bond's remaining payments and vice versa (as shown in Exhibit 13.1).
- **Decrease in the life of the bond:** As the bond gets closer to the maturity date (keeping the yield rate constant), the present value of the bond's remaining cash flow (including the redemption value) will change as the time to maturity decreases.
- **Between interest payment dates:** The price of the bond increases to reflect the increase in the present value of cash inflows as the next coupon payment approaches. As soon as the payment is made, the price of the bond falls. This pattern continues throughout the life of the bond creating a saw-tooth or zig-zag appearance on the graph of the bond price versus time period (as shown in Exhibit 13.3).

To be able to compare the price of bonds easily, the bond price is not quoted as its full price. *Instead, it is quoted as a price excluding the accrued interest.* This price is called the **quoted price** (also called clean price or market price) of the bond.

Formula 13.3(a) **Full Price of a Bond**

$$\text{Full Price} = \text{Quoted Price} + \text{Accrued Interest}$$

Accrued interest is the interest that has accumulated on a bond since the last interest payment up to, but not including, the settlement date.

Daily bond prices in the market are quoted as a percent of their face value; this is called the **market quotation** of a bond. Since bonds are issued in different denominations, the market quotation is provided on a basis of a $100 bond.

For example, if a bond has a market quotation of 108.5 (or $108.5 or 108.5%), it means that the bond has a quoted price of 108.5% of its redemption value. So if the redemption value of the bond is $1000, then the quoted price of the bond is $1.085 \times 1000 = \$1085$.

Formula 13.3(b)

Quoted Price of a Bond

$$Quoted\ Price = Market\ Quotation \times Redemption\ Value$$

It is the market practice in Canada to quote bonds on a quoted-price basis.

Exhibit 13.3 illustrates the changes in the price of a bond selling at par, selling at premium, and selling at discount with the yield rate being constant for the remaining years to maturity.

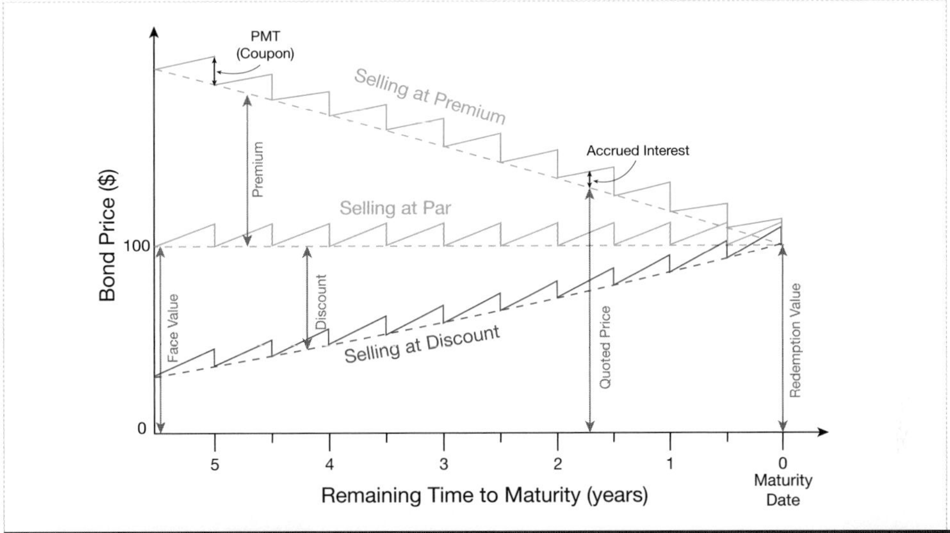

Exhibit 13.3: Comparison of Bonds Selling at Par, Premium, and Discount

Example 13.3(a)

Calculating the Purchase Price on an Interest Payment Date, Given the Market Quotation

A $5000, 4% bond is purchased five years before the redemption date. Calculate the purchase price and discount on the bond if the market quotation on the date of purchase was 98.5.

Solution

Using Formula 13.3(b), $Quoted\ Price = Market\ Quotation \times Redemption\ Value$

$$= 98.5\%\ (5000.00) = 0.985(5000.00) = \$4925.00$$

Since the purchase date is on an interest payment date, the quoted price is the purchase price of the bond.

$$Amount\ of\ Discount = Redemption\ Value - Purchase\ Price = 5000.00 - 4925.00 = \$75.00$$

Therefore, the purchase price of the bond was $4925.00 and the amount of discount was $75.00.

Example 13.3(b)

Calculating the Purchase Price between Interest Payment Dates, Given the Market Quotation

A $10,000 bond with a coupon rate of 6% was redeemable on March 01, 2017. If it was purchased on December 18, 2010 when the quote was 102.5, calculate the full price (purchase price) of the bond.

Solution

Step 1: Identifying interest payment dates

Redemption date:	March 01, 2017
Interest dates:	March 01 and September 01 every year
Purchase date:	December 18, 2010
Previous interest date:	September 01, 2010
Next interest date:	March 01, 2011

Step 2: Calculating the quoted price from the market quotation

Using Formula 13.3(b), $Quoted\ Price = Market\ Quotation \times Redemption\ Value$

$$= 102.5\%(10{,}000.00) = 1.025(10{,}000.00) = \$10{,}250.00$$

The quoted price does not include the accrued interest.

Solution *continued*

Step 3: Calculating the accrued interest

The accrued interest is a fraction of the interest payment (coupon) that the bond seller earns for holding the bond for the period of time between the interest payments.

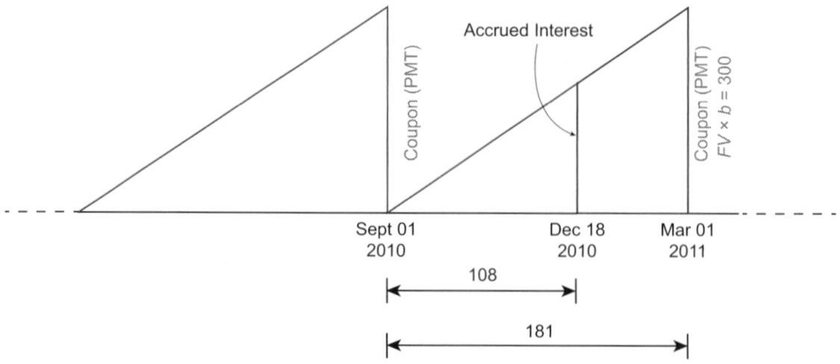

Coupon rate, $b = \frac{j}{m} = \frac{0.06}{2} = 0.03$ per half-year

Using Formula 13.2(b), $PMT = FV \times b = 10{,}000.00 \times 0.03 = \$300.00$

The accrued interest is calculated using the following formula:

$$\textit{Accrued Interest} = PMT \times \frac{\textit{Number of days from previous interest date to purchase date}}{\textit{Number of days from previous interest date to next interest date}}$$

$$= 300.00 \times \frac{\text{September 01, 2010 to December 18, 2010}}{\text{September 01, 2010 to March 01, 2011}}$$

$$= 300.00 \times \frac{108}{181} = 179.005524... = \$179.01$$

The amount of the interest payment (coupon) that the buyer will receive will be the coupon minus the accrued interest.

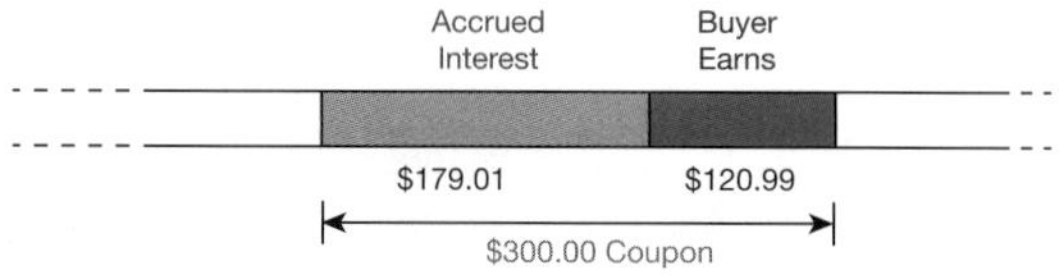

Step 4: Calculating purchase price

Using Formula 13.3(a), *Full Price* = *Quoted Price* + *Accrued Interest*

$= 10{,}250.00 + 179.01 = \$10{,}429.01$

Therefore, the full price (purchase price) of the bond was $10,429.01.

Example 13.3(c) **Calculating the Full Price, Accrued Interest, Quoted Price, and Market Quotation of a Bond**

A $5000 corporation bond with a coupon rate of 6.5% matures on June 11, 2033. An investor desiring a 3.84% compounded semi-annually yield rate purchased the bond on February 9, 2017.

(i) What is the full price (purchase price) of the bond?

(ii) What is the accrued interest?

(iii) What was the quoted price of the bond?

(iv) What was the market quotation of the bond?

Solution

Page 572

(i) *Calculating the full price (purchase price) of the bond*

Step 1: Identifying interest payment dates

Redemption date:	June 11, 2033
Interest dates:	June 11 and December 11 every year
Purchase date:	February 09, 2017
Previous interest date:	December 11, 2016
Next interest date:	June 11, 2017

Solution *continued*

Step 2: Calculating the purchase price on the previous interest payment date

Time from previous interest date to redemption date = 16 years and 6 months

$n = 2 \times 16.5 = 33$

Coupon rate, $b = \frac{j}{m} = \frac{0.065}{2} = 0.0325$ per half-year

Using Formula 13.2(b), $PMT = FV \times b = 5000.00 \times 0.0325 = \$162.50$

Periodic yield rate, $i = \frac{j}{m} = \frac{0.0384}{2} = 0.0192$ per half-year

Using Formula 13.2(a),

$$Purchase\ Price_{December\ 11,\ 2016} = PV_{PMT} + PV_{Redemption\ Value}$$

$$= 162.50\left[\frac{1-(1+0.0192)^{-33}}{0.0192}\right] + 5000.00(1+0.0192)^{-33}$$

$$= \$6614.444548...$$

Step 3: Calculating the Purchase Price on the Purchase Date

$$n = \frac{Number\ of\ days\ from\ previous\ interest\ date\ to\ purchase\ date}{Number\ of\ days\ from\ previous\ interest\ date\ to\ next\ interest\ date}$$

$$= \frac{\text{December 11, 2016 to February 09, 2017}}{\text{December 11, 2016 to June 11, 2017}} = \frac{60}{182}$$

$$Purchase\ Price_{Purchase\ Date} = 6614.444548...(1+0.0192)^{(60/182)}$$

$$= 6656.045222... = \$6656.05$$

Therefore, the purchase price of the bond was \$6656.05.

(ii) *Calculating the accrued interest*

$$Accrued\ Interest = PMT \times \frac{Number\ of\ days\ from\ previous\ interest\ date\ to\ purchase\ date}{Number\ of\ days\ from\ previous\ interest\ date\ to\ next\ interest\ date}$$

$$= 162.50 \times \frac{60}{182} = 53.571428... = \$53.57$$

Therefore, the accrued interest is \$53.57.

(iii) *Calculating the quoted price of the bond*

Rearranging Formula 13.3(a), $Quoted\ Price = Full\ Price - Accrued\ Interest$

$$= 6656.05 - 53.57 = \$6602.48$$

Therefore, the quoted price of the bond was \$6602.48.

(iv) *Calculating the market quotation of the bond*

Rearranging Formula 13.3(b),

$$Market\ Quotation = \frac{Quoted\ Price}{Redemption\ Value} = \frac{6602.48}{5000.00} = 1.320496 = 132.05\%$$

Therefore, the market quotation was 132.05.

Using the Financial Calculator to Solve Bond Problems

The preprogrammed financial calculator contains a bond worksheet that can be used to calculate purchase price and accrued interest, as shown in the following example.

Example 13.3(d) **Using the Bond Worksheet in a Financial Calculator to Solve Example 13.3(c)**

A \$5000 corporation bond with a coupon rate of 6.5% matures on June 11, 2033. An investor desiring a 3.84% compounded semi-annually yield rate purchased the bond on February 9, 2017.

(i) What was the market quotation of the bond?

(ii) What was the quoted price of the bond?

(iii) What is the accrued interest?

(iv) What is the full price (purchase price) of the bond?

Solution

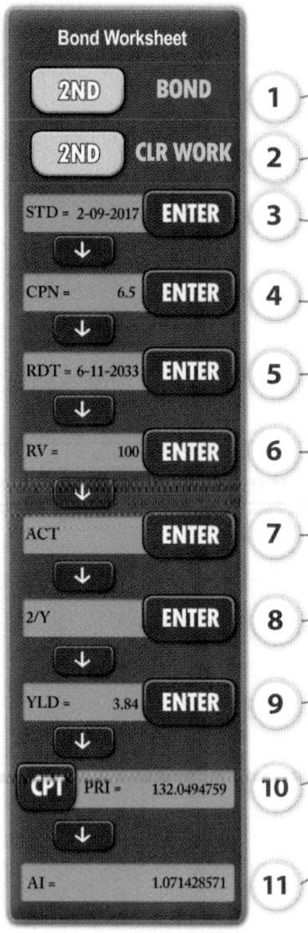

1. Press **2ND** then **BOND** (secondary function of the number **9** key) to access the bond worksheet.
2. Press **2ND** then **CRL WORK** (secondary function of the **CE/C** key) to clear the memory.
3. Input **2.0917** (representing February 09, 2017) as the settlement date. Press **ENTER**.
4. Press the **down** arrow. Input **6.5** as the coupon rate. Press **ENTER.**
5. Press the **down** arrow. Input **6.1133** (representing June 11, 2033) as the redemption date. Press **ENTER.**
6. Press the **down** arrow. Input **100** as the redemption value as it is redeemed at par on maturity. Press **ENTER.**
7. Press the **down** arrow. If necessary, press **2ND** and **SET** until *ACT* is displayed for actual day-count method.
8. Press the **down** arrow. If necessary, press **2ND** and **SET** until *2/Y* which represents two coupon payments per year.
9. Press the **down** arrow. Input **3.84** as the yield rate. Press **ENTER.**
10. Press the **down** arrow. Press **CPT** to compute the market quotation (which does not include the accrued interest).
11. Press the **down** arrow to view the accrued interest.

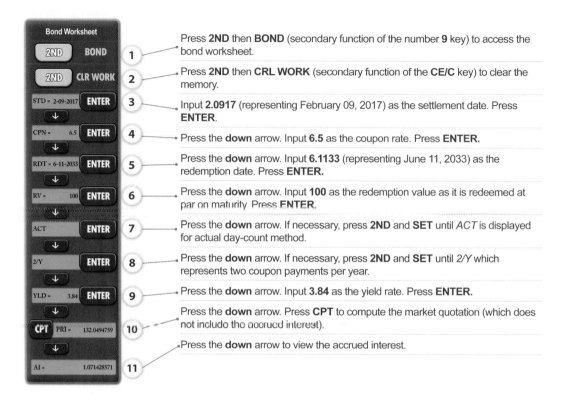

(i) From the calculator, the market quotation was 132.049475... = 132.05.

(ii) The market quotation is provided on a basis of \$100. As the redemption value is \$5000, which is 50 × 100, the quoted price will be the market quotation × 50.

$$\textit{Quoted Price} = 132.049475... \times 50 = 6602.473794... = \$6602.47$$

(iii) $\textit{Accrued Interest} = 1.071428... \times 50 = 53.571428... = \$53.57$

(iv) $\textit{Full Price} = \textit{Quoted Price} + \textit{Accrued Interest}$

$$= 6602.473794... + 53.571428... = 6656.045222... = \$6656.05$$

13.3 | Exercises

Answers to the odd-numbered problems are available at the end of the textbook.

In the following problems, assume that the coupon rates are compounded semi-annually, the coupons are paid every six months, and bonds are redeemed at par (for their face value) on maturity, unless otherwise stated.
Express the answers rounded to two decimal places, wherever applicable.

For Problems 1 and 2, determine the missing values.

1.

	Face Value	Coupon Rate	Yield Rate	Redemption Date	Purchase Date	Purchase Price	Quoted Price
a.	\$5,000.00	5.65%	6.75%	May 20, 2019	June 28, 2004	?	?
b.	\$50,000.00	6.25%	4.55%	April 07, 2017	June 19, 2011	?	?
c.	\$1000.00	4.75%	5.65%	March 26, 2020	April 12, 2014	?	?
d.	\$50,000.00	6.25%	5.15%	April 07, 2017	June 19, 2009	?	?

2.

	Face Value	Coupon Rate	Yield Rate	Redemption Date	Purchase Date	Purchase Price	Quoted Price
a.	$100,000.00	7.15%	4.55%	April 12, 2027	April 29, 2007	?	?
b.	$1000.00	3.55%	6.75%	July 23, 2018	August 12, 2005	?	?
c.	$20,000.00	6.55%	7.85%	March 26, 2020	April 12, 2014	?	?
d.	$5,000.00	4.35%	4.05%	April 07, 2017	June 19, 2009	?	?

3. A $1000 bond with a coupon rate of 5% is purchased ten years before maturity, when the market quotation was 99.4.
   a. What was the purchase price of the bond?
   b. What was the amount of discount or premium on the bond?

4. A $5000 bond with a coupon rate of 6% is purchased six years before maturity, when the market quotation was 102.5.
   a. What was the purchase price of the bond?
   b. What was the amount of discount or premium on the bond?

5. A publicly traded corporation issued a $25,000 bond on January 27, 2004 that is redeemable on January 27, 2024. It had a coupon rate of 5.25% and was purchased on January 27, 2017 when the market quotation was 98.4.
   a. What was the purchase price of the bond?
   b. What was the amount of discount or premium on the bond?

6. A $100,000 bond with a coupon rate of 6.55% was issued on June 18, 1998 and is redeemable on June 18, 2017. It was purchased on June 18, 2015 when the market quotation was 101.2.
   a. What was the purchase price of the bond?
   b. What was the amount of discount or premium on the bond?

7. A $10,000 bond at a coupon rate of 6.5% is redeemable on January 01, 2019. It was purchased on October 17, 2015 at 96.1.
   a. What was the purchase price of the bond?
   b. What was the amount of discount or premium on the bond?

8. A $5000 bond carries a 7% coupon rate and is redeemable on June 01, 2024. It was purchased at 102.15 on March 03, 2017.
   a. What was the purchase price of the bond?
   b. What was the amount of discount or premium on the bond?

9. A $25,000 bond with a coupon rate of 6% is redeemable on July 10, 2018. It was purchased on December 27, 2014 at a market quotation of 103.5.
   a. What was the quoted price of the bond?
   b. What is the accrued interest?
   c. What is the full price (purchase price) of the bond?

10. A $10,000 bond with a coupon rate of 4.55% is redeemable on September 18, 2029. It was purchased on February 12, 2018 at a market quotation of 98.5.
   a. What was the quoted price of the bond?
   b. What is the accrued interest?
   c. What is the full price (purchase price) of the bond?

11. A $100,000 bond paying 4.5% matures on August 18, 2034. The bond was purchased on July 12, 2017 when the yield rate was 3.75% compounded semi-annually.
    a. What is the purchase price of the bond?
    b. What is the accrued interest?
    c. What was the quoted price of the bond?
    d. What was the market quotation of the bond?

12. A $25,000 bond paying 6.25% matures on September 27, 2029. An investor desiring a yield rate of 7.75% compounded semi-annually purchases the bond on January 10, 2017.
    a. What is the purchase price of the bond?
    b. What is the accrued interest?
    c. What was the quoted price of the bond?
    d. What was the market quotation of the bond?

13.4 | Constructing a Bond Schedule

Bond interest payments (coupons) are considered a taxable income for an investor. Bond schedules are created to show how the interest payments are recorded using accepted accounting practices.

When a bond is purchased at par, there are no difficulties in recording the payments as the entire interest is recorded as interest revenue earned.

Amortization of Premium

When a bond is purchased at a premium, the premium amount is not recovered when the bond is redeemed at maturity. On the redemption date, the investor will have a capital loss equal to the amount of premium (the difference between the amount paid for the bond and the amount received on the redemption date). This loss can be applied to the investor's income on the redemption date, which results in a lower tax amount being owed at the time of redemption. Alternatively, an investor can choose to distribute this tax saving (that occurs on the redemption date) over each interest payment period, thereby paying a lower tax amount for each period rather than having a lump-sum tax saving (tax break) on the redemption date. In this way, the book value of the bond is gradually reduced until it reaches the redemption value on the redemption date. This process of a gradual decrease in the book value of the bond is called the *amortization of premium.*

Steps to construct a bond schedule for the amortization of premium

Bonds are recorded on a company's balance sheet at its face value plus or minus any unamortized premium or discount. This is called the book value of the bond and may differ from the market value of the bond.

- Book $\text{Value}_{\textit{Period 0}}$ = Purchase Price of the bond
- Premium to be $\text{Amortized}_{\textit{Period 0}}$ = Purchase Price – Redemption Value
- Interest Received = $FV \times b$
- Interest on $BV = BV_{\textit{Previous Period}} \times i$
- Amortized Premium = Interest Received – Interest on BV
- Book Value = Book $\text{Value}_{\textit{Previous Period}}$ – Amortized Premium
- Premium to be Amortized = Premium to be $\text{Amortized}_{\textit{Previous Period}}$ – Amortized Premium

This continues for each period until the book value is equal to the redemption value of the bond.

At the end of each period:

- Interest received is recorded as cash received.
- Interest on book value is recorded as interest earned.
- Premium on the bonds is amortized.
- Book value of bond is reduced by the amortized premium.

The following example illustrates the construction of an amortization schedule providing details of the period, interest received, interest on book value, amortized premium, premium to be amortized, and the book value.

Example 13.4(a) Constructing a Bond Schedule Illustrating the Amortization of Premium

A $1000 bond with a coupon rate of 10% is redeemable in two years. It was purchased when the yield rate was 8% compounded semi-annually. Construct the bond schedule showing the amortization of premium.

Solution

Page 573

Calculating *Purchase Price*

Set to END mode

2ND CLR TVM

2ND P/Y

P/Y = 2 ENTER

↓ C/Y = 2

2ND QUIT

4 N

8 I/Y

50 PMT

1000 FV

CPT PV

PV= -1036.298952

Coupon rate, $b = \frac{j}{m} = \frac{0.10}{2} = 0.05$ per half-year

Using Formula 13.2 (b), $PMT = FV \times b = 1000.00 \times 0.05 = \$50.00$

Periodic yield rate, $i = \frac{j}{m} = \frac{0.08}{2} = 0.04$ per half-year

$n = 2 \times 2 = 4$

Using Formula 13.2(a), $\textit{Purchase Price} = PV_{PMT} + PV_{\textit{Redemption Value}}$

$$= 50.00\left[\frac{1 - (1 + 0.04)^{-4}}{0.04}\right] + 1000.00(1 + 0.04)^{-4}$$

$$= 181.494761... + 854.804191...$$

$$= 1036.298952... = \$1036.30$$

Amount of Premium = *Purchase Price* – *Redemption Value* = 1036.30 – 1000.00 = $36.30

Constructing a bond schedule for the amortization of premium

Period	Interest Received (*FV* × *b*)	Interest on *BV* (*BV* × *i*)	Amortized Premium	Book Value (*BV*)	Premium to be Amortized
0	-	-	-	$1036.30 (a)	$36.30 (b)
1	$50.00 (c)	$41.45 (d)	$8.55 (e)	1027.75 (f)	27.75 (g)
2	50.00	41.11	8.89	1018.86	18.86
3	50.00	40.75	9.25	1009.61	9.61
4	50.00	40.38	9.62	$999.99 *	-$0.01*
Total	$200.00	$163.69	$36.31	-	-

* *Due to the rounding of amounts in each step, there is a minor difference of $0.01.*

(a) $\text{Book Value}_0 = \text{Purchase Price} = \$1036.30$

(b) $\text{Premium to be Amortized}_0 = \text{Purchase Price} - \text{Redemption Value} = 1036.30 - 1000.00 = \$36.30$

(c) $\text{Interest Received}_1 = FV \times b = 1000.00 \times 0.05 = \$50.00$

(d) $\text{Interest on } BV_1 = BV_0 \times i = 1036.30 \times 0.04 = \$41.45$

(e) $\text{Amortized Premium}_1 = \text{Interest Received}_1 - \text{Interest on } BV_1 = 50.00 - 41.45 = \$8.55$

(f) $\text{Book Value}_1 = \text{Book Value}_0 - \text{Amortized Premium}_1 = 1036.30 - 8.55 = \$1027.75$

Solution *continued*

(g) $\text{Premium to be Amortized}_1 = \text{Premium to be Amortized}_0 - \text{Amortized Premium}_1$

$= 36.30 - 8.55 = \$27.75$

***Note:** As can be seen in the schedule, the investor will end up paying taxes only on $163.69 (interest on the book value) over the life of the bond instead of $200.00 (actual amount of interest payment received).*

Accumulation of Discount

When a bond is purchased at a discount, the investor will have a capital gain equal to the amount of discount (the difference between the amount paid for the bond and the amount received on the redemption date) on the redemption date. This gain can be applied to the investor's income on the redemption date, which results in a higher tax amount being owed at the time of redemption. Alternatively, an investor can choose to distribute this tax expense (that occurs on the redemption date) over each interest payment period, thereby paying a higher tax amount for each period rather than having a lump-sum tax expense on the redemption date. In this way, the book value of the bond is gradually increased until it reaches the redemption value on the redemption date. This process of a gradual increase in the book value of the bond is called the *accumulation of discount.*

Steps to construct a bond schedule for the accumulation of discount

- $\text{Book Value}_{\textit{Period 0}} = \text{Purchase Price of the bond}$
- $\text{Discount to be Accumulated}_{\textit{Period 0}} = \text{Redemption Value} - \text{Purchase Price}$
- $\text{Interest Received} = FV \times b$
- $\text{Interest on } BV = BV_{\textit{Previous Period}} \times i$
- $\text{Accumulated Discount} = \text{Interest on } BV - \text{Interest Received}$
- $\text{Book Value} = \text{Book Value}_{\textit{Previous Period}} + \text{Accumulated Discount}$
- $\text{Discount to be Accumulated} = \text{Discount to be Accumulated}_{\textit{Previous Period}} - \text{Accumulated Discount}$

This continues for each period until the book value is equal to the redemption value of the bond.

At the end of each period:

- Interest received is recorded as cash received.
- Interest on book value is recorded as interest earned.
- Discount on the bond is accumulated.
- Book value of the bond is increased by the accumulated discount.

The following example illustrates the construction of an amortization schedule providing details of the period, interest received, interest on book value, accumulated discount, discount to be accumulated, and the book value.

Example 13.4(b) **Constructing a Bond Schedule Illustrating the Accumulation of Discount**

A $1000 bond carries an 8% coupon rate and is redeemable in two years. It was purchased when the yield-to-maturity was 10% compounded semi-annually. Construct the bond schedule showing the accumulation of discount.

Page 573

Solution

Coupon rate, $b = \frac{j}{m} = \frac{0.08}{2} = 0.04$ per half-year

Using Formula 13.2 (b), $PMT = FV \times b = 1000.00 \times 0.04 = \$40.00$

Periodic yield rate, $i = \frac{j}{m} = \frac{0.10}{2} = 0.05$ per half-year

$n = 2 \times 2 = 4$

Using Formula 13.2(a),

$$\text{Purchase Price} = PV_{PMT} + PV_{Redemption\ Value}$$

$$= 40.00\left[\frac{1-(1+0.05)^{-4}}{0.05}\right] + 1000.00(1+0.05)^{-4}$$

$$= 141.838020... + 822.702474...$$

$$= 964.540495... = \$964.54$$

Amount of Discount = Redemption Value – Purchase Price = 1000.00 – 964.54 = $35.46

Constructing the bond schedule for the accumulation of discount

Period	Interest Received ($FV \times b$)	Interest on *BV* ($BV \times i$)	Accumulated Discount	Book Value (*BV*)	Discount to be Accumulated
0	-	-	-	$964.54 (a)	$35.46 (b)
1	$40.00 (c)	$48.23 (d)	$8.23 (e)	972.77 (f)	27.23 (g)
2	40.00	48.64	8.64	981.41	18.59
3	40.00	49.07	9.07	990.48	9.52
4	40.00	49.52	9.52	1000.00	0.00
Total	$160.00	$195.46	$35.46	-	-

(a) Book Value_0 = Purchase Price = $964.54

(b) Discount to be Accumulated_0 = Redemption Value – Purchase Price = 1000.00 – 964.54 = $35.46

(c) Interest Received_1 = $FV \times b$ = 1000.00 × 0.04 = $40.00

(d) Interest on $BV_1 = BV_0 \times i$ = 964.54 × 0.05 = $48.23

(e) Accumulated Discount_1 = Interest on BV_1 – Interest Received_1 = 48.23 – 40.00 = $8.23

(f) Book Value_1 = Book Value_0 + Accumulated Discount_1 = 964.54 + 8.23 = $972.77

(g) Discount to be Accumulated_1 = Discount to be Accumulated_0 – Accumulated Discount_1

= 35.46 – 8.23 = $27.23

Note: *As can be seen in the schedule, the investor will end up paying taxes on $195.46 (interest on the book value) over the life of the bond instead of $160.00 (actual amount of interest payment received).*

13.4 | Exercises

Answers to the odd-numbered problems are available at the end of the textbook.

In the following problems, assume that the coupon rates are compounded semi-annually, the coupons are paid every six months, and bonds are redeemed at par (for their face value) on maturity, unless otherwise stated.
Express the answers rounded to two decimal places, wherever applicable.

1. A $1000 bond has a coupon rate of 4% and is redeemable in three years. It was purchased when the yield rate was 3% compounded semi-annually. Construct the bond schedule showing the amortization of the premium.

2. A corporation purchased a $50,000 bond at a coupon rate of 7.5% and redeemable in three years. If the yield rate at the time of purchase was 7% compounded semi-annually, construct the bond schedule showing the amortization of the premium.

3. A $5000 bond with a coupon rate of 6.25% and redeemable in two years was purchased when the yield rate was 7.75% compounded semi-annually. Construct the bond schedule showing the accumulation of discount.

4. A $20,000, 4.85% government bond that was due to mature in two years was purchased when the yield rate was 5.65% compounded semi-annually. Construct the bond schedule showing the accumulation of discount.

5. Mia purchased a $50,000 bond with a coupon rate of 6.25% and six years to maturity. She sold the bond, after holding it for two years when the yield rate was 5.35% compounded semi-annually. Construct the bond schedule showing the amortization of the premium.

6. Liam purchased a $25,000 bond with a coupon rate of 7.15% and eight years to maturity. He sold the bond, after holding it for six years, when the yield rate was 6.25% compounded semi-annually. Construct the bond schedule showing the amortization of the premium.

7. A $10,000 bond with a coupon rate of 3.5% is redeemable in ten years. It was purchased three years before maturity when the yield rate was 4.5% compounded quarterly. Construct the bond schedule showing the accumulation of discount.

8. Sabena purchased a $5000, 5.15% bond when it had two years to maturity and the yield rate was 6.50% compounded monthly. Construct the bond schedule showing the accumulation of discount.

13.5 | Sinking Funds

A **sinking fund** *is an interest-earning fund that is established to make periodic deposits for the purpose of retiring debts.*

A sinking fund is an interest earning fund that is set up by a corporation or government to periodically deposit money into, so that the accumulated funds will be available at a future date to repay the principal of a large debt at the time of its maturity. These funds are generally set up to assure investors (who have purchased bonds or debentures from the corporation or government) that provisions have been made to ensure repayment of their principal amount at the time of maturity of their bonds or debentures.

For example, if a business receives $1 million by issuing ten-year bonds to the public, on the date of maturity of the bonds, it would have to repay the entire principal to the holders of the bonds.

Sinking funds can also be used to prematurely clear a portion of the debt.

As the principal amount is very large, the business may establish a sinking fund to deposit money into periodically, until it accumulates $1 million by the maturity date of the bonds. This amount can then be used to repay the principal amount to the bond holders.

Sinking Fund Calculations and Constructing a Sinking Fund Schedule

As a sinking fund is generally a series of equal deposits made at regular intervals for a fixed period of time, it is treated as an annuity. Payments into the fund can be made at the end of the period (ordinary annuity) or at the beginning of the period (annuity due).

A sinking fund schedule provides details of the payment number, periodic payment into the fund, interest earned during the period, increase in the fund, the fund balance, and the book value of the fund.

Steps to construct a sinking fund schedule

- $\text{Fund Balance}_{\text{Period } 0} = \$0.00$
- $\text{Book Value}_{\text{Period } 0} = \text{Principal}$
- $\text{Interest Earned} = \text{Fund Balance}_{\text{Previous Period}} \times i$
- $\text{Increase in the Fund} = PMT + \text{Interest Earned}$
- $\text{Fund Balance} = \text{Fund Balance}_{\text{Previous Period}} + \text{Increase in the Fund}$
- $\text{Book Value} = \text{Principal} - \text{Fund Balance}$

Computing the totals

- Total Increase in the Fund = Fund Balance$_{Final\ Period}$
- Total Payment = Sum of the Payments = $n \times PMT$
- Total Interest Earned = Total Increase in the Fund – Total Payment

Example 13.5(a) **Ordinary Simple Annuity Sinking Fund Calculations and Constructing a Sinking Fund Schedule**

Acapac Industries established a sinking fund in order to accumulate at least $10,000 by depositing equal amounts of money at the end of every six months for two years. If the fund was earning interest at 4% compounded semi-annually, calculate the following and construct a sinking fund schedule to illustrate details of the fund:

(i) Size of the periodic sinking fund deposit.

(ii) Sinking fund balance at the end of the 2nd payment period.

(iii) Interest earned in the 3rd payment period.

(iv) Amount by which the sinking fund increased in the 3rd payment period.

Page 574

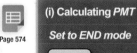

(i) Calculating *PMT*

Set to END mode

2ND CLR TVM

2ND P/Y

P/Y = 2 ENTER

↓ C/Y = 2

2ND QUIT

4 N

4 I/Y

0 PV

10,000 FV

CPT PMT

PMT= -2426.237527

(i) *Calculating the size of the periodic sinking fund deposit*

This sinking fund is an ordinary simple annuity.

$FV = \$10{,}000.00, \quad t = 2 \text{ years}, \quad i = \dfrac{j}{m} = \dfrac{0.04}{2} = 0.02$

n = 2 deposits per year × 2 years = 4 semi-annual deposits

Using Formula 10.2(a),
$$FV = PMT\left[\frac{(1+i)^n - 1}{i}\right]$$

$$10{,}000.00 = PMT\left[\frac{(1+0.02)^4 - 1}{0.02}\right] = PMT[4.121608...]$$

$$PMT = 2426.237527... = \$2426.24$$

Therefore, the periodic sinking fund deposit was $2426.24.

(ii) *Calculating the sinking fund balance at the end of the 2nd payment period*

The sinking fund balance at the end of any given period is the future value of the periodic deposits made until the end of that period.

At the end of the 2nd payment period, $n = 2$. Let the future value at the end of the 2nd period be FV_2.

Using Formula 10.2(a),
$$FV = PMT\left[\frac{(1+i)^n - 1}{i}\right]$$

$$FV_2 = 2426.24\left[\frac{(1+0.02)^2 - 1}{0.02}\right] = 2426.24\ [2.02]$$

$$= 4901.0048 = \$4901.00$$

(ii) Calculating FV_2

2 N

2426.24 +/- PMT

CPT FV

FV= 4901.0048

Therefore, the sinking fund balance at the end of the 2nd payment period was $4901.00.

(iii) *Calculating the interest earned in the 3rd payment period*

Interest that is earned in any period is on the amount that is available in the fund at the beginning of that period, which is the same as the amount that is available at the end of the previous period.

To calculate the interest earned in the 3rd period, we need to determine the fund balance at the end of the 2nd period.

From (ii), we know that the fund balance at the end of the 2nd period = FV_2 = $4901.00

The interest on this amount is: $i \times FV_2 = 0.02 \times 4901.00 = \$98.02$

Therefore, $98.02 was the interest earned by the fund in the 3rd payment period.

Solution *continued*

(iv) *Calculating the amount by which the sinking fund increased in the 3rd payment period*

The amount by which the sinking fund increased in a period is the interest earned during that period plus the deposit made in that period.

$$\left(\begin{array}{c}\textit{Amount by which the Sinking Fund}\\ \textit{Increased in the } 3^{rd} \textit{ Period}\end{array}\right) = \left(\begin{array}{c}\textit{Interest Earned}\\ \textit{in the } 3^{rd} \textit{ Period}\end{array}\right) + PMT$$

$$= 98.02 + 2426.24 = \$2524.26$$

Therefore, the amount by which the sinking fund increased in the 3rd payment period is $2524.26.

Constructing the sinking fund schedule

The Fund Balance is slightly more than the principal since the *PMT* is rounded up to the next cent, to ensure that the sinking fund accumulated *at least* $10,000.

Payment Period	Payment (*PMT*)	Interest Earned	Increase in the Fund	Fund Balance	Book Value
0	-	-	-	$0.00	$10,000.00 (a)
1	$2426.24	$0.00 (b)	$2426.24 (c)	2426.24 (d)	7573.76 (e)
2	2426.24	48.52	2474.76	4901.00	5099.00
3	2426.24	98.02	2524.26	7425.26	2574.74
4	2426.24	148.51	2574.75	$10,000.01	-$0.01
Total	$9704.96	$295.05	$10,000.01		

(a) $\text{Book Value}_0 = \text{Principal} = \$10{,}000.00$

(b) $\text{Interest Earned}_1 = \text{Fund Balance}_0 \times i = 0.00 \times 0.02 = \$0.00$

(c) $\text{Increase in the Fund}_1 = PMT + \text{Interest Earned}_1 = 2426.24 + 0.00 = \$2426.24$

(d) $\text{Fund Balance}_1 = \text{Fund Balance}_0 + \text{Increase in the Fund}_1 = 0.00 + 2426.24 = \$2426.24$

(e) $\text{Book Value}_1 = \text{Principal} - \text{Fund Balance}_1 = 10{,}000.00 - 2426.24 = \$7573.76$

Example 13.5(b) **Simple Annuity Due Sinking Fund Calculations and Constructing a Sinking Fund Schedule**

Refer to Example 13.5(a) and answer all parts of the problem assuming that Acapac Industries made deposits at the beginning of every six months instead of at the end of each period.

Solution

Page 574

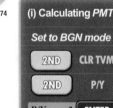

(i) Calculating *PMT*

Set to BGN mode

2ND CLR TVM

2ND P/Y

P/Y = 2 ENTER

↓ C/Y = 2

2ND QUIT

4 N

4 I/Y

0 PV

10,000 FV

CPT PMT

PMT= -2378.664242

(i) *Calculating the size of the periodic sinking fund deposit*

This sinking fund is a simple annuity due.

$FV = \$10{,}000.00,\qquad t = 2 \text{ years},\qquad i = \frac{j}{m} = \frac{0.04}{2} = 0.02$

$n = 2$ deposits per year $\times$ 2 years = 4 semi-annual deposits

Using Formula 10.4(a),
$$FV_{Due} = PMT\left[\frac{(1+i)^n - 1}{i}\right](1+i)$$

$$10{,}000.00 = PMT\left[\frac{(1+0.02)^4 - 1}{0.02}\right](1+0.02)$$

$$10{,}000.00 = PMT\,[4.121608...](1.02)$$

$$PMT = 2378.664242... = \$2378.67$$

We round *PMT* up to the next cent to ensure that the sinking fund accumulates *at least* $10,000.

Therefore, the periodic sinking fund deposit was $2378.67.

Solution
continued

(ii) *Calculating the sinking fund balance at the end of the 2nd payment period*

The sinking fund balance at the end of any given period is the future value of the periodic deposits made until the end of that period.

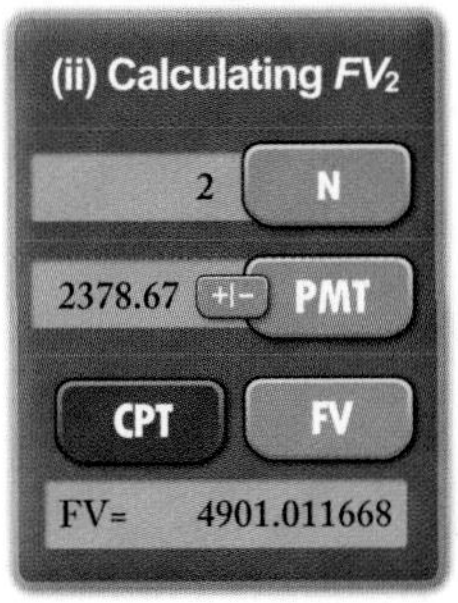

At the end of the 2nd payment period, $n = 2$. Let the future value at the end of the 2nd period be FV_2.

Using Formula 10.4(a),
$$FV = PMT\left[\frac{(1+i)^n - 1}{i}\right](1+i)$$

$$FV_2 = 2378.67\left[\frac{(1+0.02)^2 - 1}{0.02}\right](1+0.02) = 2378.67[2.02](1.02)$$

$$= 4901.011668 = \$4901.01$$

Therefore, the sinking fund balance at the end of the 2nd payment period was \$4901.01.

(iii) *Calculating the interest earned in the 3rd payment period*

The interest for a period is not only calculated on the fund balance of the previous period, but also on the periodic deposit, as the deposit is made at the beginning of the period.

Therefore, $$\left(\begin{array}{c}\textit{Interest Earned for the}\\ \textit{3rd Payment Period}\end{array}\right) = i \times \left(\begin{array}{c}\textit{2nd Period}\\ \textit{Fund Balance}\end{array} + PMT\right)$$

From (ii), we know that the fund balance at the end of the 2nd period = \$4901.01

$$\left(\begin{array}{c}\textit{Interest Earned for the}\\ \textit{3rd Payment Period}\end{array}\right) = 0.02(4901.01 + 2378.67) = 145.5936 = \$145.59$$

Therefore, \$145.59 is the interest earned by the fund in the 3rd payment period.

(iv) *Calculating the amount by which the sinking fund increased in the 3rd payment period*

The amount by which the sinking fund increased in a period is the interest earned during that period plus the deposit made in that period.

$$\left(\begin{array}{c}\textit{Amount by which the sinking fund}\\ \textit{increased in the 3rd period}\end{array}\right) = \left(\begin{array}{c}\textit{Interest Earned for the}\\ \textit{3rd Payment Period}\end{array}\right) + PMT$$

$$= 145.59 + 2378.67 = \$2524.26$$

Therefore, the amount by which the sinking fund increased in the 3rd payment period was \$2524.26.

Constructing the sinking fund schedule

Payment Period	Payment (*PMT*)	Interest Earned	Increase in the Fund	Fund Balance	Book Value
0	-	-	-	\$0.00	\$10,000.00 (a)
1	\$2378.67	\$47.57 (b)	\$2426.24 (c)	2426.24 (d)	7573.76 (e)
2	2378.67	96.10	2474.77	4901.01	5098.99
3	2378.67	145.59	2524.26	7425.27	2574.73
4	2378.67	196.08	2574.75	\$10,000.02	-\$0.02
Total	\$9514.68	\$485.34	\$10,000.02		

PMT is made at the beginning of the interval.

Interest Earned, Increase in the Fund, and Fund Balance are at the end of the interval.

In annuity due sinking funds, as payments are made at the beginning of the period, Interest Earned is calculated not only on the previous fund balance but also on the payment that is deposited into the fund.

(a) Book Value_0 = Principal = \$10,000.00

(b) Interest Earned_1 = (Fund Balance_0 + PMT) × i = (0.00 + 2378.67) × 0.02 = \$47.57

(c) Increase in the Fund_1 = PMT + Interest Earned_1 = 2378.67 + 47.57 = \$2426.24

(d) Fund Balance_1 = Fund Balance_0 + Increase in the Fund_1 = 0.00 + 2426.24 = \$2426.24

(e) Book Value_1 = Principal – Fund Balance_1 = 10,000.00 – 2426.24 = \$7573.76

Calculating the Periodic Cost and Constructing a Partial Sinking Fund Schedule

When a company issues a bond and sets up a sinking fund, it makes the following two periodic payments until the maturity of the bond:

- Periodic interest payments to the bond holder.
- Periodic deposits made into the sinking fund.

The **periodic cost** of this debt for any period is the sum of the above two payments for that period.

Example 13.5(c) **Calculating the Periodic Cost, Book Value of the Debt, and Constructing a Partial Sinking Fund Schedule**

A social networking company wanted to raise \$100,000 and issued twenty, \$5000 bonds paying a 10% coupon rate payable semi-annually for five years. It set up a sinking fund to repay the debt at the end of five years and made deposits at the end of every six months into the fund. The sinking fund was earning 6.5% compounded semi-annually.

(i) Calculate the periodic cost of the debt.

(ii) Calculate the book value of the debt after three years.

(iii) Construct a partial sinking fund schedule showing details of the first two and last two payments and the totals of the schedule.

Solution

Page 575

(i) *Calculate the periodic cost of the debt*

$$\left(\begin{array}{c}\textit{Periodic Cost}\\ \textit{of the Debt}\end{array}\right) = \left(\begin{array}{c}\textit{Periodic Interest}\\ \textit{Payment of the Bond}\end{array}\right) + \left(\begin{array}{c}\textit{Periodic Deposit into}\\ \textit{the Sinking Fund}\end{array}\right)$$

$$= PMT_{\textit{Interest on Bond}} + PMT_{\textit{Sinking Fund}}$$

Calculating periodic interest payment of the bond

$$FV = \$100{,}000.00, \quad b = \frac{j}{m} = \frac{0.10}{2} = 0.05 \text{ per half-year}$$

Using Formula 13.2(b), $PMT_{\textit{Interest on Bond}} = FV \times b = 100{,}000.00 \times 0.05 = \$5000.00$

Calculating sinking fund periodic deposit

This sinking fund is an ordinary simple annuity.

$FV = \$100{,}000.00, \quad t = 5$ years

$n = 2$ deposits per year $\times$ 5 years $= 10$ semi-annual deposits

$$i = \frac{j}{m} = \frac{0.065}{2} = 0.0325 \text{ per half-year}$$

Using Formula 10.2(a), $FV = PMT\left[\frac{(1+i)^n - 1}{i}\right]$

$$100{,}000.00 = PMT\left[\frac{(1+0.0325)^{10} - 1}{0.0325}\right] = PMT\,[11.596747...]$$

$$PMT_{\textit{Sinking Fund}} = 8623.107239... = \$8623.11$$

$$\left(\begin{array}{c}\textit{Periodic Cost}\\ \textit{of the Debt}\end{array}\right) = PMT_{\textit{Interest on Bond}} + PMT_{\textit{Sinking Fund}}$$

$$= 5000.00 + 8623.11 = \$13{,}623.11$$

Therefore, the periodic cost of the debt was \$13,623.11.

Calculating $PMT_{\textit{Sinking Fund}}$

Set to END mode

2ND CLR TVM

2ND P/Y

P/Y = 2 ENTER

↓ C/Y = 2

2ND QUIT

10 N

6.5 I/Y

0 PV

100,000 FV

CPT PMT

PMT = -8623.107239

Solution *continued*

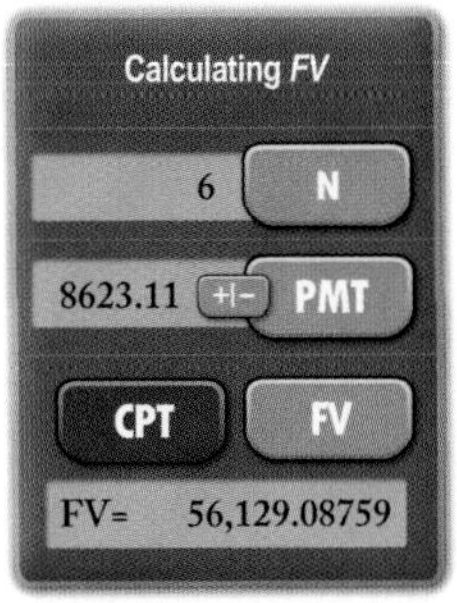

(ii) *Calculate the book value of the debt after three years*

$$\left(\begin{array}{c}\textit{Book Value of the}\\ \textit{Debt after 3 years}\end{array}\right) = \left(\begin{array}{c}\textit{Principal Amount}\\ \textit{of the Debt}\end{array}\right) - \left(\begin{array}{c}\textit{Sinking Fund Balance at}\\ \textit{the End of 3 years}\end{array}\right)$$

The sinking fund balance at the end of 3 years is the future value of the sinking fund at the end of 3 years.

$t = 3$ years, $n = 2$ deposits per year $\times$ 3 years = 6 semi-annual deposits, $i = 0.0325$

Using Formula 10.2(a), $FV = PMT\left[\frac{(1+i)^n - 1}{i}\right] = 8623.11\left[\frac{(1+0.0325)^6 - 1}{0.0325}\right]$

$= 56{,}129.08759... = \$56{,}129.09$

$$\left(\begin{array}{c}\textit{Book Value of the}\\ \textit{Debt after 3 years}\end{array}\right) = 100{,}000.00 - 56{,}129.09 = \$43{,}870.91$$

Therefore, the book value of the debt after 3 years was $43,870.91.

(iii) *Constructing the partial sinking fund schedule*

Payment Period	Payment (PMT)	Interest Earned	Increase in the Fund	Fund Balance	Book Value
0	-	-	-	$0.00	$100,000.00
1	$8623.11	$0.00	$8623.11	8623.11	91,376.89
2	8623.11	280.25	8903.36	17,526.47	82,473.53
-	-	-	-	-	-
8	-	-	-	77,363.24*	22,636.76
9	8623.11	2514.31	11,137.42	88,500.66	11,499.34
10	8623.11	2876.27	11,499.38	$100,000.04	-$0.04
Total	$86,231.10	$13,768.94	$100,000.04		

*$\textit{Fund balance}_8 = \textit{Future Value}_{\textit{8 Payments}}$

Using Formula 10.2(a),

$FV = PMT\left[\frac{(1+i)^n - 1}{i}\right] = 8623.11\left[\frac{(1+0.0325)^8 - 1}{0.0325}\right]$

$= 77{,}363.23570... = \$77{,}363.24$

13.5 | Exercises

Answers to the odd-numbered problems are available at the end of the textbook.

In the following problems, round the sinking fund payments ***up to the next cent****, to ensure the sinking fund accumulates to at least the principal. Express the answers rounded to two decimal places, wherever applicable.*

1. A $10,000 bond was cleared in four years by setting up a sinking fund that was earning 5.5% compounded semi-annually. If deposits were made to the fund at the end of every six months, calculate the size of the periodic payments deposited.

2. Rasheed Furnishings issued bonds worth $500,000 to expand its factory. It established a sinking fund to retire this debt in three years and made deposits into it at the end of every six months. If the fund was earning 7% compounded semi-annually, calculate the size of the periodic payment deposited into the fund.

3. For Problem 1, construct a sinking fund schedule illustrating the details of the fund for four years.

4. For Problem 2, construct a sinking fund schedule illustrating the details of the fund for three years.

5. Victoria Appliances sold bonds for $500,000 that were redeemable in five years. It established a sinking fund that was earning 8% compounded semi-annually to pay back the principal of the bonds on maturity. Deposits were being made to the fund at the end of every six months.
   a. Calculate the size of the periodic sinking fund deposit.
   b. Calculate the sinking fund balance at the end of the 6th payment period.
   c. Calculate the interest earned in the 7th payment period.
   d. Calculate the amount by which the sinking fund increased in the 7th payment period.
   e. Construct a partial sinking fund schedule to illustrate details of the last two payments.

6. A company issued bonds for $850,000 and established a sinking fund to retire the debt in 15 years. It made deposits at the end of every 6 months into the fund and the fund was earning 3.55% compounded semi-annually.
   a. Calculate the size of the periodic sinking fund deposit.
   b. Calculate the sinking fund balance at the end of the 11th payment period.
   c. Calculate the interest earned in the 12th payment period.
   d. Calculate the amount by which the sinking fund increased in the 12th payment period.
   e. Construct a partial sinking fund schedule to illustrate details of the last two payments.

7. A company sold $100,000 bonds and set up a sinking fund that was earning 8% compounded semi-annually to retire the bonds in four years. If it made equal deposits into the fund at the beginning of every six months, calculate the size of the periodic payments deposited.

8. Williams Software borrowed $1,250,000 through a bond issued to purchase new servers. It established a sinking fund to retire this debt in three years and made deposits into it at the beginning of every six months. The fund earned 9.5% compounded semi-annually during the period. Calculate the size of the periodic payments deposited into the fund.

9. In Problem 7, construct a sinking fund schedule illustrating the details of the fund.

10. In Problem 8, construct a sinking fund schedule illustrating the details of the fund.

11. A bank in Toronto issued bonds for $750,000 that were redeemable in ten years. It established a sinking fund that was earning 3.5% compounded semi-annually to retire this debt on maturity and made equal deposits at the beginning of every six months into the fund.
   a. Calculate the size of the periodic deposits.
   b. Calculate the fund balance at the end of the 19th payment period.
   c. Calculate the interest earned in the 20th payment period.
   d. Calculate the amount by which the sinking fund increased in the 20th payment period .
   e. Construct a partial sinking fund schedule to illustrate details of the first two payments.

12. A company borrowed $280,000 and set up a sinking fund to retire the debt in six years. It made equal deposits at the beginning of every six months into the fund and the fund was earning 8.55% compounded semi-annually.
   a. Calculate the size of the deposits made into the fund.
   b. Calculate the sinking fund balance at the end of the 4th payment period.
   c. Calculate the interest earned in the 5th payment period.
   d. Calculate the amount by which the sinking fund increased in the 5th payment period.
   e. Construct a partial sinking fund schedule to illustrate details of the first two payments.

13. To raise $5,000,000 to expand into new markets, a very successful laptop manufacturer issued bonds in the market with a coupon rate of 7%, paying interest semi-annually, and redeemable in 20 years. It established a sinking fund to retire this debt on maturity and made equal deposits into the fund at the end of every 6 months. If the fund was earning 4% compounded semi-annually, calculate the periodic cost of the debt and the book value of the debt after 10 years.

14. Wynter Tires Inc. issued $300,000 worth of 5% bonds to purchase new equipment for its showroom. It planned to retire this debt in 10 years on maturity by setting up a sinking fund and making equal deposits into it at the end of every six months. If the fund was earning 4% compounded semi-annually, calculate the periodic cost of the debt and the book value of the debt after five years.

15. For Problem 13, construct a partial amortization schedule illustrating the first three payments, last three payments, and totals of the schedule.

16. For Problem 14, construct a partial amortization schedule illustrating the first two payments, last two payments, and totals of the schedule.

17. $100,000 bonds were issued at a coupon rate of 5% payable semi-annually and redeemable in three years. To retire these bonds, a sinking fund was established, where equal deposits were made at the beginning of every six months. The fund was earning 4.5% compounded semi-annually. What was the periodic cost of the debt and the book value of the debt after two years?

18. Demarco Electronics took a loan of $345,500 from a bank to purchase testing equipment to improve the quality of its electric meters. It set up a sinking fund to retire the debt in four years and made equal payments at the beginning of every six months to this fund. If the loan was received at 6% compounded semi-annually and the sinking fund was earning 5% compounded semi-annually, calculate the periodic cost of the debt and the book value of the debt in three years.

19. For Problem 17, construct a sinking fund schedule illustrating details.

20. For Problem 18, construct a sinking fund schedule illustrating details.

13 | Review Exercises

Answers to the odd-numbered problems are available at the end of the textbook.

In the following problems, assume that the coupon rates are compounded semi-annually, the coupons are paid every six months, and bonds are redeemed at par (for their face value) on maturity, unless otherwise stated.
Express the answers rounded to two decimal places, wherever applicable.

1. Edgar purchased a $5000 bond that had a coupon rate of 5.5% payable semi-annually and was redeemable in seven years. What was his purchase price for the bond if the yield-to-maturity at the time of purchase was 6.25% compounded semi-annually? What was the discount or premium on the bond?

2. A company invested $150,000 in bonds that were issued by another company. The bonds were paying a coupon rate of 11% and were redeemable in ten years. Five years after purchasing the bonds, it needed money urgently so it sold them in the market when the yield rate was 9.5% compounded semi-annually. How much did the company sell the bonds for and what was the discount or premium on the bonds at the time of sale?

3. What was the purchase price, and the discount or premium, on a $1000 bond with a coupon rate of 8.5% payable semi-annually, if the yield rate at the time of issue was 8% compounded quarterly and the bond was redeemable in five years?

4. Heather purchased a $10,000 bond that had 4% coupons and ten years to maturity. If the yield rate at the time of purchase was 5% compounded monthly, calculate the purchase price of the bond and the discount or premium at the time of purchase.

5. Anna and her husband invested their savings of $50,000 in bonds that were paying a 10% coupon rate and were redeemable in 10 years. The yield rate at the time of their purchase was 9% compounded semi-annually. They held the bonds for four years and sold them when the yield rate was 10% compounded semi-annually. Calculate their gain or loss on this investment.

6. The Province of Ontario issued $5000 bonds with a 9% coupon rate. An investor purchased ten of these bonds when the yield rate was 8.5% compounded semi-annually and there were six years left to maturity. However, after four years, the investor sold all the bonds in the market when the yield rate was 7% compounded semi-annually. How much did the investor gain or lose on this investment?

7. A $25,000 bond paying a 12.5% coupon rate was redeemable on August 01, 2019. What was its purchase price, and its premium or discount, on October 18, 2015 when the yield rate was 8% compounded semi-annually?

8. Calculate the discount or premium on a $5000 bond with a 4% coupon rate if it was redeemable on December 31, 2020 and was purchased on February 23, 2018 when the yield rate was 5% compounded semi-annually.

9. A $5000 bond at 9% coupon rate was redeemable on June 01, 2016. It was purchased on September 27, 2014 when the quote was 104.7. Calculate the purchase price and the discount or premium on the purchase of the bonds.

10. Simon purchased a $20,000 bond at a coupon rate of 10.5% payable semi-annually that was redeemable on August 01, 2020. If he purchased it at 97.5 on April 15, 2015, calculate the purchase price of the bond.

11. Sarah purchased a $1000 bond that had a coupon rate of 6.5% payable semi-annually and was redeemable in four years. If the yield rate at the time of purchase was 5.5% compounded semi-annually, construct a bond schedule showing the amortization of the premium.

12. The Ministry of Education raised money to build a new high school by issuing $20,000 bonds at a coupon rate of 8% payable semi-annually. Three years before maturity, the bonds were purchased at 98.5. Construct the bond schedule showing the accumulation of discount.

13. A $5000, 9.5% bond was purchased at 98.2, five years before maturity. Calculate the yield rate at the time of purchase of the bond.

14. What is the yield rate on a $10,000, ten-year, 7.5% bond that was purchased at 101.5?

For Problems 15 to 18, round the sinking fund payments ***up to the next cent****, to ensure the sinking fund accumulates to at least the principal.*

15. Sigmond Inc. issued bonds for $100,000 that were redeemable in four years. It established a sinking fund that was earning 12% compounded semi-annually to repay the principal of the bonds on maturity. Deposits were being made to the fund at the end of every six months.
    a. Calculate the size of the periodic sinking fund deposit.
    b. Calculate the sinking fund balance at the end of the 5th payment period.
    c. Calculate the interest earned in the 6th payment period.
    d. Calculate the amount by which the sinking fund increased in the 6th payment period.
    e. Construct a sinking fund schedule to illustrate details of the fund.

16. A company borrowed $680,000 and set up a sinking fund to retire the debt in three years. It made deposits at the end of every six months into the fund and the fund was earning 8.5% compounded semi-annually.
    a. Calculate the size of the periodic sinking fund deposit.
    b. Calculate the sinking fund balance at the end of the 3rd payment period.
    c. Calculate the interest earned in the 4th payment period.
    d. Calculate the amount by which the sinking fund increased in the 4th payment period.
    e. Construct a sinking fund schedule to illustrate details of the fund.

17. Woldridge Brothers Inc. issued $2,000,000 bonds in the market at a coupon rate of 12% payable semi-annually and redeemable in 20 years. It established a sinking fund to retire the debt on maturity and made equal deposits into the fund every six months. If the fund was earning 10.5% compounded semi-annually, calculate the periodic cost of the debt and the book value of the debt at the end of 15 years.

18. Agatha Investments, a leading investment banking firm in Toronto, issued bonds for $250,000 at a coupon rate of 9.5% payable semi-annually to expand its operations. It set up a sinking fund to retire this debt in ten years on maturity by making equal deposits into it at the beginning of every six months. If the fund was earning 8% compounded semi-annually, calculate the periodic cost of the debt and the book value of the debt at the end of seven years.

13 | Self-Test Exercises

Answers to all the problems are available at the end of the textbook.

In the following problems, assume that the coupon rates are compounded semi-annually, the coupons are paid every six months, and bonds are redeemed at par (for their face value) on maturity, unless otherwise stated.
Express the answers rounded to two decimal places, wherever applicable.

1. Calculate the discount or premium on a $5000 bond at a coupon rate of 6% payable semi-annually if the yield rate at the time of purchase was 7% compounded semi-annually and the bond was redeemable in ten years.

2. Sally purchased a $10,000 bond at a coupon rate of 8% payable semi-annually and was redeemable in five years. How much did she pay, and what was the premium or discount for the bond if the yield rate at the time of purchase was 7% compounded monthly?

3. A company issues a $20,000 bond at a coupon rate of 7.5% payable semi-annually. Juan purchased this bond ten years before maturity when the yield rate was 7% compounded semi-annually and sold it two years later when the bond's market yield rate was 8% compounded semi-annually. Calculate his loss or gain on this investment.

4. A $1000 bond paying a 6.5% coupon rate was redeemable on May 01, 2018. What was its purchase price, and premium or discount, on July 23, 2016 when the yield rate was 9% compounded semi-annually?

5. Marcelo purchased a $25,000 bond at a coupon rate of 3.5% payable semi-annually, 5 years and 1 month before its date of maturity. If the yield rate on the date of purchase was 4% compounded semi-annually, calculate the purchase price of the bond and its discount or premium.

6. A $10,000 bond with a 7.5% coupon rate is redeemable on October 01, 2019. If it was purchased on September 18, 2014 when the quote was 103.8, calculate the purchase price, and premium or discount, on the purchase of the bond.

7. A company issued a $5000 bond at a coupon rate of 8% and redeemable in four years. If the yield rate at the time of issue was 7.5% compounded semi-annually, construct the bond schedule showing the amortization of the premium.

8. A $25,000 bond at a coupon rate of 4.75% payable semi-annually was purchased at 99.5, eight years before maturity. Calculate the yield rate of the bond.

For Problems 9 and 10, round the sinking fund payments ***up to the next cent****, to ensure the sinking fund accumulates to at least the principal.*

9. A company issued bonds worth $750,500 and set up a sinking fund to retire the debt in 15 years. It made deposits at the end of every 6 months into the fund and the fund was earning 9% compounded semi-annually.
   a. Calculate the size of the periodic sinking fund deposits.
   b. Calculate the amount by which the fund increased in the 25th payment period.
   c. Construct a partial sinking fund schedule to illustrate the details of the last two payments.

10. Irene Travels issued $100,000, 7.25% bonds in the market that were redeemable in five years. It established a sinking fund to retire the debt on maturity and made equal deposits into the fund at the end of every six months. If the fund was earning 9% compounded semi-annually, calculate the periodic cost of the debt and the book value of the debt at the end of four years.

CASE 13a

Raising Money Through Bonds

Seth, a business student in college, recently learned that bonds can be categorized as either investment grade bonds or junk bonds. Investment grade bonds are issued by established, low-risk companies, whereas junk bonds are issued by high-risk companies.

Intrigued by the concept of junk bonds, Seth followed a company called Holdings Software Developers Inc. (HSD) – a high-risk company that issued junk bonds. The company had a low credit rating in the market and its bonds were considered very risky investments, which is why it had to offer high interest payments to the holders of the bond. Although these bonds were junk bonds, surprisingly, there were many wealthy people who purchased its bonds, selling them shortly afterwards for a quick return on their investment.

In one particular case, HSD required $1,000,000 for an expansion project and raised the money by issuing $5000 bonds that were redeemable in ten years. The bonds were rated as junk bonds and offered an 11% coupon rate paid semi-annually.

HSD had wanted to increase the rating of its bond by gaining the confidence of its investors, so HSD created a ten-year sinking fund to ensure that enough money would be available at the time of maturity of the bonds. The fund was growing at 2.5% compounded monthly and they made equal deposits into the fund at the end of every six months.

a. What was the discount on the bond at the time of issue if its yield rate was 14% compounded semi-annually?

b. What was the premium on the bond at the time of issue if the yield rate was 9% compounded quarterly?

c. If an investor purchased a bond at the time of issue at a yield rate of 14% compounded semi-annually, and sold it two years later when the market required a yield rate of only 13% compounded semi-annually, how much would the investor gain or lose on this investment?

d. What was the purchase price of the bond if an investor wanted to purchase it 6 years and 2 months before its redemption date and have the bond yield 12.5% compounded semi-annually?

e. If the bond was purchased seven years before maturity for 103.4, what was its yield rate?

f. Two years before maturity, an investor purchased the bond at a yield rate of 15% compounded semi-annually. Construct a bond schedule for the investor showing the amortization of discount.

g. What was the size of the periodic sinking fund deposit (rounded up to the next cent) and what was the total interest earned during the period?

h. Construct a sinking fund schedule illustrating details of the fund.

CASE 13b

Facility Expansion Spreadsheet Project

The spreadsheet calculations should be set up in a systematic manner. Your set-up should contain a list of the given values, and as many calculated values as possible. Make your spreadsheet as 'active' as possible by using cell references (so that if one value is changed, subsequent calculations will automatically update). Use absolute cell references in special situations.

Mitchell Meat Packaging has been in business for nearly 10 years working out of the same facility. Their business has grown over the years to a point where they must expand their facilities in order to keep up with demand. The company has issued bonds worth $175,000 paying an 8% coupon rate semi-annually for five years to fund the expansion with minimal impact on current production.

Mitchell Meat Packaging will establish a sinking fund to retire this debt in five years by making deposits into the fund at the end of every six months. Interest for the fund is 6.93% compounded quarterly.

a. What is the size of the semi-annual sinking fund payment?
b. What is the periodic cost of the debt to Mitchell Meat Packaging?
c. What is the book value of the debt after three years?
d. Calculate the increase in the sinking fund balance in the second year.
e. Prepare a complete sinking fund schedule. Express totals at the bottom of each column as currency.
f. How much of the maturity value in the fund will be interest?

13 | Spreadsheet Solutions

Spreadsheet solutions to solved examples in the chapter.

13.2 Examples

Example 13.2(a)

	A	B	Formula
1		*Coupon Rate*	
2	***j***	10.00%	
3	***m***	2	
4	***b***	5.00%	= B2/B3
5			
6	(i)	*Purchase Price*	
7	***j***	10.00%	
8	***m***	2	
9	***t***	6	
10			
11	***i***	5.00%	= B7/B8
12	***n***	12	= B3*B9
13	***PMT***	$ 50.00	= B15*B4
14	***PV***	($1,000.00)	= PV(B11, B12, B13, B15) PV(rate, nper, pmt, [fv], [type])
15	***FV***	$1,000.00	
16			
17	(ii)	*Purchase Price*	
18	***j***	12.00%	
19	***m***	2	
20	***t***	6	
21			
22	***i***	6.00%	= B18/B19
23	***n***	12	= B3*B20
24	***PMT***	$50.00	= B26*B4
25	***PV***	($916.16)	= PV(B22, B23, B24, B26) PV(rate, nper, pmt, [fv], [type])
26	***FV***	$1,000.00	
27			
28	(iii)	*Purchase Price*	
29	***j***	8.00%	
30	***m***	2	
31	***t***	6	
32			
33	***i***	4.00%	= B29/B30
34	***n***	12	= B3*B31
35	***PMT***	$50.00	= B37*B4
36	***PV***	($1,093.85)	= PV(B33, B34, B35, B37) PV(rate, nper, pmt, [fv], [type])
37	***FV***	$1,000.00	
38			

Example 13.2(b)

	A	B	Formula
1		*Coupon Rate*	
2	***j***	4.60%	
3	***m***	2	
4	***b***	2.30%	= B2/B3
5			
6		*Purchase Price*	
7	***j***	5.00%	
8	***m***	1	
9	***t***	5	
10			
11	***i***	5.00%	= B7/B8
12	***c***	0.5	= B8/B3
13	i_2	2.4695%	= (1 + B11)^B12 – 1
14	***n***	10	= B3*B9
15	***PMT***	$575.00	= B17*B4
16	***PV***	($24,628.53)	= PV(B13, B14, B15, B17) PV(rate, nper, pmt, [fv], [type])
17	***FV***	$25,000.00	
18			

Example 13.2(c)

	A	B	Formula
1		*Coupon Rate*	
2	***j***	6.00%	
3	***m***	2	
4	***b***	3.00%	= B2/B3
5			
6	(i)	*Purchase Price*	
7	***j***	7.00%	
8	***m***	2	
9	***t***	10	
10			
11	***i***	3.50%	= B7/B8
12	***n***	20	= B3*B9
13	***PMT***	$600.00	= B15*B4
14	***PV***	($18,578.76)	= PV(B11, B12, B13, B15) PV(rate, nper, pmt, [fv], [type])
15	***FV***	$20,000.00	
16			
17	(ii)	*Purchase Price*	
18	***j***	5.00%	
19	***m***	2	
20	***t***	6	
21			
22	***i***	2.50%	= B18/B19
23	***n***	12	= B3*B20
24	***PMT***	$600.00	= B26*B4
25	***PV***	($21,025.78)	= PV(B22, B23, B24, B26) PV(rate, nper, pmt, [fv], [type])
26	***FV***	$20,000.00	
27			

Example 13.2(d)

	A	B	Formula
1	**Day 1**	1/1/2016	= DATE(2016, 1, 1)
2	**Day 2**	4/16/2016	= DATE(2016, 4, 16)
3	**Day 3**	7/1/2016	= DATE(2016, 7, 1) DATE(year, month, day)
4			
5		*Coupon Rate*	
6	***j***	10.00%	
7	***m***	2	
8	***b***	5.00%	= B6/B7
9			
10		*Purchase Price* Jan1	
11	***j***	7.00%	
12	***m***	2	
13	***t***	7	
14			
15	***i***	3.50%	= B11/B12
16	***n***	14	= B7*B13
17	***PMT***	$50.00	= B19*B8
18	***PV***	($1,163.81)	= PV(B15, B16, B17, B19) PV(rate, nper, pmt, [fv], [type])
19	***FV***	$1,000.00	
20			
21		*Purchase Price* Apr 16	
22	***i***	3.50%	= B15
23	***n***	0.582418	= DAYS(B2, B1)/DAYS(B3, B1) DAYS(end_date, start_date)
24	***PMT***	0	
25	***PV***	$1,163.81	= –B18
26	***FV***	($1,187.36)	= FV(B22, B23, B24, B25) FV(rate, nper, pmt, [pv], [type])
27			

Example 13.2(e)

	A	B	Formula
1		*Coupon Rate*	
2	***j***	12.00%	
3	***m***	2	
4	***b***	6.00%	= B2/B3
5			
6		Calculating *j*	
7	***j***	13.00%	= B11*B8
8	***m***	2	
9	***t***	5	
10			
11	***i***	6.50%	= RATE(B12, B13, B14, B15)
12	***n***	10	= B3*B9 RATE(nper, pmt, pv [fv], [type], [guess])
13	***PMT***	$600.00	= B15*B4
14	***PV***	($9,640.00)	
15	***FV***	$10,000.00	
16			

13.3 Examples

Example 13.3(c)

	A	B	Formula
1	**Day 1**	12/11/2016	= DATE(2016, 12, 11)
2	**Day 2**	2/9/2017	= DATE(2017, 2, 9)
3	**Day 3**	6/11/2017	= DATE(2017, 6, 11) DATE(year, month, day)
4			
5		*Coupon Rate*	
6	***j***	6.50%	
7	***m***	2	
8	***b***	3.25%	= B6/B7
9			
10	(i)	*Purchase Price* Dec 11	
11	***j***	3.84%	
12	***m***	2	
13	***t***	16.5	
14			
15	***i***	1.92%	= B11/B12
16	***n***	33	= B7*B13
17	***PMT***	$162.50	= B19*B8
18	***PV***	($6,614.44)	= PV(B15, B16, B17, B19) PV(rate, nper, pmt, [fv], [type])
19	***FV***	$5,000.00	
20			
21		*Purchase Price* Feb 09	
22	***i***	1.92%	= B15
23	***n***	0.329670	= DAYS(B2, B1)/DAYS(B3, B1) DAYS(end_date, start_date)
24	***PMT***	0	
25	***PV***	$6,614.44	= –B18
26	***FV***	($6,656.05)	= FV(B22, B23, B24, B25) FV(rate, nper, pmt, [pv], [type])
27			
28	(ii)	Accrued Interest	
29		$53.57	= B17*B23
30			
31	(iii)	Quoted Price	
32		($6,602.47)	= B26 + B29
33			
34	(iv)	Market Quotation	
35		132.05	= –B32/B19*100
36			

13.4 Examples

Example 13.4(a)

	A	B	C	D	E	F	G	H	I	J
1		Calculating *PV*			*Coupon Rate*					
2	***j***	8.00%		***j***	10.00%					
3	***m***	2		***m***	2					
4	***t***	2		***b***	5.00% = E2/E3					
5										
6	***i***	4.00% = B2/B3		Bond Schedule						
7	***n***	4 = E3*B4		**Period**	**Interest Received**	**Interest on Book Value**	**Amortized Premium**	**Book Value**	**Premium to be Amortized**	
8	***PMT***	$50.00 = B10*E4		0				$1,036.30 = –B9	$36.30 = H8 – B10	
9	***PV***	($1,036.30) = PV(B6, B7, B8, B10)		1	$50.00 = B$8	$41.45 = ROUND(H8*B$6, 2)	$8.55 = E9 – F9	$1,027.75 = H8 – G9	$27.75 = I8 – G9	
10	***FV***	$1,000.00		2	$50.00	$41.11	$8.89	$1,018.86	$18.86	
11				3	$50.00	$40.75	$9.25	$1,009.61	$9.61	
12				4	$50.00	$40.38	$9.62	$999.99	–$0.01	
13				**Total**	$200.00 = SUM(E9:E12)	$163.69 = SUM(F9:F12)	$36.31 = SUM(G9:G12)			
14										

Example 13.4(b)

	A	B	C	D	E	F	G	H	I	J
1		Calculating *PV*			*Coupon Rate*					
2	***j***	10.00%		***j***	8.00%					
3	***m***	2		***m***	2					
4	***t***	2		***b***	4.00% = E2/E3					
5										
6	***i***	5.00% = B2/B3		Bond Schedule						
7	***n***	4 = E3*B4		**Period**	**Interest Received**	**Interest on Book Value**	**Accumulated Discount**	**Book Value**	**Discount to be Accumulated**	
8	***PMT***	$40.00 = B10*E4		0				$964.54 = –B9	$35.46 = B10–H8	
9	***PV***	($964.54) = PV(B6, B7, B8, B10)		1	$40.00 = B$8	$48.23 = ROUND(H8*B$6, 2)	$8.23 = F9 – E9	$972.77 = H8 + G9	$27.23 = I8 – G9	
10	***FV***	$1,000.00		2	$40.00	$48.64	$8.64	$981.41	$18.59	
11				3	$40.00	$49.07	$9.07	$990.48	$9.52	
12				4	$40.00	$49.52	$9.52	$1,000.00	$0.00	
13				**Total**	$160.00 = SUM(E9:E12)	$195.46 = SUM(F9:F12)	$35.46 = SUM(G9:G12)			
14										

13.5 Examples

Example 13.5(a)

	A	B	C	D	E	F	G	H	I	J
1		Calculating *PMT*								
2	*j*	4.00%								
3	*m*	2		Sinking Fund Schedule						
4	*P/Y*	2		Period	Payment	Interest Earned	Increase in the Fund	Fund Balance	Book Value	
5	*t*	2		0				$0.00 = B10	$10,000.00 = B11	
6				1	$2,426.24 = ROUNDUP(–B$9,2)	$0.00 = ROUND(H5*B$7,2)	$2,426.24 = E6 + F6	$2,426.24 = H5 + G6	$7,573.76 = I$5 – H6	
7	*i*	2.00% = B2/B3		2	$2,426.24	$48.52	$2,474.76	$4,901.00	$5,099.00	
8	*n*	4 = B4*B5		3	$2,426.24	$98.02	$2,524.26	$7,425.26	$2,574.74	
9	*PMT*	($2,426.24) = PMT(B7,B8,B10,B11,B12)		4	$2,426.24	$148.51	$2,574.75	$10,000.01	–$0.01	
10	*PV*	0		**Total**	$9,704.96 = SUM(E6:E9)	$295.05 = SUM(F6:F9)	$10,000.01 = SUM(G6:G9)			
11	*FV*	$10,000.00								
11	*BGN*	0								
13										

Example 13.5(b)

	A	B	C	D	E	F	G	H	I	J
1		Calculating *PMT*								
2	*j*	4.00%								
3	*m*	2		Sinking Fund Schedule						
4	*P/Y*	2		Period	Payment	Interest Earned	Increase in the Fund	Fund Balance	Book Value	
5	*t*	2		0				$0.00 = B10	$10,000.00 = B11	
6				1	$2,378.67 = ROUNDUP(–B$9,2)	$47.57 = ROUND((H5+E6)*B$7,2)	$2,426.24 = E6 + F6	$2,426.24 = H5 + G6	$7,573.76 = I$5 – H6	
7	*i*	2.00% = B2/B3		2	$2,378.67	$96.10	$2,474.77	$4,901.01	$5,098.99	
8	*n*	4 = B4*B5		3	$2,378.67	$145.59	$2,524.26	$7,425.27	$2,574.73	
9	*PMT*	($2,378.66) = PMT(B7,B8,B10,B11,B12)		4	$2,378.67	$196.08	$2,574.75	$10,000.02	–$0.02	
10	*PV*	0		**Total**	$9,514.68 = SUM(E6:E9)	$485.34 = SUM(F6:F9)	$10,000.02 = SUM(G6:G9)			
11	*FV*	$10,000.00								
12	*BGN*	1								
13										

Example 13.5(c)

	A	B	C	D	E	F	G	H	I	J
1		Calculating *PMT*								
2	*j*	6.50%		Sinking Fund Schedule						
3	*m*	2		**Period**	**Payment**	**Interest Earned**	**Increase in the Fund**	**Fund Balance**	**Book Value**	
4	*P/Y*	2		0				$0.00 = B10	$100,000.00 = B11	
5	*t*	5		1	$8,623.11 = ROUNDUP(–B$9,2)	$0.00 = ROUND(H4*B$7,2)	$8,623.11 = E5 + F5	$8,623.11 = H4 + G5	$91,376.89 = I$4 – H5	
6				2	$8,623.11	$280.25	$8,903.36	$17,526.47	$82,473.53	
7	*i*	3.25% = B2/B3		-	-	-	-	-	-	
8	*n*	10 = B4*B5		8	-	-	-	$77,363.24 = FV(B7, 8, –E5, B10, B12)	$22,636.76 = I$4 – H8	
9	*PMT*	($8,623.11) = PMT(B7,B8,B10,B11,B12)		9	$8,623.11 = ROUNDUP(–B$9,2)	$2,514.31 =ROUND(H8*B$7,2)	$11,137.42 = E9 + F9	$88,500.66 = H8 + G9	$11,499.34	
10	*PV*	0		10	$8,623.11	$2,876.27	$11,499.38	$100,000.04	–$0.04	
11	*FV*	$100,000.00		**Total**	$86,231.10 = E5*10	$13,768.94 = G11 – E11	$100,000.04 = H10			
12	*BGN*	0								
13										

13 | Summary of Notation and Formulas

NOTATION

b = Coupon rate

FV = Face value of the bond

PMT = Bond Payment

i = Yield or market rate of interest

FORMULAS

Purchase Price of a Bond | 13.2(a)

$$Purchase\ Price = PV_{PMT} + PV_{Redemption\ Value}$$

Periodic Interest Payment of a Bond | 13.2(b)

$$PMT = FV \times b$$

Full Price of a Bond | 13.3(a)

$$Full\ Price = Quoted\ Price + Accrued\ Interest$$

Quoted Price of a Bond | 13.3(b)

$$Quoted\ Price = Market\ Quotation \times Redemption\ Value$$

Chapter

14 BUSINESS INVESTMENT DECISIONS

LEARNING OBJECTIVES

- Calculate the discounted cash flow (DCF) of investments and evaluate and compare investment decisions using the DCF method.
- Calculate the net present value (NPV) of an investment and evaluate and compare investment decisions using the NPV method.
- Calculate the internal rate of return (IRR) of an investment and evaluate and compare investment decisions using the IRR method.
- Calculate the payback period of an investment and evaluate and compare investment decisions using the payback rule.

CHAPTER OUTLINE

14.1 Discounted Cash Flow (DCF)

14.2 Net Present Value (NPV)

14.3 Internal Rate of Return (IRR)

14.4 Payback Period

Introduction

Investment is the purchase or creation of assets using financial resources with the objective of making gains in the future. Individuals and businesses alike invest money to obtain future benefits. For example, individuals may invest money to benefit from its returns during their retirement, use these returns to purchase a property, or finance a child's education. Similarly, businesses make investments for the long-term to benefit from returns in the future. For example, businesses may invest in:

Investments **are expenditures with determinable future benefits.**

- Machinery to increase productivity.
- Training and development for their employees to improve performance.
- Equipment upgrades to improve product/service quality.
- Software to automate operations.
- Advertising to improve brand awareness.
- New business acquisition to expand their product offering or to own a larger market share.

Investors and business owners expect high returns on the money they invest. When various options and alternatives are available, it is necessary to assess, evaluate, and compare them to make the best investment decision. The main consideration in making investment decisions will include the following:

1. The required and affordable investment amount.
2. The waiting period to receive benefits from the investment.
3. The expected profit or the required rate of return from the investment.
4. The other available investment options and a comparison of benefits.
5. The required time period to pay back the investment.

Capital investments *are investments that generate monetary returns in the long-term.*

In this chapter, using concepts we have learned, we will focus on investments that result in monetary gains over a period of time. These are referred to as **capital investments**, with the word 'capital' implying that the investments generate returns in the long-term. In accounting terms, such investments would be regarded as capital assets on the balance sheet (long-term) and not expenses on the income statement (short-term).

As these investments are often large, it is important for business managers to carefully analyze their decision to invest. Utilizing the concept of time value of money (money growing over time when it is invested at an interest rate) there are different methods of comparing investments or evaluating the feasibility of investing in projects. We will look at the following four methods:

1. Discounted Cash Flow (DCF)
2. Net Present Value (NPV)
3. Internal Rate of Return (IRR)
4. Payback Period

14.1 | Discounted Cash Flow (DCF)

Discounted cash flow (DCF) *is when all the expected future cash flows are discounted to a particular date.*

In the **Discounted Cash Flow** (DCF) method, all of the expected future cash flows from investing in a project are discounted to determine their present value on a particular date (focal date), which is then used to evaluate the investment option.

$$PV_{All\ Cash\ Flows} = PV_{Cash\ Flow\ 1} + PV_{Cash\ Flow\ 2} + PV_{Cash\ Flow\ 3} \ldots$$

If the present value of all cash flows is greater than the cost of investing in a project, then the project may be considered a good investment option. The discounted cash inflows of different investment options are compared on a particular focal date and the one with the highest discounted cash flows is accepted.

The rate of return used to calculate the present value of cash flows is the **required rate of return** that the business expects from investing in this project. This required rate of return is generally the **cost of capital,** which is the opportunity cost of investing; i.e., the rate of return that the business would otherwise earn if the amount is invested in another investment that has the same level of risk as this project.

Note: *While solving problems, investments (cash outflows) are generally considered to be made at the beginning of the year and net returns or profits (cash inflows) are generally considered to be received at the end of the year, unless otherwise stated.*

Example 14.1(a) Calculating the Discounted Cash Flow (DCF) of a Project

A marketing company is evaluating an investment in a marketing project devised by one of its interns. The project will generate net returns of \$15,000 one year from now, \$10,000 two years from now, and \$7000 three years from now. The company's required rate of return is 10%. What is the discounted cash flow of the net returns?

Solution

Page 601

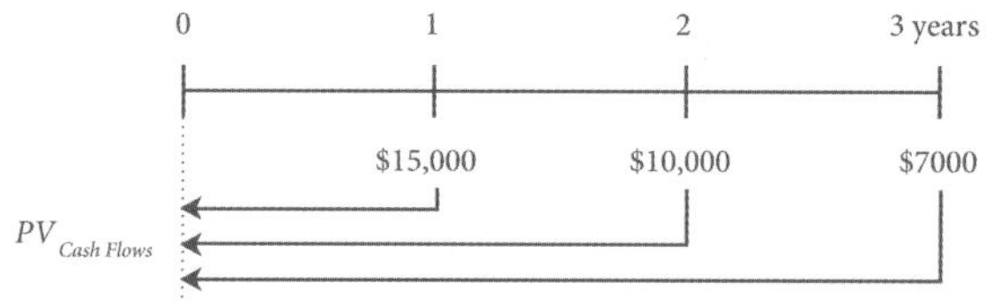

If the compounding period is not provided, assume it to be an annually compounding interest rate.

$j = 0.10, \quad m = 1, \quad i = \frac{j}{m} = \frac{0.10}{1} = 0.10$

Using Formula 9.1(b), $PV = FV(1 + i)^{-n}$

Calculating the Present Value of the cash flows:

$$PV_{Cash\ Flows} = 15{,}000.00(1 + 0.10)^{-1} + 10{,}000.00(1 + 0.10)^{-2} + 7000.00(1 + 0.10)^{-3}$$

$$= 13{,}636.36364... + 8264.462810... + 5259.203606...$$

$$= 27{,}160.03005... = \$27{,}160.03$$

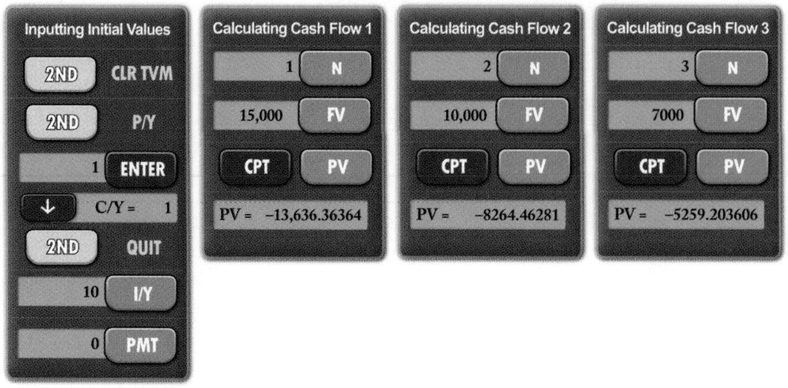

Therefore, the discounted cash flow of the project is \$27,160.03.

Using the Cash Flow Worksheet to Solve DCF Problems

The preprogrammed financial calculator has a cash flow worksheet that can be used to discount uneven cash flows. We will solve Example 14.1(a) using the cash flow worksheet of the Texas Instruments BA II Plus financial calculator.

Example 14.1(b) **Using the Cash Flow Worksheet to Solve Example 14.1(a)**

Solve Example 14.1(a) using the cash flow worksheet of the financial calculator.

Solution

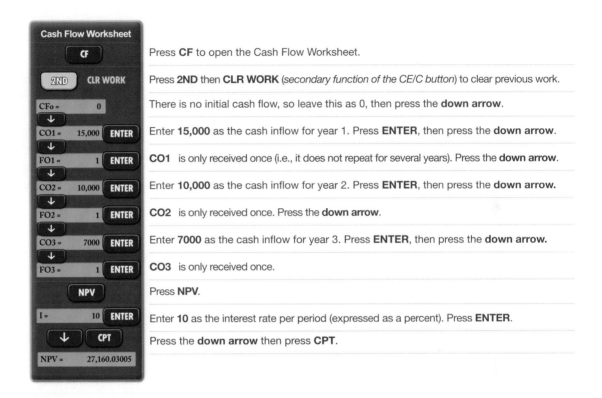

Cash Flow Worksheet	
CF	Press **CF** to open the Cash Flow Worksheet.
2ND CLR WORK	Press **2ND** then **CLR WORK** (*secondary function of the CE/C button*) to clear previous work.
CFo = 0 ↓	There is no initial cash flow, so leave this as 0, then press the **down arrow**.
CO1 = 15,000 ENTER ↓	Enter **15,000** as the cash inflow for year 1. Press **ENTER**, then press the **down arrow**.
FO1 = 1 ENTER ↓	**CO1** is only received once (i.e., it does not repeat for several years). Press the **down arrow**.
CO2 = 10,000 ENTER ↓	Enter **10,000** as the cash inflow for year 2. Press **ENTER**, then press the **down arrow.**
FO2 = 1 ENTER ↓	**CO2** is only received once. Press the **down arrow**.
CO3 = 7000 ENTER ↓	Enter **7000** as the cash inflow for year 3. Press **ENTER**, then press the **down arrow.**
FO3 = 1 ENTER	**CO3** is only received once.
NPV	Press **NPV**.
I = 10 ENTER	Enter **10** as the interest rate per period (expressed as a percent). Press **ENTER**.
↓ CPT	Press the **down arrow** then press **CPT**.
NPV = 27,160.03005	

Therefore, the discounted cash flow of the project is $27,160.03.

Example 14.1(c) **Comparing Two Investment Options Using the DCF Method**

The CEO of a software development company has to choose between investing in either Project *A* or Project *B*, which will generate the same return.

- Project *A* requires investments of $60,000 one year from now and $70,000 two years from now.
- Project *B* requires investments of $40,000 one year from now and $80,000 two years from now.

Which project is economically better if cost of capital is 6% compounded monthly?

Solution

Page 601

$$j = 0.06,\ m = 12,\ i = \frac{0.06}{12} = 0.005$$

Project A

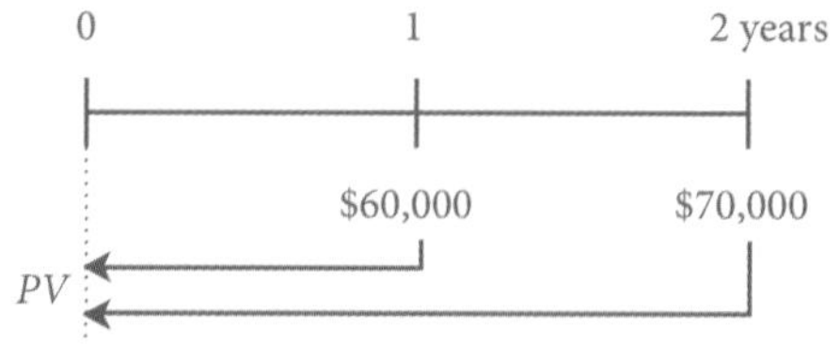

$$PV = 60{,}000.00(1 + 0.005)^{-12} + 70{,}000.00(1 + 0.005)^{-24}$$
$$= 56{,}514.32038... + 62{,}102.99682...$$
$$= 118{,}617.3172... = \$118{,}617.32$$

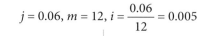

Project B

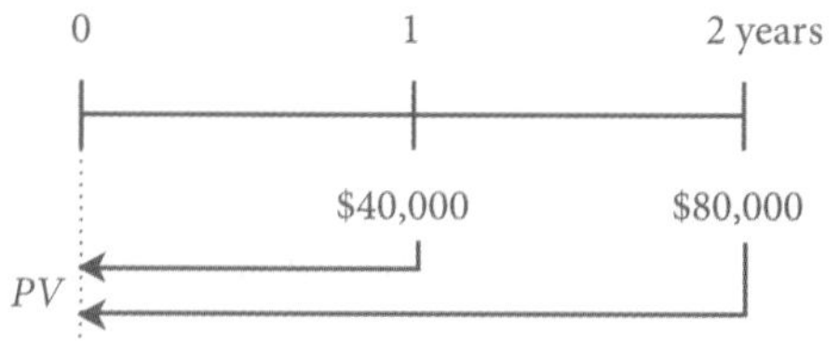

$$PV = 40{,}000.00(1 + 0.005)^{-12} + 80{,}000.00(1 + 0.005)^{-24}$$
$$= 37{,}676.21359... + 70{,}974.85351...$$
$$= 108{,}651.0671... = \$108{,}651.07$$

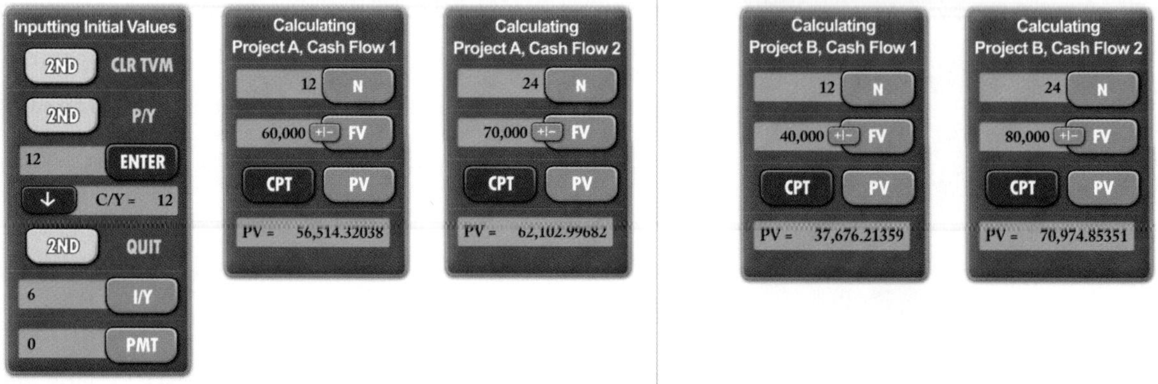

Cash Flow Worksheet

Since the cash flows are occurring annually, we must use the annually compounded interest rate in the cash flow worksheet.

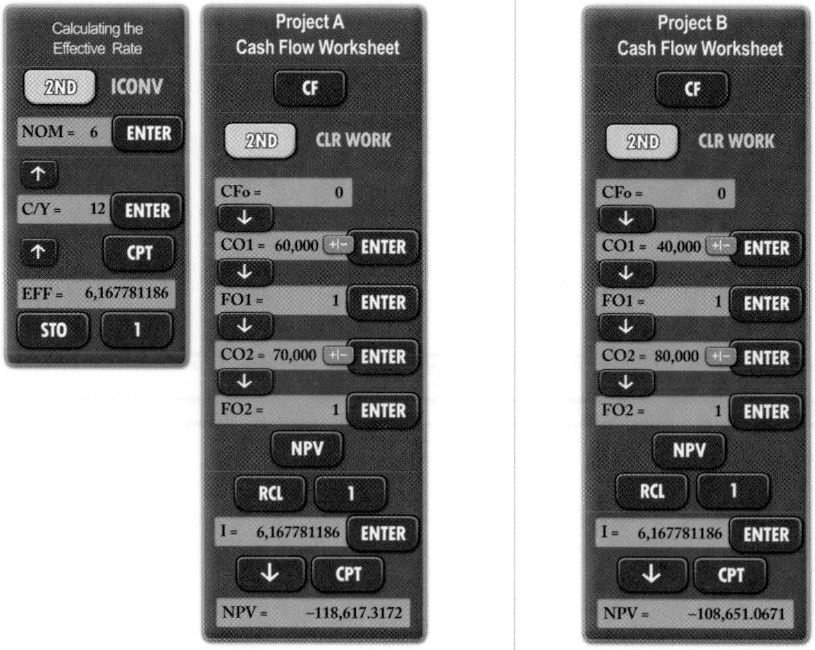

Therefore, Project *B* is economically better because it has a lower discounted cash flow than Project *A*.

Example 14.1(d) **Evaluating Lease vs. Buy Option Using the DCF Method**

A car salesman offered Meghan the following two options:

- Lease Option: Pay lease amounts of $330 at the beginning of every month for four years. At the end of four years, purchase the car for $15,000.
- Buy Option: Purchase the car immediately for $25,000.

Which option should she choose if money is worth 9% compounded monthly?

Page 601

Solution

Lease Option

Calculating $PV_{Lease\ Option}$

Set to BGN mode

2ND CLR TVM
2ND P/Y
12 ENTER
↓ C/Y= 12
2ND QUIT
48 N
9 I/Y
330 +/- PMT
15,000 +/- FV
CPT PV
PV = 23,839.6474

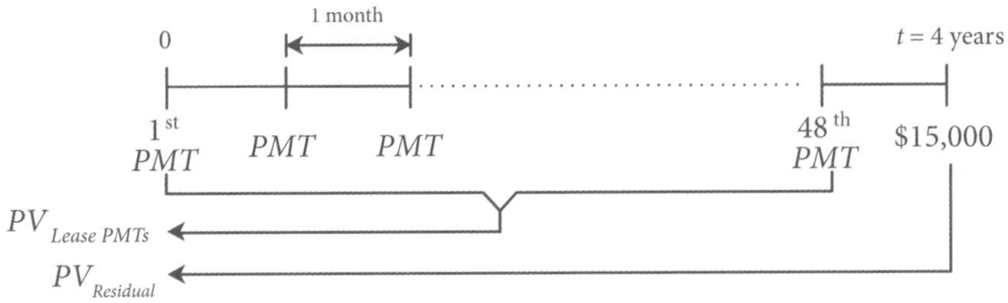

$$PMT = \$330$$

$$n = 12 \text{ payments/year} \times 4 \text{ years}$$
$$= 48 \text{ monthly payments}$$

$$j = 0.09, \quad m = 12, \quad i = \frac{j}{m} = \frac{0.09}{12} = 0.0075 \text{ per month}$$

The lease payments form a simple annuity due.

Using Formula 10.4(b), $$PV_{Due} = PMT\left[\frac{1-(1+i)^{-n}}{i}\right](1+i)$$

$$PV_{Lease\ PMTs} = 330.00\left[\frac{1-(1+0.0075)^{-48}}{0.0075}\right](1+0.0075)$$

$$= \$13{,}360.43536...$$

Using Formula 9.1(b), $$PV = FV(1+i)^{-n}$$

$$PV_{Residual} = 15{,}000.00(1+0.0075)^{-48}$$

$$= \$10{,}479.21204...$$

Therefore, $$PV_{Lease\ Option} = 13{,}360.43536... + 10{,}479.21204...$$

$$= 23{,}839.64740... = \$23{,}839.65$$

Cash Flow Worksheet

CF
2ND CLR WORK
CFo = 330 +/- ENTER
↓
CO1 = 330 +/- ENTER
↓
FO1 = 47 ENTER
↓
CO2 = 15,000 +/- ENTER
↓
FO2 = 1 ENTER
NPV
I = 0.75 ENTER
↓ CPT
NPV = -23,839.6474

Buy Option

The PV of the lease option is less than the buy option of purchasing it for $25,000.

Therefore, Meghan should choose the lease option.

Since the cash flows are occurring monthly, we must use the periodic monthly compounded interest rate in the cash flow worksheet.

14.1 | Exercises

Answers to the odd-numbered problems are available at the end of the textbook.

1. The innovation centre of a company has come up with an idea for a new product. It is expected that if produced, the product will generate returns of $10,000 one year from now, and $8000 two years from now. The required rate of return is 5%. Calculate the DCF of the returns.

2. The marketing department of a company is evaluating a new campaign. It is expected to generate returns of $8000 in the first year and $4000 in the second year. If the required rate of return is 6%, calculate the DCF of the investment option.

3. A company can settle a loan by making a payment of $60,000 one year from now and $85,000 two years from now. It also has the option of settling the same loan by paying $40,000 one year from now and $100,000 two years from now. If the cost of capital is 8%, compute the DCF for each option and determine the most economical option for the company.

4. Project *A* requires investments of $50,000 one year from now and $60,000 two years from now. Project *B* requires investments of $30,000 one year from now and $90,000 two years from now. Assume that the returns on each project are the same and that the required rate of return is 8%. Compute the DCF for each project and determine the most economical option.

5. A company is deciding between two projects:
   - Project *A* will generate net returns of $120,000 one year from now and $30,000 two years from now.
   - Project *B* will generate net returns of $40,000 one year from now and $120,000 three years from now.

   Compute the DCF for each project and determine the most economical option if the required rate of return is 11%.

6. A young investor is deciding between two investment options with equal costs.
   - Option 1 will provide net returns of $30,000 two years from now and $5000 four years from now.
   - Option 2 will provide net returns of $20,000 two years from now and $26,000 four years from now.

   Compute the DCF for each option and determine the most economical option if the cost of capital is 9%.

7. Amy was offered two options for a car:
   - Lease Option: Pay lease amounts of $400 at the beginning of every month for five years. At the end of five years, purchase the car for $15,000.
   - Buy Option: Purchase the car immediately for $25,000.

   Compute the DCF for the lease option and determine the most economical option, if money is worth 8% compounded monthly.

8. William is deciding between purchasing a machine for $120,000 or taking advantage of a leasing option that requires him to pay $1600 at the beginning of every month for eight years. At the end of eight years, he will have to pay $20,000 to own the machine. Compute the DCF for the lease option and determine the most economical option, if money is worth 6.5% compounded monthly.

• 9. Amanda was on a work contract in Alberta for five years and had the following two options:
   - Renting Option: pay $1000 at the beginning of every month for five years to rent an apartment.
   - Purchasing Option: pay $165,000 to own an apartment and pay $500 towards maintenance and tax at the beginning of every month for five years. At the end of five years, she estimated that she will receive $181,500 from the sale of the apartment.

   Compute the DCF of both options and determine the most economical option, if money is worth:

   a. 6% compounded monthly. b. 5% compounded monthly.

• 10. Harris was evaluating the benefits of purchasing or leasing a machine. The cost of the machine is $19,800 and he estimated that he could sell it at the end of five years for $4500. He would also have to spend $1000 at the beginning of every month for supplies and maintenance. However, if he leases the machine, he would only have to pay $1290 at the beginning of every month for the entire period and this amount would include supplies and maintenance too. Compute the DCF and determine the most economical option, if money is worth:

   a. 3% compounded monthly. b. 4% compounded monthly.

14.2 | Net Present Value (NPV)

Net present value (NPV) is a method of evaluating the feasibility of an investment decision by determining the difference between the present value of all cash inflows (returns) and the present value of all cash outflows (investments).

Net present value (NPV) is the difference between the present value of all cash inflows and the present value of all cash outflows.

Formula 14.2

Net Present Value

$$NPV = PV_{Cash\ Inflows} - PV_{Cash\ Outflows}$$

Therefore, when:

$PV_{Cash\ Inflows} > PV_{Cash\ Outflows}$	NPV is greater than zero.
$PV_{Cash\ Inflows} < PV_{Cash\ Outflows}$	NPV is less than zero.
$PV_{Cash\ Inflows} = PV_{Cash\ Outflows}$	NPV is zero.

To calculate the NPV of a project, a business must first determine its **required rate of return**. The required rate of return is used in discounting a project's cash flows in NPV calculations, which inform business decision makers as to whether projects will produce an acceptable return.

Accept the project if $\boldsymbol{NPV > 0}$. The investment in the project will provide an expected return better than the required rate of return.

Accept the project if $\boldsymbol{NPV = 0}$. The investment in the project will provide an expected return equal to the required rate of return.

Reject the project if $\boldsymbol{NPV < 0}$. The investment in the project will provide an expected return less than the required rate of return.

When comparing different investment projects, the project with the highest NPV should be chosen.

Example 14.2(a)

Evaluating Investment Decisions when Cash Flows are Capital Investments

The senior management team at Blue Dreams Resort is evaluating a project, which will require an $80,000 investment today. Based on its analysis, the project will generate net returns of $15,000 in the first year, $30,000 in the second year, $45,000 in the third year, and $25,000 in the fourth year. Given that the company requires a 10% rate of return on all of its investments, should it accept this project?

Solution

Page 601

This project can be evaluated by calculating its NPV.

Method 1

$$NPV = PV_{Cash\ Inflows} - PV_{Cash\ Outflows}$$

Calculating the Present Value of Cash Inflows

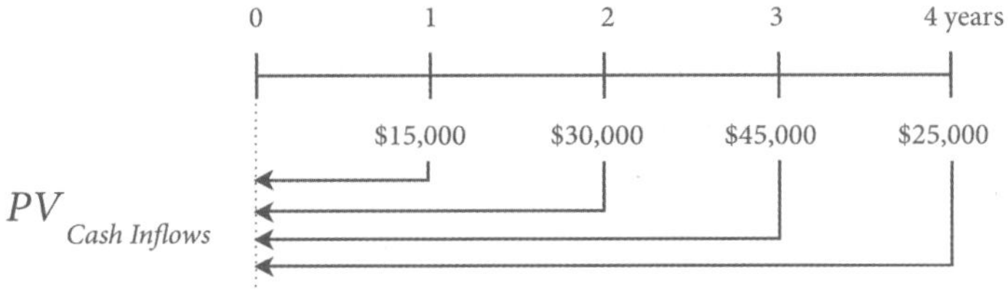

Investments (cash outflows) are generally considered to be made at the beginning of the year and net returns or profits (cash inflows) are generally considered to be received at the end of the year, unless otherwise stated.

Solution *continued*

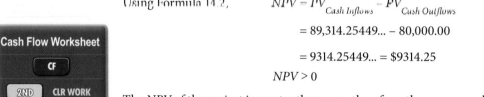

$$PV_{Cash\ Inflows} = 15{,}000.00(1 + 0.10)^{-1} + 30{,}000.00(1 + 0.10)^{-2} + 45{,}000.00(1 + 0.10)^{-3} + 25{,}000.00(1 + 0.10)^{-4}$$

$$= 13{,}636.36364... + 24{,}793.38843... + 33{,}809.16604... + 17{,}075.33638...$$

$$= \$89{,}314.25449...$$

Calculating the Present Value of Cash Outflows

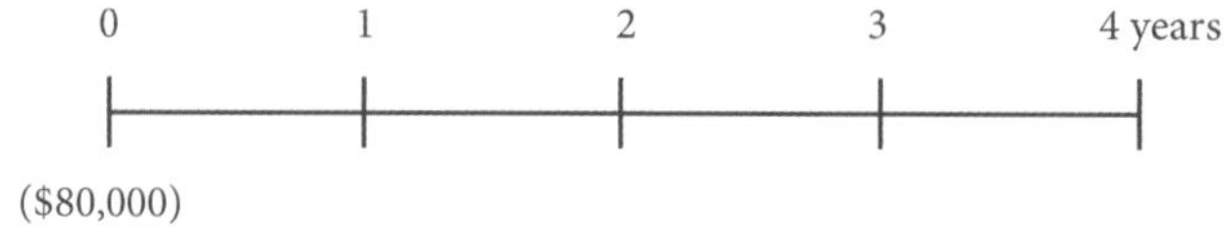

$$PV_{Cash\ Outflows} = \$80{,}000.00$$

Using Formula 14.2, $NPV = PV_{Cash\ Inflows} - PV_{Cash\ Outflows}$

$$= 89{,}314.25449... - 80{,}000.00$$

$$= 9314.25449... = \$9314.25$$

$$NPV > 0$$

The *NPV* of the project is greater than zero; therefore, the company should accept this project.

Method 2

Rather than seperately calculating the present value of all cash inflows and the present value of the cash outflows, we can calculate the cash inflows less cash outflows for every period (the Net Cash Flow) and calculate the present value of those amounts, to determine the Net Present Value. Most financial calculators require this format for evaluating the Net Present Value.

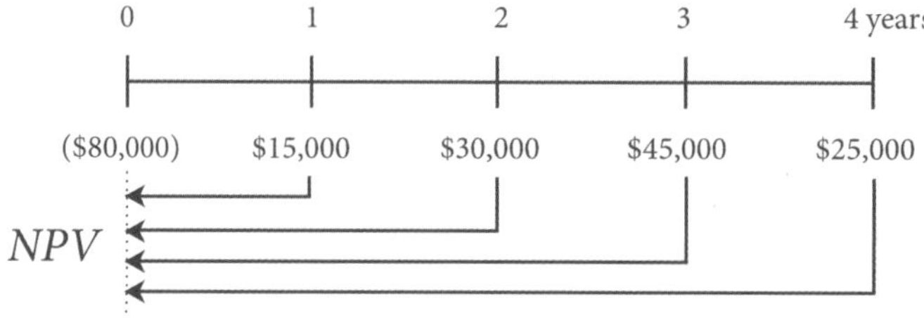

$$NPV = -80{,}000.00 + 15{,}000.00(1 + 0.10)^{-1} + 30{,}000.00(1 + 0.10)^{-2} + 45{,}000.00(1 + 0.10)^{-3} + 25{,}000.00(1 + 0.10)^{-4}$$

$$= -80{,}000.00 + 13{,}636.36364... + 24{,}793.38843... + 33{,}809.16604... + 17{,}075.33638...$$

$$= 9314.254491... = \$9314.25$$

$$NPV > 0$$

The *NPV* of the project is greater than zero; therefore, the company should accept this project.

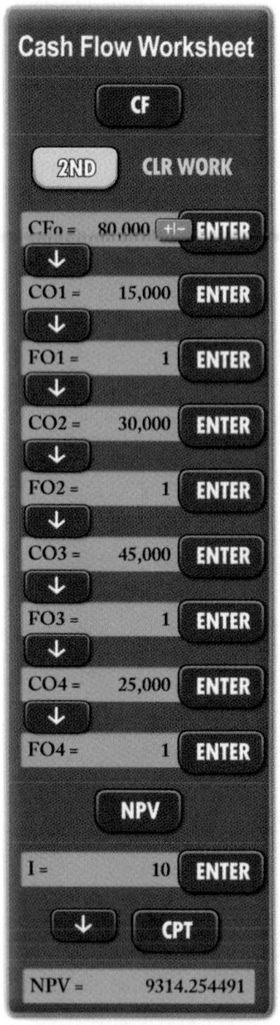

Example 14.2(b) **Comparing Investment Decisions when Cash Flows are Capital Investments**

The operations team at Hairpin Engineering Inc. was evaluating the feasibility of the following two projects that were required for the business:

- Milling Project: Investment of $260,000 in an automatic milling machine that would reduce wastage by $180,000 in the first year and $120,000 in the second year.
- Grinding Project: Investment of $120,860 in an automatic grinding machine that would reduce wastage by $85,000 in the first year and $116,000 in the second year.

Compute the NPV of each project and determine if the team should accept or reject them if the cost of capital is 12%.

Page 601

Solution

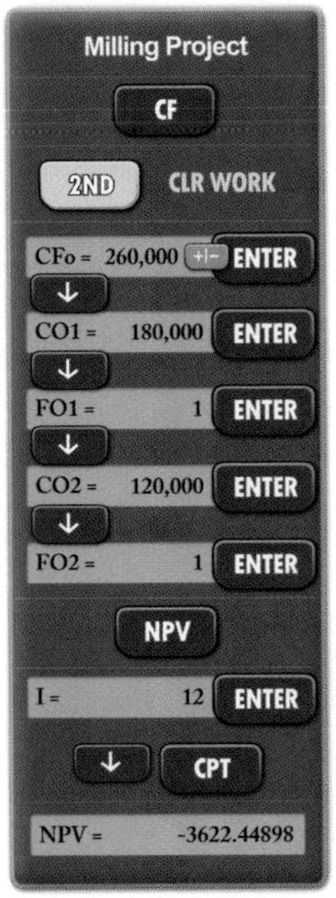

The reduction of wastage would be cash saved for the business and is considered a cash inflow.

Milling Project

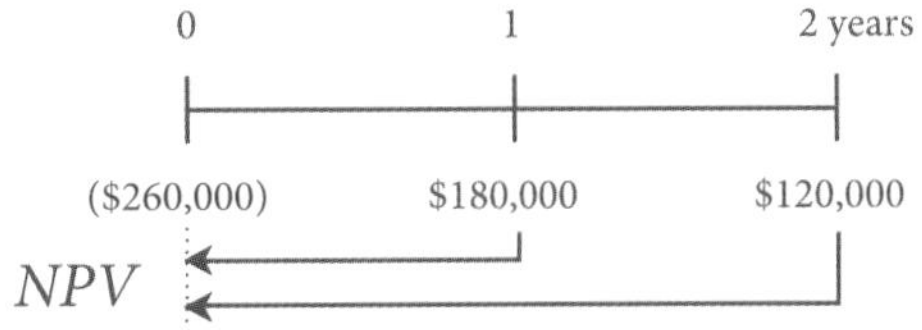

$$NPV_{Milling} = -260{,}000.00 + 180{,}000.00(1 + 0.12)^{-1} + 120{,}000.00(1 + 0.12)^{-2}$$
$$= -260{,}000.00 + 160{,}714.2857... + 95{,}663.26531...$$
$$= -3622.448980... = -\$3622.45$$

$NPV_{Milling}$ is negative; therefore, the team should reject the milling project.

Grinding Project

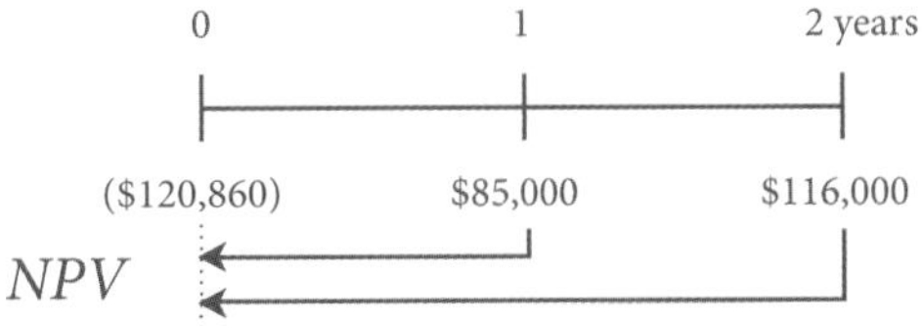

$$NPV_{Grinding} = -120{,}860.00 + 85{,}000.00(1 + 0.12)^{-1} + 116{,}000.00(1 + 0.12)^{-2}$$
$$= -120{,}860.00 + 75{,}892.85714... + 92{,}474.48980...$$
$$= 47{,}507.34694... = \$47{,}507.35$$

$NPV_{Grinding}$ is positive; therefore, the team should accept the grinding project.

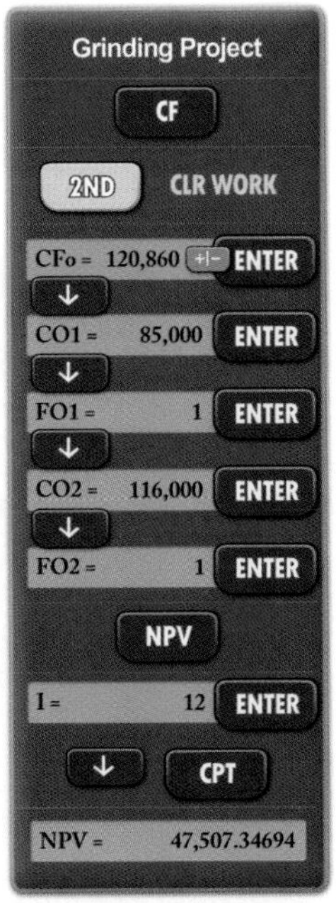

Example 14.2(c) Evaluating an Investment Decision when Cash Flows Form an Annuity

Martin was evaluating the feasibility of purchasing a factory. He would have to make an upfront payment of $1,470,000. He would then need to invest $900,000 one year from now and $950,000 two years from now to upgrade and expand the facilities. The factory would generate net returns of $380,000 from the second year onwards. He planned to sell the factory at the end of eight years for $4,000,000. If the required rate of return is 15%, should he accept or reject this plan?

Solution

Page 601

Method 1

$$NPV = PV_{Cash\ Inflows} - PV_{Cash\ Outflows}$$

Calculating the Present Value of Cash Inflows

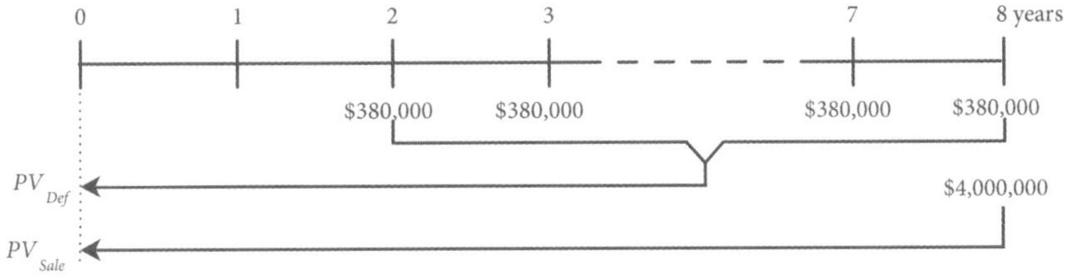

The present value of cash inflows at the focal date can be calculated using the different approaches discussed in the Compound Interest and Annuities chapters. Let us consider the $380,000 annual net income from year 2 to year 8 as an ordinary deferred annuity (deferral period of one year), and the $4,000,000 single payment as shown on the line diagram.

Solution
continued

$$PV_{Def} = 380,000.00\left[\frac{1-(1+0.15)^{-7}}{0.15}\right](1+0.15)^{-1} = \$1,374,747.390...$$

$$PV_{Sale} = 4,000,000.00(1+0.15)^{-8} = \$1,307,607.095...$$

$$PV_{Cash\ Inflows} = PV_{Def} + PV_{Sale}$$
$$= 1,374,747.390... + 1,307,607.095...$$
$$= \$2,682,354.486...$$

Calculating the Present Value of Cash Outflows

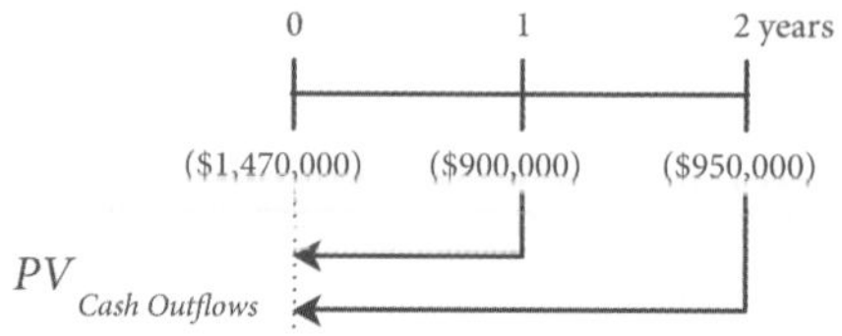

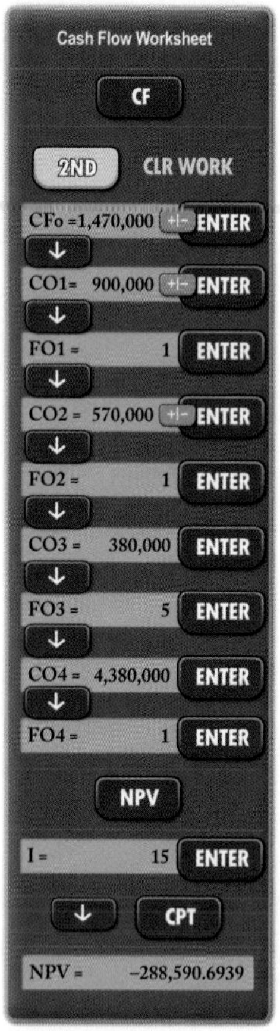

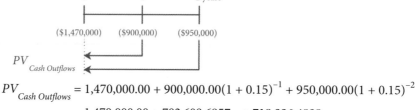

$$PV_{Cash\ Outflows} = 1,470,000.00 + 900,000.00(1+0.15)^{-1} + 950,000.00(1+0.15)^{-2}$$
$$= 1,470,000.00 + 782,608.6957... + 718,336.4839...$$
$$= \$2,970,945.180...$$

Using Formula 14.2, $NPV = PV_{Cash\ Inflows} - PV_{Cash\ Outflows}$

$$= 2,682,354.486... - 2,970,945.180...$$
$$= -288,590.6939... = -\$288,590.69$$

As the *NPV* is negative, he should reject the plan.

Method 2

The net cash flow for each period must be calculated by subtracting all of the cash outflows from all of the cash inflows for each period.

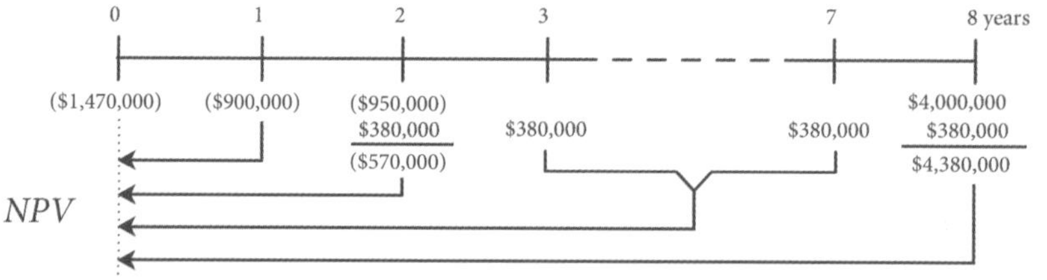

Note: *When using the cash flow worksheet of a financial calculator, a cash flow amount must be entered for every period. If no cash flow exists for a particular period, enter 0 for that C0 and 1 for the F0. If more than one cash flow exists in a specific period, enter the net cash flow for that period.*

Example 14.2(d) **Evaluating an Investment Decision when Payments are Not Annual**

Ella, the CEO of a small tech start-up, was debating whether to invest her company's profits in an annuity in which she would need to invest $10,000 now, and receive 48 monthly payments of $400, with the first payment being received in one year. By computing the NPV, determine whether Ella should invest her company's profits in the annuity. Assume the rate of return is 13%, compounded semi-annually.

Page 602

Solution

Since the cash flows are occurring monthly, we must use the periodic monthly compounded interest rate in the cash flow worksheet.

$$i = \frac{j}{m} = \frac{0.13}{2} = 0.065$$

$$c = \frac{\textit{Number of compounding periods per year}}{\textit{Number of payments per year}} = \frac{2}{12}$$

$$i_2 = (1 + i)^c - 1 = (1 + 0.065)^{(2/12)} - 1 = 0.010551...$$

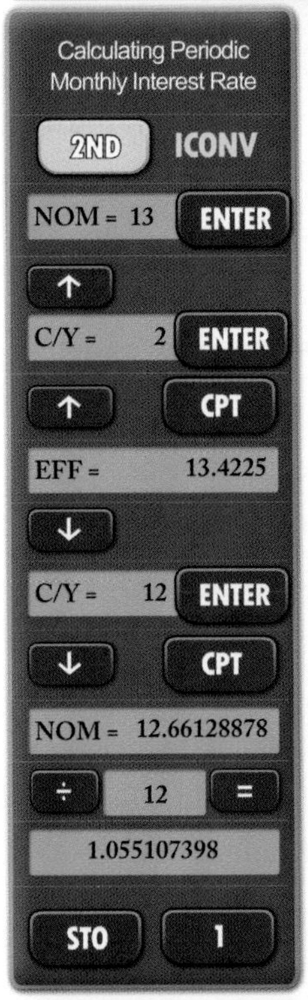

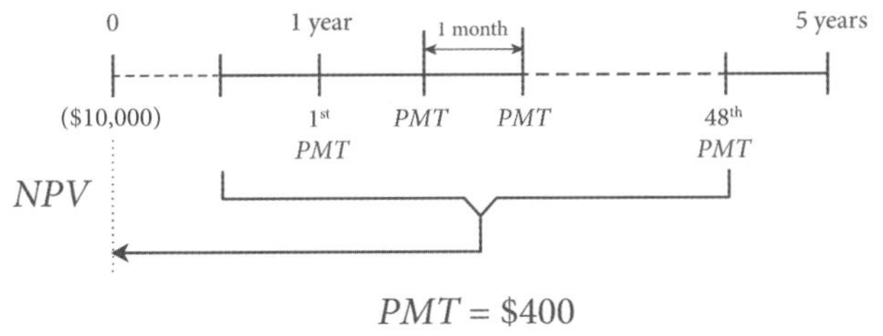

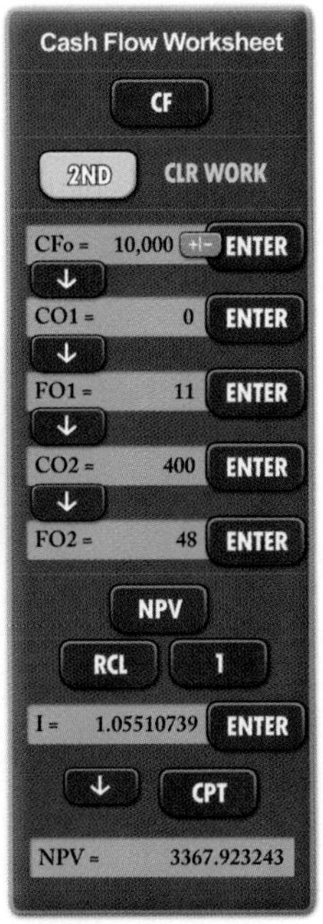

The 48 monthly payments of \$400 starting in one year can be considered as an ordinary deferred annuity (deferral period of 11 months).

Since there are no cash flows for 11 months, we enter 0 for CO1 and 11 for F01.

$$NPV = -10{,}000.00 + 400.00\left[\frac{1 - (1 + 0.010551...)^{-48}}{0.010551...}\right](1 + 0.010551...)^{-11}$$

$$= -10{,}000.00 + 13{,}367.92324...$$

$$= 3367.923243... = \$3367.92$$

As the NPV is positive, Ella should invest her company's profits in the annuity.

14.2 | Exercises

Answers to the odd-numbered problems are available at the end of the textbook.

1. Martha's hair salon is considering buying airtime for a television commercial to spread the word about its services and attract clients during non-peak hours. Alternatively, it could invest in a cheaper newspaper advertisement campaign. It forecasted the following cash flows for the two options:
   - Television: Investment of \$9500 today would increase profits by \$7350 in the first year and \$5650 in the second year.
   - Newspaper: Investment of \$1350 today would increase profits by \$3250 in the first year and \$1600 in the second year.

   If the cost of capital is 8%, compute the NPV for each option and determine the most economical one.

2. A printing shop is evaluating the following two investment options to improve its process.
   - Upgrade the printing equipment: Investment of \$35,000 today would increase profits by \$40,000 in the first year and \$20,000 in the second year.
   - Replace the printing equipment with automated equipment: Investment of \$150,000 today would increase profits by \$70,000 in the first year and \$120,000 in the second year.

   If the cost of capital is 7%, compute the NPV of each investment option and determine the most economical one.

3. A construction company is evaluating the feasibility of purchasing a fleet of trucks for a total investment of \$4,250,000 today. It forecasted that the purchase would generate profits of \$880,500 in the first year, \$900,000 in the second year, and \$750,000 in the third year. At the end of the third year, it would sell the trucks for \$3,000,000. Compute the NPV and determine if this is a feasible investment decision for a cost of capital of:

   a. 11% b. 12% c. 13%

4. The project manager of a steel manufacturing factory in Hamilton puts forth a proposal to the senior management for the immediate purchase of a specialized machine that costs $2,750,000. She forecasted that it would increase the profits through improved productivity by $1,200,000 in the first year, $1,150,000 in the second year, and $960,400 in the third year. At the end of the third year, the machine would have a salvage value of $500,000. Compute the NPV and determine if this is a sound investment proposal for a cost of capital of:

   a. 7% b. 10% c. 11%

5. Harold purchased two trucks for his warehouse for a total of $65,000. This investment saved him $13,500 every year for ten years. At the end of the tenth year, he sold both the trucks for a total of $10,000. Compute the NPV and determine if this was a sound investment decision. The cost of capital is 8.5%.

6. Gabrielle was spending a lot of money on outsourcing her printing jobs to a local printer. To save costs, she purchased an $18,500 colour laser printer for her office. This investment saved her $3250 every year for eight years. At the end of the eighth year, she sold the printer for $2500. Compute the NPV and determine if this was a sound investment decision. The cost of capital is 12%.

7. Samuel Semiconductors plans to invest $1,500,000 today and $1,650,000 one year from now on a research project. The company forecasted that it would start making net returns of $640,000 every year from the third year onwards, for ten years, at the end of which, it would sell the project for $2,500,000. Compute the NPV and determine if the project is feasible. The cost of capital is 8%.

8. Coupix Inc. was developing a complex mobile application that required an investment of $1,200,000 today and $1,350,000 one year from now. It was forecasted that the application will generate net returns of $1,000,000 every year from the third year onwards, for three years, at the end of which, Coupix will sell the application to a competitor for $1,500,000. Compute the NPV and determine if this was a sound investment decision. The cost of capital was 11%.

9. Madrid Development Inc. was evaluating the feasibility of a construction project. Construction would require an initial outlay of $3,230,000 today, $1,600,000 one year from now, and $450,000 two years from now. Net returns of $900,000 are expected every year starting from the second year onwards, for nine years, at the end of which, the project will be sold for $4,850,000. Compute the NPV and determine if the project is feasible. The cost of capital is 12%.

10. Microhaul Inc. was planning on building a private transportation network in London, Ontario. Construction would require an initial outlay of $1,230,000 today, $350,000 one year from now, and $200,000 two years from now. Net returns of $375,000 were expected every year starting from the second year onwards, for seven years, at the end of which, the network would be sold to the government for $1,000,000. Compute the NPV and determine if the plan is feasible. The cost of capital is 10%.

• 11. A company was evaluating the feasibility of investing in machinery to manufacture an automotive component. It would need to make an investment of $550,000 today, after which, it would have to spend $7000 every year starting one year from now for ten years. At the end of the period, the machine would have a salvage value of $10,000. The company confirmed that it can produce and sell 8000 components every year for ten years and the net return will be $12.50 per component. Compute the NPV and determine if the investment option is feasible. The cost of capital is 9%.

• 12. Vera Fabrics was evaluating the feasibility of investing in machinery that would improve the production process of its clothing line. An initial investment of $650,000 was required to purchase the machine today, and additional investments of $40,000 one year from now and $35,000 two years from now for upgrades and maintenance. The machinery would have an economic life of seven years, at the end of which, the salvage value would be $12,000. Investment in the machinery will result in cost savings of $5 per metre of the 30,000 metres of fabric that is produced every year, starting one year from now, for the entire economic life of the machinery. Compute the NPV and determine if the investment decision is feasible. The cost of capital is 8%.

- 13. By evaluating the NPV of both options, determine which of the following plans is a better investment:

  Plan A: Invest $25,000 now, and receive 24 quarterly payments of $2000, with the first payment being received in two years.

  Plan B: Make 5 annual deposits of $5000 starting now, and receive $40,000 in eight years.

  The cost of capital is 11%, compounded semi-annually.

- 14. By evaluating the NPV of both options, determine which of the following plans is a better investment:

  Plan A: Invest $100,000 now, and receive 14 annual payments of $10,000, with the first payment being received in one year.

  Plan B: Make 8 semi-annual deposits of $10,000 starting now, and receive $120,000 in 5 years.

  The cost of capital is 9%, compounded monthly.

14.3 | Internal Rate of Return (IRR)

The **Internal Rate of Return** (IRR) is the effective (annually compounding) rate of return for an investment. The IRR is the discount rate at which the NPV of an investment is zero; i.e., the IRR is the rate of return that makes the present value of all cash inflows equal to the present value of all cash outflows ($PV_{Cash\ Inflows} = PV_{Cash\ Outflows}$). It is also called the **Return on Investment** (ROI).

As described earlier, the rate of return used to calculate the NPV is the **required rate of return** that the business expects from investing in this project. This required rate of return is generally the **cost of capital** *(i)*, which is the opportunity cost of investing, i.e., the rate of return the business would otherwise earn when the amount is invested in another investment that has the same risk level as this project.

Projects are accepted if the internal rate of return is greater than or equal to the cost of capital (*i*) and projects are rejected if the IRR is less than the cost of capital (*i*).

In summary,

If $\boldsymbol{NPV = 0, IRR = i}$, Project is acceptable.

If $\boldsymbol{NPV > 0, IRR > i}$, Project is acceptable.

If $\boldsymbol{NPV < 0, IRR < i}$, Project should be rejected.

The higher a project's IRR, the more profitable the project is (relative to the initial investment). As such, the IRR can be used to rank the projects that a business is considering. When comparing investment projects, the project that has the highest IRR should be accepted.

Solving for a project's IRR using algebra alone is difficult and can only be computed by trial and error. Using a preprogrammed financial calculator (such as the Texas Instruments BAII Plus) automates this trial and error process, and it becomes much more feasible to compute the IRR for several projects. We will be using this approach in the following example.

Example 14.3 **Calculating the IRR for a Project**

A project required investments of $40,000 today, $60,000 one year from now, $60,000 two years from now, and $60,000 three years from now. It generated net returns of $35,000 in the fourth year and continued generating net returns of $40,000 from the fifth year onwards, for nine years. The project had a salvage value of $55,000.

(i) Calculate the internal rate of return of this project.

(ii) If the cost of capital is 7%, is it feasible to undertake this project?

Page 602

Solution

The internal rate of return can be algebraically calculated by trial and error. This is a time consuming process, especially if we want to arrive at an accurate answer. However, the cash flow worksheet on a financial calculator can be used to accurately calculate the internal rate of return.

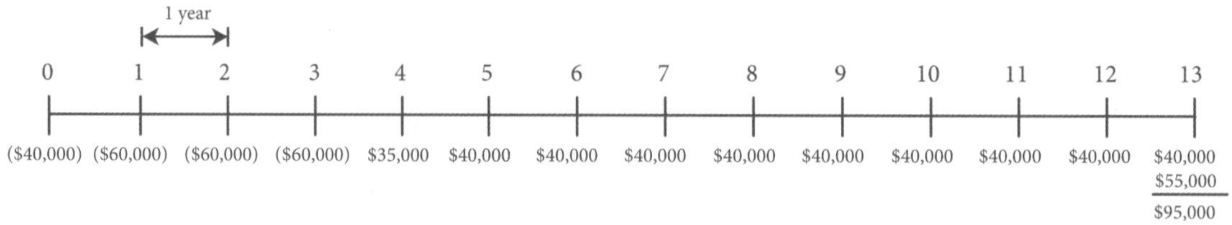

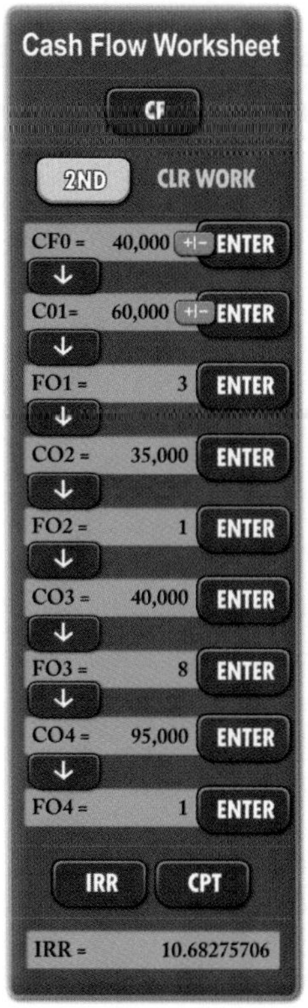

Press **CF** to open the Cash Flow Worksheet

Press **2ND** then **CLR WORK** (secondary function of the CE|C key) to clear previous work.

Enter the **$40,000** cash outflow (as a **negative** value).

Enter the **$60,000** cash outflow (as a **negative** value).

Enter the number of cash flows for CO1. The $60,000 payment will be made **3** times.

Enter the **$35,000** cash inflow.

Enter the number of cash flows for CO2 (**1** cash flow).

Enter the **$40,000** cash inflow.

Enter the number of cash flows for CO3. There are **8** years in which the total inflow is $40,000.

Enter the total cash inflow of **$95,000** in the final year.

Enter the number of cash flows for CO4 (**1** cash flow).

Press **IRR** and **CPT** to compute the internal rate of return.

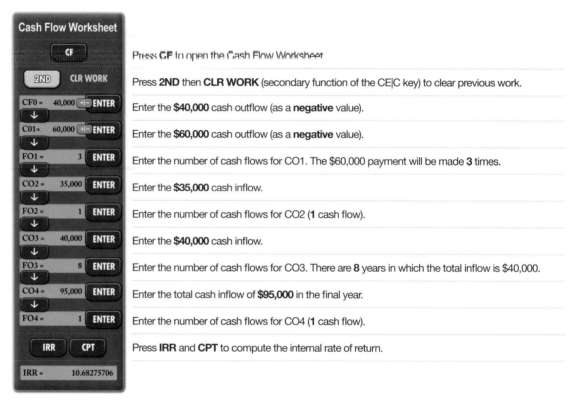

(i) Therefore, the internal rate of return for this project is 10.68%.

(ii) The IRR of 10.68% is higher than the cost of capital of 7%. It is therefore feasible to undertake this project.

14.3 | Exercises

Answers to the odd-numbered problems are available at the end of the textbook.

For the following problems, express the answers rounded to two decimal places, wherever applicable.

1. Calculate the IRR for a project that requires an investment of $60,000 today and $50,000 one year from now. The project will generate profits of $20,000 every year, from the second year onwards, for ten years, and it has no terminal value.

2. A research project requires an investment of $1,500,000 today and $450,000 one year from today. It would generate cost savings of $650,000 every year starting from the second year onwards, for five years. Calculate the IRR of the project.

3. Cheng is evaluating the feasibility of a project that requires an investment of $750,000 today and $300,000 one year from today. It will generate cost savings of $200,000 every year from the second year onwards, for seven years. If the project has a terminal value of $25,000, calculate the IRR. Should the project be accepted if the company's cost of capital is 8%?

4. Umar and Adam were evaluating the feasibility of a project which requires an investment of $350,000 today and $300,000 one year from today. The project would generate operating profits of $150,000 every year from the second year onwards, for five years. The project would have a terminal value of $100,000. Calculate the IRR of the project and determine whether it is feasible if the cost of capital is 8%.

5. Andrew purchased a franchisee agreement to distribute electronic gadgets for ten years. The agreement requires an investment of $1,500,000 today, $950,000 one year from today, and $350,000 two years from today to establish the showroom. The franchise generated $550,000 in profits each year from the first year onwards, for ten years. At the end of the tenth year, he anticipates that he can sell the furniture in his showroom for $20,000. Calculate the IRR and determine if he should proceed if the cost of capital is 9%.

6. Production Co. hired a management consulting firm to execute a new project launch. The consulting firm charged the company $180,000 as an initial appraisal fee. A year later, it charged them $750,000, and two years later, $800,000. Through the launch, Production Co. had profits of $250,000 every year from the first year onwards, for ten years. If the project had no terminal value, calculate the IRR of this consulting engagement. If the company's required rate of return is 11%, was it worthwhile for it to hire this consulting firm?

7. Harold purchased two trucks for his warehouse for a total of $65,000. This investment saved him $13,500 every year for ten years. At the end of the tenth year, he sold both the trucks for a total of $10,000. Calculate the IRR of Harold's investment. If the cost of capital is 8.5%, is the IRR higher than the cost of capital?

8. Gabrielle was spending a lot of money on outsourcing her printing jobs to a local printer. To save costs, she purchased an $18,500 colour laser printer for her office. This investment saved her $3250 every year for eight years. At the end of the eighth year, she sold the printer for $2500. Calculate the IRR of Gabrielle's investment. If the cost of capital is 12%, is the IRR higher than the cost of capital?

9. Samuel Semiconductors plans to invest $1,500,000 today and $1,650,000 one year from now on a research project. The company forecasted that it would start making net returns of $640,000 every year from the third year onwards, for ten years, at the end of which it would sell the project for $2,500,000. Calculate the IRR of Samuel Semiconductors' project. If the cost of capital is 8%, is the IRR higher than the cost of capital?

10. Coupix Inc. was developing a complex mobile application that required an investment of $1,200,000 today and $1,350,000 one year from now. It was forecasted that the application will generate net returns of $1,000,000 every year from the third year onwards, for three years, at the end of which Coupix will sell the application to a competitor for $1,500,000. Calculate the IRR of Coupix Inc.'s investment. If the cost of capital is 11%, is the IRR higher than the cost of capital?

11. Madrid Development Inc. was evaluating the feasibility of a construction project. Construction would require an initial outlay of $3,230,000 today, $1,600,000 one year from now, and $450,000 two years from now. Net returns of $900,000 are expected every year starting from the second year onwards, for nine years, at the end of which the project will be sold for $4,850,000. Calculate the IRR of Madrid Development's project. If the cost of capital is 12%, is the IRR higher than the cost of capital?

12. Microhaul Inc. was planning on building a private transportation network in London, Ontario. Construction would require an initial outlay of $1,230,000 today, $350,000 one year from now, and $200,000 two years from now. Net returns of $375,000 were expected every year starting from the second year onwards, for seven years, at the end of which the network would be sold to the government for $1,000,000. Calculate the IRR of Microhaul Inc.'s construction project. If the cost of capital is 10%, is the IRR higher than the cost of capital?

• 13. A company was evaluating the feasibility of investing in machinery to manufacture an automotive component. It would need to make an investment of $550,000 today, after which, it would have to spend $7000 every year starting one year from now for ten years. At the end of the period, the machine would have a salvage value of $10,000. The company confirmed that it can produce and sell 8000 components every year for ten years and that the net return will be $12.50 per component. Calculate the IRR of the manufacturing company's investment. If the cost of capital is 9%, is the IRR higher than the cost of capital?

• 14. Vera Fabrics was evaluating the feasibility of investing in machinery that would improve the production process of its clothing line. An initial investment of $650,000 was required to purchase the machine today, and additional investments of $40,000 one year from now and $35,000 two years from now for upgrades and maintenance. The machinery would have an economic life of seven years, at the end of which the salvage value would be $12,000. Investment in the machinery will result in cost savings of $5 per metre of the 30,000 metres of fabric that is produced every year, starting one year from now, for the entire economic life of the machinery. Calculate the IRR of Vera Fabrics' investment. If the cost of capital is 8%, is the IRR higher than the cost of capital?

14.4 | Payback Period

The payback period is the length of time required for an investment to break even, where the cash inflows reach the amount of the inital cash outlay.

The payback period is calculated as the ratio of the project's cost to the annual cash inflows. For example, if a project costs $275,000 and it produces regular annual cash inflows of $50,000, then,

$$\textit{Payback Period} = \frac{275{,}000}{50{,}000} = 5.5 \text{ years} = 5 \text{ years and } 6 \text{ months}$$

We can also find this value using a table (which is necessary if cash flows are not the same from year to year). The first two columns in the table show Cash Outflows (negative) and Cash Inflows (positive). The third column, Net Cash Flow, shows the difference between cash inflows and cash outflows for every year. The Cumulative Cash Flow column represents the total Net Cash Flow for the current year and all previous years. Once the Cumulative Cash Flow reaches zero, the project has reached its payback period.

	Cash Outflow	Cash Inflow	Net Cash Flow	Cumulative Cash Flow
Year 1	($275,000)	$50,000	($225,000)	($225,000)
Year 2	-	50,000	50,000	(175,000)
Year 3	-	50,000	50,000	(125,000)
Year 4	-	50,000	50,000	(75,000)
Year 5	-	50,000	50,000	(25,000)
Year 6	-	50,000	50,000	25,000

The cumulative cash flow shows that the company will break even in Year 6 (it only needs $25,000 in Year 6 to break even, which it will exceed).

$$\textit{Payback Period} = \left(5 + \frac{25{,}000}{50{,}000}\right) = \left(5 + \frac{1}{2}\right) \text{ years}$$
$$= 5 \text{ years and } 6 \text{ months}$$

The Payback Period Method ignores the time value of money and also ignores any benefits that occur after the payback period. Despite these deficiencies, the method is often used due to its simplicity.

Investors and businesses often employ a 'Payback Rule', which requires that all projects that are undertaken have a payback period within a certain amount of time, such as 5 years. If the investment costs are recovered sooner, then the additional cash inflows can be reinvested into other projects. For this reason, investments with shorter payback periods may be considered less risky.

Example 14.4(a) **Evaluating Invesment Decisions Using a Payback Rule**

Stewart Bradley Inc. is evaluating a project which will require a $40,000 investment. Based on analysis, the project will generate future net returns of $7000 in year one, $15,000 in year two, $22,000 in year three, and $10,000 in year four. Should the company accept the project if it has a payback rule of three years?

Solution

	Cash Outflow	Cash Inflow	Net Cash Flow	Cumulative Cash Flow
Year 1	($40,000)	$7000	($33,000)	($33,000)
Year 2	-	15,000	15,000	(18,000)
Year 3	-	22,000	22,000	4000
Year 4	-	10,000	10,000	14,000

The cumulative cash flow shows that the company will break even in year three (it only needs $18,000 in year three to break even, which it will exceed).

$$\textit{Payment Period} = \left(2 + \frac{18{,}000}{22{,}000}\right) = \left(2 + \frac{9}{11}\right) \text{ years}$$

$$= 2 \text{ years and } 10 \text{ months (rounded up to the next month)}$$

The payback period is below the payback rule; therefore, the company should accept the project.

Example 14.4(b) **Evaluating Invesment Decisions Using a Payback Rule**

A software company invested $120,000 to acquire a product from a competitor and invested an additional $100,000 every year for the next two years to convert the product into a new service offering. When the service entered the market, it generated yearly profits of $60,000 from the fourth year onwards, for eight years, at the end of which, the underlying technology was sold for $800,000.

(i) Calculate this project's payback period.

(ii) Does this satisfy the company's payback rule of seven years?

Solution

	Cash Outflow	Cash Inflow	Net Cash Flow	Cumulative Cash Flow
Year 1	($120,000)	-	($120,000)	($120,000)
Year 2	(100,000)	-	(100,000)	(220,000)
Year 3	(100,000)	-	(100,000)	(320,000)
Year 4	-	$60,000	60,000	(260,000)
Year 5	-	60,000	60,000	(200,000)
Year 6	-	60,000	60,000	(140,000)
Year 7	-	60,000	60,000	(80,000)
Year 8	-	60,000	60,000	(20,000)
Year 9	-	60,000	60,000	40,000
Year 10	-	60,000	60,000	100,000
Year 11	-	860,000	860,000	960,000

Solution *continued*

(i) The cumulative cash flow shows that the company will break even in year nine. Only $20,000 is needed to break even in year nine, but there are cash inflows of $60,000.

$$\textit{Payback Period} = \left(8 + \frac{20{,}000}{60{,}000}\right) = \left(8 + \frac{1}{3}\right) \text{ years}$$
$$= 8 \text{ years and } 4 \text{ months}$$

Therefore, the project's payback period is 8 years and 4 months.

(ii) The payback period exceeds seven years; therefore, it does not satisfy the company's payback rule.

14.4 | Exercises

Answers to the odd-numbered problems are available at the end of the textbook.

For the following problems, express the answers in years and months rounded up to the next month.

1. KFX Corporation is considering a $40,000 investment, which will provide net returns of $5000, $20,000, $25,000, and $45,000 in the second, third, fourth, and fifth years, respectively. The company has a payback rule of four years. What is the payback period and should the company undertake the investment?

2. Kabab Co. is considering a $260,000 investment, which will provide net returns of $100,000, $150,000, and $200,000 in the second, third, and fourth years, respectively. The company has a payback rule of three years. What is the payback period and should the company undertake the investment?

3. In 2015, a distributor of fishing and camping equipment paid $225,000 to sponsor an event. It also paid $175,000 in 2016 and $100,000 in 2017 towards the sponsorship of the event. The sponsorship increased the company's brand awareness, leading to increased profits of $120,000 every year from 2017 onwards for five years. What is the payback period of the sponsorship and does it satisfy the distributor's payback rule of six years?

4. A movie studio invested $60 million to produce a film. This budget was exhausted in the first year, before the film was completed. It cost an additional $15 million in the second year to complete the film. The film generated net returns of $40 million in the third year, $25 million in the fourth year, and went on to generate net returns of $3 million every year from the fifth year for five years. Calculate the payback period on the film project and determine whether this satisfies the studio's eight-year payback rule.

• 5. Richard purchased a business for $200,000, borrowing from a family member to finance the purchase. The business generated revenues of $50,000 every year from the first year. From the second year onwards, Richard withdrew a salary of $45,000 per annum. In the fourth year, he spent $20,000 to renovate his showroom to attract more customers. This increased his profits to $130,000 every year starting from the fifth year. What was the payback period on the business? Does this meet his payback rule of four and a half years?

• 6. Clara operates a specialized financial services business in Toronto. She's currently considering purchasing an exclusive service agreement from a competitor for $120,000, but would like to ensure that the investment would meet her payback rule of five years. The service agreement would guarantee net returns of $30,000 per year, but would also require her to pay $15,000 for a regulatory audit every other year (starting from the first year). What is the payback period on this investment and does it satisfy Clara's payback rule?

14 | Review Exercises

Answers to the odd-numbered problems are available at the end of the textbook.

For the following problems, express the answers rounded to two decimal places, wherever applicable.

1. Gabriel is deciding between purchasing farm equipment for $100,000 or taking advantage of a leasing option. The leasing option would require him to make a down-payment of $5000 immediately, and a payment of $2000 at the beginning of every month for four years. At the end of four years, he would have to pay $15,000 to own the equipment. Using the DCF method, calculate which option is cheaper, and by how much, if money is worth 7% compounded monthly.

2. A new car model is available for $23,000. There is also a leasing option available which requires payments of $350 at the beginning of every month for four years, at the end of which, there is an option to purchase the vehicle for $10,000. Using the DCF method, calculate which option would be cheaper, and by how much, if money is worth 5.75% compounded monthly.

3. The government spent an initial amount of $1,960,000 to lay the foundation for a new toll road. It spent an additional $2,350,000 one year from now and $2,200,000 two years from now to construct the roads. The toll road generated net returns of $700,000 every year from the third year onwards, for ten years, at the end of which, it sold the toll road for $5,000,000 to a private company. What is the NPV of this investment if the cost of capital was 5%?

4. A consulting firm offered a company the following proposal for its consulting services: (i) an upfront payment of $200,000 for a thorough analysis of the current situation, and (ii) payments of $300,000 one year from now and $300,000 two years from now to develop and implement a cost-savings strategy. It guaranteed $310,000 in annual cost savings starting from the third year onwards, for four years. If the project has no terminal value, calculate the NPV of this consulting engagement. If the company's required rate of return is 11%, was it feasible for it to hire this consulting firm?

5. In Problem 3, calculate the IRR of the provincial government's investment. Was it higher than its cost of capital?

6. In Problem 4, calculate the IRR of the company's investment in the consulting engagement. Was it higher than its required rate of return?

7. Louise, a senior manager at Tulip Waters LLP, is evaluating a proposal for the purchase of an automatic machine that costs $3,000,000. She forecasts that it would increase profits by $600,000, $1,500,000, and $1,800,000 in the first, second, and third years, respectively. At the end of the third year, the machine would have a salvage value of $125,000. By calculating the NPV, is this investment economical for it if the cost of capital is:

   a. 12%? b. 13%? c. 14%?

8. Henry is considering the purchase of a new machine at a cost of $24,000. This will enable him to save $6000, $12,000, and $11,000 in the first, second, and third years, respectively. He could sell the machine at a scrap value of $500 at the end of the third year. By calculating the NPV, is this investment economical for him if the cost of capital is:

   a. 8%? b. 9%? c. 10%?

9. In an attempt to save on their electricity bill, Mr. and Mrs. Gloucester spent $7000 to install solar panels on the roof of their home. This saved them $1000 every year (from the first year) for 12 years. At the end of the 12th year, they spent $500 to uninstall the panels and scrap them. Was this installation worthwhile if their cost of capital was 7.5%? What was the NPV of the installation?

10. Bluestine Inc. opened a sales office at a cost of $1,100,000. The office generated consistent profits of $300,000 every year (from the first year) for five years. At the end of five years, it closed the office and sold all the furniture for $20,000. Calculate the NPV of the venture if the cost of capital was 10%.

11. An investment of $500,000 in a project will generate cost savings of $100,000 every year for the first six years and $45,000 every year for the next four years. If there is no terminal value for the project, calculate its IRR.

12. An investment of $180,000 in a project will generate operating profits of $50,000 every year for the first two years and $30,000 every year for the next five years. If the project has a terminal value of $5000, calculate its IRR.

13. A pharmaceutical company is developing a new pill that requires investments of $1,550,000 today, $600,000 one year from now, and $780,000 two years from now. The company anticipates that it will generate profits of $750,000, $1,000,000 and $1,250,000 in the third, fourth, and fifth years, respectively. At the end of the fifth year, the patent on the pill can be sold for $1,000,000. What is the IRR of this project? Is the development feasible if the cost of capital is 8%?

14. The development of a new robotic machine required investments of $1,600,000 today, $900,000 one year from today, and $890,000 two years from today. The team forecasted cost savings of $1,150,000, $1,200,000, and $1,610,000 in the third, fourth, and fifth years, respectively. At the end of the fifth year, the machine would have a salvage value of $540,000. Calculate the IRR of this project. Will the development be feasible if the company's cost of capital is 9%?

15. Hydra Corp. is analyzing a decision that would require an initial investment of $300,000 that will provide net returns of $200,000 in the first year, $120,000 in the second year, and $25,000 in the third year. What is the IRR of the investment? Does it meet the company's IRR of 10%?

16. Massey is assessing an investment in which she would have to pay $25,000 today to receive net returns of $15,000 in the first year, $5000 in the second year, and $10,000 in the third year. If the investment has no terminal value, what is its IRR and does it meet Massey's IRR of 11%?

17. A farmer purchased a machine for $60,000 in the hopes of increasing the productivity of his farm. The machine had a positive impact resulting in increased profits of $20,000 every year from the second year onwards, for six years. In the third year, the machine required repairs costing $8000. What is the payback period of the machine? Does it satisfy the farmer's four-year payback rule?

18. Heartlife Finance lent $40,000 to a businesswoman to start a new business. The business did not earn any revenues in its first year and required an additional $20,000 investment from Heartlife Finance to continue operating into the second year. From the second year onwards, the business was able to generate profits of $25,000 for seven consecutive years. Being a relatively small financier, Heartlife uses a three-year payback rule on all of its business investments. What is the payback period of this investment and does it satisfy the payback rule?

19. Hillary wanted to grow a small orchard on a property she owned in Niagara. She spent $20,000 in the first year to plant the trees and $6000 per year for the next four years to grow the trees. The orchard generated profits of $12,000 per year from the fifth year onwards. What is the payback period on the orchard and would it have satisfied a seven-year payback rule?

20. A large corporation purchased a start-up company for $600,000. The start-up generated profits of $120,000 in the first year, $80,000 in the second year, and $75,000 in the third year. In the third year, the parent corporation invested $135,000 in a change initiative to transform the start-up into a high performer. It was successful in increasing profits to $200,000 per year from the fourth year onwards. What is the payback period on the investment in the start-up company and would it have satisfied a six-year payback rule?

14 | Self-Test Exercises

Answers to all the problems are available at the end of the textbook.

For the following problems, express the answers rounded to two decimal places, wherever applicable.

1. A young investor is deciding between two equal investments that will provide the following net returns:
   - Option 1 will provide net returns of $40,000 one year from now and $11,000 five years from now.
   - Option 2 will provide net returns of $15,000 two years from now and $40,000 five years from now.

   Determine which option is better, and by how much, if his cost of capital is 10%.

2. A fast-food restaurant chain would like to introduce a new ice cream to its menu, but will need to invest in ice cream machines for all of its restaurants. This upgrade will cost $200,000 and is expected to generate net returns of $125,000, $70,000, and $60,000, in the first, second, and third years, respectively. What is the NPV of this investment? Should it make this investment if the required rate of return is 14%?

3. In Problem 2, calculate the IRR of the investment. Was it higher than the required rate of return?

4. A cell phone manufacturer is evaluating the following two investments to improve its process:
   - Upgraded plastic molder: Investment of $85,000 today would increase profits by $60,000 in the first year and $45,000 in the second year.
   - Upgraded conveyer system: Investment of $320,000 today would increase profits by $150,000 in the first year and $250,000 in the second year.

   Which of these investments is economically better and what is its IRR?

5. A research organization had to justify the economic viability of a patent development project. The project would require investments in salaries and other expenses in the amount of $650,000, $725,000, and $550,000, in the first, second, and third years, respectively. The patent would generate annual royalties of $500,000 from the fourth year onwards, for four years. The royalty rights would subsequently be sold to a manufacturer for $800,000. What is the NPV and is the project viable if the cost of capital of 9%?

6. A software development project would require investments of $400,000 every year for four years. It would generate profits of $425,000 from the second year onwards, for six years. Calculate its NPV if the cost of capital is 8%.

7. FC Corp. purchased a license which would allow it to provide a financial product to Canadian banks for the next 12 years. It costs the company $1,250,000 to purchase the license and it had to allow for a regulatory audit that cost $10,000 today and $10,000 one year from now. The agreement resulted in profits of $125,000 every year from the first year onwards, for 12 years. At the end of 12 years, the company sold the license to another organization for $400,000. What was the NPV and is the investment feasible if the company's required rate of return of 6%?

8. Jason is considering a $50,000 investment which will provide cash net returns of $6000, $25,000, $30,000, and $55,000 in the second, third, fourth, and fifth years, respectively. What is the payback period and should Jason undertake the investment if his payback rule is three years?

9. Holdon Ltd. purchased a small paragliding business for $300,000. The business is expected to provide net returns of $250,000 every year, starting from the first year, and has annual expenses of $120,000, as well as special licensing fees of $10,000 every year. What is the payback period on this investment and does it meet the company's two-year payback rule?

CASE 14

Investing in the Stock Market

Olena manages an investment company that has a portfolio of investments in various sectors including technology, social media, construction, auto manufacturing, and pharmaceutical industries. In 2014, she purchased 750 shares of a publicly traded social media company and 1800 shares of a publicly traded automobile company. She held the shares for three years and sold them at the beginning of 2017.

The following table summarizes the price per share when she purchased them on January 01, 2014 and sold them on January 01, 2017:

Company	Price Per Share 2014	Price Per Share 2017
Social Media Company	$45.21	$72.33
Automobile Company	$18.12	$29.50

The following table summarizes cash dividends that she received from the investments during the holding period:

Year	Social Media Company Dividends Per Share	Automobile Company Dividends Per Share
2014	$0.42	$0.24
2015	$0.38	$0.27
2016	$0.51	$0.23

Her required rate of return for investments in the stock market is 15%.

a. What is the NPV of the investment in the social media company shares?

b. What is the NPV of the investment in the automobile company shares?

c. What is the NPV of the total investment in the stock market?

d. What is the maximum amount she should have paid for the social media company's shares?

e. What is the maximum amount she should have paid for the automobile company's shares?

f. What rate of return was realized over the holding period for the social media company shares?

g. What rate of return was realized over the holding period for the automobile company shares?

h. What rate of return was realized over the holding period of the entire investment?

14 | Spreadsheet Solutions

Spreadsheet solutions to solved examples in the chapter.

14.1 Examples

Example 14.1(a)

	A	B	
1	Calculating *DCF*		
2	**Rate**	10.00%	
3	**Year 1**	$15,000.00	
4	**Year 2**	$10,000.00	
5	**Year 3**	$7,000.00	
6			
7	***DCF***	$27,160.03	= NPV(B2, B3:B5) NPV(rate, value1, [value2],...)
8			

Example 14.1(c)

	A	B	
1	Calculating *f*		
2	***j***	6.00%	
3	***m***	12	
4	***f***	6.1678%	= EFFECT(B2, B3) EFFECT(nominal_rate, npery)
5			
6	Calculating DCF_A		
7	**Year 1**	($60,000.00)	
8	**Year 2**	($70,000.00)	
9			
10	***DCF***	($118,617.32)	= NPV(B4, B7:B8) NPV(rate, value1,[value2],...)
11			
12	Calculating DCF_B		
13	**Year 1**	($40,000.00)	
14	**Year 2**	($80,000.00)	
15			
16	***DCF***	($108,651.07)	= NPV(B4, B13:B14) NPV(rate, value1,[value2],...)
17			

Example 14.1(d)

	A	B	
1	Calculating $PV_{Lease\ Option}$		
2	***j***	9.00%	
3	***m***	12	
4	***P/Y***	12	
5	***t***	4	
6			
7	***i***	0.75%	= B2/B3
8	***n***	48	= B4*B5
9	***PMT***	($330.00)	
10	***PV***	$23,839.65	= PV(B7, B8, B9, B11, B12) PV(rate, nper, pmt, [fv], [type])
11	***FV***	($15,000.00)	
12	***BGN***	1	
13			

14.2 Examples

Example 14.2(a)

	A	B	
1	Calculating *NPV*		
2	**Rate**	10.00%	
3	**Year 0**	($80,000.00)	
4	**Year 1**	$15,000.00	
5	**Year 2**	$30,000.00	
6	**Year 3**	$45,000.00	
7	**Year 4**	$25,000.00	
8			
9	***NPV***	$9,314.25	= B3+NPV(B2, B4:B7) NPV(rate, value1, [value2],...)
10			

Example 14.2(b)

	A	B	
1	$NPV_{Milling}$		
2	**Rate**	12.00%	
3	**Year 0**	($260,000.00)	
4	**Year 1**	$180,000.00	
5	**Year 2**	$120,000.00	
6			
7	***NPV***	($3,622.45)	= B3+NPV(B2, B4:B5) NPV(rate, value1, [value2],...)
8			
9	$NPV_{Grinding}$		
10	**Rate**	12.00%	
11	**Year 0**	($120,860.00)	
12	**Year 1**	$85,000.00	
13	**Year 2**	$116,000.00	
14			
15	***NPV***	$47,507.35	= B11+NPV(B10, B12:B13) NPV(rate, value1, [value2],...)
16			

Example 14.2(c)

	A	B	
1	Calculating *NPV*		
2	**Rate**	15.00%	
3	**Year 0**	($1,470,000.00)	
4	**Year 1**	($900,000.00)	
5	**Year 2**	($570,000.00)	= −950000+380000
6	**Year 3**	$380,000.00	
7	**Year 4**	$380,000.00	
8	**Year 5**	$380,000.00	
9	**Year 6**	$380,000.00	
10	**Year 7**	$380,000.00	
11	**Year 8**	$4,380,000.00	= 4000000+380000
12			
13	***NPV***	($288,590.69)	= B3+NPV(B2, B4:B11) NPV(rate, value1, [value2],...)
14			

Example 14.2(d)

	A	B	
1	Calculating *NPV*		
2	***j***	13.00%	
3	***m***	2	
4	***P/Y***	12	
5	***t***	4	
6			
7	***i***	6.50%	= B2/B3
8	***c***	0.166667	= B3/B4
9	i_2	1.0551%	= (1 + B7)^B8 – 1
10	***n***	48	= B4*B5
11	***PMT***	$400.00	
12	***PV***	($15,003.93)	= PV(B9, B10, B11, B13, B14) PV(rate, nper, pmt, [fv], [type])
13	***FV***	0	
14	***BGN***	0	
15			
16	***j***	13.00%	
17	***m***	2	
18	***t***	0.916667	= 11/12
19			
20	***i***	6.50%	= B16/B17
21	***n***	1.833333	= B17*B18
22	***PMT***	0	
23	***PV***	($13,367.92)	= PV(B20, B21, B22, B24) PV(rate, nper, pmt, [fv], [type])
24	***FV***	$15,003.93	= –B12
25			
26	***NPV***	$3,367.92	= –10000 – B23
27			

14.3 Examples

Example 14.3

	A	B	
1		Calculating *IRR*	
2	**Year 0**	($40,000.00)	
3	**Year 1**	($60,000.00)	
4	**Year 2**	($60,000.00)	
5	**Year 3**	($60,000.00)	
6	**Year 4**	$35,000.00	
7	**Year 5**	$40,000.00	
8	**Year 6**	$40,000.00	
9	**Year 7**	$40,000.00	
10	**Year 8**	$40,000.00	
11	**Year 9**	$40,000.00	
12	**Year 10**	$40,000.00	
13	**Year 11**	$40,000.00	
14	**Year 12**	$40,000.00	
15	**Year 13**	$95,000.00	
16			
17	***IRR***	10.68%	= IRR(B2:B15) IRR(values, [guess])
18			

14 | Summary of Notation and Formulas

NOTATION

DCF: Discounted Cash Flow

NPV: Net Present Value

IRR: Internal Rate of Return

FORMULAS

Net Present Value | 14.2

$$NPV = PV_{Cash\ Inflows} - PV_{Cash\ Outflows}$$

Answer Key

Chapter 1

Exercises 1.1

1. a. **(i)** 7,000 + 60 + 1 **(ii)** seven thousand, sixty-one
b. **(i)** 40,000 + 300 + 10 + 8 **(ii)** forty thousand, three hundred eighteen
c. **(i)** 5,000,000 + 200,000 + 40,000 + 9,000 + 300 + 40 + 6 **(ii)** five million, two hundred forty-nine thousand, three hundred forty-six
d. **(i)** 90,000,000 + 5,000,000 + 200,000 + 70,000 + 5,000 + 300 + 80 + 5 **(ii)** ninety-five million, two hundred seventy-five thousand, three hundred eighty-five

3. a. **(i)** 0.3 + 0.05 **(ii)** thirty-five hundredths
b. **(i)** 0.06 + 0.007 **(ii)** sixty-seven thousandths
c. **(i)** 40 + 1 + 0.08 **(ii)** forty-one and eight hundredths
d. **(i)** 10 + 9 + 0.006 **(ii)** nineteen and six thousandths

5. a. **(i)** 65,244.34 **(ii)** 60,000 + 5,000 + 200 + 40 + 4 + 0.3 + 0.04
b. **(i)** 12,452,832 **(ii)** 10,000,000 + 2,000,000 + 400,000 + 50,000 + 2,000 + 800 + 30 + 2
c. **(i)** 500,000,000 **(ii)** 500,000,000
d. **(i)** 7.4 **(ii)** 7 + 0.4

7. a. 89,613,522.13 **b.** 16,217,567
c. 500,000 **d.** 87.5

9. a. 1650 **b.** 10,000
c. $26,000 **d.** $900

11. a.132.1 **b.** 3
c. $85.43 **d.** $34.99

13. a. six and seven tenths
b. forty-five hundredths
c. thirty-four thousandths
d. one and six thousandths

15. a. **(i)** 6% **(ii)** 5.6% **(iii)** 5.57%
b. **(i)** 30% **(ii)** 29.9% **(iii)** 29.88%

17. a. **(i)** 75% **(ii)** 75.3% **(iii)** 75.25%
b. **(i)** 116% **(ii)** 115.8% **(iii)** 115.80%

19. a. **(i)** 1800 **(ii)** 1790 **b.** **(i)** 690 **(ii)** 683
c. **(i)** 1890 **(ii)** 1881

21. a. **(i)** 190 **(ii)** 194 **b.** **(i)** 500 **(ii)** 494
c. **(i)** 610 **(ii)** 604

23. a. **(i)** 4800 **(ii)** 4350 **b.** **(i)** 23,500 **(ii)** 22,656
c. **(i)** 7000 **(ii)** 6745

25. a. **(i)** 9 **(ii)** 9.44 **b.** **(i)** 20 **(ii)** 16.5
c. **(i)** 5 **(ii)** 5.58

27. 1700, 700, 1900, 100, 400, 600

29. $0.03 **31.** 8%

33 a. 0.3 **b.** 17.09 **c.** 15.297 **d.** 0.007

35. 30 months **37.** $20 **39.** $26,980

Exercises 1.2

1. a. **(i)** 2, 3, 5, 7 **(ii)** 4, 6, 8, 9
b. **(i)** 17, 19, 23 **(ii)** 15, 16, 18, 20, 21, 22, 24, 25, 26, 27

3. a. **(i)** 37, 41 **(ii)** 33, 34, 35, 36, 38, 39, 40
b. **(i)** 47, 53 **(ii)** 45, 46, 48, 49, 50, 51, 52, 54, 55, 56, 57

5. a. 2, 3 **b.** 2, 7

7. a. 2, 3 **b.** 5, 13

9. a. 2, 7 **b.** 2, 3, 5,

11. a. 15 **b.** 24

13. a. 36 **b.** 60

15. a. 240 **b.** 84

17. a. 14 **b.** 33

19. a. 60 **b.** 42

21. a. 56 **b.** 20

23. a. **(i)** factors of 36: 1, 2, 3, 4, 6, 9, 12, 18, 36; factors of 84: 1, 2, 3, 4, 6, 7, 12, 14, 21, 28, 42, 84 **(ii)** 2, 4, 8, 16 **(iii)** 16
b. **(i)** factors of 48: 1, 2, 3, 4, 6, 8, 12, 16, 24, 48; factors of 160: 1, 2, 4, 5, 8, 10, 16, 20, 32, 40, 80, 160 **(ii)** 2, 4, 8, 16 **(iii)** 16

25. a. **(i)** factors of 35: 1, 5, 7, 35; factors of 75: 1, 3, 5, 15, 25, 75 **(ii)** 5 **(iii)** 5
b. **(i)** factors of 24: 1, 2, 3, 4, 6, 8, 12, 24; factors of 64: 1, 2, 4, 8, 16, 32, 64 **(ii)** 2, 4, 8 **(iii)** 8

27. a. **(i)** factors of 50: 1, 2, 5, 10, 25, 50; factors of 75: 1, 3, 5, 15, 25, 75; factors of 125: 1, 5, 25, 125 **(ii)** 5, 25 **(iii)** 25
b. **(i)** factors of 30: 1, 2, 3, 5, 6, 10, 15, 30; factors of 75: 1, 3, 5, 15, 25, 75; factors of 90: 1, 2, 3, 5, 6, 9, 10, 15, 18, 30, 45, 90 **(ii)** 3, 5, 15 **(iii)** 15

29 a. **(i)** factors of 76: 1, 2, 4, 19, 38, 76; factors of 114: 1, 2, 3, 6, 19, 38, 57, 114; factors of 152: 1, 2, 4, 8, 19, 38, 76, 152 **(ii)** 2, 19, 38 **(iii)** 38
b. **(i)** factors of 96: 1, 2, 3, 4, 6, 8, 12, 16, 24, 32, 48, 96; factors of 144: 1, 2, 3, 4, 6, 8, 9, 12, 16, 18, 24, 36, 48, 72, 144; factors of 216: 1, 2, 3, 4, 6, 8, 9, 12, 18, 24, 27, 36, 54, 72, 108, 216 **(ii)** 2, 3, 4, 6, 8, 12, 24 **(iii)** 24

31. 32 cm **33.** Feb 28

Exercises 1.3

1. a. $\frac{11}{8}$ b. $\frac{51}{4}$
   c. $\frac{38}{5}$ d. $\frac{29}{3}$
3. a. $1\frac{5}{7}$ b. $2\frac{1}{8}$
   c. $3\frac{4}{9}$ d. $2\frac{4}{5}$
5. a. 8, 18
   b. 5, 21
   c. 11, 30
   d. 15, 30
7. a. $\frac{20}{3}$ b. $\frac{26}{3}$
   c. $\frac{34}{5}$ d. $\frac{1}{4}$
9. a. $\frac{11}{20}$ b. $\frac{8}{7}$
   c. $\frac{16}{39}$ d. $\frac{15}{23}$
11. a. $1\frac{11}{18}$ b. $1\frac{7}{20}$
    c. $16\frac{11}{12}$ d. $7\frac{1}{12}$
13. a. $1\frac{11}{39}$ b. $1\frac{4}{9}$
    c. $3\frac{11}{12}$ d. $16\frac{1}{21}$
15. a. $2\frac{2}{45}$ b. $1\frac{1}{18}$
    c. 15 d. $12\frac{1}{2}$
17. a. $1\frac{1}{3}$ b. $\frac{5}{21}$
    c. $1\frac{1}{2}$ d. 4
19. $\frac{11}{12}$
21. $15\frac{1}{2}$ h
23. $\frac{7}{8}$ m
25. $2\frac{2}{5}$
27. 66
29. 32
31. 304
33. $\frac{1}{4}$
35. 1350
37. $3\frac{1}{2}$ km
39. $981

Exercises 1.4

1. a. −99 b. 20
3. a. 4 b. 40
5. a. 540 b. −49
7. a. 208 b. −192
9. 29
11. 2
13. −6
15. 16
17. 158
19. a. $\frac{4}{9}$ b. 125
21. a. $\frac{32}{243}$ b. $\frac{243}{32}$
23. 4514.79
25. 1535
27. 2498.97
29. 1763.27
31. 16,911.28
33. 37,618.52
35. 5619.82
37. 1968.84
39. 17,581.16
41. 11,341.04
43. 13,091.64
45. 114,942.37
47. 106,257.38
49. 238,447.63

Exercises 1.5

1. a. 22 b. 52.50
3. 37.125 h
5. 117
7. 75
9. $7875
11. 56.67
13. a. $103.79 b. $112.50
15. $216.86
17. a. 12 b. 4 c. 1.14
19. 6.33%

Review Exercises 1

1. a. 6.29 b. 2.32
   c. 7.31 d. 1846.15
3. a. $42.59 b. $74.96
   c. $91.69 d. $498.42
5. a. 660 b. 576 c. 990
7. a. 5 b. 2 c. 25
9. 28 h
11. $1500
13. a. 76 b. 4
15. a. 90,691.77 b. 43,278.27
17. $5150
19. 50 kg
21. $26.05

Self-Test Exercises 1

1. $1220.70
2. 79,000
3. a. 72 b. 80 c. 576
4. a. 4 b. 7 c. 12
5. $1830
6. a. 2 b. 1
7. a. 52,141.33 b. 2856.13
8. $38,962.50
9. 92%
10. a. 36 b. 0.17
11. $23.57

Chapter 2

Exercises 2.1

1. a. $7xy; -4y$ b. $-y; 3$
   c. $9xy; -6y$
3. a. 5; 5, −3
   b. 1; −2, 3
   c. 7; −2, −2
   d. −4; 8
5. a. $11x^2 + 17x$
   b. $-7y^2 + y$
   c. $3x + 3y^2$
7. a) $\frac{8}{5}$ b) $\frac{3}{2}$ c) 4
9. a. $-75x - 3$ b. −38
11. a. $-5x + 7$ b. $2x - 4$
13. a. $12x - 4y - 36$
    b. $-32y^2 - 288y$
15. a. $-7y^2 - 12y + 6$
    b. $4x + 25$
    c. $24x^2 - 70x + 11$
17. a. $-x - y$
    b. $5x - 3y + 1$
    c. $\frac{x^2}{2y}$
19. a. $\frac{3x+9}{2}$
    b. $\frac{3x+15}{8}$
    c. $\frac{15y}{16}$
21. a. $\frac{23}{9}$ b. 24
    c. $\frac{5}{2}$ d. 22
23. a. $3y$; 30 b. $8z$; 56
25. a. $-2x^2$; −18
    b. $54x^3$; 6750
27. a. $5A + 3B$
    b. $x + 5y + 7$
29. a. $-6x + 12y$
    b. $x^2y - 2x^2 + 8xy^2 + 4$
31. a. $2a + 14b - 12c + 2$; 24
    b. $3x^2 - 2x$; 65
33. a. $3y(2x^2 - x - 3)$
    b. $3(5y^2 - 4y - 1)$
    c. $2ab(3b - 4a)$
35. a. $2b(5a - 4c)$
    b. $4a^2(2a - 1)$
    c. $6x(x - 1)$
37. a. $(y + 2)(5x + 3)$
    b. $(x - 5)(4y - x)$
    c. $(x - 2)(y + 5)$
39. a. $(x + 1)(x - y)$
    b. $(x + 1)(2x + 3y)$

Exercises 2.2

1. a. $2x - 3$ b. $\frac{2x}{5}$
   c. $25 + 3x$ d. $6(3 + x)$
3. a. $x + 6 = 10; x = 4$
   b. $6x = 72; x = 12$
5. a. $\frac{x}{5} = 4; x = 20$
   b. $\frac{2x}{3} = 12; x = 18$
7. a. $x = 30$ b. $x = 18$
9. a. $x = -17$ b. $x = 6$
11. a. $x = \frac{7}{5}$ or 1.4
    b. $x = 2$
13. a. $x = 4$ b. $x = 1.18$
15. a. $x = 66.37$ b. $x = 101.85$
17. $x = -2.2$
19. $x = 4.33$
21. $x = 51.4$
23. $y = 11$
25. $x = -5$
27. $x = 16$
29. $y = 42$
31. $x = 5$
33. 5
35. 9 m; 16 m
37. Andy: $175; Becky: $325
39. $76/h
41. 15 m; 5 m
43. 27
45. Adult: $10
    Child: $7
47. Ryan: $16/h
    Hailey: $19.50/h
49. $2000

Exercises 2.3

1. a. 609 b. −255
3. a. 1,000,000 b. 81
5. a. 729 b. 256
7. a. −10,000,000 b. 400
9. a. 3 b. 104,976
11. a. 97.66 b. 59,049
13. a. 4 b. 27
15. a. 4 b. 9
17. a. 25 b. 36
19. a. x^4 b. x^6
21. a. x^6 b. x^{17}
23. a. $20x^3$ b. x^6
25. a. $-x^7$ b. y^6
27. a. x^4y^8 b. x^2
29. a. $\frac{x^3}{y^3}$ b. $\frac{y}{x}$
31. a. x^9 b. $3x^2$
33. a. x^2 b. $-x^2$
35. a. x^4 b. x^5

Exercises 2.4

1. a. $\log 100{,}000 = 5$
   b. $\log_2 64 = 6$
   c. $\log_3 9 = 2$
3. a. $\log_4 1024 = 5$
   b. $\log_6 7776 = 5$
   c. $\log_9 6561 = 4$
5. a. $10^2 = 100$
   b. $2^5 = 32$
   c. $3^6 = 729$
7. a. $4^3 = 64$
   b. $5^4 = 625$
   c. $6^3 = 216$
9. a. 7.7187 b. 5.0370
   c. 3.2958
11. a. 2.3076 b. 0.0050
   c. −0.3930
13. a. 1.62 b. 2.33
15. a. 8.83 b. 5.53
17. a. $\ln 3 - \ln 7$
   b. $\ln 4 + \ln 9$
19. a. $\ln A + \ln B - \ln C$
   b. $\ln X - \ln Y - \ln Z$
21. a. $\ln 40$ b. $\ln 5$
23. a. $\ln 675$
   b. $\ln\left(\frac{32}{9}\right)$
25. a. $\ln 25$ b. $\ln 216$
27. a. $\ln\left(\frac{a}{b}\right)^5$ b. $\ln(ab)^4$
29. $\ln\left(\frac{a^3b^2}{c^5}\right)$ 31. $\ln 40.5$
33. a. 0.07 b. 0.52
35. a. 42.33 b. 31.00
37. 52.60 39. 10.49

Exercises 2.5

1. $C = S - M$
3. $E = S - C - P$
5. $B = \frac{P}{R}$
7. $r = \frac{S - P}{Pt}$
9. $L = \frac{N}{1 - d}$
11. $a = \frac{b}{b + c}$,
   $c = \frac{b(1 - a)}{a}$
13. $a = c(b + 1)$,
   $b = \frac{a - c}{c}$
15. a. \$187.50 b. \$1752.17
17. a. 0.06 b. 0.66
19. a. \$6816.88
   b. \$7999.98
21. a. \$5000.00
   b. 0.25
23. \$5793.25 25. \$2501.42
27. \$7102.18 29. 0.13
31. 0.01 33. 0.02
35. $V_f = V_iC + V_i$
37. $n = \frac{\ln\left(\frac{FV}{PV}\right)}{\ln(1 + i)}$
39. $m = \frac{\ln f}{\ln(1 + i)}$

Review Exercises 2

1. a. $3x^2 + x - 2$; 12
   b. $2x^2 + 6x - 8$; −12
   c. $-10x^2 + 3xy - 7y^2$; −32
   d. $x^2 + x - 2$; 10
3. a. $2x(3x - 2)$; 2
   b. $3y^2(y - 4)$; −72
   c. $7x(y + 2x)$; 28
   d. $3x(3x^2 - 2x + 1)$; 198
5. a. $12 + 3x$
   b. $x - 5$
   c. $x(x + 3)$
   d. $10x + 15$
7. a. $5x + 17 = 42$; $x = 5$
   b. $\frac{x}{15} = 45$; $x = 675$
9. a. $x - 10 = 10$; $x = 20$
   b. $4x(3) = 36$; $x = 3$
11. a. 3 b. 18
13. a. −9 b. 2
15. \$12.50
17. a. 17 b. 72
   c. 16
19. a. $125^{\frac{1}{3}}$ b. $\left(\frac{9}{4}\right)^{\frac{1}{2}}$
   c. 4^2
21. a. $3x^7$ b. x^4
   c. $\frac{x^4}{4y^5}$
23. a. $2x^2$ b. $\frac{8x^9}{y^6}$
   c. x^{14}
25. a. 26.25 b. 1691.63
27. a. 28.36 b. 55.48
29. $r = \sqrt{\frac{3V}{\pi h}}$

Self-Test Exercises 2

1. a. $x^2 + 2x - 3$; 5
   b. $-x^2 - 6x + 10$; 19
   c. $19x^2 - 7xy - 5y^2$; −15
   d. $4x - 11y + 7$; 4
2. a. $6y(3y - 2)$; 96
   b. $3y(5y^2 + 4y + 1)$; 30
   c. $7x(2y - 3x)$; −56
   d. $2xy(4y - 3x)$; 14
3. a. $3x - 25$
   b. $x + 18$
   c. $2x - 6$
   d. $\frac{x}{3}$
4. a. $2x - 9 = 21$; 15
   b. $5x - 3 = 22$; 5
5. a. $4(8) = 16x$; 2
   b. $6x = 30$; 5
6. a. 4 b. $-\frac{4}{7}$
   c. 18 d. $\frac{14}{3}$
7. 12 m, 18 m
8. −25
9. a. −128 b. −121
   c. −1000 d. 3
   e. 6 f. 3125
10. a. $9x^6$ b. $16x^4y^6$
   c. $4y^2$ d. x^4
   e. $\frac{y^2}{x^6}$ f. 1
11. a. 15.45 b. 3.17
12. a. 55.48 b. 13.33
13. a. 102.70 b. 4
14. a. 0.0084 b. 0.0100
15. a. $t = \frac{S - P}{Pr}$ b. 2

Chapter 3

Exercises 3.1

1. a. 0.8, $\frac{4}{5}$
   b. 25%, $\frac{1}{4}$
   c. 150%, 1.5
   d. 0.065, $\frac{13}{200}$
   e. $4\frac{4}{5}$% or 4.8%, $\frac{6}{125}$
   f. 8%, 0.08
3. a. 0.106, $\frac{53}{500}$
   b. 225%, $\frac{9}{4}$
   c. $\frac{1}{4}$% or 0.25%, 0.0025
   d. −0.26, $-\frac{13}{50}$

e. −15%, $-\frac{3}{20}$
f. $-58\frac{1}{3}$% or −58.33%, −0.58

5. a. 70 b. 100 c. 52
7. a. 0.1875 b. 0.5 km c. $55
9. a. 90% b. 111.11% c. 14%
11. a. $186 b. $130 c. $2200
13. a. $16.50 b. $0.27 c. $9.45
15. $32.50
17. $25,000 19. 74%
21. 13,729,688
23. $10,278.72
25. 0.50%
27. $89,400
29. $45
31. $1,163,636.36
33. Class *A*
35. 91,200
37. $16,880
39. a. 42,875 b. 39,487,180

Exercises 3.2

1. a. $306 b. $9 c. $11,250 d. 680 kg e. $530 f. $7.38 g. 75% h. 25%
3. $3,270,888
5. $90,000
7. $81,818.18
9. 7.17%
11. 22.22% 13. 20.27%
15. −2% 17. −25%
19. $468,000
21. a. $450 b. $30,450
23. a. Tudor b. $17.85
25. −2.5%
27. 4.17%
29. −13.51%; −21.56%; −32.16%
31. 16.67%
33. 4.76%

Exercises 3.3

1. a. $5000 b. $2500 c. $2307.69 d. $1153.85
3. $3575 5. $1638
7. $2578.33 9. $33.13
11. $3080 13. 9 h
15. $11,250
17. $5820
19. a. $62,000 b. 3.44%
21. a. $100; $570; $2800 b. 7.78%
23. a. $2712.50 b. $42,000
25. $48,400
27. $2800
29. $47,500
31. $23,000
33. $1260
35. $1484.98
37. 4.5%
39. $1160

Exercises 3.4

1. $36,725
3. $44,850 5. $1625
7. a. $10,170; $1170 b. $10,350
9. $3538.25 11. $30.33
13. $666.67; $766.67
15. $21,492.25
17. $3000 19. $6
21. $7
23. a. $4180 b. $5684.80
25. a. $2244 b. $4600
27. 3.05% 29. 15

Review Exercises 3

1. $180,200 3. 5.80%
5. $3022.50
7. $2830; 6.29%
9. 12.25%
11. $144.15 13. $135.45
15. $5041.54
17. $2385.10
19. a. 2570 b. 28,555,556
21. a. 33.33% b. 22.54%
23. 13.04%

Self-test Exercises 3

1. $71,080.81
2. a. 60% b. $500; 25%
3. $150.54
4. a. −7.67%; −16.61% b. 23.01%
5. Depreciated by 4%
6. $931.66 7. $47,294
8. a. $3166.67 b. $1583.33 c. $1461.54 d. $730.77
9. $2191.16
10. $45,250
11. $7.45
12. $1375

Chapter 4

Exercises 4.1

1. b, d
3. c
5. a. 5 : 4 : 8; 1.25 : 1 : 2 b. 36 : 5 : 9; 7.2 : 1 : 1.8 c. 3 : 15 : 20; 1 : 5 : 6.67
7. a. 7 : 2 : 5; 3.5 : 1 : 2.5 b. 20 : 18 : 21; 1.11 : 1 : 1.17 c. 9 : 10 : 15; 1 : 1.11 : 1.67
9. a. 1 : 6 b. 4 : 35 c. 1 : 16 d. 25 : 3
11. 1 : 10
13. 500 km/h
15. 2 kg of flour for $3.30
17. 8 pencils for $2.88
19. 0.8 litres of juice for $1.40
21. 800 g box of cereal for $5.00; $0.15/kg
23. *A*; $2.45/h
25. 191 : 240
27. a. 2: 3: 5: 1 b. 4: 6: 9: 2
29. $144; $216
31. $8400; $1400; $4200
33. $22,727.27; $12,121.21; $15,151.52
35. $7150; $5850
37. $11,250
39. 15 : 20 : 24

Exercises 4.2

1. a. 10 b. 0.70 c. 0.61 or $\frac{11}{18}$ d. 2.625 or $2\frac{5}{8}$ e. 0.375 or $\frac{3}{8}$ f. 4.33 or $\frac{13}{3}$ or $4\frac{1}{3}$
3. 1 year and 9 months
5. $254.55
7. 4.96 km
9. $200; $1000
11. a. $50,000; $20,000 b. $158,888.89; $72,222.22; $28,888.89 c. $27,272.73; $10,909.09
13. $865.38 15. $175
17. $2250 19. 3 : 5 : 4
21. $20,769.23
23. $15,000; $25,000; $20,000
25. a. 33 b. 5 : 3
27. 12 : 9 : 16 29. 325

Exercises 4.3

1. a. £161.20 b. US$2248.54 c. C$6671.00 d. C$16.44
3. a. C$1793.25 b. C$41.27
5. C$581.63
7. Lost C$140.10
9. $1334.13
11. A$1 = £0.6223
13. A$481.80
15. C$4884.57

17. C$1220.28
19. C$723,413.49
21. 4%
23. a. Depreciate
b. Depreciate
c. Appreciate
25. USA
27. C$1.1614
29. C$1601.12; no

Exercises 4.4

1. 115.63; 134.38
3. 143.29; 134.53
5. a. 102.0; 103.1
b. 1.1%
7. a. 97.0; 98.9
b. 2.0%
9. $2683.57; $2766.61
11. $2274.77; $2366.36
13. $56,762.88
15. 5.5%
17. $3601.05
19. No; $5824.41
21. 0.8217; 0.7899
23. $28,431.15
25. $41,015.83

Review Exercises 4

1. $46,350
3. $1000; $2500
5. $1057.69
7. 6 : 7 : 8
9. Gina; $0.75/h
11. $1093.75; $2333.33; $1822.92
13. 4.2% 15. $591.59
17. 21 19. C$2032.94
21. 4 : 6 : 3

Self-Test Exercises 4

1. US$1 = C$1.325
2. C$1334.20
3. $2125 4. 4.3125 m
5. $208.33 6. C$42.75
7. Yes; C$4.96
8. $845.18 9. $25,000
10. 25 : 30 : 42
11. $488.24

Chapter 5

Exercises 5.1

1. a. $1875.00; $1500.00
b. $230.00; 12%
c. 54%; $432.00
d. 2%; $490.00
3. a. 28%; $388.80; $151.20
b. $1970.19; 38.58%; $1210.19
c. $2768.09; 9.25%; $256.09
d. 3%; 17.94%; $215.26
5. $671.20
7. a. $13.20 b. $151.80
9. a. $871.51 b. $91.51
11. a. $408,000.00
b. $387,600.00
13. 18% 15. 5%
17. $58.24 19. Yes
21. 10.65%
23. a. $1028.85
b. $171.15
25. a. $295.00
b. 35.4%
27. a. retail store; $10.22
b. 12.79%
29. a. electronic store; $16.50
b. 3.59%
31. 6.63%
33. a. $6915.46; $7205.44; $6942.00
b. Northern Canada
35. a. Orillia
b. 2.21%

Exercises 5.2

1. a. Jan 11, 2017; Jan 31, 2017
b. Mar 22, 2017; Apr 29, 2017
c. May 25, 2017; Jun 9, 2017
d. Aug 21, 2017; Sept 20, 2017
3. a. $20,090.00
b. $20,500.00
c. $20,500.00
5. $2223.98
7. $18,612.00
9. $49,275.00
11. $99,980.50
13. $10,134.79
15. $1974.36
17. $480.96
19. $80,025.00
21. $29,400.00
23. a. $146,632.65
b. $45,109.81
25. a. Sept 10, 2016; Sept 30, 2016
b. Aug 10, 2016; Aug 30, 2016
c. Mar 06, 2017; Mar 29, 2017
d. Jul 26, 2017; Aug 30, 2017
27. a. $117,176.00
b. $117,176.00
c. $120,800.00
29. a. $918.00
b. $918.00
c. Nil
31. $2462.50
33. a. $4243.75
b. $1970.00
35. a. $12,450.72
b. $7301.71
c. $22,301.71

Exercises 5.3

1. a. $60.00; 25%; 20%
b. $120.00; $72.00; 37.50%
c. $22.00; $110.00; 20%
d. $21.00; $63.00; 50%
e. $23.33; $46.67; 200.04%
3. a. $630.00; $1830.00; 52.50%; 34.43%
b. $3049.50; $1674.10; 40.93%; 29.04%
c. $2926.83; $600.00; $3526.83; 17.01%
d. $4.40; $11.00; $0.90; 66.67%
e. $410.00; $430.50; $12.30; 4.76%
5. a. 20% b. 16.67%
7. a. 55.56% b. 35.71%
9. a. $360.00 b. $78.75
11. $120.00
13. $600.94
15. $2.31
17. a. $195.31
b. 36.00%
19. a. $38.57
b. 75.01%
21. 16.67%
23. 21.95%
25. $38.80
27. a. $9.50 b. $1.70
29. a. $170,477.50
b. $378,838.89
31. a. $21.00
b. $9.00
33. 2nd; $16.67
35. $2489.76

Exercises 5.4

1. a. $65.00; 28.08%; 21.92%; 8.46%; $59.50
b. $38.75; $250.00; 18.34%; 15.50%; $237.50
c. $2128.88; $2230.00; 4.75%; 4.53%; $55.75
d. $135.00; $450.00; 42.86%; 46.67%; $240.00
e. $247.00; $1197.00; 20.63%; $143.64; $1053.36
f. $12,000.00; $3000.00; 20%; $2250.00; 15%

3. a. $40.00 b. $160.00
5. $120.00; 15%
7. $3333.33; $2333.33
9. 20.38% 11. 37.89%
13. 12.28% 15. 45.00%
17. $1087.50; $652.50
19. $440.00; $308.00
21. a. $1250.00
b. $312.50
23. $140.00; $119.00
25. a. 20% b. $23.40
27. a. $75.00 b. 30%
29. 6.50%
31. a. $480.00 b. $336.00

Exercises 5.5

1. a. $1000.00; $1150.00; 115%; 53.49%; $1612.50; $312.50
b. $800.50; $1700.75; 88.92%; 47.07%; $1105.49; $4.74
c. $2.44; $18.19; $0.26; 13.41%; $17.19; $1.18
d. $509.06; $169.69; $93.19; 33.33%; $593.91; $8.35
e. $3899.00; $515.75; 16.84%; 14.41%; 8.24%; $140.25
f. $21.50; $11.50; 56.58%; 36.13%; 21.01%; $47.00
3. a. $3220.00; profit: $140.00
b. $2737.00; loss: $343.00
5. a. $0.40
b. $3.40; profit: $1.00
7. $28.00 profit
9. a. $15.00 profit b. $105.00
11. $10.00 profit
13. a. $864.00
b. $86.40 profit
c. $172.80
15. 20%
17. $50.00 profit
19. a. $210.00
b. $5.25 profit
c. 10%
21. a. $550.00
b. 10%
c. 37.5%
23. a. $642.86
b. 2.16%
c. $31.14 profit
25. a. $316.20
b. $280.63
c. 11.25%
27. a. $56.00; $42.00; $26.25
b. $1365.00
29. a. $4080.00 profit
b. 50%; $6.00

Exercises 5.6

1. a. $520.00 b. $634.20
c. $114.20 d. 21.96%
3. a. $4760.00 b. $10,178.75
c. $5418.75 d. 53.24%
5. a. $192.50 b. $157.50
c. 45%
7. a. $85.50 b. $34.50
c. 28.75%
9. a. 35% b. 32.5%
11. 70.38% 13. 33.33%
15. a. $252.00 b. 40.48%

Review Exercises 5

1. $1.19 3. $2914.00
5. 2.03%
7. a. $286.88 b. 68.13%
9. a. $43,875.00
b. $44,100.00
c. $45,000.00
11. $5.85
13. a. $84.00 b. 28.57%
c. $18.00
15. a. $2.22 b. $1.78
17. a. $45.00 b. $36.00
19. a. $29.25
b. $94.25
c. $28.28
d. $65.97
e. $0.97
21. a. $108,330.41
b. $57,163.80
c. $182,163.80
23. a. $177.87
b. $6.88 loss
c. 16.13%
25. a. $1080.00
b. 15%

Self-Test Exercises 5

1. a. $2100.00 b. 48.7% c. $1022.70
2. a. Ajax b. 2.78%
3. a. $3610.80 b. $2708.10
c. Nil
4. $43,670.10
5. $10,312.50 loss
6. a. $450.00 b. 25.93%
7. 66.67%
8. a. $181.25 b. $108.75
c. $45.31 d. $135.94
e. $63.44
9. a. $19,400.00 b. $29,100.00
10. a. $25,670.10
b. $5261.94
c. $5261.94
11. $54.54 loss
12. a. 9.24% b. 23.08%

Chapter 6

Exercises 6.1

1.

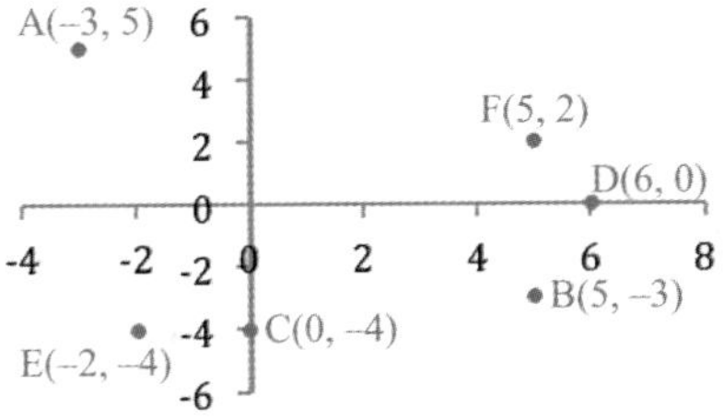

3. a. 2nd b. 4th c. 1st d. X-axis
e. 3rd f. Y-axis
5. a. 2 units

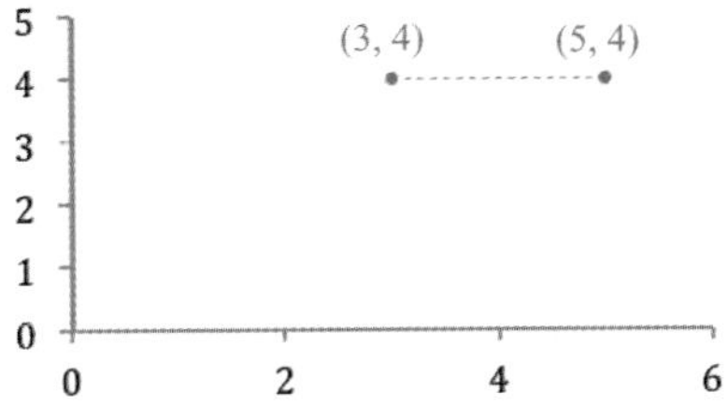

b. 9 units

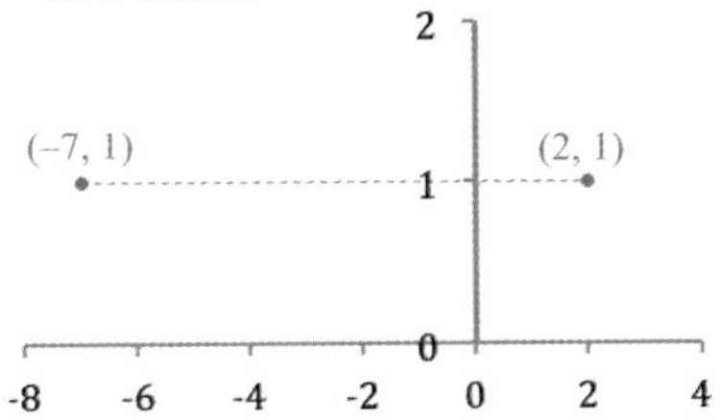

c. 5 units

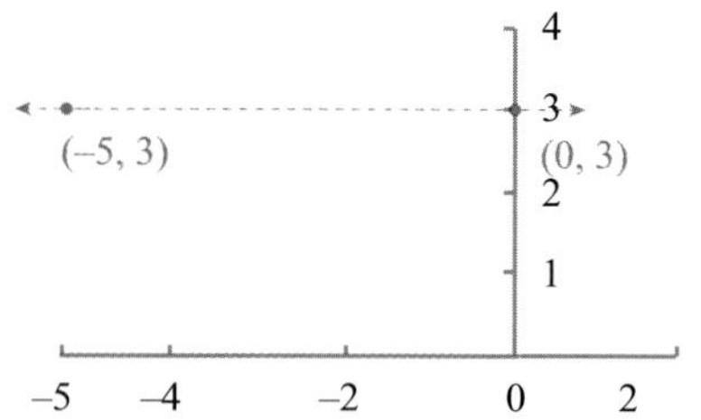

d. 8 units

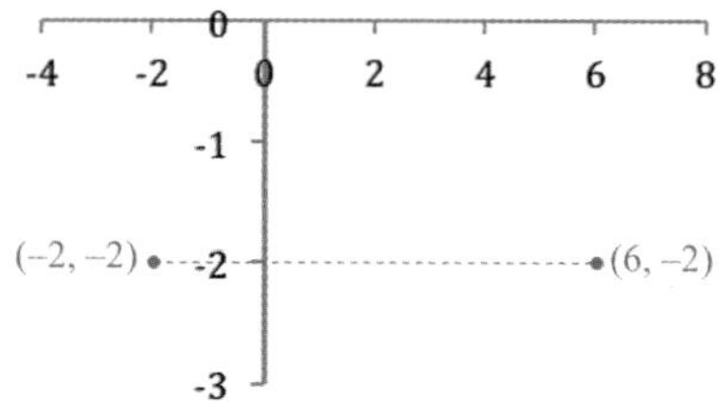

7. (–3, –1)

9. (1, 12) and (1, –2)

Exercises 6.2

1. a. 4 **b.** 10 **c.** 6 **d.** 9 **e.** 15 **f.** 6

3. a. $y = -\frac{3}{2}x - \frac{3}{4}$

b. $y = \frac{2}{3}x + 5$

5. a. $5x - 2y = -2$

b. $3x + 4y = -12$

7. a.

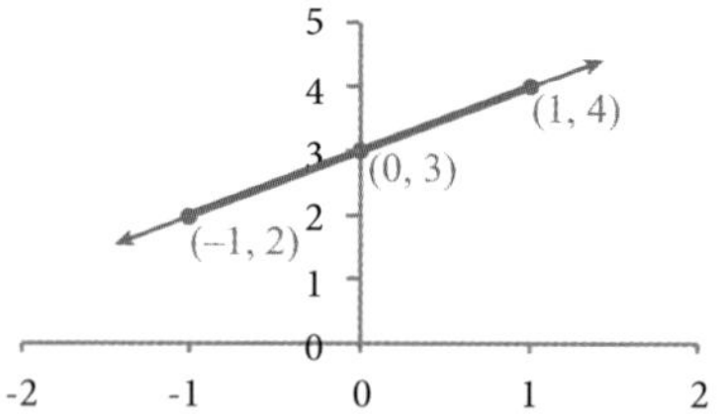

b.

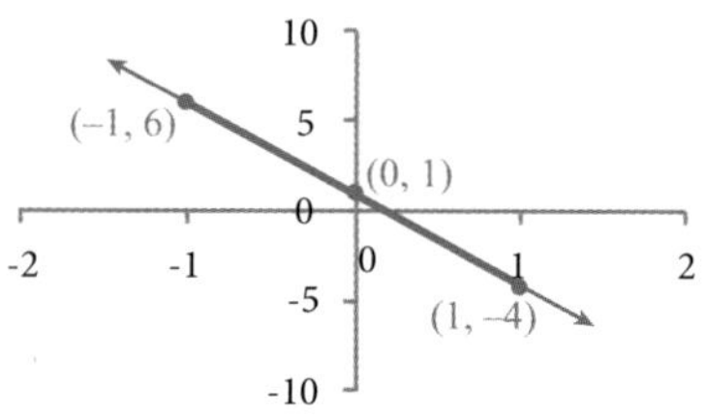

9. a.

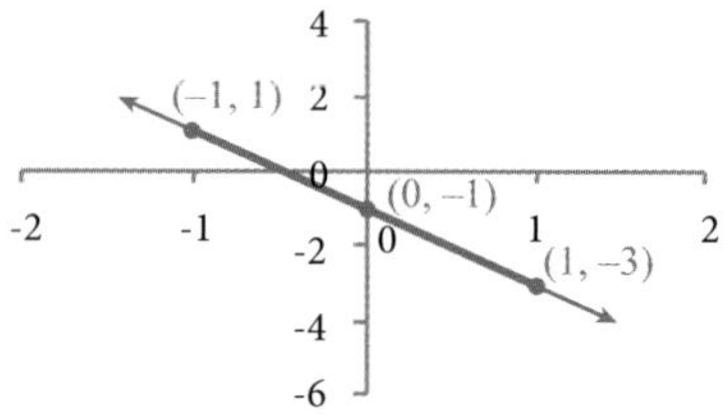

b.

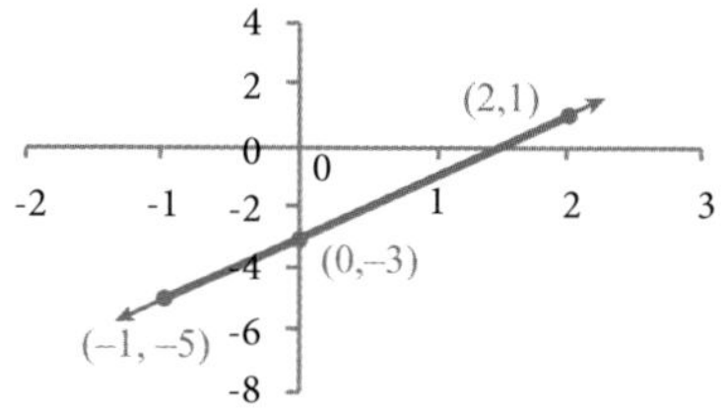

11. a. $\left(-\frac{2}{3}, 0\right)$; (0, –2)

b. (7, 0); (0, 7)

c. (–2, 0); (0, 4)

13. Positive

15. $\frac{2}{3}$; (0, –6)

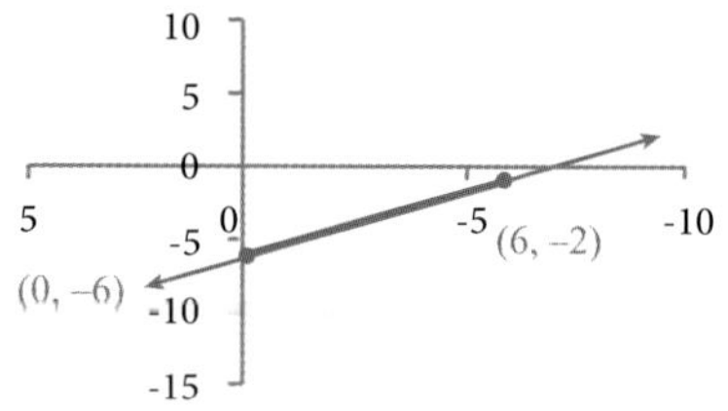

17. $\frac{4}{7}$; (0, 3)

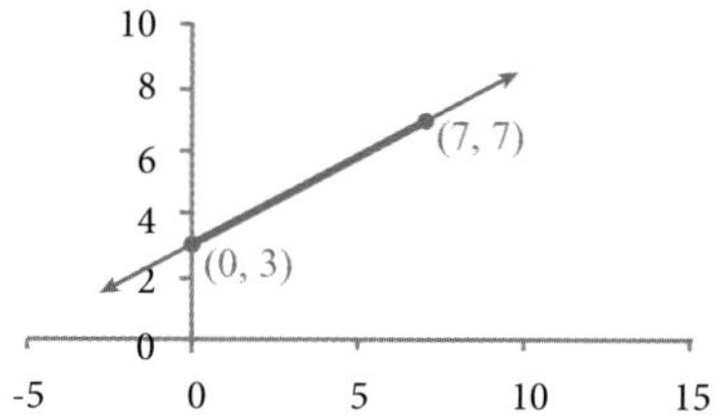

19. $y = 2$ **21.** $y = x - 2$

23. $y = x + 4$ **25.** $y = 2x$

27. $y = \frac{5}{4}x - 5$ **29.** 0

31. 0 **33.** 2

35. 7 **37.** $y = -\frac{5}{3}x + 5$

39. $y = 15x + 5$; (0, 5); 15

Exercises 6.3

1. (1, 1) **3.** Many solutions

5. $\left(-\frac{6}{7}, \frac{30}{7}\right)$

7. Problem 3: dependent; problem 5: independent

9. Problem 3: consistent; problem 5: consistent

11. 4 **13.** 4

15. (–2, 1) **17.** Many solutions

19. No solution

Exercises 6.4

1. a. (2, –2) **b.** $\left(\frac{54}{11}, \frac{37}{11}\right)$

3. a. (2, 1) **b.** (6, –1)

5. a. (3, –3) **b.** (1, 2)

7. a. (9, 2) **b.** (2, 3)

9. a. (1, –2) **b.** (2, 4)

11. a. (–1, –2) **b.** (3, –2)

13. (–3, –1) **15.** (3, 4)

17. (3, –2) **19.** (10, 6)

21. (15, 12) **23.** $\left(\frac{9}{7}, \frac{27}{7}\right)$

25. (1, 3) **27.** (3, –2)

29. (2, 1) **31.** $12

33. 32; 60

35. 3% p.a.: $10,000; 4% p.a.: $15,000

37. a. Company *B* **b.** 300

39. Adults: 300; children: 150

Review Exercises 6

1. a. 4th **b.** 2nd **c.** X-axis **d.** 4th **e.** X-axis **f.** Y-axis

3. Rectangle; 24 units^2; 22 units

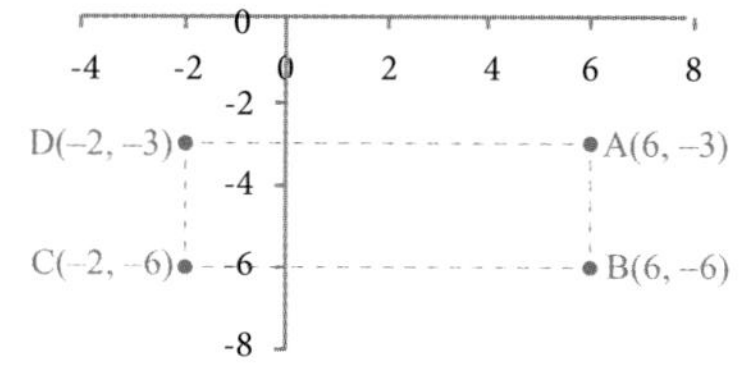

5. a.

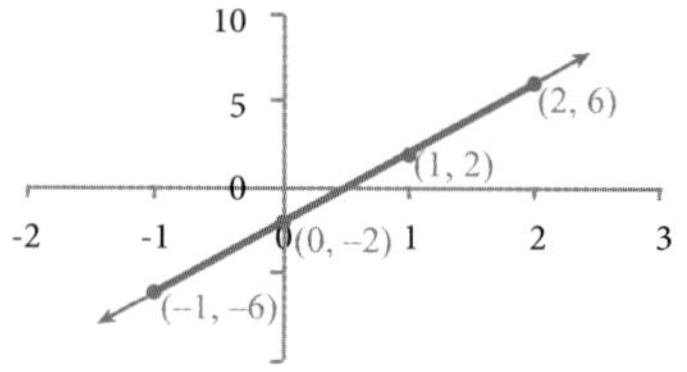

b.

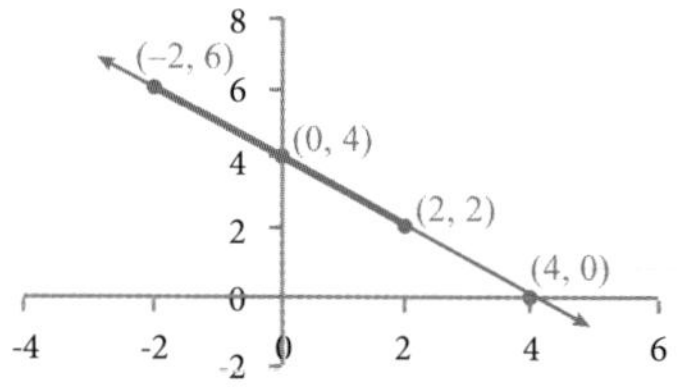

c.

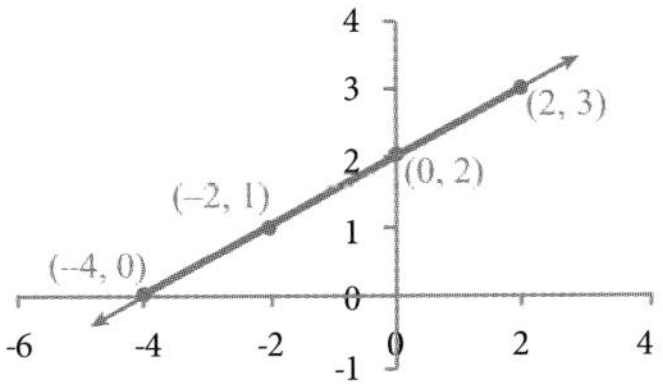

7. a.

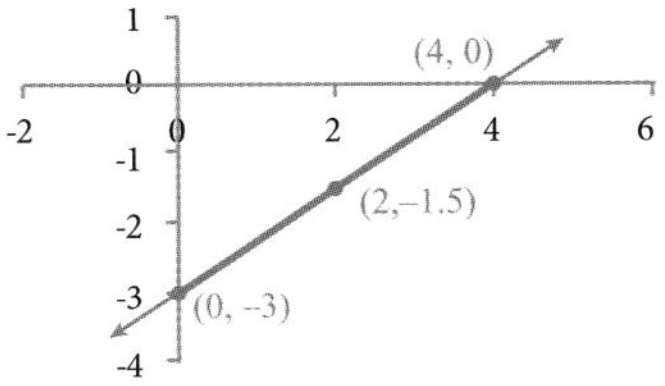

b.

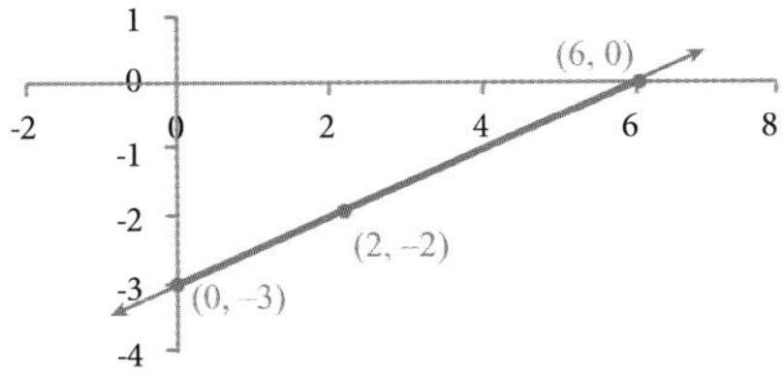

c.

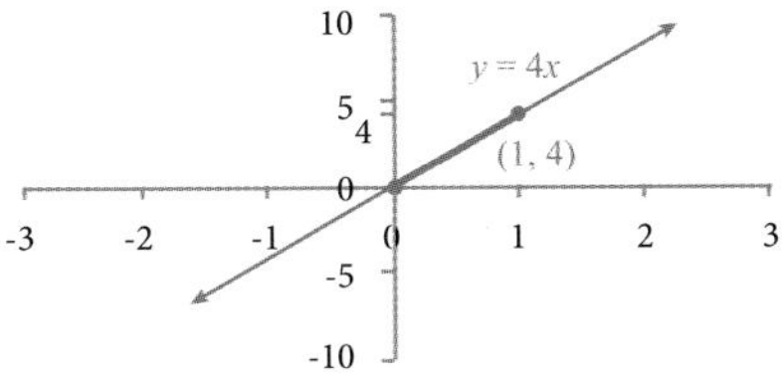

9. a.

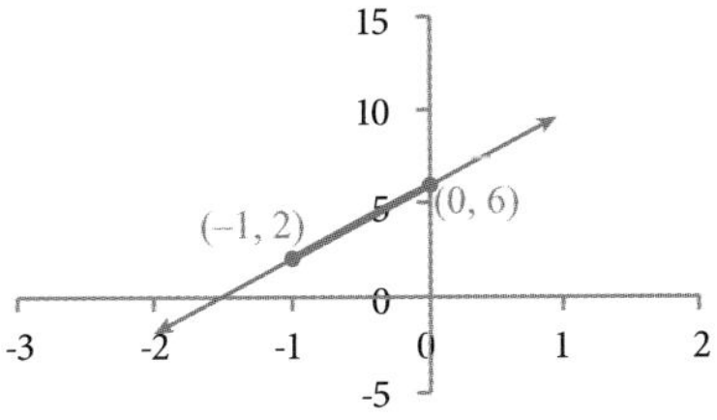

b.

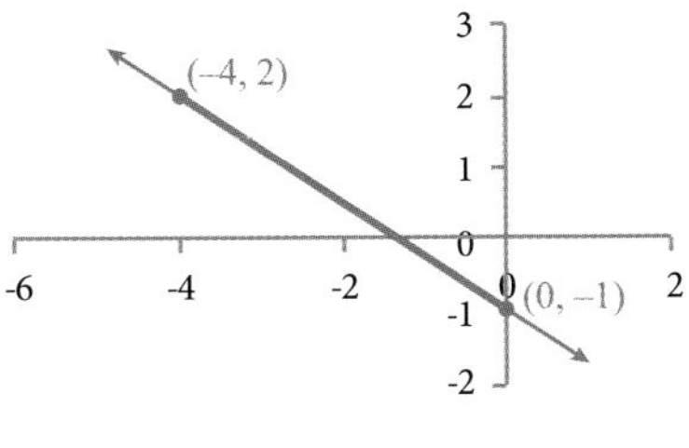

c.

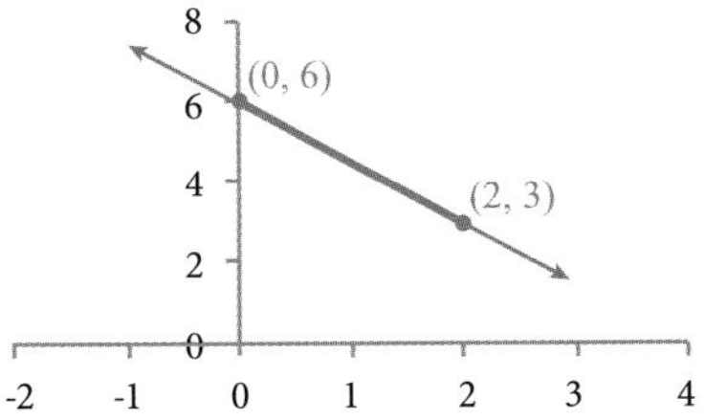

11. a. $y = \frac{3}{4}x - \frac{1}{4}$

b. $y = -\frac{4}{3}x + \frac{8}{3}$

c. $y = 3x - 5$

13. -3; $y = 2x - 1$

15. a. \$13,500 **b.** \$25,500

17. a. (2, −5) **b.** (6, 2)

c. (2, 1)

19. a. (4, 1) **b.** $\left(\frac{52}{19}, -\frac{70}{19}\right)$ **c.** (1, 1)

21. a. (2, 1) **b.** (−4, −2)

c. (3, 0)

23. 2 and 7

Self-Test Exercises 6

1. (−3, −1); 40 units^2 **2.** $\frac{2}{3}$; 2

3. $4x + 5y = 9$

4. a. $x + 2y = -8$

b. $2x - 3y = 6$

5. a.

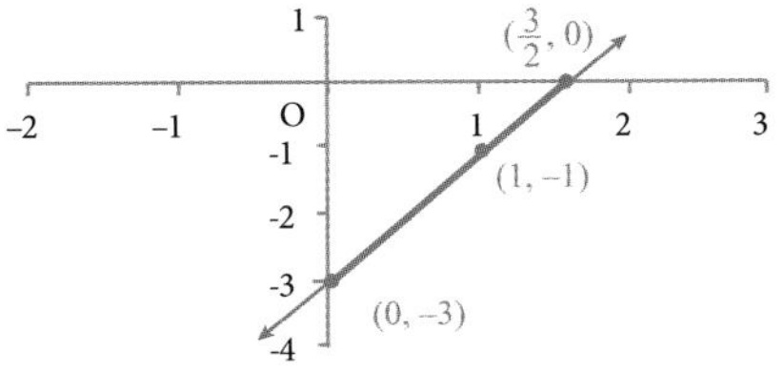

b.

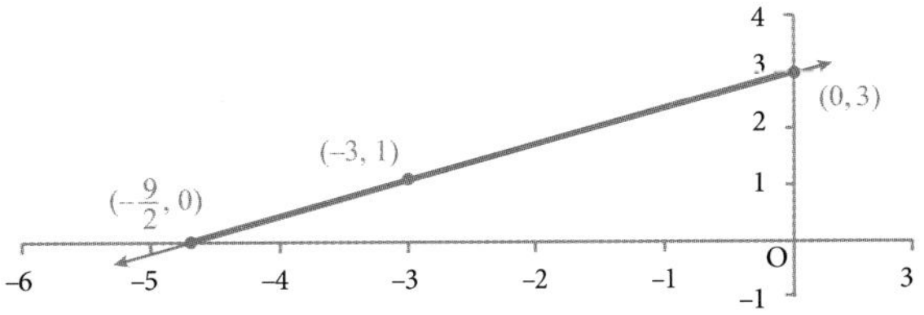

6. $3x - 2y = -12$

7. a. Many solutions **b.** $\left(-\frac{25}{11}, \frac{2}{11}\right)$

8. a. $\left(\frac{15}{7}, -\frac{18}{7}\right)$ **b.** (−4, 4)

9. a. $\left(-\frac{3}{2}, -\frac{3}{2}\right)$ **b.** $\left(-\frac{17}{31}, \frac{128}{31}\right)$

10. -1; $y = -8x + 6$

11. Adult: 125; child: 75

12. 5.5% p.a.: \$6000, 3.5% p.a.: \$4000

Chapter 7

Exercises 7.1

1. a. 100; \$300; \$1300

b. \$110; \$14,000; \$22,000

c. $61; $3782; $9672

d. $2300; $2250; $4550

3. 250 **5.** 800

7. a. $7560.00 **b.** $90.00

9. $300.00 **11.** $67.12

13. a. $296,000.00 **b.** $81,400.00

15. a. $147.69 **b.** $457,839.00

Exercises 7.2

1. a. 760; $2280.00; 76% **b.**$300 profit

3. a. 5140; $411,200.00; 85.67%

b. $3000.00 loss **c.** $64,500.00 profit

5. a. 127 **b.** 495

7. a. 625 **b.** $226.00

9. $90.50 **11.** 915

13. a. 240 **b.** 492

15. a. 8 **b.** 45 **c.** 6

Exercises 7.3

1. a. $22.50; $22,500.00; $65,000.00; 1000

b. $78,500.00; $90,000.00; $174,000.00; $5500.00

c. $30.00; $45.00; $23,940.00; $9810.00

d. $77,800.00; $41.67; $202,500.00; $140,300.00

3. a. $520.00 **b.** 86

5. $10,670.00 profit

7. a. $8.71 **b.** $19.29 **c.** $1306.50

9. a. 2250 **b.** $60,750.00 **c.** $90,000.00

11. 700

13. a. 650 **b.** 241

15. $8347.50

Exercises 7.4

1. $375,000.00

3. a. $880,000.00 **b.** $1,200,000.00 **c.** $17,500.00

5. a. $120,000.00 **b.** $65,000.00 **c.** $52,000.00

7. 7.50% **9.** $100,000.00

Exercises 7.5

1. a.

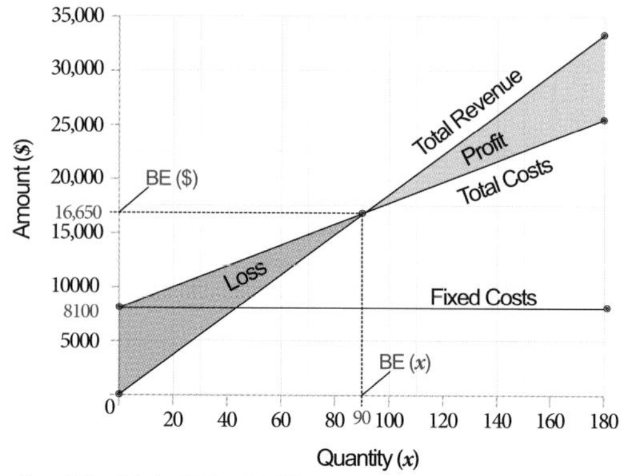

b. 90; $16,650; 50%

3. a.

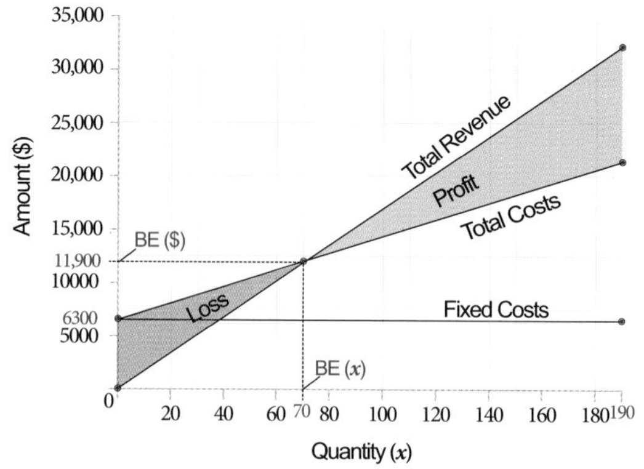

b. 70; $11,900; 36.84% **c.** $1800 loss **d.** $10,800

5. a.

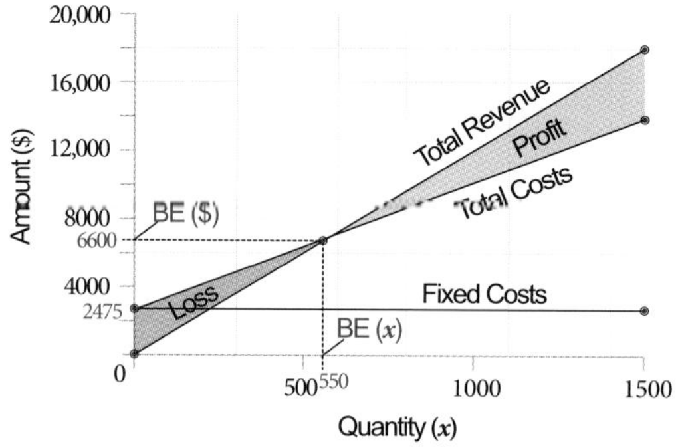

b. 550; $6600; 36.67%; **c.** 700

7. a.

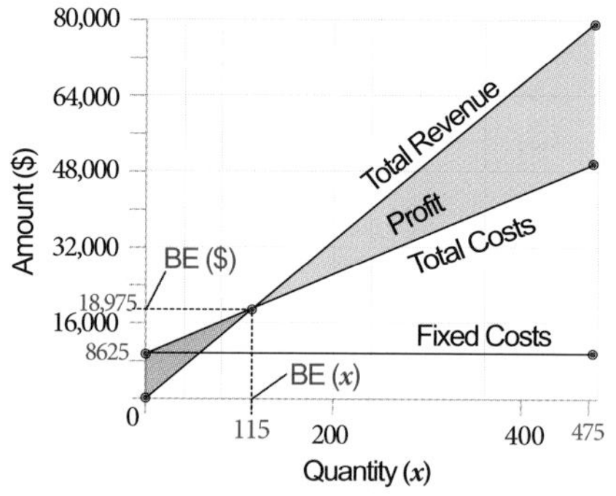

b. 115; $18,975; 24.21% **c.** 145

9. a.

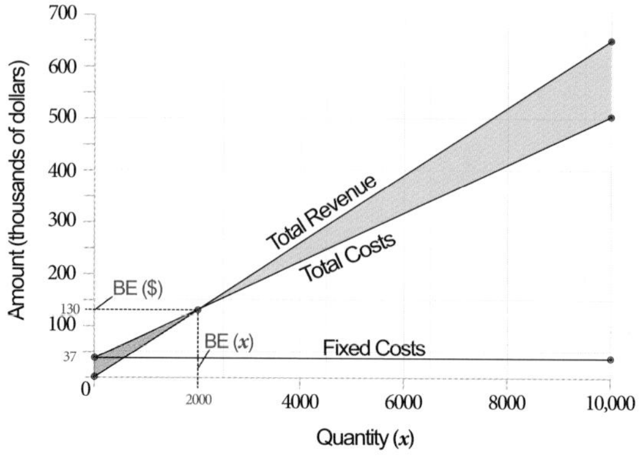

b. 2000; $130,000; 20% **c.** 1645; $131,600

Review Exercises 7

1. a. 491 **b.** $2250.00 **c.** 673

3. a. $5.00; 40% **b.** 13,600 **c.** $30,000.00

5. a. 950 **b.** $184,875.00 **c.** 6950

7. a. $270.00 **b.** 400 **c.** 66.67%

9. a. 2680 **b.** 1560

11. a.

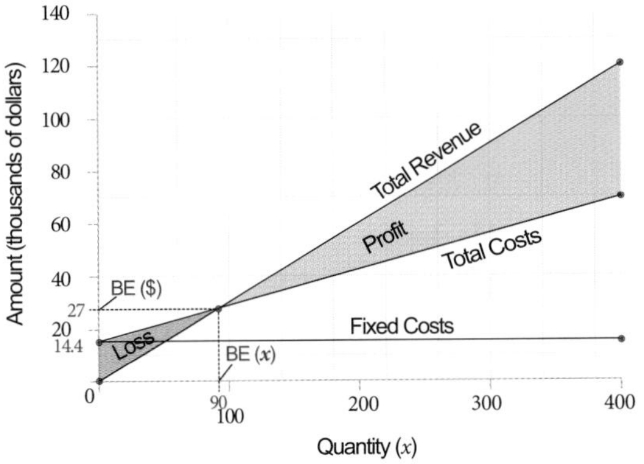

b. 90; $27,000; 22.50% **c.** 98

13. a. $6.40; 40% **b.** 600 **c.** $1600.00

15. 7.01%

17. a. $13,000.00; 200 **b.** 334 **c.** $7350.00

19. a. 640 **b.** $50,000.00 **c.** 915

21. a. $15,000.00 **b.** $9000.00 **c.** $60,000,000.00

Self-Test Exercises 7

1. a. 5000 **b.** 7500

2. a. 69.44% **b.** $95,000.00

3. a. 90 **b.** 633

4. a. $38.75 **b.** $6.25 **c.** $1800.00

5. a. 18,000 **b.** $75,000.00

6. a. –$150,000.00 **b.** 3554

7. a. $625,000.00 **b.** $262,500.00

8. a. $280.00 **b.** $8,503,367.35; $109.59

9. a. 625 **b.** $126,000.00 **c.** 853

10. a. $21,156.00 **b.** 1763 **c.** $60,000.00

Chapter 8

Exercises 8.1

1. a. 49 days; 0.13 years
b. 279 days; 0.76 years
c. 132 days; 0.36 years
d. 378 days; 1.04 years

3. a. $10.96 **b.** $48.22
c. $855.77 **d.** $25.20

5. $106.85 **7.** $29.23

9. $312.50 **11.** $37.81

13. $384.00 **15.** $17.12

17. $110.96

19. 0.85% p.m.

21. $225.00; $172.50

23. Aba; $14.96

25. $235.33

27. $43.59 more

29. $50.00

Exercises 8.2

1. a. 14.24%
b. $3976.15
c. December 24, 2017
d. September 11, 2016

3. $5115.17 **5.** $2931.76

7. $6000.00 **9.** $6653.65

11. 3.75% **13.** 7.84%

15. 1.03% **17.** 7 months

19. July 07, 2017

21. January 12, 2018

23. 1 year and 2 months **25.** $460.00; $60.00

27. $454.11; $50,454.11 **29.** $20,018.00; $702.00

31. $3644.56; $39.94

33. $10,058.42; $10,308.42

35. $286.38

37. $19,271.88

39. 13 years and 4 months

41. $2553.33

43. $2750.00; 4%

Exercises 8.3

1. $37,975.00

3. $2627.02

5. $6118.55

7. a. $21,987.20 **b.** $21,987.94

9. $793.88

11. Option *B*; $1830.76

13. $1027.50

15. $6052.68

17. $6516.53; $3258.26

19. $1083.59

Exercises 8.4

1. Option *A*; $338.75

3. $235.52

5. February 18, 2017; $37,638.70

7. $10,000.00

9. $9832.84

11. $10,040.56

13. 4.30%

15. $4991.79; $8.21

17. $4972.11

19. $8999.21

21. $16,761.39

23. a. $74,723.62 b. 4.50%

25. a. $988.66

b. $992.55; $3.89 profit

c. 3.19%

Review Exercises 8

1. 1 year and 5 months

3. $4477.53; $252.53

5. $19,489.79

7. $4560.00

9. $3044.68

11. $6041.80

13. $7527.01

15. $1717.91

17. $1325.35

19. $4457.54; $8915.08

21. $2666.25

23. 4.00%; $4500.00

Self-Test Exercises 8

1. $192.50

2. 0.47%

3. $277.17

4. $6685.80; $54.95

5. $4768.12

6. $2109.06

7. $191.78

8. a. $24,511.12

b. $24,735.03; profit: $223.91

c. 3.70%

9. $25,184.02

10. $1951.39

11. 2.00%

12. 6.00%

Chapter 9

Exercises 9.1

1. a. 2; 2.5%; 2; 4

b. 4; 2.85%; 1.5; 6

c. 8.4%; 12; 1.5; 18

d. 7.3%; 365; 0.4; 146

3. 16.2% 5. 4

7. 44 9. 4

11. 16 13. 2%

Exercises 9.2

1. a. 2.555%; 11; $1319.85

b. 4.65%; 9; $3939.72

c. 12; 7.2; $17,133.94

d. 11 years and 3 months; 6.57%; $19,744.88

3. $3611.91; $611.91

5. $3294.95; $494.95

7. a. $273,190.61

b. $23,190.61

9. a. $22,905.47

b. $23,113.54, $3113.54, $208.07

11. $13,804.35; $1804.35

13. $33,440.59

15. $39,333.63

17. Option B

19. $388.39 21. $400.96

23. $162.02 more in Option B

25. $43,708.11

27. $61,066.44

29. $43,367.83

31. $4367.09

Exercises 9.3

1. a. $4984.62; 2.69%; 10

b. $8597.29; 5.82%; 43

c. $12,000.00; 12; 84

d. $7500.00; 2 years and 3 months; 7.42%

3. $22,005.32

5. $17,703.44

7. $37,340.28

9. $4014.06

11. $12,492.36

13. $430,047.90

15. Yes 17. $27,679.87

19. Option B; $174.34

21. $45,000.00; $10,021.80

23. Option B

25. $6451.69

Exercises 9.4

1. a. $7021.97

b. $3557.52

c. $1789.34

d. $4337.95

3. a. $3561.16 b. $1740.32

5. a. $623.58 b. $5322.98

7. $46,275.48 9. $1501.09

11. $12,190.18 13. $2936.90

15. $59,703.28 17. $16,131.46

19. $16,994.24 21. $666,532.39

23. $4760.16 25. $3477.50

Exercises 9.5

1. a. 4.77% b. 3.84%

c. 4.24% d. 4.07%

3. 6.95%; 0.58%

5. 9.65% 7. 21.22%

9. 7.35%

11. 3.45%

13. 8.04%; 5.07%

Exercises 9.6

1. a. 5.00 years; 5 years; 5 years

b. 4.67 years; 4 years and 8 months; 4 years and 244 days

c. 3.25 years; 3 years and 3 months; 3 years and 92 days

d. 2.58 years; 2 years and 7 months; 2 years and 211 days

3. 5.74 years; 5 years and 9 months; 5 years and 269 days

5. 4.08 years; 4 years and 1 month; 4 years and 29 days

7. 4.00 years; 4 years; 4 years

9. 3.67 years; 3 years and 8 months; 3 years and 244 days

11. 20.50 years; 20 years and 6 months; 20 years and 183 days

13. 43.82 years; 43 years and 10 months; 43 years and 298 days

15. 2.86 years; 2 years and 11 months; 2 years and 313 days

Exercises 9.7

1. a. 4.86% b. 4.89%

c. 4.91% d. 4.92%

3. 3.99% 5. 10.47%

7. 9.7% compounded daily

9. 34.49%

11. Bank of London

13. 8.46%

15. $29,564.48; $4564.48; 5.75%

17. 4.58%

19. Credit card company

21. 3.97%; $18,501.64

Exercises 9.8

1. **a.** 6.94% **b.** 6.08%
   c. 7.92%
3. 7.85% **5.** 12.25%
7. 3.48% **9.** Option (a)
11. **a.** 5.92% compounded quarterly
    b 5.84% compounded monthly
13. 1.2% p.m.
15. 12.55%; 12.00%
17. 5.88%

Review Exercises 9

1. $459,448.89; $259,448.89
3. $35,919.80 **5.** $91.92
7. $8075.66; $3924.34
9. $27,795.83
11. 8.70%; 8.85%
13. 1.61%; 3.21%
15. 18.16 years; 18 years and 2 months; 18 years and 59 days
17. Either bank; equivalent rates
19. 6.34% **21.** 4.92%

Self-Test Exercises 9

1. $671,345.81; $90,445.81
2. $34,191.94
3. $15,888.60
4. $23,368.76
5. Nil
6. $10,225.90
7. 6.89%
8. 8.26 years; 8 years and 4 months; 8 years and 94 days
9. 4.25%
10. $135,605.89
11. $7720.41

Chapter 10

Exercises 10.1

1. General annuity due; 71
3. Ordinary simple annuity; 21
5. Simple annuity due; 48
7. Ordinary general annuity; 240
9. RRSP: general annuity due, 120; RRIF: ordinary general annuity, 60

Exercises 10.2

1. **a.** $30,720.52
   b. $31,495.31
   c. $20,109.07
   d. $29,362.93
3. **a.** $19,781.80
   b. $21,587.93
   c. $15,998.32
   d. $22,430.14
5. **a.** $3382.26
   b. $382.26
7. **a.** $153,848.80
   b. $168,309.07
9. $7865.50
11. $107,741.14
13. $147,162.90
15. $9715.94
17. $78,527.85
19. $28,747.63; $3547.63
21. $21,664.25; $2664.25
23. **a.** $107,452.69
    b. $7547.31
25. $172,657.10
27. Pay the entire amount; $PV(\text{loan}) = \$6325.12 > \$5000$

Exercises 10.3

1. **a.** $\frac{4}{2}$; 0.025156
   b. $\frac{365}{12}$; 0.003506
   c. $\frac{12}{2}$; 0.024241
   d. $\frac{2}{4}$; 0.012176
3. **a.** $47,071.42
   b. $64,744.95
   c. $55,604.70
   d. $51,432.10
5. **a.** $23,010.52
   b. $33,500.26
   c. $36,609.18
   d. $42,046.38
7. $6802.36
9. **a.** $18,604.04
   b. $18,586.65
11. $49,030.59
13. $26,182.16; $26,169.76; RRSP 1
15. Option *A*; $4747.47
17. $120,010.68
19. $39,661.64
21. $8404.14
23. Second option; $7667.23
25. $12,680.33; $1189.67
27. Annuity *A*; $42.98
29. $44,014.81
31. **a.** Gerard; $3937.64
    b. Gabriella; $92,062.36
33. $55,444.13

Exercises 10.4

1. **a.** $54,994.99
   b. $51,612.58
   c. $23,027.61
   d. $20,469.92
3. **a.** $35,450.26
   b. $28,701.70
   c. $16,948.76
   d. $17,000.37
5. $27,477.32
7. **a.** $35,546.28
   b. $27,000.00
   c. $8546.28
9. $341,438.22
11. **a.** $32,446.22
    b. $8446.22
13. $17,750.33
15. $22,218.23
17. $149,961.38
19. $78,763.17
21. **a.** Purchase option
    b. $10,388.64
23. $61,115.85; $16,115.85
25. $148,522.94
27. $13,805.50; $17,305.63

Exercises 10.5

1. **a.**$92,369.28 **b.** $63,795.94
   c. $70,957.19 **d.** $108,116.61
3. **a.** $42,919.50 **b.** $38,790.41
   c. $49,228.39 **d.** $83,841.79
5. $28,706.93
7. $42,176.93; $15,176.93
9. $23,432.95

11. $47,717.63

13. a. $121,951.97
b. $21,951.97

15. $176,120.76; $64,120.76

17. a. $38,900.61
b. $38,726.01

19. $744.82

21. $146,698.06

23. $59,144.42

25. a. Purchase option
b. $11,588.47

27. Ryder; $17,905.90

29. First option; $6246.55

Exercises 10.6

1. $1909.24

3. $225.92

5. $6253.77

7. $12,044.38

9. $4351.18

11. $439.88

13. $899.14

15. $1285.65

17. $10,183.15

19. $761.91

21. $3482.98

23. $298.12

25. $2955.21

27. $2729.91

29. $640.42

31. a. $364.01 **b.** $0.14

33. $32,500.62

Exercises 10.7

1. 1 year and 4 months

3. 8 years

5. 5 payments

7. 4 years

9. 2 years and 6 months

11. 2 years and 5 months

13. 18 years

15. 191 payments

17. a. 73 withdrawals
b. 36 years

19. 45 payments

21. $330.40; 6 years and 1 month

Exercises 10.8

1. 4.77% **3.** 5.60%

5. 5.05% **7.** 4.11%

9. 5.72% **11.** 9.64%

13. a. 8.26% **b.** 14.19%

15. 6.55% **17.** 5.77%

19. 4.36% **21.** 7.63%

23. 6.88%, 6.42%; Bank's loan

Review Exercises 10

1. $1171.10 **3.** $78,941.69

5. $14,780.21; $4780.21

7. $167,600.31

9. $228,596.35

11. $14,289.05; $4289.05

13. $1289.97 **15.** $548.24

17. $26,116.57 **19.** $969.45

21. 4 years and 10 months

23. 5 years and 11 months

25. 8.87% **27.** 24.13%

29. $12.33

Self-Test Exercises 10

1. $14,745.75; $1745.75

2. $50,000.00, $47,155.52, $45,596.35; Option A

3. $41,925.08, $41,921.59; Option A

4. $198,594.46

5. 7 years and 4 months **6.** 29

7. $416.41 **8. a.** $11,453.21 **b.** $158,128.40

9. 10 years

10. $38,988.14; $6011.86

11. $534,395.07; $259,200.00; $275,195.07

12. $4219.56

13. 59

14. $0.52

15. a. 4.67%
b. $3557.10

Chapter 11

Exercises 11.1

1. a. 4 months; 3 years
b. 5 months; 3 years

3. $120,967.49

5. $143,291.95

7. $73,415.59

9. $13,167.65

11. 4 years and 9 months

13. 7 years and 6 months

15. $198.75
17. a. $1130.26
b. $50,631.20
19. $462.68
21. Deferred Annuity Due: 4 years
Ordinary Deferred Annuity: 3.92 years
23. $207,645.76

Exercises 11.2

1. $166,666.67
3. $67,162.97
5. $202.50
7. $410,435.81
9. $15,750
11. 6.55%
13. $3094.06
15. $4770.51
17. $500,484.39
19. $5101.39
21. a. $1000
b. $995.02
c. $1342.14
d. $987.72

Exercises 11.3

1. a. $11,203.38
b. $11,697.49
c. $1235.28
3. a. $128,614.69
b. $14,563.15
5. a. $57,832.31
b. $10,200.33
7. $20,757.70
9. $3099.42
11. $23,524.95

Review Exercises 11

1. $895,467.91
3. $16,851.31
5. 3 years
7. $1886.93
9. $7500
11. $9961.22
13. $3099.27
15. $2,542,515.72
17. $82,604.34
19. $7786.66

Self-Test Exercises 11

1. $46,554.48
2. $3013.67
3. 5 years and 4 months
4. $140.76
5. $24,891.84
6. $2901.84
7. $7593.75
8. $130,724.69
9. $57,573.27
10. $8219.50

Chapter 12

Exercises 12.1

1. a. $2562.81
b.

Payment Number	Amount Paid	Interest Portion	Principal Portion	Principal Balance
0				$10,000.00
1	$2562.81	$100.00	$2462.81	7537.19
2	2562.81	75.37	2487.44	5049.75
3	2562.81	50.50	2512.31	2537.44
4	2562.81	25.37	2537.44	0.00
Total	**$10,251.24**	**$251.24**	**$10,000.00**	

c. $10,251.24
d. $251.24

3. a. 7 years
b.

Payment Number	Amount Paid	Interest Portion	Principal Portion	Principal Balance
0				$45,240.00
1	$2098.25	$859.29	$1238.96	44,001.04
2	2098.25	835.76	1262.49	42,738.55
...	.	.	.	.
26	.	.	.	4078.40
27	2098.25	77.47	2020.78	2057.62
28	2096.70	39.08	2057.62	0.00
Total	**$58,749.45**	**$13,509.45**	**$45,240.00**	

c. $13,509.45
5. $16,798.16
7. $20,602.62
9. a. 184
b. $1791.04
11. a. 77
b. $349.26
13. a. 121
b. $72,301.00
c. $1345.58
d. $245,345.58
15. a. $1588.96
b. $11.04
17. $1359.92
19. a. $708.37
b. $352.78
c. $83,787.68
21.

Payment Number	Amount Paid	Interest Portion	Principal Portion	Principal Balance
0				$100,000.00
1	$1061.15	$417.51	$643.64	99,356.36
2	1061.15	414.82	646.33	98,710.03
...	.	.	.	.
118	.	.	.	2108.82
119	1061.15	8.80	1052.35	1056.47
120	1060.88	4.41	1056.47	0.00
Total	**$127,337.73**	**$27,337.73**	**$100,000.00**	

23. a. $6042.04
b. $557.96
25.

Payment Number	Amount Paid	Interest Portion	Principal Portion	Principal Balance
0				$18,750.00
1	$550.00	$84.77	$465.23	18,284.77
2	550.00	82.67	467.33	17,817.44
...	.	.	.	.
36	.	.	.	606.17
37	550.00	2.74	547.26	58.91
38	59.18	0.27	58.91	0.00
Total	**$20,409.18**	**$1659.18**	**$18,750.00**	

27. a. $7598.58 b. $4101.42
29.

Payment Number	Amount Paid	Interest Portion	Principal Portion	Principal Balance
0				$75,000.00
1	$1300.00	$548.81	$751.19	74,248.81
2	1300.00	543.31	756.69	73,492.12
...	.	.	.	.
74	.	.	.	1581.03
75	1300.00	11.57	1288.43	292.60
76	294.74	2.14	292.60	0.00
Total	**$97,794.74**	**$22,794.74**	**$75,000.00**	

Exercises 12.2

1. a. $1437.90 **b.** $248,486.25 **c.** $1463.15
3. a. $1100.00 **b.** $479.91
5.

Payment Number	Amount Paid	Interest Portion	Principal Portion	Principal Balance
0				$100,000.00
1	$1100.00	$453.17	$646.83	99,353.17
2	1100.00	450.24	649.76	98,703.41
...	.	.	.	.
116	.	.	.	1570.63
117	1100.00	7.11	1092.89	477.74
118	479.91	2.17	477.74	0.00
Total	$129,179.91	$29,179.91	$100,000.00	

7. a. $1050.00 **b.** 6 months **c.** $445.97
9. a. $1560.00 **b.** $82,744.20 **c.** $1550.00; $948.77
11. $280,049.82
13. a. $1682.56 **b.** $266,900.87 **c.** 4 years and 4 months
15. a. $1206.93 **b.** $169,289.62 **c.** 2 years and 2 months
17. a. 20 years **b.** 17 years and 18 weeks **c.** $29,202.30

Review Exercises 12

1. $1585.72; $1528.64;

Payment Number	Amount Paid	Interest Portion	Principal Portion	Principal Balance
0				$17,500.00
1	$1585.72	$229.69	$1356.03	16,143.97
2	1585.72	211.89	1373.83	14,770.14
...	.	.	.	.
10	.	.	.	3110.08
11	1585.72	40.82	1544.90	1565.18
12	1585.72	20.54	1565.18	0.00
Total	$19,028.64	$1528.64	$17,500.00	

3. $2507.07; $35.47 **5.** $12.94; $487.06
7.

Payment Number	Amount Paid	Interest Portion	Principal Portion	Principal Balance
0	.	.	.	$16,850.00
1	$500.00	$62.60	$437.40	16,412.60
2	500.00	60.97	439.03	15,973.57
...	.	.	.	.
35	.	.	.	533.36
36	500.00	1.98	498.02	35.34
37	35.47	0.13	35.34	0.00
Total	$18,035.47	$1185.47	$16,850.00	

9.

Payment Number	Amount Paid	Interest Portion	Principal Portion	Principal Balance
0				$1,250,000.00
1	$285,547.43	$57,521.95	$228,025.48	1,021,974.52
2	285,547.43	47,028.78	238,518.65	783,455.87
3	285,547.43	36,052.73	249,494.70	533,961.17
4	285,547.43	24,571.59	260,975.84	272,985.33
5	285,547.45	12,562.12	272,985.33	0.00
Total	$1,427,737.17	$177,737.17	$1,250,000.00	

11. $1354.03; $6736.83 **13.** $1354.03; $379.12; $974.91
15. a. $2133.12 **b.** $291,938.85 **c.** $2190.71
17. a. $800.00 **b.** $560.23 **19.** $156,080.51

Self-Test Exercises 12

1. $176.95;

Payment Number	Amount Paid	Interest Portion	Principal Portion	Principal Balance
0	-	-	-	$20,000.00
1	$176.95	$20.00	$156.95	19,843.05
2	176.95	19.84	157.11	19,685.94
...	.	.	.	.
118	.	.	.	353.35
119	176.95	0.35	176.60	176.75
120	176.93	0.18	176.75	0.00
Total	$21,233.98	$1233.98	$20,000.00	

2. $5236.56; $261.39 **3.** $30.35; $319.65
4.

Payment Number	Amount Paid	Interest Portion	Principal Portion	Principal Balance
0				$18,400.00
1	$350.00	$113.53	$236.47	18,163.53
2	350.00	112.07	237.93	17,925.60
3	350.00	110.60	239.40	17,686.20
...	.	.	.	.
61	.	.	.	950.19
62	350.00	5.86	344.14	606.05
63	350.00	3.74	346.26	259.79
64	261.39	1.60	259.79	0.00
Total	$22,311.39	$3911.39	$18,400.00	

5. $457.42; $10,102.57 **6.** $457.59; $128.61; $328.81
7. a. $988.56 **b.** $170,834.05 **c.** $1076.95
8. a. $180.00 **b.** $170.52
9. 2 years **10.** 4 years and 2 months

Chapter 13

Exercises 13.1

1. a. $5000.00; 12 years; Sold at a Discount
b. $30,000.00; March 15, 2023; Sold at a Premium
c. $10,000.00; June 10, 2019; Sold at Par
3. $1000.00; November 01, 2021; Sold at a Discount
5. $5000.00; December 15, 2026; Sold at Par
7. $3000.00; March 14, 2022; Sold at a Premium
9. $10,000.00; March 31, 2022; Sold at a Premium

Exercises 13.2

1. a. $1000.00; $0.00 **b.** $4281.27; $718.73 discount
c. $14,994.83; $4994.83 premium
3. a. $1000.00 **b.** $786.45; $213.55
c. $1136.78; $136.78
5. a. $82,031.87 **b.** $17,968.13 discount
7. a. $51,601.31 **b.** $1601.31 premium
9. a. $9715.37 **b.** $284.63 discount
11. a. $978.40 **b.** $1013.89
c. $35.49 gain **d.** 3.63% gain

13. a. $11,384.87; $1384.87 premium
b. $21,012.32; $1012.32 premium
c. 4.33%; $24.00 premium
d. 10.40%; $1001.50 discount

15. a. $9734.16 **b.** $265.84 discount

17. 8.64% **19.** 4.16%

Exercises 13.3

1. a. $4517.88; $4487.94
b. $54,910.07; $54,286.78
c. $957.20; $955.00
d. $54,115.32; $53,492.02

3. a. $994.00 **b.** $6.00 discount

5. a. $24,600.00 **b.** $400.00 discount

7. a. $9800.76 **b.** $199.24 discount

9. a. $25,875.00 **b.** $692.93
c. $26,567.93

11. a. $111,192.12 **b.** $1790.06
c. $109,402.07 **d.** 109.40

Exercises 13.4

1.

Period	Interest Received	Interest on *BV*	Amortized Premium	Book Value (*BV*)	Premium to be Amortized
0	-	-	-	$1028.49	$28.49
1	$20.00	$15.43	$4.57	1023.92	23.92
2	20.00	15.36	4.64	1019.28	19.28
3	20.00	15.29	4.71	1014.57	14.57
4	20.00	15.22	4.78	1009.79	9.79
5	20.00	15.15	4.85	1004.94	4.94
6	20.00	15.07	4.93	1000.01*	0.01*
Total	$120.00	$91.52	$28.48		

**Due to the rounding of amounts in each step, there is a minor difference of $0.01.*

3.

Period	Interest Received	Interest on *BV*	Accumulated Discount	Book Value (*BV*)	Discount to be Accumulated
0	-	-	-	$4863.48	$136.52
1	$156.25	$188.46	$32.21	4895.69	104.31
2	156.25	189.71	33.46	4929.15	70.85
3	156.25	191.00	34.75	4963.90	36.10
4	156.25	192.35	36.10	5000.00	0.00
Total	$625.00	$761.52	$136.52		

5.

Period	Interest Received	Interest on *BV*	Amortized Premium	Book Value (*BV*)	Premium to be Amortized
0	-	-	-	$51,601.31	$1601.31
1	$1562.50	$1380.34	$182.16	51,419.15	1419.15
2	1562.50	1375.46	187.04	51,232.11	1232.11
3	1562.50	1370.46	192.04	51,040.07	1040.07
4	1562.50	1365.32	197.18	50,842.89	842.89
5	1562.50	1360.05	202.45	50,640.44	640.44
6	1562.50	1354.63	207.87	50,432.57	432.57
7	1562.50	1349.07	213.43	50,219.14	219.14
8	1562.50	1343.36	219.14	50,000.00	0.00
Total	$12,500.00	$10,898.69	$1601.31		

7.

Period	Interest Received	Interest on BV	Accumulated Discount	Book Value (BV)	Discount to be Accumulated
0	-	-	-	$9715.37	$284.63
1	$175.00	$219.83	$44.83	9760.20	239.80
2	175.00	220.84	45.84	9806.04	193.96
3	175.00	221.88	46.88	9852.92	147.08
4	175.00	222.94	47.94	9900.86	99.14
5	175.00	224.02	49.02	9949.88	50.12
6	175.00	225.13	50.13	10,000.01*	–0.01*
Total	$1050.00	$1334.64	$284.64		

**Due to the rounding of amounts in each step, there is a minor difference of $0.01.*

Exercises 13.5

1. $1134.58

3.

Payment Period	Payment (PMT)	Interest Earned	Increase in the Fund	Fund Balance	Book Value
0	-	-	-	$0.00	$10,000.00
1	$1134.58	$0.00	$1134.58	1134.58	$8865.42
2	1134.58	31.20	1165.78	2300.36	7699.64
3	1134.58	63.26	1197.84	3498.20	6501.80
4	1134.58	96.20	1230.78	4728.98	5271.02
5	1134.58	130.05	1264.63	5993.61	4006.39
6	1134.58	164.82	1299.40	7293.01	2706.99
7	1134.58	200.56	1335.14	8628.15	1371.85
8	1134.58	237.27	1371.85	10,000.00	0.00
Total	$9076.64	$923.36	$10,000.00		

5. a. $41,645.48 **b.** $276,233.45
c. $11,049.34 **d.** $52,694.82
e.

Payment Period	Payment (PMT)	Interest Earned	Increase in the Fund	Fund Balance	Book Value
8	-	-	-	$383,730.88	$116,269.12
9	$41,645.48	$15,349.24	$56,994.72	440,725.60	59,274.40
10	41,645.48	17,629.02	59,274.50	500,000.10	–0.10

7. $10,435.37

9.

Payment Period	Payment (PMT)	Interest Earned	Increase in the Fund	Fund Balance	Book Value
0	-	-	-	$0.00	$100,000.00
1	$10,435.37	$417.41	$10,852.78	10,852.78	89,147.22
2	10,435.37	851.53	11,286.90	22,139.68	77,860.32
3	10,435.37	1303.00	11,738.37	33,878.05	66,121.95
4	10,435.37	1772.54	12,207.91	46,085.96	53,914.04
5	10,435.37	2260.85	12,696.22	58,782.18	41,217.82
6	10,435.37	2768.70	13,204.07	71,986.25	28,013.74
7	10,435.37	3296.86	13,732.23	85,718.48	14,281.51
8	10,435.37	3846.15	14,281.52	100,000.00	0.00
Total	$83,482.96	$16,517.05	$100,000.00		

11. **a.** $31,099.19 **b.** $706,001.72
c. $12,899.27 **d.** $43,998.46
e.

Payment Period	Payment (PMT)	Interest Earned	Increase in the Fund	Fund Balance	Book Value
0	-	-	-	$0.00	$750,000.00
1	$31,099.19	$544.24	$31,643.43	31,643.43	718,356.57
2	31,099.19	1098.00	32,197.19	63,840.62	686,159.38

13. $257,778.74; $2,988,694.34

15.

Payment Period	Payment (PMT)	Interest Earned	Increase in the Fund	Fund Balance	Book Value
0			-	$0.00	$5,000,000.00
1	$82,778.74	$0.00	$82,778.74	82,778.74	4,917,221.26
2	82,778.74	1655.57	84,434.31	167,213.05	4,832,786.95
3	82,778.74	3344.26	86,123.00	253,336.06	4,746,663.94
...	-	-	-	-	-
37	-	-	-	4,472,887.51	527,112.49
38	82,778.74	89,457.75	172,236.49	4,645,124.00	354,876.00
39	82,778.74	92,902.48	175,681.22	4,820,805.22	179,194.78
40	82,778.74	96,416.10	179,194.84	5,000,000.06	−0.06
Total	**$3,311,149.60**	**$1,688,850.46**	**$5,000,000.06**		

17. $17,906.85; $34,827.18

19.

Payment Period	Payment (PMT)	Interest Earned	Increase in the Fund	Fund Balance	Book Value
0	-	-	-	$0.00	$100,000.00
1	$15,406.85	$346.65	$15,753.50	15,753.50	84,246.50
2	15,406.85	701.11	16,107.96	31,861.46	68,138.54
3	15,406.85	1063.54	16,470.39	48,331.85	51,668.15
4	15,406.85	1434.12	16,840.97	65,172.82	34,827.18
5	15,406.85	1813.04	17,219.89	82,392.71	17,607.29
6	15,406.85	2200.49	17,607.34	100,000.05	-0.05
Total	**$92,441.04**	**$7,558.95**	**$100,000.05**		

Review Exercises 13

1. $4789.99; $210.01 discount
3. $1017.00; $17.00 premium
5. $3251.98 loss
7. $29,269.79; $4269.79 premium
9. $5380.08; $380.08 premium
11.

Period	Interest Received	Interest on BV	Amortized Premium	Book Value (BV)	Premium to be Amortized
0	-	-	-	$1035.47	$35.47
1	$32.50	$28.48	$4.02	1031.45	31.45
2	32.50	28.36	4.14	1027.31	27.31
3	32.50	28.25	4.25	1023.06	23.06
4	32.50	28.13	4.37	1018.69	18.69
5	32.50	28.01	4.49	1014.20	14.20
6	32.50	27.89	4.61	1009.59	9.59
7	32.50	27.76	4.74	1004.85	4.85
8	32.50	27.63	4.87	999.98*	-0.02*
Total	**$260.00**	**$224.51**	**$35.49**		

**Due to the rounding of amounts in each step, there is a minor difference of $0.02.*

13. 9.97%
15. **a.** $10,103.60 **b.** $56,954.93
c. $3417.30 **d.** $13,520.90
e.

Payment Period	Payment (PMT)	Interest Earned	Increase in the Fund	Fund Balance	Book Value
0	-	-	-	$0.00	$100,000.00
1	$10,103.60	$0.00	$10,103.60	10,103.60	89,896.40
2	10,103.60	606.22	10,709.82	20,813.42	79,186.58
3	10,103.60	1248.81	11,352.41	32,165.83	67,834.17
4	10,103.60	1929.95	12,033.55	44,199.38	55,800.62
5	10,103.60	2651.96	12,755.56	56,954.94	43,045.06
6	10,103.60	3417.30	13,520.90	70,475.84	29,524.16
7	10,103.60	4228.55	14,332.15	84,807.99	15,192.01
8	10,103.60	5088.50	15,192.08	100,000.07	−0.07
Total	**$80,828.80**	**$19,171.29**	**$100,000.07**		

17. $135,572.74; $919,829.94

Self-Test Exercises 13

1. $355.31 discount
2. $10,372.08; $372.08 premium
3. $1293.23 loss
4. $974.31; $25.69 discount
5. $24,794.12; $205.88 discount
6. $10,728.36; $728.36 premium
7.

Period	Interest Received	Interest on BV	Amortized Premium	Book Value (BV)	Premium to be Amortized
0	-	-	-	$5085.03	$85.03
1	$200.00	$190.69	$9.31	5075.72	75.72
2	200.00	190.34	9.66	5066.06	66.06
3	200.00	189.98	10.02	5056.04	56.04
4	200.00	189.60	10.40	5045.64	45.64
5	200.00	189.21	10.79	5034.85	34.85
6	200.00	188.81	11.19	5023.66	23.66
7	200.00	188.39	11.61	5012.05	12.05
8	200.00	187.95	12.05	5000.00	0.00
Total	**$1600.00**	**$1514.97**	**$85.03**		

8. 4.83%
9. **a.** $12,301.86 **b.** $35,380.32
c.

Payment Period	Payment (PMT)	Interest Earned	Increase in the Fund	Fund Balance	Book Value
28				$664,218.43	$86,281.57
29	$12,301.86	$29,889.83	$42,191.69	706,410.12	44,089.88
30	12,301.86	31,788.46	44,090.32	750,500.44	−0.44

10. $11,762.89; $23,666.48

Chapter 14

Exercises 14.1

1. $16,780.05
3. $128,429.36, $122,770.92; Option 2
5. $132,456.78, $123,779.00; Project *A*
7. $29,927.05; Buy Option
9. a. $51,984.19, $56,433.04; Renting Option
b. $53,211.50, $50,179.97; Purchasing Option

Exercises 14.2

1. $2149.52, $3031.00; Newspaper
3. a. $15,671.11; yes
b. –$77,188.87; no
c. –$167,026.34; no
5. $28,001.05; yes
7. $1,646,807.11; yes
9. $825,890.82; yes
11. $51,066.27; yes
13. $3970.83; –$3429.33; Plan *A*

Exercises 14.3

1. 11.22%
3. 6.80%; no
5. 16.98%; yes
7. 16.99%; yes
9. 14.78%; yes
11. 14.89%; yes
13. 11.05%; yes

Exercises 14.4

1. 3 years and 8 months; yes
3. 6 years and 2 months; no
5. 5 years and 10 months; no

Review Exercises 14

1. Purchase option; $353.59
3. $1,493,315.84
5. 7.98%; yes
7. a. $101,682.08; yes
b. $39,815.04; yes
c. –$20,162.75; no
9. Yes; $525.35
11. 10.87%
13. 8.92%; yes
15. 9.94%; no
17. 4 years and 5 months; no
19. 7 years and 8 months; no

Self-Test Exercises 14

1. Option 1; $5960.22
2. $4010.14; Yes
3. 15.37%; Yes
4. Upgrade plastic molder; 16.16%
5. –89,605.13; no
6. $388,349.96
7. –$22,665.72; no
8. 3 years and 8 months; no
9. 2 years and 6 months; no

Glossary

Algebra a branch of mathematics that deals with different relations and operations by using letters and symbols to represent numbers, values, etc.

Algebraic expression consists of one or more terms with a combination of variables, numbers, and operation signs. Equations and formulas are formed using algebraic expressions.

Algebraic term a number, variable, or a combination of numbers and variables, which forms a part of an expression.

Amortization the process of repaying a loan through periodic payments.

Amortization period the time taken to repay a loan.

Amortization schedule a table showing the reduction of a loan's principal balance from period to period, including the payment size, the interest portion, and the principal portion for each period.

Amount of interest the amount charged for using a principal amount for a period of time.

Amount of markup (also known as margin or gross profit) the difference between the selling price and the cost of merchandise.

Annual salary the salary that an employee receives for his or her service over the period of a year.

Annuity a series of payments (usually in equal amounts) made at regular intervals for a fixed period of time.

Annuity due an annuity where payments are made at the beginning of each payment period.

Base (B) the number that represents the whole (100%) quantity or value; used in percent calculations.

Base salary plus commission when an employee receives a commission on the sales made, in addition to his/her base salary.

BEDMAS the acronym for the order of arithmetic operations: Bracket, Exponent, Division and Multiplication, Addition and Subtraction.

Binomial a polynomial with 2 terms.

Bi-weekly pay period when an employee is paid once every two weeks.

Bond an (often transferrable) contract that promises regular payments over time, as well as a larger lump-sum payment at the end of the contract's term. These contracts are generally sold to investors with the promise of a return on their investment.

Break-even point the point at which the total sales or total revenue equals the total costs. At the break-even point, there are no profits made and no losses incurred.

Break-even price the selling price of an item, which includes only the cost and overhead expenses. When a product is sold at the break-even price, neither is profit made nor loss incurred.

Cash discount the amount of discount on the net price (invoice amount) offered by a seller to a buyer to encourage early payment of an invoice.

Cash-inflow when money is received.

Cash-outflow when money is paid out.

Coefficient the number factor in front of the variable(s) of an algebraic term.

Collateral the legal claim that a lender holds over a borrower's property, assigned in a lending agreement, which grants the lender the right to take the property if the borrower has shown an inability to pay the debt.

Commercial paper similar to T-bills, except that it is issued by large corporations rather than by governments.

Commission a percent of sales for a given pay period that is given to an employee as part of his/her salary.

Common logarithms the logarithm of a number to the base 10; referred to by the symbol 'log'.

Complex fraction a fraction in which one or more fractions are found in the numerator or denominator.

Composite number a whole number that has at least one factor other than 1 and the number itself.

Compound interest a procedure where interest is added to the principal at the end of each compounding period to earn interest in the subsequent compounding period.

Compounding frequency the number of times interest is compounded every year.

Compounding period the time interval between two successive interest dates.

Constant a letter used in an algebraic expression that only represents a single number.

Constant-growth annuity an annuity where the periodic payment amount increases by a constant rate over the preceding payment amount.

Contribution Margin per unit the amount remaining from the selling price per unit after deducting the variable costs per unit.

Contribution Ratio the ratio of the contribution margin to the selling price per unit; expressed as a percent.

Cost the amount paid for an item after trade discounts and cash discounts have both been deducted.

Cost of capital the cost of spending money in a business (either through direct interest charges on borrowed money, or relative opportunity costs through profits lost from alternative projects), expressed as a compounded rate.

Deferred annuity an annuity in which the first periodic payment is made after a certain interval of time, known as the deferral period.

Deferred annuity due a deferred annuity where periodic payments are made at the beginning of each payment period.

Demand loan a loan that becomes payable when it is demanded by the lender who issued the loan.

Discounted Cash Flow a method of valuing an investment by discounting all future cash inflows and outflows, to their present value.

Down payment a lump sum payment made at the start of a loan, mortgage, or lease.

Effective interest rate the annually compounding interest rate.

End-of-Month dating (EOM) a cash payment term where the credit period and discount period start from the end of the month in which the invoice is dated.

Equivalent algebraic equations equations with the same solutions.

Equivalent fraction the resulting fraction when both the numerator and denominator of a fraction are either multiplied by the same number or divided by the same number.

Equivalent interest rates nominal interest rates with different compounding periods that result in the same future value of a given principal for any fixed period of time.

Equivalent ratio the resulting ratio when all the terms of the ratio are multiplied by the same number or divided by the same number.

Exchange rate (also called the foreign exchange rate or forex rate) used to convert currencies between countries.

Exponents mathematical notation for representing the product of a repeated number. For example, $2 \times 2 \times 2 \times 2 \times 2$ is represented as 2^5 using exponents.

Face Value the amount that is to be transferred from the issuer to the holder of a promissory note; the redemption value of the note.

Factors of a number whole numbers that can divide the number with no remainder.

Fixed Costs costs that remain the same irrespective of how many items are produced and sold.

Fraction a rational number written as one integer divided by another non-zero integer.

Fractional exponent when the exponent of a term is a fraction.

Future value the accumulated value of a payment or a series of payments.

General annuity due an annuity due where the compounding period and the payment period are not the same.

Goods and Services Tax (GST) sales taxes that are levied by the federal government. The federal GST rate for all provinces and territories in Canada is 5%.

Graduated commission when an employee's commission increases gradually with increased sales.

Graduated piecework rate when the rate per unit increases above a pre-determined output level.

Greatest Common Factor (GCF) the largest common number that divides two or more numbers with no remainder.

Gross pay the total amount of earnings before any deductions are made.

Guaranteed Investment Certificate (GIC) investment where the investor is guaranteed to receive the full principal investment plus interest at the end of the specified time period.

Harmonized Sales Tax (HST) a single tax which combines the GST and PST. In New Brunswick, Newfoundland, Nova Scotia, and Ontario, the Canada Revenue Agency collects the HST and remits the appropriate amounts to the participating provinces.

Hourly wages when employees are paid on an hour-by-hour basis.

Improper fraction a fraction in which the absolute value of the numerator is greater than the absolute value of the denominator.

Interest a fee paid by borrowers to lenders for using money temporarily.

Interest bearing promissory note a promissory note where the face value is the amount of loan that must be repaid with the interest calculated based on the interest rate specified on the note.

Internal Rate of Return (IRR) the annually compounding rate at which an investment produces a gain.

Lease an agreement in which a lessee makes regular payments to essentially borrow an asset from a lessor; the ownership of the asset remains with the lessor.

Least or Lowest Common Denominator (LCD) the smallest whole number that is divisible by each of two or more fractions' denominators.

Least or Lowest Common Multiple (LCM) the smallest multiple that is common to two or more whole numbers.

Like terms two or more algebraic terms that have the same variables and exponents.

Linear equation a first degree algebraic equation with one or two variables which produces a straight line when plotted on a graph.

List price (also known as the manufacturer's suggested retail price or MSRP) the price of a merchandise item before discounts have been applied.

Markdown the amount by which the selling price of a product is reduced to determine the sale price or reduced selling price.

Markup the amount that a business adds to the cost of the product to arrive at the selling price of the product.

Maturity value the accumulated value of a principal amount that is invested or borrowed at an interest rate for a period of time.

Merchandising a process that involves the buying and selling of goods (merchandise) from a manufacturer to the final sale of those goods to consumers.

Mill rate the amount of property tax per thousand dollars of property value.

Mixed number a number consisting of both a whole number and a fraction, which are written side-by-side and imply that the whole number and proper fraction are added together.

Monomial an algebraic expression that only has one term.

Monthly pay period when an employee is paid once a month.

Mortgage a loan issued by a financial lending institution to a borrower for the purpose of purchasing real-estate property, generally with the lender holding a legal claim over the property until the loan has been repaid.

Multiples of a number whole numbers that can be divided by the number with no remainder.

Natural logarithms the logarithm of a number to the base '*e*', where $e = 2.718282...$; referred to by the symbol 'ln'.

Net Income the difference between the total revenue collected and the total costs incurred in a business.

Net loss when the total revenue is less than the total costs.

Net pay the actual payment that an employee receives after all payroll deductions.

Net Present Value the present value of all future cash inflows less the present value of all future cash outflows. This represents the total gain of an investment over its life, taking the time value of money into account.

Net price the price of a merchandise item after deducting all discounts.

Net profit when the total revenue of a business exceeds its total costs.

Nominal interest rate the quoted or stated interest rate per annum on which the compound interest calculation is based for a given compounding period.

Non-interest bearing promissory note a promissory note where the face value is the maturity value of the note.

Operating profit also known as profit, is the amount of desired profit necessary to stay in the business.

Ordinary annuity an annuity where payments are made at the end of each payment period.

Ordinary dating cash payment terms where the credit period and the discount period start on the invoice date.

Ordinary deferred annuity a deferred annuity where periodic payments are made at the end of each payment period.

Ordinary general annuity an ordinary annuity where the compounding period and the payment period are not the same.

Ordinary simple annuity an ordinary annuity where the compounding period and the payment period are the same.

Overhead expenses (also known as operating expenses) expenses that are necessary to operate the business.

Overtime factor used to calculate the overtime rate of pay for an employee.

Overtime rate the hourly rate of pay for working overtime.

Pay period how often payments are made to an employee. They could be monthly, semi-monthly, bi-weekly, or weekly.

Payback period the length of time required for an investment's cash inflows to match and/or cross its cash outflows (ignoringing the time value of money).

Payment interval (or payment period) the time between two successive payments.

Payroll a record that employers maintain to register employees' names, the types of payment, and the amount of payment made towards them.

Payroll deductions deductions from the employees' salary to pay towards taxes, the employees' pension, savings, etc.

Percent used to express a quantity out of 100 units and is represented by the symbol %.

Percent change the percent by which a quantity increases or decreases from its initial value.

Periodic interest rate the interest rate for a given compounding period.

Perpetuity an annuity where the periodic payments begin on a fixed date and continue indefinitely.

Perpetuity due a perpetuity where periodic payments are made at the beginning of the payment period.

Piecework rate when employment is based on the number of units produced or task completed (output), employees' gross pay is calculated based on an agreed flat rate called piecework rate for each item or task completed.

Place value the value of a digit in a number based on its place or position.

Polynomial an algebraic expression that has two or more terms.

Portion (P) a part of the whole quantity or value (portion of the base); used in percent calculations.

Present value the discounted value or principal amount of a payment or a series of payments.

Prime number a whole number that has no factors other than 1 and the number itself.

Principal the amount of money borrowed or invested at the beginning of a period.

Promissory note a written promise to repay a borrowed amount of money to a lender on an agreed date.

Proper fraction a fraction in which the absolute value of the numerator is less than the absolute value of the denominator.

Property tax the amount the owner of a property is required to pay the municipal government and is generally calculated as a percent of the value of the property that is being assessed.

Proportions when two sets of ratios are equal, we say that they are proportionate to each other.

Pro-ration sharing or allocating quantities, usually amounts, on a proportionate basis.

Provincial Sales Tax (PST) the sales tax levied by Canadian provinces. No PST is levied in Alberta, the Northwest Territories, Nunavut, or the Yukon.

Quoted price of a bond a number above or below 100 which represents the discount or premium applicable to a bond's face value.

Rate (R) the percent relationship between base and portion.

Rate of markdown markdown expressed as a percent of selling price.

Rate of markup markup expressed as a percent of cost or selling price.

Ratio a comparison or relationship between two or more quantities.

Receipt-of-Goods dating (ROG) cash payment terms where the credit period and discount period start from the date of receipt of goods.

Redemption in the case of bonds, repayment of the face value and the end of coupon payments.

Residual value the expected value of an asset at the end of a lease term.

Savings account a convenience account, where the interest is often calculated on the daily balance and posted monthly.

Selling price the price at which merchandise is sold to customers.

Semi-monthly pay period when an employee is paid two payments per month.

Simple annuity due an annuity due where the compounding period and the payment period are the same.

Simple arithmetic average (also called arithmetic mean or mean) the sum of all the values of the terms divided by the number of terms.

Simple interest rate the rate at which a principal amount is borrowed or invested.

Sinking fund an interest-earning fund that is built up over time with periodic deposits, so that the accumulated funds may later be withdrawn to make large payments to settle debts (such as the repayment of a bond's face value).

Straight commission when an employee is paid a single percent of the sales for the pay period as salary.

Straight piecework rate when a certain amount of pay per unit of output is given regardless of the output quantity.

Taxes fees that federal, provincial, or municipal governments charge organizations and individuals on income and property.

Term deposits (also known as fixed deposits or time deposits) investments where money is invested for a fixed period of time.

Term of an annuity the time from the beginning of the first payment interval to the end of the last payment interval.

Time period the period of time for which the principal amount is borrowed or invested during which interest is charged or earned.

Time value of money money grows with time when it is invested or borrowed at a particular interest rate.

Total costs the sum of the fixed costs and the total variable costs of a business.

Total Revenue the amount of money received or brought into the business from the sale of merchandise.

Total Variable Costs costs that vary directly with the number of units of items produced.

Trade discount the discount offered on the list price.

Treasury bill (also known as a T-bill) is a written agreement or contract issued to investors for a short term; issued by the federal government on every other Tuesday through major financial institutions as their agents.

Trinomial a polynomial with three terms.

Unlike terms two or more algebraic terms that have different variables or the same variables with different exponents.

Variable when a certain letter represents various numbers it is called a variable; i.e., a variable is used to represent a value that can change in an algebraic expression.

Variable Cost per unit the cost of producing one unit of merchandise.

Weekly pay period when an employee is paid every week.

Weighted arithmetic mean a method of calculating an average for a set of values, where each value is given a weight which determines its contribution to the final average.

Workweek the number of working hours in a week.

Yield to Maturity (YTM) indicates the internal rate of return of an investment to the end of its term. As an interest rate, indicates the periodically compounding rate of growth of the investment.

Index

Notes

Notes

Notes

Notes

Financial Calculator Instructions

	TEXAS INSTRUMENTS BAII Plus	SHARP EL-738
Set the calculator to Financial Mode	*Set by default*	MODE 0
Set to 9 decimal places	2ND FORMAT 9 ENTER 2ND QUIT	SETUP 0 0 9
Set to floating-decimal format	*Setting to 9 decimals also sets to floating-decimal format*	SETUP 0 2
Set to Algebraic operating system	2ND FORMAT DEC = ↓ DEG ↓ US ↓ US ↓ Chn 2ND SET AOS	
Store and recall from the memory	STO Press any digit from 0 to 9 to store a value in that digit RCL Press any digit from 0 to 9 to recall a value from that digit	STO Press any letter from A to H, M, or X to Z to store a value in that letter RCL Press any letter from A to H, M, or X to Z to recall a value from that letter
Clear the memory and the display	2ND MEM 2ND CLRWORK	2nd F M-CLR 0 0
Clear the display	CE/C	ON/C
Clear the TVM worksheet	2ND CLR TVM	2nd F CA
Clear the Worksheets	2ND CLRWORK	2nd F CA
Close a worksheet	2ND QUIT	ON/C
Set the TVM worksheet to BGN or END mode	2ND BGN 2ND SET	2nd F BGN/END
Open the date worksheet	2ND DATE	DATE
Enter the first date	Enter date 1 as mm.ddyy ENTER	Enter date 1 as mmddyyyy ENT
Enter the second date	↓ Enter date 2 as mm.ddyy ENTER	▼ Enter date 2 as mmddyyyy ENT
Compute the days between dates	↓ CPT	▼ COMP
Record TVM Values		
Number of compounding periods or number of payments	Enter Value N	Enter Value N
Nominal interest rate	Enter Value I/Y as a %	Enter Value I/Y as a %
Number of payments per year	2ND P/Y P/Y = ENTER	2nd F P/Y P/Y = ENT
Compounding frequency	2ND P/Y ↓ C/Y = ENTER	2nd F P/Y ▼ C/Y = ENT
Present value	Enter Value PV	Enter Value PV
Size of the periodic payment	Enter Value PMT	Enter Value PMT
Future value	Enter Value FV	Enter Value FV
Compute an unknown TVM variable	CPT Press the variable key	COMP Press the variable key
Recall a TVM variable	RCL Press the variable key	RCL Press the variable key
Calculate the Effective Interest Rate		
Enter the nominal interest rate (%)	2ND ICONV Enter j ENTER	Enter C/Y (x,y) Enter j
Enter the compounding frequency	↑ Enter C/Y ENTER	2nd F →EFF
Compute the effective interest rate	↑ CPT	

	TEXAS INSTRUMENTS BAII Plus	SHARP EL-738
Calculate the Nominal Interest Rate		
Enter the effective interest rate	2ND ICONV ↓ Enter f ENTER	Enter C/Y Y (x,y) Enter f
Enter the compounding frequency	↓ Enter C/Y ENTER	2nd F → APR
Compute the nominal interest rate	↓ CPT	
Amortization Worksheet		
Open the worksheet	2ND AMORT	A AMRT
Enter the number of the starting payment	P1 = ENTER	AMRT P1 = Z ENT
Enter the number of the ending payment	↓ P2 = ENTER	▼ AMRT P2 = Z ENT
Principal balance after payment in P2	↓ BAL =	▼ BALANCE =
Total principal paid from P1 to P2	↓ PRN =	▼ Σ PRINCIPAL =
Total interest paid from P1 to P2	↓ INT =	▼ Σ INTEREST =
Cash Flow Worksheet		
Opens the worksheet	CF	F CFi
Clears the worksheet	2ND CLRWORK	2nd F CA
Enter initial cash flow	CFo = ENTER	CF DO = Z ENT
Enter first cash value/group of cash flows	↓ CO1 = ENTER	CF D1 = Y (x,y)
Enter FO as the number of occurences	↓ FO1 = ENTER	CF N1 = Z ENT
Continue for further cash values/groups of cash flows		
Calculate the NPV		
Press NPV	NPV	ON/C 2nd F CASH
Enter the interest rate per period (as a percent)	I = ENTER	RATE (I/Y) = Z ENT
Compute the NPV	↓ CPT NPV =	▼ COMP NET_PV =
Calculate the IRR		
Press IRR and CPT	IRR CPT IRR =	▼ COMP RATE (I/Y) =

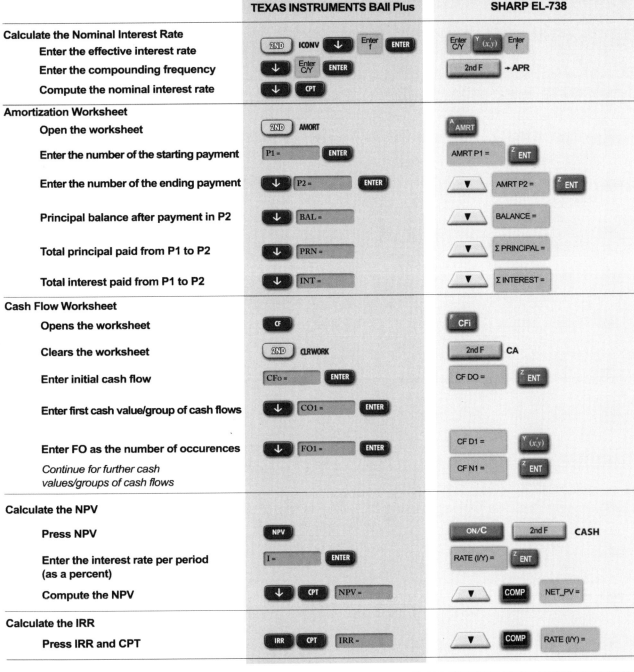

Bond Worksheet (BAII PLUS)

Opens the worksheet	2ND BOND
Clear the worksheet	2ND CLRWORK
Enter the settlement date	STD = ENTER
Enter the coupon rate (%)	↓ CPN = ENTER
Enter the redemption date	↓ RDT = ENTER
Enter the redemption value	↓ RV = ENTER
Press 2ND and SET for ACT	↓ ACT = ENTER
Press 2ND and SET for 2/Y	↓ 2/Y = ENTER
Enter the yield rate (%)	↓ YLD = ENTER
Market quotation	↓ CPT PRI =
Accrued Interest	↓ AI =

Bond Worksheet (SHARP EL-738)

Open the worksheet	B BOND
Clear the worksheet	2nd F CA
Enter the coupon rate (%)	COUPON (PMT) = Z ENT
Enter the redemption value	▼ REDEMPT (FV) = Z ENT
Enter the settlement date	▼ M-D-Y 1 = Z ENT
Enter the redemption date	▼ M-D-Y 2 = Z ENT
Enter 2 for 2 coupons per year	▼ CPN/Y(N) = Z ENT
Enter the yield rate	▼ YIELD (I/Y) = Z ENT
Press 2nd F and 360/ACT	2nd F 360/ACT
Market quotation	▼ COMP PRICE (PV) =
Accrued Interest	▼ COMP ACCU INT =

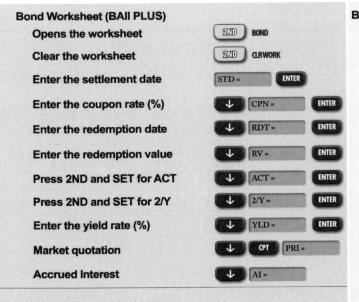

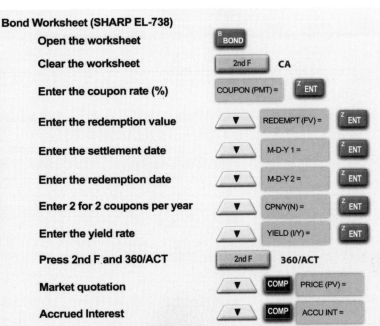

Summary of Formulas

PERCENTS, PERCENT CHANGES, AND APPLICATIONS

3.1 $P = R \times B$

3.2 $\%C = \dfrac{V_f - V_i}{V_i} \times 100\%$

3.3(a) $\text{Pay for pay period} = \dfrac{\text{Annual Salary}}{\text{Number of pay periods per year}}$

3.3(b) $\text{Hourly rate of pay} = \dfrac{\text{Weekly Pay}}{\text{Number of working hours per week}} = \dfrac{\text{Weekly Pay}}{\text{Workweek}}$

3.4(a) $\text{Property Tax} = \text{Assessed value of property} \times \text{Tax Rate}$

3.4(b) $\text{Property Tax} = \dfrac{\text{Assessed value of the property}}{1000} \times \text{Mill Rate}$

MATHEMATICS OF MERCHANDISING

5.1(a) $\text{Amount of trade discount} = d \times L$

5.1(b) $N = L(1 - d)$

5.1(c) $N = L(1 - d_1)(1 - d_2)(1 - d_3) \ldots (1 - d_n)$

5.1(d) $d_e = 1 - [(1 - d_1)(1 - d_2)(1 - d_3) \ldots (1 - d_n)]$

5.2 $\text{Amount Credited} = \dfrac{\text{Amount Paid}}{(1 - d)}$

5.3(a) $S = C + M$

5.3(b) $M = E + P$

5.3(c) $S = C + E + P$

5.3(d) $\text{Rate of markup on cost} = \dfrac{M}{C} \times 100\%$

5.3(e) $\text{Rate of markup on selling price} = \dfrac{M}{S} \times 100\%$

5.3(f) $BE = C + E$

5.4(a) $S_{Red} = S - D$

5.4(b) $D = S - S_{Red}$

5.4(c) $\text{Rate of markdown} = \dfrac{D}{S} \times 100\%$

5.5(a) $P_{Red} = S_{Red} - C - E$

5.5(b) $P_{Red} = P - D$ If P_{Red} is negative, then there is a loss at sale price.

Table 5.5: Merchandising Calculation Table

	Amount	Rate on C	Rate on S
P			
$+E$			
M			
$+C$			
S			
$-D$			
S_{Red}			
$-BE$: $-C$			
$-BE$: $-E$			
P_{Red}			

5.6(a) $\text{Net Amount of Markup} = \text{Total Sales} - \text{Total Cost}$

5.6(b) $\text{Net Rate of Markup based on Total Cost} = \dfrac{\text{Net Amount of Markup}}{\text{Total Cost}} \times 100\%$

5.6(c) $\text{Net Rate of Markup based on Total Sales} = \dfrac{\text{Net Amount of Markup}}{\text{Total Sales}} \times 100$

BREAK-EVEN AND COST-VOLUME-PROFIT ANALYSIS

7.1(a) $TVC = VC \times x$

7.1(b) $TC = FC + TVC$

7.1(c) $TR = S \times x$

7.1(d) $NI = TR - TC$

7.1(e) At the break-even point, $TR = TC$

7.1(f) $CM = S - VC$

7.1(g) $CR = \dfrac{CM}{S} \times 100\%$

7.2(a) $S \times x = FC + (VC \times x) + NI$

7.2(b) $x = \dfrac{FC + NI}{(S - VC)}$

7.3 $x_{BE} = \dfrac{FC}{CM}$

7.4(a) $\text{CM Percent} = \dfrac{TR - TVC}{TR} \times 100\%$

7.4(b) $NI = (\text{CM Percent} \times TR) - FC$ **or** $NI = TCM - FC$

SIMPLE INTEREST AND APPLICATIONS

8.1 $I = Prt$

8.2(a) $S = P + I$

8.2(b) $S = P(1 + rt)$

8.2(c) $P = \dfrac{S}{(1 + rt)}$ **or** $P = S(1 + rt)^{-1}$